IMPORTANT:

HERE IS YOUR REGISTRATION CODE TO ACCESS
YOUR PREMIUM McGRAW-HILL ONLINE RESOURCES.

For key premium online resources you need THIS CODE to gain access. Once the code is entered, you will be able to use the Web resources for the length of your course.

If your course is using **WebCT** or **Blackboard**, you'll be able to use this code to access the McGraw-Hill content within your instructor's online course.

Access is provided if you have purchased a new book. If the registration code is missing from this book, the registration screen on our Website, and within your WebCT or Blackboard course, will tell you how to obtain your new code.

Registering for McGraw-Hill Online Resources

TO gain access to your McGraw-Hill web resources simply follow the steps below:

1. USE YOUR WEB BROWSER TO GO TO: **http://www.mhhe.com/dugopolski**
2. CLICK ON **FIRST TIME USER**.
3. ENTER THE REGISTRATION CODE* PRINTED ON THE TEAR-OFF BOOKMARK ON THE RIGHT.
4. AFTER YOU HAVE ENTERED YOUR REGISTRATION CODE, CLICK **REGISTER**.
5. FOLLOW THE INSTRUCTIONS TO SET-UP YOUR PERSONAL UserID AND PASSWORD.
6. WRITE YOUR UserID AND PASSWORD DOWN FOR FUTURE REFERENCE. KEEP IT IN A SAFE PLACE.

TO GAIN ACCESS to the McGraw-Hill content in your instructor's **WebCT** or **Blackboard** course simply log in to the course with the UserID and Password provided by your instructor. Enter the registration code exactly as it appears in the box to the right when prompted by the system. You will only need to use the code the first time you click on McGraw-Hill content.

Thank you, and welcome to your McGraw-Hill online Resources!

* YOUR REGISTRATION CODE CAN BE USED ONLY ONCE TO ESTABLISH ACCESS. IT IS NOT TRANSFERABLE.

0-07-291887-X DUGOPOLSKI: ALGEBRA FOR COLLEGE STUDENTS, 3E

MCGRAW-HILL
ONLINE RESOURCES

REGISTRATION CODE

HA2K-WYAN-KB0A-FT1U-LNTP

Algebra for College Students

EDITION 3

Algebra for College Students

EDITION 3

Mark Dugopolski

Southeastern Louisiana University

 Higher Education

Boston   Burr Ridge, IL   Dubuque, IA   Madison, WI
New York   San Francisco   St. Louis   Bangkok
Bogotá   Caracas   Kuala Lumpur   Lisbon   London   Madrid
Mexico City   Milan   Montreal   New Delhi   Santiago
Seoul   Singapore   Sydney   Taipei   Toronto

ALGEBRA FOR COLLEGE STUDENTS, THIRD EDITION

Published by McGraw-Hill, a business unit of The McGraw-Hill Companies, Inc., 1221
Avenue of the Americas, New York, NY 10020. Copyright © 2004, 2000 by The McGraw-
Hill Companies, Inc. All rights reserved. Previous editions © 1996 by Addison-Wesley
Publishing Company, Inc. All rights reserved. No part of this publication may be reproduced
or distributed in any form or by any means, or stored in a database or retrieval system,
without the prior written consent of The McGraw-Hill Companies, Inc., including, but not
limited to, in any network or other electronic storage or transmission, or broadcast for
distance learning.

Some ancillaries, including electronic and print components, may not be available to
customers outside the United States.

This book is printed on acid-free paper.

2 3 4 5 6 7 8 9 0 VNH/VNH 0 9 8 7 6 5 4 3

ISBN 0–07–291886–1

Publisher: *William K. Barter*
Senior sponsoring editor: *David Dietz*
Developmental editor: *Erin Brown*
Executive marketing manager: *Marianne C. P. Rutter*
Senior marketing manager: *Mary K. Kittell*
Senior project manager: *Vicki Krug*
Lead production supervisor: *Sandy Ludovissy*
Lead media project manager: *Audrey A. Reiter*
Media technology producer: *Jeff Huettman*
Coordinator of freelance design: *Rick D. Noel*
Cover designer: *Todd Damotte/Rokusek Design*
Cover image: *@Corbis, Volume 622, Architectural Details, No.*5
Lead photo research coordinator: *Carrie K. Burger*
Supplement producer: *Brenda A. Ernzen*
Compositor: *Interactive Composition Corporation*
Typeface: *10.5/12 Times Roman*
Printer: *Von Hoffmann Corporatio*n

Photo Credits
Page 1: © Robert Brenner/PhotoEdit; p. 30, p. 57: U.S. Army Corps of Engineers; p. 54:
© Digital Vision/Volume 185; p. 78, p. 204, p. 399, p. 717: © Susan Van Etten; p. 125,
659: © Reuters NewMedia Inc./CORBIS; p. 168 (bottom), p. 310, p. 374, p. 467, p. 545,
p. 721: © The McGraw-Hill Companies, Inc.; p. 255: © Paul Conklin/PhotoEdit; p. 327:
© Digital Vision/Volume 285; p. 393: © Herb Snitzer/Stock Boston; p. 623: Courtesy
Molly McCallister; p. 682: Courtesy Friedrich von Huene Workshop. All other photos
© PhotoDisc, Inc.

Library of Congress Cataloging-in-Publication Data

Dugopolski, Mark.
  Algebra for college students / Mark Dugopolski. — 3rd ed.
     p.   cm.
  Includes index.
  ISBN 0–07–291886–1 (hard copy : alk. paper)
   1. Algebra. I. Title.

QA152.3 .D837 2004
512.9—dc21   2002153999
                                                     CIP

www.mhhe.com

*To my wife and daughters,
Cheryl, Sarah, and Alisha*

CONTENTS

Appendix   A-1

Answers   A-7

Index   I-1

Algebra for College Students, Third Edition, is designed to provide students with the algebra background needed for further college-level mathematics courses. The unifying theme of this text is the development of the skills necessary for solving equations and inequalities, followed by the application of those skills to solving applied problems. My primary goal in writing the third edition of *Algebra for College Students,* has been to retain the features that made the second edition so successful, while incorporating the comments and suggestions of second-edition users. As always, I endeavor to write texts that students can read, understand, and enjoy, while gaining confidence in their ability to use mathematics. Although a complete development of each topic is provided in *Algebra for College Students,* Third Edition, the text *Elementary Algebra,* Fourth Edition, in this series would be more appropriate for students with no prior experience in algebra.

Content Changes

While the essence of previous editions remains, the topics have been rearranged to reflect the current needs of instructors.

- Functions are introduced in Section 3.5. After that, function topics are revisited where appropriate. For example, polynomial functions appear in Section 5.3, the domain of rational expressions and functions is covered in Section 6.1, and the domain of radical functions is covered in Section 7.1. Functions also appear in Chapter 8, with quadratic equations, and again in Chapters 9, 10, and 11.

- Section 3.5 on functions and relations has been revised with expanded coverage of the concepts of domain and range and the different forms of a function. *Graphs of Functions*, previously Section 3.6, which included graphs of constant functions, quadratic functions, absolute value functions, and square-root functions has been moved to Chapter 9, Section 1.

- The distance and midpoint formulas now appear in Section 3.1, where graphing lines is introduced. The distance formula also appears in Section 12.2, where it is used to develop the equation of a parabola from the geometric definition.

- In Chapter 4, the two sections on determinants and Cramer's rule have been condensed into one, Section 4.5.

- To streamline Chapter 5, the section covering division of polynomials has been moved to Chapter 6 on rational expressions.

- Sections 7.1 and 7.2 have been swapped from the second edition so that radicals now appears as the first topic in Chapter 7, Section 1, and rational exponents now appears in Section 7.2.

- **NEW!** Transformations of graphs has been added to Chapter 9 and appears in Section 9.2.

- **NEW!** The factor theorem has been added to Chapter 10 and appears in Section 10.1.

- NEW! In Section 12.2, the discussion of parabolas was expanded to include parabolas that open right or left. In Section 12.4 the discussion of hyperbolas was expanded to include hyperbolas that are not centered at the origin.

- NEW! Appendix A Geometry Review has been updated to include review exercises to help students recall geometry concepts and formulas.

In addition to these changes, the text and exercise sets have been carefully revised where necessary. Many new, applied examples have been added to the text and many new, applied exercises have been added to the exercise sets. Particular care has been given to achieving an appropriate balance of problems that progressively increase in difficulty from routine exercises in the beginning of the set to more challenging exercises at the end of the set. As in earlier editions, fractions and decimals are used in the exercises and throughout the text discussions to help reinforce the basic arithmetic skills that are necessary for success in algebra.

Features

- Each chapter begins with a Chapter Opener that discusses a real application of algebra. The discussion is accompanied by a photograph and, in most cases by a real-data application graph that helps students visualize algebra and more fully understand the concepts discussed in the chapter. In addition, each chapter contains a Math at Work feature, which profiles a real person and the mathematics that he or she uses on the job. These two features have corresponding real data exercises.

- The third edition continues to emphasize real-data applications that involve graphs. Applications appear throughout the text to help demonstrate concepts, motivate students, and to give students practice using new skills. Many of the real-data exercises contain data obtained from the Internet. Internet addresses are provided as a resource for both students and teachers. An Index of Selected Applications listing applications by subject matter is included at the front of the text.

- Every section begins with In This Section, a list of topics that shows the student what will be covered. Because the topics correspond to the headings within each section, students will find it easy to locate and study specific concepts.

- Important ideas, such as definitions, rules, summaries, and strategies, are set apart in boxes for quick reference. Color is used to highlight these boxes as well as other important points in the text.

- The third edition contains margin features that appear throughout the text:

  Calculator Close-ups give students an idea of how and when to use a graphing calculator. Some Calculator Close-ups simply introduce the features of a graphing calculator, where others enhance understanding of algebraic concepts. For this reason, many of the Calculator Close-ups will benefit even those students who do not use a graphing calculator. A graphing calculator is not required for studying from this text.

  Study Tips are included in the margins throughout the text. These short tips are meant to continually reinforce good study habits and to remind students that it is never too late to make improvements in the manner in which they study.

  Helpful Hints are short comments that enhance the material in the text, provide another way of approaching a problem, or clear up misconceptions.

- At the end of every section are Warm-up exercises, a set of ten simple statements that are to be answered true or false. These exercises are designed to provide a smooth transition between the ideas and the exercise sets. They help students understand that every statement in mathematics is either true or false. They are also good for discussion or group work.

- Most section-ending exercise sets in the third edition begin with six simple writing exercises. These exercises are designed to get students to review the definitions and rules of the section before doing more traditional exercises. For example, the student might simply be asked what properties of equality were discussed in this section.

- The end-of-section Exercises follow the same order as the textual material and contain exercises that are keyed to examples, as well as numerous exercises that are not keyed to examples. This organization enables the instructor to cover only part of a section if necessary and easily determine which exercises are appropriate to assign. The *keyed exercises* give the student a place to start practicing and building confidence, whereas the *nonkeyed exercises* are designed to wean the student from following examples in a step-by-step manner. *Getting More Involved exercises* are designed to encourage *writing, discussion, exploration,* and *cooperative learning. Graphing Calculator exercises* require a graphing calculator and are identified with a graphing calculator logo. Exercises for which a scientific calculator would be helpful are identified with a scientific calculator logo. Please refer to page xxiii for a visual guide of the icons.

- Every chapter ends with a four-part Wrap-up, which includes the following:

    The chapter Summary lists important concepts along with brief illustrative examples.

    Enriching Your Mathematical Word Power appears at the end of each chapter and consists of multiple-choice questions in which the important terms are to be matched with their meanings. This feature emphasizes the importance of proper terminology.

    The Review Exercises contain problems that are keyed to the sections of the chapter as well as numerous miscellaneous exercises.

    The Chapter Test is designed to help the student assess his or her readiness for a test. The Chapter Test has no keyed exercises, thus encouraging the student to work independently of the sections and examples.

- **UPDATED!** At the end of each chapter is a Collaborative Activities feature that is designed to encourage interaction and learning in groups. Many of the Collaborative Activities for the third edition have been updated. Instructions and suggestions for using these activities and answers to all problems can be found in the Instructor's Solutions Manual.

- Making Connections, at the end of Chapters 2–13, are cumulative exercises designed to help students review and synthesize new material with ideas from previous chapters, and in some cases, review material necessary for success in upcoming chapters. Every Making Connections exercise set includes at least one applied exercise that requires ideas from one or more of the previous chapters.

Topic Reinforcement

Several methods are employed in this text to help students retain what they learn and expand and build on previously learned concepts. Most notably, the Making Connections appear at the end of each chapter through Chapter 13 and beginning with Chapter 2. Making Connections are cumulative sets of exercises that help students to continually practice what they learn. Also, functions are introduced in Section 3.5 and revisited where appropriate throughout the text. This constant reinforcement helps students retain and strengthen their understanding of this important concept. The distance formula is covered in Section 3.1 and reviewed in Section 12.2 where it is used to develop the equations of the conic sections. In Chapter 9, solving quadratics by factoring and the square root property are reviewed prior to the new ideas of completing the square and the quadratic formula. Through these, and similar methods, students retain what they learn and apply what they learn to new concepts.

Supplements for the Instructor
ANNOTATED INSTRUCTOR'S EDITION

This ancillary includes answers to all section ending exercises, review exercises, Making Connections exercises, and chapter tests. Each answer is printed next to each problem on the page where the problem appears. The answers are printed in a second color for ease of use by instructors.

INSTRUCTOR'S TESTING AND RESOURCE CD-ROM

This CD-ROM contains a computerized test bank that utilizes Brownstone Diploma® testing software. The computerized test bank enables instructors to create well-formatted quizzes or tests using a large bank of algorithmically generated and static questions. When creating a quiz or test, the user can manually choose individual questions or have the software randomly select questions based on section, question type, difficulty level, and other criteria. Instructors also have the ability to add or edit test bank questions to create their own customized test bank. In addition to printed tests, the test generator can deliver tests over a local area network or the World Wide Web, with automatic grading.

Also available on the CD-ROM are pre-formatted tests that appear in two forms: Adobe Acrobat (pdf) and Microsoft Word files. These files are provided for convenient access to "ready to use" tests. The tests can also be downloaded as a Word (.doc) file or can be viewed and printed as a (.pdf) file at www.mhhe.com/dugopolski.

INSTRUCTOR'S SOLUTIONS MANUAL

Prepared by Mark Dugopolski, this supplement contains detailed worked solutions to all of the exercises in the text. The solutions are based on by the techniques used in the text. Instructions and suggestions for using the Collaborative Activities feature in the text are also included in the Instructor's Solutions Manual.

PageOut

PageOut is McGraw-Hill's unique point-and-click course website tool, enabling instructors to create a full-featured, professional quality course Website without knowing HTML coding. With PageOut instructors can post a syllabus online, assign McGraw-Hill Online Learning Center content, add links to important off-site resources, and maintain student results in the online grade book. Instructors can also send class announcements, copy a course site to share with colleagues, and upload original files. PageOut is free for every McGraw-Hill user. For those instructors who are short on time, there is a team on hand, ready to help build a site!

Learn more about PageOut and other McGraw-Hill digital solutions at www.mhhe.com/solutions.

Supplements for the Student

STUDENT'S SOLUTIONS MANUAL

Prepared by Mark Dugopolski, the *Student's Solutions Manual* contains complete worked-out solutions to all of the odd-numbered exercises in the text. It also contains solutions for all exercises in the Chapter Tests. It may be purchased from McGraw-Hill.

DUGOPOLSKI VIDEO SERIES (Videotapes or CD-ROMs)

The videos are text-specific and cover all chapters of the text. The videos feature an instructor who introduces topics and works through selected problems from the exercise sets. Students are encouraged to work the problems on their own and to check their results with those provided.

DUGOPOLSKI TUTORIAL CD-ROM

This interactive CD-ROM is a self-paced tutorial specifically linked to the text that reinforces topics through unlimited opportunities to review concepts and practice problem solving. The CD-ROM contains algorithmically generated chapter-, and section-specific questions. It requires virtually no computer training on the part of students and supports Windows and Macintosh computers.

ONLINE LEARNING CENTER

The Online Learning Center (OLC), located at www.mhhe.com/dugopolski, contains resources for students and instructors.

Through the Instructor Resource Site, instructors can access links to professional resources, a PowerPoint presentation (transparencies), printable tests, group projects, and a link to PageOut.

To access the Instructor Resource Site, instructors must have a passcode that can be obtained by contacting a McGraw-Hill Higher Education representative.

The Student Learning Site is also passcode-protected. Passcodes for students can be found at the front of their texts when newly purchased. *Passcodes are available free to students when they purchase a new text.* Students also have access to algorithmically generated "bookmarkable" practice exercises (including hints), section- and chapter-level testing, audiovisual tutorials, interactive applications, and links to NetTutor™ and other interesting websites.

The Information Center can be accessed by students and instructors without a passcode. Through the Information Center, users can access general information about the text and its supplements.

ALEKS®

ALEKS® (**A**ssessment and **LE**arning in **K**nowledge **S**paces) is an artificial intelligence-based system for individualized math learning, available over the World Wide Web. ALEKS® delivers precise, qualitative diagnostic assessments of students' math knowledge, guides them in the selection of appropriate new study material, and records their progress toward mastery of curricular goals in a robust classroom management system. It interacts with the student much as a skilled human tutor would, moving between explanation and practice as needed, correcting and analyzing errors, defining terms, and changing topics on request. By sophisticated modeling of a student's "knowledge state" for a given subject matter, ALEKS® can focus clearly on what the student is most ready to learn next, building a learning momentum that fuels success.

To learn more about ALEKS® including purchasing information, visit the ALEKS® website at www.highedmath.aleks.com.

NetTutor

NetTutor is a revolutionary system that enables students to interact with a live tutor over the World Wide Web by using NetTutor's Web-based, graphical chat capabilities. Students can also submit questions and receive answers, browse previously answered questions, and view previous live chat sessions.

NetTutor can be accessed on the Online Learning Center through the Student Learning Site.

Acknowledgments

First of all I thank all of the students and professors who used the previous editions of this text, for without their support there would not be a third edition. I sincerely appreciate the efforts of the reviewers who made many helpful suggestions for improving the second edition:

Henry C. Bailey, *Cuyahoga Community College*
Carole Bergen, *Mercy College*
Adrian M. DeWindt-King, *Cumberland County College*
Suzanne Doviak, *Old Dominion University*
Paul C. Rokicky, *Cuyahoga Community College*
Alexis Thurman, *County College of Morris*

In addition, I would also like to thank the following reviewers of *Intermediate Algebra*, Third Edition. Their suggestions were also helpful in improving this volume.

Corinna Goehring, *Jackson State Community College*
Domingo Javier-Litong, *Houston Community College*
Joselle D. Kehoe, *DeVry Institute of Technology*
Susann Kyriazopoulos, *DeVry University–Chicago Campus*
Mitchel Levy, *Broward Community College*
Margaret Michener, *University of Nebraska–Kearney*
Joyce Nemeth, *Broward Community College–South Campus*
Charles Odion, *Houston Community College*
Avis Proctor, *Broward Community College*
Togba Sapolucia, *Houston Community College*
Donald W. Solomon, *University of Wisconsin–Milwaukee*
Burnette Thompson, *Houston Community College–Northwest*
Emmanuel Ekwere Usen, *Houston Community College*
Pam Wahl, *Middlesex Community College*
Joel D. Williams, *Houston Community College System*
Walter Wooden, *Broward Community College*

I also want to express my sincere appreciation to my wife, Cheryl, for her invaluable patience and support.

Hammond, Louisiana   M.D.

CHAPTER 1

The Real Numbers

E verywhere you look people are running, riding, dancing, and exercising their way to fitness. In the past year more than $25 billion has been spent on sports equipment alone, and this amount is growing steadily.

Proponents of exercise claim that it can increase longevity, improve body image, decrease appetite, and generally enhance a person's health. While many sports activities can help you to stay fit, experts have found that aerobic, or dynamic, workouts provide the most fitness benefit. Some of the best aerobic exercises include cycling, running, and even jumping rope. Whatever athletic activity you choose, trainers recommend that you set realistic goals and work your way toward them consistently and slowly. To achieve maximum health benefits, experts suggest that you exercise three to five times a week for 15 to 60 minutes at a time.

There are many different ways to measure exercise. One is to measure the energy used, or the rate of oxygen consumption. Since heart rate rises as a function of increased oxygen, another easier measure of intensity of exercise is your heart rate during exercise. The desired heart rate, or target heart rate, for beneficial exercise varies for each individual depending on conditioning, age, and gender. In Exercises 101 and 102 of Section 1.4 you will see how an algebraic expression can determine your target heart rate for beneficial exercise.

Chapter Opener

Each **chapter opener** features a real-world situation that can be modeled using mathematics. Each chapter contains exercises that relate back to the chapter opener.

Evaluate each expression for $a = -1$, $b = 3$, and $c = -4$. See Example 7.

57. $b^2 - 4ac$ **58.** $\sqrt{a^2 - 4bc}$

59. $\dfrac{a-b}{a-c}$ **60.** $\dfrac{b-c}{b-a}$

61. $(a-b)(a+b)$ **62.** $(a-c)(a+c)$

63. $\sqrt{c^2 - 2c + 1}$ **64.** $b^2 - 2b - 3$

65. $\dfrac{2}{a} + \dfrac{b}{c} - \dfrac{1}{c}$ **66.** $\dfrac{c}{a} + \dfrac{c}{b} - \dfrac{a}{b}$

67. $|a-b|$ **68.** $|b+c|$

Find the value of $\dfrac{y_2 - y_1}{x_2 - x_1}$ for each choice of y_1, y_2, x_1, and x_2. See Example 8.

69. $y_1 = 4$, $y_2 = -6$, $x_1 = 2$, $x_2 = -7$

70. $y_1 = -3$, $y_2 = -3$, $x_1 = 4$, $x_2 = -5$

71. $y_1 = -1$, $y_2 = 2$, $x_1 = -3$, $x_2 = 1$

72. $y_1 = -2$, $y_2 = 5$, $x_1 = 2$, $x_2 = 6$

73. $y_1 = 2.4$, $y_2 = 5.6$, $x_1 = 5.9$, $x_2 = 4.7$

74. $y_1 = -5.7$, $y_2 = 6.9$, $x_1 = 3.5$, $x_2 = 4.2$

Evaluate each expression without a calculator. Use a calculator to check.

75. $-2^2 + 5(3)^2$ **76.** $-3^2 + 3(6)^2$

77. $(-2 + 5)3^2$ **78.** $(-3 + 3)6^2$

79. $\sqrt{5^2 - 4(1)(6)}$ **80.** $\sqrt{6^2 - 4(2)(4)}$

81. $[13 + 2(-5)]^2$ **82.** $[6 + 2(-4)]^2$

83. $\dfrac{4 - (-1)}{-3 - 2}$ **84.** $\dfrac{2 - (-3)}{3 - 5}$

85. $3(-2)^2 - 5(-2) + 4$

86. $3(-1)^2 + 5(-1) - 6$

87. $-4\left(\dfrac{1}{2}\right)^2 + 3\left(\dfrac{1}{2}\right) - 2$ **88.** $8\left(\dfrac{1}{2}\right)^2 - 6\left(\dfrac{1}{2}\right) + 1$

89. $-\dfrac{1}{2}|6 - 2|$ **90.** $-\dfrac{1}{3}|9 - 6|$

91. $\dfrac{1}{2} - \dfrac{1}{3}\left|\dfrac{1}{4} - \dfrac{1}{2}\right|$ **92.** $\dfrac{1}{3} - \dfrac{1}{2}\left|\dfrac{1}{3} - \dfrac{1}{2}\right|$

93. $|6 - 3 \cdot 7| + |7 - 5|$

94. $|12 - 4| - |3 - 4 \cdot 5|$

95. $3 - 7[4 - (2 - 5)]$

96. $9 - 2[3 - (4 + 6)]$

97. $3 - 4(2 - |4 - 6|)$

98. $3 - (|-4| - |-5|)$

99. $4[2 - (5 - |-3|)^2]$

100. $[5 - (-3)]^2 + [4 - (-2)]^2$

Solve each problem. See Example 9.

101. *Female target heart rate.* The algebraic expression $0.65(220 - A)$ gives the target heart rate for beneficial exercise for women, where A is the age of the woman. How much larger is the target heart rate of a 25-year-old woman than that of a 65-year-old woman? Use the accompanying graph to estimate the age at which a woman's target heart rate is 115.

FIGURE FOR EXERCISES 101 AND 102

102. *Male target heart rate.* The algebraic expression $0.75(220 - A)$ gives the target heart rate for beneficial exercise for men, where A is the age of the man. Use the algebraic expression to find the target heart rate for a 20-year-old man and a 50-year-old man. Use the accompanying graph to estimate the age at which a man's target heart rate is 115.

Solve each problem.

103. *Perimeter of a pool.* The algebraic expression $2L + 2W$ gives the perimeter of a rectangle with length L and width W. Find the perimeter of a rectangular swimming pool that has length 34 feet and width 18 feet.

104. *Area of a lot.* The algebraic expression for the area of a trapezoid, $0.5h(b_1 + b_2)$, gives the area of the property shown in the figure. Find the area if $h = 150$ feet, $b_1 = 260$ feet, and $b_2 = 220$ feet.

FIGURE FOR EXERCISE 104

105. *Saving for retirement.* The expression $P(1 + r)^n$ gives the amount of an investment of P dollars invested for n years at interest rate r compounded

Margin Notes

Margin notes include **helpful hints**, **study tips,** and **calculator close-ups.** The **helpful hints** point out common errors or reminders. The **study tips** provide practical suggestions for improving study habits. The optional **calculator close-ups** provide tips on using a graphing calculator to aid in your understanding of the material. They also include insightful suggestions for increasing calculator proficiency.

The solution set is $(-\infty, 4]$, and its graph is shown in Fig. 2.13.

FIGURE 2.13

EXAMPLE 5   An inequality with fractions

Solve $\frac{1}{2}x - \frac{2}{3} \le x + \frac{4}{3}$. State and graph the solution set.

Helpful Hint

Notice that we use the same strategy for solving inequalities as we do for solving equations. But we must remember to reverse the inequality symbol when we multiply or divide by a negative number. For inequalities it is usually best to isolate the variable on the left-hand side.

Solution

First multiply each side of the inequality by 6, the LCD:

$$\frac{1}{2}x - \frac{2}{3} \le x + \frac{4}{3} \qquad \text{Original inequality}$$

$$6\left(\frac{1}{2}x - \frac{2}{3}\right) \le 6\left(x + \frac{4}{3}\right) \qquad \text{Multiplying by positive 6 does not reverse the inequality.}$$

$$3x - 4 \le 6x + 8 \qquad \text{Distributive property}$$

$$3x \le 6x + 12 \qquad \text{Add 4 to each side.}$$

$$-3x \le 12 \qquad \text{Subtract 6x from each side.}$$

$$x \ge -4 \qquad \text{Divide each side by } -3 \text{ and reverse the inequality.}$$

The solution set is the interval $[-4, \infty)$. Its graph is shown in Fig. 2.14.

FIGURE 2.14

In Example 6 we see an inequality that is satisfied by all real numbers and one that has no solution.

EXAMPLE 6   All or nothing

Solve each inequality and graph the solution set.

a) $6 - 4x < -4x + 7$ **b)** $2(4x - 5) \ge 4(2x - 1)$

Solution

FIGURE 2.15

a) Adding $4x$ to each side will greatly simplify the inequality:

$$6 - 4x < -4x + 7 \qquad \text{Original inequality}$$

$$6 < 7 \qquad \text{Add 4x to each side.}$$

Since $6 < 7$ is correct no matter what real number is used in place of x, the solution set is the set of all real numbers $(-\infty, \infty)$. Its graph is shown in Fig. 2.15.

b) Start by simplifying each side of the inequality.

$$2(4x - 5) \ge 4(2x - 1) \qquad \text{Original inequality}$$

$$8x - 10 \ge 8x - 4 \qquad \text{Distributive property}$$

$$-10 \ge -4 \qquad \text{Subtract 8x from each side.}$$

Since $-10 \ge -4$ is false no matter what real number is used in place of x, the solution set is the empty set $\varnothing$ and there is no graph to draw.

Study Tip

When you get a test back, don't simply file it in your notebook or the waste basket. While the material is fresh in your mind, rework all the problems that you missed. Ask questions about anything that you don't understand and save your test for future reference.

Linear Equation in One Variable

A **linear equation in one variable** x is an equation of the form $ax + b = 0$, where a and b are real numbers, with $a \ne 0$.

The equations in Examples 2 through 5 are called linear equations in one variable, or simply linear equations, because they could all be rewritten in the form $ax + b = 0$. At first glance the equations in Example 6 appear to be linear equations. However, they cannot be written in the form $ax + b = 0$, with $a \ne 0$, so they are not linear equations. A linear equation has exactly one solution. The strategy that we use for solving linear equations is summarized in the following box.

Strategy for Solving a Linear Equation

1. If fractions are present, multiply each side by the LCD to eliminate them.
2. Use the distributive property to remove parentheses.
3. Combine any like terms.
4. Use the addition property of equality to get all variables on one side and numbers on the other side.
5. Use the multiplication property of equality to get a single variable on one side.
6. Check by replacing the variable in the original equation with your solution.

Note that not all equations require all of the steps.

EXAMPLE 7   Using the equation-solving strategy

Solve the equation $\frac{y}{2} - \frac{y - 4}{5} = \frac{23}{10}$.

Calculator Close-Up

You can use the fraction feature of a graphing calculator to check that 5 satisfies the equation. If you make a mistake entering an expression, you can recall the expression by pressing the ENTRY key and modify the expression.

```
5/2-(5-4)/5▸Frac
                23/10
```

Solution

We first multiply each side of the equation by 10, the LCD for 2, 5, and 10. However, we do not have to write down that step. We can simply use the distributive property to multiply each term of the equation by 10.

$$\frac{y}{2} - \frac{y - 4}{5} = \frac{23}{10}$$

$$\overset{5}{\cancel{10}}\left(\frac{y}{2}\right) - \overset{2}{\cancel{10}}\left(\frac{y - 4}{5}\right) = \overset{}{\cancel{10}}\left(\frac{23}{\cancel{10}}\right) \qquad \text{Multiply each side by 10.}$$

$$5y - 2(y - 4) = 23 \qquad \text{Divide each denominator into 10 to eliminate fractions.}$$

$$5y - 2y + 8 = 23 \qquad \text{Be careful to change all signs: } -2(y - 4) = -2y + 8$$

$$3y + 8 = 23 \qquad \text{Combine like terms.}$$

$$3y + 8 - 8 = 23 - 8 \qquad \text{Subtract 8 from each side.}$$

$$3y = 15 \qquad \text{Simplify.}$$

$$\frac{3y}{3} = \frac{15}{3} \qquad \text{Divide each side by 3.}$$

$$y = 5$$

Check that 5 satisfies the original equation. The solution set is {5}.

Helpful Hint

Making a guess can be a good way to become familiar with the problem. For example, let's guess that the answers to Example 2 are 50, 51, and 52. Since $50 + 51 + 52 = 153$, these are not the correct numbers. But now we realize that we should use x, $x + 1$, and $x + 2$ and that the equation should be

$$x + x + 1 + x + 2 = 228.$$

Since the sum of these three expressions for the consecutive integers is 228, we can write the following equation and solve it:

$$x + (x + 1) + (x + 2) = 228 \quad \text{The sum of the integers is 228.}$$
$$3x + 3 = 228$$
$$3x = 225$$
$$x = 75$$
$$x + 1 = 76 \quad \text{Identify the other unknown quantities.}$$
$$x + 2 = 77$$

To verify that these values are the correct integers, we compute

$$75 + 76 + 77 = 228.$$

The three consecutive integers that have a sum of 228 are 75, 76, and 77. ■

General Strategy for Problem Solving

The steps to follow in providing a complete solution to a verbal problem can be stated as follows.

Study Tip

Don't simply work exercises to get answers. Keep reminding yourself of what you are actually doing. Keep trying to obtain the big picture. How does this section relate to what we did in the previous section? Where are we going next? When is the picture complete?

> **Strategy for Solving Word Problems**
>
> 1. Read the problem until you understand the problem. Making a guess and checking it will help you to understand the problem.
> 2. If possible, draw a diagram to illustrate the problem.
> 3. Choose a variable and write down what it represents.
> 4. Represent any other unknowns in terms of that variable.
> 5. Write an equation that models the situation.
> 6. Solve the equation.
> 7. Be sure that your solution answers the question posed in the original problem.
> 8. Check your answer by using it to solve the original problem (not the equation).

We will now see how this strategy can be applied to various types of problems.

Geometric Problems

Any problem that involves a geometric figure may be referred to as a **geometric problem.** For geometric problems the equation is often a geometric formula.

EXAMPLE 3

Finding the length and width of a rectangle
The length of a rectangular piece of property is 1 foot more than twice the width. If the perimeter is 302 feet, find the length and width.

Solution
First draw a diagram as in Fig. 2.4. Because the length is 1 foot more than twice the width, we let

x

$2x + 1$

FIGURE 2.4

$$x = \text{the width}$$

and

$$2x + 1 = \text{the length.}$$

Strategy Boxes

The **strategy boxes** provide a numbered list of concepts from a section or a set of steps to follow in problem solving. They can be used by students who prefer a more structured approach to problem solving or they can be used as a study tool to review important points within sections.

Solution
If x represents the number of AM ads and y represents the number of FM ads, then x and y must satisfy the inequality $50x + 75y \leq 3000$. Because the number of ads cannot be negative, we also have $x \geq 0$ and $y \geq 0$. So we graph only points in the first quadrant that satisfy $50x + 75y \leq 3000$. The line $50x + 75y = 3000$ goes

FIGURE 3.35

MATH AT WORK

"We will return after these messages." We often hear these words on television and radio just before several minutes of commercials. Carolanne Johnson, Account Executive and Media Salesperson for WBOQ, a classical radio station, is involved in every step of creating such advertisements.

The first step is finding clients that are consistent with the station's image. Ms. Johnson generates her own leads from a number of sources, such as print ads and billboards. The next steps are sitting down with the client, gathering information about the product or service, assessing the competition, and finally determining how much of the client's advertising budget should be spent on radio. Typically, this can be 2% to 4% of the total budget.

Radio ads usually run for 60 seconds, but reminder ads can be as short as 30 seconds. Some of the radio spots are time-sensitive and run 40 to 60 times a month for a specific month. Other clients are concerned with image building and may sponsor one particular broadcast every day for the whole year.

Ms. Johnson is concerned that the clients receive an adequate return on their investment. She is constantly reviewing the budget and making sure that the commercials present what the client wishes to project.

Example 7 and Exercise 77 of this section give problems that involve allocation of advertising dollars.

MEDIA SALESPERSON

Math at Work

The **Math at Work** feature that appears in each chapter explores the careers of individuals who use the mathematics presented in the chapter in their work. Students are referred to exercises that directly relate to the occupation highlighted in **Math at Work.**

Warm-ups

Warm-ups appear before each set of exercises at the end of every section. They are true or false statements that can be used to check conceptual understanding of material within each section.

Helpful Hint

A problem involving two unknowns can often be solved with one variable as in Chapter 2. Likewise, you can often solve a problem with three unknowns using only two variables. Solve Example 5 by letting a, b, and $2a$ be the rent for a one-bedroom, two-bedroom, and a three-bedroom condo.

equation for the total repairs, and a third equation expressing the fact that the rent for the three-bedroom condo is twice that for the one-bedroom condo:

$$x + y + z = 1240$$
$$0.1x + 0.2y + 0.3z = 276$$
$$z = 2x$$

Substitute $z = 2x$ into both of the other equations to eliminate z:

$$x + y + 2x = 1240$$
$$0.1x + 0.2y + 0.3(2x) = 276$$

$$3x + \quad y = 1240$$
$$0.7x + 0.2y = 276$$

$$-2(3x + y) = -2(1240) \qquad \text{Multiply each side by } -2.$$
$$10(0.7x + 0.2y) = 10(276) \qquad \text{Multiply each side by 10.}$$

$$-6x - 2y = -2480$$
$$\underline{7x + 2y = 2760} \qquad \text{Add.}$$
$$x = 280$$

$$z = 2(280) = 560 \qquad \text{Because } z = 2x$$
$$280 + y + 560 = 1240 \qquad \text{Because } x + y + z = 1240$$
$$y = 400$$

Check that (280, 400, 560) satisfies all three of the original equations. The condos rent for \$280, \$400, and \$560 per week. ■

WARM-UPS

True or false? Explain your answer.

1. The point $(1, -2, 3)$ is in the solution set to the equation $x + y - z = 4$.

2. The point $(4, 1, 1)$ is the only solution to the equation $x + y - z = 4$.

3. The ordered triple $(1, -1, 2)$ satisfies $x + y + z = 2$, $x - y - z = 0$, and $2x + y - z = -1$.

4. Substitution cannot be used on three equations in three variables.

5. Two distinct planes are either parallel or intersect in a single point.

6. The equations $x - y + 2z = 6$ and $x - y + 2z = 4$ are inconsistent.

7. The equations $3x + 2y - 6z = 4$ and $-6x - 4y + 12z = -8$ are dependent.

8. The graph of $y = 2x - 3z + 4$ is a straight line.

9. The value of x nickels, y dimes, and z quarters is $0.05x + 0.10y + 0.25z$ cents.

10. If $x = -2$, $z = 3$, and $x + y + z = 6$, then $y = 7$.

---

32. **Buying texts.** Melissa purchased an English text, a math text, and a chemistry text for a total of \$276. The English text was \$20 more than the math text and the chemistry text was twice the price of the math text. What was the price of each text?

33. **Three-day drive.** In three days, Carter drove 2196 miles in 36 hours behind the wheel. The first day he averaged 64 mph, the second day 62 mph, and the third day 58 mph. If he drove 4 more hours on the third day than on the first day, then how many hours did he drive each day?

34. **Three-day trip.** In three days, Katy traveled 146 miles down the Mississippi River in her kayak with 30 hours of paddling. The first day she averaged 6 mph, the second day 5 mph, and the third day 4 mph. If her distance on the third day was equal to her distance on the first day, then for how many hours did she paddle each day?

35. **Diversification.** Ann invested a total of \$12,000 in stocks, bonds, and a mutual fund. She received a 10% return on her stock investment, an 8% return on her bond investment, and a 12% return on her mutual fund. Her total return was \$1,230. If the total investment in stocks and bonds equaled her mutual fund investment, then how much did she invest in each?

36. **Paranoia.** Fearful of a bank failure, Norman split his life savings of \$60,000 among four banks. He received 5%, 6%, and 7% on the three deposits. In the account earning 7% interest, he deposited twice as much as in the account earning 5% interest. If his total earnings were \$3,760, then how much did he deposit in each account?

37. **Weighing in.** Anna, Bob, and Chris will not disclose their weights but agree to be weighed in pairs. Anna and Bob together weigh 226 pounds. Bob and Chris together weigh 210 pounds. Anna and Chris together weigh 200 pounds. How much does each student weigh?

FIGURE FOR EXERCISE 37

Anna & Bob   Bob & Chris   Anna & Chris

38. **Big tipper.** On Monday Headley paid \$1.70 for two cups of coffee and one doughnut, including the tip. On Tuesday he paid \$1.65 for two doughnuts and a cup of coffee, including the tip. On Wednesday he paid \$1.30 for one coffee and one doughnut, including the tip. If he always tips the same amount, then what is the amount of each item?

39. **Three coins.** Nelson paid \$1.75 for his lunch with 13 coins, consisting of nickels, dimes, and quarters. If the number of dimes was twice the number of nickels, then how many of each type of coin did he use?

40. **Pocket change.** Harry has \$2.25 in nickels, dimes, and quarters. If he had twice as many nickels, half as many dimes, and the same number of quarters, he would have \$2.50. If he has 27 coins altogether, then how many of each does he have?

41. **Working overtime.** To make ends meet, Ms. Farnsby works three jobs. Her total income last year was \$48,000. Her income from teaching was just \$6,000 more than her income from house painting. Royalties from her textbook sales were one-seventh of the total money she received from teaching and house painting. How much did she make from each source last year?

42. **Lunch-box special.** Salvador's Fruit Mart sells variety packs. The small pack contains three bananas, two apples, and one orange for \$1.80. The medium pack contains four bananas, three apples, and three oranges for \$3.05. The family size contains six bananas, five apples, and four oranges for \$4.65. What price should Salvador charge for his lunch-box special that consists of one banana, one apple, and one orange?

43. **Three generations.** Edwin, his father, and his grandfather have an average age of 53. One-half of his grandfather's age, plus one-third of his father's age, plus one-fourth of Edwin's age is 65. If 4 years ago, Edwin's grandfather was four times as old as Edwin, then how old are they all now?

44. **Three-digit number.** The sum of the digits of a three-digit number is 11. If the digits are reversed, the new number is 46 more than five times the old number. If the hundreds digit plus twice the tens digit is equal to the units digit, then what is the number?

GETTING MORE INVOLVED

45. **Exploration.** Draw diagrams showing the possible ways to position three planes in three-dimensional space.

46. **Discussion.** Make up a system of three linear equations in three variables for which the solution set is $\{(0, 0, 0)\}$. A system with this solution set is called a *homogeneous* system. Why do you think it is given that name?

Exercises

The theme of mathematics in everyday situations is carried over to the exercise sets. Applications based on real-world data are included in each set. The **Index of Selected Applications** can help students to quickly identify exercises that associate the mathematics that may be used in their areas of interest.

MISCELLANEOUS

55. The points $(3, \quad)$ and $(\quad, -7)$ are on the line that passes through $(2, 1)$ and has slope 4. Find the missing coordinates of the points.

56. If a line passes through $(5, 2)$ and has slope $\frac{2}{3}$, then what is the value of y on this line when $x = 8$, $x = 11$, and $x = 12$?

57. Find k so that the line through $(2, k)$ and $(-3, -5)$ has slope $\frac{1}{2}$.

58. Find k so that the line through $(k, 3)$ and $(-2, 0)$ has slope 3.

59. What is the slope of a line that is perpendicular to a line with slope 0.247?

60. What is the slope of a line that is perpendicular to the line through $(3.27, -1.46)$ and $(-5.48, 3.61)$?

GETTING MORE INVOLVED

61. *Writing.* What is the difference between zero slope and undefined slope?

62. *Writing.* Is it possible for a line to be in only one quadrant? Two quadrants? Write a rule for determining whether a line has positive, negative, zero, or undefined slope from knowing in which quadrants the line is found.

63. *Exploration.* A rhombus is a quadrilateral with four equal sides. Draw a rhombus with vertices $(-3, -1)$, $(0, 3)$, $(2, -1)$, and $(5, 3)$. Find the slopes of the diagonals of the rhombus. What can you conclude about the diagonals of this rhombus?

64. *Exploration.* Draw a square with vertices $(-5, 3)$, $(-3, -3)$, $(1, 5)$, and $(3, -1)$. Find the slopes of the diagonals of the square. What can you conclude about the diagonals of this square?

GRAPHING CALCULATOR EXERCISES

65. Graph $y = 1x$, $y = 2x$, $y = 3x$, and $y = 4x$ together in the standard viewing window. These equations are all of the form $y = mx$. What effect does increasing m have on the graph of the equation? What are the slopes of these four lines?

66. Graph $y = -1x$, $y = -2x$, $y = -3x$, and $y = -4x$ together in the standard viewing window. These equations are all of the form $y = mx$. What effect does decreasing m have on the graph of the equation? What are the slopes of these four lines?

In This Section
- Point-Slope Form
- Slope-Intercept Form
- Standard Form
- Using Slope-Intercept Form for Graphing
- Applications

3.3 THREE FORMS FOR THE EQUATION OF A LINE

In Section 3.1 you learned how to graph a straight line corresponding to a linear equation. The line contains all of the points that satisfy the equation. In this section we start with a line or a description of a line and write an equation corresponding to the line.

Point-Slope Form

Figure 3.20 shows the line that has slope $\frac{2}{3}$ and contains the point $(3, 5)$. In Section 3.2 you learned that the slope is the same no matter which two points of the line are used to calculate it. So if we find the slope m for this line using an arbitrary point of the line, say (x, y), and the specific point $(3, 5)$, we get

$$m = \frac{y - 5}{x - 3}.$$

Getting More Involved appears within selected exercise sets. This feature may contain

 Writing,

Cooperative Learning,

 Exploration, and/or

Discussion exercises. Each of these components is designed to give students an opportunity to improve and develop the ways in which they express mathematical ideas.

The exercise sets contain exercises that are keyed to examples, as well as exercises that are not keyed to examples.

---

c) Write the equation of the line through $(0, 3)$ and $(-5, 0)$ in intercept form.

d) Which lines cannot be written in intercept form?

GRAPHING CALCULATOR EXERCISES

98. Graph the equation $y = 0.5x - 1$ using the standard viewing window. Adjust the range of y-values so that the line goes from the lower left corner of your viewing window to the upper right corner.

99. Graph $y = x - 3000$, using a viewing window that shows both the x-intercept and the y-intercept.

100. Graph $y = 2x - 400$ and $y = -0.5x + 1$ on the same screen, using the viewing window $-500 \leq x \leq 500$ and $-1000 \leq y \leq 1000$. Should these lines be perpendicular? Explain.

101. The lines $y = 2x - 3$ and $y = 1.9x + 2$ are not parallel. Find a viewing window in which the lines intersect. Estimate the point of intersection.

In This Section
- Definition
- Graphing Linear Inequalities
- The Test Point Method
- Graphing Compound Inequalities
- Applications

3.4 LINEAR INEQUALITIES AND THEIR GRAPHS

In the first three sections of this chapter you studied linear equations. We now turn our attention to linear inequalities.

Definition

A linear inequality is a linear equation with the equal sign replaced by an inequality symbol.

Linear Inequality

If A, B, and C are real numbers with A and B not both zero, then

$$Ax + By \leq C$$

is called a **linear inequality.** In place of $\leq$, we can also use $\geq$, $<$, or $>$.

Graphing Linear Inequalities

Consider the inequality $-x + y > 1$. If we solve the inequality for y, we get

$$y > x + 1.$$

Which points in the xy-plane satisfy this inequality? We want the points where the y-coordinate is larger than the x-coordinate plus 1. If we locate a point on the line $y = x + 1$, say $(2, 3)$, then the y-coordinate is equal to the x-coordinate plus 1. If we move upward from that point, to say $(2, 4)$, the y-coordinate is larger than the x-coordinate plus 1. Because this argument can be made at every point on the line, all points above the line satisfy $y > x + 1$. Likewise, points below the line satisfy $y < x + 1$. The solution sets, or graphs, for the inequality $y > x + 1$ and the inequality $y < x + 1$ are the shaded regions shown in Figs. 3.24(a) and 3.24(b) on the next page. In each case the line $y = x + 1$ is dashed to indicate that points on the line do not satisfy the inequality and so are not in the solution set. If the inequality symbol is $\leq$ or $\geq$, then points on the boundary line also satisfy the inequality, and the line is drawn solid.

Study Tip

Working problems one hour per day every day of the week is better than working problems for 7 hours on one day of the week. It is usually better to spread out your study time than to try and learn everything in one big session.

Calculator Exercises

Calculator Exercises are optional. They provide an opportunity for students to learn how a scientific or graphing calculator might be useful in solving various problems.

318 (5-64) Chapter 5 Exponents and Polynomials

you get $x^2 - x = 0$, which has two solutions. Which method is correct? Explain.

96. Cooperative learning. Work with a group to examine the following solution to $x^2 - 2x = -1$:

$$x(x - 2) = -1$$
$$x = -1 \quad \text{or} \quad x - 2 = -1$$
$$x = -1 \quad \text{or} \quad x = 1$$

Is this method correct? Explain.

97. Cooperative learning. Work with a group to examine the following steps in the solution to $5x^2 - 5 = 0$

$$5(x^2 - 1) = 0$$
$$5(x - 1)(x + 1) = 0$$
$$x - 1 = 0 \quad \text{or} \quad x + 1 = 0$$
$$x = 1 \quad \text{or} \quad x = -1$$

What happened to the 5? Explain.

COLLABORATIVE ACTIVITIES

Magic Tricks

Jim and Sadar are talking one day after class.

Sadar: Jim, I have a trick for you. Think of a number between 1 and 10. I will ask you to do some things to this number. Then at the end tell me your result, and I will tell you your number.

Jim: Oh, yeah you probably rig it so the result is my number.

Sadar: Come on Jim, give it a try and see.

Jim: Okay, okay, I thought of a number.

Sadar: Good, now write it down, and don't let me see your paper. Now add x. Got that? Now multiply everything by 2.

Jim: Hey, I didn't know you were going to make me think! This is algebra!

Sadar: I know, now just do it. Okay, now square the polynomial. Got that? Now subtract $4x^2$.

Jim: How did you know I had a $4x^2$? I told you this was rigged!

Sadar: Of course it's rigged, or it wouldn't work. Do you want to finish or not?

Jim: Yeah, I guess so. Go ahead, what do I do next?

Sadar: Divide by 4. Okay, now subtract the x-term.

Grouping: Two students per group
Topic: Practice with exponent rules, multiplying polynomials

Jim: Just any old x-term? Got any particular coefficient in mind?

Sadar: Now stop teasing me. I know you only have one x-term left, so subtract it.

Jim: Ha, ha, I *could* give you a hint about the coefficient, but that wouldn't be fair, would it?

Sadar: Well you could, and then I could tell you your number, or you could just tell me the number you have left after subtracting.

Jim: Okay, the number I had left at the end was 25. Let's see if you can tell me what the coefficient of the x-term I subtracted is.

Sadar: Aha, then the number you chose at the beginning was 5, and the coefficient was 10!

Jim: Hey, you're right! How did you do that?

In your group, follow Sadar's instructions and determine why she knew Jim's number. Make up another set of instructions to use as a magic trick. Be sure to use variables and some of the exponent rules or rules for multiplying polynomials that you learned in this chapter. Exchange instructions with another group and see whether you can figure out how their trick works.

WRAP-UP CHAPTER 5

SUMMARY

Definitions		Examples
Definition of negative integral exponents	If a is a nonzero real number and n is a positive integer, then $$a^{-n} = \frac{1}{a^n}.$$	$2^{-3} = \dfrac{1}{2^3} = \dfrac{1}{8}$

Collaborative Activities

Collaborative Activities appear at the end of each chapter. The activities are designed to encourage interaction and learning in a group setting.

WRAP-UP CHAPTER 8

SUMMARY

Quadratic Equations		Examples
Quadratic equation	An equation of the form $ax^2 + bx + c = 0$, where a, b, and c are real numbers, with $a \neq 0$	$x^2 = 11$ $(x - 5)^2 = 99$ $x^2 + 3x - 20 = 0$ $x^2 + x - 6 = 0$ $(x + 3)(x - 2) = 0$

504 (8-52) Chapter 8 Quadratic Equations, Functions, and Inequalities

ENRICHING YOUR MATHEMATICAL WORD POWER

For each mathematical term, choose the correct meaning.

1. qu...
a. ...
b. ...

6. quadratic function
a. $y = ax + b$ with $a \neq 0$
b. a parabola
c. $y = ax^2 + bx + c$ with $a \neq 0$
d. the quadratic formula

...quadratic in form
...$x = 0$

2. ...

87. $\dfrac{x - 4}{x + 2} \geq 0$

88. $\dfrac{x - 3}{x + 5} < 0$

89. $\dfrac{x - 2}{x + 3} < 1$

90. $\dfrac{x - 3}{x + 4} > 2$

91. $\dfrac{3}{x + 2} > \dfrac{1}{x + 1}$

92. $\dfrac{1}{x + 1} < \dfrac{1}{x - 1}$

MISCELLANEOUS

In Exercises 93–104, find all real or imaginary solutions to each equation.

93. $144x^2 - 120x + 25 = 0$

Chapter 8 Review Exercises (8-55) **507**

103. $x^{1/2} - 15x^{1/4} + 50 = 0$

104. $x^{-2} - 9x^{-1} + 18 = 0$

Find exact and approximate solutions to each problem.

105. Missing numbers. Find two positive real numbers that differ by 4 and have a product of 4.

106. One on one. Find two positive real numbers that differ by 1 and have a product of 1.

107. Big screen TV. On a 19-inch diagonal measure television picture screen, the height is 4 inches less than the width. Find the height and width.

19 in.
$x - 4$ in.
x in.

FIGURE FOR EXERCISE 107

108. Boxing match. A boxing ring is in the shape of a square, 20 ft on each side. How far apart are the fighters when they are in opposite corners of the ring?

Wrap-up

Every chapter ends with a four-part **Wrap-up:**

The **Summary** lists important concepts along with brief illustrative examples.

Enriching Your Mathematical Word Power enables students to review terms introduced in each chapter. It is intended to help reinforce students' command of mathematical terminology.

Review Exercises contain problems that are keyed to each section of the chapter as well as **miscellaneous exercises,** which are not keyed to the sections. The *miscellaneous exercises* are designed to test the student's ability to synthesize various concepts.

Chapter 8   Test   (8-57) **509**

CHAPTER 8 TEST

Calculate the value of $b^2 - 4ac$, and state how many real solutions each equation has.

1. $2x^2 - 3x + 2 = 0$

2. $-3x^2 + 5x - 1 = 0$

3. $4x^2 - 4x + 1 = 0$

Solve by using the quadratic formula.

4. $2x^2 + 5x - 3 = 0$

5. $x^2 + 6x + 6 = 0$

Solve by completing the square.

6. $x^2 + 10x + 25 = 0$

7. $2x^2 + x - 6 = 0$

Solve by any method.

8. $x(x + 1) = 12$

9. $a^4 - 5a^2 + 4 = 0$

10. $x - 2 - 8\sqrt{x - 2} + 15 = 0$

Find the complex solutions to the quadratic equations.

11. $x^2 + 36 = 0$

12. $x^2 + 6x + 10 = 0$

13. $3x^2 - x + 1 = 0$

Graph each quadratic function. State the domain and range.

14. $f(x) = 16 - x^2$

15. $g(x) = x^2 - 3x$

Write a quadratic equation that has each given pair of solutions.

16. $-4, 6$

17. $-5i, 5i$

Solve each inequality. State and graph the solution set.

18. $w^2 + 3w < 18$

19. $\dfrac{2}{x - 2} < \dfrac{3}{x + 1}$

Find the exact solution to each problem.

20. The length of a rectangle is 2 ft longer than the width. If the area is 16 ft², then what are the length and width?

21. A new computer can process a company's monthly payroll in 1 hour less time than the old computer. To really save time, the manager used both computers and finished the payroll in 3 hours. How long would it take the new computer to do the payroll by itself?

Solve each problem.

22. Find the x-intercepts for the parabola $y = x^2 - 6x + 5$.

23. The height in feet for a ball thrown upward at 48 feet per second is given by $s(t) = -16t^2 + 48t$, where t is the time in seconds after the ball is tossed. What is the maximum height that the ball will reach?

Chapter Test

This is designed to help the student assess his or her readiness for a test. The **Chapter Test** has no keyed exercises, which affords students an opportunity to synthesize concepts found within the chapter.

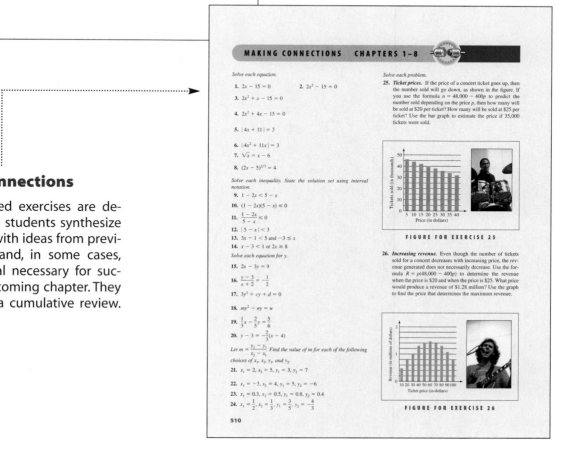

MAKING CONNECTIONS   CHAPTERS 1–8

Solve each equation.

1. $2x - 15 = 0$

2. $2x^2 - 15 = 0$

3. $2x^2 + x - 15 = 0$

4. $2x^2 + 4x - 15 = 0$

5. $|4x + 11| = 3$

6. $|4x^2 + 11x| = 3$

7. $\sqrt{x} = x - 6$

8. $(2x - 5)^{2/3} = 4$

Solve each inequality. State the solution set using interval notation.

9. $1 - 2x < 5 - x$

10. $(1 - 2x)(5 - x) \le 0$

11. $\dfrac{1 - 2x}{5 - x} \le 0$

12. $|5 - x| < 3$

13. $3x - 1 < 5$ and $-3 \le x$

14. $x - 3 < 1$ or $2x \ge 8$

Solve each equation for y.

15. $2x - 3y = 9$

16. $\dfrac{y - 3}{x + 2} = \dfrac{1}{2}$

17. $3y^2 + cy + d = 0$

18. $my^2 - ny = w$

19. $\dfrac{1}{3}x - \dfrac{2}{5}y = \dfrac{5}{6}$

20. $y - 3 = -\dfrac{2}{3}(x - 4)$

Let $m = \dfrac{y_2 - y_1}{x_2 - x_1}$. Find the value of m for each of the following choices of x_1, x_2, y_1, and y_2.

21. $x_1 = 2, x_2 = 5, y_1 = 3, y_2 = 7$

22. $x_1 = -3, x_2 = 4, y_1 = 5, y_2 = -6$

23. $x_1 = 0.3, x_2 = 0.5, y_1 = 0.8, y_2 = 0.4$

24. $x_1 = \dfrac{1}{2}, x_2 = \dfrac{1}{3}, y_1 = \dfrac{3}{5}, y_2 = -\dfrac{4}{3}$

Solve each problem.

25. *Ticket prices.* If the price of a concert ticket goes up, then the number sold will go down, as shown in the figure. If you use the formula $n = 48,000 - 400p$ to predict the number sold depending on the price p, then how many will be sold at $20 per ticket? How many will be sold at $25 per ticket? Use the bar graph to estimate the price if 35,000 tickets were sold.

FIGURE FOR EXERCISE 25

26. *Increasing revenue.* Even though the number of tickets sold for a concert decreases with increasing price, the revenue generated does not necessarily decrease. Use the formula $R = p(48,000 - 400p)$ to determine the revenue when the price is $20 and when the price is $25. What price would produce a revenue of $1.28 million? Use the graph to find the price that determines the maximum revenue.

FIGURE FOR EXERCISE 26

510

Making Connections

These nonkeyed exercises are designed to help students synthesize new material with ideas from previous chapters and, in some cases, review material necessary for success in the upcoming chapter. They may serve as a cumulative review.

The Real Numbers

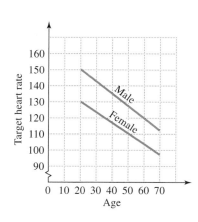

E verywhere you look people are running, riding, dancing, and exercising their way to fitness. In the past year more than $25 billion has been spent on sports equipment alone, and this amount is growing steadily.

Proponents of exercise claim that it can increase longevity, improve body image, decrease appetite, and generally enhance a person's health. While many sports activities can help you to stay fit, experts have found that aerobic, or dynamic, workouts provide the most fitness benefit. Some of the best aerobic exercises include cycling, running, and even jumping rope. Whatever athletic activity you choose, trainers recommend that you set realistic goals and work your way toward them consistently and slowly. To achieve maximum health benefits, experts suggest that you exercise three to five times a week for 15 to 60 minutes at a time.

There are many different ways to measure exercise. One is to measure the energy used, or the rate of oxygen consumption. Since heart rate rises as a function of increased oxygen, another easier measure of intensity of exercise is your heart rate during exercise. The desired heart rate, or target heart rate, for beneficial exercise varies for each individual depending on conditioning, age, and gender. In Exercises 101 and 102 of Section 1.4 you will see how an algebraic expression can determine your target heart rate for beneficial exercise.

1.1   S E T S

Every subject has its own terminology, and **algebra** is no different. In this section we will learn the basic terms and facts about sets.

Set Notation

A **set** is a collection of objects. At home you may have a set of dishes and a set of steak knives. In algebra we generally discuss sets of numbers. For example, we refer to the numbers 1, 2, 3, 4, 5, and so on as the set of **counting numbers** or **natural numbers.** Of course, these are the numbers that we use for counting.

The objects or numbers in a set are called the **elements** or **members** of the set. To describe sets with a convenient notation, we use braces, { }, and name the sets with capital letters. For example,

$$A = \{1, 2, 3\}$$

means that set A is the set whose members are the natural numbers 1, 2, and 3. The letter N is used to represent the entire set of natural numbers.

A set that has a fixed number of elements such as $\{1, 2, 3\}$ is a **finite** set, whereas a set without a fixed number of elements such as the natural numbers is an **infinite** set. When listing the elements of a set, we use a series of three dots to indicate a continuing pattern. For example, the set of natural numbers is written as

$$N = \{1, 2, 3, \ldots\}.$$

The set of natural numbers *between* 4 and 40 can be written

$$\{5, 6, 7, 8, \ldots, 39\}.$$

Note that since the members of this set are *between* 4 and 40, it does not include 4 or 40.

Set-builder notation is another method of describing sets. In this notation we use a variable to represent the numbers in the set. A **variable** is a letter that is used to stand for some numbers. The set is then built from the variable and a description of the numbers that the variable represents. For example, the set

$$B = \{1, 2, 3, \ldots, 49\}$$

is written in set-builder notation as

$$B = \{x \mid x \text{ is a natural number less than 50}\}.$$

The set of numbers   such that   condition for membership

This notation is read as "B is the set of numbers x such that x is a natural number less than 50." Notice that the number 50 is not a member of set B.

The symbol $\in$ is used to indicate that a specific number is a member of a set, and $\notin$ indicates that a specific number is not a member of a set. For example, the statement $1 \in B$ is read as "1 is a member of B," "1 belongs to B," "1 is in B," or "1 is an element of B." The statement $0 \notin B$ is read as "0 is not a member of B," "0 does not belong to B," "0 is not in B," or "0 is not an element of B."

Two sets are **equal** if they contain exactly the same members. Otherwise, they are said to be not equal. To indicate equal sets, we use the symbol $=$. For sets that are not equal we use the symbol $\neq$. The elements in two equal sets do not need to be written in the same order. For example, $\{3, 4, 7\} = \{3, 4, 7\}$ and $\{2, 4, 1\} = \{1, 2, 4\}$, but $\{3, 5, 6\} \neq \{3, 5, 7\}$.

E X A M P L E   1

Set notation

Let $A = \{1, 2, 3, 5\}$ and $B = \{x \mid x$ is an even natural number less than 10$\}$. Determine whether each statement is true or false.

a) $3 \in A$ **b)** $5 \in B$ **c)** $4 \notin A$ **d)** $A = N$

e) $A = \{x \mid x$ is a natural number less than 6$\}$ **f)** $B = \{2, 4, 6, 8\}$

Solution

a) True, because 3 is a member of set A.

b) False, because 5 is not an even natural number.

c) True, because 4 is not a member of set A.

d) False, because A does not contain all of the natural numbers.

e) False, because 4 is a natural number less than 6, and $4 \notin A$.

f) True, because the even counting numbers less than 10 are 2, 4, 6, and 8. ■

Union of Sets

Any two sets A and B can be combined to form a new set called their union that consists of all elements of A together with all elements of B.

Union of Sets

If A and B are sets, the **union** of A and B, denoted $A \cup B$, is the set of all elements that are either in A, in B, or in both. In symbols,

$$A \cup B = \{x \mid x \in A \text{ or } x \in B\}.$$

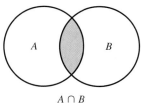

$A \cup B$

F I G U R E   1 . 1

In mathematics the word "or" is always used in an inclusive manner (allowing the possibility of both alternatives). The diagram in Fig. 1.1 can be used to illustrate $A \cup B$. Any point that lies within circle A, circle B, or both is in $A \cup B$. Diagrams (like Fig. 1.1) that are used to illustrate sets are called **Venn diagrams.**

E X A M P L E   2

Helpful Hint

To remember what "union" means think of a labor union, which is a group formed by joining together many individuals.

Union of sets

Let $A = \{0, 2, 3\}$, $B = \{2, 3, 7\}$, and $C = \{7, 8\}$. List the elements in each of these sets.

a) $A \cup B$ **b)** $A \cup C$

Solution

a) $A \cup B$ is the set of numbers that are in A, in B, or in both A and B.

$$A \cup B = \{0, 2, 3, 7\}$$

b) $A \cup C = \{0, 2, 3, 7, 8\}$ ■

$A \cap B$

F I G U R E   1 . 2

Intersection of Sets

Another way to form a new set from two known sets is by considering only those elements that the two sets have in common. The diagram shown in Fig. 1.2 illustrates the intersection of two sets A and B.

Helpful Hint

To remember the meaning of "intersection," think of the intersection of two roads. At the intersection you are on both roads.

Intersection of Sets

If A and B are sets, the **intersection** of A and B, denoted $A \cap B$, is the set of all elements that are in both A and B. In symbols,

$$A \cap B = \{x \mid x \in A \text{ and } x \in B\}.$$

It is possible for two sets to have no elements in common. A set with no members is called the **empty set** and is denoted by the symbol $\varnothing$. Note that $A \cup \varnothing = A$ and $A \cap \varnothing = \varnothing$ for any set A.

CAUTION   The set $\{0\}$ is not the empty set. The set $\{0\}$ has one member, the number 0. Do not use the number 0 to represent the empty set.

EXAMPLE 3   **Intersection of sets**
Let $A = \{0, 2, 3\}$, $B = \{2, 3, 7\}$, and $C = \{7, 8\}$. List the elements in each of these sets.

a) $A \cap B$ **b)** $B \cap C$ **c)** $A \cap C$

Solution

a) $A \cap B$ is the set of all numbers that are in both A and B. So $A \cap B = \{2, 3\}$.

b) $B \cap C = \{7\}$ **c)** $A \cap C = \varnothing$ ■

EXAMPLE 4   **Membership and equality**
Let $A = \{1, 2, 3, 5\}$, $B = \{2, 3, 7, 8\}$, and $C = \{6, 7, 8, 9\}$. Place one of the symbols $=$, $\neq$, $\in$, or $\notin$ in the blank to make each statement correct.

a) 5 _____ $A \cup B$ **b)** 5 _____ $A \cap B$
c) $A \cup B$ _____ $\{1, 2, 3, 5, 7, 8\}$ **d)** $A \cap B$ _____ $\{2\}$

Solution

a) $5 \in A \cup B$ because 5 is a member of A.

b) $5 \notin A \cap B$ because 5 must belong to *both* A and B to be a member of $A \cap B$.

c) $A \cup B = \{1, 2, 3, 5, 7, 8\}$ because the elements of A together with those of B are listed. Note that 2 and 3 are members of both sets but are listed only once.

d) $A \cap B \neq \{2\}$ because $A \cap B = \{2, 3\}$.   ■

Subsets

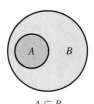

$A \subseteq B$

FIGURE 1.3

If every member of set A is also a member of set B, then we write $A \subseteq B$ and say that A is a **subset** of B. See Fig. 1.3. For example,

$$\{2, 3\} \subseteq \{2, 3, 4\}$$

because $2 \in \{2, 3, 4\}$ and $3 \in \{2, 3, 4\}$. Note that the symbol for membership ($\in$) is used between a single element and a set, whereas the symbol for subset ($\subseteq$) is used between two sets. If A is not a subset of B, we write $A \nsubseteq B$.

CAUTION   To claim that $A \nsubseteq B$, there *must* be an element of A that does *not* belong to B. For example,

$$\{1, 2\} \nsubseteq \{2, 3, 4\}$$

because 1 is a member of the first set but not of the second.

Is the empty set $\varnothing$ a subset of $\{2, 3, 4\}$? If we say that $\varnothing$ is *not* a subset of $\{2, 3, 4\}$, then there must be an element of $\varnothing$ that does not belong to $\{2, 3, 4\}$. But that cannot happen because $\varnothing$ is empty. So $\varnothing$ is a subset of $\{2, 3, 4\}$. In fact, by the same reasoning, *the empty set is a subset of every set.*

E X A M P L E   5

Subsets

Determine whether each statement is true or false.

a) $\{1, 2, 3\}$ is a subset of the set of natural numbers.

b) The set of natural numbers is not a subset of $\{1, 2, 3\}$.

c) $\{1, 2, 3\} \not\subseteq \{2, 4, 6, 8\}$

d) $\{2, 6\} \subseteq \{1, 2, 3, 4, 5\}$

e) $\varnothing \subseteq \{2, 4, 6\}$

Helpful Hint

The symbols $\subseteq$ and $\subset$ are often used interchangeably. The symbol $\subseteq$ combines the subset symbol $\subset$ and the equal symbol $=$. We use it when sets are equal, $\{1, 2\} \subseteq \{1, 2\}$, and when they are not, $\{1\} \subseteq \{1, 2\}$. When sets are not equal, we could simply use $\subset$, as in $\{1\} \subset \{1, 2\}$.

Solution

a) True, because 1, 2, and 3 are natural numbers.

b) True, because 5, for example, is a natural number and $5 \notin \{1, 2, 3\}$.

c) True, because 1 is in the first set but not in the second.

d) False, because 6 is in the first set but not in the second.

e) True, because we cannot find anything in $\varnothing$ that fails to be in $\{2, 4, 6\}$.   ∎

Combining Three or More Sets

We know how to find the union and intersection of two sets. For three or more sets we use parentheses to indicate which pair of sets to combine first. In Example 6, notice that different results are obtained from different placements of the parentheses.

E X A M P L E   6

Operations with three sets

Let $A = \{1, 2, 3, 4\}$, $B = \{2, 5, 6, 8\}$, and $C = \{4, 5, 7\}$. List the elements of each of these sets.

a) $(A \cup B) \cap C$ **b)** $A \cup (B \cap C)$

Study Tip

Exercise sets are designed to increase gradually in difficulty. So start from the beginning and work lots of exercises. If you get stuck, go back and study the corresponding examples. If you are still stuck, move ahead to a new type of exercise.

Solution

a) The parentheses indicate that the union of A and B is to be found first and then the result, $A \cup B$, is to be intersected with C.

$$A \cup B = \{1, 2, 3, 4, 5, 6, 8\}$$

Now examine $A \cup B$ and C to find the elements that belong to both sets:

$$A \cup B = \{1, 2, 3, 4, 5, 6, 8\}$$
$$C = \{4, 5, 7\}$$

The only numbers that are members of $A \cup B$ and C are 4 and 5. Thus

$$(A \cup B) \cap C = \{4, 5\}.$$

b) In $A \cup (B \cap C)$, first find $B \cap C$:

$$B \cap C = \{5\}$$

Now $A \cup (B \cap C)$ consist of all members of A together with 5 from $B \cap C$:

$$A \cup (B \cap C) = \{1, 2, 3, 4, 5\}$$ ∎

WARM-UPS

True or false? Explain your answer.

Let $A = \{1, 2, 3, 4\}$, $B = \{3, 4, 5\}$, and $C = \{3, 4\}$.

 1. $A = \{x \mid x \text{ is a counting number}\}$
 2. The set B has an infinite number of elements.
 3. The set of counting numbers less than 50 million is an infinite set.
 4. $1 \in A \cap B$
 5. $3 \in A \cup B$
 6. $A \cap B = C$
 7. $C \subseteq B$
 8. $A \subseteq B$
 9. $\varnothing \subseteq C$
 10. $A \nsubseteq C$

1.1   EXERCISES

Reading and Writing   *After reading this section, write out the answers to these questions. Use complete sentences.*

 1. What is a set?
 2. What is the difference between a finite set and an infinite set?

 3. What is a Venn diagram used for?

 4. What is the difference between the intersection and the union of two sets?

 5. What does it mean to say that set A is a subset of set B?

 6. Which set is a subset of every set?

For Exercises 7–52 let N represent the natural numbers, $A = \{x \mid x \text{ is an odd counting number smaller than } 10\}$, $B = \{2, 4, 6, 8\}$, and $C = \{1, 2, 3, 4, 5\}$.

Determine whether each statement is true or false. Explain your answer. See Example 1.

 7. $6 \in A$
 8. $8 \in A$

 9. $A \neq B$
 10. $A = \{1, 3, 5, 7, \ldots\}$

 11. $3 \in C$
 12. $4 \notin B$

 13. $A = \{1, 3, 7, 9\}$
 14. $B \neq C$

 15. $0 \in N$
 16. $2.5 \in N$

 17. $C = N$
 18. $N = A$

List the elements in each set. If the set is empty, write $\varnothing$. See Examples 2 and 3.

 19. $A \cap B$
 20. $A \cup B$

 21. $A \cap C$
 22. $A \cup C$

 23. $B \cup C$
 24. $B \cap C$

 25. $A \cup \varnothing$
 26. $B \cup \varnothing$
 27. $A \cap \varnothing$
 28. $B \cap \varnothing$
 29. $A \cap N$
 30. $A \cup N$

Use one of the symbols $\in$, $\notin$, $=$, $\neq$, $\cup$, or $\cap$ in the blank of each statement to make it correct. See Example 4.

 31. $A \cap B$ _____ $\varnothing$
 32. $A \cap C$ _____ $\varnothing$
 33. A _____ $B = \{1, 2, 3, 4, 5, 6, 7, 8, 9\}$
 34. A _____ $B = \varnothing$
 35. B _____ $C = \{2, 4\}$
 36. B _____ $C = \{1, 2, 3, 4, 5, 6, 8\}$
 37. 3 _____ $A \cap B$
 38. 3 _____ $A \cap C$
 39. 4 _____ $B \cap C$
 40. 8 _____ $B \cup C$

Determine whether each statement is true or false. Explain your answer. See Example 5.

 41. $A \subseteq N$
 42. $B \subseteq N$
 43. $\{2, 3\} \subseteq C$
 44. $C \subseteq A$
 45. $B \nsubseteq C$
 46. $C \nsubseteq A$
 47. $\varnothing \subseteq B$
 48. $\varnothing \subseteq C$
 49. $A \subseteq \varnothing$
 50. $B \subseteq \varnothing$
 51. $A \cap B \subseteq C$
 52. $B \cap C \subseteq \{2, 4, 6, 8\}$

For Exercises 53–78, let $D = \{3, 5, 7\}$, $E = \{2, 4, 6, 8\}$, and $F = \{1, 2, 3, 4, 5\}$.

List the elements in each set. If the set is empty, write $\varnothing$. See Example 6.

 53. $D \cup E$
 54. $D \cap E$

 55. $D \cap F$
 56. $D \cup F$

57. $E \cup F$ **58.** $E \cap F$

59. $(D \cup E) \cap F$ **60.** $(D \cup F) \cap E$

61. $D \cup (E \cap F)$ **62.** $D \cup (F \cap E)$

63. $(D \cap F) \cup (E \cap F)$ **64.** $(D \cap E) \cup (F \cap E)$

65. $(D \cup E) \cap (D \cup F)$ **66.** $(D \cup F) \cap (D \cup E)$

Use one of the symbols $\in, \subseteq, =, \cup,$ *or* $\cap$ *in the blank of each statement to make it correct.*

67. D _____ $\{x \mid x$ is an odd natural number$\}$
68. E _____ $\{x \mid x$ is an even natural number smaller than 9$\}$

69. 3 _____ D **70.** $\{3\}$ _____ D
71. D _____ $E = \varnothing$ **72.** $D \cap E$ _____ D
73. $D \cap F$ _____ F **74.** $3 \notin E$ _____ F
75. $E \not\subseteq E$ _____ F **76.** $E \subseteq E$ _____ F
77. D _____ $F = F \cup D$ **78.** E _____ $F = F \cap E$

List the elements in each set.

79. $\{x \mid x$ is an even natural number less than 20$\}$

80. $\{x \mid x$ is a natural number greater than 6$\}$

81. $\{x \mid x$ is an odd natural number greater than 11$\}$

82. $\{x \mid x$ is an odd natural number less than 14$\}$

83. $\{x \mid x$ is an even natural number between 4 and 79$\}$

84. $\{x \mid x$ is an odd natural number between 12 and 57$\}$

Write each set using set-builder notation. Answers may vary.
85. $\{3, 4, 5, 6\}$

86. $\{1, 3, 5, 7\}$

87. $\{5, 7, 9, 11, \ldots\}$

88. $\{4, 5, 6, 7, \ldots\}$

89. $\{6, 8, 10, 12, \ldots, 82\}$

90. $\{9, 11, 13, 15, \ldots, 51\}$

GETTING MORE INVOLVED

91. *Discussion.* If A and B are finite sets, could $A \cup B$ be infinite? Explain.

92. *Cooperative learning.* Work with a small group to answer the following questions. If $A \subseteq B$ and $B \subseteq A$, then what can you conclude about A and B? If $(A \cup B) \subseteq (A \cap B)$, then what can you conclude about A and B?

93. *Discussion.* What is wrong with each statement? Explain.
a) $3 \subseteq \{1, 2, 3\}$
b) $\{3\} \in \{1, 2, 3\}$
c) $\varnothing = \{\varnothing\}$

94. *Exploration.* There are only two possible subsets of $\{1\}$, namely, $\varnothing$ and $\{1\}$.
a) List all possible subsets of $\{1, 2\}$. How many are there?
b) List all possible subsets of $\{1, 2, 3\}$. How many are there?
c) Guess how many subsets there are of $\{1, 2, 3, 4\}$. Verify your guess by listing all the possible subsets.
d) How many subsets are there for $\{1, 2, 3, \ldots, n\}$?

In This Section

- The Rational Numbers
- Graphing on the Number Line
- The Irrational Numbers
- Intervals of Real Numbers

1.2 # THE REAL NUMBERS

The set of real numbers is the basic set of numbers used in algebra. There are many different types of real numbers. To understand better the set of real numbers, we will study some of the subsets of numbers that make up this set.

The Rational Numbers

We have already discussed the set of counting or natural numbers. The set of natural numbers together with the number 0 is called the set of **whole numbers.** The whole numbers together with the negatives of the counting numbers form the set of

integers. We use the letters N, W, and J to name these sets:

$$N = \{1, 2, 3, \ldots\} \qquad \text{The natural numbers}$$
$$W = \{0, 1, 2, 3, \ldots\} \qquad \text{The whole numbers}$$
$$J = \{\ldots, -3, -2, -1, 0, 1, 2, 3, \ldots\} \qquad \text{The integers}$$

Rational numbers are numbers that are written as ratios or as quotients of integers. We use the letter Q (for quotient) to name the set of rational numbers and write the set in set-builder notation as follows:

$$Q = \left\{ \frac{a}{b} \middle| a \text{ and } b \text{ are integers, with } b \neq 0 \right\} \qquad \text{The rational numbers}$$

Examples of rational numbers are

$$7, \quad \frac{9}{4}, \quad -\frac{17}{10}, \quad 0, \quad \frac{0}{4}, \quad \frac{3}{1}, \quad -\frac{47}{3}, \quad \text{and} \quad \frac{-2}{-6}.$$

Note that the rational numbers are the numbers that can be expressed as a ratio (or quotient) of integers. The integer 7 is rational because we can write it as $\frac{7}{1}$.

Another way to describe rational numbers is by using their decimal form. To obtain the decimal form, we divide the denominator into the numerator. For some rational numbers the division terminates, and for others it continues indefinitely. These examples show some rational numbers and their equivalent decimal forms:

$$\frac{26}{100} = 0.26 \qquad \text{Terminating decimal}$$

$$\frac{4}{1} = 4.0 \qquad \text{Terminating decimal}$$

$$\frac{1}{4} = 0.25 \qquad \text{Terminating decimal}$$

$$\frac{2}{3} = 0.6666\ldots \qquad \text{The single digit 6 repeats.}$$

$$\frac{25}{99} = 0.252525\ldots \qquad \text{The pair of digits 25 repeats.}$$

$$\frac{4177}{990} = 4.2191919\ldots \qquad \text{The pair of digits 19 repeats.}$$

Rational numbers are defined as ratios of integers, but they can be described also by their decimal form. *The rational numbers are those decimal numbers whose digits either repeat or terminate.*

E X A M P L E   1

Subsets of the rational numbers

Determine whether each statement is true or false.

a) $0 \in W$ b) $N \subseteq J$ c) $0.75 \in J$ d) $J \subseteq Q$

Solution

a) True, because 0 is a whole number.

b) True, because every natural number is also a member of the set of integers.

c) False, because the rational number 0.75 is not an integer.

d) True, because the rational numbers include the integers.

Graphing on the Number Line

To construct a number line, we draw a straight line and label any convenient point with the number 0. Now we choose any convenient length and use it to locate points to the right of 0 as points corresponding to the positive integers and points to the left of 0 as points corresponding to the negative integers. See Fig. 1.4. The numbers corresponding to the points on the line are called the **coordinates** of the points. The distance between two consecutive integers is called a **unit,** and it is the same for any two consecutive integers. The point with coordinate 0 is called the **origin.** The numbers on the number line increase in size from left to right. When we compare the size of any two numbers, the larger number lies to the right of the smaller one on the number line.

FIGURE 1.4

It is often convenient to illustrate sets of numbers on a number line. The set of integers, *J*, is illustrated or **graphed** as in Fig. 1.5. The three dots to the right and left on the number line indicate that the integers go on indefinitely in both directions.

FIGURE 1.5

E X A M P L E   2

Graphing on the number line

List the elements of each set and graph each set on a number line.

a) $\{x \mid x$ is a whole number less than $4\}$

b) $\{a \mid a$ is an integer between 3 and $9\}$

c) $\{y \mid y$ is an integer greater than $-3\}$

Solution

a) The whole numbers less than 4 are 0, 1, 2, and 3. Figure 1.6 shows the graph of this set.

FIGURE 1.6

b) The integers between 3 and 9 are 4, 5, 6, 7, and 8. The graph is shown in Fig. 1.7.

FIGURE 1.7

c) The integers greater than -3 are -2, -1, 0, 1, and so on. To indicate the continuing pattern, we use a series of dots on the graph in Fig. 1.8.

FIGURE 1.8

■

The Irrational Numbers

Some numbers can be expressed as ratios of integers and some cannot. Numbers that cannot be expressed as a ratio of integers are called **irrational numbers.** To better understand irrational numbers consider the positive square root of 2 (in symbols $\sqrt{2}$). The square root of 2 is a number that you can multiply by itself to get 2. So we can write (using a raised dot for times)

$$\sqrt{2} \cdot \sqrt{2} = 2.$$

If we look for $\sqrt{2}$ on a calculator or in Appendix B, we find 1.414. But if we multiply 1.414 by itself, we get

$$(1.414)(1.414) = 1.999396.$$

So $\sqrt{2}$ is not equal to 1.414 (in symbols, $\sqrt{2} \neq 1.414$). The square root of 2 is approximately 1.414 (in symbols, $\sqrt{2} \approx 1.414$). There is no terminating or repeating decimal that will give exactly 2 when multiplied by itself. So $\sqrt{2}$ is an irrational number. It can be shown that other square roots such as $\sqrt{3}$, $\sqrt{5}$, and $\sqrt{7}$ are also irrational numbers.

In decimal form the rational numbers either repeat or terminate. The irrational numbers neither repeat nor terminate. Examine each of these numbers to see that it has a continuing pattern that guarantees that its digits will neither repeat nor terminate:

$$0.606000600000600000006\ldots$$
$$0.15115111511115\ldots$$
$$3.12345678910111213\ldots$$

So each of these numbers is an irrational number.

Since we generally work with rational numbers, the irrational numbers may seem to be unnecessary. However, irrational numbers occur in some very real situations. Over 2000 years ago people in the Orient and Egypt observed that the ratio of the circumference and diameter is the same for any circle. This constant value was proven to be an irrational number by Johann Heinrich Lambert in 1767. Like other irrational numbers, it does not have any convenient representation as a decimal number. This number has been given the name π (Greek letter pi). See Fig. 1.9. The value of π rounded to nine decimal places is 3.141592654. When using π in computations, we frequently use the rational number 3.14 as an approximate value for π.

The set of irrational numbers I and the set of rational numbers Q have no numbers in common and together form the set of **real numbers** R. The set of real numbers can be visualized as the set of all points on the number line. Two real numbers are **equal** if they correspond to the same point on the number line. See Fig. 1.10.

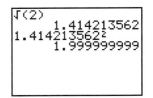
$$\pi = \frac{\text{Circumference}}{\text{Diameter}} \qquad \pi = \frac{C}{D}$$

FIGURE 1.9

FIGURE 1.10

Figure 1.11 illustrates the relationship between the set of real numbers and the various subsets that we have been discussing.

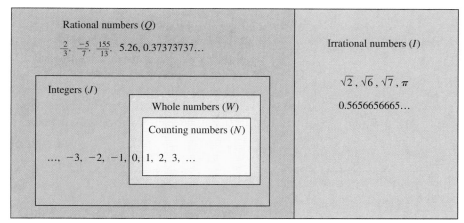

FIGURE 1.11

EXAMPLE 3   **Classifying real numbers**
Determine which elements of the set

$$\left\{-\sqrt{7}, -\frac{1}{4}, 0, \sqrt{5}, \pi, 4.16, 12\right\}$$

are members of each of these sets.
a) Real numbers   b) Rational numbers   c) Integers

Solution
a) All of the numbers are real numbers.
b) The numbers $-\frac{1}{4}$, 0, 4.16, and 12 are rational numbers.
c) The only integers in this set are 0 and 12.   ∎

EXAMPLE 4   **Subsets of the real numbers**
Determine whether each of these statements is true or false.
a) $\sqrt{7} \in Q$ b) $J \subseteq W$ c) $I \cap Q = \varnothing$ d) $-3 \in N$
e) $J \cap I = \varnothing$ f) $Q \subseteq R$ g) $R \subseteq N$ h) $\pi \in R$

Solution
a) False   b) False   c) True   d) False
e) True   f) True   g) False   h) True   ∎

Intervals of Real Numbers

An **interval of real numbers** is the set of real numbers that lie between two real numbers, which are called the **endpoints** of the interval. **Interval notation** is used to represent intervals. For example, the interval notation (2, 3) is used to represent the real numbers that lie between 2 and 3 on the number line. The graph of (2, 3) is shown in Fig. 1.12. Parentheses are used to indicate that the endpoints do not belong

FIGURE 1.12

[2, 3]

FIGURE 1.13

to the interval, whereas brackets are used to indicate that the endpoints do belong to the interval. The interval [2, 3] consists of the real numbers between 2 and 3 including the endpoints. It is graphed in Fig. 1.13.

The infinity symbol may also be used as an endpoint, even though it does not represent a number. The interval (3, ∞) consists of the real numbers greater than 3 and extending infinitely far to the right on the number line. See Fig. 1.14. The interval (−∞, 3) consists of the real numbers less than 3, as shown in Fig. 1.15. The entire set of real numbers is written in interval notation as (−∞, ∞) and graphed as in Fig. 1.16. Parentheses are always used next to −∞ and ∞.

(3, ∞)

FIGURE 1.14

(−∞, 3)

FIGURE 1.15

(−∞, ∞)

FIGURE 1.16

E X A M P L E   5

Interval notation

Write each interval of real numbers in interval notation and graph it.

a) The set of real numbers greater than or equal to 2

b) The set of real numbers less than −3

c) The set of real numbers between 1 and 5 inclusive

d) The set of real numbers greater than or equal to 2 and less than 4

Solution

a) The set of real numbers greater than or equal to 2 includes 2. It is written as [2, ∞) and graphed in Fig. 1.17.

b) The set of real numbers less than −3 does not include −3. It is written as (−∞, −3) and graphed in Fig. 1.18.

c) The set of real numbers between 1 and 5 inclusive includes both 1 and 5. It is written as [1, 5] and graphed in Fig. 1.19.

d) The set of real numbers greater than or equal to 2 and less than 4 includes 2 but not 4. It is written as [2, 4) and graphed in Fig. 1.20.

[2, ∞)

FIGURE 1.17

(−∞, −3)

FIGURE 1.18

[1, 5]

FIGURE 1.19

[2, 4)

FIGURE 1.20

Intervals are sometimes graphed using a hollow circle to indicate that an endpoint is not in the interval and a solid circle to indicate that an endpoint is in the interval. The advantage of using parentheses and brackets on the graph is that they match the interval notation and the interval notation looks like an abbreviated version of the graph.

The intersection of two intervals is the set of real numbers that belong to both intervals. The union of two intervals is the set of real numbers that belong to one, or the other, or both of the intervals.

EXAMPLE 6   **Combining intervals**

Write each union or intersection as a single interval.

a) $(2, 4) \cup (3, 6)$

b) $(2, 4) \cap (3, 6)$

c) $(-1, 2) \cup [0, \infty)$

d) $(-1, 2) \cap [0, \infty)$

Solution

a) Graph $(2, 4)$ and $(3, 6)$ as in Fig. 1.21. The union of the two intervals consists of the real numbers between 2 and 6, which is written as $(2, 6)$.

b) Examining the graphs in Fig. 1.21, we see that only the real numbers between 3 and 4 belong to both $(2, 4)$ and $(3, 6)$. So the intersection of $(2, 4)$ and $(3, 6)$ is $(3, 4)$.

c) Graph $(-1, 2)$ and $[0, \infty)$ as in Fig. 1.22. The union of these intervals consists of the real numbers greater than -1, which is written as $(-1, \infty)$.

d) Examining the graphs in Fig. 1.22, we see that the real numbers between 0 and 2 belong to both intervals. Note that 0 also belongs to both intervals but 2 does not. So the intersection is $[0, 2)$.

FIGURE 1.21

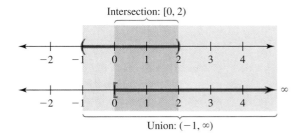

FIGURE 1.22

WARM-UPS

True or false? Explain your answer.

1. The number π is a rational number.

2. The set of rational numbers is a subset of the set of real numbers.

3. Zero is the only number that is a member of both Q and I.

4. The set of real numbers is a subset of the set of irrational numbers.

5. The decimal number $0.44444 \ldots$ is a rational number.

6. The decimal number $4.212112111211112 \ldots$ is a rational number.

7. Every irrational number corresponds to a point on the number line.

8. The intervals $(2, 6)$ and $(3, 9)$ both contain the number 6.

9. $(1, 3) \cup [3, 4) = (1, 4)$

10. $(1, 5) \cap [2, 8) = (2, 8)$

Reading and Writing   *After reading this section, write out the answers to these questions. Use complete sentences.*

1. What are the integers?

2. What are the rational numbers?

3. What kinds of decimal numbers are rational numbers?

4. What kinds of decimal numbers are irrational?

5. What are the real numbers?

6. What is the ratio of the circumference and diameter of any circle?

Determine whether each statement is true or false. Explain your answer. See Example 1.

7. $-6 \in Q$

8. $\frac{2}{7} \in Q$

9. $0 \notin Q$

10. $0 \notin N$

11. $0.6666\ldots \in Q$

12. $0.00976 \notin Q$

13. $N \subseteq Q$

14. $Q \subseteq J$

List the elements in each set and graph each set on a number line. See Example 2.

15. $\{x \mid x \text{ is a whole number smaller than } 6\}$

16. $\{x \mid x \text{ is a natural number less than } 7\}$

17. $\{a \mid a \text{ is an integer greater than } -5\}$

18. $\{z \mid z \text{ is an integer between } 2 \text{ and } 12\}$

19. $\{w \mid w \text{ is a natural number between } 0 \text{ and } 5\}$

20. $\{y \mid y \text{ is a whole number greater than } 0\}$

21. $\{x \mid x \text{ is an integer between } -3 \text{ and } 5\}$

22. $\{y \mid y \text{ is an integer between } -4 \text{ and } 7\}$

Determine which elements of the set

$$A = \left\{ -\sqrt{10},\ -3,\ -\frac{5}{2},\ -0.025,\ 0,\ \sqrt{2},\ 3\frac{1}{2},\ \frac{8}{2} \right\}$$

are members of these sets. See Example 3.

23. Real numbers

24. Natural numbers

25. Whole numbers

26. Integers

27. Rational numbers

28. Irrational numbers

Determine whether each statement is true or false. Explain. See Example 4.

29. $Q \subseteq R$

30. $I \subseteq Q$

31. $I \cap Q = \{0\}$

32. $J \subseteq Q$

33. $I \cup Q = R$

34. $J \cap Q = \varnothing$

35. $0.2121121112\ldots \in Q$ **36.** $0.3333\ldots \in Q$

37. $3.252525\ldots \in I$ **38.** $3.1010010001\ldots \in I$

39. $0.999\ldots \in I$ **40.** $0.666\ldots \in Q$

41. $\pi \in I$ **42.** $\pi \in Q$

Place one of the symbols $\subseteq$, $\not\subseteq$, $\in$, or $\notin$ in each blank so that each statement is true.

43. N ___ W **44.** J ___ Q

45. J ___ N **46.** Q ___ W

47. Q ___ R **48.** I ___ R

49. $\varnothing$ ___ I **50.** $\varnothing$ ___ Q

51. N ___ R **52.** W ___ R

53. 5 ___ J **54.** -6 ___ J

55. 7 ___ Q
56. 8 ___ Q
57. $\sqrt{2}$ ___ R
58. $\sqrt{2}$ ___ I
59. 0 ___ I
60. 0 ___ Q
61. $\{2, 3\}$ ___ Q
62. $\{0, 1\}$ ___ N
63. $\{3, \sqrt{2}\}$ ___ R
64. $\{3, \sqrt{2}\}$ ___ Q

Write each interval of real numbers in interval notation and graph it. See Example 5.

65. The set of real numbers greater than 1

66. The set of real numbers greater than -2

67. The set of real numbers less than -1

68. The set of real numbers less than 5

69. The set of real numbers between 3 and 4

70. The set of real numbers between -1 and 3

71. The set of real numbers between 0 and 2 inclusive

72. The set of real numbers between -1 and 1 inclusive

73. The set of real numbers greater than or equal to 1 and less than 3

74. The set of real numbers greater than 2 and less than or equal to 5.

Write the interval notation for the interval of real numbers shown in each graph.

75.

76.

77.

78.

79.

80.

81.

82.

Write each union or intersection as a single interval. See Example 6.

83. $(1, 5) \cup (4, 9)$

84. $(-1, 2) \cup (0, 8)$

85. $(0, 3) \cap (2, 8)$

86. $(1, 8) \cap (2, 10)$

87. $(-2, 4) \cup (0, \infty)$

88. $(-\infty, 4) \cup (1, 5)$

89. $(-\infty, 2) \cap (0, 6)$

90. $(3, 6) \cap (0, \infty)$

91. $[2, 5) \cup (4, 9]$

92. $[-2, 2] \cup [2, 6)$

93. $[2, 6) \cap [2, 8)$

94. $[1, 5] \cap [2, 9]$

GETTING MORE INVOLVED

95. *Writing.* What is the difference between a rational and an irrational number? Why is $\sqrt{9}$ rational and $\sqrt{3}$ irrational?

96. *Cooperative learning.* Work in a small group to make a list of the real numbers of the form $\sqrt{n}$, where n is a natural number between 1 and 100 inclusive. Decide on a method for determining which of these numbers are rational and find them. Compare your group's method and results with other groups' work.

97. *Exploration.* Find the decimal representations of

$$\frac{2}{9}, \quad \frac{2}{99}, \quad \frac{23}{99}, \quad \frac{23}{999}, \quad \frac{234}{999}, \quad \frac{23}{9999}, \quad \text{and} \quad \frac{1234}{9999}.$$

a) What do these decimals have in common?
b) What is the relationship between each fraction and its decimal representation?

1.3   OPERATIONS ON THE SET OF REAL NUMBERS

Computations in algebra are performed with positive and negative numbers. In this section we will extend the basic operations of arithmetic to the negative numbers.

Absolute Value

The real numbers are the coordinates of the points on the number line. However, we often refer to the points as numbers. For example, the numbers 5 and −5 are both five units away from 0 on the number line shown in Fig. 1.23. A number's *distance* from 0 on the number line is called the **absolute value** of the number. We write $|a|$ for "the absolute value of a." Therefore $|5| = 5$ and $|-5| = 5$.

FIGURE 1.23

EXAMPLE 1

Absolute value

Find the value of $|4|$, $|-4|$, and $|0|$.

Solution

Because both 4 and −4 are four units from 0 on the number line, we have $|4| = 4$ and $|-4| = 4$. Because the distance from 0 to 0 on the number line is 0, we have $|0| = 0$. ■

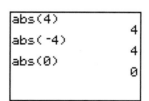

Note that $|a|$ represents distance, and distance is never negative. So $|a|$ is greater than or equal to zero for any number a.

Two numbers that are located on opposite sides of zero and have the same absolute value are called **opposites** of each other. The opposite of zero is zero. Every number has a unique opposite. The numbers 9 and −9 are opposites of one another. The minus sign, −, is used to signify "opposite" in addition to "negative." When the minus sign is used in front of a number, it is read as "negative." When it is used in front of parentheses or a variable, it is read as "opposite." For example,

$$-(9) = -9$$

is read as "the opposite of 9 is negative 9," and

$$-(-9) = 9$$

is read as "the opposite of negative 9 is 9." In general, $-a$ is read "the opposite of a." If a is positive, $-a$ is negative. If a is negative, $-a$ is positive. Opposites have the following property.

Opposite of an Opposite

For any number a,

$$-(-a) = a.$$

E X A M P L E   2

Opposite of an opposite

Evaluate.

a) $-(-12)$ **b)** $-(-(-8))$

Solution

a) The opposite of negative 12 is 12. So $-(-12) = 12$.

b) The opposite of the opposite of -8 is -8. So $-(-(-8)) = -8$.   ■

Remember that we have defined $|\,a\,|$ to be the distance between 0 and a on the number line. Using opposites, we can give a symbolic definition of absolute value.

Absolute Value

$$|\,a\,| = \begin{cases} a & \text{if } a \text{ is positive or zero} \\ -a & \text{if } a \text{ is negative} \end{cases}$$

Using this definition, we write

$$|\,7\,| = 7$$

because 7 is positive. To find the absolute value of -7, we use the second line of the definition and write

$$|\,-7\,| = -(-7) = 7.$$

Addition

A good way to understand positive and negative numbers is to think of the *positive numbers as assets* and the *negative numbers as debts*. For this illustration we can think of assets simply as cash. Think of debts as unpaid bills such as the electric bill, the phone bill, and so on. If you have assets of $4 and $11 and no debts, then your net worth is $15. **Net worth** is the total of your debts and assets. If you have debts of $6 and $7 and no assets, then your net worth is $-\$13$. In symbols,

$$(-6) \quad + \quad (-7) \quad = \quad -13.$$

| $\uparrow$ | $\uparrow$ | $\uparrow$ | $\uparrow$ |
| $6 debt | Added to | $7 debt | $13 debt |

We can think of this addition as adding the absolute values of -6 and -7 (that is, $6 + 7 = 13$) and then putting a negative sign on that result to get -13. These examples illustrate the next rule.

Sum of Two Numbers with Like Signs

To find the sum of two numbers with the same sign, add their absolute values. The sum has the same sign as the original numbers.

If you have a debt of $5 and have only $5 in cash, then your debts equal your assets (in absolute value), and your net worth is $0. In symbols,

$$-5 \quad + \quad 5 \quad = \quad 0.$$

| $\uparrow$ | $\uparrow$ | $\uparrow$ |
| Debt of $5 | Asset of $5 | Net worth |

The number a and its opposite $-a$ have a sum of zero for any a. For this reason, a and $-a$ are called **additive inverses** of each other. Note that the words "negative," "opposite," and "additive inverse" are often used interchangeably.

Additive Inverse Property

For any real number a, there is a unique number $-a$ such that

$$a + (-a) = -a + a = 0.$$

To understand the sum of a positive and a negative number, consider this situation. If you have a debt of $7 and $10 in cash, you may have $10 in hand, but your net worth is only $3. Your assets exceed your debts (in absolute value), and you have a positive net worth. In symbols,

$$-7 + 10 = 3.$$

Note that to get 3, we actually subtract 7 from 10. If you have a debt of $8 but have only $5 in cash, then your debts exceed your assets (in absolute value). You have a net worth of $-$3. In symbols,

$$-8 + 5 = -3.$$

Note that to get the 3 in the answer, we subtract 5 from 8.

As you can see from these examples, the sum of a positive number and a negative number (with different absolute values) may be either positive or negative. These examples illustrate the rule for adding numbers with unlike signs and different absolute values.

Helpful Hint

The sum of two numbers with unlike signs and the same absolute value is zero because of the additive inverse property.

Sum of Two Numbers with Unlike Signs (and Different Absolute Values)

To find the sum of two numbers with unlike signs, subtract their absolute values.

The sum is positive if the number with the larger absolute value is positive.
The sum is negative if the number with the larger absolute value is negative.

E X A M P L E   3

Calculator Close-Up

A graphing calculator can add signed numbers in any form. If you use the fraction feature, the answer is given as a fraction.

```
-9+ -7
              -16
-35.4+2.51
           -32.89
1/5+ -3/4▸Frac
            -11/20
```

No one knows what calculators will be like in 10 or 20 years. So concentrate on understanding the mathematics and you will have no trouble with changing technology.

Adding signed numbers

Find each sum.

a) $-6 + 13$ b) $-9 + (-7)$ c) $2 + (-2)$

d) $-35.4 + 2.51$ e) $-7 + 0.05$ f) $\dfrac{1}{5} + \left(-\dfrac{3}{4}\right)$

Solution

a) The absolute values of -6 and 13 are 6 and 13. Subtract 6 from 13 to get 7. Because the number with the larger absolute value is 13 and it is positive, the result is 7.

b) $-9 + (-7) = -16$

c) $2 + (-2) = 0$

d) Line up the decimal points and subtract 2.51 from 35.40 to get 32.89. Because 35.4 is larger than 2.51 and 35.4 has a negative sign, the answer is negative.

$$-35.4 + 2.51 = -32.89$$

e) Line up the decimal points and subtract 0.05 from 7.00 to get 6.95. Because 7.00 is larger than 0.05 and 7.00 has a negative sign, the answer is negative.

$$-7 + 0.05 = -6.95$$

f) $\dfrac{1}{5} + \left(-\dfrac{3}{4}\right) = \dfrac{4}{20} + \left(-\dfrac{15}{20}\right)$ The LCD for 5 and 4 is 20.

$\qquad\qquad\quad = -\dfrac{11}{20}$ Add.   ■

Subtraction

Think of subtraction as removing debts or assets, and think of addition as receiving debts or assets. For example, if you have $10 in cash and $4 is taken from you, your resulting net worth is the same as if you have $10 and a water bill for $4 arrives in the mail. In symbols,

$$10 \quad - \quad 4 \quad = \quad 10 \quad + \quad (-4).$$

↑   ↑   ↑   ↑
Remove   Cash   Receive   Debt

Removing cash is equivalent to receiving a debt.

Suppose that you have $17 in cash but owe $7 in library fines. Your net worth is $10. If the debt of $7 is canceled or forgiven, your net worth will increase to $17, the same as if you received $7 in cash. In symbols,

$$10 \quad - \quad (-7) \quad = \quad 10 \quad + \quad 7.$$

↑   ↑   ↑   ↑
Remove   Debt   Receive   Cash

Removing a debt is equivalent to receiving cash.

Notice that each preceding subtraction problem is equivalent to an addition problem in which we add the opposite of what we were going to subtract. These examples illustrate the definition of subtraction.

> **Subtraction of Real Numbers**
>
> For any real numbers a and b,
>
> $$a - b = a + (-b).$$

E X A M P L E   4

Calculator Close-Up

A graphing calculator can subtract signed numbers in any form. If your calculator has a subtraction symbol and a negative symbol, you will get an error message if you do not use them appropriately.

```
-3.6--7
            3.4
0.02-7
           -6.98
1/3--1/6▶Frac
             1/2
```

Subtracting signed numbers

Find each difference.

a) $-7 - 3$ **b)** $7 - (-3)$ **c)** $48 - 99$

d) $-3.6 - (-7)$ **e)** $0.02 - 7$ **f)** $\dfrac{1}{3} - \left(-\dfrac{1}{6}\right)$

Solution

a) To subtract 3 from -7, add the opposite of 3 and -7:

$$-7 - 3 = -7 + (-3) \quad a - b = a + (-b)$$
$$= -10 \qquad\qquad \text{Add.}$$

b) To subtract -3 from 7, add the opposite of -3 and 7. The opposite of -3 is 3:

$$7 - (-3) = 7 + (3) \quad a - b = a + (-b)$$
$$= 10 \qquad\qquad \text{Add.}$$

c) To subtract 99 from 48, add -99 and 48:

$$48 - 99 = 48 + (-99) \quad a - b = a + (-b)$$
$$= -51 \qquad \text{Add.}$$

d) $-3.6 - (-7) = -3.6 + 7 \quad a - b = a + (-b)$
$$= 3.4 \qquad \text{Add.}$$

e) $0.02 - 7 = 0.02 + (-7) \quad a - b = a + (-b)$
$$= -6.98 \qquad \text{Add.}$$

f) $\dfrac{1}{3} - \left(-\dfrac{1}{6}\right) = \dfrac{1}{3} + \left(\dfrac{1}{6}\right) \quad a - b = a + (-b)$

$$= \frac{2}{6} + \frac{1}{6} \qquad \text{Get common denominators.}$$

$$= \frac{3}{6} \qquad \text{Add.}$$

$$= \frac{1}{2} \qquad \text{Reduce.} \qquad \blacksquare$$

Multiplication

The result of multiplying two numbers is called the **product** of the numbers. The numbers multiplied are **factors.** In algebra we use a raised dot to indicate multiplication, or we place symbols next to one another. For example, the product of a and b is written as $a \cdot b$ or ab. The product of 4 and x is $4x$. We also use parentheses to indicate multiplication. For example, the product of 4 and 3 is written as $4 \cdot 3$, $4(3)$, $(4)3$, or $(4)(3)$.

Multiplication is just a short way to do repeated additions. Adding five 2's gives

$$2 + 2 + 2 + 2 + 2 = 10.$$

So we have the multiplication fact $5 \cdot 2 = 10$. Adding together five negative 2's gives

$$(-2) + (-2) + (-2) + (-2) + (-2) = -10.$$

So we must have $5(-2) = -10$. We can think of $5(-2) = -10$ as saying that taking on five debts of \$2 each is equivalent to a debt of \$10. Losing five debts of \$2 each is equivalent to gaining \$10, so we must have $-5(-2) = 10$.

The rules for multiplying signed numbers are easy to state and remember.

Product of Signed Numbers

To find the product of two nonzero real numbers, multiply their absolute values.

The product is *positive* if the numbers have the *same* sign.
The product is *negative* if the numbers have *unlike* signs.

For example, to multiply -4 and -5, we multiply their absolute values ($4 \cdot 5 = 20$). Since -4 and -5 have the same sign, $(-4)(-5) = 20$. To multiply -6 and 3, we multiply their absolute values ($6 \cdot 3 = 18$). Since -6 and 3 have unlike signs, $-6 \cdot 3 = -18$.

EXAMPLE 5

Multiplying signed numbers

Find each product.

a) $(-3)(-6)$ b) $-4(10)$ c) $(-0.01)(0.02)$ d) $\dfrac{4}{9} \cdot \left(-\dfrac{1}{5}\right)$

Solution

a) First multiply the absolute values ($3 \cdot 6 = 18$). Because -3 and -6 have the same sign, we get $(-3)(-6) = 18$.

b) $-4(10) = -40$ Opposite signs, negative result

c) When multiplying decimals, we total the number of decimal places used in the numbers multiplied to get the number of decimal places in the answer. Thus $(-0.01)(0.02) = -0.0002$.

d) $\dfrac{4}{9} \cdot \left(-\dfrac{1}{5}\right) = -\dfrac{4}{45}$ Opposite signs, negative result   ∎

Division

Just as every real number has an additive inverse or opposite, every nonzero real number a has a **multiplicative inverse** or **reciprocal** $\dfrac{1}{a}$. The reciprocal of 3 is $\dfrac{1}{3}$, and

$$3 \cdot \dfrac{1}{3} = 1.$$

> **Multiplicative Inverse Property**
>
> For any nonzero real number a, there is a unique number $\dfrac{1}{a}$ such that
>
> $$a \cdot \dfrac{1}{a} = \dfrac{1}{a} \cdot a = 1.$$

EXAMPLE 6

Finding multiplicative inverses

Find the multiplicative inverse (reciprocal) of each number.

a) -2 b) $\dfrac{3}{8}$ c) -0.2

Solution

a) The multiplicative inverse (reciprocal) of -2 is $-\dfrac{1}{2}$ because

$$-2\left(-\dfrac{1}{2}\right) = 1.$$

b) The reciprocal of $\dfrac{3}{8}$ is $\dfrac{8}{3}$ because

$$\dfrac{3}{8} \cdot \dfrac{8}{3} = 1.$$

c) First convert the decimal number -0.2 to a fraction:

$$-0.2 = -\dfrac{2}{10}$$

$$= -\dfrac{1}{5}$$

So the reciprocal of -0.2 is -5 and $-0.2(-5) = 1$.   ∎

Note that the reciprocal of any negative number is negative.

Earlier we defined subtraction for real numbers as addition of the additive inverse. We now define division for real numbers as multiplication by the multiplicative inverse (reciprocal).

Division of Real Numbers

For any real numbers a and b with $b \neq 0$,

$$a \div b = a \cdot \frac{1}{b}.$$

If $a \div b = c$, then a is called the **dividend,** b the **divisor,** and c the **quotient.** We also refer to $a \div b$ and $\frac{a}{b}$ as the quotient of a and b.

EXAMPLE 7

Dividing signed numbers

Find each quotient.

a) $-60 \div (-2)$ **b)** $-24 \div \frac{3}{8}$ **c)** $6 \div (-0.2)$

Solution

a) $-60 \div (-2) = -60 \cdot \left(-\frac{1}{2}\right)$ Multiply by $-\frac{1}{2}$, the reciprocal of -2.

$\qquad = 30$ Same sign, positive product

b) $-24 \div \frac{3}{8} = -24 \cdot \frac{8}{3}$ Multiply by $\frac{8}{3}$, the reciprocal of $\frac{3}{8}$.

$\qquad = -64$ Opposite signs, negative product

c) $6 \div (-0.2) = 6(-5)$ Multiply by -5, the reciprocal of -0.2.

$\qquad = -30$ Opposite signs, negative product ∎

Calculator Close-Up

A graphing calculator uses a forward slash to indicate division. Note that to divide by the fraction $\frac{3}{8}$ you must use parentheses around the fraction.

```
-60/-2
              30
-24/(3/8)
             -64
-24/3/8
              -1
```

You can see from Examples 6 and 7 that a product or quotient is positive when the signs are the same and is negative when the signs are opposite:

$$\text{same signs} \leftrightarrow \text{positive result,}$$
$$\text{opposite signs} \leftrightarrow \text{negative result.}$$

Even though all division can be done as multiplication by a reciprocal, we generally use reciprocals only when dividing fractions. Instead, we find quotients using our knowledge of multiplication and the fact that

$$a \div b = c \quad \text{if and only if} \quad c \cdot b = a.$$

For example, $-72 \div 9 = -8$ because $-8 \cdot 9 = -72$. Using long division or a calculator, you can get

$$-43.74 \div 1.8 = -24.3$$

and check that you have it correct by finding $-24.3 \cdot 1.8 = -43.74$.

We use the same rules for division when division is indicated by a fraction bar. For example,

$$\frac{-6}{3} = -2, \qquad \frac{6}{-3} = -2, \qquad \frac{-1}{3} = \frac{1}{-3} = -\frac{1}{3}, \qquad \text{and} \qquad \frac{-6}{-3} = 2.$$

Helpful Hint

Some people remember that "two positives make a positive, a negative and a positive make a negative, and two negatives make a positive." Of course, that is true only for multiplication, division, and cute stories like this: If a good person comes to town, that's good. If a bad person comes to town, that's bad. If a good person leaves town, that's bad. If a bad person leaves town, that's good.

Note that if one negative sign appears in a fraction, the fraction has the same value whether the negative sign is in the numerator, in the denominator, or in front of the fraction. If the numerator and denominator of a fraction are both negative, then the fraction has a positive value.

Division by Zero

Why do we omit division by zero from the definition of division? If we write $10 \div 0 = c$, we need to find c such that $c \cdot 0 = 10$. But there is no such number. If we write $0 \div 0 = c$, we need to find c such that $c \cdot 0 = 0$. But $c \cdot 0 = 0$ is true for any number c. Having $0 \div 0$ equal to any number would be confusing. Thus $a \div b$ is defined only for $b \neq 0$. Quotients such as

$$5 \div 0, \qquad 0 \div 0, \qquad \frac{7}{0}, \qquad \text{and} \qquad \frac{0}{0}$$

are said to be *undefined*.

WARM-UPS

True or false? Explain your answer.

1. The additive inverse of -6 is 6.

2. The opposite of negative 5 is positive 5.

3. The absolute value of 6 is -6.

4. The result of a subtracted from b is the same as $b + (-a)$.

5. If a is positive and b is negative, then ab is negative.

6. If a is positive and b is negative, then $a + b$ is negative.

7. $(-3) - (-6) = -9$

8. $6 \div \left(-\dfrac{1}{2}\right) = -3$

9. $-3 \div 0 = 0$

10. $0 \div (-7) = 0$

1.3   **EXERCISES**

Reading and Writing   *After reading this section, write out the answers to these questions. Use complete sentences.*

1. What is absolute value?

2. How do you add two numbers with the same sign?

3. How do you add two numbers with unlike signs and different absolute values?

4. What is the relationship between subtraction and addition?

5. How do you multiply signed numbers?

6. What is the relationship between division and multiplication?

Evaluate. See Examples 1 and 2.

7. $|-34|$

8. $|17|$

9. $|0|$

10. $|-15|$

11. $|-6| - |-6|$

12. $|8| - |-8|$

13. $-|-9|$

14. $-|-3|$

15. $-(-9)$

16. $-(-(8))$

17. $-(-(-3))$

18. $-(-(-2))$

Find each sum. See Example 3.

19. $(-5) + 9$

20. $(-3) + 10$

21. $(-4) + (-3)$

22. $(-15) + (-11)$

23. $-6 + 4$

24. $5 + (-15)$

25. $7 + (-17)$

26. $-8 + 13$

27. $(-11) + (-15)$

28. $-18 + 18$

29. $18 + (-20)$

30. $7 + (-19)$

31. $-14 + 9$

32. $-6 + (-7)$

33. $-4 + 4$

34. $-7 + 9$

35. $-\dfrac{1}{10} + \dfrac{1}{5}$

36. $-\dfrac{1}{8} + \left(-\dfrac{1}{8}\right)$

37. $\dfrac{1}{2} + \left(-\dfrac{2}{3}\right)$

38. $\dfrac{3}{4} + \dfrac{1}{2}$

39. $-15 + 0.02$

40. $0.45 + (-1.3)$

41. $-2.7 + (-0.01)$

42. $0.8 + (-1)$

43. $47.39 + (-44.587)$

44. $0.65357 + (-2.375)$

45. $0.2351 + (-0.5)$

46. $-1.234 + (-4.756)$

Find each difference. See Example 4.

47. $7 - 10$

48. $8 - 19$

49. $-4 - 7$

50. $-5 - 12$

51. $7 - (-6)$

52. $3 - (-9)$

53. $-1 - 5$

54. $-4 - 6$

55. $-12 - (-3)$

56. $-15 - (-6)$

57. $20 - (-3)$

58. $50 - (-70)$

59. $\dfrac{9}{10} - \left(-\dfrac{1}{10}\right)$

60. $\dfrac{1}{8} - \dfrac{1}{4}$

61. $1 - \dfrac{3}{2}$

62. $-\dfrac{1}{2} - \left(-\dfrac{1}{3}\right)$

63. $2 - 0.03$

64. $-0.02 - 3$

65. $5.3 - (-2)$

66. $-4.1 - 0.13$

67. $-2.44 - 48.29$

68. $-8.8 - 9.164$

69. $-3.89 - (-5.16)$

70. $0 - (-3.5)$

Find each product. See Example 5.

71. $(25)(-3)$

72. $(5)(-7)$

73. $\left(-\dfrac{1}{3}\right)\left(-\dfrac{1}{2}\right)$

74. $\left(-\dfrac{1}{2}\right)\left(-\dfrac{6}{7}\right)$

75. $(0.3)(-0.3)$

76. $(-0.1)(-0.5)$

77. $(-0.02)(-10)$

78. $(0.05)(-2.5)$

Find the multiplicative inverse of each number. See Example 6.

79. 20

80. -5

81. $-\dfrac{6}{5}$

82. $-\dfrac{1}{8}$

83. -0.3

84. 0.125

Evaluate. See Example 7.

85. $-6 \div 3$

86. $84 \div (-2)$

87. $30 \div (-0.8)$

88. $(-9)(-6)$

89. $(-0.8)(0.1)$

90. $7 \div (-0.5)$

91. $(-0.1) \div (-0.4)$

92. $(-18) \div (-0.9)$

93. $9 \div \left(-\dfrac{3}{4}\right)$

94. $-\dfrac{1}{3} \div \left(-\dfrac{5}{8}\right)$

95. $-\dfrac{2}{3}\left(-\dfrac{9}{10}\right)$

96. $\dfrac{1}{2}\left(-\dfrac{2}{5}\right)$

97. $(0.25)(-365)$

98. $7.5 \div (-0.15)$

99. $(-51) \div (-0.003)$

100. $(-2.8)(5.9)$

Perform these computations.

101. $-62 + 13$

102. $-88 + 39$

103. $-32 - (-25)$

104. $-71 - (-19)$

105. $|-15|$

106. $-|-75|$

107. $\dfrac{1}{2}(-684)$

108. $\dfrac{1}{3}(-123)$

109. $\dfrac{1}{2} - \left(-\dfrac{1}{4}\right)$

110. $\dfrac{1}{8} - \left(-\dfrac{1}{4}\right)$

111. $-57 \div 19$

112. $0 \div (-36)$

113. $|-17| + |-3|$

114. $64 - |-12|$

115. $0 \div (-0.15)$

116. $-20 \div \left(-\dfrac{8}{3}\right)$

117. $27 \div (-0.15)$

118. $33 \div (-0.2)$

119. $-\dfrac{1}{3} + \dfrac{1}{6}$

120. $-\dfrac{2}{3} + \dfrac{1}{6}$

121. $-63 + |8|$

122. $|-34| - 27$

123. $-\dfrac{1}{2} + \left(-\dfrac{1}{2}\right)$

124. $-\dfrac{2}{3} + \left(-\dfrac{2}{3}\right)$

125. $-\dfrac{1}{2} - 19$

126. $-\dfrac{1}{3} - 22$

127. $28 - 0.01$

128. $55 - 0.1$

129. $-29 - 0.3$

130. $-0.241 - 0.3$

131. $(-2)(0.35)$

132. $(-3)(0.19)$

133. $(-10)(-0.2)$

134. $\left(-\dfrac{1}{2}\right)(-50)$

Use an operation with signed numbers to solve each problem.

135. *Net worth of a family.* The average American family has an $85,000 house, a $45,000 mortgage, $2,300 in credit card debt, $1,500 in other debts, $1,200 in savings, and two cars worth $3,500 each. What is the net worth of the average American family?

136. *Net worth of a bank.* Just before the recession, First Federal Homestead had $15.6 million in mortgage loans, had $23.3 million on deposit, and owned $8.5 million worth of real estate. After the recession started, the value of the real estate decreased to $4.8 million. What was the net worth of First Federal before the recession and after the recession started? (To a financial institution a loan is an asset and a deposit is a liability.)

137. *Warming up.* On January 11 the temperature at noon was 14°F in St. Louis and −6°F in Duluth. How much warmer was it in St. Louis?

138. *Bitter cold.* On January 16 the temperature at midnight was −31°C in Calgary and −20°C in Toronto. How much warmer was it in Toronto?

139. *Below sea level.* The altitude of the floor of Death Valley is −282 feet (282 feet below sea level); the altitude of the shore of the Dead Sea is −1,296 feet (*Rand McNally World Atlas*). How many feet above the shore of the Dead Sea is the floor of Death Valley?

FIGURE FOR EXERCISE 137

140. *Highs and lows.* The altitude of the peak of Mt. Everest, the highest point on earth, is 29,028 feet. The world's greatest known ocean depth of −36,201 feet was recorded in the Marianas Trench (*Rand McNally World Atlas*). How many feet above the bottom of the Marianas Trench is a climber who has reached the top of Mt. Everest?

FIGURE FOR EXERCISE 140

GETTING MORE INVOLVED

141. *Discussion.* Why is it necessary to learn addition of signed numbers before learning subtraction of signed numbers and to learn multiplication of signed numbers before learning division of signed numbers?

142. *Writing.* Explain why 0 is the only real number that does not have a multiplicative inverse.

1.4 EVALUATING EXPRESSIONS

In algebra you will learn to work with variables. However, there is often nothing more important than finding a numerical answer to a question. This section is concerned with computation.

Arithmetic Expressions

The result of writing numbers in a meaningful combination with the ordinary operations of arithmetic is called an **arithmetic expression** or simply an **expression.** An expression that involves more than one operation is called a **sum, difference, product,** or **quotient** if the last operation to be performed is addition, subtraction, multiplication, or division, respectively. Parentheses are used as **grouping symbols** to indicate which operations are performed first. The expression

$$5 + (2 \cdot 3)$$

is a sum because the parentheses indicate that the product of 2 and 3 is to be found before the addition is performed. So we evaluate this expression as follows:

$$5 + (2 \cdot 3) = 5 + 6 = 11$$

If we write $(5 + 2)3$, the expression is a product and it has a different value.

$$(5 + 2)3 = 7 \cdot 3 = 21$$

Brackets [ ] are also used to indicate grouping. If an expression occurs within absolute value bars | |, it is evaluated before the absolute value is found. So absolute value bars also act as grouping symbols. We perform first the operations within the innermost grouping symbols.

EXAMPLE 1

Grouping symbols

Evaluate each expression.

a) $5[(2 \cdot 3) - 8]$ **b)** $2[(4 \cdot 5) - |3 - 6|]$

Solution

a) $5[(2 \cdot 3) - 8] = 5[6 - 8]$ Innermost grouping first

$$= 5[-2]$$
$$= -10$$

b) $2[(4 \cdot 5) - |3 - 6|] = 2[20 - |-3|]$ Innermost grouping first

$$= 2[20 - 3]$$
$$= 2[17]$$
$$= 34$$

∎

Calculator Close-Up

You can use parentheses to control the order in which your calculator performs the operations in an expression.

```
5((2*3)-8)
            -10
2((4*5)-abs(3-6)
)
             34
```

Exponential Expressions

We use the notation of exponents to simplify the writing of repeated multiplication. The product $5 \cdot 5 \cdot 5 \cdot 5$ is written as 5^4. The number 4 in 5^4 is called the exponent, and it indicates the number of times that the factor 5 occurs in the product.

Exponential Expression

For any natural number n and real number a,

$$a^n = \underbrace{a \cdot a \cdot a \cdot \ldots \cdot a}_{n \text{ factors of } a}.$$

We call a the **base,** n the **exponent,** and a^n an **exponential expression.**

We read a^n as "the nth power of a" or "a to the nth power." The exponential expressions 3^5 and 10^6 are read as "3 to the fifth power" and "10 to the sixth power." We can also use the words "squared" and "cubed" for the second and third powers, respectively. For example, 5^2 and 2^3 are read as "5 squared" and "2 cubed," respectively.

E X A M P L E   2

Exponential expressions

Evaluate.

a) 2^3 **b)** $(-3)^4$ **c)** $\left(-\dfrac{1}{2}\right)^5$

Solution

a) $2^3 = 2 \cdot 2 \cdot 2$ The factor 2 is used three times.
$ = 8$

b) $(-3)^4 = (-3)(-3)(-3)(-3)$ The factor -3 is used four times.
$ = 81$ Even number of negative signs, positive product

c) $\left(-\dfrac{1}{2}\right)^5 = \left(-\dfrac{1}{2}\right)\left(-\dfrac{1}{2}\right)\left(-\dfrac{1}{2}\right)\left(-\dfrac{1}{2}\right)\left(-\dfrac{1}{2}\right)$ The factor $-\dfrac{1}{2}$ is used five times.

$\phantom{\left(-\dfrac{1}{2}\right)^5} = -\dfrac{1}{32}$ Odd number of negative signs, negative product ∎

Square Roots

Because $3^2 = 9$ and $(-3)^2 = 9$, both 3 and -3 are square roots of 9. We use the **radical symbol** $\sqrt{}$ to indicate the nonnegative or principal square root of 9. We write $\sqrt{9} = 3$.

> **Square Roots**
>
> If $a^2 = b$, then a is called a **square root** of b. If $a \geq 0$, then a is called the **principal square root** of b and we write $\sqrt{b} = a$.

The radical symbol is a grouping symbol. We perform all operations within the radical symbol before the square root is found.

E X A M P L E   3

Evaluating square roots

Evaluate.

a) $\sqrt{64}$ **b)** $\sqrt{9 + 16}$ **c)** $\sqrt{3(17 - 5)}$

Solution

a) Because $8^2 = 64$, we have $\sqrt{64} = 8$.

b) Because the radical symbol is a grouping symbol, add 9 and 16 before finding the square root:

$$\sqrt{9 + 16} = \sqrt{25}$$ Add first.
$$\phantom{\sqrt{9 + 16}} = 5$$ Find square root.

Calculator Close-Up

Powers are indicated on a graphing calculator using a caret (^). Most calculators also have an x^2-key for squaring. Note that parentheses are necessary in $(-3)^4$. Without parentheses, your calculator should get $-3^4 = -81$. Try it.

```
2^3
               8
(-3)^4
              81
(-1/2)^5▶Frac
           -1/32
```

Note that $\sqrt{9} + \sqrt{16} = 3 + 4 = 7$. So $\sqrt{9 + 16} \neq \sqrt{9} + \sqrt{16}$.

c) $\sqrt{3(17 - 5)} = \sqrt{3(12)} = \sqrt{36} = 6$ ■

Order of Operations

To simplify the writing of expressions, we often omit some grouping symbols. If we saw the expression

$$5 + 2 \cdot 3$$

written without parentheses, we would not know how to evaluate it unless we had a rule for which operations to perform first. Expressions in which some or all grouping symbols are omitted, are evaluated consistently by using a rule called the **order of operations.**

Order of Operations

Evaluate inside any grouping symbols first. Where grouping symbols are missing use this order.
1. Evaluate each exponential expression (in order from left to right).
2. Perform multiplication and division (in order from left to right).
3. Perform addition and subtraction (in order from left to right).

"In order from left to right" means that we evaluate the operations in the order in which they are written. For example,

$$20 \cdot 3 \div 6 = 60 \div 6 = 10 \quad \text{and} \quad 10 - 3 + 6 = 7 + 6 = 13.$$

If an expression contains grouping symbols, we evaluate within the grouping symbols using the order of operations.

E X A M P L E   4

Order of operations

Evaluate each expression.

a) $5 + 2 \cdot 3$ **b)** $9 \cdot 2^3$ **c)** $(6 - 4^2)^2$ **d)** $40 \div 8 \cdot 2 \div 5 \cdot 3$

Solution

a) $5 + 2 \cdot 3 = 5 + 6$ Multiply first.

$= 11$ Then add.

b) $9 \cdot 2^3 = 9 \cdot 8$ Evaluate the exponential expression first.

$= 72$ Then multiply.

c) $(6 - 4^2)^2 = (6 - 16)^2$ Evaluate 4^2 within the parentheses first.

$= (-10)^2$ Then subtract.

$= 100$ $(-10)(-10) = 100$

d) Multiplication and division are done from left to right.

$$40 \div 8 \cdot 2 \div 5 \cdot 3 = 5 \cdot 2 \div 5 \cdot 3$$
$$= 10 \div 5 \cdot 3$$
$$= 2 \cdot 3$$
$$= 6$$

■

C A U T I O N   Don't confuse -3^2 and $(-3)^2$. We interpret -3^2 as the opposite of 3^2. So $-3^2 = -(3^2) = -9$, whereas $(-3)^2 = (-3)(-3) = 9$.

Calculator Close-Up

Because the radical symbol on most calculators cannot be extended, parentheses are used to group the expression that is inside the radical.

```
√(64)
            8
√(9+16)
            5
√(3(17-5))
            6
```

Calculator Close-Up

When parentheses are omitted, most (but not all) calculators follow the same order of operations that we use in this text. Try these computations on your calculator. To use a calculator effectively, you must practice with it.

```
5+2*3
            11
(6-4²)²
            100
40/8*2/5*3
            6
```

E X A M P L E   5

The order of negative signs

Evaluate each expression.

a) -2^4 **b)** -5^2 **c)** $(3 - 5)^2$ **d)** $-(5^2 - 4 \cdot 7)^2$

Helpful Hint

"Everybody Loves My Dear Aunt Sally" is often used as a memory aid for the order of operations. Do **E**xponents and **L**ogarithms, **M**ultiplication and **D**ivision, and then **A**ddition and **S**ubtraction. Logarithms are discussed later in this text.

Solution

a) To evaluate -2^4, find 2^4 first and then take the opposite. So $-2^4 = -16$.

b) $-5^2 = -(5^2)$ The exponent applies to 5 only.

$\qquad = -25$

c) Evaluate within the parentheses first, then square that result.

$$(3 - 5)^2 = (-2)^2 \quad \text{Evaluate within parentheses first.}$$
$$= 4 \quad \text{Square } -2 \text{ to get 4.}$$

d) $-(5^2 - 4 \cdot 7)^2 = -(25 - 28)^2$ Evaluate 5^2 within the parentheses first.

$\qquad\qquad\qquad\quad = -(-3)^2$ Then subtract.

$\qquad\qquad\qquad\quad = -9$ Square -3 to get 9, then take the opposite of 9 to get -9.   ■

When an expression involves a fraction bar, the numerator and denominator are each treated as if they are in parentheses. Example 6 illustrates how the fraction bar groups the numerator and denominator.

E X A M P L E   6

Order of operations in fractions

Evaluate each quotient.

a) $\dfrac{10 - 8}{6 - 8}$ **b)** $\dfrac{-6^2 + 2 \cdot 7}{4 - 3 \cdot 2}$

Calculator Close-Up

Some calculators use the built-up form for fractions $\left(\frac{1}{2}\right)$, but some do not (1/2). If your calculator does not use the built-up form, then you must enclose numerators and denominators (that contain operations) in parentheses as shown here.

```
(10-8)/(6-8)
               -1
(-6²+2*7)/(4-3*2
)
               11
```

Solution

a) $\dfrac{10 - 8}{6 - 8} = \dfrac{2}{-2}$ Evaluate the numerator and denominator separately.

$\qquad\qquad = -1$ Then divide.

b) $\dfrac{-6^2 + 2 \cdot 7}{4 - 3 \cdot 2} = \dfrac{-36 + 14}{4 - 6}$

$\qquad\qquad\quad = \dfrac{-22}{-2}$ Evaluate the numerator and denominator separately.

$\qquad\qquad\quad = 11$ Then divide.   ■

Algebraic Expressions

The result of combining numbers and variables with the ordinary operations of arithmetic (in some meaningful way) is called an **algebraic expression.** For example,

$$2x - 5y, \quad 5x^2, \quad (x - 3)(x + 2), \quad b^2 - 4ac, \quad 5, \quad \text{and} \quad \frac{x}{2}$$

are algebraic expressions, or simply **expressions.** An expression such as $2x - 5y$ has no definite value unless we assign values to x and y. For example, if $x = 3$ and $y = 4$, then the value of $2x - 5y$ is found by replacing x with 3 and y with 4 and evaluating:

$$2x - 5y = 2(3) - 5(4) = 6 - 20 = -14$$

MATH AT WORK

Nancy Gittins, Assistant Director of Financial Aid at Babson College, helps graduate and undergraduate students to achieve their goal of financing their educations. Because recent tuition and fees can be as high as $20,000 a year, many students need financial aid to help defray these expenses. Federal loans and state loans, as well as grants from the federal and state levels, can be given to students who qualify. Ms. Gittins administers many of these loans and grants and helps students to understand the different options that are available. The interest rate for these loans is now a variable rate that is tied to treasury bills. The rate can be as high as 9.0% and as low as 7.3%. In Exercise 107 of this section you will work with interest rates compounded annually.

FINANCIAL AID DIRECTOR

Note the importance of the order of operations in evaluating an algebraic expression. To find the value of the difference $2x - 5y$ when $x = -2$ and $y = -3$, replace x and y by -2 and -3, respectively, and then evaluate.

$$2x - 5y = 2(-2) - 5(-3) = -4 - (-15) = -4 + 15 = 11$$

EXAMPLE 7

Value of an algebraic expression

Evaluate each expression for $a = 2$, $b = -3$, and $c = 4$.

a) $a - c^2$ **b)** $a - b^2$ **c)** $b^2 - 4ac$ **d)** $\dfrac{a - b}{c - b}$

Calculator Close-Up

To evaluate $a - c^2$, first store the values for a and c using the STO key. Then enter the expression.

```
2→A
            2
4→C
            4
A-C²
          -14
```

Solution

a) Replace a by 2 and c by 4 in the expression $a - c^2$.

$$a - c^2 = 2 - 4^2 = 2 - 16 = -14$$

b) $a - b^2 = 2 - (-3)^2$ Let $a = 2$ and $b = -3$.

$\qquad\quad = 2 - 9$ Evaluate the exponential expression first.

$\qquad\quad = -7$ Then subtract.

c) $b^2 - 4ac = (-3)^2 - 4(2)(4)$ Let $a = 2$, $b = -3$, and $c = 4$.

$\qquad\qquad = 9 - 32$ Evaluate the exponential expression and product.

$\qquad\qquad = -23$ Subtract last.

d) $\dfrac{a - b}{c - b} = \dfrac{2 - (-3)}{4 - (-3)}$ Let $a = 2$, $b = -3$, and $c = 4$.

$\qquad\qquad = \dfrac{5}{7}$ Evaluate the numerator and denominator.   ■

CAUTION   When you replace a variable by a negative number, be sure to use parentheses around the negative number. If we were to omit the parentheses in Example 7(c), we would get $-3^2 - 4(2)(4) = -41$ instead of -23.

A symbol such as y_1 is treated like any other variable. We read y_1 as "y one" or "y sub one." The 1 is called a **subscript.** We can think of y_1 as the "first y" and y_2 as the "second y." We use the subscript notation in Example 8.

EXAMPLE   8

An algebraic expression with subscripts

Let $y_1 = -12$, $y_2 = -5$, $x_1 = -3$, and $x_2 = 4$. Find the value of $\dfrac{y_2 - y_1}{x_2 - x_1}$.

Solution

Substitute the appropriate values into the expression:

$$\frac{y_2 - y_1}{x_2 - x_1} = \frac{-5 - (-12)}{4 - (-3)} \quad \text{Let } y_1 = -12, y_2 = -5,\; x_1 = -3, \text{ and } x_2 = 4.$$

$$= \frac{7}{7} = 1 \quad \text{Evaluate.}$$

■

Helpful Hint

Many of the expressions that we evaluate in this section are expressions that we will study later in this text. We use the expression in Example 8 to find the slope of a line in Chapter 3.

When we evaluate an algebraic expression involving only one variable for many values of that variable, we get a collection of data. A graph (picture) of these data can give us useful information.

EXAMPLE   9

Reading a graph

The expression $0.85(220 - A)$ gives the target heart rate for beneficial exercise for an athlete who is A years old. Use the graph in Fig. 1.24 to estimate the target heart rate for a 40-year-old athlete. Use the graph to estimate the age of an athlete with a target heart rate of 170.

Study Tip

If you don't know how to get started on the exercises, go back to the examples. Cover the solution in the text with a piece of paper and see if you can solve the example. After mastering the examples, then try the exercises again.

FIGURE   1.24

Solution

To find the target heart rate for a 40-year-old athlete, first draw a vertical line from age 40 up to the graph as shown in Fig. 1.24. From the point of intersection, draw a horizontal line to the heart rate scale. So the target heart rate for a 40-year-old athlete is about 153. To find the age corresponding to a heart rate of 170, first draw a horizontal line from heart rate 170 to the graph as shown in the figure. From the point of intersection, draw a vertical line down to the age scale. The heart rate of 170 corresponds to an age of about 20.

■

True or false? Explain your answer.

1. $2^3 = 6$
2. $-1 \cdot 2^2 = -4$
3. $-2^2 = -4$
4. $6 + 3 \cdot 2 = 18$
5. $(6 + 3) \cdot 2 = 81$
6. $(6 + 3)^2 = 18$
7. $6 + 3^2 = 15$
8. $(-3)^3 = -3^3$
9. $|-3 - (-2)| = 5$
10. $|7 - 8| = |7| - |8|$

1.4   EXERCISES

Reading and Writing   *After reading this section, write out the answers to these questions. Use complete sentences.*

1. What is an arithmetic expression?

2. How do you know whether to call an expression a sum, a difference, a product, or a quotient?

3. Why are grouping symbols used?

4. What is an exponential expression?

5. What is the purpose of the order of operations?

6. What is the difference between -3^2 and $(-3)^2$?

Evaluate each expression. See Example 1.

7. $(-3 \cdot 4) - (2 \cdot 5)$
8. $|-3 - 2| - |2 - 6|$
9. $4[5 - |3 - (2 \cdot 5)|]$
10. $-2|(-3 \cdot 4) - 6|$
11. $(6 - 8)(|2 - 3| + 6)$
12. $-5(6 + [(5 - 7) - 4])$

Evaluate each exponential expression. See Example 2.

13. 2^5
14. 3^4
15. $(-1)^4$
16. $(-1)^5$
17. $\left(-\dfrac{1}{3}\right)^2$
18. $\left(-\dfrac{1}{2}\right)^6$

Evaluate each radical. See Example 3.

19. $\sqrt{49}$
20. $\sqrt{100}$

21. $\sqrt{36 + 64}$
22. $\sqrt{25 - 9}$
23. $\sqrt{4(7 + 9)}$
24. $\sqrt{(11 + 2)(18 - 5)}$

Evaluate each expression. See Examples 4 and 5.

25. $4 - 6 \cdot 2$
26. $8 - 3 \cdot 9$
27. $5 - 6(3 - 5)$
28. $8 - 3(4 - 6)$
29. $\left(\dfrac{1}{3} - \dfrac{1}{2}\right)\left(\dfrac{1}{4} - \dfrac{1}{2}\right)$
30. $\left(\dfrac{1}{2} - \dfrac{1}{4}\right)\left(\dfrac{1}{2} - \dfrac{3}{4}\right)$
31. $-3^2 + (-8)^2 + 3$
32. $-6^2 + (-3)^3$
33. $-(2 - 7)^2$
34. $-(1 - 3 \cdot 2)^3$
35. $-5^2 \cdot 2^3$
36. $2^4 - 4^2$
37. $(-5)(-2)^3$
38. $(-1)(2 - 8)^3$
39. $-(3^2 - 4)^2$
40. $-(6 - 2^3)^4$
41. $-60 \div 10 \cdot 3 \div 2 \cdot 5 \div 6$
42. $75 \div (-5)(-3) \div \dfrac{1}{2} \cdot 6$
43. $5.5 - 2.3^4$
44. $5.3^2 - 4 \cdot 6.1$
45. $(1.3 - 0.31)(2.9 - 4.88)$
46. $(6.7 - 9.88)^3$
47. $-388.8 \div (13.5)(9.6)$
48. $(-4.3)(5.5) \div (3.2)(-1.2)$

Evaluate each expression. See Example 6.

49. $\dfrac{2 - 6}{9 - 7}$
50. $\dfrac{9 - 12}{4 - 5}$
51. $\dfrac{-3 - 5}{6 - (-2)}$
52. $\dfrac{-14 - (-2)}{-3 - 3}$
53. $\dfrac{4 + 2 \cdot 7}{3 \cdot 2 - 9}$
54. $\dfrac{-6 - 2(-3)}{8 - 3(-3)}$
55. $\dfrac{-3^2 - (-9)}{2 - 3^2}$
56. $\dfrac{-2^4 - 5}{3^2 - 2^4}$

Evaluate each expression for $a = -1$, $b = 3$, and $c = -4$. See Example 7.

57. $b^2 - 4ac$

58. $\sqrt{a^2 - 4bc}$

59. $\dfrac{a - b}{a - c}$

60. $\dfrac{b - c}{b - a}$

61. $(a - b)(a + b)$

62. $(a - c)(a + c)$

63. $\sqrt{c^2 - 2c + 1}$

64. $b^2 - 2b - 3$

65. $\dfrac{2}{a} + \dfrac{b}{c} - \dfrac{1}{c}$

66. $\dfrac{c}{a} + \dfrac{c}{b} - \dfrac{a}{b}$

67. $|a - b|$

68. $|b + c|$

Find the value of $\dfrac{y_2 - y_1}{x_2 - x_1}$ for each choice of y_1, y_2, x_1, and x_2. See Example 8.

69. $y_1 = 4$, $y_2 = -6$, $x_1 = 2$, $x_2 = -7$

70. $y_1 = -3$, $y_2 = -3$, $x_1 = 4$, $x_2 = -5$

71. $y_1 = -1$, $y_2 = 2$, $x_1 = -3$, $x_2 = 1$

72. $y_1 = -2$, $y_2 = 5$, $x_1 = 2$, $x_2 = 6$

 73. $y_1 = 2.4$, $y_2 = 5.6$, $x_1 = 5.9$, $x_2 = 4.7$

74. $y_1 = -5.7$, $y_2 = 6.9$, $x_1 = 3.5$, $x_2 = 4.2$

Evaluate each expression without a calculator. Use a calculator to check.

75. $-2^2 + 5(3)^2$

76. $-3^2 + 3(6)^2$

77. $(-2 + 5)3^2$

78. $(-3 + 3)6^2$

79. $\sqrt{5^2 - 4(1)(6)}$

80. $\sqrt{6^2 - 4(2)(4)}$

81. $[13 + 2(-5)]^2$

82. $[6 + 2(-4)]^2$

83. $\dfrac{4 - (-1)}{-3 - 2}$

84. $\dfrac{2 - (-3)}{3 - 5}$

85. $3(-2)^2 - 5(-2) + 4$

86. $3(-1)^2 + 5(-1) - 6$

87. $-4\left(\dfrac{1}{2}\right)^2 + 3\left(\dfrac{1}{2}\right) - 2$

88. $8\left(\dfrac{1}{2}\right)^2 - 6\left(\dfrac{1}{2}\right) + 1$

89. $-\dfrac{1}{2}|6 - 2|$

90. $-\dfrac{1}{3}|9 - 6|$

91. $\dfrac{1}{2} - \dfrac{1}{3}\left|\dfrac{1}{4} - \dfrac{1}{2}\right|$

92. $\dfrac{1}{3} - \dfrac{1}{2}\left|\dfrac{1}{3} - \dfrac{1}{2}\right|$

93. $|6 - 3 \cdot 7| + |7 - 5|$

94. $|12 - 4| - |3 - 4 \cdot 5|$

95. $3 - 7[4 - (2 - 5)]$

96. $9 - 2[3 - (4 + 6)]$

97. $3 - 4(2 - |4 - 6|)$

98. $3 - (|-4| - |-5|)$

99. $4[2 - (5 - |-3|)^2]$

100. $[5 - (-3)]^2 + [4 - (-2)]^2$

Solve each problem. See Example 9.

101. *Female target heart rate.* The algebraic expression $0.65(220 - A)$ gives the target heart rate for beneficial exercise for women, where A is the age of the woman. How much larger is the target heart rate of a 25-year-old woman than that of a 65-year-old woman? Use the accompanying graph to estimate the age at which a woman's target heart rate is 115.

FIGURE FOR EXERCISES 101 AND 102

102. *Male target heart rate.* The algebraic expression $0.75(220 - A)$ gives the target heart rate for beneficial exercise for men, where A is the age of the man. Use the algebraic expression to find the target heart rate for a 20-year-old and a 50-year-old man. Use the accompanying graph to estimate the age at which a man's target heart rate is 115.

Solve each problem.

103. *Perimeter of a pool.* The algebraic expression $2L + 2W$ gives the perimeter of a rectangle with length L and width W. Find the perimeter of a rectangular swimming pool that has length 34 feet and width 18 feet.

104. *Area of a lot.* The algebraic expression for the area of a trapezoid, $0.5h(b_1 + b_2)$, gives the area of the property shown in the figure. Find the area if $h = 150$ feet, $b_1 = 260$ feet, and $b_2 = 220$ feet.

220 ft

150 ft

260 ft

FIGURE FOR EXERCISE 104

105. *Saving for retirement.* The expression $P(1 + r)^n$ gives the amount of an investment of P dollars invested for n years at interest rate r compounded annually. Long-term corporate bonds have had an average yield of 6.2% annually over the last 40 years (Fidelity Investments, www.fidelity.com).

a) Use the accompanying graph to estimate the amount of a $10,000 investment in corporate bonds after 30 years.

b) Use the given expression to calculate the value of a $10,000 investment after 30 years of growth at 6.2% compounded annually.

FIGURE FOR EXERCISE 105

 106. *Saving for college.* The average cost of a B.A. at a private college in 2021 will be $100,000 (U.S. Department of Education, www.ed.gov). The principal that must be invested at interest rate r compounded annually to have A dollars in n years is given by the algebraic expression

$$\frac{A}{(1 + r)^n}.$$

What amount must Melanie's generous grandfather invest in 2003 at 7% compounded annually so that Melanie will have $100,000 for her college education in 2021?

 107. *Student loan.* A college student borrowed $4000 at 8% compounded annually in her freshman year and did not have to make payments until four years later.

Use the accompanying graph to estimate the amount that she owes at the time the payments start. Use the expression $P(1 + r)^n$ to find the actual amount of the debt at the time the payments start.

FIGURE FOR EXERCISE 107

 108. *Nursing home costs.* The average cost of a one-year stay in a nursing home in 2002 was $45,600 (www.medicare.gov). In n years from 2002 the average cost will be $45,600(1.05)^n$ dollars. Find the projected cost for a one-year stay in 2012.

 109. *Higher nursing home costs.* Some economists project that the average cost of a one-year stay in a nursing home n years from 2002 will be $45,600(1.08)^n$ dollars. How much more would you pay for a one-year stay in 2012 using this expression rather than the expression in the last exercise?

GETTING MORE INVOLVED

110. *Discussion.* Evaluate $5(5(5 \cdot 3 + 6) + 4) + 7$ and $3 \cdot 5^3 + 6 \cdot 5^2 + 4 \cdot 5 + 7$. Explain why these two expressions must have the same value.

111. *Cooperative learning.* Find some examples of algebraic expressions that are not mentioned in this text and explain to your class what they are used for.

In This Section

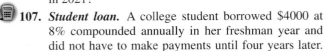

- Commutative Properties
- Associative Properties
- Distributive Property
- Identity Properties
- Inverse Properties
- Multiplication Property of Zero

1.5   PROPERTIES OF THE REAL NUMBERS

You know that the price of a hamburger plus the price of a Coke is the same as the price of a Coke plus the price of a hamburger. But, do you know which property of the real numbers is at work in this situation? In arithmetic we may be unaware when to use properties of the real numbers, but in algebra we need a better understanding of those properties. In this section we will study the properties of the basic operations on the set of real numbers.

Commutative Properties

We get the same result whether we evaluate $3 + 7$ or $7 + 3$. With multiplication, we have $4 \cdot 5 = 5 \cdot 4$. These examples illustrate the commutative properties.

Commutative Property of Addition

For any real numbers a and b,

$$a + b = b + a.$$

Commutative Property of Multiplication

For any real numbers a and b,

$$ab = ba.$$

In writing the product of a number and a variable, it is customary to write the number first. We write $3x$ rather than $x3$. In writing the product of two variables, it is customary to write them in alphabetical order. We write cd rather than dc.

Addition and multiplication are commutative operations, but what about subtraction and division? Because $7 - 3 = 4$ and $3 - 7 = -4$, subtraction is not commutative. To see that division is not commutative, consider the amount each person gets when a \$1 million lottery prize is divided between two people and when a \$2 prize is divided among 1 million people.

Associative Properties

Consider the expression $2 + 3 + 7$. Using the order of operations, we add from left to right to get 12. If we first add 3 and 7 to get 10 and then add 2 and 10, we also get 12. So

$$(2 + 3) + 7 = 2 + (3 + 7).$$

Now consider the expression $2 \cdot 3 \cdot 5$. Using the order of operations, we multiply from left to right to get 30. However, we can first multiply 3 and 5 to get 15 and then multiply by 2 to get 30. So

$$(2 \cdot 3) \cdot 5 = 2 \cdot (3 \cdot 5).$$

These examples illustrate the associative properties.

Associative Property of Addition

For any real numbers a, b, and c,

$$(a + b) + c = a + (b + c).$$

Associative Property of Multiplication

For any real numbers a, b, and c,

$$(ab)c = a(bc).$$

Consider the expression

$$4 - 9 + 8 - 5 - 8 + 6 - 13.$$

According to the accepted order of operations, we could evaluate this expression by computing from left to right. However, if we use the definition of subtraction, we can rewrite this expression as

$$4 + (-9) + 8 + (-5) + (-8) + 6 + (-13).$$

The commutative and associative properties of addition allow us to add these numbers in any order we choose. A good way to add them is to add the positive numbers, add the negative numbers, and then combine the two totals:

$$4 + 8 + 6 + (-9) + (-5) + (-8) + (-13) = 18 + (-35)$$
$$= -17$$

For speed we usually do not rewrite the expression. We just sum the positive numbers and sum the negative numbers, and then combine their totals.

E X A M P L E   1

Using commutative and associative properties

Evaluate.

a) $4 - 7 + 10 - 5$ **b)** $6 - 5 - 9 + 7 - 2 + 5 - 8$

Solution

a) $4 - 7 + 10 - 5 = 14 + (-12) = 2$

    ↑   ↑
Sum of the positive   Sum of the negative
    numbers   numbers

b) $6 - 5 - 9 + 7 - 2 + 5 - 8 = 18 + (-24)$ Add positive numbers;
$$= -6$$ add negative numbers.

∎

Not all operations are associative. Using subtraction, for example, we have

$$(8 - 4) - 1 \neq 8 - (4 - 1)$$

because $(8 - 4) - 1 = 3$ and $8 - (4 - 1) = 5$. For division we have

$$(8 \div 4) \div 2 \neq 8 \div (4 \div 2)$$

because $(8 \div 4) \div 2 = 1$ and $8 \div (4 \div 2) = 4$. So subtraction and division are not associative.

Helpful Hint

Imagine a parade in which 6 rows of horses are followed by 4 rows of horses with 3 horses in each row.

+ + + + + +   + + + +
+ + + + + +   + + + +
+ + + + + +   + + + +

There are 10 rows of 3 horses or 30 horses, or there are 18 horses followed by 12 horses for a total of 30 horses.

Distributive Property

Using the order of operations, we evaluate the product $3(6 + 4)$ first by adding 6 and 4 and then multiplying by 3:

$$3(6 + 4) = 3 \cdot 10 = 30$$

Note that we also have

$$3 \cdot 6 + 3 \cdot 4 = 18 + 12 = 30.$$

Therefore

$$3(6 + 4) = 3 \cdot 6 + 3 \cdot 4.$$

Note that multiplication by 3 from outside the parentheses is *distributed* over each term inside the parentheses. This example illustrates the distributive property.

Distributive Property

For any real numbers a, b, and c,

$$a(b + c) = ab + ac.$$

Because subtraction is defined in terms of addition, multiplication distributes over subtraction as well as over addition. For example,

$$3(x - 2) = 3(x + (-2))$$
$$= 3x + (-6)$$
$$= 3x - 6.$$

Because multiplication is commutative, we can write the multiplication before or after the parentheses. For example,

$$(y + 6)3 = 3(y + 6)$$
$$= 3y + 18.$$

The distributive property is used in two ways. If we start with the product $5(x + 4)$ and write

$$5(x + 4) = 5x + 20,$$

we are writing a product as a sum. We are removing the parentheses. If we start with the difference $6x - 18$ and write

$$6x - 18 = 6(x - 3),$$

we are using the distributive property to write a difference as a product.

E X A M P L E   2

Using the distributive property

Use the distributive property to rewrite each sum or difference as a product and each product as a sum or difference.

a) $9x - 9$ b) $b(2 - a)$ c) $3a + ac$ d) $-2(x - 3)$

Solution

a) $9x - 9 = 9(x - 1)$

b) $b(2 - a) = 2b - ab$ Note that $b \cdot 2 = 2b$ by the commutative property.

c) $3a + ac = a(3 + c)$

d) $-2(x - 3) = -2x - (-2)(3)$ Distributive property
$$= -2x - (-6)$$ Multiply.
$$= -2x + 6$$ $a - (-b) = a + b$ ∎

Identity Properties

The numbers 0 and 1 have special properties. Addition of 0 to a number does not change the number, and multiplication of a number by 1 does not change the number. For this reason, 0 is called the **additive identity** and 1 is called the **multiplicative identity.**

Additive Identity Property

For any real number a,

$$a + 0 = 0 + a = a.$$

Multiplicative Identity Property

For any real number a,

$$a \cdot 1 = 1 \cdot a = a.$$

Inverse Properties

The ideas of *additive inverses* and *multiplicative inverses* were introduced in Section 1.3. Every real number a has a unique additive inverse or opposite, $-a$, such that $a + (-a) = 0$. Every nonzero real number a also has a unique multiplicative inverse (reciprocal), written $\frac{1}{a}$, such that $a\left(\frac{1}{a}\right) = 1$. For rational numbers the multiplicative inverse is easy to find. For example, the multiplicative inverse of $\frac{2}{5}$ is $\frac{5}{2}$ because

$$\frac{2}{5} \cdot \frac{5}{2} = \frac{10}{10} = 1.$$

Calculator Close-Up

Most scientific calculators have a key labeled 1/x, which gives the reciprocal of the number on the display. Graphing calculators do not have a reciprocal key, but you can find reciprocals as shown here.

```
1/0.002+1/0.0012
5
            1300
```

Additive Inverse Property

For any real number a, there is a unique number $-a$ such that

$$a + (-a) = -a + a = 0.$$

Multiplicative Inverse Property

For any nonzero real number a, there is a unique number $\frac{1}{a}$ such that

$$a \cdot \frac{1}{a} = \frac{1}{a} \cdot a = 1.$$

Reciprocals are used in problems involving rates. For example, if Brandon washes one car in $\frac{1}{3}$ of an hour, then he is washing cars at the rate of $1/\left(\frac{1}{3}\right)$ or 3 cars/hour (3 cars per hour). If Gilda washes one car in $\frac{1}{4}$ of an hour, then she is washing at the rate of $1/\left(\frac{1}{4}\right)$ or 4 cars/hour. In general, if one task is completed in x hours, then the rate is $\frac{1}{x}$ tasks/hour. If Brandon and Gilda maintain the same rates when working together, then their rate together is the sum of their individual rates, or 7 cars/hour.

EXAMPLE 3

Work rates

An old computer system can process one water bill in 0.002 hour. A new computer system can process one water bill in 0.00125 hour. If the old system is used simultaneously with the new one, then at what rate will the processing of the water bills be accomplished?

Solution

Since the old system does one bill in 0.002 hour, its rate is $\frac{1}{0.002}$ bills per hour. Since the new system does one bill in 0.00125 hour, its rate is $\frac{1}{0.00125}$ bills per hour. Their rate when working together is the sum of their individual rates:

$$\frac{1}{0.002} + \frac{1}{0.00125} = 1300$$

They are working together at the rate of 1300 bills per hour. ∎

Multiplication Property of Zero

Zero has a property that no other number has. Multiplication involving zero always results in zero. It is the multiplication property of zero that prevents 0 from having a reciprocal.

> **Multiplication Property of Zero**
>
> For any real number a,
>
> $$0 \cdot a = a \cdot 0 = 0.$$

E X A M P L E 4

Recognizing properties

Identify the property that is illustrated in each case.

a) $5 \cdot 9 = 9 \cdot 5$

b) $3 \cdot \dfrac{1}{3} = 1$

c) $1 \cdot 865 = 865$

d) $3 + (5 + a) = (3 + 5) + a$

e) $4x + 6x = (4 + 6)x$

f) $7 + (x + 3) = 7 + (3 + x)$

g) $4567 \cdot 0 = 0$

h) $239 + 0 = 239$

i) $-8 + 8 = 0$

j) $-4(x - 5) = -4x + 20$

Solution

a) Commutative property of multiplication

b) Multiplicative inverse property

c) Multiplicative identity property

d) Associative property of addition

e) Distributive property

f) Commutative property of addition

g) Multiplication property of zero

h) Additive identity property

i) Additive inverse property

j) Distributive property ■

WARM-UPS

True or false? Explain your answer.

1. Addition is a commutative operation.

2. $8 \div (4 \div 2) = (8 \div 4) \div 2$

3. $10 \div 2 = 2 \div 10$

4. $5 - 3 = 3 - 5$

5. $10 - (7 - 3) = (10 - 7) - 3$

6. $4(6 \div 2) = (4 \cdot 6) \div (4 \cdot 2)$

7. The multiplicative inverse of 0.02 is 50.

8. Division is not an associative operation.

9. $3 + 2x = 5x$ for any value of x.

10. A machine that washes one car in 0.04 hour is washing at the rate of 25 cars per hour.

1.5   EXERCISES

Reading and Writing   *After reading this section, write out the answers to these questions. Use complete sentences.*

1. What are the commutative properties?

2. What are the associative properties?

3. What is the difference between the commutative property of addition and the associative property of addition?

4. What is the distributive property?

5. Why is 0 called the additive identity?

6. Why is 1 called the multiplicative identity?

Evaluate. See Example 1.

7. $9 - 4 + 6 - 10$

8. $-3 + 4 - 12 + 9$

9. $6 - 10 + 5 - 8 - 7$

10. $5 - 11 + 6 - 9 + 12 - 2$

11. $-4 - 11 + 6 - 8 + 13 - 20$

12. $-8 + 12 - 9 - 15 + 6 - 22 + 3$

13. $-3.2 + 1.4 - 2.8 + 4.5 - 1.6$

14. $4.4 - 5.1 + 3.6 - 2.3 + 8.1$

15. $3.27 - 11.41 + 5.7 - 12.36 - 5$

16. $4.89 - 2.1 + 7.58 - 9.06 - 5.34$

Use the distributive property to rewrite each sum or difference as a product and each product as a sum or difference. See Example 2.

17. $4(x - 6)$

18. $5(a - 1)$

19. $2m + 10$

20. $3y + 9$

21. $a(3 + t)$

22. $b(y + w)$

23. $-2(w - 5)$

24. $-4(m - 7)$

25. $-2(3 - y)$

26. $-5(4 - p)$

27. $5x - 5$

28. $3y + 3$

29. $-1(-2x - y)$

30. $-1(-4y - w)$

31. $-3(-2w - 3y)$

32. $-4(-x - 6)$

33. $3y - 15$

34. $5x + 10$

35. $3a + 9$

36. $7b - 49$

37. $\frac{1}{2}(4x + 8)$

38. $\frac{1}{3}(3x + 6)$

39. $-\frac{1}{2}(2x - 4)$

40. $-\frac{1}{3}(9x - 3)$

Find the multiplicative inverse (reciprocal) of each number.

41. $\frac{1}{2}$

42. $\frac{1}{3}$

43. 1

44. -1

45. 6

46. 8

47. 0.25

48. 0.75

49. -0.7

50. -0.9

51. -1.8

52. -2.6

 Use a calculator to evaluate each expression. Round answers to four decimal places.

53. $\frac{1}{2.3} + \frac{1}{5.4}$

54. $\frac{1}{13.5} - \frac{1}{4.6}$

55. $\dfrac{\dfrac{1}{4.3}}{\dfrac{1}{5.6} + \dfrac{1}{7.2}}$

56. $\dfrac{\dfrac{1}{4.5} - \dfrac{1}{5.6}}{\dfrac{1}{3.2} + \dfrac{1}{2.7}}$

 Solve each problem. See Example 3.

57. *Fastest airliner.* The Concorde travels 1 mile in 0.0006897 hour and carries 128 passengers (www.british-airways.com/concorde). Find its rate in miles per hour.

58. *Fastest jet plane.* On March 6, 1990, the SR-71 Blackbird set a record by flying coast to coast in 68 minutes (National Air and Space Museum, www.nasm.si.edu). The Blackbird averaged one mile every 0.000471 hour. Find the rate in miles per hour.

59. *Who's got the button.* A small clothing factory has three workers who attach buttons. Rita, Mary, and Sam can attach a single button in 0.01 hour, 0.02 hour, and 0.015 hour, respectively. At what hourly rate are they attaching buttons when working simultaneously?

60. *Modern art.* Emilio can paint the exterior of a certain house in 36.5 hours. Alex can paint the same house in 30 hours. If they work together without interfering with each other, then at what hourly rate will the house be painted?

Name the property that is illustrated in each case. See Example 4.

61. $3 + x = x + 3$
62. $x \cdot 5 = 5x$
63. $5(x - 7) = 5x - 35$
64. $a(3b) = (a \cdot 3)b$
65. $3(xy) = (3x)y$
66. $3(x - 1) = 3x - 3$
67. $4(0.25) = 1$
68. $0.3 + 9 = 9 + 0.3$
69. $y^3 x = xy^3$
70. $0 \cdot 52 = 0$
71. $1 \cdot x = x$
72. $(0.1)(10) = 1$
73. $2x + 3x = (2 + 3)x$
74. $8 + 0 = 8$
75. $7 + (-7) = 0$
76. $1 \cdot y = y$
77. $(36 + 79)0 = 0$
78. $5x + 5 = 5(x + 1)$
79. $xy + x = x(y + 1)$
80. $ab + 3ac = a(b + 3c)$

Complete each statement using the property named.

81. $5 + w =$ _____, commutative property of addition

82. $2x + 2 =$ _____, distributive property

83. $5(xy) =$ _____, associative property of multiplication

84. $x + \dfrac{1}{2} =$ _____, commutative property of addition

85. $\dfrac{1}{2}x - \dfrac{1}{2} =$ _____, distributive property

86. $3(x - 7) =$ _____, distributive property
87. $6x + 9 =$ _____, distributive property
88. $(x + 7) + 3 =$ _____, associative property of addition

89. $8(0.125) =$ _____, multiplicative inverse property
90. $-1(a - 3) =$ _____, distributive property
91. $0 = 5($_____$)$, multiplication property of zero
92. $8 \cdot ($_____$) = 8$, multiplicative identity property
93. $0.25 ($_____$) = 1$, multiplicative inverse property
94. $45(1) =$ _____, multiplicative identity property

GETTING MORE INVOLVED

95. *Discussion.* Does the order in which your groceries are placed on the checkout counter make any difference in your total bill? Which properties are at work here?

96. *Discussion.* Suppose that you just bought 10 grocery items and paid a total bill that included 6% sales tax. Would there be any difference in your total bill if you purchased the items one at a time? Which property is at work here?

In This Section

- Using the Properties in Computation
- Like Terms
- Combining Like Terms
- Products and Quotients
- Removing Parentheses

1.6   **USING THE PROPERTIES**

The properties of the real numbers can be helpful when we are doing computations. In this section we will see how the properties can be applied in arithmetic and algebra.

Using the Properties in Computation

Consider the product of 36 and 200. Using the associative property of multiplication, we can write

$$(36)(200) = (36)(2 \cdot 100) = (36 \cdot 2)(100).$$

To find this product mentally, first multiply 36 by 2 to get 72, then multiply 72 by 100 to get 7200.

E X A M P L E   1   **Using properties in computation**
Evaluate each expression mentally by using an appropriate property.

a) $536 + 25 + 75$ b) $5 \cdot 426 \cdot \dfrac{1}{5}$ c) $7 \cdot 45 + 3 \cdot 45$

Solution

a) To perform this addition mentally, the associative property of addition can be applied as follows:

$$536 + (25 + 75) = 536 + 100 = 636$$

b) Use the commutative and associative properties of multiplication to rearrange mentally this product.

$$5 \cdot 426 \cdot \frac{1}{5} = 426 \cdot 5 \cdot \frac{1}{5} \quad \text{Commutative property of multiplication}$$

$$= 426\left(5 \cdot \frac{1}{5}\right) \quad \text{Associative property of multiplication}$$

$$= 426 \cdot 1 \quad \text{Multiplicative inverse property}$$

$$= 426$$

c) Use the distributive property to rewrite the expression, then evaluate it.

$$7 \cdot 45 + 3 \cdot 45 = (7 + 3)45 = 10 \cdot 45 = 450 \qquad ■$$

Like Terms

The properties of the real numbers are used also with algebraic expressions. Simple algebraic expressions such as

$$-2, \qquad 4x, \qquad -5x^2y, \qquad b, \qquad \text{and} \qquad -abc$$

are called terms. A **term** is a single number or the product of a number and one or more variables raised to powers. The number preceding the variables in a term is called the **coefficient.** In the term $4x$ the coefficient of x is 4. In the term $-5x^2y$ the coefficient of x^2y is -5. In the term b the coefficient of b is 1, and in the term $-abc$ the coefficient of abc is -1. If two terms contain the same variables with the same powers, they are called **like terms.** For example, $3x^2$ and $-5x^2$ are like terms, whereas $3x^2$ and $-2x^3$ are not like terms.

Combining Like Terms

We can combine any two like terms involved in a sum by using the distributive property. For example,

$$2x + 5x = (2 + 5)x \quad \text{Distributive property}$$
$$= 7x \quad \text{Add 2 and 5.}$$

Because the distributive property is valid for any real numbers, we have $2x + 5x = 7x$ for any real number x.

We can also use the distributive property to combine any two like terms involved in a difference. For example,

$$-3xy - (-2xy) = [-3 - (-2)]xy \quad \text{Distributive property}$$
$$= -1xy \quad \text{Subtract.}$$
$$= -xy \quad \text{Multiplying by } -1 \text{ is the same as taking the opposite.}$$

Of course, we do not want to write out these steps every time we combine like terms. We can combine like terms as easily as we can add or subtract their coefficients.

E X A M P L E   2

Combining like terms

Perform the indicated operation.

a) $b + 3b$ **b)** $5x^2 - 7x^2$

c) $5xy - (-13xy)$ **d)** $-2a + (-9a)$

Solution

a) $b + 3b = 1b + 3b = 4b$ **b)** $5x^2 - 7x^2 = -2x^2$

c) $5xy - (-13xy) = 18xy$ **d)** $-2a + (-9a) = -11a$ ∎

C A U T I O N   The distributive property allows us to combine only *like* terms. Expressions such as

$$3xw + 5, \qquad 7xy + 9t, \qquad 5b + 6a, \qquad \text{and} \qquad 6x^2 + 7x$$

do not contain like terms, so their terms cannot be combined.

Products and Quotients

We can use the associative property of multiplication to simplify the product of two terms. For example,

$$4(7x) = (4 \cdot 7)x \qquad \text{Associative property of multiplication}$$
$$= (28)x$$
$$= 28x. \qquad \text{Remove unnecessary parentheses.}$$

C A U T I O N   Multiplication does not distribute over multiplication. For example, $2(3 \cdot 4) \neq 6 \cdot 8$ because $2(3 \cdot 4) = 2(12) = 24$.

In the next example we use the fact that dividing by 3 is equivalent to multiplying by $\frac{1}{3}$, the reciprocal of 3:

$$3\left(\frac{x}{3}\right) = 3\left(x \cdot \frac{1}{3}\right) \qquad \text{Definition of division}$$

$$= 3\left(\frac{1}{3} \cdot x\right) \qquad \text{Commutative property of multiplication}$$

$$= \left(3 \cdot \frac{1}{3}\right)x \qquad \text{Associative property of multiplication}$$

$$= 1 \cdot x \qquad 3 \cdot \frac{1}{3} = 1 \text{ (Multiplicative inverse property)}$$

$$= x \qquad \text{Multiplicative identity property}$$

To find the product $(3x)(5x)$, we use both the commutative and associative properties of multiplication:

$$(3x)(5x) = (3x \cdot 5)x \qquad \text{Associative property of multiplication}$$
$$= (3 \cdot 5x)x \qquad \text{Commutative property of multiplication}$$
$$= (3 \cdot 5)(x \cdot x) \qquad \text{Associative property of multiplication}$$
$$= (15)(x^2) \qquad \text{Simplify.}$$
$$= 15x^2 \qquad \text{Remove unnecessary parentheses.}$$

All of the steps in finding the product $(3x)(5x)$ are shown here to illustrate that every step is justified by a property. However, you should write $(3x)(5x) = 15x^2$ without doing any intermediate steps.

E X A M P L E   3   **Multiplying terms**

Find each product.

a) $(-5)(6x)$ **b)** $(-3a)(-8a)$ **c)** $(-4y)(-6)$ **d)** $(-5a)\left(\dfrac{b}{5}\right)$

Solution

a) $-30x$ **b)** $24a^2$ **c)** $24y$ **d)** $-ab$ ■

In Example 4 we use the properties to find quotients. Try to identify the property that is used at each step.

E X A M P L E   4   **Dividing terms**

Find each quotient.

a) $\dfrac{5x}{5}$ **b)** $\dfrac{4x + 8}{2}$

Study Tip

Solution

a) First use the definition of division to change the division by 5 to multiplication by $\frac{1}{5}$.

$$\frac{5x}{5} = 5x \cdot \frac{1}{5} = \left(\frac{1}{5} \cdot 5\right)x = 1 \cdot x = x$$

b) First use the definition of division to change division by 2 to multiplication by $\frac{1}{2}$.

$$\frac{4x + 8}{2} = (4x + 8) \cdot \frac{1}{2} = \frac{1}{2} \cdot (4x + 8) = 2x + 4$$

Since both $4x$ and 8 are divided by 2, we could have written

$$\frac{4x + 8}{2} = \frac{4x}{2} + \frac{8}{2} = 2x + 4.$$ ■

C A U T I O N   Do not divide a number into just one term of a sum. For example,

$$\frac{2 + 7}{2} \neq 1 + 7$$

because

$$\frac{2 + 7}{2} = \frac{9}{2} \quad \text{and} \quad 1 + 7 = 8.$$

Removing Parentheses

Multiplying a number by -1 merely changes the sign of the number. For example,

$$(-1)(6) = -6 \qquad \text{and} \qquad (-1)(-15) = 15.$$

Thus -1 times a number is the same as the *opposite* of the number. Using variables, we have

$$(-1)x = -x \qquad \text{or} \qquad -1(a + 2) = -(a + 2).$$

When a minus sign appears in front of a sum, we can think of it as multiplication by -1 and use the distributive property. For example,

$$
\begin{aligned}
-(a + 2) &= -1(a + 2) \\
&= (-1)a + (-1)2 \quad \text{Distributive property} \\
&= -a + (-2) \\
&= -a - 2.
\end{aligned}
$$

If a minus sign occurs in front of a difference, we can rewrite the expression as a sum. For example,

$$
\begin{aligned}
-(x - 5) &= -1(x - 5) \quad {\scriptstyle -a \,=\, -1 \cdot a} \\
&= (-1)x - (-1)5 \quad \text{Distributive property} \\
&= -x + 5. \quad \text{Simplify.}
\end{aligned}
$$

Note that a minus sign in front of a set of parentheses affects each term in the parentheses, changing the sign of each term.

EXAMPLE 5

Removing parentheses

Simplify each expression.

a) $6 - (x + 8)$ **b)** $4x - 6 - (7x - 4)$ **c)** $3x - (-x + 7)$

Solution

a)
$$
\begin{aligned}
6 - (x + 8) &= 6 - x - 8 \quad \text{Change the sign of each term in parentheses.} \\
&= 6 - 8 - x \quad \text{Rearrange the terms.} \\
&= -2 - x \quad \text{Combine like terms.}
\end{aligned}
$$

b)
$$
\begin{aligned}
4x - 6 - (7x - 4) &= 4x - 6 - 7x + 4 \quad \text{Remove parentheses.} \\
&= 4x - 7x - 6 + 4 \quad \text{Rearrange the terms.} \\
&= -3x - 2 \quad \text{Combine like terms.}
\end{aligned}
$$

c)
$$
\begin{aligned}
3x - (-x + 7) &= 3x + x - 7 \quad \text{Remove parentheses.} \\
&= 4x - 7 \quad \text{Combine like terms.}
\end{aligned}
$$ ■

The commutative and associative properties of addition allow us to rearrange the terms so that we may combine like terms. However, it is not necessary actually to write down the rearrangement. We can identify like terms and combine them without rearranging.

EXAMPLE 6

More parentheses and like terms

Simplify each expression.

a) $(-5x + 7) + (2x - 9)$ **b)** $-4x + 7x + 3(2 - 5x)$

c) $-3x(4x - 9) - (x - 5)$ **d)** $x - 0.03(x + 300)$

Solution

a) $(-5x + 7) + (2x - 9) = -3x - 2$ Combine like terms.

b) $-4x + 7x + 3(2 - 5x) = -4x + 7x + 6 - 15x$ Distributive property
$$= -12x + 6$$ Combine like terms.

c) $-3x(4x - 9) - (x - 5) = -12x^2 + 27x - x + 5$ Remove parentheses.
$$= -12x^2 + 26x + 5$$ Combine like terms.

d) $x - 0.03(x + 300) = 1x - 0.03x - 9$ Distributive property; $(-0.03)(300) = -9$
$$= 0.97x - 9$$ Combine like terms: $1.00 - 0.03 = 0.97$ ■

WARM-UPS

True or false? Explain your answer.

A statement involving variables should be marked true only if it is true for all values of the variable.

1. $5(x + 7) = 5x + 35$
2. $-4x + 8 = -4(x + 8)$
3. $-1(a - 3) = -(a - 3)$
4. $5y + 4y = 9y$
5. $(2x)(5x) = 10x$
6. $-2t(5t - 3) = -10t^2 + 6t$
7. $a + a = a^2$
8. $b \cdot b = 2b$
9. $1 + 7x = 8x$
10. $(3x - 4) - (8x - 1) = -5x - 3$

1.6   EXERCISES

Reading and Writing   After reading this section, write out the answers to these questions. Use complete sentences.

1. What is a term?

2. What are like terms?

3. What is the coefficient of a term?

4. Which property is used to combine like terms?

5. What operations can you perform with unlike terms?

6. How do you remove parentheses that are preceded by a negative sign?

Perform each computation. Make use of appropriate rules to simplify each problem. See Example 1.

7. $45(200)$
8. $25(300)$
9. $\frac{4}{3}(0.75)$
10. $5(0.2)$

11. $(427 + 68) + 32$
12. $(194 + 78) + 22$
13. $47 \cdot 4 + 47 \cdot 6$
14. $53 \cdot 3 + 53 \cdot 7$
15. $19 \cdot 5 \cdot 2 \cdot \frac{1}{5}$
16. $17 \cdot 4 \cdot 2 \cdot \frac{1}{4}$
17. $(120)(400)$
18. $150 \cdot 300$
19. $13 \cdot 377(-5 + 5)$
20. $(456 \cdot 8)\frac{1}{8}$
21. $(348 + 5) + 45$
22. $(135 + 38) + 12$
23. $\frac{2}{3}(1.5)$
24. $(1.25)(0.8)$
25. $17 \cdot 101 - 17 \cdot 1$
26. $33 \cdot 2 - 12 \cdot 33$
27. $354 + 7 + 8 + 3 + 2$
28. $564 + 35 + 65 + 72 + 28$
29. $(567 + 874)(-2 \cdot 4 + 8)$
30. $(567^2 + 48)[3(-5) + 15]$

Combine like terms where possible. See Example 2.

31. $-4n + 6n$
32. $-3a + 15a$
33. $3w - (-4w)$
34. $3b - (-7b)$

35. $4mw^2 - 15mw^2$ **36.** $2b^2x - 16b^2x$

37. $-5x - (-2x)$ **38.** $-11 - 7t$

39. $-4 - 7z$ **40.** $-19m - (-3m)$

41. $4t^2 + 5t^2$ **42.** $5a + 4a^2$

43. $-4ab + 3a^2b$ **44.** $-7x^2y + 5x^2y$

45. $9mn - mn$ **46.** $3cm - cm$

47. $x^3y - 3x^3y$ **48.** $s^4t - 5s^4t$

49. $-kz^6 - kz^6$ **50.** $m^7w - m^7w$

Find each product or quotient. See Examples 3 and 4.
51. $4(7t)$ **52.** $-3(4r)$ **53.** $(-2x)(-5x)$

54. $(-3h)(-7h)$ **55.** $(-h)(-h)$ **56.** $x(-x)$

57. $7w(-4)$ **58.** $-5t(-1)$ **59.** $-x(1 - x)$

60. $-p(p - 1)$ **61.** $(5k)(5k)$ **62.** $(-4y)(-4y)$

63. $3\left(\dfrac{y}{3}\right)$ **64.** $5z\left(\dfrac{z}{5}\right)$ **65.** $9\left(\dfrac{2y}{9}\right)$

66. $8\left(\dfrac{y}{8}\right)$ **67.** $\dfrac{6x^3}{2}$ **68.** $\dfrac{-8x^2}{4}$

69. $\dfrac{3x^2y + 15x}{3}$ **70.** $\dfrac{6xy^2 - 8w}{2}$ **71.** $\dfrac{2x - 4}{-2}$

72. $\dfrac{-6x - 9}{-3}$ **73.** $\dfrac{-xt + 10}{-2}$ **74.** $\dfrac{-2xt^2 + 8}{-4}$

Simplify each expression. See Example 5.
75. $a - (4a - 1)$
76. $5x - (2x - 7)$
77. $6 - (x - 4)$
78. $9 - (w - 5)$
79. $4m + 6 - (m + 5)$
80. $5 - 6t - (3t + 4)$
81. $-5b - (-at + 7b)$
82. $-4x^2 - (-7x^2 + 2y)$
83. $t^2 - 5w - (-2w - t^2)$
84. $n^2 - 6m - (-n^2 - 2m)$

85. $x^2 - (x^2 - y^2 - z)$
86. $5w - (6w - 3xy - zy)$

Simplify each expression. See Example 6.
87. $(2x + 7x) + (3 + 5)$
88. $(3x + 4x) + (5 + 12)$
89. $(-3x + 4) + (5x - 6)$
90. $(-4x + 11) + (6x - 8)$
91. $4a^2 - 5c - (6a^2 - 7c)$
92. $3x^2 - 4 - (x^2 - 5)$
93. $5(t^2 - 3w) - 2(-3w - t^2)$
94. $6(xy^2 + 2) - 5(-xy^2 - 1)$
95. $-7m + 3(m - 4) + 5m$
96. $-6m + 4(m - 3) + 7m$
97. $8 - 7(k^3 + 3) - 4$
98. $6 + 5(k^3 - 2) - k^3 + 5$
99. $x - 0.04(x + 50)$
100. $x - 0.03(x + 500)$
101. $0.1(x + 5) - 0.04(x + 50)$
102. $0.06x + 0.14(x + 200)$
103. $3k + 5 - 2(3k - 4) - k + 3$
104. $5w - 2 + 4(w - 3) - 6(w - 1)$
105. $5.7 - 4.5(x - 3.9) - 5.42$
106. $0.04(5.6x - 4.9) + 0.07(7.3x - 34)$

Simplify.
107. $3(1 - xy) - 2(xy - 5) - (35 - xy)$
108. $2(x^2 - 3) - (6x^2 - 2) + 2(-7x^2 - 4)$
109. $w \cdot 3w + 5w(-6w) - w(2w)$
110. $3w^3 + 5w^3 - 4w^3 + 12w^3 - 2w^2$
111. $3a^2w^2 - 5w^2 \cdot a^2 - 2aw \cdot 2aw$
112. $-3(aw^2 + 5a^2w) - 2(-a^2w - a^2w)$

113. $\dfrac{1}{6} - \dfrac{1}{3}\left(-6x^2y - \dfrac{1}{2}\right)$

114. $-\dfrac{1}{2}bc - \dfrac{1}{2}bc(3 - a)$

115. $-\dfrac{1}{2}m\left(-\dfrac{1}{2}m\right) - \dfrac{1}{2}m - \dfrac{1}{2}m$

116. $\dfrac{4wyt}{4} + \dfrac{-8wyt}{2} - \dfrac{-2wy}{2}$

117. $\dfrac{-8t^3 - 6t^2 + 2}{-2}$

118. $\dfrac{7x^3 - 5x^3 - 4}{-2}$

119. $\dfrac{-6xyz - 3xy + 9z}{-3}$

120. $\dfrac{20a^2b^4 - 10a^2b^4 + 5}{-5}$

Write an algebraic expression for each problem.

121. *Triangle.* The lengths of the sides of a triangular flower bed are s feet, $s + 2$ feet, and $s + 4$ feet. What is its perimeter?

122. *Parallelogram.* The lengths of the sides of a lot in the shape of a parallelogram are w feet and $w + 50$ feet. What is its perimeter? Is it possible to find the area from this information?

w + 50 ft

w ft   w ft

w + 50 ft

FIGURE FOR EXERCISE 122

123. *Parthenon.* To obtain a pleasing rectangular shape, the ancient Greeks constructed buildings with a length that was about $\frac{1}{6}$ longer than the width. If the width of the

Parthenon is x meters and its length is $x + \frac{1}{6}x$ meters, then what is the perimeter? What is the area?

124. *Square.* If the length of each side of a square sign is x inches, then what are the perimeter and area of the square?

FIGURE FOR EXERCISE 124

COLLABORATIVE ACTIVITIES

OOOP! Order of Operations Game

This game reviews the established order of operations for real numbers.

1. Before Play Begins

You will need three to five players on a team. Assign each player one of the roles or operations listed in part (3). Write one of these expressions on a sheet of paper.

a) $\dfrac{5^2 - 2(-3)}{-2^3 - 6}$ **b)** $\dfrac{(-2)^2 + 3(-5)}{4 \cdot 5 + 2}$

c) $75 \div 3(2 + 6) - (4^2 \div 2)$

d) $[13 - 5 + 4 \div (-2^2)(7 + 8)] + (-4)$

2. Determining a Player's Turn at Play

All players working together analyze the expression and decide which part to complete. If there are parentheses, then the players decide whether what is inside the parentheses needs simplification. **E** *performs his or her operation before* **M**, *and* **M** *performs his or her operation before* **A**. Each player's turn ends when he or she encounters an operation that precedes his or hers or when he or she reaches the end of the expression.

Grouping: Three to five students per group
Topic: Order of operations, learning to work in groups

3. Each Player's Task

    E—Exponents: Working left to right, **E** evaluates exponential expressions in order.

    M—Multiply/Divide: Working left to right, **M** performs multiplications and divisions in order. Multiplication and division may be done by two players working as a team. If these tasks are split, then the two players perform their assigned operations in order, taking turns as needed.

    A—Add/Subtract: Working left to right, **A** performs additions and subtractions in order. Addition and subtraction may be done by two players working as a team. If these tasks are split, then the two players perform their assigned operations in order, taking turns as needed.

4. Recording Results

Results are recorded on one sheet of paper. As each player finishes his or her operation, she or he passes the paper to the player with the next task. Each player rewrites the new form of the expression on the next line of the page and initials his or her work with **E**, **M**, or **A**.

WRAP-UP

CHAPTER 1

SUMMARY

Sets		**Examples**
Set-builder notation	Notation for describing a set using variables.	$C = \{x \mid x$ is a natural number smaller than 4$\}$ $D = \{3, 4\}$
Membership	The symbol $\in$ means "is an element of."	$1 \in C, 4 \notin C$
Union	$A \cup B = \{x \mid x \in A$ or $x \in B\}$	$C \cup D = \{1, 2, 3, 4\}$
Intersection	$A \cap B = \{x \mid x \in A$ and $x \in B\}$	$C \cap D = \{3\}$
Subset	A is a subset of B if every element of A is also an element of B. $\varnothing \subseteq A$ for any set A.	$\{1, 2\} \subseteq C$ $\varnothing \subseteq C, \varnothing \subseteq D$

Real Numbers		**Examples**
Rational numbers	$Q = \left\{ \dfrac{a}{b} \mid a$ and b are integers with $b \neq 0 \right\}$	$\dfrac{3}{2}, 5, -6, 0, 0.25252525\ldots$
Irrational numbers	$I = \{x \mid x$ is a real number that is not rational$\}$	$\sqrt{2}, \sqrt{3}, \pi, 0.1515515551\ldots$
Real numbers	$R = \{x \mid x$ is the coordinate of a point on the number line$\}$	$R = Q \cup I$
Intervals of real numbers	An interval of real numbers is the set of real numbers that lie between two real numbers, which are called the endpoints of the interval. We may use $-\infty$ or ∞ as endpoints.	The real numbers between 3 and 4: $(3, 4)$ The real numbers greater than or equal to 6: $[6, \infty)$

Operations with Real Numbers		**Examples**
Absolute value	$\lvert a \rvert = \begin{cases} a & \text{if } a \text{ is positive or zero} \\ -a & \text{if } a \text{ is negative} \end{cases}$	$\lvert 6 \rvert = 6, \lvert 0 \rvert = 0$ $\lvert -6 \rvert = 6$
Addition and subtraction	To find the sum of two numbers with the same sign, add their absolute values. The sum has the same sign as the original numbers.	$-2 + (-7) = -9$
	To find the sum of two numbers with unlike signs, subtract their absolute values. The sum is positive if the number with the larger absolute value is positive. The sum is negative if the number with the larger absolute value is negative.	$-6 + 9 = 3$ $-9 + 6 = -3$

| | Subtraction: $a - b = a + (-b)$ | $4 - 7 = 4 + (-7) = -3$ |
| | (Change the sign and add.) | $5 - (-3) = 5 + 3 = 8$ |

Multiplication and division

To find the product or quotient of two numbers, multiply or divide their absolute values:
Same signs $\leftrightarrow$ positive result
Opposite signs $\leftrightarrow$ negative result

$(-4)(-2) = 8, (-4)(2) = -8$

$-8 \div (-2) = 4, -8 \div 2 = -4$

Exponential expressions

In the expression a^n, a is the base and n is the exponent.

$2^3 = 2 \cdot 2 \cdot 2 = 8$

Square roots

If $a^2 = b$, then a is a square root of b.
If $a \geq 0$ and $a^2 = b$, then $\sqrt{b} = a$.

Both 3 and -3 are square roots of 9.
Because $3 \geq 0$, $\sqrt{9} = 3$.

Order of operations

In an expression without parentheses or absolute value:
1. Evaluate exponential expressions.
2. Perform multiplication and division.
3. Perform addition and subtraction.
With parentheses or absolute value:
First evaluate within each set of parentheses or absolute value, using the above order.

$7 + 2^3 = 15$
$3 + 4 \cdot 6 = 27$
$5 + 4 \cdot 3^2 = 41$

$(2 + 4)(5 - 9) = -24$
$3 + 4|2 - 3| = 7$

Properties of the Real Numbers   **Examples**

For any real numbers a, b, and c:

Commutative property of
  addition $a + b = b + a$ $3 + 7 = 7 + 3$
  multiplication $ab = ba$ $4 \cdot 3 = 3 \cdot 4$

Associative property of
  addition $(a + b) + c = a + (b + c)$ $(1 + 3) + 5 = 1 + (3 + 5)$
  multiplication $(ab)c = a(bc)$ $(3 \cdot 5)7 = 3(5 \cdot 7)$

Distributive property $a(b + c) = ab + ac$ $3(4 + x) = 12 + 3x$
    $5x - 10 = 5(x - 2)$

Additive identity property $a + 0 = 0 + a = a$ $6 + 0 = 0 + 6 = 6$

Multiplicative identity property $1 \cdot a = a \cdot 1 = a$ $1 \cdot 6 = 6 \cdot 1 = 6$

Additive inverse property $a + (-a) = -a + a = 0$ $8 + (-8) = 0, -8 + 8 = 0$

Multiplicative inverse property $a \cdot \dfrac{1}{a} = \dfrac{1}{a} \cdot a = 1$ for $a \neq 0$ $8 \cdot \dfrac{1}{8} = 1, -2\left(-\dfrac{1}{2}\right) = 1$

Multiplication property of zero	$0 \cdot a = a \cdot 0 = 0$	$9 \cdot 0 = 0$ $(0)(-4) = 0$

Algebraic Concepts

		Examples
Algebraic expressions	Any meaningful combination of numbers, variables, and operations	$x^2 + y^2, -5abc$
Term	An expression containing a number or the product of a number and one or more variables raised to powers	$3x^2, -7x^2y, 8$
Like terms	Terms with identical variable parts	$4bc - 8bc = -4bc$

ENRICHING YOUR MATHEMATICAL WORD POWER

For each mathematical term, choose the correct meaning.

1. term
   a. an expression containing a number or the product of a number and one or more variables raised to powers
   b. the amount of time spent in this course
   c. a word that describes a number
   d. a variable

2. like terms
   a. terms that are identical
   b. the terms of a sum
   c. terms that have the same variables with the same exponents
   d. terms with the same variables

3. variable
   a. a letter that is used to represent some numbers
   b. the letter x
   c. an equation with a letter in it
   d. not the same

4. additive inverse
   a. the number -1
   b. the number 0
   c. the opposite of addition
   d. opposite

5. order of operations
   a. the order in which operations are to be performed in the absence of grouping symbols
   b. the order in which the operations were invented
   c. the order in which operations are written
   d. a list of operations in alphabetical order

6. absolute value
   a. a definite value
   b. a positive number
   c. the distance from 0 on the number line
   d. the opposite of a number

7. natural numbers
   a. the counting numbers
   b. numbers that are not irrational
   c. the nonnegative numbers
   d. numbers that we find in nature

8. rational numbers
   a. the numbers 1, 2, 3, and so on
   b. the integers
   c. numbers that make sense
   d. numbers of the form $\frac{a}{b}$ where a and b are integers with $b \neq 0$

9. irrational numbers
   a. cube roots
   b. numbers that cannot be expressed as a ratio of integers
   c. numbers that do not make sense
   d. integers

10. additive identity
   a. the number 0
   b. the number 1
   c. the opposite of a number
   d. when two sums are identical

11. multiplicative identity
   a. the number 0
   b. the number 1
   c. the reciprocal
   d. when two products are identical

12. dividend
   a. a in $\dfrac{a}{b}$ b. b in $\dfrac{a}{b}$
   c. the result of $\dfrac{a}{b}$ d. what a bank pays on deposits

13. divisor

a: a in $\dfrac{a}{b}$ b: b in $\dfrac{a}{b}$

c: the result of $\dfrac{a}{b}$ d: two visors

14. quotient

a: a in $\dfrac{a}{b}$ b: b in $\dfrac{a}{b}$

c: $\dfrac{a}{b}$ d: the divisor plus the remainder

REVIEW EXERCISES

1.1 *Let* $A = \{1, 2, 3\}$, $B = \{3, 4, 5\}$, $C = \{1, 2, 3, 4, 5\}$, $D = \{3\}$, *and* $E = \{4, 5\}$. *Determine whether each statement is true or false.*

1. $A \cap B = D$
2. $A \cap B = E$
3. $A \cup B = E$
4. $A \cup B = C$
5. $B \cup C = C$
6. $A \cap C = B$
7. $A \cap \varnothing = A$
8. $A \cup \varnothing = \varnothing$
9. $(A \cap B) \cup E = B$
10. $(C \cap B) \cap A = D$
11. $B \subseteq C$
12. $A \subseteq E$
13. $A = B$
14. $B = C$
15. $3 \in D$
16. $5 \notin A$
17. $0 \in E$
18. $D \subseteq \varnothing$
19. $\varnothing \subseteq E$
20. $1 \in A$

Study Tip

Note how the review exercises are arranged according to the sections in this chapter. If you are having trouble with a certain type of problem, refer back to the appropriate section for examples and explanations.

1.2 *Which elements of the set*

$$\left\{-\sqrt{2}, -1, 0, 1, 1.732, \sqrt{3}, \pi, \frac{22}{7}, 31\right\}$$

are members of these sets?

21. Whole numbers
22. Natural numbers
23. Integers
24. Rational numbers

25. Irrational numbers
26. Real numbers

Write each interval of real numbers in interval notation and graph it.

27. The set of real numbers greater than 0

28. The set of real numbers less than 4

29. The set of real numbers between 5 and 6

30. The set of real numbers between 5 and 6 inclusive

31. The set of real numbers greater than or equal to -1 and less than 2

32. The set of real numbers greater than 3 and less than or equal to 6

Write each union or intersection as a single interval.

33. $(0, 2) \cup (1, 5)$
34. $(0, 2) \cap (1, 5)$
35. $(2, 4) \cap (3, \infty)$
36. $(-\infty, 3) \cup (1, 6)$
37. $[2, 6) \cup (4, 8)$
38. $[-2, 1] \cap [0, 5)$

1.3 *Evaluate.*
39. $-4 + 9$
40. $-3 + (-5)$
41. $25 - 37$
42. $-6 - 10$
43. $(-4)(6)$
44. $(-7)(-6)$
45. $(-8) \div (-4)$

46. $40 \div (-8)$

47. $-\dfrac{1}{4} + \dfrac{1}{12}$

48. $\dfrac{1}{3} - \left(-\dfrac{1}{12}\right)$

49. $\dfrac{-20}{-2}$

50. $\dfrac{30}{-6}$

51. $-0.04 + 10$

52. $-0.05 + (-3)$

53. $-6 - (-2)$

54. $-0.2 - (-0.04)$

55. $-0.5 + 0.5$

56. $-0.04 \div 0.2$

57. $3.2 \div (-0.8)$

58. $(0.2)(-0.9)$

59. $0 \div (-0.3545)$

60. $(-6)(-0.5)$

1.4 *Evaluate each expression.*

61. $4 + 7(5)$

62. $(4 + 7)5$

63. $(4 + 7)^2$

64. $4 + 7^2$

65. $5 + 3 \cdot |6 - 4 \cdot 3|$

66. $6 - (7 - 8)$

67. $(6 - 8) - (5 - 9)$

68. $5 - 6 - 8 - 10$

69. $3 - 5(6 - 2 \cdot 5)$

70. $4^2 - 9 + 3^2$

71. $5^2 - (6 + 5)^2$

72. $|3 - 4 \cdot 2| - |5 - 8|$

73. $\sqrt{3^2 + 4^2}$

74. $\sqrt{13^2 - 5^2}$

75. $\dfrac{-4 - 5}{7 - (-2)}$

76. $\dfrac{5 - 9}{2 - 4}$

77. $1 - (0.8)(0.3)$

78. $5 - (0.2)(0.1)$

79. $(-3)^2 - (4)(-1)(-2)$

80. $3^2 - 4(1)(-3)$

81. $3 - 2|4 - 7|$

82. $3|4 - 6| + 1$

83. $\dfrac{-5 - 3}{-4 + 2}$

84. $\dfrac{-6 + 3}{3 - 9}$

Let $a = -2$, $b = 3$, and $c = -1$. Find the value of each algebraic expression.

85. $\sqrt{b^2 - 4ac}$

86. $\sqrt{a^2 + 4b}$

87. $(c - b)(c + b)$

88. $(a + b)(a - b)$

89. $a^2 + 2ab + b^2$

90. $a^2 - 2ab + b^2$

91. $a^3 - b^3$

92. $a^3 + b^3$

93. $\dfrac{b + c}{a + b}$

94. $\dfrac{b - c}{2b - a}$

95. $|a - b|$

96. $|b - a|$

97. $(a + b)c$

98. $ac + bc$

1.5 *Name the property that justifies each equation.*

99. $a + x = x + a$

100. $0 \cdot 5 = 0$

101. $3(x - 1) = 3x - 3$

102. $10 + (-10) = 0$

103. $5(2x) = (5 \cdot 2)x$

104. $w + y = y + w$

105. $1 \cdot y = y$

106. $4 \cdot \dfrac{1}{4} = 1$

107. $5(0.2) = 1$

108. $3 \cdot 1 = 3$

109. $12 \cdot 0 = 0$

110. $x + 1 = 1 + x$

111. $18 + 0 = 18$

112. $2w + 2m = 2(w + m)$

113. $-5 + 5 = 0$

114. $2 + (3 + 4) = (2 + 3) + 4$

Use the distributive property to rewrite each sum or difference as a product, and each product as a sum of difference, whichever is appropriate.

115. $3x - 3a$

116. $5x - 5y$

117. $3(w + 1)$

118. $2(m + 14)$

119. $7x + 7$

120. $3w + 3$

121. $5(x - 5)$

122. $13(b - 3)$

123. $-3(2x - 5)$

124. $-2(5 - 4x)$

125. $p - pt$

126. $ab + b$

1.6 *Simplify each expression.*

127. $3a + 7 + 4a - 5$

128. $2m + 6 + m - 2$

129. $5(t - 4) - 3(2t - 6)$

130. $2(x - 3) + 2(3 - x)$

131. $-(a - 2) + 2 - a$

132. $-(w - y) + 3(y - w)$

133. $5 - 3(x - 2) + 7(x + 4) - 6$

134. $7 - 2(x - 7) + 7 - x$

135. $0.2(x + 0.1) - (x + 0.5)$

136. $0.1(x - 0.2) - (x + 0.1)$

137. $0.05(x + 3) - 0.1(x + 20)$

138. $0.02(x + 100) - 0.2(x + 50)$

139. $\dfrac{1}{2}(x + 4) - \dfrac{1}{4}(x - 8)$

140. $\dfrac{1}{2}(2x - 1) + \dfrac{1}{4}(x + 1)$

141. $\dfrac{-9x^2 - 6x + 3}{3}$

142. $\dfrac{4x - 2}{-2} + \dfrac{4x + 2}{2}$

MISCELLANEOUS

Evaluate these expressions for $w = 24$, $x = -6$, $y = 6$, and $z = 4$. Name the property or properties used.

143. $32z(x + y)$

144. $(wz)\dfrac{1}{w}$

145. $768z + 768y$

146. $28z + 28y$

147. $(12z + x) + y$

148. $(42 + x) + y$

149. $752x + 752y$

150. $37y + 37x$

151. $(47y)\dfrac{z}{w}$

152. $3w + 3y$

153. $(xw)\dfrac{1}{y}$

154. $(xz)\dfrac{1}{x}$

155. $5(x + y)(z + w)$

156. $(4x + 7y)(w + xz)$

Solve each problem.

157. *Teamwork.* Istvan can attach one shingle using a nail gun in 0.2 minute while Robin takes 0.5 minute to attach one shingle using a hammer. How many shingles per minute will they be attaching if they work together?

158. *Carpeting costs.* Write an algebraic expression for the cost of carpeting a rectangular room that is x yards by $x + 2$ yards if carpeting costs \$20 per square yard?

159. *Inflationary spiral.* If car prices increase 5% annually, then in n years a car that currently costs P dollars will cost $P(1.05)^n$ dollars.

    a) Use this algebraic expression to predict the price of a new 2010 Camaro Z28 Convertible, if the price of the 2002 model was \$27,759 (www.edmunds.com).

    b) Use the accompanying graph to predict the first year in which the price of this car will be over \$50,000.

FIGURE FOR EXERCISE 159

160. *Lots of water.* The volume of water in a round swimming pool with radius r feet and depth h feet is $7.5\pi r^2 h$ gallons. Find the volume of water in a pool that has diameter 24 feet and depth 3 feet.

FIGURE FOR EXERCISE 160

CHAPTER 1 TEST

Let $A = \{2, 4, 6, 8, 10\}$, $B = \{3, 4, 5, 6, 7\}$, and $C = \{6, 7, 8, 9, 10\}$. List the elements in each of these sets.

1. $A \cup B$ **2.** $B \cap C$

3. $A \cap (B \cup C)$

Study Tip

Before you take an in-class exam on this chapter, work the sample test given here. Set aside one hour to work this test and use the answers in the back of this book to grade yourself. Even though your instructor might not ask exactly the same questions, you will get a good idea of your test readiness.

Which elements of $\left\{-4, -\sqrt{3}, -\dfrac{1}{2}, 0, 1.65, \sqrt{5}, \pi, 8\right\}$ are members of these sets?

4. Whole numbers   **5.** Integers

6. Rational numbers

7. Irrational numbers

Graph each of these sets.

8. The integers between -3 and 5

9. The interval $(-3, 5]$

Write each union or intersection as a single interval.

10. $(-\infty, 2) \cup (1, 4)$

11. $(2, 8) \cap [4, 9)$

Evaluate each expression.

12. $6 + 3(-5)$

13. $\sqrt{(-2)^2 - 4(3)(-5)}$

14. $-5 + 6 - 12$

15. $0.02 - 2$

16. $\dfrac{-3 - (-7)}{3 - 5}$

17. $\dfrac{-6 - 2}{4 - 2}$

18. $\left(\dfrac{2}{3} - 1\right)\left(\dfrac{1}{3} - \dfrac{1}{2}\right)$

19. $-\dfrac{4}{7} - \dfrac{1}{2}\left(24 - \dfrac{8}{7}\right)$

20. $|\,3 - 5(2)\,|$

21. $5 - 2\,|\,6 - 10\,|$

22. $(452 + 695)[2(-4) + 8]$

23. $478(8) + 478(2)$

24. $-8 \cdot 3 - 4(6 - 9 \cdot 2^3)$

Evaluate each expression for $a = -3$, $b = -4$, and $c = 2$.

25. $b^2 - 4ac$ **26.** $\dfrac{a^2 - b^2}{b - a}$ **27.** $\dfrac{ab - 6c}{b^2 - c^2}$

Identify the property that justifies each equation.

28. $2(5 + 7) = 10 + 14$

29. $57 \cdot 4 = 4 \cdot 57$

30. $2 + (6 + x) = (2 + 6) + x$

31. $-6 + 6 = 0$

32. $1 \cdot (-6) = (-6) \cdot 1$

Simplify each expression.

33. $3(m - 5) - 4(-2m - 3)$

34. $x + 3 - 0.05(x + 2)$

35. $\dfrac{1}{2}(x - 4) + \dfrac{1}{4}(x + 3)$

36. $-3(x^2 - 2y) - 2(3y - 4x^2)$

37. $\dfrac{-6x^2 - 4x + 2}{-2}$

Use the distributive property to rewrite each expression as a product.

38. $5x - 40$

39. $7t - 7$

Solve each problem.

40. If Celeste and her crew of loggers can cut and load one tree in 0.0625 hour, then how many trees per hour can they cut and load?

41. The rectangular table for table tennis is x feet long and $x - 4$ feet wide. Write algebraic expressions for the perimeter and the area of the table. Find the actual perimeter and area using $x = 9$.

 42. If the population of the earth grows at 3% annually, then in n years the present population P will grow to $P(1.03)^n$. Assuming an annual growth rate of 3% and a present population of 6 billion people, what will the population be in 25 years?

2

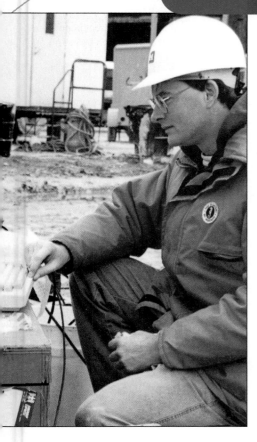

Linear Equations and Inequalities in One Variable

On April 13, 1992, the headline of *The Chicago Tribune* read, "Flood Cripples Loop Businesses." Workers driving pilings around a bridge had ruptured an abandoned freight tunnel under the Chicago River. Water was gushing into the 40 miles of open tunnels below the 12 square blocks of Chicago's downtown area called the Loop. The rapidly rising water entered basements, saturated foundations, and quickly forced the shutdown of most utilities. Some subway lines were closed, and eventually thousands of workers were evacuated. While divers were used to survey the problem, the Army Corps of Engineers was called in. Their solution was to seal off the portion of the tunnel that was ruptured, using a steel-reinforced concrete plug. Once the plug was in place, the engineers worked on reversing the flow of the water. For over a month, millions of gallons of water were drained off to a water reclamation plant, and the Loop slowly returned to normal.

In this chapter we will study algebraic equations and formulas. In Exercises 89 and 90 of Section 2.2 you will see how the engineers used very simple algebraic formulas to calculate the amount of force the water would have on the plug and how much force the concrete plug would withstand. The story of the Chicago flood is just one example of how algebraic formulas are used daily in practical situations.

2.1 LINEAR EQUATIONS IN ONE VARIABLE

The applications of algebra often lead to equations. The skills that you learned in Chapter 1, such as combining like terms and performing operations with algebraic expressions, will now be used to solve equations.

Basic Ideas and Definitions

An **equation** is a sentence that expresses the equality of two algebraic expressions. Consider the equation

$$2x + 1 = 7.$$

Because $2(3) + 1 = 7$ is true, we say that 3 **satisfies** the equation. No other number in place of x will make the statement $2x + 1 = 7$ true. However, an equation might be satisfied by more than one number. For example, both 3 and -3 satisfy $x^2 = 9$. Any number that satisfies an equation is called a **solution** or **root** to the equation.

> ### Solution Set
>
> The set of all solutions to an equation is called the **solution set** to the equation.

The solution set to $2x + 1 = 7$ is $\{3\}$. To determine whether a number is in the solution set to an equation, we simply replace the variable by the number and see whether the equation is correct.

E X A M P L E 1

Satisfying an equation

Determine whether each equation is satisfied by the number following the equation.

a) $3x + 7 = -8,\quad -5$ **b)** $2(x - 1) = 2x + 3,\quad 4$

Solution

a) Replace x by -5 and evaluate each side of the equation.

$$3x + 7 = -8$$
$$3(-5) + 7 = -8$$
$$-15 + 7 = -8$$
$$-8 = -8 \quad \text{Correct}$$

Because -5 satisfies the equation, -5 is in the solution set to the equation.

b) Replace x by 4 and evaluate each side of the equation.

$$2(x - 1) = 2x + 3$$
$$2(4 - 1) = 2(4) + 3 \quad \text{Replace } x \text{ by 4.}$$
$$2(3) = 8 + 3$$
$$6 = 11 \quad \text{Incorrect}$$

The two sides of the equation have different values when $x = 4$. So 4 is *not* in the solution set to the equation. ∎

Solving Equations

To **solve** an equation means to find its solution set. It is easy to determine whether a given number is in the solution set of an equation as in Example 1, but that example does not provide a method for *solving* equations. The most basic method for solving equations involves the **properties of equality.**

Properties of Equality

Addition Property of Equality
Adding the same number to both sides of an equation does not change the solution set to the equation. In symbols, if $a = b$, then $a + c = b + c$.

Multiplication Property of Equality
Multiplying both sides of an equation by the same nonzero number does not change the solution set to the equation. In symbols, if $a = b$ and $c \neq 0$, then $ca = cb$.

Because subtraction is defined in terms of addition, the addition property of equality also allows us to subtract the same number from both sides. For example, subtracting 3 from both sides is equivalent to adding -3 to both sides. Because division is defined in terms of multiplication, the multiplication property of equality also allows us to divide both sides by the same nonzero number. For example, dividing both sides by 2 is equivalent to multiplying both sides by $\frac{1}{2}$.

Equations that have the same solution set are called **equivalent equations.** In Example 2 we use the properties of equality to solve an equation by writing an equivalent equation with x isolated on one side of the equation.

E X A M P L E   2

Using the properties of equality
Solve the equation $6 - 3x = 8 - 2x$.

Solution
We want to obtain an equivalent equation with only a single x on the left-hand side and a number on the other side.

$$6 - 3x = 8 - 2x$$
$$6 - 3x - 6 = 8 - 2x - 6 \qquad \text{Subtract 6 from each side.}$$
$$-3x = 2 - 2x \qquad \text{Simplify.}$$
$$-3x + 2x = 2 - 2x + 2x \qquad \text{Add } 2x \text{ to each side.}$$
$$-x = 2 \qquad \text{Combine like terms.}$$
$$-1 \cdot (-x) = -1 \cdot 2 \qquad \text{Multiply each side by } -1.$$
$$x = -2$$

Replacing x by -2 in the original equation gives us

$$6 - 3(-2) = 8 - 2(-2),$$

which is correct. So the solution set to the original equation is $\{-2\}$.   ■

The addition property of equality allows us to add $2x$ to each side of the equation in Example 2 because $2x$ represents a real number.

CAUTION If you add an expression to each side that does not always represent a real number, then the equations might not be equivalent. For example,

$$x = 0 \quad \text{and} \quad x + \frac{1}{x} = 0 + \frac{1}{x}$$

are *not* equivalent because 0 satisfies the first equation but not the second one. (The expression $\frac{1}{x}$ is not defined if x is 0.)

To solve some equations, we must simplify the equation before using the properties of equality.

E X A M P L E 3

Simplifying the equation first

Solve the equation $2(x - 4) + 5x = 34$.

Solution

Before using the properties of equality, we simplify the expression on the left-hand side of the equation:

$$2(x - 4) + 5x = 34$$
$$2x - 8 + 5x = 34 \qquad \text{Distributive property}$$
$$7x - 8 = 34 \qquad \text{Combine like terms.}$$
$$7x - 8 + 8 = 34 + 8 \qquad \text{Add 8 to each side.}$$
$$7x = 42 \qquad \text{Simplify.}$$
$$\frac{7x}{7} = \frac{42}{7} \qquad \text{Divide each side by 7 to get a single } x \text{ on the left side.}$$
$$x = 6$$

To check, we replace x by 6 in the original equation and simplify:

$$2(6 - 4) + 5 \cdot 6 = 34$$
$$2(2) + 30 = 34$$
$$34 = 34$$

The solution set to the equation is $\{6\}$. ∎

When an equation involves fractions, we can simplify it by multiplying each side by a number that is evenly divisible by all of the denominators. The smallest such number is called the **least common denominator (LCD).** Multiplying each side of the equation by the LCD will eliminate all of the fractions.

E X A M P L E 4

An equation with fractions

Find the solution set for the equation

$$\frac{x}{2} - \frac{1}{3} = \frac{x}{3} + \frac{5}{6}.$$

Solution

To solve this equation, we multiply each side by 6, the LCD for 2, 3, and 6:

$$6\left(\frac{x}{2} - \frac{1}{3}\right) = 6\left(\frac{x}{3} + \frac{5}{6}\right) \qquad \text{Multiply each side by 6.}$$

$$6 \cdot \frac{x}{2} - 6 \cdot \frac{1}{3} = 6 \cdot \frac{x}{3} + 6 \cdot \frac{5}{6} \qquad \text{Distributive property}$$

$$3x - 2 = 2x + 5 \qquad \text{Simplify.}$$

$$3x - 2 - 2x = 2x + 5 - 2x \qquad \text{Subtract } 2x \text{ from each side.}$$

$$x - 2 = 5 \qquad \text{Combine like terms.}$$

$$x - 2 + 2 = 5 + 2 \qquad \text{Add 2 to each side.}$$

$$x = 7 \qquad \text{Combine like terms.}$$

Check 7 in the original equation. The solution set is {7}.   ■

Equations that involve decimal numbers can be solved like equations involving fractions. If we multiply a decimal number by 10, 100, or 1000, the decimal point is moved one, two, or three places to the right, respectively. If the decimal points are all moved far enough to the right, the decimal numbers will be replaced by whole numbers. Example 5 shows how to use the multiplication property of equality to eliminate decimal numbers in an equation.

E X A M P L E   5

An equation with decimals

Solve the equation $x - 0.1x = 0.75x + 4.5$.

Solution

Because the number with the most decimal places in this equation is 0.75 (75 hundredths), multiplying each side by 100 will eliminate all decimals.

$$100(x - 0.1x) = 100(0.75x + 4.5) \qquad \text{Multiply each side by 100.}$$

$$100x - 10x = 75x + 450 \qquad \text{Distributive property}$$

$$90x = 75x + 450 \qquad \text{Combine like terms.}$$

$$90x - 75x = 75x + 450 - 75x \qquad \text{Subtract } 75x \text{ from each side.}$$

$$15x = 450 \qquad \text{Combine like terms.}$$

$$\frac{15x}{15} = \frac{450}{15} \qquad \text{Divide each side by 15.}$$

$$x = 30$$

Check that 30 satisfies the original equation. The solution set is {30}.   ■

Types of Equations

We often think of an equation such as $3x + 4x = 7x$ as an "addition fact" because the equation is satisfied by all real numbers. However, some equations that we think of as facts are not satisfied by all real numbers. For example, $\frac{x}{x} = 1$ is satisfied by every real number except 0 because $\frac{0}{0}$ is undefined. The equation $x + 1 = x + 1$ is satisfied by all real numbers because both sides are identical. All of these equations are called *identities*.

The equation $2x + 1 = 7$ is true only on condition that we choose $x = 3$. For this reason, it is called a *conditional equation*. The equations in Examples 2 through 5 are conditional equations.

Some equations are false no matter what value is used to replace the variable. For example, no number satisfies $x = x + 1$. The solution set to this *inconsistent* equation is the empty set, $\varnothing$.

Identity, Conditional Equation, Inconsistent Equation

An **identity** is an equation that is satisfied by every number for which both sides are defined.

A **conditional equation** is an equation that is satisfied by at least one number but is not an identity.

An **inconsistent equation** is an equation whose solution set is the empty set.

It is easy to classify $2x = 2x$ as an identity and $x = x + 2$ as an inconsistent equation, but some equations must be simplified before they can be classified.

E X A M P L E 6

An inconsistent equation and an identity

Solve each equation.

a) $8 - 3(x - 5) + 7 = 3 - (x - 5) - 2(x - 11)$

b) $5 - 3(x - 6) = 4(x - 9) - 7x$

Helpful Hint

Removing parentheses with the distributive property and combining like terms was discussed in Chapter 1. If you are having trouble with these equations, your problem might be in the preceding chapter.

Solution

a) First simplify each side of the equation:

$$8 - 3(x - 5) + 7 = 3 - (x - 5) - 2(x - 11)$$
$$8 - 3x + 15 + 7 = 3 - x + 5 - 2x + 22 \quad \text{Distributive property}$$
$$30 - 3x = 30 - 3x \quad \text{Combine like terms.}$$

This last equation is satisfied by any value of x because the two sides are identical. Because the last equation is equivalent to the original equation, the original equation is satisfied by any value of x and is an identity. The solution set is R, the set of all real numbers.

b) First simplify each side of the equation.

$$5 - 3(x - 6) = 4(x - 9) - 7x$$
$$5 - 3x + 18 = 4x - 36 - 7x \quad \text{Distributive property}$$
$$23 - 3x = -36 - 3x \quad \text{Combine like terms.}$$
$$23 - 3x + 3x = -36 - 3x + 3x \quad \text{Add } 3x \text{ to each side.}$$
$$23 = -36 \quad \text{Combine like terms.}$$

The equation $23 = -36$ is false for any choice of x. Because these equations are all equivalent, the original equation is also false for any choice of x. The solution set to this inconsistent equation is the empty set, $\varnothing$. ■

Strategy for Solving Linear Equations

The most basic equations of algebra are linear equations. In Chapter 3 we will see a connection between linear equations in one variable and straight lines.

Study Tip

When you get a test back, don't simply file it in your notebook or the waste basket. While the material is fresh in your mind, rework all the problems that you missed. Ask questions about anything that you don't understand and save your test for future reference.

Linear Equation in One Variable

A **linear equation in one variable** x is an equation of the form $ax + b = 0$, where a and b are real numbers, with $a \neq 0$.

The equations in Examples 2 through 5 are called linear equations in one variable, or simply linear equations, because they could all be rewritten in the form $ax + b = 0$. At first glance the equations in Example 6 appear to be linear equations. However, they cannot be written in the form $ax + b = 0$, with $a \neq 0$, so they are not linear equations. A linear equation has exactly one solution. The strategy that we use for solving linear equations is summarized in the following box.

Strategy for Solving a Linear Equation

1. If fractions are present, multiply each side by the LCD to eliminate them.
2. Use the distributive property to remove parentheses.
3. Combine any like terms.
4. Use the addition property of equality to get all variables on one side and numbers on the other side.
5. Use the multiplication property of equality to get a single variable on one side.
6. Check by replacing the variable in the original equation with your solution.

Note that not all equations require all of the steps.

E X A M P L E   7

Using the equation-solving strategy

Solve the equation $\dfrac{y}{2} - \dfrac{y-4}{5} = \dfrac{23}{10}$.

Calculator Close-Up

You can use the fraction feature of a graphing calculator to check that 5 satisfies the equation. If you make a mistake entering an expression, you can recall the expression by pressing the ENTRY key and modify the expression.

```
5/2-(5-4)/5▶Frac
                23/10
```

Solution

We first multiply each side of the equation by 10, the LCD for 2, 5, and 10. However, we do not have to write down that step. We can simply use the distributive property to multiply each term of the equation by 10.

$$\frac{y}{2} - \frac{y-4}{5} = \frac{23}{10}$$

$$\overset{5}{\cancel{10}}\left(\frac{y}{\cancel{2}}\right) - \overset{2}{\cancel{10}}\left(\frac{y-4}{\cancel{5}}\right) = \cancel{10}\left(\frac{23}{\cancel{10}}\right) \quad \text{Multiply each side by 10.}$$

$$5y - 2(y - 4) = 23 \qquad \text{Divide each denominator into 10 to eliminate fractions.}$$

$$5y - 2y + 8 = 23 \qquad \text{Be careful to change all signs:} \\ -2(y-4) = -2y + 8$$

$$3y + 8 = 23 \qquad \text{Combine like terms.}$$

$$3y + 8 - 8 = 23 - 8 \quad \text{Subtract 8 from each side.}$$

$$3y = 15 \qquad \text{Simplify.}$$

$$\frac{3y}{3} = \frac{15}{3} \qquad \text{Divide each side by 3.}$$

$$y = 5$$

Check that 5 satisfies the original equation. The solution set is $\{5\}$. ∎

Techniques

Writing down every step when solving an equation is not always necessary. Solving an equation is often part of a larger problem, and anything that we can do to make the process more efficient will make solving the entire problem faster and easier. For example, we can combine some steps.

Combining Steps	*Writing Every Step*

$$4x - 5 = 23$$

$$4x = 28 \quad \text{Add 5 to each side.}$$

$$x = 7 \quad \text{Divide each side by 4.}$$

$$4x - 5 = 23$$

$$4x - 5 + 5 = 23 + 5$$

$$4x = 28$$

$$\frac{4x}{4} = \frac{28}{4}$$

$$x = 7$$

The same steps are used in each of the solutions. However, when 5 is added to each side in the solution on the left, only the result is written. When each side is divided by 4, only the result is written.

The equation $-x = -5$ says that the additive inverse of x is -5. Since the additive inverse of 5 is -5, we conclude that x is 5. So instead of multiplying each side of $-x = -5$ by -1, we solve the equation as follows:

$$-x = -5$$

$$x = 5 \qquad \text{Additive inverse property}$$

Sometimes it is simpler to isolate x on the right-hand side of the equation:

$$3x + 1 = 4x - 5$$

$$6 = x \qquad \text{Subtract } 3x \text{ from each side and add 5 to each side.}$$

You can rewrite $6 = x$ as $x = 6$ or leave it as is. Either way, 6 is the solution.

For some equations with fractions it is more efficient to multiply by a multiplicative inverse instead of multiplying by the LCD:

$$-\frac{2}{3}x = \frac{1}{2}$$

$$-\frac{3}{2}\left(-\frac{2}{3}x\right) = -\frac{3}{2}\left(\frac{1}{2}\right) \qquad \text{Multiply each side by } -\frac{3}{2}, \text{ the reciprocal of } -\frac{2}{3}.$$

$$x = -\frac{3}{4}$$

The techniques shown here should not be attempted until you have become proficient at solving equations by writing out every step. The more efficient techniques shown here are not a requirement of algebra, but they can be a labor-saving tool that will be useful when we solve more complicated problems.

E X A M P L E   8   **Efficient solutions**

Solve each equation.

a) $3x + 4 = 0$

b) $2 - (x + 5) = -2(3x - 1) + 6x$

Solution

a) Combine steps to solve the equation efficiently.

$$3x + 4 = 0$$
$$3x = -4 \qquad \text{Subtract 4 from each side.}$$
$$x = -\frac{4}{3} \qquad \text{Divide each side by 3.}$$

Check $-\frac{4}{3}$ in the original equation:

$$3\left(-\frac{4}{3}\right) + 4 = -4 + 4 = 0$$

The solution set is $\left\{-\frac{4}{3}\right\}$.

b) $2 - (x + 5) = -2(3x - 1) + 6x$

$$-x - 3 = 2 \qquad \text{Simplify each side.}$$
$$-x = 5 \qquad \text{Add 3 to each side.}$$
$$x = -5 \qquad \text{Additive inverse property}$$

Check that -5 satisfies the original equation. The solution set is $\{-5\}$. ■

Applications

In Example 9 we show how a linear equation can occur in an application.

E X A M P L E   9

Completing high school

The percentage of persons 25 years and over who had completed 4 years of high school was only 25% in 1940 (Census Bureau, www.census.gov). See Fig. 2.1. The expression $0.96n + 25$ gives the percentage of persons 25 and over who have completed 4 years of high school in the year $1940 + n$.

a) What was the percentage in 1990?

b) When will the percentage reach 95%?

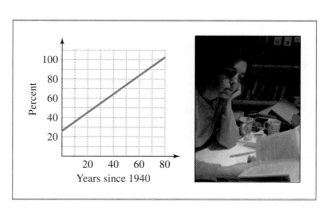

FIGURE 2.1

Solution

a) Since 1990 is 50 years after 1940, $n = 50$ and

$$0.96(50) + 25 = 73.$$

So in 1990 approximately 73% of persons 25 and over had completed 4 years of high school.

b) To find when the percentage will reach 95%, solve this equation:

$$0.96n + 25 = 95$$
$$0.96n = 70$$
$$n = \frac{70}{0.96} \approx 73$$

So 73 years after 1940 or in 2013 the percentage will reach 95%. ∎

WARM-UPS

True or false? Explain your answer.

1. The equation $-2x + 3 = 8$ is equivalent to $-2x = 11$.
2. The equation $x - (x - 3) = 5x$ is equivalent to $3 = 5x$.
3. To solve $\frac{3}{4}x = 12$, we should multiply each side by $\frac{3}{4}$.
4. The equation $-x = -6$ is equivalent to $x = 6$.
5. To eliminate fractions, we multiply each side of an equation by the LCD.
6. The solution set to $3x + 5 = 7$ is $\left\{\frac{2}{3}\right\}$.
7. The equation $2(3x + 4) = 6x + 12$ is an inconsistent equation.
8. The equation $4(x + 3) = x + 3$ is a conditional equation.
9. The equation $x - 0.2x = 0.8x$ is an identity.
10. The equation $3x - 5 = 7$ is a linear equation.

2.1   EXERCISES

Reading and Writing   *After reading this section, write out the answers to these questions. Use complete sentences.*

1. What is an equation?

2. How do you know if a number satisfies an equation?

3. What are equivalent equations?

4. What is a linear equation in one variable?

5. What is the usual first step in solving an equation that involves fractions?

6. What is an identity?

7. What is a conditional equation?

8. What is an inconsistent equation?

Determine whether each equation is satisfied by the given number. See Example 1.

9. $3x + 7 = -5$, -4
10. $-3x - 5 = 13$, -6
11. $\frac{1}{2}x - 4 = \frac{1}{3}x - 2$, 12
12. $\frac{y - 7}{2} - \frac{1}{3} = \frac{y - 7}{3}$, 9

13. $0.2(x - 50) = 20 - 0.05x$,   200
14. $0.12x - (4 - x) = 1.02x + 1$,   50
15. $0.1x - 30 = 16 - 0.06x$,   80
16. $0.08x + 3.2 = 0.1x + 2.8$,   20

Solve each linear equation. Show your work and check your answer. See Examples 2 and 3.

17. $-72 - x = 15$ **18.** $51 - x = -9$

19. $-3x - 19 = 5 - 2x$ **20.** $-5x + 4 = -9 - 4x$

21. $2x - 3 = 0$ **22.** $5x + 7 = 0$

23. $-2x + 5 = 7$ **24.** $-3x - 4 = 11$

25. $-12x - 15 = 21$ **26.** $-13x + 7 = -19$

27. $26 = 4x + 16$ **28.** $14 = -5x - 21$

29. $-3(x - 16) = 12 - x$ **30.** $-2(x + 17) = 13 - x$

31. $2(x + 9) - x = 36$ **32.** $3(x - 13) - x = 9$

33. $2 + 3(x - 1) = x - 1$ **34.** $x + 9 = 1 - 4(x - 2)$

Solve each equation. See Example 4.

35. $-\dfrac{3}{7}x = 4$ **36.** $\dfrac{5}{6}x = -2$

37. $-\dfrac{5}{7}x - 1 = 3$ **38.** $4 - \dfrac{3}{5}x = -6$

39. $\dfrac{x}{3} + \dfrac{1}{2} = \dfrac{7}{6}$ **40.** $\dfrac{1}{4} + \dfrac{1}{5} = \dfrac{x}{2}$

41. $\dfrac{2}{3}x + 5 = -\dfrac{1}{3}x + 17$ **42.** $\dfrac{1}{4}x - 6 = -\dfrac{3}{4}x + 14$

43. $\dfrac{1}{2}x + \dfrac{1}{4} = \dfrac{1}{4}(x - 6)$ **44.** $\dfrac{1}{3}(x - 2) = \dfrac{2}{3}x - \dfrac{13}{3}$

45. $8 - \dfrac{x - 2}{2} = \dfrac{x}{4}$ **46.** $\dfrac{x}{3} - \dfrac{x - 5}{5} = 3$

47. $\dfrac{y - 3}{3} - \dfrac{y - 2}{2} = -1$ **48.** $\dfrac{x - 2}{2} - \dfrac{x - 3}{4} = \dfrac{7}{4}$

Solve each equation. See Example 5.

49. $x - 0.2x = 72$
50. $x - 0.1x = 63$
51. $0.03(x + 200) + 0.05x = 86$
52. $0.02(x - 100) + 0.06x = 62$
53. $0.1x + 0.05(x - 300) = 105$
54. $0.2x - 0.05(x - 100) = 35$

Solve each equation. Identify each as a conditional equation, an inconsistent equation, or an identity. See Example 6.

55. $2(x + 1) = 2(x + 3)$
56. $2x + 3x = 6x$
57. $x + x = 2x$
58. $4x - 3x = x$
59. $x + x = 2$
60. $4x - 3x = 5$
61. $\dfrac{4x}{4} = x$
62. $5x \div 5 = x$
63. $x \cdot x = x^2$
64. $\dfrac{2x}{2x} = 1$
65. $2(x + 3) - 7 = 5(5 - x) + 7(x + 1)$

66. $2(x + 4) - 8 = 2x + 1$
67. $2\left(\dfrac{1}{2}x + \dfrac{3}{2}\right) - \dfrac{7}{2} = \dfrac{3}{2}(x + 1) - \left(\dfrac{1}{2}x + 2\right)$
68. $2\left(\dfrac{1}{4}x + 1\right) - 2 = \dfrac{1}{2}x$
69. $2(0.5x + 1.5) - 3.5 = 3(0.5x + 0.5)$

70. $2(0.25x + 1) - 2 = 0.75x - 1.75$

Solve each equation. See Example 7.
71. $4 - 6(2x - 3) + 1 = 3 + 2(5 - x)$

72. $3x - 5(6 - 2x) = 4(x - 8) + 3$

73. $\dfrac{1}{2}\left(y - \dfrac{1}{6}\right) + \dfrac{2}{3} = \dfrac{5}{6} + \dfrac{1}{3}\left(\dfrac{1}{2} - 3y\right)$

74. $\dfrac{3}{4} - \dfrac{1}{3}\left(\dfrac{1}{2}y - 2\right) = 3\left(y - \dfrac{1}{4}\right)$

75. $8 - \dfrac{2}{3}(60x - 900) = \dfrac{1}{2}(400x + 6)$

76. $\dfrac{40x - 5}{2} + \dfrac{5}{2} = \dfrac{33 - 2x}{3} - 11$

77. $\dfrac{a - 3}{4} - \dfrac{2a - 5}{2} = \dfrac{a + 1}{3} - \dfrac{1}{6}$

78. $\dfrac{1}{2}\left(\dfrac{b}{3} - \dfrac{4b}{5}\right) + \dfrac{1}{6} = \dfrac{1}{3} - \dfrac{b - 1}{2}$

79. $1.3 - 0.2(6 - 3x) = 0.1(0.2x + 3)$

80. $0.01(500 - 30x) = 5.4x + 200$

Solve each equation. Practice combining some steps. Look for more efficient ways to solve each equation. See Example 8.

81. $3x - 9 = 0$

82. $5x + 1 = 0$

83. $7 - z = -9$

84. $-3 - z = 3$

85. $\frac{2}{3}x = \frac{1}{2}$

86. $\frac{3}{2}x = -\frac{9}{5}$

87. $-\frac{3}{5}y = 9$

88. $-\frac{2}{7}w = 4$

89. $3y + 5 = 4y - 1$

90. $2y - 7 = 3y + 1$

91. $5x + 10(x + 2) = 110$

92. $1 - 3(x - 2) = 4(x - 1) - 3$

Solve each equation.

93. $\dfrac{P + 7}{3} - \dfrac{P - 2}{5} = \dfrac{7}{3} - \dfrac{P}{15}$

94. $\dfrac{w - 3}{8} - \dfrac{5 - w}{4} = \dfrac{4w - 1}{8} - 1$

95. $x - 0.06x = 50,000$

96. $x - 0.05x = 800$

97. $2.365x + 3.694 = 14.8095$

98. $-3.48x + 6.981 = 4.329x - 6.851$

Solve each problem. See Example 9.

99. *Public school enrollment.* The expression

$$0.45x + 39.05$$

can be used to approximate in millions the total enrollment in public elementary and secondary schools in the

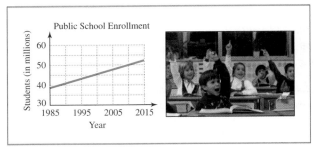

FIGURE FOR EXERCISE 99

year $1985 + x$ (National Center for Education Statistics, www.nces.ed.gov).

a) What was the public school enrollment in 1992?

b) In which year will enrollment reach 50 million students?

c) Judging from the accompanying graph, is enrollment increasing or decreasing?

100. *Teacher's average salary.* The expression

$$553.7x + 27,966$$

can be used to approximate the average annual salary in dollars of public school teachers in the year $1985 + x$ (National Center for Education Statistics, www.nces.ed.gov).

a) What was the average teacher's salary in 1993?

b) In which year will the average salary reach $45,000?

GETTING MORE INVOLVED

101. *Writing.* Explain how to eliminate the decimals in an equation that involves numbers with decimal points. Would you use the same technique when using a calculator?

102. *Discussion.* Explain why the multiplication property of equality does not allow us to multiply each side of an equation by zero.

In This Section

- Solving for a Variable
- Finding the Value of a Variable
- Geometric Formulas

2.2 FORMULAS

A real-life problem may involve many variable quantities that are related to each other. The relationship between these variables may be expressed by a formula. In this section we will combine our knowledge of evaluating expressions from Chapter 1 with the equation-solving skills of Section 2.1 to work with formulas.

Solving for a Variable

A **formula** or **literal equation** is an equation involving two or more variables. For example, the formula

$$A = LW$$

expresses the known relationship among the length L, width W, and area A of a rectangle. The formula

$$C = \frac{5}{9}(F - 32)$$

expresses the relationship between the Fahrenheit and Celsius measurements of temperature. The Celsius temperature is determined by the Fahrenheit temperature. For example, if the Fahrenheit temperature F is 95°, we can use the formula to find the Celsius temperature C as follows:

$$C = \frac{5}{9}(95 - 32) = \frac{5}{9}(63) = 35$$

A temperature of 95°F is equivalent to 35°C.

Sometimes it is necessary to solve a formula for one variable in terms of the others without substituting numbers for the variables. We will use the same steps in solving for a particular variable as we did in solving linear equations.

EXAMPLE 1

Solving for a variable

Solve the formula $C = \frac{5}{9}(F - 32)$ for F.

Solution

To solve the formula for F, we isolate F on one side of the equation. We can eliminate both the 9 and the 5 from the right-hand side of the equation by multiplying by $\frac{9}{5}$, the reciprocal of $\frac{5}{9}$:

$$C = \frac{5}{9}(F - 32)$$

$$\frac{9}{5}C = \frac{9}{5} \cdot \frac{5}{9}(F - 32) \qquad \text{Multiply each side by } \tfrac{9}{5}.$$

$$\frac{9}{5}C = F - 32 \qquad\qquad \tfrac{9}{5} \cdot \tfrac{5}{9} = 1$$

$$\frac{9}{5}C + 32 = F \qquad\qquad \text{Add 32 to each side.}$$

So the formula $F = \frac{9}{5}C + 32$ expresses F in terms of C. With this formula, we can use the value of C to determine the corresponding value of F. ∎

Note that both $F = \frac{9}{5}C + 32$ and $C = \frac{5}{9}(F - 32)$ express the relationship between C and F. The formula $F = \frac{9}{5}C + 32$ gives F in terms of C and $C = \frac{5}{9}(F - 32)$ gives C in terms of F. If we substitute 35 for C in $F = \frac{9}{5}C + 32$, we get

$$F = \frac{9}{5}(35) + 32 = 63 + 32 = 95.$$

In Chapter 3 we will study linear equations involving x and y. We often need to solve such equations for one of the variables.

EXAMPLE 2

Equations involving x and y

Write y in terms of x, if $3x - 2y = 6$.

Helpful Hint

There may be more than one correct answer when solving for a variable. For example,

$$y = \frac{3x - 6}{2}$$

also expresses y in terms of x. The main thing is to isolate y.

Solution

We can isolate y on the left-hand side:

$$3x - 2y = 6$$
$$-2y = -3x + 6 \qquad \text{Subtract } 3x \text{ from each side.}$$
$$\frac{-2y}{-2} = \frac{-3x + 6}{-2} \qquad \text{Divide each side by } -2.$$
$$y = \frac{3}{2}x - 3 \qquad \text{This equation expresses } y \text{ in terms of } x.$$

The formula $A = P + Prt$ is used to find the amount A after t years for an investment of P dollars at simple interest rate r. Note that the variable P occurs twice in the formula. To solve the formula for P, we use the distributive property as shown in the next example.

EXAMPLE 3

Helpful Hint

The key step in Example 3 is the distributive property. We cannot make P occur only once without it.

Specified variable occurring twice

Solve $A = P + Prt$ for P.

Solution

We can use the distributive property to write the sum $P + Prt$ as a product of P and $1 + rt$:

$$A = P + Prt$$
$$A = P(1 + rt) \qquad \text{Distributive property}$$
$$\frac{A}{1 + rt} = \frac{P(1 + rt)}{1 + rt} \qquad \text{Divide each side by } 1 + rt.$$
$$\frac{A}{1 + rt} = P$$

The formula $P = \dfrac{A}{1 + rt}$ expresses P in terms of A, r, and t. Note that parentheses are not needed around the expression $1 + rt$ in the denominator because the fraction bar acts as a grouping symbol.

CAUTION If you write $A = P + Prt$ as $P = A - Prt$, then you have not solved the formula for P. When a formula is solved for a specified variable, that variable must be isolated on one side, and it must not occur on the other side.

When the variable for which we are solving occurs on opposite sides of the equation, we must move all terms involving that variable to the same side and then use the distributive property to write the expression as a product.

EXAMPLE 4

Specified variable occurring on both sides

Suppose $3a + 7 = -5ab + b$. Solve for a.

Solution

Get all terms involving a onto one side and all other terms onto the other side:

$$3a + 7 = -5ab + b$$
$$3a + 5ab + 7 = b \qquad \text{Add } 5ab \text{ to each side.}$$
$$3a + 5ab = b - 7 \qquad \text{Subtract 7 from each side.}$$
$$a(3 + 5b) = b - 7 \qquad \text{Use the distributive property to write the left-hand side as a product.}$$

Helpful Hint

If you do the steps in Example 4 in a different way, you might end up with

$$a = \frac{7 - b}{-3 - 5b}.$$

This answer is correct because a is isolated. However, we usually prefer to see fewer negative signs. So we multiply this numerator and denominator by -1 and get the answer in Example 4.

E X A M P L E   5

Calculator Close-Up

A graphing calculator allows you to enter the entire expression in Example 5 and to evaluate it in one step. The ANS key holds the last value calculated. If we use ANS for x in the original equation, the calculator returns a 1, indicating that the equation is satisfied.

```
(6.31*23.45+6.78
)/(3.24-6.31)
        -50.40700326
3.24*Ans-6.78=6.
31(Ans+23.45)
                    1
```

$$\frac{a(3 + 5b)}{3 + 5b} = \frac{b - 7}{3 + 5b} \qquad \text{Divide each side by } 3 + 5b.$$

$$a = \frac{b - 7}{3 + 5b} \qquad\qquad \blacksquare$$

When solving an equation in one variable that contains many decimal numbers, we usually use a calculator for the arithmetic. However, if you use a calculator at every step and round off the result of every computation, the final answer can differ greatly from the correct answer. Example 5 shows how to avoid this problem. The numbers are treated as if they were variables and no arithmetic is performed until all of the numbers are on one side of the equation. This technique is similar to solving an equation for a specified variable.

Doing computations last

Solve $3.24x - 6.78 = 6.31(x + 23.45)$.

Solution

Use the distributive property on the right-hand side, but simply write $(6.31)(23.45)$ rather than the result obtained on a calculator.

$$3.24x - 6.78 = 6.31x + (6.31)(23.45) \qquad \text{Distributive property}$$

$$3.24x - 6.31x = (6.31)(23.45) + 6.78 \qquad \text{Get all } x\text{-terms on the left.}$$

$$(3.24 - 6.31)x = (6.31)(23.45) + 6.78 \qquad \text{Distributive property}$$

$$x = \frac{(6.31)(23.45) + 6.78}{3.24 - 6.31} \qquad \text{Divide each side by } (3.24 - 6.31).$$

$$\approx -50.407 \qquad \text{Round to three decimal places.}$$

Check -50.407 in the original equation. When you check an approximate answer, you will get approximately the same value for each side of the equation. The solution set is $\{-50.407\}$. $\qquad\qquad \blacksquare$

Finding the Value of a Variable

In many situations we know the values of all of the variables in a formula except one. We can use the formula to determine the unknown value. A list of common formulas and their meanings is given at the back of the text. This list may be helpful for doing the exercises at the end of this section.

E X A M P L E   6

Helpful Hint

It doesn't matter what form to use when solving for y here. If you use

$$y = \frac{2x + 9}{3}$$

and let $x = -3$, you get $y = 1$.

Finding the value of a variable

Use the formula $-2x + 3y = 9$ to find y given that $x = -3$.

Solution

To find y, we first write y in terms of x:

$$-2x + 3y = 9 \qquad\qquad \text{Original equation}$$

$$3y = 2x + 9 \qquad \text{Add } 2x \text{ to each side.}$$

$$y = \frac{2}{3}x + 3 \qquad \text{Divide each side by 3.}$$

Now replace x by -3:

$$y = \frac{2}{3}(-3) + 3$$

$$y = 1 \qquad\qquad \blacksquare$$

E X A M P L E   7

Finding the interest rate

The simple interest on a loan is \$50, the principal is \$500, and the time is 2 years. What is the simple interest rate?

Solution

The formula $I = Prt$ expresses the interest I in terms of the principal P, rate r, and time t. To find the rate, we first solve the formula for r, then insert the values of P, I, and t:

$$Prt = I$$

$$\frac{Prt}{Pt} = \frac{I}{Pt} \qquad \text{Divide each side by } Pt.$$

$$r = \frac{I}{Pt} \qquad \text{This formula expresses the rate in terms of } I, P, \text{ and } t.$$

$$r = \frac{50}{500(2)} \qquad \text{Substitute values for } I, P, \text{ and } t.$$

$$r = 0.05 = 5\% \qquad \text{A rate is usually written as a percent.} \qquad \blacksquare$$

In Example 7 we solved the formula for r and then inserted the values of the other variables. If we had to find the interest rate for many different loans, this method would be the most direct. But we could also have inserted the values of I, P, and t into the original formula and then solved for r. Examples 8 and 9 illustrate this second approach.

Geometric Formulas

Appendix A contains some geometric formulas that will be useful in problems that involve geometric shapes. In geometry it is common to use variables with subscripts. A subscript is a slightly lowered number following the variable. For example, the areas of two triangles might be referred to as A_1 and A_2. (We read A_1 as "A sub one" or simply "A one.") You will see subscripts in the next example.

E X A M P L E   8

Area of a trapezoid

The wildlife sanctuary shown in Fig. 2.2 on the next page has a trapezoidal shape with an area of 30 square kilometers. If one base, b_1, of the trapezoid is 10 kilometers and its height is 5 kilometers, find the length of the other base, b_2.

Solution

In any geometric problem it is helpful to have a diagram, as in Fig. 2.2. Substitute the given values into the formula for the area of a trapezoid, found in Appendix A, and then solve for b_2:

$$A = \frac{1}{2}h(b_1 + b_2) \qquad \text{The area depends on } h, b_1, \text{ and } b_2.$$

$$30 = \frac{1}{2} \cdot 5(10 + b_2) \qquad \text{Substitute given values into the formula for the area of a trapezoid.}$$

$$60 = 5(10 + b_2) \qquad \text{Multiply each side by 2.}$$

$$12 = 10 + b_2 \qquad \text{Divide each side by 5.}$$

$$2 = b_2 \qquad \text{Subtract 10 from each side.}$$

b_2

5 km

10 km

FIGURE 2.2

The length of the base b_2 is 2 kilometers. $\qquad \blacksquare$

EXAMPLE 9

Volume of a rectangular solid

Millie has just completed pouring 14 cubic yards of concrete to construct a rectangular driveway. If the concrete is 4 inches thick and the driveway is 18 feet wide, then how long is her driveway?

Solution

FIGURE 2.3

First draw a diagram as in Fig. 2.3. The driveway is a rectangular solid. The formula for the volume of a rectangular solid is $V = LWH$ (from Appendix A). Before we insert the values of the variables into the formula, we must convert all of them to the same unit of measurement. We will convert feet and inches to yards:

$$4 \text{ inches} = 4 \text{ in.} \cdot \frac{1 \text{ yd}}{36 \text{ in.}} = \frac{1}{9} \text{ yard}$$

$$18 \text{ feet} = 18 \text{ ft} \cdot \frac{1 \text{ yd}}{3 \text{ ft}} = 6 \text{ yards}$$

Now replace W, H, and V by the appropriate values:

$$V = LWH \qquad \text{The volume is determined by the length, width, and height.}$$

$$14 = L \cdot 6 \cdot \frac{1}{9}$$

$$\frac{9}{6} \cdot 14 = L \qquad \text{Multiply each side by } \frac{9}{6}.$$

$$21 = L$$

The length of the driveway is 21 yards, or 63 feet. ■

True or false? Explain your answer.

1. The formula $A = P + Prt$ solved for P is $P = A - Prt$.

2. In solving $A = P + Prt$ for P, we do not need the distributive property.

3. Solving $I = Prt$ for t gives us $t = I - Pr$.

4. If $a = \dfrac{bh}{2}$, $b = 5$, and $h = 6$, then $a = 15$.

5. The perimeter of a rectangle is found by multiplying its length and width.

6. The volume of a rectangular box is the product of its length, width, and height.

7. The area of a trapezoid with parallel sides b_1 and b_2 is $\frac{1}{2}(b_1 + b_2)$.

8. If $x - y = 5$, then $y = x - 5$ expresses y in terms of x.

9. If $x = -3$ and $y = -2x - 4$, then $y = 2$.

10. The area of a rectangle is the total distance around the outside edge.

2.2 EXERCISES

Reading and Writing *After reading this section, write out the answers to these questions. Use complete sentences.*

1. What is a formula?

2. What is a formula used for?

3. What does it mean to solve a formula for a particular variable?

4. How do you solve for a variable that occurs twice in a formula?

5. How do you find the value of a variable in a formula?

6. What formula expresses the volume of a rectangular solid in terms of its length, width, and height?

Solve each formula for the specified variable. See Example 1.

7. $I = Prt$ for t

8. $d = rt$ for r

9. $F = \dfrac{9}{5}C + 32$ for C

10. $A = \dfrac{1}{2}bh$ for h

11. $A = LW$ for W

12. $C = 2\pi r$ for r

13. $A = \dfrac{1}{2}(b_1 + b_2)$ for b_1

14. $A = \dfrac{1}{2}(b_1 + b_2)$ for b_2

15. $P = 2L + 2W$ for L

16. $P = 2L + 2W$ for W

17. $V = \pi r^2 h$ for h

18. $V = \dfrac{1}{3}\pi r^2 h$ for h

Write y in terms of x. See Example 2.

19. $2x + 3y = 9$

20. $4y + 5x = 8$

21. $x - y = 4$

22. $y - x = 6$

23. $\dfrac{1}{2}x - \dfrac{1}{3}y = 2$

24. $\dfrac{1}{3}x - \dfrac{1}{4}y = 1$

25. $y - 2 = \dfrac{1}{2}(x - 3)$

26. $y - 3 = \dfrac{1}{3}(x - 4)$

Solve for the specified variable. See Examples 3 and 4.

27. $A = P + Prt$ for t

28. $A = P + Prt$ for r

29. $ab + a = 1$ for a

30. $y - wy = m$ for y

31. $xy + 5 = y - 7$ for y

32. $xy + 5 = x + 7$ for x

33. $xy^2 + xz^2 = xw^2 - 6$ for x

34. $xz^2 + xw^2 = xy^2 + 5$ for x

35. $\dfrac{1}{R} = \dfrac{1}{R_1} + \dfrac{1}{R_2}$ for R_1

36. $\dfrac{1}{a} + \dfrac{1}{b} = \dfrac{1}{2}$ for a

 Solve each equation. Use a calculator only on the last step. Round answers to three decimal places and use your calculator to check your answer. See Example 5.

37. $3.35x - 54.6 = 44.3 - 4.58x$

38. $-4.487x - 33.41 = 55.83 - 22.49x$

39. $4.59x - 66.7 = 3.2(x - 5.67)$

40. $457(36x - 99) = 34(28x - 239)$

41. $\dfrac{x}{19} - \dfrac{3}{23} = \dfrac{4}{31} - \dfrac{3x}{7}$

42. $\dfrac{1}{8} - \dfrac{5}{7}\left(x - \dfrac{5}{22}\right) = \dfrac{4x}{9} + \dfrac{1}{12}$

Find y given that x = 3. See Example 6.

43. $2x - 3y = 5$

44. $-3x - 4y = 4$

45. $-4x + 2y = 1$

46. $x - y = 7$

47. $y = -2x + 5$ **48.** $y = -3x - 6$

49. $-x + 2y = 5$ **50.** $-x - 3y = 6$

51. $y - 1.046 = 2.63(x - 5.09)$

52. $y - 2.895 = -1.07(x - 2.89)$

Find x in each formula given that y = 2, z = -3, and w = 4. See Example 6.

53. $wxy = 5$ **54.** $wxz = 4$

55. $x + xz = 7$ **56.** $xw - x = 3$

57. $w(x - z) = y(x - 4)$

58. $z(x - y) = y(x + 5)$

59. $w = \dfrac{1}{2}xz$ **60.** $y = \dfrac{1}{2}wx$

61. $\dfrac{1}{w} + \dfrac{1}{x} = \dfrac{1}{y}$ **62.** $\dfrac{1}{w} + \dfrac{1}{y} = \dfrac{1}{x}$

Find the geometric formula in each case.

63. The area of a circle in terms of its radius

64. The circumference of a circle in terms of its diameter

65. The radius of a circle in terms of its circumference

66. The diameter of a circle in terms of its circumference

67. The width of a rectangle in terms of its length and perimeter

68. The length of a rectangle in terms of its width and area

Solve each problem. Draw a diagram for each geometric problem. See Examples 7–9.

69. *Simple interest.* If the simple interest on $1000 for 2 years is $300, then what is the rate?

70. *Finding time.* If the simple interest on $2000 at 18% is $180, then what is the time?

71. *Rectangular floor.* The area of a rectangular floor is 23 square yards. The width is 4 yards. Find the length.

72. *Rectangular garden.* The area of a rectangular garden is 55 square meters. The length is 7 meters. Find the width.

73. *Ice sculpture.* The volume of a rectangular block of ice is 36 cubic feet. The bottom is 2 feet by 2.5 feet. Find the height of the block.

74. *Cardboard box.* A shipping box has a volume of 2.5 cubic meters. The box measures 1 meter high by 1.25 meters wide. How long is the box?

75. *Fish tank.* The volume of a rectangular aquarium is 900 gallons. The bottom is 4 feet by 6 feet. Find the height of the tank. (*Hint:* There are 7.5 gallons per cubic foot.)

FIGURE FOR EXERCISE 75

76. *Reflecting pool.* A rectangular reflecting pool with a horizontal bottom holds 60,000 gallons of water. If the pool is 40 feet by 100 feet, how deep is the water?

77. *Area of a triangle.* The area of a triangle is 30 square feet. If the base is 4 feet, then what is the height?

78. *Larger triangle.* The area of a triangle is 40 square meters. If the height is 10 meters, then what is the length of the base?

79. *Second base.* The area of a trapezoid is 300 square inches. If the height is 20 inches and the lower base is 16 inches, then what is the length of the upper base?

FIGURE FOR EXERCISE 79

80. *Height of a trapezoid.* The area of a trapezoid is 200 square centimeters. The bases are 16 centimeters and 24 centimeters. Find the height.

81. *Fencing.* If it takes 600 feet of fence to enclose a rectangular lot that is 132 feet wide, then how deep is the lot?

82. Football. The perimeter of a football field in the NFL, excluding the end zones, is $306\frac{2}{3}$ yards. How wide is the field?

x yd

FIGURE FOR EXERCISE 82

83. Radius of a circle. If the circumference of a circle is 3π meters, then what is the radius?

84. Diameter of a circle. If the circumference of a circle is 12π inches, then what is the diameter?

85. Radius of the earth. If the circumference of the earth is 25,000 miles, then what is the radius?

86. Altitude of a satellite. If a satellite travels 26,000 miles in each circular orbit of the earth, then how high above the earth is the satellite orbiting? See Exercise 85.

h

FIGURE FOR EXERCISE 86

87. Height of a can. If the volume of a can is 30 cubic inches and the diameter of the top is 3 inches, then what is the height of the can?

3 in.

SANTA FE
BEANS

h

FIGURE FOR EXERCISE 87

88. Height of a cylinder. If the volume of a cylinder is 6.3 cubic meters and the diameter of the lid is 1.2 meters, then what is the height of the cylinder?

89. Great Chicago flood. The great Chicago flood of April 1992 occurred when an old freight tunnel connecting buildings in the Loop ruptured. As shown in the figure,

engineers plugged the tunnel with concrete on each side of the hole. They used the formula $F = WDA$ to find the force F of the water on the plug. In this formula the weight of water W is 62 pounds per cubic foot (lb/ft^3), the average depth D of the tunnel below the surface of the river is 32 ft, and the cross-sectional area A of the tunnel is 48 ft^2. Find the force on the plug.

5 ft

river bottom

32 ft

hole

48 ft^2 concrete plug   tunnel

FIGURE FOR EXERCISE 89

90. Will it hold? To plug the tunnel described in the previous exercise, engineers drilled a 5-foot-diameter shaft down to the tunnel. The concrete plug was made so that it extended up into the shaft. For the plug to remain in place, the shear strength of the concrete in the shaft would have to be greater than the force of the water. The amount of force F that it would take for the water to shear the concrete in the shaft is given by $F = s\pi r^2$, where s is the shear strength of concrete and r is the radius of the shaft in inches. If the shear strength of concrete is 38 lb/in.^{2}, then what force of water would shear the concrete in the shaft? Use the result from Exercise 89 to determine whether the concrete would be strong enough to hold back the water.

91. Estimating armaments. During World War II the Allies captured some German tanks on which the smallest serial number was S and the biggest was B. Assuming the entire production of tanks was numbered 1 through N, the Allies used the formula $N = B + S - 1$ to estimate the number of tanks in the German army (*New Scientist*, May 1998).
a) Find N if $B = 2003$ and $S = 455$.
b) If this formula was used to estimate $N = 1452$ and the largest serial number was 1033, what was the smallest serial number?

92. Cigarette usage. The percentage of Americans 18 to 25 who use cigarettes has been decreasing at an approximately constant rate since 1974 (National Institute on Drug Abuse, www.nida.nih.gov). The formula

$$P = 47.9 - 0.94n$$

can be used to estimate the percentage of smokers in this age group n years after 1974.
a) Use the formula to find the percentage of smokers in this age group in 2004.

$$P = 47.9 - 0.94n$$

P
50
40
Percent
30
20
10

10 20 30 40 50 60 n
Years since 1974

FIGURE FOR EXERCISE 92

b) Use the accompanying graph to estimate the year in which smoking will be eliminated from this age group.
c) Use the formula to find the year in which smoking will be eliminated from this age group.
93. *Distance between streets.* Harold Johnson lives on a four-sided, 50,000-square-foot lot that is bounded on two sides by parallel streets. The city has assessed him

h

FIGURE FOR EXERCISES 93–95

$1,000 for curb repair, $2 for each foot of property bordering on these two streets. How far apart are the streets?

94. *Assessed for repairs.* Harold's sister, Maude, lives next door on a triangular lot of 25,000 square feet that also extends from street to street but has frontage only on one street. What will her assessment be? (See Exercise 93.)

95. *Juniper's lot.* Harold's other sister, Juniper, lives on the other side of him on a lot of 60,000 square feet in the shape of a parallelogram. What will her assessment be? (See Exercise 93.)

96. *Mother's driveway.* Harold's mother, who lives across the street, is pouring a concrete driveway, 12 feet wide and 4 inches thick, from the street straight to her house. This is too much work for Harold to do in one day, so his mother has agreed to buy 4 cubic yards of concrete each Saturday for three consecutive Saturdays. How far is it from the street to her house?

GETTING MORE INVOLVED

97. *Exploration.* Electric companies often point out the low cost of electricity in performing common household tasks.
 a) Find the cost of a kilowatt-hour of electricity in your area.
 b) Write a formula for finding the cost of electricity for a household appliance to perform a certain task and to explain what each variable represents.
 c) Use your formula to find the cost in your area for baking a $1\frac{1}{2}$-pound loaf of bread for 5 hours in a 750-watt Welbilt breadmaker.

In This Section

- Writing Algebraic Expressions
- Solving Problems
- General Strategy for Problem Solving
- Geometric Problems
- Investment Problems
- Mixture Problems
- Uniform Motion Problems
- Commission Problems

2.3   **APPLICATIONS**

We often use algebra to solve problems by translating them into algebraic equations. Sometimes we can use formulas such as those in Appendix A. More often we have to set up a new equation that represents or **models** the problem. We begin with translating verbal expressions into algebraic expressions.

Writing Algebraic Expressions

Consider the three consecutive integers 5, 6, and 7. Note that each integer is 1 larger than the previous integer. To represent three *unknown* consecutive integers, we let

$$x = \text{the first integer,}$$
$$x + 1 = \text{the second integer,}$$
and $$x + 2 = \text{the third integer.}$$

Consider the three consecutive odd integers 7, 9, and 11. Note that each odd integer is 2 larger than the previous odd integer. To represent three *unknown*

consecutive odd integers, we let

$$x = \text{the first odd integer,}$$
$$x + 2 = \text{the second odd integer,}$$

and
$$x + 4 = \text{the third odd integer.}$$

Note that consecutive even integers as well as consecutive odd integers differ by 2. So the same expressions are used in either case.

How would we represent two numbers that have a sum of 8? If one of the numbers is 2, the other is certainly 6, or $8 - 2$. So if x is one of the numbers, then $8 - x$ is the other number. The expressions x and $8 - x$ have a sum of 8 for any value of x.

E X A M P L E   1   Writing algebraic expressions

Write algebraic expressions to represent each verbal expression.

a) Two numbers that differ by 12

b) Two consecutive even integers

c) Two investments that total $5000

d) The length of a rectangle if the width is x meters and the perimeter is 10 meters

Solution

a) The expressions x and $x + 12$ differ by 12. Note that we could also use x and $x - 12$ for two numbers that differ by 12.

b) The expressions x and $x + 2$ represent two consecutive even integers.

c) If x represents the amount of one investment, then $5000 - x$ represents the amount of the other investment.

d) Because the perimeter is 10 meters and $P = 2L + 2W = 2(L + W)$, the sum of the length and width is 5 meters. Because the width is x, the length is $5 - x$.

∎

M A T H   A T   W O R K

Mark Cromett, General Manager of the Charles Street Starbucks Coffee Store, arrives at work early in the morning to make sure each customer receives a perfect cup of coffee. Coffee beans from Central and South America, East Africa, and the Pacific are ground daily. Careful calibrations for the grinding are done by weighing each specific type of coffee. Even humidity frequently becomes part of the equation on how coffee is prepared. Besides the geographical area where the beans originate, customers have many choices for coffee. Selections are made among full city, espresso, Italian, and French roasts. Even seven decaffeinated coffees are available. But even with all of the choices, customers sometimes prefer their own special blend, requesting a mixture of different types of beans. Mr. Cromett is glad to brew or grind any special blend for a customer, and his charge depends on the different prices of the coffees mixed together. In Exercise 49 of this section you will determine the price of a specially blended coffee.

**COFFEE STORE
MANAGER**

Many verbal phrases occur repeatedly in applications. This list of some frequently occurring verbal phrases and their translations into algebraic expressions will help you to translate words into algebra.

Translating Words into Algebra

	Verbal Phrase	Algebraic Expression
Addition:	The sum of a number and 8	$x + 8$
	Five is added to a number	$x + 5$
	Two more than a number	$x + 2$
	A number increased by 3	$x + 3$
Subtraction:	Four is subtracted from a number	$x - 4$
	Three less than a number	$x - 3$
	The difference between 7 and a number	$7 - x$
	Some number decreased by 2	$x - 2$
	A number less 5	$x - 5$
Multiplication:	The product of 5 and a number	$5x$
	Seven times a number	$7x$
	Twice a number	$2x$
	One-half of a number	$\frac{1}{2}x \left(\text{or } \frac{x}{2}\right)$
Division:	The ratio of a number to 6	$\frac{x}{6}$
	The quotient of 5 and a number	$\frac{5}{x}$
	Three divided by some number	$\frac{3}{x}$

More than one operation can be combined in a single expression. For example, 7 less than twice a number is written as $2x - 7$.

Solving Problems

We will now see how algebraic expressions can be used to form an equation. If the equation correctly models a problem, then we may be able to solve the equation to get the solution to the problem. Some problems in this section could be solved without using algebra. However, the purpose of this section is to gain experience in setting up equations and using algebra to solve problems. We will show a complete solution to each problem so that you can gain the experience needed to solve more complex problems. We begin with a simple number problem.

EXAMPLE 2   **A number problem**

The sum of three consecutive integers is 228. Find the integers.

Solution

We first represent the unknown quantities with variables. The unknown quantities are the three consecutive integers. Let

$$x = \text{the first integer,}$$
$$x + 1 = \text{the second integer,}$$
and
$$x + 2 = \text{the third integer.}$$

Helpful Hint

Making a guess can be a good way to become familiar with the problem. For example, let's guess that the answers to Example 2 are 50, 51, and 52. Since $50 + 51 + 52 = 153$, these are not the correct numbers. But now we realize that we should use x, $x + 1$, and $x + 2$ and that the equation should be

$$x + x + 1 + x + 2 = 228.$$

Since the sum of these three expressions for the consecutive integers is 228, we can write the following equation and solve it:

$$x + (x + 1) + (x + 2) = 228 \quad \text{The sum of the integers is 228.}$$
$$3x + 3 = 228$$
$$3x = 225$$
$$x = 75$$
$$x + 1 = 76 \quad \text{Identify the other unknown quantities.}$$
$$x + 2 = 77$$

To verify that these values are the correct integers, we compute

$$75 + 76 + 77 = 228.$$

The three consecutive integers that have a sum of 228 are 75, 76, and 77.

General Strategy for Problem Solving

The steps to follow in providing a complete solution to a verbal problem can be stated as follows.

Study Tip

Don't simply work exercises to get answers. Keep reminding yourself of what you are actually doing. Keep trying to obtain the big picture. How does this section relate to what we did in the previous section? Where are we going next? When is the picture complete?

Strategy for Solving Word Problems

1. Read the problem until you understand the problem. Making a guess and checking it will help you to understand the problem.
2. If possible, draw a diagram to illustrate the problem.
3. Choose a variable and write down what it represents.
4. Represent any other unknowns in terms of that variable.
5. Write an equation that models the situation.
6. Solve the equation.
7. Be sure that your solution answers the question posed in the original problem.
8. Check your answer by using it to solve the original problem (not the equation).

We will now see how this strategy can be applied to various types of problems.

Geometric Problems

Any problem that involves a geometric figure may be referred to as a **geometric problem.** For geometric problems the equation is often a geometric formula.

E X A M P L E   3

Finding the length and width of a rectangle

The length of a rectangular piece of property is 1 foot more than twice the width. If the perimeter is 302 feet, find the length and width.

Solution

First draw a diagram as in Fig. 2.4. Because the length is 1 foot more than twice the width, we let

$$x = \text{the width}$$

and

$$2x + 1 = \text{the length.}$$

$2x + 1$

FIGURE 2.4

x

Helpful Hint

To become familiar with the problem, let's guess that the width is 20 feet. The length would be 41 feet (1 foot more than twice the width). The perimeter of a 20 foot by 41 foot rectangle is 2(20) + 2(41) or 122 feet, which is not correct, but now we understand the problem.

The perimeter of a rectangle is modeled by the equation $2L + 2W = P$:

$$2L + 2W = P$$
$$2(2x + 1) + 2(x) = 302 \quad \text{Replace } L \text{ by } 2x + 1 \text{ and } W \text{ by } x.$$
$$4x + 2 + 2x = 302 \quad \text{Remove the parentheses.}$$
$$6x = 300$$
$$x = 50$$
$$2x + 1 = 101 \quad \text{Because } 2(50) + 1 = 101$$

Because $P = 2(101) + 2(50) = 302$ and 101 is 1 more than twice 50, we can be sure that the answer is correct. So the length is 101 feet, and the width is 50 feet. ■

Investment Problems

Investment problems involve sums of money invested at various interest rates. In this chapter we consider simple interest only.

E X A M P L E   4

Investing at two rates

Greg Smith invested some money in a certificate of deposit (CD) with an annual yield of 9%. He invested twice as much money in a mutual fund with an annual yield of 12%. His interest from the two investments at the end of the year was $396. How much money was invested at each rate?

Solution

Recall the formula $I = Prt$. In this problem the time t is 1 year, so $I = Pr$. If we let x represent the amount invested at the 9% rate, then $2x$ is the amount invested at 12%. The interest on these investments is the principal times the rate, or $0.09x$ and $0.12(2x)$. It is often helpful to make a table for the unknown quantities.

Helpful Hint

To become familiar with the problem, let's guess that he invested $400 in a CD at 9% and $800 (twice as much) in a mutual fund at 12%. His total interest is

0.09(400) + 0.12(800)

or $132, which is not correct, but now we understand the problem.

	Principal	Rate	Interest
Certificate of deposit	x dollars	9%	$0.09x$ dollars
Mutual fund	$2x$ dollars	12%	$0.12(2x)$ dollars

The fact that the total interest from the investments was $396 is expressed in this equation:

$$0.09x + 0.12(2x) = 396$$
$$0.09x + 0.24x = 396 \quad \text{We could multiply each side by 100}$$
$$0.33x = 396 \quad \text{to eliminate the decimals.}$$
$$x = \frac{396}{0.33}$$
$$x = 1200$$
$$2x = 2400$$

To check this answer, we find that $0.09(\$1200) = \$108$ and $0.12(\$2400) = \$288$. Now $\$108 + \$288 = \$396$. So Greg invested $1200 at 9% and $2400 at 12%. ■

Mixture Problems

Mixture problems involve solutions containing various percentages of a particular ingredient.

EXAMPLE 5

Mixing milk

How many gallons of milk containing 5% butterfat must be mixed with 90 gallons of 1% milk to obtain 2% milk?

Solution

If x represents the number of gallons of 5% milk, then $0.05x$ represents the amount of fat in that milk. If we mix x gallons of 5% milk with 90 gallons of 1% milk, we will have $x + 90$ gallons of 2% milk. See Fig. 2.5. We can make a table to classify all of the unknown amounts.

	Amount of milk	% fat	Amount of fat
5% milk	x gal	5	$0.05x$ gal
1% milk	90 gal	1	$0.01(90)$ gal
2% milk	$x + 90$ gal	2	$0.02(x + 90)$ gal

In mixture problems we always write an equation that accounts for one of the ingredients in the process. In this case we write an equation to express the fact that the total amount of fat from the first two types of milk is the same as the amount of fat in the mixture.

$$0.05x + 0.01(90) = 0.02(x + 90)$$
$$0.05x + 0.9 = 0.02x + 1.8 \quad \text{Remove parentheses.}$$
$$0.03x = 0.9 \quad \text{Note that we chose to work with the decimals}$$
$$x = 30 \quad \text{rather than eliminate them.}$$

We should use 30 gallons of 5% milk. There are 1.5 gallons of fat in the 30 gallons of 5% milk. The 1% milk will contribute 0.9 gallon of fat, and there will be 2.4 gallons of fat in 120 gallons of 2% milk. Because $1.5 + 0.9 = 2.4$, we have the correct solution. ∎

Helpful Hint

To become familiar with the problem, let's guess that 100 gallons of 5% milk should be mixed with 90 gallons of 1% milk. The total amount of fat would be 0.05(100) + 0.01(90) or 5.9 gallons of fat. But 2% of 190 is 3.8 gallons of fat. Since the amounts of fat should be equal, our guess is incorrect.

FIGURE 2.5

EXAMPLE 6

Blending gasoline

A dealer has 10,000 gallons of unleaded gasoline. He wants to add just enough ethanol to make the fuel a 10% ethanol mixture. How many gallons of ethanol should be added?

Solution

Let x represent the number of gallons of 100% pure ethanol that should be added. (The original gasoline has no ethanol in it.) We can classify all of this information in a table.

	Amount of gasoline	% ethanol	Amount of ethanol
Gasoline	10,000 gal	0	0 gal
Ethanol	x gal	100	x gal
Mixture	$x + 10,000$ gal	10	$0.1(x + 10,000)$ gal

We can write $0 + x = 0.1(x + 10,000)$ to express the fact that the amount of ethanol in the gasoline plus the amount of ethanol added is equal to the amount of ethanol in the final mixture. This model accounts for all of the ethanol in the process.

$$0 + x = 0.1(x + 10,000)$$

$$x = 0.1x + 1000 \quad \text{Remove parentheses.}$$

$$0.9x = 1000 \qquad \text{Subtract } 0.1x \text{ from each side of the equation.}$$

$$x = \frac{1000}{0.9} \qquad \text{Divide each side by 0.9.}$$

$$x \approx 1,111.1 \text{ gallons}$$

The amount of ethanol has been rounded to the nearest tenth of a gallon, so we cannot expect checking to be exact. If we combine 10,000 gallons of gasoline with 1,111.1 gallons of ethanol, we obtain 11,111.1 gallons of fuel. Notice that the amount of ethanol is 10% of the total mixture, 10% of $(10,000 + x)$. ■

Uniform Motion Problems

Problems that involve motion at a constant rate are referred to as **uniform motion problems.**

E X A M P L E   7

Driving Miss Jennifer

Jennifer drove her car for 3 hours in a dust storm. When the skies cleared, she increased her speed by 30 miles per hour and drove for 4 more hours, completing her 295-mile trip. How fast did she travel during the dust storm?

Solution

If x was Jennifer's speed during the dust storm, then her speed under clear skies was $x + 30$. For problems involving motion we use the formula $D = RT$ (distance equals rate times time). It is again helpful to make a table to classify the given information.

	Rate	Time	Distance
Dust storm	x mph	3 hr	$3x$ mi
Clear skies	$x + 30$ mph	4 hr	$4(x + 30)$ mi

This equation indicates that the total distance traveled was 295 miles:

$$3x + 4(x + 30) = 295$$

$$3x + 4x + 120 = 295 \quad \text{Remove parentheses.}$$

$$7x = 175$$

$$x = 25 \text{ miles per hour}$$

Check this answer in the original problem. Jennifer traveled 25 miles per hour (mph) during the storm. ■

Commission Problems

When property is sold, the percentage of the selling price that the selling agent receives is the **commission.**

E X A M P L E   8

Helpful Hint

To become familiar with the problem, let's guess that the selling price is $100,000. The commission is 6% of the selling price: 0.06(100,000) or $6,000. So Sonia receives $94,000, which is incorrect.

Selling price of a house

Sonia is selling her house through a real estate agent whose commission is 6% of the selling price. What should be the selling price so that Sonia can get $84,600?

Solution

Let x be the selling price. The commission is 6% of x (not 6% of $84,600). Sonia receives the selling price less the sales commission.

$$\text{Selling price} - \text{commission} = \text{Sonia's share}$$
$$x - 0.06x = 84{,}600$$
$$0.94x = 84{,}600$$
$$x = \frac{84{,}600}{0.94}$$
$$= \$90{,}000$$

The commission is 0.06($90,000), or $5,400. Sonia's share is $90,000 − $5,400, or $84,600. The house should sell for $90,000. ■

WARM-UPS

True or false? Explain your answer.

1. The recommended first step in solving a word problem is to write the equation.
2. When solving word problems, always write what the variable stands for.
3. Any solution to your equation must solve the word problem.
4. To represent two consecutive odd integers, we use x and $x + 1$.
5. We can represent two numbers that have a sum of 6 by x and $6 - x$.
6. Two numbers that differ by 7 can be represented by x and $x + 7$.
7. If $5x$ feet is 2 feet more than $3(x + 20)$ feet, then $5x + 2 = 3(x + 20)$.
8. If x is the selling price and the commission is 8% of the selling price, then the commission is $0.08x$.
9. If you need $80,000 for your house and the agent gets 10% of the selling price, then the agent gets $8,000, and the house sells for $88,000.
10. When we mix a 10% acid solution with a 14% acid solution, we can obtain a solution that is 24% acid.

2.3   EXERCISES

Reading and Writing *After reading this section, write out the answers to these questions. Use complete sentences.*

1. How do you algebraically represent three unknown consecutive integers?

2. What is the difference between representing three unknown consecutive even or odd integers?

3. What formula expresses the perimeter of a rectangle in terms of length and width?

4. What verbal phrases are used to indicate the operation of addition?

5. What is the commission when a real estate agent sells property?

6. What is uniform motion?

Find algebraic expressions for each of these verbal expressions. See Example 1.

7. Two consecutive even integers

8. Two consecutive odd integers

9. Two numbers with a sum of 10

10. Two numbers with a difference of 3

11. Eighty-five percent of the selling price

12. The product of a number and 3

13. The distance traveled in 3 hours at x miles per hour

14. The time it takes to travel 100 miles at $x + 5$ miles per hour

15. The perimeter of a rectangle if the width is x feet and the length is 5 feet longer than the width

16. The width of a rectangle if the length is x meters and the perimeter is 20 meters

Show a complete solution for each number problem. See Example 2.

17. The sum of three consecutive integers is 84. Find the integers.

18. Find three consecutive integers whose sum is 171.

19. Find three consecutive even integers whose sum is 252.

20. Find three consecutive even integers whose sum is 84.

21. Two consecutive odd integers have a sum of 128. What are the integers?

22. Four consecutive odd integers have a sum of 56. What are the integers?

Show a complete solution to each geometric problem. See Example 3.

23. *Length and width.* If the perimeter of a rectangle is 278 meters and the length is 1 meter longer than twice the width, then what are the length and width?

24. *Dimensions of a frame.* A frame maker made a large picture frame using 10 feet of frame molding. If the length of the finished frame was 2 feet more than the width, then what were the dimensions of the frame?

25. *Perimeter of a lot.* Having finished fencing the perimeter of a triangular piece of land, Lance observed that the second side was just 10 feet short of being twice as long as the first side, and the third side was exactly 50 feet longer than the first side. If he used 684 feet of fencing, what are the lengths of the three sides?

26. *Isosceles triangle.* A flag in the shape of an isosceles triangle has a base that is 3.5 inches shorter than either of the equal sides. If the perimeter of the triangle is 49 inches, what is the length of the equal sides?

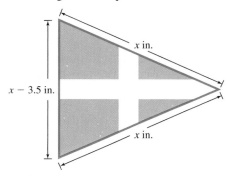

FIGURE FOR EXERCISE 26

27. *Hog heaven.* Farmer Hodges has 50 feet of fencing to make a rectangular hog pen beside a very large barn. He needs to fence only three sides because the barn will form the fourth side. Studies have shown that under those conditions the side parallel to the barn should be 5 feet longer than twice the width. If Farmer Hodges uses all of the fencing, what should the dimensions be?

FIGURE FOR EXERCISE 27

28. *Doorway dimensions.* A carpenter made a doorway that is 1 foot taller than twice the width. If she used three pieces of door edge molding with a total length of 17 feet, then what are the approximate dimensions of the doorway?

Show a complete solution to each investment problem. See Example 4.

29. Investing money. Mr. and Mrs. Jackson invested some money at 6% simple interest and some money at 10% simple interest. In the second investment they put $1000 more than they put in the first. If the income from both investments for one year was $340, then how much did they invest at each rate?

30. Sibling rivalry. Samantha lent her brother some money at 9% simple interest and her sister one-half as much money at 16% simple interest. If she received a total of 34 cents in interest, then how much did she lend to each one?

31. Investing inheritance. Norman invested one-half of his inheritance in a CD that had a 10% annual yield. He lent one-quarter of his inheritance to his brother-in-law at 12% simple interest. His income from these two investments was $6400 for one year. How much was the inheritance?

32. Insurance settlement. Gary invested one-third of his insurance settlement in a CD that yielded 12%. He also invested one-third in Tara's computer business. Tara paid Gary 15% on this investment. If Gary's total income from these investments was $10,800 for one year, then what was the amount of his insurance settlement?

Show a complete solution to each mixture problem. See Examples 5 and 6.

33. Acid solutions. How many gallons of 5% acid solution should be mixed with 20 gallons of a 10% acid solution to obtain an 8% acid solution?

34. Alcohol solutions. How many liters of a 10% alcohol solution should be mixed with 12 liters of a 20% alcohol solution to obtain a 14% alcohol solution?

35. Increasing acidity. A gallon of Del Monte White Vinegar is labeled 5% acidity. How many fluid ounces of pure acid must be added to get 6% acidity?

36. Chlorine bleach. A gallon of Clorox bleach is labeled "5.25% sodium hypochlorite by weight." If a gallon of bleach weighs 8.3 pounds, then how many ounces of sodium hypochlorite must be added so that the bleach will be 6% sodium hypochlorite?

Show a complete solution to each uniform motion problem. See Example 7.

37. Driving in a fog. Carlo drove for 3 hours in a fog, then increased his speed by 30 miles per hour (mph) and drove 6 more hours. If his total trip was 540 miles, then what was his speed in the fog?

38. Walk, don't run. Louise walked for 2 hours then ran for $1\frac{1}{2}$ hours. If she runs twice as fast as she walks and the total trip was 20 miles, then how fast does she run?

39. Commuting to work. A commuter bus takes 2 hours to get downtown; an express bus, averaging 25 mph faster, takes 45 minutes to cover the same route. What is the average speed for the commuter bus?

FIGURE FOR EXERCISE 39

40. Passengers versus freight. A freight train takes $1\frac{1}{4}$ hours to get to the city; a passenger train averaging 40 mph faster takes only 45 minutes to cover the same distance. What is the average speed of the passenger train?

Show a complete solution to each problem. See Example 8.

41. Listing a house. Karl wants to get $80,000 for his house. The real estate agent charges 8% of the selling price for selling the house. What should the selling price be?

42. Hot tamales. Martha sells hot tamales at a sidewalk stand. Her total receipts including the 5% sales tax were $915.60. What amount of sales tax did she collect?

43. Mustang Sally. Sally bought a used Mustang. The selling price plus the 7% state sales tax was $9041.50. What was the selling price?

44. Choosing a selling price. Roy is selling his car through a broker. Roy wants to get $3000 for himself, but the broker gets a commission of 10% of the selling price. What should the selling price be?

Show a complete solution to each problem.

45. Tennis. The distance from the baseline to the service line on a tennis court is 3 feet longer than the distance from the service line to the net. If the distance from the

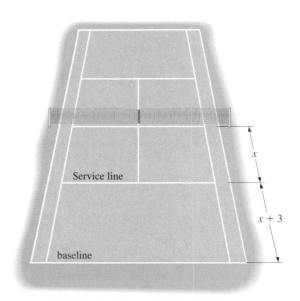

FIGURE FOR EXERCISE 45

baseline to the net is 39 feet, then what is the distance from the service line to the net?

46. *Mixed doubles.* The doubles court in tennis is one-third wider than the singles court. If the doubles court is 36 feet wide, then what is the width of the singles court?

47. *First Super Bowl.* In the first Super Bowl game in the Los Angeles Coliseum in 1967, the Green Bay Packers out-scored the Kansas City Chiefs by 25 points. If 45 points were scored in that game, then what was the final score?

48. *Toy sales.* In 1998 Toys "R" Us and Wal-Mart together held 36% of the toy market share (*Fortune,* June 1, 1998, www.fortune.com). If the market share for Toys "R" Us was 4 percentage points higher than the market share for Wal-Mart, then what was the market share for each company?

49. *Blending coffee.* Mark blends $\frac{3}{4}$ of a pound of premium Brazilian coffee with $1\frac{1}{2}$ pounds of standard Colombian coffee. If the Brazilian coffee sells for $10 per pound and the Colombian coffee sells for $8 per pound, then what should the price per pound be for the blended coffee?

FIGURE FOR EXERCISE 49

50. *'Tis the seasoning.* Cheryl's Famous Pumpkin Pie Seasoning consists of a blend of cinnamon, nutmeg, and cloves. When Cheryl mixes up a batch, she uses 200 ounces of cinnamon, 100 ounces of nutmeg, and 100 ounces of cloves. If cinnamon sells for $1.80 per ounce, nutmeg sells for $1.60 per ounce, and cloves sell for $1.40 per ounce, what should be the price per ounce of the mixture?

51. *Health food mix.* Dried bananas sell for $0.80 per quarter-pound, and dried apricots sell for $1.00 per quarter-pound. How many pounds of apricots should be mixed with 10 pounds of bananas to get a mixture that sells for $0.95 per quarter-pound?

52. *Mixed nuts.* Cashews sell for $1.20 per quarter-pound, and Brazil nuts sell for $1.50 per quarter-pound. How many pounds of cashews should be mixed with 20 pounds of Brazil nuts to get a mix that sells for $1.30 per quarter-pound?

53. *Antifreeze mixture.* A mechanic finds that a car with a 20-quart radiator has a mixture containing 30% antifreeze in it. How much of this mixture would he have to drain out and replace with pure antifreeze to get a 50% antifreeze mixture?

54. *Increasing the percentage.* A mechanic has found that a car with a 16-quart radiator has a 40% antifreeze mixture in the radiator. She has on hand a 70% antifreeze solution. How much of the 40% solution would she have to replace with the 70% solution to get the solution in the radiator up to 50%?

55. *Profit.* The profit for General Electric was $12,735 million in 2001 (www.forbes.com). This figure represents an increase of 18.8% from the previous year. What was the profit in 2000?

56. *Market Value.* The market value for General Electric was $406,525 million in 2001 (www.forbes.com). This figure represents a 6.3% decrease from the previous year. What was the market value in 2000?

57. *Dividing the estate.* Uncle Albert's estate is to be divided among his three nephews. The will specifies that Daniel receive one-half of the amount that Brian receives and that Raymond receive $1000 less than one-third of the amount that Brian receives. If the estate amounts to $25,400, then how much does each inherit?

58. *Mary's assets.* Mary Hall's will specifies that her lawyer is to liquidate her assets and divide the proceeds among her three sisters. Lena's share is to be one-half of Lisa's, and Lisa's share is to be one-half of Lauren's. If the lawyer has agreed to a fee that is equal to 10% of the largest share and the proceeds amount to $164,428, then how much does each person get?

59. *Missing integers.* If the larger of two consecutive integers is subtracted from twice the smaller integer, then the result is 21. Find the integers.

60. *Really odd integers.* If the smaller of two consecutive odd integers is subtracted from twice the larger one, then the result is 13. Find the integers.

61. *Highway miles.* Berenice and Jarrett drive a rig for Continental Freightways. In one day Berenice averaged 50 mph and Jarrett averaged 56 mph, but Berenice drove for two more hours than Jarrett. If together they covered 683 miles, then for how many hours did Berenice drive?

62. *Spring break.* Fernell and Dabney shared the driving to Florida for spring break. Fernell averaged 50 mph, and Dabney averaged 64 mph. If Fernell drove for 3 hours longer than Dabney but covered 18 miles less than Dabney, then for how many hours did Fernell drive?

63. *Stacy's square.* Stacy has 70 meters of fencing and plans to make a square pen. In one side she is going to leave an opening that is one-half the length of the side. If she uses all 70 meters of fencing, how large can the square be?

64. *Shawn's shed.* Shawn is building a tool shed with a square foundation and has enough siding to cover 32 linear feet of walls. If he leaves a 4-foot space for a door, then what size foundation would use up all of his siding?

FIGURE FOR EXERCISE 64

65. *Splitting investments.* Joan had $3000 to invest. She invested part of it in an investment paying 8% and the remainder in an investment paying 10%. If the total income on these investments was $290, then how much did she invest at each rate?

66. *Financial independence.* Dorothy had $8000 to invest. She invested part of it in an investment paying 6% and the rest in an investment paying 9%. If the total income from these investments was $690, then how much did she invest at each rate?

67. *Alcohol solutions.* Amy has two solutions available in the laboratory, one with 5% alcohol and the other with 10% alcohol. How much of each should she mix together to obtain 5 gallons of an 8% solution?

68. *Alcohol and water.* Joy has a solution containing 12% alcohol. How much of this solution and how much water must she use to get 6 liters of a solution containing 10% alcohol?

69. *Chance meeting.* In 6 years Todd will be twice as old as Darla was when they met 6 years ago. If their ages total 78 years, then how old are they now?

70. *Centennial Plumbing Company.* The three Hoffman brothers advertise that together they have a century of plumbing experience. Bart has twice the experience of Al, and in 3 years Carl will have twice the experience that Al had a year ago. How many years of experience does each of them have?

In This Section

- Inequality Symbols
- Interval Notation and Graphs
- Solving Linear Inequalities
- Applications

2.4 INEQUALITIES

An equation is a statement that indicates that two algebraic expressions are equal. An **inequality** is a statement that indicates that two algebraic expressions are not equal in a specific way, one expression being greater than or less than the other.

Inequality Symbols

The inequality symbols that we will be using are listed along with their meanings in the box.

Inequality Symbols

Symbol	Meaning
$<$	Is less than
$\leq$	Is less than or equal to
$>$	Is greater than
$\geq$	Is greater than or equal to

It is clear that 5 is less than 10, but how do we compare -5 and -10? If we think of negative numbers as debts, we would say that -10 is the larger debt. However,

Helpful Hint

A good way to learn inequality symbols is to notice that the inequality symbol always points at the smaller number. An inequality symbol can be read in either direction. For example, we can read $-4 < x$ as "-4 is less than x" or as "x is greater than -4." It is usually easier to understand an inequality if you read the variable first.

in algebra the size of a number is determined only by its position on the number line. For two numbers a and b we say that a *is less than* b if and only if a is to the *left* of b on the number line. To compare -5 and -10, we locate each point on the number line in Fig. 2.6. Because -10 is to the left of -5 on the number line, we say that -10 is less than -5. In symbols,

$$-10 < -5.$$

FIGURE 2.6

We say that a is greater than b if and only if a is to the *right* of b on the number line. Thus we can also write

$$-5 > -10.$$

The statement $a \le b$ is true if a is less than b or if a is equal to b. The statement $a \ge b$ is true if a is greater than b or if a equals b. For example, the statement $3 \le 5$ is true, and so is the statement $5 \le 5$.

EXAMPLE   1

Inequalities

Determine whether each statement is true or false.

a) $-5 < 3$ **b)** $-9 > -6$

c) $-3 \le 2$ **d)** $4 \ge 4$

Calculator Close-Up

We can use a calculator to check whether an inequality is satisfied in the same manner that we check equations. The calculator returns a 1 if the inequality is correct or a 0 if it is not correct.

```
-5<3
              1
-9>-6
              0
-3≤2
              1
```

Solution

a) The statement $-5 < 3$ is true because -5 is to the left of 3 on the number line. In fact, any negative number is less than any positive number.

b) The statement $-9 > -6$ is false because -9 lies to the left of -6.

c) The statement $-3 \le 2$ is true because -3 is less than 2.

d) The statement $4 \ge 4$ is true because $4 = 4$ is true.   ■

Interval Notation and Graphs

If an inequality involves a variable, then which real numbers can be used in place of the variable to obtain a correct statement? The set of all such numbers is the **solution set** to the inequality. For example, $x < 3$ is correct if x is replaced by any number that lies to the left of 3 on the number line:

$$1.5 < 3, \qquad 0 < 3, \qquad \text{and} \qquad -2 < 3$$

Using interval notation from Section 1.2, the solution set to $x < 3$ is the interval of real numbers $(-\infty, 3)$. The graph of the solution set or the graph of $x < 3$ is shown in Fig. 2.7.

FIGURE 2.7

An inequality such as $x \geq 1$ is satisfied by 1 and any real number that lies to the right of 1 on the number line. So the solution set to $x \geq 1$ is the interval $[1, \infty)$. Its graph is shown in Fig. 2.8.

FIGURE 2.8

The solution set and graph for each of the four basic inequalities are given in the box. Note that a bracket indicates that a number is included in the solution set and a parenthesis indicates that a number is not included.

Basic Interval Notation (*k* any real number)		
Inequality	**Solution Set with Interval Notation**	**Graph**
$x > k$	(k, ∞)	
$x \geq k$	$[k, \infty)$	
$x < k$	$(-\infty, k)$	
$x \leq k$	$(-\infty, k]$	

E X A M P L E 2

Interval notation and graphs

Write the solution set to each inequality in interval notation and graph it.

a) $x > -5$ **b)** $x \leq 2$

Solution

a) Every real number to the right of -5 satisfies $x > -5$. So the solution set is the interval $(-5, \infty)$. The graph is shown in Fig. 2.9.

FIGURE 2.9

b) The inequality $x \leq 2$ is satisfied by 2 and every real number to the left of 2. So the solution set is $(-\infty, 2]$. The graph is in Fig. 2.10.

FIGURE 2.10

Solving Linear Inequalities

In Section 2.1 we defined a linear equation as an equation of the form $ax + b = 0$. If we replace the equality symbol in a linear equation with an inequality symbol, we have a linear inequality.

Linear Inequality

A **linear inequality** in one variable x is any inequality of the form $ax + b < 0$, where a and b are real numbers, with $a \neq 0$. In place of $<$ we may also use $\leq$, $>$, or $\geq$.

Inequalities that can be *rewritten* in the form of a linear inequality are also called linear inequalities.

Before we solve linear inequalities, let's examine the results of performing various operations on each side of an inequality. If we start with the inequality $2 < 6$ and add 2 to each side, we get the true statement $4 < 8$. Examine the results in the table shown here.

Perform these operations on each side of $2 < 6$:

	Add 2	Subtract 2	Multiply by 2	Divide by 2
Resulting inequality	$4 < 8$	$0 < 4$	$4 < 12$	$1 < 3$

All of the resulting inequalities are correct. However, if we perform operations on each side of $2 < 6$ using -2, the situation is not as simple. For example, $-2 \cdot 2 = -4$ and $-2 \cdot 6 = -12$, but -4 is greater than -12. To get a correct inequality when each side is multiplied or divided by -2, we must reverse the inequality symbol, as shown in this table.

Perform these operations on each side of $2 < 6$:

	Add -2	Subtract -2	Multiply by -2	Divide by -2
Resulting inequality	$0 < 4$	$4 < 8$	$-4 > -12$	$-1 > -3$

Inequality reverses

These examples illustrate the properties that we use for solving inequalities.

Properties of Inequality

Addition Property of Inequality
If the same number is added to both sides of an inequality, then the solution set to the inequality is unchanged.

Multiplication Property of Inequality
If both sides of an inequality are multiplied by the same *positive number,* then the solution set to the inequality is unchanged.
If both sides of an inequality are multiplied by the same *negative number* and *the inequality symbol is reversed*, then the solution set to the inequality is unchanged.

Because subtraction is defined in terms of addition, the addition property of inequality also allows us to subtract the same number from both sides. Because division is defined in terms of multiplication, the multiplication property of inequality also allows us to divide both sides by the same nonzero number *as long as we reverse the inequality symbol when dividing by a negative number.*

Equivalent inequalities are inequalities with the same solution set. We find the solution to a linear inequality by using the properties to convert it into an equivalent inequality with an obvious solution set, just as we do when solving equations.

E X A M P L E   3

Solving inequalities

Solve each inequality. State the solution set in interval notation and graph it.

a) $2x - 7 < -1$ **b)** $5 - 3x < 11$

Solution

a) We proceed exactly as we do when solving equations:

$$2x - 7 < -1 \quad \text{Original inequality}$$
$$2x < 6 \quad \text{Add 7 to each side.}$$
$$x < 3 \quad \text{Divide each side by 2.}$$

The solution set is the interval $(-\infty, 3)$. The graph is shown in Fig. 2.11.

FIGURE 2.11

b) We divide by a negative number to solve this inequality.

$$5 - 3x < 11 \quad \text{Original inequality}$$
$$-3x < 6 \quad \text{Subtract 5 from each side.}$$
$$x > -2 \quad \text{Divide each side by } -3 \text{ and reverse the inequality symbol.}$$

The solution set is the interval $(-2, \infty)$. The graph is shown in Fig. 2.12. ■

FIGURE 2.12

Calculator Close-Up

To check the solution to Example 3, press the Y = key and let $y_1 = 5 - 3x$.

Press TBLSET to set the starting point for x and the distance between the x-values.

Now press TABLE and scroll through values of x until y_1 gets smaller than 11.

```
Plot1 Plot2 Plot3
\Y1∎5-3X
\Y2=
\Y3=
\Y4=
\Y5=
\Y6=
\Y7=
```

```
TABLE SETUP
 TblStart=0
 ∆Tbl=1
Indpnt: Auto Ask
Depend: Auto Ask
```

```
  X  │ Y1
─────┼─────
 -4  │ 17
 -3  │ 14
 -2  │ 11
 -1  │ 8
  0  │ 5
  1  │ 2
  2  │ -1
Y1∎5-3X
```

This table supports the conclusion that if $x > -2$, then $5 - 3x < 11$.

E X A M P L E   4

Solving inequalities

Solve $\dfrac{8 + 3x}{-5} \geq -4$. State and graph the solution set.

Solution

$$\frac{8 + 3x}{-5} \geq -4 \quad \text{Original inequality}$$

$$-5\left(\frac{8 + 3x}{-5}\right) \leq -5(-4) \quad \text{Multiply each side by } -5 \text{ and reverse the inequality symbol.}$$

$$8 + 3x \leq 20 \quad \text{Simplify.}$$
$$3x \leq 12 \quad \text{Subtract 8 from each side.}$$
$$x \leq 4 \quad \text{Divide each side by 3.}$$

The solution set is $(-\infty, 4]$, and its graph is shown in Fig. 2.13.

F I G U R E   2 . 1 3

E X A M P L E   5

An inequality with fractions

Solve $\frac{1}{2}x - \frac{2}{3} \leq x + \frac{4}{3}$. State and graph the solution set.

Solution

First multiply each side of the inequality by 6, the LCD:

$$\frac{1}{2}x - \frac{2}{3} \leq x + \frac{4}{3} \qquad \text{Original inequality}$$

$$6\left(\frac{1}{2}x - \frac{2}{3}\right) \leq 6\left(x + \frac{4}{3}\right) \qquad \text{Multiplying by positive 6 does not reverse the inequality.}$$

$$3x - 4 \leq 6x + 8 \qquad \text{Distributive property}$$

$$3x \leq 6x + 12 \qquad \text{Add 4 to each side.}$$

$$-3x \leq 12 \qquad \text{Subtract } 6x \text{ from each side.}$$

$$x \geq -4 \qquad \text{Divide each side by } -3 \text{ and reverse the inequality.}$$

The solution set is the interval $[-4, \infty)$. Its graph is shown in Fig. 2.14.

F I G U R E   2 . 1 4

In Example 6 we see an inequality that is satisfied by all real numbers and one that has no solution.

E X A M P L E   6

All or nothing

Solve each inequality and graph the solution set.

a) $6 - 4x < -4x + 7$ **b)** $2(4x - 5) \geq 4(2x - 1)$

Solution

a) Adding $4x$ to each side will greatly simplify the inequality:

$$6 - 4x < -4x + 7 \qquad \text{Original inequality}$$

$$6 < 7 \qquad \text{Add } 4x \text{ to each side.}$$

Since $6 < 7$ is correct no matter what real number is used in place of x, the solution set is the set of all real numbers $(-\infty, \infty)$. Its graph is shown in Fig. 2.15.

b) Start by simplifying each side of the inequality.

$$2(4x - 5) \geq 4(2x - 1) \qquad \text{Original inequality}$$

$$8x - 10 \geq 8x - 4 \qquad \text{Distributive property}$$

$$-10 \geq -4 \qquad \text{Subtract } 8x \text{ from each side.}$$

Since $-10 \geq -4$ is false no matter what real number is used in place of x, the solution set is the empty set $\varnothing$ and there is no graph to draw.

Helpful Hint

Notice that we use the same strategy for solving inequalities as we do for solving equations. But we must remember to reverse the inequality symbol when we multiply or divide by a negative number. For inequalities it is usually best to isolate the variable on the left-hand side.

F I G U R E   2 . 1 5

Applications

There are a variety of ways to express inequalities verbally. Some of the most common are illustrated in this table.

Verbal Sentence	Inequality
x is greater than 6; x is more than 6	$x > 6$
y is smaller than 0; y is less than 0	$y < 0$
w is at least 9; w is not less than 9	$w \geq 9$
m is at most 7; m is not greater than 7	$m \leq 7$

EXAMPLE 7   **Writing inequalities**

Identify the variable and write an inequality that describes the situation.

a) Chris paid more than $200 for a suit.

b) A candidate for president must be at least 35 years old.

c) The capacity of an elevator is at most 1500 pounds.

d) The company must hire no fewer than 10 programmers.

Solution

a) If c is the cost of the suit in dollars, then $c > 200$.

b) If a is the age of the candidate in years, then $a \geq 35$.

c) If x is the capacity of the elevator in pounds, then $x \leq 1500$.

d) If n represents the number of programmers and n is not less than 10, then $n \geq 10$. ■

In Example 7(d) we knew that n was not less than 10. So there were exactly two other possibilities: n was greater than 10 or equal to 10. The fact that there are only three possible ways to position two real numbers on a number line is called the **trichotomy property.**

Trichotomy Property

For any two real numbers a and b, exactly one of these is true:

$$a < b, \quad a = b, \quad \text{or} \quad a > b$$

We follow the same steps to solve problems involving inequalities as we do to solve problems involving equations.

EXAMPLE 8   **Price range**

Lois plans to spend less than $500 on an electric dryer, including the 9% sales tax and a $64 setup charge. In what range is the selling price of the dryer that she can afford?

Solution

If we let x represent the selling price in dollars for the dryer, then the amount of sales tax is $0.09x$. Because her total cost must be less than $500, we can write the following inequality:

$$x + 0.09x + 64 < 500$$
$$1.09x < 436 \quad \text{Subtract 64 from each side.}$$
$$x < \frac{436}{1.09} \quad \text{Divide each side by 1.09.}$$
$$x < 400$$

The selling price of the dryer must be less than \$400. ■

Note that if we had written the equation $x + 0.09x + 64 = 500$ for the last example, we would have gotten $x = 400$. We could then have concluded that the selling price must be less than \$400. This would certainly solve the problem, but it would not illustrate the use of inequalities. The original problem describes an inequality, and we should solve it as an inequality.

E X A M P L E   9

Paying off the mortgage

Tessie owns a piece of land on which she owes \$12,760 to a bank. She wants to sell the land for enough money to at least pay off the mortgage. The real estate agent gets 6% of the selling price, and her city has a \$400 real estate transfer tax paid by the seller. What should the range of the selling price be for Tessie to get at least enough money to pay off her mortgage?

Solution

If x is the selling price in dollars, then the commission is $0.06x$. We can write an inequality expressing the fact that the selling price minus the real estate commission minus the \$400 tax must be at least \$12,760:

$$x - 0.06x - 400 \geq 12{,}760$$
$$0.94x - 400 \geq 12{,}760 \quad 1 - 0.06 = 0.94$$
$$0.94x \geq 13{,}160 \quad \text{Add 400 to each side.}$$
$$x \geq \frac{13{,}160}{0.94} \quad \text{Divide each side by 0.94.}$$
$$x \geq 14{,}000$$

The selling price must be at least \$14,000 for Tessie to pay off the mortgage. ■

WARM-UPS

True or false? Explain your answer.

1. $0 < 0$ **2.** $-300 > -2$ **3.** $-60 \leq -60$

4. The inequality $6 < x$ is equivalent to $x < 6$.

5. The inequality $-2x < 10$ is equivalent to $x < -5$.

6. The solution set to $3x \geq -12$ is $(-\infty, -4]$.

7. The solution set to $-x > 4$ is $(-\infty, -4)$.

8. If x is no larger than 8, then $x \leq 8$.

9. If m is any real number, then exactly one of these is true: $m < 0$, $m = 0$, or $m > 0$.

10. The number -2 is a member of the solution set to the inequality $3 - 4x \leq 11$.

2.4 EXERCISES

Reading and Writing *After reading this section, write out the answers to these questions. Use complete sentences.*

1. What is an inequality?

2. What symbols are used to express inequality?

3. What does it mean when we say that a is less than b?

4. What is a linear inequality?

5. How does solving linear inequalities differ from solving linear equations?

6. What verbal phrases are used to indicate an inequality?

Determine whether each inequality is true or false. See Example 1.

7. $-3 < -9$

8. $-8 > -7$

9. $0 \le 8$

10. $-6 \ge -8$

11. $(-3)20 > (-3)40$

12. $(-1)(-3) < (-1)(5)$

13. $9 - (-3) \le 12$

14. $(-4)(-5) + 2 \ge 21$

Determine whether each inequality is satisfied by the given number.

15. $2x - 4 < 8, -3$

16. $5 - 3x > -1, 6$

17. $2x - 3 \le 3x - 9, 5$

18. $6 - 3x \ge 10 - 2x, -4$

19. $5 - x < 4 - 2x, -1$

20. $3x - 7 \ge 3x - 10, 9$

Write the solution set in interval notation and graph it. See Example 2.

21. $x \le -1$

22. $x \ge -7$

23. $x > 20$

24. $x < 30$

25. $3 \le x$

26. $-2 > x$

27. $x < 2.3$

28. $x \le 4.5$

Fill in the blank with an inequality symbol so that the two statements are equivalent.

29. $x + 5 > 12$
   x ___ 7

30. $2x - 3 \le -4$
   $2x$ ___ -1

31. $-x < 6$
   x ___ -6

32. $-5 \ge -x$
   5 ___ x

33. $-2x \ge 8$
   x ___ -4

34. $-5x > -10$
   x ___ 2

35. $4 < x$
   x ___ 4

36. $-9 \le -x$
   x ___ 9

Solve each of these inequalities. Express the solution set in interval notation and graph it. See Examples 3–5.

37. $7x > -14$

38. $4x \le -8$

39. $-3x \le 12$

40. $-2x > -6$

41. $2x - 3 > 7$

42. $3x - 2 < 6$

43. $18 \ge 3 - 5x$

44. $19 \le 5 - 4x$

45. $\dfrac{x - 3}{-5} < -2$

46. $\dfrac{2x - 3}{4} > 6$

47. $2 \geq \dfrac{5 - 3x}{4}$

48. $-1 \leq \dfrac{7 - 5x}{-2}$

49. $3 - \dfrac{1}{4}x \geq 2$

50. $5 - \dfrac{1}{3}x > 2$

51. $\dfrac{1}{4}x - \dfrac{1}{2} < \dfrac{1}{2}x - \dfrac{2}{3}$

52. $\dfrac{1}{3}x - \dfrac{1}{6} < \dfrac{1}{6}x - \dfrac{1}{2}$

53. $\dfrac{y - 3}{2} > \dfrac{1}{2} - \dfrac{y - 5}{4}$

54. $\dfrac{y - 1}{3} - \dfrac{y + 1}{5} > 1$

Solve each inequality and graph the solution set. See Example 6.

55. $3(x + 2) \leq 9 + 3x$

56. $2x + 3 > 2(x - 4)$

57. $-2(5x - 1) \leq -5(5 + 2x)$
58. $-4(2x - 5) \leq 2(6 - 4x)$
59. $3x - (4 - 2x) < 5 - (2 - 5x)$

60. $6 - (5 - 3x) > 7x - (3 + 4x)$

61. $\dfrac{1}{2}x + \dfrac{1}{4}x < \dfrac{1}{8}(6x - 4)$

62. $\dfrac{3}{8}x - \dfrac{1}{4}x < \dfrac{1}{6}\left(\dfrac{3}{4}x - 6\right)$

Identify the variable and write an inequality that describes each situation. See Example 7.
63. Tony is taller than 6 feet.

64. Glenda is under 60 years old.

65. Wilma makes less than $80,000 per year.

66. Bubba weighs over 80 pounds.

67. The maximum speed for the Concorde is 1450 miles per hour (mph).

68. The minimum speed on the freeway is 45 mph.

69. Julie can afford at most $400 per month.

70. Fred must have at least a 3.2 grade point average.

71. Burt is no taller than 5 feet.

72. Ernie cannot run faster than 10 mph.

73. Tina makes no more than $8.20 per hour.

74. Rita will not take less than $12,000 for the car.

Solve each problem by using an inequality. See Examples 8 and 9.
75. *Car shopping.* Jennifer is shopping for a new car. In addition to the price of the car, there is an 8% sales tax and a $172 title and license fee. If Jennifer decides that she will spend less than $10,000 total, then what is the price range for the car?
76. *Sewing machines.* Charles wants to buy a sewing machine in a city with a 10% sales tax. He has at most $700 to spend. In what price range should he look?

77. *Truck shopping.* Linda and Bob are shopping for a new truck in a city with a 9% sales tax. There is also an $80 title and license fee to pay. They want to get a good truck and plan to spend at least $10,000. What is the price range for the truck?

78. *DVD rental.* For $19.95 per month you can rent an unlimited number of DVD movies through an Internet rental service. You can rent the same DVDs at a local store for $3.98 each. How many movies would you have to rent per month for the Internet service to be the better deal?
79. *Declining birth rate.* The graph on the next page shows the number of births per 1000 women per year since 1980 in the United States (www.census.gov).
a) Has the number of births per 1000 women been increasing or decreasing since 1980?
b) The formula $B = -0.52n + 71.1$ can be used to approximate the number of births per 1000 women,

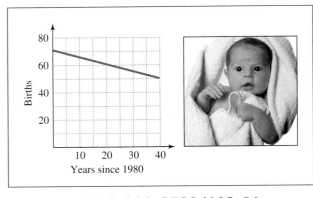

FIGURE FOR EXERCISE 79

Grading	Scale
90–100	A
80–89	B
70–79	C
60–69	D

TABLE FOR EXERCISES 81 AND 82

where n is the number of years since 1980. What is the first year in which the number of births will be less than 55?

80. Bachelor's degrees. The number of bachelor's degrees in thousands awarded in the United States can be approximated using the formula

$$B = 16.45n + 980.2,$$

where n is the number of years since 1985 (National Center for Education Statistics, www.nces.ed.gov). What is the first year in which the number of bachelor's degrees will exceed 1.5 million?

81. Weighted average. Professor Jorgenson gives only a midterm exam and a final exam. The semester average is computed by taking $\frac{1}{3}$ of the midterm exam score plus $\frac{2}{3}$ of the final exam score. The grade is determined from the semester average by using the grading scale given in the table. If Stanley scored only 56 on the midterm, then for what range of scores on the final exam would he get a C or better in the course?

82. C or better. Professor Brown counts her midterm as $\frac{2}{3}$ of the grade and her final as $\frac{1}{3}$ of the grade. Wilbert scored only 56 on the midterm. If Professor Brown also uses the grading scale given in the table, then what range of scores on the final exam would give Wilbert a C or better in the course?

83. Designer jeans. A pair of ordinary jeans at A-Mart costs $50 less than a pair of designer jeans at Enrico's. In fact, you can buy four pairs of A-Mart jeans for less than one pair of Enrico's jeans. What is the price range for a pair of A-Mart jeans?

84. United Express. Al and Rita both drive parcel delivery trucks for United Express. Al averages 20 mph less than Rita. In fact, Al is so slow that in 5 hours he covered fewer miles than Rita did in 3 hours. What are the possible values for Al's rate of speed?

GETTING MORE INVOLVED

85. Discussion. If 3 is added to every number in $(4, \infty)$, the resulting set is $(7, \infty)$. In each of the following cases, write the resulting set of numbers in interval notation. Explain your results.
  a) The number -6 is subtracted from every number in $[2, \infty)$.
  b) Every number in $(-\infty, -3)$ is multiplied by 2.
  c) Every number in $(8, \infty)$ is divided by 4.
  d) Every number in $(6, \infty)$ is multiplied by -2.
  e) Every number in $(-\infty, -10)$ is divided by -5.

86. Writing. Explain why saying that x is *at least* 9 is equivalent to saying that x is *greater than or equal to* 9. Explain why saying that x is *at most* 5 is equivalent to saying that x is *less than or equal to* 5.

2.5   COMPOUND INEQUALITIES

In This Section

• Basics

• Graphing the Solution Set

• Applications

In this section we will use the ideas of union and intersection from Chapter 1 along with our knowledge of inequalities from Section 2.4 to work with compound inequalities.

Basics

The inequalities that we studied in Section 2.4 are referred to as **simple inequalities.** If we join two simple inequalities with the connective "and" or the connective "or," we get a **compound inequality.** A compound inequality using the connective "and" is true if and only if *both* simple inequalities are true.

E X A M P L E   1

Compound inequalities using the connective "and"

Determine whether each compound inequality is true.

a) $3 > 2$ and $3 < 5$

b) $6 > 2$ and $6 < 5$

Solution

a) The compound inequality is true because $3 > 2$ is true and $3 < 5$ is true.

b) The compound inequality is false because $6 < 5$ is false.   ■

A compound inequality using the connective "or" is true if one or the other or both of the simple inequalities are true. It is false only if both simple inequalities are false.

E X A M P L E   2

Compound inequalities using the connective "or"

Determine whether each compound inequality is true.

a) $2 < 3$ or $2 > 7$

b) $4 < 3$ or $4 \geq 7$

Helpful Hint

There is a big difference between "and" and "or." To get money from an automatic teller you must have a bank card *and* know a secret number (PIN). There would be a lot of problems if you could get money by having a bank card *or* knowing a PIN.

Solution

a) The compound inequality is true because $2 < 3$ is true.

b) The compound inequality is false because both $4 < 3$ and $4 \geq 7$ are false.   ■

If a compound inequality involves a variable, then we are interested in the solution set to the inequality. The solution set to an "and" inequality consists of all numbers that satisfy both simple inequalities, whereas the solution set to an "or" inequality consists of all numbers that satisfy at least one of the simple inequalities.

E X A M P L E   3

Solutions of compound inequalities

Determine whether 5 satisfies each compound inequality.

a) $x < 6$ and $x < 9$

b) $2x - 9 \leq 5$ or $-4x \geq -12$

Solution

a) Because $5 < 6$ and $5 < 9$ are both true, 5 satisfies the compound inequality.

b) Because $2 \cdot 5 - 9 \leq 5$ is true, it does not matter that $-4 \cdot 5 \geq -12$ is false. So 5 satisfies the compound inequality.   ■

Graphing the Solution Set

The solution set to a compound inequality using the connective "and" is the intersection of the two solutions sets, because it consists of all real numbers that satisfy both simple inequalities.

E X A M P L E   4

Graphing compound inequalities

Graph the solution set to the compound inequality $x > 2$ and $x < 5$.

Solution

First sketch the graph of $x > 2$ and then the graph of $x < 5$, as shown in the top two number lines in Fig. 2.16. The intersection of these two solution sets is the portion of the number line that is shaded on both graphs, just the part between 2 and 5, not including the endpoints. So the solution set is the interval $(2, 5)$ and its graph is shown at the bottom of Fig. 2.16.

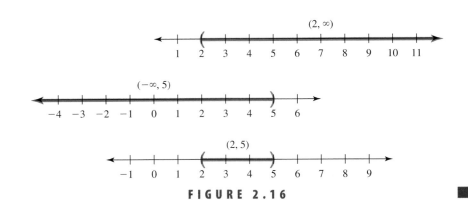

FIGURE 2.16

The solution set to a compound inequality using the connective "or" is the union of the two solution sets, because it consists of all real numbers that satisfy one or the other or both simple inequalities.

E X A M P L E   5

Graphing compound inequalities

Graph the solution set to the compound inequality $x > 4$ or $x < -1$.

Solution

First graph the solution sets to the simple inequalities as shown in Fig. 2.17. The union of these two intervals is shown at the bottom of Fig. 2.17. Since the union does not simplify to a single interval, the solution set is written using the symbol for union as $(-\infty, -1) \cup (4, \infty)$.

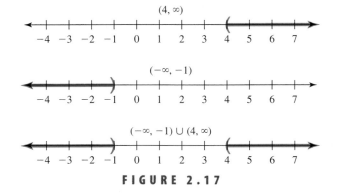

FIGURE 2.17

CAUTION   When graphing the intersection of two simple inequalities, do not draw too much. For the intersection, graph only numbers that satisfy *both* inequalities. Omit numbers that satisfy one but not the other inequality. Graphing a union is usually easier because we can simply draw both solution sets on the same number line.

It is not always necessary to graph the solution set to each simple inequality before graphing the solution set to the compound inequality. We can save time and work if we learn to think of the two preliminary graphs but draw only the final one.

E X A M P L E   6

Overlapping intervals

Sketch the graph and write the solution set in interval notation to each compound inequality.

a) $x < 3$ and $x < 5$

b) $x > 4$ or $x > 0$

Solution

a) To graph $x < 3$ and $x < 5$, we shade only the numbers that are both less than 3 and less than 5. So numbers between 3 and 5 are not shaded in Fig. 2.18. The compound inequality $x < 3$ and $x < 5$ is equivalent to the simple inequality $x < 3$. The solution set can be written as $(-\infty, 3)$.

FIGURE 2.18

b) To graph $x > 4$ or $x > 0$, we shade both regions on the same number line as shown in Fig. 2.19. The compound inequality $x > 4$ or $x > 0$ is equivalent to the simple inequality $x > 0$. The solution set is $(0, \infty)$.

FIGURE 2.19

Example 7 shows a compound inequality that has no solution and one that is satisfied by every real number.

E X A M P L E   7

All or nothing

Sketch the graph and write the solution set in interval notation to each compound inequality.

a) $x < 2$ and $x > 6$

b) $x < 3$ or $x > 1$

Solution

a) A number satisfies $x < 2$ and $x > 6$ if it is both less than 2 *and* greater than 6. There are no such numbers. The solution set is the empty set, $\varnothing$.

b) To graph $x < 3$ or $x > 1$, we shade both regions on the same number line as shown in Fig. 2.20. Since the two regions cover the entire line, the solution set is the set of all real numbers $(-\infty, \infty)$.

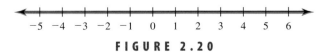

FIGURE 2.20

If we start with a more complicated compound inequality, we first simplify each part of the compound inequality and then find the union or intersection.

EXAMPLE 8

Calculator Close-Up

To check Example 8, press Y= and let $y_1 = x + 2$ and $y_2 = x - 6$. Now scroll through a table of values for y_1 and y_2. From the table you can see that y_1 is greater than 3 and y_2 is less than 7 precisely when x is between 1 and 13.

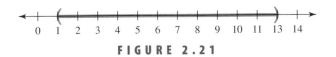

Intersection

Solve $x + 2 > 3$ and $x - 6 < 7$. Graph the solution set.

Solution

First simplify each simple inequality:

$$x + 2 - 2 > 3 - 2 \quad \text{and} \quad x - 6 + 6 < 7 + 6$$
$$x > 1 \qquad\qquad \text{and} \qquad\qquad x < 13$$

The intersection of these two solution sets is the set of numbers between (but not including) 1 and 13. Its graph is shown in Fig. 2.21. The solution set is written in interval notation as $(1, 13)$.

FIGURE 2.21   ∎

EXAMPLE 9

Calculator Close-Up

To check Example 9, press Y= and let $y_1 = 5 - 7x$ and $y_2 = 3x - 2$. Now scroll through a table of values for y_1 and y_2. From the table you can see that either $y_1 \geq 12$ or $y_2 < 7$ is true for $x < 3$. Note also that for $x \geq 3$ both $y_1 \geq 12$ and $y_2 < 7$ are incorrect. The table supports the conclusion of Example 9.

Union

Graph the solution set to the inequality

$$5 - 7x \geq 12 \qquad \text{or} \qquad 3x - 2 < 7.$$

Solution

First solve each of the simple inequalities:

$$5 - 7x - 5 \geq 12 - 5 \qquad \text{or} \qquad 3x - 2 + 2 < 7 + 2$$
$$-7x \geq 7 \qquad\qquad \text{or} \qquad\qquad 3x < 9$$
$$x \leq -1 \qquad\qquad \text{or} \qquad\qquad x < 3$$

The union of the two solution intervals is $(-\infty, 3)$. The graph is shown in Fig. 2.22.

FIGURE 2.22   ∎

An inequality may be read from left to right or from right to left. Consider the inequality $1 < x$. If we read it in the usual way, we say, "1 is less than x." The meaning is clearer if we read the variable first. Reading from right to left, we say, "x is greater than 1."

Another notation is commonly used for the compound inequality

$$x > 1 \qquad \text{and} \qquad x < 13.$$

This compound inequality can also be written as

$$1 < x < 13.$$

Reading from left to right, we read $1 < x < 13$ as "1 is less than x is less than 13." The meaning of this inequality is clearer if we read the variable first and read the first inequality symbol from right to left. Reading the variable first, $1 < x < 13$ is read as "x is greater than 1 and less than 13." So x is between 1 and 13, and reading x first makes it clear.

CAUTION   We write $a < x < b$ only if $a < b$, and we write $a > x > b$ only if $a > b$. Similar rules hold for $\leq$ and $\geq$. So $4 < x < 9$ and $-6 \geq x \geq -8$ are correct uses of this notation, but $5 < x < 2$ is not correct. Also, the inequalities should *not* point in opposite directions as in $5 < x > 7$.

E X A M P L E   1 0

Another notation

Solve the inequality and graph the solution set:

$$-2 \leq 2x - 3 < 7$$

Solution

This inequality could be written as the compound inequality

$$2x - 3 \geq -2 \qquad \text{and} \qquad 2x - 3 < 7.$$

However, there is no need to rewrite the inequality because we can solve it in its original form.

$$-2 + 3 \leq 2x - 3 + 3 < 7 + 3 \quad \text{\small Add 3 to each part.}$$
$$1 \leq 2x < 10$$
$$\frac{1}{2} \leq \frac{2x}{2} < \frac{10}{2} \qquad \text{\small Divide each part by 2.}$$
$$\frac{1}{2} \leq x < 5$$

The solution set is $\left[\frac{1}{2}, 5\right)$, and its graph is shown in Fig. 2.23.

F I G U R E   2 . 2 3

Calculator Close-Up

Do not use a table on your calculator as a method for solving an inequality. Use a table to check your algebraic solution and you will get a better understanding of inequalities.

E X A M P L E   1 1

Solving a compound inequality

Solve the inequality $-1 < 3 - 2x < 9$ and graph the solution set.

Solution

$$-1 - 3 < 3 - 2x - 3 < 9 - 3 \quad \text{\small Subtract 3 from each part of the inequality.}$$
$$-4 < -2x < 6$$
$$2 > x > -3 \qquad \text{\small Divide each part by } -2 \text{ and reverse both inequality symbols.}$$
$$-3 < x < 2 \qquad \text{\small Rewrite the inequality with the smallest number on the left.}$$

The solution set is $(-3, 2)$, and its graph is shown in Fig. 2.24.

F I G U R E   2 . 2 4

Calculator Close-Up

Let $y_1 = 3 - 2x$ and make a table. Scroll through the table to see that y_1 is between -1 and 9 when x is between -3 and 2. The table supports the conclusion of Example 11.

Applications

When final exams are approaching, students are often interested in finding the final exam score that would give them a certain grade for a course.

EXAMPLE 12

Final exam scores

Fiana made a score of 76 on her midterm exam. For her to get a B in the course, the average of her midterm exam and final exam must be between 80 and 89 inclusive. What possible scores on the final exam would give Fiana a B in the course?

Solution

Let x represent her final exam score. Between 80 and 89 inclusive means that an average between 80 and 89 as well as an average of exactly 80 or 89 will get a B. So the average of the two scores must be greater than or equal to 80 and less than or equal to 89.

$$80 \leq \frac{x + 76}{2} \leq 89$$
$$160 \leq x + 76 \leq 178 \quad \text{Multiply by 2.}$$
$$160 - 76 \leq x \leq 178 - 76 \quad \text{Subtract 76.}$$
$$84 \leq x \leq 102$$

If Fiana scores between 84 and 102 inclusive, she will get a B in the course. ∎

WARM-UPS

True or false? Explain your answer.

1. $3 < 5$ and $3 \leq 10$
2. $3 < 5$ or $3 < 10$
3. $3 > 5$ and $3 < 10$
4. $3 \geq 5$ or $3 \leq 10$
5. $4 < 8$ and $4 > 2$
6. $4 < 8$ or $4 > 2$
7. $-3 < 0 < -2$
8. $(3, \infty) \cap (8, \infty) = (8, \infty)$
9. $(3, \infty) \cup [8, \infty) = [8, \infty)$
10. $(-2, \infty) \cap (-\infty, 9) = (-2, 9)$

2.5 EXERCISES

Reading and Writing *After reading this section, write out the answers to these questions. Use complete sentences.*

1. What is a compound inequality?

2. When is a compound inequality using "and" true?

3. When is a compound inequality using "or" true?

4. How do we solve compound inequalities?

5. What is the meaning of $a < b < c$?

6. What is the meaning of $5 < x > 7$?

Determine whether each compound inequality is true. See Examples 1 and 2.

7. $-6 < 5$ and $-6 > -3$
8. $3 < 5$ or $0 < -3$
9. $4 \leq 4$ and $-4 \leq 0$
10. $1 < 5$ and $1 > -3$
11. $6 < 5$ or $-4 > -3$
12. $4 \leq -4$ or $0 \leq 0$

Determine whether -4 satisfies each compound inequality. See Example 3.

13. $x < 5$ and $x > -3$
14. $x < 5$ or $x > -3$

15. $x - 3 \geq -7$ or $x + 1 > 1$

16. $2x \leq -8$ and $5x \leq 0$

17. $2x - 1 < -7$ or $-2x > 18$

18. $-3x > 0$ and $3x - 4 < 11$

Graph the solution set to each compound inequality. See Examples 4–7.

19. $x > -1$ and $x < 4$

20. $x \leq 3$ and $x \leq 0$

21. $x \geq 2$ or $x \geq 5$

22. $x < -1$ or $x < 3$

23. $x \leq 6$ or $x > -2$

24. $x > -2$ and $x \leq 4$

25. $x \leq 6$ and $x > 9$

26. $x < 7$ or $x > 0$

27. $x \leq 6$ or $x > 9$

28. $x \geq 4$ and $x \leq -4$

29. $x \geq 6$ and $x \leq 1$

30. $x > 3$ or $x < -3$

Solve each compound inequality. Write the solution set using interval notation and graph it. See Examples 8 and 9.

31. $x - 3 > 7$ or $3 - x > 2$

32. $x - 5 > 6$ or $2 - x > 4$

33. $3 < x$ and $1 + x > 10$

34. $-0.3x < 9$ and $0.2x > 2$

35. $\frac{1}{2}x > 5$ or $-\frac{1}{3}x < 2$

36. $5 < x$ or $3 - \frac{1}{2}x < 7$

37. $2x - 3 \leq 5$ and $x - 1 > 0$

38. $\frac{3}{4}x < 9$ and $-\frac{1}{3}x \leq -15$

39. $\frac{1}{2}x - \frac{1}{3} \geq -\frac{1}{6}$ or $\frac{2}{7}x \leq \frac{1}{10}$

40. $\frac{1}{4}x - \frac{1}{3} > -\frac{1}{5}$ and $\frac{1}{2}x < 2$

41. $0.5x < 2$ and $-0.6x < -3$

42. $0.3x < 0.6$ or $0.05x > -4$

Solve each compound inequality. Write the solution set in interval notation and graph it. See Examples 10 and 11.

43. $5 < 2x - 3 < 11$

44. $-2 < 3x + 1 < 10$

45. $-1 < 5 - 3x \leq 14$

46. $-1 \leq 3 - 2x < 11$

47. $-3 < \dfrac{3m + 1}{2} \leq 5$

48. $0 \leq \dfrac{3 - 2x}{2} < 5$

49. $-2 < \dfrac{1 - 3x}{-2} < 7$

50. $-3 < \dfrac{2x - 1}{3} < 7$

51. $3 \leq 3 - 5(x - 3) \leq 8$

52. $2 \leq 4 - \dfrac{1}{2}(x - 8) \leq 10$

Write each union or intersection of intervals as a single interval if possible.

53. $(2, \infty) \cup (4, \infty)$ **54.** $(-3, \infty) \cup (-6, \infty)$

55. $(-\infty, 5) \cap (-\infty, 9)$

56. $(-\infty, -2) \cap (-\infty, 1)$

57. $(-\infty, 4] \cap [2, \infty)$

58. $(-\infty, 8) \cap [3, \infty)$

59. $(-\infty, 5) \cup [-3, \infty)$

60. $(-\infty, -2] \cup (2, \infty)$

61. $(3, \infty) \cap (-\infty, 3]$

62. $[-4, \infty) \cap (-\infty, -6]$

63. $(3, 5) \cap [4, 8)$

64. $[-2, 4] \cap (0, 9]$

65. $[1, 4) \cup (2, 6]$

66. $[1, 3) \cup (0, 5)$

Write either a simple or a compound inequality that has the given graph as its solution set.

67.

68.

69.

70.

71.

72.

73.

74.

75.

76.

Solve each problem by using a compound inequality. See Example 12.

77. Aiming for a C. Professor Johnson gives only a midterm exam and a final exam. The semester average is computed by taking $\frac{1}{3}$ of the midterm exam score plus $\frac{2}{3}$ of the final exam score. To get a C, Beth must have a semester average between 70 and 79 inclusive. If Beth scored only 64 on the midterm, then for what range of scores on the final exam would Beth get a C?

78. Two tests only. Professor Davis counts his midterm as $\frac{2}{3}$ of the grade, and his final as $\frac{1}{3}$ of the grade. Jason scored only 64 on the midterm. What range of scores on the final exam would put Jason's average between 70 and 79 inclusive?

79. Keep on truckin'. Abdul is shopping for a new truck in a city with an 8% sales tax. There is also an $84 title and license fee to pay. He wants to get a good truck and plans to spend at least $12,000 but no more than $15,000. What is the price range for the truck?

80. Selling-price range. Renee wants to sell her car through a broker who charges a commission of 10% of the selling price. The book value of the car is $14,900, but Renee still owes $13,104 on it. Although the car is in only fair condition and will not sell for more than the book value, Renee must get enough to at least pay off the loan. What is the range of the selling price?

81. Hazardous to her health. Trying to break her smoking habit, Jane calculates that she smokes only three full cigarettes a day, one after each meal. The rest of the time she smokes on the run and smokes only half of the cigarette. She estimates that she smokes the equivalent of 5 to 12 cigarettes per day. How many times a day does she light up on the run?

82. Possible width. The length of a rectangle is 20 meters longer than the width. The perimeter must be between 80 and 100 meters. What are the possible values for the width of the rectangle?

83. Higher education. The formulas

$$B = 16.45n + 1062.45$$

and

$$M = 7.79n + 326.82$$

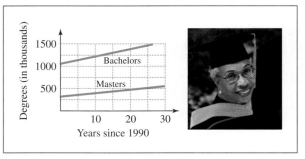

FIGURE FOR EXERCISE 83

can be used to approximate the number of bachelor's and master's degrees in thousands, respectively, awarded per year, n years after 1990 (National Center for Educational Statistics, www.nces.ed.gov).
a) How many bachelor's degrees were awarded in 2000?
b) In what year will the number of bachelor's degrees that are awarded reach 1.4 million?
c) What is the first year in which both B is greater than 1.4 million and M is greater than 0.55 million?

d) What is the first year in which either B is greater than 1.4 million or M is greater than 0.55 million?

84. Senior citizens. The number of senior citizens (65 and over) in the United States in millions n years after 1990 can be estimated by using the formula

$$s = 0.38n + 31.2$$

(U.S. Bureau of the Census, www.census.gov). The percentage of senior citizens living below the poverty level

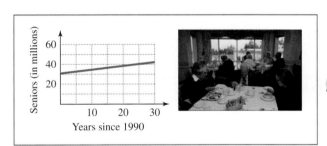

FIGURE FOR EXERCISE 84

n years after 1990 can be estimated by using the formula

$$p = -0.25n + 12.2.$$

a) How many senior citizens were there in 2000?

b) In what year will the percentage of seniors living below the poverty level reach 7%?
c) What is the first year in which we can expect both the number of seniors to be greater than 40 million and fewer than 7% living below the poverty level?

GETTING MORE INVOLVED

85. Discussion. If $-x$ is between a and b, then what can you say about x?
86. Discussion. For which of the inequalities is the notation used correctly?
a) $-2 \le x < 3$ b) $-4 \ge x < 7$ c) $-1 \le x > 0$
d) $6 < x \le -8$ e) $5 \ge x \ge -9$

87. Discussion. In each case, write the resulting set of numbers in interval notation. Explain your answers.
a) Every number in $(3, 8)$ is multiplied by 4.
b) Every number in $[-2, 4)$ is multiplied by -5.

c) Three is added to every number in $(-3, 6)$.
d) Every number in $[3, 9]$ is divided by -3.
88. Discussion. Write the solution set using interval notation for each of these inequalities in terms of s and t. State any restrictions on s and t. For what values of s and t is the solution set empty?
a) $x > s$ and $x < t$
b) $x > s$ and $x > t$

2.6 ABSOLUTE VALUE EQUATIONS AND INEQUALITIES

In This Section

- Absolute Value Equations
- Absolute Value Inequalities
- Applications

In Chapter 1 we learned that absolute value measures the distance of a number from 0 on the number line. In this section we will learn to solve equations and inequalities involving absolute value.

Absolute Value Equations

Solving equations involving absolute value requires some techniques that are different from those studied in previous sections. For example, the solution set to the equation

$$|x| = 5$$

is $\{-5, 5\}$ because both 5 and -5 are five units from 0 on the number line, as shown in Fig. 2.25. So $|x| = 5$ is equivalent to the compound equation

$$x = 5 \text{ or } x = -5.$$

FIGURE 2.25

The equation $|x| = 0$ is equivalent to the equation $x = 0$ because 0 is the only number whose distance from 0 is zero. The solution set to $|x| = 0$ is $\{0\}$.

The equation $|x| = -7$ is inconsistent because absolute value measures distance, and distance is never negative. So the solution set is empty. These ideas are summarized as follows.

Helpful Hint

Some students grow up believing that the only way to solve an equation is to "do the same thing to each side." Then along comes absolute value equations. For an absolute value equation we write an equivalent compound equation that is not obtained by "doing the same thing to each side."

Basic Absolute Value Equations		
Absolute Value Equation	**Equivalent Equation**	**Solution Set**
$|x| = k \ (k > 0)$	$x = k \text{ or } x = -k$	$\{k, -k\}$
$|x| = 0$	$x = 0$	$\{0\}$
$|x| = k \ (k < 0)$		$\varnothing$

We can use these ideas to solve more complicated absolute value equations.

E X A M P L E   1

Absolute value equal to a positive number
Solve each equation.

a) $|x - 7| = 2$ **b)** $|3x - 5| = 7$

Calculator Close-Up

Use $Y=$ to set $y_1 = \text{abs}(x - 7)$. Make a table to see that y_1 has value 2 when $x = 5$ or $x = 9$. The table supports the conclusion of Example 1(a).

X	Y1
5	2
6	1
7	0
8	1
9	2
10	3
11	4

Y1 ∎abs(X-7)

Solution

a) First rewrite $|x - 7| = 2$ without absolute value:

$$x - 7 = 2 \quad \text{or} \quad x - 7 = -2 \quad \text{Equivalent equation}$$
$$x = 9 \quad \text{or} \quad x = 5$$

The solution set is $\{5, 9\}$. The distance from 5 to 7 or from 9 to 7 is 2 units.

b) First rewrite $|3x - 5| = 7$ without absolute value:

$$3x - 5 = 7 \quad \text{or} \quad 3x - 5 = -7 \quad \text{Equivalent equation}$$
$$3x = 12 \quad \text{or} \quad 3x = -2$$
$$x = 4 \quad \text{or} \quad x = -\frac{2}{3}$$

The solution set is $\left\{-\frac{2}{3}, 4\right\}$. ∎

E X A M P L E   2

Absolute value equal to zero

Solve $| \, 2(x - 6) + 7 \, | = 0$.

Solution

Since 0 is the only number whose absolute value is 0, the expression within the absolute value bars must be 0.

$$2(x - 6) + 7 = 0 \quad \text{Equivalent equation}$$
$$2x - 12 + 7 = 0$$
$$2x - 5 = 0$$
$$2x = 5$$
$$x = \frac{5}{2}$$

The solution set is $\left\{ \frac{5}{2} \right\}$.   ■

Helpful Hint

Examples 1, 2, and 3 show the three basic types of absolute value equations—absolute value equal to a positive number, zero, or a negative number. These equations have 2, 1, and no solutions, respectively.

E X A M P L E   3

Absolute value equal to a negative number

Solve each equation.

a) $| \, x - 9 \, | = -6$ **b)** $-5 \, | \, 3x - 7 \, | + 4 = 14$

Solution

a) The equation indicates that $| \, x - 9 \, | = -6$. However, the absolute value of any quantity is greater than or equal to zero. So there is no solution to the equation.

b) First subtract 4 from each side to isolate the absolute value expression:

$$-5 \, | \, 3x - 7 \, | + 4 = 14 \quad \text{Original equation}$$
$$-5 \, | \, 3x - 7 \, | = 10 \quad \text{Subtract 4 from each side.}$$
$$| \, 3x - 7 \, | = -2 \quad \text{Divide each side by } -5.$$

There is no solution because no number has a negative absolute value.   ■

The equation in Example 4 has an absolute value on both sides.

E X A M P L E   4

Absolute value on both sides

Solve $| \, 2x - 1 \, | = | \, x + 3 \, |$.

Solution

Two quantities have the same absolute value only if they are equal or opposites. So we can write an equivalent compound equation:

$$2x - 1 = x + 3 \quad \text{or} \quad 2x - 1 = -(x + 3)$$
$$x - 1 = 3 \quad \text{or} \quad 2x - 1 = -x - 3$$
$$x = 4 \quad \text{or} \quad 3x = -2$$
$$x = 4 \quad \text{or} \quad x = -\frac{2}{3}$$

Check 4 and $-\frac{2}{3}$ in the original equation. The solution set is $\left\{ -\frac{2}{3}, 4 \right\}$.   ■

Absolute Value Inequalities

Since absolute value measures distance from 0 on the number line, $| \, x \, | > 5$ indicates that x is more than five units from 0. Any number on the number line to the right of 5 or to the left of -5 is more than five units from 0. So $|x| > 5$ is equivalent to

$$x > 5 \quad \text{or} \quad x < -5.$$

The solution set to this inequality is the union of the solution sets to the two simple inequalities. The solution set is $(-\infty, -5) \cup (5, \infty)$. The graph of $|x| > 5$ is shown in Fig. 2.26.

FIGURE 2.26

The inequality $|x| \leq 3$ indicates that x is less than or equal to three units from 0. Any number between -3 and 3 inclusive satisfies that condition. So $|x| \leq 3$ is equivalent to

$$-3 \leq x \leq 3.$$

The graph of $|x| \leq 3$ is shown in Fig. 2.27. These examples illustrate the basic types of absolute value inequalities.

FIGURE 2.27

Basic Absolute Value Inequalities ($k > 0$)			
Absolute Value Inequality	Equivalent Inequality	Solution Set	Graph of Solution Set
$\|x\| > k$	$x > k$ or $x < -k$	$(-\infty, -k) \cup (k, \infty)$	
$\|x\| \geq k$	$x \geq k$ or $x \leq -k$	$(-\infty, -k] \cup [k, \infty)$	
$\|x\| < k$	$-k < x < k$	$(-k, k)$	
$\|x\| \leq k$	$-k \leq x \leq k$	$[-k, k]$	

We can solve more complicated inequalities in the same manner as simple ones.

EXAMPLE 5

Absolute value inequality

Solve $|x - 9| < 2$ and graph the solution set.

Solution

Because $|x| < k$ is equivalent to $-k < x < k$, we can rewrite $|x - 9| < 2$ as follows:

$$-2 < x - 9 < 2$$
$$-2 + 9 < x - 9 + 9 < 2 + 9 \quad \text{Add 9 to each part of the inequality.}$$
$$7 < x < 11$$

The graph of the solution set $(7, 11)$ is shown in Fig. 2.28. Note that the graph consists of all real numbers that are within two units of 9.

FIGURE 2.28

EXAMPLE 6

Absolute value inequality

Solve $|3x + 5| > 2$ and graph the solution set.

Solution

$$3x + 5 > 2 \qquad \text{or} \qquad 3x + 5 < -2 \qquad \text{Equivalent compound inequality}$$

$$3x > -3 \qquad \text{or} \qquad 3x < -7$$

$$x > -1 \qquad \text{or} \qquad x < -\frac{7}{3}$$

The solution set is $\left(-\infty, -\frac{7}{3}\right) \cup (-1, \infty)$, and its graph is shown in Fig. 2.29.

FIGURE 2.29

EXAMPLE 7

Absolute value inequality

Solve $|5 - 3x| \leq 6$ and graph the solution set.

Calculator Close-Up

Use Y= to set $y_1 = \text{abs}(5 - 3x)$. The table supports the conclusion that $y \leq 6$ when x is between $-\frac{1}{3}$ and $\frac{11}{3}$ even though $-\frac{1}{3}$ and $\frac{11}{3}$ do not appear in the table. For more accuracy, make a table in which the change in x is $\frac{1}{3}$.

X	Y1
-1	8
0	5
1	2
2	1
3	4
4	7
5	10

Y1◻abs(5-3X)

Solution

$$-6 \leq 5 - 3x \leq 6 \qquad \text{Equivalent inequality}$$

$$-11 \leq -3x \leq 1 \qquad \text{Subtract 5 from each part.}$$

$$\frac{11}{3} \geq x \geq -\frac{1}{3} \qquad \text{Divide by } -3 \text{ and reverse each inequality symbol.}$$

$$-\frac{1}{3} \leq x \leq \frac{11}{3} \qquad \text{Write } -\frac{1}{3} \text{ on the left because it is smaller than } \frac{11}{3}.$$

The solution set is $\left[-\frac{1}{3}, \frac{11}{3}\right]$ and its graph is shown in Fig. 2.30.

FIGURE 2.30

Some absolute value inequalities that do not fit the preceding categories can be solved by using the definition of absolute value.

EXAMPLE 8

Special case

Solve $3 + |7 - 2x| \geq 3$.

Solution

Subtract 3 from each side to isolate the absolute value expression.

$$|7 - 2x| \geq 0$$

Because the absolute value of any real number is greater than or equal to 0, the solution set is R, the set of all real numbers.

E X A M P L E   9

An impossible case

Solve $|5x - 12| < -2$.

Solution

We write an equivalent inequality only when the value of k is positive. With -2 on the right-hand side, we do not write an equivalent inequality. Since the absolute value of any quantity is greater than or equal to 0, no value for x can make this absolute value less than -2. The solution set is $\varnothing$, the empty set. ■

Applications

A simple example will show how absolute value inequalities can be used in applications.

E X A M P L E   1 0

Controlling water temperature

The water temperature in a certain manufacturing process must be kept at 143°F. The computer is programmed to shut down the process if the water temperature is more than 7° away from what it is supposed to be. For what temperature readings is the process shut down?

Study Tip

When taking a test, try not to spend too much time on a single problem. If a problem is taking a long time, then you might be approaching it incorrectly. Move on to another problem and make sure that you get finished with the test.

Solution

If we let x represent the water temperature, then $x - 143$ represents the difference between the actual temperature and the desired temperature. The quantity $x - 143$ could be positive or negative. The process is shut down if the absolute value of $x - 143$ is greater than 7.

$$|x - 143| > 7$$

$$x - 143 > 7 \qquad \text{or} \qquad x - 143 < -7$$
$$x > 150 \qquad \text{or} \qquad x < 136$$

The process is shut down for temperatures greater than 150°F or less than 136°F. ■

WARM-UPS

True or false? Explain your answer.

1. The equation $|x| = 2$ is equivalent to $x = 2$ or $x = -2$.
2. All absolute value equations have two solutions.
3. The equation $|2x - 3| = 7$ is equivalent to $2x - 3 = 7$ or $2x + 3 = 7$.

4. The inequality $|x| > 5$ is equivalent to $x > 5$ or $x < -5$.
5. The equation $|x| = -5$ is equivalent to $x = 5$ or $x = -5$.
6. There is only one solution to the equation $|3 - x| = 0$.
7. We should write the inequality $x > 3$ or $x < -3$ as $3 < x < -3$.
8. The inequality $|x| < 7$ is equivalent to $-7 \le x \le 7$.
9. The equation $|x| + 2 = 5$ is equivalent to $|x| = 3$.
10. If x is any real number, then the absolute value of x is positive.

2.6 EXERCISES

Reading and Writing *After reading this section, write out the answers to these questions. Use complete sentences.*

1. What does absolute value measure?

2. Why does $|x| = 0$ have only one solution?

3. Why does $|x| = 4$ have two solutions?

4. Why is $|x| = -3$ inconsistent?

5. Why do all real numbers satisfy $|x| \geq 0$?

6. Why do no real numbers satisfy $|x| < -3$?

Solve each absolute value equation. See Examples 1–3.

7. $|a| = 5$ **8.** $|x| = 2$ **9.** $|x - 3| = 1$

10. $|x - 5| = 2$ **11.** $|3 - x| = 6$ **12.** $|7 - x| = 6$

13. $|3x - 4| = 12$ **14.** $|5x + 2| = -3$

15. $\left|\dfrac{2}{3}x - 8\right| = 0$ **16.** $\left|3 - \dfrac{3}{4}x\right| = \dfrac{1}{4}$

17. $|6 - 0.2x| = 10$

18. $|5 - 0.1x| = 0$

19. $|7(x - 6)| = -3$

20. $|2(a + 3)| = 15$

21. $|2(x - 4) + 3| = 5$

22. $|3(x - 2) + 7| = 6$

23. $|7.3x - 5.26| = 4.215$

24. $|5.74 - 2.17x| = 10.28$

Solve each absolute value equation. See Examples 3 and 4.

25. $3 + |x| = 5$

26. $|x| - 10 = -3$

27. $2 - |x + 3| = -6$

28. $4 - 3|x - 2| = -8$

29. $5 - \dfrac{|3 - 2x|}{3} = 4$

30. $3 - \dfrac{1}{2}\left|\dfrac{1}{2}x - 4\right| = 2$

31. $|x - 5| = |2x + 1|$

32. $|w - 6| = |3 - 2w|$

33. $\left|\dfrac{5}{2} - x\right| = \left|2 - \dfrac{x}{2}\right|$

34. $\left|x - \dfrac{1}{4}\right| = \left|\dfrac{1}{2}x - \dfrac{3}{4}\right|$

35. $|x - 3| = |3 - x|$

36. $|a - 6| = |6 - a|$

Write an absolute value inequality whose solution set is shown by the graph. See Examples 5–7.

37.

38.

39.

40.

41.

42.

43.

44.

Determine whether each absolute value inequality is equivalent to the inequality following it. See Examples 5–7.

45. $|x| < 3, \ x < 3$ **46.** $|x| > 3, \ x > 3$

47. $|x - 3| > 1, \ x - 3 > 1$ or $x - 3 < -1$

48. $|x - 3| \leq 1, \ -1 \leq x - 3 \leq 1$

49. $|x - 3| \geq 1, \ x - 3 \geq 1$ or $x - 3 \leq 1$

50. $|x - 3| > 0, x - 3 > 0$

51. $|4 - x| < 1, 4 - x < 1$ and $-(4 - x) < 1$

52. $|4 - x| > 1, 4 - x > 1$ or $-(4 - x) > 1$

Solve each absolute value inequality and graph the solution set. See Examples 5–7.

53. $|x| > 6$

54. $|w| > 3$

55. $|2a| < 6$

56. $|3x| < 21$

57. $|x - 2| \geq 3$

58. $|x - 5| \geq 1$

59. $\frac{1}{5}|2x - 4| < 1$

60. $\frac{1}{3}|2x - 1| < 1$

61. $-2|5 - x| \geq -14$

62. $-3|6 - x| \geq -3$

63. $2|3 - 2x| - 6 \geq 18$

64. $2|5 - 2x| - 15 \geq 5$

Solve each absolute value inequality and graph the solution set. See Examples 8 and 9.

65. $|x - 2| > 0$

66. $|6 - x| \geq 0$

67. $|x - 5| \geq 0$

68. $|3x - 7| \geq -3$

69. $-2|3x - 7| > 6$

70. $-3|7x - 42| > 18$

71. $|2x + 3| + 6 > 0$

72. $|5 - x| + 5 > 5$

Solve each inequality. Write the solution set using interval notation.

73. $1 < |x + 2|$

74. $5 \geq |x - 4|$

75. $5 > |x| + 1$

76. $4 \leq |x| - 6$

77. $3 - 5|x| > -2$

78. $1 - 2|x| < -7$

79. $|5.67x - 3.124| < 1.68$

80. $|4.67 - 3.2x| \geq 1.43$

Solve each problem by using an absolute value equation or inequality. See Example 10.

81. *Famous battles.* In the Hundred Years' War, Henry V defeated a French army in the battle of Agincourt and Joan of Arc defeated an English army in the battle of Orleans (*The Doubleday Almanac*). Suppose you know only that these two famous battles were 14 years apart and that the battle of Agincourt occurred in 1415. Use an absolute value equation to find the possibilities for the year in which the battle of Orleans occurred.

82. *World records.* In July 1985 Steve Cram of Great Britain set a world record of 3 minutes 29.67 seconds for the 1500-meter race and a world record of 3 minutes 46.31 seconds for the 1-mile race (*The Doubleday Almanac*). Suppose you know only that these two events occurred 11 days apart and that the 1500-meter record was set on July 16. Use an absolute value equation to find the possible dates for the 1-mile record run.

83. *Weight difference.* Research at a major university has shown that identical twins generally differ by less than 6 pounds in body weight. If Kim weighs 127 pounds, then in what range is the weight of her identical twin sister Kathy?

84. *Intelligence quotient.* Jude's IQ score is more than 15 points away from Sherry's. If Sherry scored 110, then in what range is Jude's score?

85. *Unidentified flying objects.* The formula

$$S = -16t^2 + v_0 t + s_0$$

gives height in feet above the earth at time t seconds for an object projected into the air with an initial velocity of v_0 feet per second (ft/sec) from an initial height of s_0 feet. Two balls are tossed into the air simultaneously, one from the ground at 50 ft/sec and one from a height of 10 feet at 40 ft/sec. See the accompanying graph.

a) Use the graph to estimate the time at which the balls are at the same height.

b) Find the time from part (a) algebraically.

c) For what values of t will their heights above the ground differ by less than 5 feet (while they are both in the air)?

FIGURE FOR EXERCISE 85

FIGURE FOR EXERCISE 86

86. *Playing catch.* A circus clown at the top of a 60-foot platform is playing catch with another clown on the ground. The clown on the platform drops a ball at the same time as the one on the ground tosses a ball upward at 80 ft/sec. For what length of time is the distance between the balls less than or equal to 10 feet? (*Hint:* Use the formula given in Exercise 85. The initial velocity of a ball that is dropped is 0 ft/sec.)

GETTING MORE INVOLVED

87. *Discussion.* For which real numbers m and n is each equation satisfied?

a) $|m - n| = |n - m|$

b) $|mn| = |m| \cdot |n|$

c) $\left|\dfrac{m}{n}\right| = \dfrac{|m|}{|n|}$

88. *Exploration.* **a)** Evaluate $|m + n|$ and $|m| + |n|$ for
   i) $m = 3$ and $n = 5$
   ii) $m = -3$ and $n = 5$
   iii) $m = 3$ and $n = -5$
   iv) $m = -3$ and $n = -5$

b) What can you conclude about the relationship between $|m + n|$ and $|m| + |n|$?

COLLABORATIVE ACTIVITIES

Adjusting Your Position

Before algebra was invented (circa 800 A.D.) people used many techniques for solving problems. One technique found in the Ahmes papyrus (circa 1650 B.C.) is called "the rule of false position." In this activity you will explore this technique.

This problem is very similar to one found in the Ahmes papyrus:

A quantity, $\frac{2}{3}$ of the quantity, $\frac{1}{2}$ of the quantity, and $\frac{1}{6}$ of the quantity, added together, become 33. What is the quantity?

This problem is solved using the rule of false position as follows:

a) Make a guess for the desired quantity. This is our "false position." Since this problem involves fractions, we use a

Grouping: Three students per group

Topic: Solving linear equations in one variable

common multiple of the denominators. So we guess the number 6.

b) Then we use our guess in the calculation described in the problem:

$$6 + \frac{2}{3} \cdot 6 + \frac{1}{2} \cdot 6 + \frac{1}{6} \cdot 6 = 6 + 4 + 3 + 1$$
$$= 14$$

Since we got 14 instead of 33, we must adjust our guess. In order to "adjust" 14 to 33 we multiply it by $\frac{33}{14}$. This is our adjustment factor:

$$\text{Adjustment factor} = \frac{\text{Required value}}{\text{Calculated value}}$$

c) Multiply 6 by the adjustment factor to find the desired quantity:

$$6 \cdot \frac{33}{14} = \frac{99}{7}$$

d) Check $\frac{99}{7}$ in the original calculation to see if we get 33:

$$\frac{99}{7} + \frac{2}{3} \cdot \frac{99}{7} + \frac{1}{2} \cdot \frac{99}{7} + \frac{1}{6} \cdot \frac{99}{7} = 33$$

Now work with your group on these exercises. Have one person keep track of the steps you need to follow, have a second person decide on your guess and perform the steps, and have the third person check the calculations to make sure they are done correctly. After you have solved the problem by the rule of false position, let x represent the unknown quantity and solve the problem algebraically.

1. Try the same problem from the Ahmes papyrus with a different multiple of 6.

2. Sally received her paycheck on Friday but cannot find the check stub. She knows she paid $\frac{1}{3}$ of her check for rent, $\frac{1}{4}$ for groceries, and $\frac{1}{6}$ for some outstanding bills. She has $150 left from her check. What was her take-home pay on Friday?

3. Vangie, Arik, and Calvin work at a bagel store. Vangie can make three times as many bagels in a day as Calvin and Arik can make half as many bagels in a day as Calvin. If they all work together one day and make 450 bagels, how many bagels can Calvin make in one day?

W R A P - U P

CHAPTER 2

SUMMARY

Equations

		Examples
Solution set	The set of all numbers that satisfy an equation (or inequality)	$x + 2 = 6$ has solution set $\{4\}$.
Equivalent equations	Equations with the same solution set	$2x + 1 = 5$ $2x = 4$
Properties of equality	We may perform the same operation $(+, -, \cdot, \div)$ with the same real number on each side of an equation without changing the solution set (excluding multiplication and division by 0).	$x = 4$ $x + 1 = 5$ $x - 1 = 3$ $2x = 8$ $\dfrac{x}{2} = 2$
Identity	An equation that is satisfied by every number for which both sides are defined	$x + x = 2x$
Conditional equation	An equation whose solution set contains at least one real number but is not an identity	$5x - 10 = 0$
Inconsistent equation	An equation whose solution set is $\varnothing$	$x = x + 1$
Linear equation in one variable	An equation of the form $ax + b = 0$ with $a \neq 0$	$3x + 8 = 0$ $5x - 1 = 2x - 9$

Strategy for solving a linear equation	1. If fractions are present, multiply each side by the LCD to eliminate the fractions. 2. Use the distributive property to remove parentheses. 3. Combine any like terms. 4. Use the addition property of equality to get all variables on one side and numbers on the other side. 5. Use the multiplication property of equality to get a single variable on one side. 6. Check your work by replacing the variable in the original equation with your solution.
Strategy for solving word problems	1. Read the problem until you understand the problem. 2. If possible, draw a diagram to illustrate the problem. 3. Choose a variable and write down what it represents. 4. Represent any other unknowns in terms of that variable. 5. Write an equation that models the situation. 6. Solve the equation. 7. Be sure that your solution answers the question posed in the original problem. 8. Check your answer by using it to solve the original problem (not the equation).

Inequalities   **Examples**

Linear inequality in one variable	Any inequality of the form $ax + b < 0$ with $a \neq 0$ In place of $<$ we can use $\leq$, $>$ or $\geq$.	$2x + 9 < 0$ $x - 2 \geq 7$ $-3x - 1 \geq 2x + 5$
Properties of inequality	We may perform the same operation $(+, -, \cdot, \div)$ on each side of an inequality just as we do in solving equations, with one exception: When multiplying or dividing by a negative number, the inequality symbol is reversed.	$-3x > 6$ $x < -2$
Trichotomy property	For any two real numbers a and b, exactly one of the following statements is true: $a < b$, $a = b$, or $a > b$	If w is not greater than 7, then $w \leq 7$.

Compound inequality	Two simple inequalities connected with the word "and" or "or"
	    And corresponds to *intersection*.
	    Or corresponds to *union*.
		$x > 1$ and $x < 5$
		$x > 3$ or $x < 1$

Absolute Value

	Absolute Value Equation	**Equivalent Equation**	**Solution Set**
Basic absolute value equations	$\lvert x \rvert = k \ (k > 0)$ $\lvert x \rvert = 0$ $\lvert x \rvert = k \ (k < 0)$	$x = k$ or $x = -k$ $x = 0$	$\{k, -k\}$ $\{0\}$ $\varnothing$

	Absolute Value Inequality	Equivalent Inequality	Solution Set	Graph of Solution Set
Basic absolute value inequalities ($k > 0$)	$\lvert x \rvert > k$	$x > k$ or $x < -k$	$(-\infty, -k) \cup (k, \infty)$	
	$\lvert x \rvert \geq k$	$x \geq k$ or $x \leq -k$	$(-\infty, -k] \cup [k, \infty)$	
	$\lvert x \rvert < k$	$-k < x < k$	$(-k, k)$	
	$\lvert x \rvert \leq k$	$-k \leq x \leq k$	$[-k, k]$	

ENRICHING YOUR MATHEMATICAL WORD POWER

For each mathematical term, choose the correct meaning.

1. **equation**
   a. an expression
   b. an inequality
   c. a sentence that expresses the equality of two algebraic expressions
   d. an algebraic sentence

2. **linear equation**
   a. an equation in which the terms are in line
   b. an equation of the form $ax + b = 0$, where $a \neq 0$
   c. the equation of a line
   d. an equation of the form $a^2 + b^2 = c^2$

3. **identity**
   a. an equation that is satisfied by all real numbers
   b. an equation that is satisfied by every real number
   c. an equation that is identical
   d. an equation that is satisfied by every real number for which both sides are defined

4. **conditional equation**
   a. an equation that has at least one real solution
   b. an equation that is correct
   c. an equation that is satisfied by at least one real number but is not an identity
   d. an equation that we are not sure how to solve

5. **inconsistent equation**
   a. an equation that is wrong
   b. an equation that is only sometimes consistent
   c. an equation that has no solution
   d. an equation with two variables

6. **equivalent equations**
   a. equations that are identical
   b. equations that are correct
   c. equations that are equal
   d. equations that have the same solution

7. **formula**
   a. a form
   b. a type of race car
   c. a process
   d. an equation involving two or more variables

8. **literal equation**
   a. a formula
   b. an equation with words
   c. a false equation
   d. a fact

9. **uniform motion**
   a. movement of an army
   b. movement in a straight line
   c. consistent motion
   d. motion at a constant rate

10. **least common denominator**
    a. the smallest divisor of all denominators
    b. the denominator that appears the least
    c. the smallest identical denominator
    d. the least common multiple of the denominators

11. **equivalent inequalities**
    a. the inequality reverses when dividing by a negative number
    b. $a < b$ and $b < c$
    c. $a < b$ and $a \leq b$
    d. inequalities that have the same solution set

12. **inequality**
    a. an equation that is not correct
    b. two different numbers
    c. a statement that expresses the inequality of two algebraic expressions
    d. a larger number

13. **compound inequality**
    a. an inequality that is complicated
    b. an inequality that reverses when divided by a negative number
    c. an inequality of negative numbers
    d. two simple inequalities joined with "and" or "or"

REVIEW EXERCISES

2.1 *Solve each equation.*

1. $2x - 7 = 9$ **2.** $5x - 7 = 38$

3. $11 = 5 - 4x$ **4.** $-8 = 7 - 3x$

5. $x - 6 - (x - 6) = 0$ **6.** $x - 6 - 2(x - 3) = 0$

7. $2(x - 3) - 5 = 5 - (3 - 2x)$

8. $2(x - 4) + 5 = -(3 - 2x)$

9. $\dfrac{3}{17}x = 0$ **10.** $-\dfrac{3}{8}x = \dfrac{1}{2}$

11. $\dfrac{1}{4}x - \dfrac{1}{5} = \dfrac{1}{5}x + \dfrac{4}{5}$ **12.** $\dfrac{1}{2}x - 1 = \dfrac{1}{3}x$

13. $\dfrac{t}{2} - \dfrac{t - 2}{3} = \dfrac{3}{2}$

14. $\dfrac{y + 1}{4} - \dfrac{y - 1}{6} = y + 5$

15. $1 - 0.4(x - 4) + 0.6(x - 7) = -0.6$

16. $0.04x - 0.06(x - 8) = 0.1x$

2.2 *Solve each equation for x.*

17. $ax + b = 0$ **18.** $mx + c = d$ **19.** $ax + 2 = cx$

20. $mx = 3 - x$ **21.** $mwx = P$ **22.** $xyz = 2$

23. $\dfrac{1}{x} + \dfrac{1}{2} = w$ **24.** $\dfrac{1}{x} + \dfrac{1}{a} = 2$

Write y in terms of x.

25. $3x - 2y = -6$ **26.** $4x - 3y + 9 = 0$

27. $y - 2 = -\dfrac{1}{3}(x - 6)$ **28.** $y + 6 = \dfrac{1}{2}(x - 4)$

29. $\dfrac{1}{2}x - \dfrac{1}{4}y = 5$ **30.** $-\dfrac{x}{3} + \dfrac{y}{2} = \dfrac{5}{8}$

2.3 *Solve each problem.*

31. *Legal pad.* If the perimeter of a legal-size note pad is 45 inches and the pad is 5.5 inches longer than it is wide, then what are its length and width?

Study Tip

Note how the review exercises are arranged according to the sections in this chapter. If you have trouble with a certain type of problem, refer back to the appropriate section for examples and explanations.

32. *Area of a trapezoid.* The height of a trapezoid is 5 feet, and the upper base is 2 feet shorter than the lower base. If the area of the trapezoid is 45 square feet, then how long is the lower base?

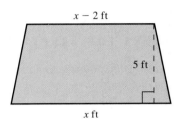

$x - 2$ ft

5 ft

x ft

FIGURE FOR EXERCISE 32

33. *Saving for retirement.* Roy makes $8000 more per year than his wife. Roy saves 10% of his income for retirement, and his wife saves 8%. Together they save $5660 per year. How much does each make?

34. *Charitable contributions.* Duane makes $1000 less per year than his wife. Duane gives 5% of his income to charity, and his wife gives 10% of her income to charity. Together they contribute $2500 to charity. How much does each make?

35. *Dealer discounts.* Sarah is buying a car for $7600. The dealer gave her a 20% discount off the list price. What was the list price?

36. *Gold sale.* At 25% off, a jeweler is selling a gold chain for $465. What was the list price?

37. *Nickels and dimes.* Rebecca has 15 coins consisting of dimes and nickels. The total value of the coins is $0.95. How many of each does she have?

38. *Nickels, dimes, and quarters.* Camille has 19 coins consisting of nickels, dimes, and quarters. The value of the coins is $1.60. If she has six times as many nickels as quarters, then how many of each does she have?

39. *Tour de desert.* On a recent bicycle trip across the desert Barbara rode for 5 hours. Her bicycle then developed mechanical difficulties, and she walked the bicycle for 3 hours to the nearest town. Altogether, she covered 85 miles. If she rides 9 miles per hour (mph) faster than she walks, then how far did she walk?

40. *Motor city.* Delmas flew to Detroit in 90 minutes and drove his new car back home in 6 hours. If he drove 150 mph slower than he flew, then how fast did he fly?

Speed to Detroit = x mph

Speed from Detroit = $x - 150$ mph

FIGURE FOR EXERCISE 40

2.4 *Solve each inequality. State the solution set using interval notation and graph it.*

41. $3 - 4x < 15$

42. $5 - 6x > 35$

43. $2(x - 3) > -6$

44. $4(5 - x) < 20$

45. $-\frac{3}{4}x \geq 6$

46. $-\frac{2}{3}x \leq 4$

47. $3(x + 2) > 5(x - 1)$

48. $4 - 2(x - 3) < 0$

49. $\frac{1}{2}x + 7 \leq \frac{3}{4}x - 5$

50. $\frac{5}{6}x - 3 \geq \frac{2}{3}x + 7$

2.5 *Solve each compound inequality. State the solution set using interval notation and graph it.*

51. $x + 2 > 3$ or $x - 6 < -10$

52. $x - 2 > 5$ or $x - 2 < -1$

53. $x > 0$ and $x - 6 < 3$

54. $x \leq 0$ and $x + 6 > 3$

55. $6 - x < 3$ or $-x < 0$

56. $-x > 0$ or $x + 2 < 7$

57. $2x < 8$ and $2(x - 3) < 6$

58. $\frac{1}{3}x > 2$ and $\frac{1}{4}x > 2$

59. $x - 6 > 2$ and $6 - x > 0$

60. $-\frac{1}{2}x < 6$ or $\frac{2}{3}x < 4$

61. $0.5x > 10$ or $0.1x < 3$

62. $0.02x > 4$ and $0.2x < 3$

63. $-2 \leq \dfrac{2x - 3}{10} \leq 1$

64. $-3 < \dfrac{4 - 3x}{5} < 2$

Write each union or intersection of intervals as a single interval.

65. $[1, 4) \cup (2, \infty)$

66. $(2, 5) \cup (-1, \infty)$

67. $(3, 6) \cap [2, 8]$

68. $[-1, 3] \cap [0, 8]$

69. $(-\infty, 5) \cup [5, \infty)$

70. $(-\infty, 1) \cup (0, \infty)$

71. $(-3, -1] \cap [-2, 5]$

72. $[-2, 4] \cap (4, 7]$

2.6 *Solve each absolute value equation and graph the solution set.*

73. $|x| + 2 = 16$

74. $\left|\dfrac{x}{2}\right| - 5 = -1$

75. $|4x - 12| = 0$

76. $|2x - 8| = 0$

77. $|x| = -5$

78. $\left|\dfrac{x}{2} - 5\right| = -1$

79. $|2x - 1| - 3 = 0$

80. $|5 - x| - 2 = 0$

Solve each absolute value inequality and graph the solution set.

81. $|2x| \geq 8$

82. $|5x - 1| \leq 14$

83. $\left|1 - \dfrac{x}{5}\right| > \dfrac{9}{5}$

84. $\left|1 - \dfrac{1}{6}x\right| < \dfrac{1}{2}$

85. $|x - 3| < -3$ **86.** $|x - 7| \leq -4$

87. $|x + 4| \geq -1$

88. $|6x - 1| \geq 0$

89. $1 - \dfrac{3}{2}|x - 2| < -\dfrac{1}{2}$

90. $1 > \dfrac{1}{2}|6 - x| - \dfrac{3}{4}$

MISCELLANEOUS

Solve each problem by using equations or inequalities.

91. *Rockbuster video.* Stephen plans to open a video rental store in Edmonton. Industry statistics show that 45% of the rental price goes for overhead. If the maximum that anyone will pay to rent a tape is $5 and Stephen wants a profit of at least $1.65 per tape, then in what range should the rental price be?

92. *Working girl.* Regina makes $6.80 per hour working in the snack bar. To keep her grant, she may not earn more than $51 per week. What is the range of the number of hours per week that she may work?

93. *Skeletal remains.* Forensic scientists use the formula $h = 60.089 + 2.238F$ to predict the height h (in centimeters) for a male whose femur measures F centimeters. (See the accompanying figure.) In what range is the length of the femur for males between 150 centimeters and 180 centimeters in height? Round to the nearest tenth of a centimeter.

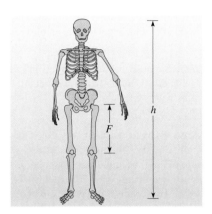

FIGURE FOR EXERCISE 93

94. *Female femurs.* Forensic scientists use the formula $h = 61.412 + 2.317F$ to predict the height h in centimeters for a female whose femur measures F centimeters.

a) Use the accompanying graph to estimate the femur length for a female with height of 160 centimeters.

b) In what range is the length of the femur for females who are over 170 centimeters tall?

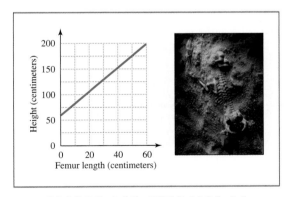

FIGURE FOR EXERCISE 94

95. *Car trouble.* Dane's car was found abandoned at mile marker 86 on the interstate. If Dane was picked up by the police on the interstate exactly 5 miles away, then at what mile marker was he picked up?

96. *Comparing scores.* Scott scored 72 points on the midterm, and Katie's score was more than 16 points away from Scott's. What was Katie's score?

97. *Year-end bonus.* A law firm has agreed to distribute 20% of its profits to its employees as a year-end bonus. To the firm's accountant, the bonus is an expense that must be used to determine the profit. That is, bonus = 20% × (profit before bonus − bonus). Given that the profit before the bonus is $300,000, find the amount of the bonus using the accountant's method. How does this answer compare to 20% of $300,000, which is what the employees want?

98. *Higher rate.* Suppose that the employees in Exercise 97 got the bonus that they wanted. To the accountant, what percent of the profits was given in bonuses?

99. *Dairy cattle.* Thirty percent of the dairy cattle in Washington County are Holsteins, whereas 60% of the dairy cattle in neighboring Cade County are Holsteins. In the combined two-county area, 50% of the 3600 dairy cattle are Holsteins. How many dairy cattle are in each county?

100. *Profitable business.* United Home Improvement (UHI) makes 20% profit on its good grade of vinyl siding, 30% profit on its better grade, and 60% profit on its best grade. So far this year, UHI has $40,000 in sales of good siding and $50,000 in sales of better siding. The company goal is to have at least an overall profit of 50% of total sales. What would the sales figures for the best grade of siding have to be to reach this goal?

For each graph in Exercises 101–118, write an equation or inequality that has the solution set shown by the graph. Use absolute value when possible.

101.

102.

103.

104.

105.

106.

107.

108.

109.

110.

111.

112.

113.

114.

115.

116.

117.

118.

CHAPTER 2 TEST

Solve each equation.

1. $-10x - 5 + 4x = -4x + 3$

2. $\dfrac{y}{2} - \dfrac{y - 3}{3} = \dfrac{y + 6}{6}$

3. $|w| + 3 = 9$

4. $|3 - 2(5 - x)| = 3$

Write y in terms of x.

5. $2x - 5y = 20$ **6.** $y = 3xy + 5$

Solve each inequality. State the solution set using interval notation and graph the solution set.

7. $|m - 6| \leq 2$

8. $2|x - 3| - 5 > 15$

9. $2 - 3(w - 1) < -2w$

10. $2 < \dfrac{5 - 2x}{3} < 7$

11. $3x - 2 < 7$ and $-3x \leq 15$

12. $\dfrac{2}{3}y < 4$ or $y - 3 < 12$

Solve each equation or inequality.

13. $|2x - 7| = -3$

14. $x - 4 > 1$ or $x < 12$ **15.** $3x < 0$ and $x - 5 > 2$

16. $|2x - 5| \leq 0$ **17.** $|x - 3| < 0$

18. $x + 3x = 4x$ **19.** $2(x + 7) = 2x + 9$

20. $|x - 6| > -6$ **21.** $x - 0.04(x - 10) = 96.4$

Write a complete solution to each problem.

22. The perimeter of a rectangle is 84 meters. If the width is 16 meters less than the length, then what is the width of the rectangle?

23. If the area of a triangle is 21 square inches and the base is 3 inches, then what is the height?

24. Joan bought a gold chain marked 30% off. If she paid $210, then what was the original price?

25. How many liters of an 11% alcohol solution should be mixed with 60 liters of a 5% alcohol solution to obtain a mixture that is 7% alcohol?

26. Al and Brenda do the same job, but their annual salaries differ by more than $3,000. Assume, Al makes $28,000 per year and write an absolute value inequality to describe this situation. What are the possibilities for Brenda's salary?

Study Tip

Before you take an in-class exam on this chapter, work the sample test given here. Set aside one hour to work this test and use the answers in the back of this book to grade yourself. Even though your instructor might not ask exactly the same questions, you will get a good idea of your test readiness.

Simplify each expression.

1. $5x + 6x$

2. $5x \cdot 6x$

3. $\dfrac{6x + 2}{2}$

4. $5 - 4(2 - x)$

5. $(30 - 1)(30 + 1)$

6. $(30 + 1)^2$

7. $(30 - 1)^2$

8. $(2 + 3)^2$

9. $2^2 + 3^2$

10. $(8 - 3)(3 - 8)$

11. $(-1)(3 - 8)$

12. -2^2

13. $3x + 8 - 5(x - 1)$

14. $(-6)^2 - 4(-3)2$

15. $3^2 \cdot 2^3$

16. $4(-6) - (-5)(3)$

17. $-3x \cdot x \cdot x$

18. $(-1)(-1)(-1)(-1)(-1)(-1)$

Solve each equation.

19. $5x + 6x = 8x$

20. $5x + 6x = 11x$

21. $5x + 6x = 0$

22. $5x + 6 = 11x$

23. $3x + 1 = 0$

24. $5 - 4(2 - x) = 1$

25. $3x + 6 = 3(x + 2)$

26. $x - 0.01x = 990$

27. $|5x + 6| = 11$

Solve the problem.

28. *Cost analysis.* Diller Electronics can rent a copy machine for 5 years from American Business Supply for $75 per month plus 6 cents per copy. The same copier can be purchased for $8000, but then it costs only 2 cents per copy for supplies and maintenance. The purchased copier has no value after 5 years.

a) Use the accompanying graph to estimate the number of copies for 5 years for which the cost of renting would equal the cost of buying.

b) Write a formula for the 5-year cost under each plan.

c) Algebraically find the number of copies for which the 5-year costs would be equal.

d) If Diller makes 120,000 copies in 5 years, which plan is cheaper and by how much?

e) For what range of copies do the two plans differ by less than $500?

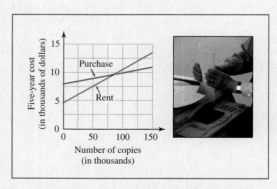

FIGURE FOR EXERCISE 28

Study Tip

Don't wait until the final exam to review material. Do some review on a regular basis. The Making Connections exercises on this page can be used to review, compare, and contrast different concepts that you have studied. A good time to work these exercises is between a test and the start of new material.

Linear Equations and Inequalities in Two Variables

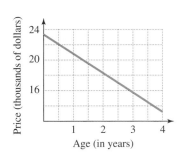

T he first self-propelled automobile to carry passengers was built in 1801 by the British inventor Richard Trevithick. By 1911 about 600,000 automobiles were operated in the United States alone. Some were powered by steam and some by electricity, but most were powered by gasoline. In 1913, to meet the ever growing demand, Henry Ford increased production by introducing a moving assembly line to carry automobile parts. Today the United States is a nation of cars. Over 11 million automobiles are produced here annually, and total car registrations number over 114 million.

Prices for new cars rise every year. Today the most basic Ford Focus sells for $13,000 to $15,000, whereas Henry Ford's early model T sold for $850. Unfortunately, the moment you buy your new car its value begins to decrease. Much of the behavior of automobile prices can be modeled with linear equations. In Exercises 81 and 82 of Section 3.1 you will use linear equations to find increasing new car prices and depreciating used car prices.

3.1

GRAPHING LINES IN THE COORDINATE PLANE

In Chapter 2 we used the number line to illustrate the solution sets to equations and inequalities in one variable. In this chapter we will use a new coordinate system made from a pair of number lines to illustrate the solution sets to equations and inequalities in two variables.

Graphing Ordered Pairs

The **rectangular** or **Cartesian coordinate system** consists of a horizontal number line, the *x*-axis, and a vertical number line, the *y*-axis, as shown in Fig. 3.1. The intersection of the axes is the **origin.** The axes divide the coordinate plane, or the *xy*-plane, into four regions called **quadrants.** The quadrants are numbered as shown in Fig. 3.1, and they do not include any points on the axes.

Helpful Hint

In this chapter you will be doing a lot of graphing. Using graph paper will help you to understand the concepts and to recognize errors. For your convenience, a page of graph paper can be found at the end of this chapter. Make as many copies of it as you wish.

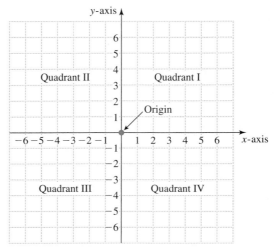

FIGURE 3.1

Just as every real number corrresponds to a point on the number line, every pair of real numbers corresponds to a point in the rectangular coordinate system. Locating a point in the rectangular coordinate system that corresponds to a pair of real numbers is referred to as **plotting** or **graphing** the point.

EXAMPLE 1

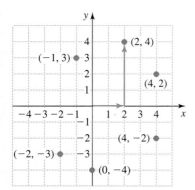

FIGURE 3.2

Plotting points

Graph the points corresponding to the pairs (2, 4), (4, 2), (−2, −3), (−1, 3), (0, −4), and (4, −2).

Solution

To plot (2, 4), start at the origin, move two units to the right, then up four units as shown in Fig. 3.2. To plot (4, 2), start at the origin, move four units to the right, then two units up as shown in Fig. 3.2. To plot (−2, −3), start at the origin, move two units to the left, then down three units. All six points are shown in Fig. 3.2. ■

A pair of numbers, such as (2, 4), is called an **ordered pair** because the order of the numbers is important. The pairs (4, 2) and (2, 4) correspond to different points in Fig. 3.2. The first number in an ordered pair is the *x*-coordinate and the second number is the *y*-coordinate.

Note that we use the same notation for ordered pairs that we use for intervals of real numbers, but the meaning should always be clear from the context. The ordered pair (2, 4) represents a single pair of real numbers and a single point in the xy-plane, whereas the interval (2, 4) represents all real numbers between 2 and 4. Since ordered pairs correspond to points, we often refer to them as points.

The Midpoint and Distance Formulas

The **midpoint** of a line segment is a point that is on the line segment and equidistant from the end points. We use the notation $(\bar{x}, \bar{y})$ (read "x bar, y bar") for the midpoint of a line segment. The midpoint is found by "averaging" the x-coordinates and y-coordinates of the endpoints, in the same manner that you would average two test scores:

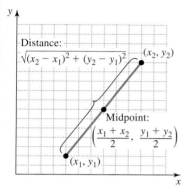

FIGURE 3.3

Midpoint Formula

The midpoint of the line segment with endpoints (x_1, y_1) and (x_2, y_2) is given by

$$(\bar{x}, \bar{y}) = \left(\frac{x_1 + x_2}{2}, \frac{y_1 + y_2}{2}\right).$$

The length of a line segment or the distance between the endpoints is given by the **distance formula.** See Fig. 3.3.

Distance Formula

The distance between the points (x_1, y_1) and (x_2, y_2) is

$$\sqrt{(x_2 - x_1)^2 + (y_2 - y_1)^2}.$$

We will see a proof of the distance formula later in this text.

EXAMPLE 2

Finding the midpoint and length of a line segment

Find the midpoint and length of the line segment with endpoints (1, 7) and (5, 4).

Solution

Use the midpoint formula with $(x_1, y_1) = (1, 7)$ and $(x_2, y_2) = (5, 4)$:

$$(\bar{x}, \bar{y}) = \left(\frac{1 + 5}{2}, \frac{7 + 4}{2}\right) = \left(3, \frac{11}{2}\right)$$

Use the distance formula to find the length of the line segment:

$$\sqrt{(x_2 - x_1)^2 + (y_2 - y_1)^2} = \sqrt{(5 - 1)^2 + (4 - 7)^2}$$
$$= \sqrt{16 + 9}$$
$$= \sqrt{25} = 5$$

Note that $(x_1, y_1) = (5, 4)$ and $(x_2, y_2) = (1, 7)$ gives the same midpoint and length. Try it.   ■

Graphing a Linear Equation

An equation in two variables, such as $y = 2x + 3$, is satisfied only if we find a number for x and a number for y that make it true. For example, if $x = 4$ and $y = 11$, then the equation becomes $11 = 2 \cdot 4 + 3$, which is a true statement. So the ordered pair (4, 11) satisfies the equation. The solution set to this equation consists of all ordered pairs that satisfy the equation. In set notation it is written as $\{(x, y) \mid y = 2x + 3\}$. However, this set notation does not shed any light on the solution set to $y = 2x + 3$. We can get a better understanding of the solution set if we graph all of the points in the solution set.

EXAMPLE 3

Graphing a linear equation

Graph the solution set to $y = 2x + 3$.

Solution

We arbitrarily choose some values for x and find corresponding y-values:

Choose x,   then $y = 2(x) + 3$.

If $x = -4$,   then $y = 2(-4) + 3 = -5$.

If $x = -3$,   then $y = 2(-3) + 3 = -3$.

If $x = -2$,   then $y = 2(-2) + 3 = -1$.

If $x = -1$,   then $y = 2(-1) + 3 = 1$.

If $x = 0$,   then $y = 2(0) + 3 = 3$.

If $x = 1$,   then $y = 2(1) + 3 = 5$.

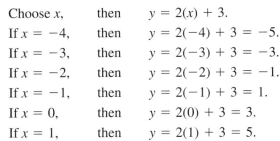

FIGURE 3.4

We can display the corresponding x- and y-values in this table:

x	-4	-3	-2	-1	0	1
$y = 2x + 3$	-5	-3	-1	1	3	5

Now plot the points $(-4, -5)$, $(-3, -3)$, $(-2, -1)$, $(-1, 1)$, $(0, 3)$, and $(1, 5)$, as shown in Fig. 3.4, and draw a line through them. There are infinitely many ordered pairs that satisfy $y = 2x + 3$, but they all lie on this line. The arrows on the ends of the line indicate that it extends without bound in both directions. The line in Fig. 3.4 is the graph of the solution set to $y = 2x + 3$ or simply the graph of $y = 2x + 3$. ∎

Since the value of y in $y = 2x + 3$ is determined from the value of x, y is the **dependent variable** and x is the **independent variable.** Because the graph of $y = 2x + 3$ is a line, the equation is a **linear equation.**

When we draw any graph, we are attempting to put on paper an image that exists in our minds. The line for $y = 2x + 3$ that we have in mind has no thickness, is perfectly straight, and extends infinitely. All attempts to draw it on paper fall short. The best we can do is to use a sharp pencil to keep it as thin as possible, a ruler to make it as straight as possible, and arrows to indicate that it does not end.

Study Tip

It is a good idea to work with others, but don't be misled. Working a problem with help is not the same as working a problem on your own. In the end, mathematics is personal. Make sure that you can do it.

EXAMPLE 4

Graphing a linear equation

Graph $y + 2x = 1$. Plot at least four points.

Solution

First rewrite $y + 2x = 1$ as $y = -2x + 1$. Now arbitrarily select some values for x and find the corresponding y-values:

If $x = -1$,   then $y = -2(-1) + 1 = 3$.

If $x = 0$,   then $y = -2(0) + 1 = 1$.

If $x = 1$,   then $y = -2(1) + 1 = -1$.

If $x = 2$,   then $y = -2(2) + 1 = -3$.

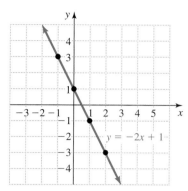

FIGURE 3.5

We can display the corresponding x- and y-coordinates in a table:

x	-1	0	1	2
$y = -2x + 1$	3	1	-1	-3

Plot the points $(-1, 3)$, $(0, 1)$, $(1, -1)$, and $(2, -3)$ and draw a line through them, as shown in Fig. 3.5. ∎

Calculator Close-Up

To graph $y + 2x = 1$ with a graphing calculator, first press Y= and enter $y_1 = -2x + 1$.

Next press WINDOW to set the viewing window as follows:

Xmin = −10, X max = 10, Xscl = 1, Ymin = −10, Ymax = 10, Yscl = 1 These settings are referred to as the standard window.

Press GRAPH to draw the graph. Even though the calculator does not draw a very good straight line, it supports our conclusion that Fig. 3.5 is the graph of $y + 2x = 1$.

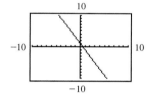

If the coefficient of a variable in a linear equation is 0, then that variable is usually omitted from the equation. For example, the equation $y = 0 \cdot x + 2$ is written as $y = 2$. Because x is multiplied by 0, any value of x can be used as long as y is 2. Because the y-coordinates are all the same, the graph is a horizontal line.

E X A M P L E   5

Graphing a horizontal line

Graph $y = 2$. Plot at least four points.

Solution

This table gives four points that satisfy $y = 2$, or $y = 0 \cdot x + 2$. Note that it is easy to determine y in this case because y is always 2.

x	-2	-1	0	1
$y = 0 \cdot x + 2$	2	2	2	2

The horizontal line through these points is shown in Fig. 3.6. ∎

If the coefficient of y is 0 in a linear equation, then the graph is a vertical line.

FIGURE 3.6

E X A M P L E   6

Graphing a vertical line

Graph $x = 4$. Plot at least four points.

Solution

We can think of the equation $x = 4$ as $x = 4 + 0 \cdot y$. Now arbitrarily select some y-values and find the corresponding x-values:

$$\text{If } y = -2, \quad \text{then} \quad x = 4 + 0(-2) = 4.$$
$$\text{If } y = -1, \quad \text{then} \quad x = 4 + 0(-1) = 4.$$
$$\text{If } y = 0, \quad \text{then} \quad x = 4 + 0(0) = 4.$$

Because y is multiplied by 0, the equation is satisfied by every ordered pair with an x-coordinate of 4:

x	4	4	4	4	4	4
y	-2	-1	0	1	2	3

Graphing these points produces the vertical line shown in Fig. 3.7. ∎

FIGURE 3.7

Using Intercepts for Graphing

The **x-intercept** is the point where the line crosses the x-axis. The x-intercept has a y-coordinate of 0. Similarly, the **y-intercept** is the point where the line crosses the y-axis. The y-intercept has an x-coordinate of 0. If a line has distinct x- and y-intercepts, then they can be used as two points that determine the location of the line. Since horizontal lines, vertical lines, and lines through the origin do not have two distinct intercepts, they cannot be graphed using only the intercepts.

E X A M P L E   7

Using intercepts to graph

Use the intercepts to graph the line $3x - 4y = 6$.

Solution

Let $x = 0$ in $3x - 4y = 6$ to find the y-intercept:

$$3(0) - 4y = 6$$
$$-4y = 6$$
$$y = -\frac{3}{2}$$

Let $y = 0$ in $3x - 4y = 6$ to find the x-intercept:

$$3x - 4(0) = 6$$
$$3x = 6$$
$$x = 2$$

The y-intercept is $\left(0, -\frac{3}{2}\right)$, and the x-intercept is $(2, 0)$. The line through the intercepts is shown in Fig. 3.8. To check, find another point that satisfies the equation. The point $(-2, -3)$ satisfies the equation and is on the line in Fig. 3.8. ∎

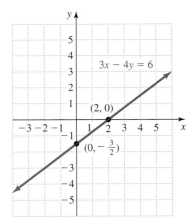

FIGURE 3.8

> **C A U T I O N**   Even though two points determine the location of a line, finding at least three points will help you to avoid errors.

Applications

When we graph equations involving the variables x and y we always put the independent variable x on the horizontal axis and the dependent variable y on the vertical axis. When we use variables such as C for cost, n for the number of items, r for radius, and A for area, we usually have one variable (the dependent variable) written in terms of the other (the independent variable). For example, in $C = 2n + 9$ and $A = \pi r^2$, C and A are the dependent variables, whereas n and r are the independent variables. When we graph these equations, we always put the independent variable on the horizontal axis and the dependent variable on the vertical axis.

E X A M P L E   8   **Graphing a linear equation in an application**

The cost per week C (in dollars) of producing n pairs of shoes for the Reebop Shoe Company is given by the linear equation $C = 2n + 8000$. Graph the equation for n between 0 and 800 inclusive ($0 \leq n \leq 800$).

Solution

Make a table of values for n and C as follows:

n	0	200	400	600	800
$C = 2n + 8000$	8000	8400	8800	9200	9600

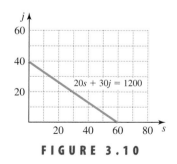

Cost (in thousands of dollars)

Number of pairs

F I G U R E   3 . 9

Graph the line as shown in Fig. 3.9. Because $C = 2n + 8000$ expresses C in terms of n, C is the dependent variable and the vertical axis is labeled C. To accommodate the large numbers, we let each unit on the n-axis represent 200 pairs and each unit on the C-axis represent $1000. ∎

Note how the axes in Fig. 3.9 are labeled. The n-axis starts at 0 and each tick mark represents 200 pairs. Because all of the costs were between $8000 and $9600 we omitted the tick marks for 1 through 7 and put a wave in the C-axis to indicate that some numbers are missing. Omitting the numbers from 1 through 7 makes the difference between the $8000 and $9600 costs look greater.

E X A M P L E   9   **Writing a linear equation**

A store manager is ordering shirts at $20 each and jackets at $30 each. The total cost of the order must be $1200. Write an equation for the total cost and graph it. If she orders 15 shirts, then how many jackets can she order?

Solution

Let s be the number of shirts in the order and j be the number of jackets in the order. Since the total cost is $1200 we can write

$$20s + 30j = 1200.$$

If $s = 0$, then $30j = 1200$ or $j = 40$. If $j = 0$, then $20s = 1200$ or $s = 60$. Graph the line through $(0, 40)$ and $(60, 0)$ as in Fig. 3.10. Note that we arbitrarily put s on the horizontal axis and j on the vertical axis. If $s = 15$, find j as follows:

$$20(15) + 30j = 1200$$
$$300 + 30j = 1200$$
$$30j = 900$$
$$j = 30$$

F I G U R E   3 . 1 0

$20s + 30j = 1200$

If she orders 15 shirts then she must order 30 jackets.

In Example 9, the numbers of shirts and jackets in the order must be whole numbers and every possible order corresponds to a point on the line in Fig. 3.10. However, points on the line whose coordinates are not whole numbers do not correspond to possible orders. Even though the line does not show the possible orders exactly, we draw it because it is more convenient than finding every possible order and then plotting just those points. ∎

WARM-UPS

True or false? Explain your answer.

1. The point (2, 5) satisfies the equation $3y - 2x = -4$.
2. The vertical axis is usually called the x-axis.
3. The point (0, 0) is in quadrant I.
4. The point (0, 1) is on the y-axis.
5. The graph of $x = 7$ is a vertical line.
6. The graph of $8 - y = 0$ is a horizontal line.
7. The y-intercept for the line $y = 2x - 3$ is (0, −3).
8. If $C = 3n + 4$, then $C = 10$ when $n = 2$.
9. If $P = 3x$ and $P = 12$, then $x = 36$.
10. The vertical axis should be A when graphing $A = \pi r^2$.

3.1 EXERCISES

Reading and Writing *After reading this section, write out the answers to these questions. Use complete sentences.*

1. What is the point called at the intersection of the x- and y-axis?

2. What is an ordered pair?

3. What are the x- and y-intercepts?

4. What type of equation has a graph that is a horizontal line?

5. What type of equation has a graph that is a vertical line?

6. Which variable usually goes on the vertical axis?

Plot the following points in a rectangular coordinate system. For each point, name the quadrant in which it lies or the axis on which it lies. See Example 1.

7. (2, 5)
8. (−5, 1)
9. $\left(-3, -\dfrac{1}{2}\right)$
10. (−2, −6)
11. (0, 4)
12. (0, 2)

13. $(\pi, -1)$
14. $\left(\dfrac{4}{3}, 0\right)$
15. (−4, 3)
16. (0, −3)
17. $\left(\dfrac{3}{2}, 0\right)$
18. (3, 2)
19. $\left(0, -\dfrac{7}{3}\right)$
20. $\left(4, -\dfrac{10}{3}\right)$

Find the midpoint and length of the line segment with the given endpoints. See Example 2.

21. (2, 5) and (5, 1)

22. (1, 7) and (5, 10)

23. (−2, 4) and (6, −2)

24. (−3, 5) and (3, −3)

25. $(3, 1)$ and $(-9, -4)$

26. $(-3, -4)$ and $(2, 8)$

27. $(-1, 4)$ and $(1, 1)$

28. $(-3, -4)$ and $(-6, 1)$

Graph each linear equation. Plot four points for each line. See Examples 3–6.

29. $y = x + 1$ **30.** $y = x - 1$

31. $y = -2x + 3$ **32.** $y = 2x - 3$

33. $y = x$ **34.** $y = -x$

35. $y = 3$ **36.** $y = -2$

37. $y = 1 - x$ **38.** $y = 2 - x$

39. $x = 2$ **40.** $x = -3$

41. $y = \dfrac{1}{2}x - 1$ **42.** $y = \dfrac{1}{3}x - 2$

43. $y + 3 = 0$ **44.** $y + 4 = 0$

45. $x - 4 = 0$ **46.** $x + 5 = 0$

47. $y = \dfrac{1}{2}x$

48. $y = -\dfrac{2}{3}x$

57. $x - y + 5 = 0$

58. $x + y + 7 = 0$

49. $3x + y = 5$

50. $x + 2y = 4$

59. $2x + 3y = 5$

60. $3x - 4y = 7$

51. $6x + 3y = 0$

52. $2x + 4y = 0$

61. $2x - 3y = 60$

62. $2x + 3y = 30$

53. $y = 2x - 20$

54. $y = 40 - 2x$

63. $y = 2x - 4$

64. $y = -3x + 6$

Find the x- and y-intercepts for each line and use them to graph the line. See Example 7.

55. $4x - 3y = 12$

56. $2x + 5y = 20$

65. $y = -\dfrac{1}{2}x - 20$

66. $y = \dfrac{1}{3}x + 10$

Find all intercepts for each line. Some of these lines have only one intercept.

67. $3x - 5y = 15$

68. $9x + 8y = 72$

69. $y = 5x$

70. $y = -4x$

71. $6x + 3 = 0$

72. $40x + 5 = 0$

73. $12 + 18y = 0$

74. $2 - 10y = 0$

75. $2 - 4y = 8x$

76. $9x + 3 = 12y$

Complete the given ordered pairs so that each ordered pair satisfies the given equation.

77. $(2, \ ), (\ , -3), \quad y = -3x + 6$

78. $(-1, \ ), (\ , 4), \quad y = \dfrac{1}{2}x + 2$

79. $(-4, \ ), (\ , 6), \quad \dfrac{1}{2}x - \dfrac{1}{3}y = 9$

80. $(3, \ ), (\ , -1), \quad 2x - 3y = 5$

Solve each problem. See Examples 8 and 9.

81. *Camaro inflation.* The rising list price P (in dollars) for a new Camaro Z28 Coupe can be modeled by the equation $P = 320n + 22{,}765$, where n is the number of years since 2000 (www.edmunds.com).
a) What will be the list price for a new Z28 Coupe in 2008?
b) What is the annual increase in list price?
c) Graph the equation for $0 \le n \le 10$.

82. *Camaro Z28 depreciation.* The 2002 average retail price P (in dollars) for an n-year-old Camaro Z28 Coupe can be modeled by the equation $P = 23{,}405 - 2{,}530n$, where $0 \le n \le 4$ (www. edmunds.com).
a) What was the average retail price of a 4-year-old Z28 in 2002?

b) How much does this model depreciate each year?
c) Graph the equation for $0 \le n \le 4$.

83. *Rental cost.* For a one-day car rental the X-press Car Company charges C dollars, where C is determined by the formula $C = 0.26m + 42$ and m is the number of miles driven.
a) What is the charge for a car driven 400 miles?
b) Sketch a graph of the equation for m ranging from 0 to 1000.

84. *Measuring risk.* The Friendly Bob Loan Company gives each applicant a rating, t, from 0 to 10 according to the applicant's ability to repay, a higher rating indicating higher risk. The interest rate, r, is then determined by the formula $r = 0.02t + 0.15$.
a) If your rating were 8, then what would be your interest rate?
b) Sketch the graph of the equation for t ranging from 0 to 10.

85. *Little Chicago pizza.* The equation $C = 0.50t + 8.95$ gives the customer's cost in dollars for a pan pizza, where t is the number of toppings.
a) Find the cost of a five-topping pizza.
b) Find t if $C = 14.45$ and interpret your result.

86. *Long distance charges.* The formula $L = 0.10n + 4.95$ gives the monthly bill in dollars for AT&T's one-rate

Monthly bill (in dollars) — L, 25, 20, 15, 10, 5, 0

Time (minutes) — 0, 50, 100, 150, 200 n

FIGURE FOR EXERCISE 86

plan, where n is the number of minutes of long distance used during the month.

a) Find n if the long distance charge is $23.45.
b) Find L for 120 minutes.
c) Estimate the L-intercept from the accompanying graph.
d) Use the formula to find the L-intercept.
e) Use the formula to find the n-intercept.

87. Note pads and binders. An office manager is placing an order for note pads at $1 each and binders at $2 each. The total cost of the order must be $100. Write an equation for the total cost and graph it. If he orders 30 note pads, then how many binders must he order?

88. Tacos and burritos. Jessenda is ordering tacos at $0.75 each and burritos at $2 each for a large group. She must spend $300. Write an equation for the total cost and graph it. If she orders 200 tacos, then how many burritos must she order?

89. Cost, revenue, and profit. Hillary sells roses at a busy Los Angeles intersection. The formulas

$$C = 0.55x + 50,$$
$$R = 1.50x,$$

and

$$P = 0.95x - 50$$

give her weekly cost, revenue, and profit in terms of x, where x is the number of roses that she sells in one week.

a) Find C, R, and P if $x = 850$. Interpret your results.
b) Find x if $P = 995$ and interpret your result.
c) Find $R - C$ if $x = 1100$ and interpret your result.

90. Velocity of a pop up. A pop up off the bat of Mark McGwire goes straight into the air at 88 feet per second (ft/sec). The formula $v = -32t + 88$ gives the velocity of the ball in feet per second, t seconds after the ball is hit.

a) Find the velocity for $t = 2$ and $t = 3$ seconds. What does a negative velocity mean?
b) For what value of t is $v = 0$? Where is the ball at this time?
c) What are the two intercepts on the accompanying graph? Interpret this answer.
d) If the ball takes the same time going up as it does coming down, then what is its velocity as it hits the ground?

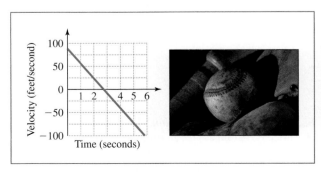

Velocity (feet/second) — 100, 50, 0, −50, −100

Time (seconds) — 1 2 4 5 6

FIGURE FOR EXERCISE 90

GRAPHING CALCULATOR EXERCISES

Graph each linear equation on a graphing calculator. Choose a viewing window that shows both intercepts. Answers may vary.

91. $y = -3x + 20$ **92.** $y = 5 - 50x$

93. $y = 300x - 2$

94. $y = 5x - 800$

95. $x + 2y = 600$

96. $3x - 2y = 1500$

In This Section

- Slope
- Using Coordinates to Find Slope
- Parallel Lines
- Perpendicular Lines
- Applications of Slope

3.2 SLOPE OF A LINE

In Section 3.1 we saw some equations whose graphs were straight lines. In this section we look at graphs of straight lines in more detail and study the concept of slope of a line.

Slope

If a highway has a 6% grade, then in 100 feet (measured horizontally) the road rises 6 feet (measured vertically). See Fig. 3.11. The ratio of 6 to 100 is 6%. If a roof rises 9 feet in a horizontal distance (or run) of 12 feet, then the roof has a 9–12 pitch. A roof with a 9–12 pitch is steeper than a roof with a 6–12 pitch. The grade of a road and the pitch of a roof are measurements of steepness. In each case the measurement is a ratio of rise (vertical change) to run (horizontal change).

FIGURE 3.11

We measure the steepness of a line in the same way that we measure steepness of a road or a roof. The slope of a line is the ratio of the change in y-coordinate, or the **rise,** to the change in x-coordinate, or the **run,** between two points on the line.

Slope

$$\text{Slope} = \frac{\text{change in } y\text{-coordinate}}{\text{change in } x\text{-coordinate}} = \frac{\text{rise}}{\text{run}}$$

Consider the line in Fig. 3.12(a). In going from (0, 1) to (1, 3), there is a change of $+1$ in the x-coordinate and a change of $+2$ in the y-coordinate, or a run of 1 and a rise of 2. So the slope is $\frac{2}{1}$ or 2. If we move from (1, 3) to (0, 1) as in Fig. 3.12(b) the rise is -2 and the run is -1. So the slope is $\frac{-2}{-1}$ or 2. If we start at either point and move to the other point, we get the same slope.

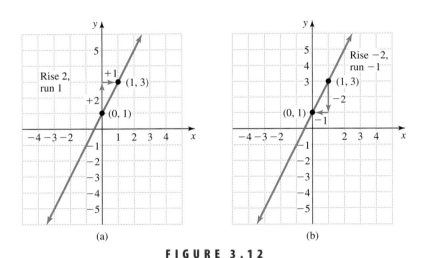

(a)   (b)

FIGURE 3.12

EXAMPLE 1

Finding the slope from a graph

Find the slope of each line by going from point A to point B.

a)

b)

c)
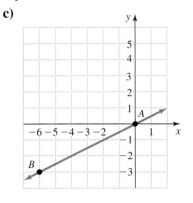

Solution

a) *A* is located at $(0, 3)$ and *B* at $(2, 0)$. In going from *A* to *B*, the change in *y* is -3 and the change in *x* is 2. So

$$\text{slope} = \frac{-3}{2} = -\frac{3}{2}.$$

b) In going from $A(2, 1)$ to $B(6, 3)$, we must rise 2 and run 4. So

$$\text{slope} = \frac{2}{4} = \frac{1}{2}.$$

c) In going from $A(0, 0)$ to $B(-6, -3)$, we find that the rise is -3 and the run is -6. So

$$\text{slope} = \frac{-3}{-6} = \frac{1}{2}.$$ ■

Note that in Example 1(c) we found the slope of the line of Example 1(b) by using two different points. The slope is the ratio of the lengths of the two legs of a right triangle whose hypotenuse is on the line. See Fig. 3.13. As long as one leg is vertical and the other leg is horizontal, all such triangles for a given line have the same shape: They are similar triangles. Because ratios of corresponding sides in similar triangles are equal, the slope has the same value no matter which two points of the line are used to find it.

FIGURE 3.13

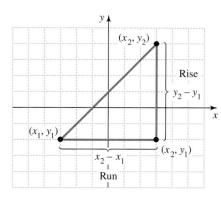

FIGURE 3.14

Using Coordinates to Find Slope

We can obtain the rise and run from a graph, or we can get them without a graph by subtracting the *y*-coordinates to get the rise and the *x*-coordinates to get the run for two points on the line. See Fig. 3.14.

Slope Using Coordinates

The slope *m* of the line containing the points (x_1, y_1) and (x_2, y_2) is given by

$$m = \frac{y_2 - y_1}{x_2 - x_1}, \qquad \text{provided that } x_2 - x_1 \neq 0.$$

E X A M P L E   2

Finding slope from coordinates

Find the slope of each line.

a) The line through $(2, 5)$ and $(6, 3)$

b) The line through $(-2, 3)$ and $(-5, -1)$

c) The line through $(-6, 4)$ and the origin

Solution

a) Let $(x_1, y_1) = (2, 5)$ and $(x_2, y_2) = (6, 3)$. The assignment of (x_1, y_1) and (x_2, y_2) is arbitrary.

$$m = \frac{y_2 - y_1}{x_2 - x_1} = \frac{3 - 5}{6 - 2} = \frac{-2}{4} = -\frac{1}{2}$$

b) Let $(x_1, y_1) = (-5, -1)$ and $(x_2, y_2) = (-2, 3)$:

$$m = \frac{y_2 - y_1}{x_2 - x_1} = \frac{3 - (-1)}{-2 - (-5)} = \frac{4}{3}$$

c) Let $(x_1, y_1) = (0, 0)$ and $(x_2, y_2) = (-6, 4)$:

$$m = \frac{4 - 0}{-6 - 0} = \frac{4}{-6} = -\frac{2}{3}$$

■

C A U T I O N   Do not reverse the order of subtraction from numerator to denominator when finding the slope. If you divide $y_2 - y_1$ by $x_1 - x_2$, you will get the wrong sign for the slope.

E X A M P L E   3

Slope for horizontal and vertical lines

Find the slope of each line.

a)

b)

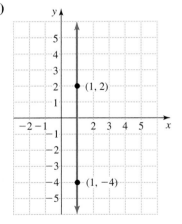

Solution

a) Using $(-3, 2)$ and $(4, 2)$ to find the slope of the horizontal line, we get

$$m = \frac{2 - 2}{-3 - 4}$$

$$= \frac{0}{-7} = 0.$$

Helpful Hint

Think about what slope means to skiers. No one skis on cliffs or even refers to them as slopes.

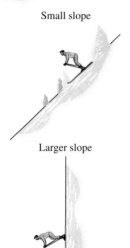

Zero slope

Small slope

Larger slope

Undefined slope

b) Using $(1, -4)$ and $(1, 2)$ to find the slope of the vertical line, we get $x_2 - x_1 = 0$. Because the definition of slope using coordinates says that $x_2 - x_1$ must be nonzero, the slope is undefined for this line. ∎

Since the y-coordinates are equal for any two points on a horizontal line, $y_2 - y_1 = 0$ and the slope is 0. Since the x-coordinates are equal for any two points on a vertical line, $x_2 - x_1 = 0$ and the slope is undefined.

Horizontal and Vertical Lines

The slope of any horizontal line is 0.
Slope is undefined for any vertical line.

CAUTION   Do not say that a vertical line has no slope because "no slope" could be confused with 0 slope, the slope of a horizontal line.

As you move the tip of your pencil from left to right along a line with positive slope, the y-coordinates are increasing. As you move the tip of your pencil from left to right along a line with negative slope, the y-coordinates are decreasing. See Fig. 3.15.

FIGURE 3.15

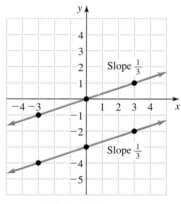

FIGURE 3.16

Parallel Lines

Consider the two lines shown in Fig. 3.16. Each of these lines has a slope of $\frac{1}{3}$, and these lines are parallel. In general, we have the following fact.

Parallel Lines

Nonvertical parallel lines have equal slopes.

Of course, any two vertical lines are parallel, but we cannot say that they have equal slopes because slope is not defined for vertical lines.

E X A M P L E 4

Parallel lines

Line l goes through the origin and is parallel to the line through $(-2, 3)$ and $(4, -5)$. Find the slope of line l.

Solution

The line through $(-2, 3)$ and $(4, -5)$ has slope

$$m = \frac{-5 - 3}{4 - (-2)} = \frac{-8}{6} = -\frac{4}{3}.$$

Because line l is parallel to a line with slope $-\frac{4}{3}$, the slope of line l is $-\frac{4}{3}$ also. ∎

Perpendicular Lines

The lines shown in Fig. 3.17 have slopes 2 and $-\frac{1}{2}$. These two lines appear to be perpendicular to each other. It can be shown that *a line is perpendicular to another line if its slope is the negative of the reciprocal of the slope of the other.*

Perpendicular Lines

Two lines with slopes m_1 and m_2 are perpendicular if and only if

$$m_1 = -\frac{1}{m_2}.$$

FIGURE 3.17

Note that the relationship between slopes of perpendicular lines can also be expressed by the equation $m_1 \cdot m_2 = -1$. Of course, any vertical line and any horizontal line are perpendicular, but their slopes do not satisfy this equation because slope is undefined for vertical lines.

E X A M P L E 5

Perpendicular lines

Line l contains the point $(1, 6)$ and is perpendicular to the line through $(-4, 1)$ and $(3, -2)$. Find the slope of line l.

Solution

The line through $(-4, 1)$ and $(3, -2)$ has slope

$$m = \frac{1 - (-2)}{-4 - 3} = \frac{3}{-7} = -\frac{3}{7}.$$

Because line l is perpendicular to a line with slope $-\frac{3}{7}$, the slope of line l is $\frac{7}{3}$. ∎

Applications of Slope

When a geometric figure is located in a coordinate system, we can use slope to determine whether it has any parallel or perpendicular sides.

E X A M P L E   6

Using slope with geometric figures

Determine whether $(-3, 2)$, $(-2, -1)$, $(4, 1)$, and $(3, 4)$ are the vertices of a rectangle.

Solution

Figure 3.18 shows the quadrilateral determined by these points. If a parallelogram has at least one right angle, then it is a rectangle. Calculate the slope of each side.

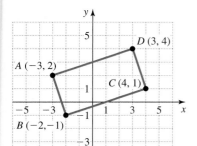

FIGURE 3.18

$$m_{AB} = \frac{2 - (-1)}{-3 - (-2)} \qquad m_{BC} = \frac{-1 - 1}{-2 - 4}$$

$$= \frac{3}{-1} = -3 \qquad = \frac{-2}{-6} = \frac{1}{3}$$

$$m_{CD} = \frac{1 - 4}{4 - 3} \qquad m_{AD} = \frac{2 - 4}{-3 - 3}$$

$$= \frac{-3}{1} = -3 \qquad = \frac{-2}{-6} = \frac{1}{3}$$

Because the opposite sides have the same slope, they are parallel, and the figure is a parallelogram. Because $\frac{1}{3}$ is the opposite of the reciprocal of -3, the intersecting sides are perpendicular. Therefore the figure is a rectangle. ∎

The slope of a line is a rate. The slope tells us how much the dependent variable changes for a change of 1 in the independent variable. For example, if the horizontal axis is hours and the vertical axis is miles, then the slope is miles per hour (mph). If the horizontal axis is days and the vertical axis is dollars, then the slope is dollars per day.

E X A M P L E   7

Interpreting slope

Worldwide carbon dioxide (CO_2) emissions have increased from 14 billion tons in 1970 to 26 billion tons in 2000 (World Resources Institute, www.wri.org).

a) Find and interpret the slope of the line in Fig. 3.19.

b) Use the slope to predict the amount of worldwide CO_2 emissions in 2010.

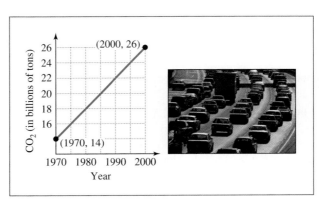

FIGURE 3.19

Study Tip

Finding out what happened in class and attending class are not the same. Attend every class and be attentive. Don't just take notes and let your mind wander. Use class time as a learning time.

Solution

a) Find the slope of the line through (1970, 14) and (2000, 26):

$$m = \frac{26 - 14}{2000 - 1970} = \frac{12}{30} = 0.4$$

So CO_2 emissions are increasing 0.4 billion tons per year.

b) If the CO_2 emissions keep increasing 0.4 billion tons per year, then in 10 years the level will go up 10(0.4) or 4 billion tons. So in 2010 CO_2 emissions will be 30 billion tons. ■

WARM-UPS

True or false? Explain your answer.

1. Slope is a measurement of the steepness of a line.

2. Slope is run divided by rise.

3. The line through (4, 5) and (−3, 5) has undefined slope.

4. The line through (−2, 6) and (−2, −5) has undefined slope.

5. Slope cannot be negative.

6. The slope of the line through (0, −2) and (5, 0) is $-\frac{2}{5}$.

7. The line through (4, 4) and (5, 5) has slope $\frac{5}{4}$.

8. If a line contains points in quadrants I and III, then its slope is positive.

9. Lines with slope $\frac{2}{3}$ and $-\frac{2}{3}$ are perpendicular to each other.

10. Any two parallel lines have equal slopes.

3.2   EXERCISES

Reading and Writing   *After reading this section, write out the answers to these questions. Use complete sentences.*

1. What does slope measure?

2. What is the rise and what is the run?

3. Why does a horizontal line have zero slope?

4. Why is slope undefined for vertical lines?

5. What is the relationship between the slopes of perpendicular lines?

6. What is the relationship between the slopes of parallel lines?

Determine the slope of each line. See Example 1.

7.

8.

9.

10.

11.

12.

13.

14.

15.

16.

17.

18.

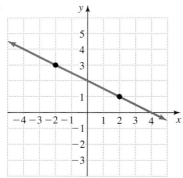

Find the slope of the line that contains each of the following pairs of points. See Examples 2 and 3.

19. $(2, 6), (5, 1)$

20. $(3, 4), (6, 10)$

21. $(-3, -1), (4, 3)$

22. $(-2, -3), (1, 3)$

23. $(-2, 2), (-1, 7)$

24. $(-3, 5), (1, -6)$

25. $(3, -5), (0, 0)$

26. $(0, 0), (-2, -1)$

27. $(0, 3), (5, 0)$

28. $(3, 0), (0, 10)$

29. $\left(\frac{3}{4}, -1\right), \left(-\frac{1}{2}, -\frac{1}{2}\right)$

30. $\left(\frac{1}{2}, 2\right), \left(\frac{1}{4}, \frac{1}{2}\right)$

31. $(6, 212), (7, 209)$

32. $(1988, 306), (1990, 315)$

33. $(4, 7), (-12, 7)$

34. $(5, -3), (9, -3)$

35. $(2, 6), (2, -6)$

36. $(-3, 2), (-3, 0)$

37. $(24.3, 11.9), (3.57, 8.4)$

38. $(-2.7, 19.3), (5.46, -3.28)$

39. $\left(\frac{\pi}{4}, 1\right), \left(\frac{\pi}{2}, 0\right)$

40. $\left(\frac{\pi}{3}, -1\right), \left(\frac{\pi}{6}, 0\right)$

In each case, make a sketch and find the slope of line l. See Examples 4 and 5.

41. Line *l* contains the point (3, 4) and is perpendicular to the line through $(-5, 1)$ and $(3, -2)$.

42. Line *l* goes through $(-3, -5)$ and is perpendicular to the line through $(-2, 6)$ and $(5, 3)$.

43. Line *l* goes through (2, 5) and is parallel to the line through $(-3, -2)$ and (4, 1).

44. Line *l* goes through the origin and is parallel to the line through $(-3, -5)$ and $(4, -1)$.

45. Line *l* is perpendicular to a line with slope $\frac{4}{5}$. Both lines contain the origin.

46. Line *l* is perpendicular to a line with slope -5. Both lines contain the origin.

Solve each geometric figure problem. See Example 6.

47. If the opposite sides of a quadrilateral are parallel, then it is a parallelogram. Use slope to determine whether the points $(-6, 1)$, $(-2, -1)$, $(0, 3)$, and $(4, 1)$ are the vertices of a parallelogram.

48. Use slope to determine whether the points $(-7, 0)$, $(-1, 6)$, $(-1, -2)$, and $(6, 5)$ are the vertices of a parallelogram. See Exercise 47.

49. A trapezoid is a quadrilateral with one pair of parallel sides. Use slope to determine whether the points $(-3, 2)$, $(-1, -1)$, $(3, 6)$, and $(6, 4)$ are the vertices of a trapezoid.

50. A parallelogram with at least one right angle is a rectangle. Determine whether the points $(-4, 4)$, $(-1, -2)$, $(0, 6)$, and $(3, 0)$ are the vertices of a rectangle.

51. If a triangle has one right angle, then it is a right triangle. Use slope to determine whether the points $(-3, 3)$, $(-1, 6)$, and $(0, 0)$ are the vertices of a right triangle.

52. Use slope to determine whether the points $(0, -1)$, $(2, 5)$, and $(5, 4)$ are the vertices of a right triangle. See Exercise 51.

Solve each problem. See Example 7.

53. *Pricing the Crown Victoria.* The list price for a new Ford Crown Victoria four-door sedan was \$21,135 in 1998 and \$23,635 in 2002 (www.edmunds.com).
  a) Find the slope of the line shown in the accompanying figure.
  b) Use the accompanying figure to predict the price in 2010.
  c) Use the slope to predict the price in 2010.

FIGURE FOR EXERCISE 53

54. *Depreciating Monte Carlo.* In 2002 the average retail price of a one-year-old Chevrolet Monte Carlo was \$13,690, whereas the average retail price of a 4-year-old Monte Carlo was \$7381 (www.edmunds.com).
  a) Use the accompanying graph to estimate the average retail price of a 3-year-old car in 2002.

  b) Find the slope of the line in the figure.

  c) Use the slope to predict the price of a 3-year-old car in 2002.

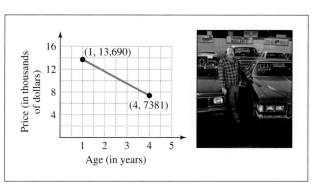

FIGURE FOR EXERCISE 54

MISCELLANEOUS

55. The points (3,) and (, −7) are on the line that passes through (2, 1) and has slope 4. Find the missing coordinates of the points.

56. If a line passes through (5, 2) and has slope $\frac{2}{3}$, then what is the value of y on this line when $x = 8$, $x = 11$, and $x = 12$?

57. Find k so that the line through (2, k) and (−3, −5) has slope $\frac{1}{2}$.

58. Find k so that the line through (k, 3) and (−2, 0) has slope 3.

59. What is the slope of a line that is perpendicular to a line with slope 0.247?

60. What is the slope of a line that is perpendicular to the line through (3.27, −1.46) and (−5.48, 3.61)?

GETTING MORE INVOLVED

61. Writing. What is the difference between zero slope and undefined slope?

62. Writing. Is it possible for a line to be in only one quadrant? Two quadrants? Write a rule for determining whether a line has positive, negative, zero, or undefined slope from knowing in which quadrants the line is found.

63. Exploration. A rhombus is a quadrilateral with four equal sides. Draw a rhombus with vertices (−3, −1), (0, 3), (2, −1), and (5, 3). Find the slopes of the diagonals of the rhombus. What can you conclude about the diagonals of this rhombus?

64. Exploration. Draw a square with vertices (−5, 3), (−3, −3), (1, 5), and (3, −1). Find the slopes of the diagonals of the square. What can you conclude about the diagonals of this square?

GRAPHING CALCULATOR EXERCISES

65. Graph $y = 1x$, $y = 2x$, $y = 3x$, and $y = 4x$ together in the standard viewing window. These equations are all of the form $y = mx$. What effect does increasing m have on the graph of the equation? What are the slopes of these four lines?

66. Graph $y = -1x$, $y = -2x$, $y = -3x$, and $y = -4x$ together in the standard viewing window. These equations are all of the form $y = mx$. What effect does decreasing m have on the graph of the equation? What are the slopes of these four lines?

In This Section

- Point-Slope Form
- Slope-Intercept Form
- Standard Form
- Using Slope-Intercept Form for Graphing
- Applications

3.3

THREE FORMS FOR THE EQUATION OF A LINE

In Section 3.1 you learned how to graph a straight line corresponding to a linear equation. The line contains all of the points that satisfy the equation. In this section we start with a line or a description of a line and write an equation corresponding to the line.

Point-Slope Form

Figure 3.20 shows the line that has slope $\frac{2}{3}$ and contains the point (3, 5). In Section 3.2 you learned that the slope is the same no matter which two points of the line are used to calculate it. So if we find the slope m for this line using an arbitrary point of the line, say (x, y), and the specific point (3, 5), we get

$$m = \frac{y - 5}{x - 3}.$$

Because the slope of this line is $\frac{2}{3}$, we can write

$$\frac{y - 5}{x - 3} = \frac{2}{3}.$$

Multiplying each side by $x - 3$, we get

$$y - 5 = \frac{2}{3}(x - 3).$$

Because (x, y) was an arbitrary point on the line, this equation is satisfied by every point on the line.

If we use (x_1, y_1) as the specific point and (x, y) as an arbitrary point on a line with slope m, we can write

$$\frac{y - y_1}{x - x_1} = m.$$

Multiplying each side of this equation by $x - x_1$ gives us the **point-slope form** of the equation of the line.

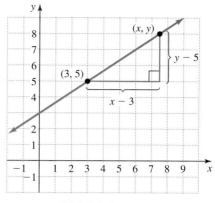

FIGURE 3.20

Point-Slope Form

The equation of the line through (x_1, y_1) with slope m in point-slope form is

$$y - y_1 = m(x - x_1).$$

E X A M P L E   1

Writing an equation for a line given a point and the slope

Find an equation for the line through $(-2, 5)$ with slope -3 and solve it for y.

Solution

Use $x_1 = -2$, $y_1 = 5$, and $m = -3$ in the point-slope form:

$$y - 5 = -3[x - (-2)]$$

Now solve the equation for y:

$$y - 5 = -3[x + 2]$$
$$y - 5 = -3x - 6$$
$$y = -3x - 1$$

■

If you know two points on a line, then you can graph the line (two points determine a line). In Example 2 we will see that two points of a line also determine an equation for the line.

E X A M P L E   2

Writing an equation for a line given two points on the line

Find the equation of the line through the given pair of points and solve it for y.

a) $(3, 5)$ and $(4, 7)$ **b)** $(3, -2)$ and $(-1, 1)$

Calculator Close-Up

Graph $y = \left(-\frac{3}{4}\right)x + \frac{1}{4}$ and check that the line goes through $(3, -2)$ and $(-1, 1)$ by using the TRACE feature.

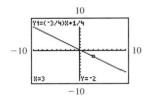

Solution

a) First find the slope:

$$m = \frac{y_2 - y_1}{x_2 - x_1} = \frac{7 - 5}{4-3} = 2$$

Now use the slope and one point, say $(3, 5)$, in the point-slope form:

$$y - y_1 = m(x - x_1) \quad \text{Point-slope form}$$
$$y - 5 = 2(x - 3) \quad \text{Substitute } m = 2, (x_1, y_1) = (3, 5).$$
$$y - 5 = 2x - 6 \quad \text{Distributive property}$$
$$y = 2x - 1 \quad \text{Solve for } y.$$

Because $(3, 5)$ and $(4, 7)$ both satisfy $y = 2x - 1$, we can be sure that we have the correct equation.

b) First find the slope of the line through $(3, -2)$ and $(-1, 1)$:

$$m = \frac{1 - (-2)}{-1 - 3}$$
$$= \frac{3}{-4} = -\frac{3}{4}$$

Now use this slope and one of the points, say $(3, -2)$, to write the equation in point-slope form:

$$y - (-2) = -\frac{3}{4}(x - 3) \quad \text{Point-slope form}$$
$$y + 2 = -\frac{3}{4}x + \frac{9}{4} \quad \text{Distributive property}$$
$$y = -\frac{3}{4}x + \frac{1}{4} \quad \text{Solve for } y: \frac{9}{4} - 2 = \frac{9}{4} - \frac{8}{4} = \frac{1}{4}.$$

Note that we would get the same equation if we had used slope $-\frac{3}{4}$ and the other point $(-1, 1)$. Try it. ■

We know that if a line has slope m, then the slope of any line perpendicular to it is $-\frac{1}{m}$, provided $m \neq 0$. We also know that nonvertical parallel lines have equal slopes. These facts are used in Example 3.

E X A M P L E   3

Writing equations of perpendicular and parallel lines

In each case find the equation for line l and then solve it for y.

a) Line l goes through $(2, 0)$ and is perpendicular to the line through $(5, -1)$ and $(-1, 3)$.

b) Line l goes through $(-1, 6)$ and is parallel to the line through $(2, 4)$ and $(7, -11)$.

Solution

a) First find the slope of the line through $(5, -1)$ and $(-1, 3)$:

$$m = \frac{3 - (-1)}{-1 - 5} = \frac{4}{-6} = -\frac{2}{3}$$

Study Tip

When taking a test, put a check mark beside every question that you have answered and checked. When you have finished the test, then you can go back and spend the remaining time on the problems that are not yet checked. You will not waste time reworking problems that you know are correct.

Because line l is perpendicular to this line, line l has slope $\frac{3}{2}$. Now use $(2, 0)$ and the slope $\frac{3}{2}$ in the point-slope formula to get the equation of line l:

$$y - 0 = \frac{3}{2}(x - 2)$$

$$y = \frac{3}{2}x - 3 \quad \text{Distributive property}$$

b) First find the slope of the line through $(2, 4)$ and $(7, -11)$:

$$m = \frac{-11 - 4}{7 - 2} = \frac{-15}{5} = -3$$

Since parallel lines have equal slopes, use the slope -3 and the point $(-1, 6)$:

$$y - 6 = -3(x - (-1)) \quad \text{Point-slope form}$$
$$y - 6 = -3(x + 1) \quad \text{Simplify.}$$
$$y - 6 = -3x - 3 \quad \text{Distributive property}$$
$$y = -3x + 3 \quad \text{Solve for } y. \quad \blacksquare$$

Calculator Close-Up

With slope-intercept form and a graphing calculator, it is easy to see how the slope affects the steepness of a line. The graphs of $y_1 = \frac{1}{2}x$, $y_2 = x$, $y_3 = 2x$, and $y_4 = 3x$ are all shown on the accompanying screen.

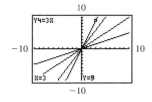

Slope-Intercept Form

The line $y = -3x - 1$ in Example 1 has slope -3. To find the y-intercept of this line, let $x = 0$ in $y = -3x - 1$: $y = -3(0) - 1 = -1$. The y-intercept is $(0, -1)$. Its y-coordinate appears in the equation:

$$y = -3x - 1$$

Slope y-intercept $(0, -1)$

Because the slope and y-intercept can be read from the equation when it is solved for y, this form of the equation of the line is called slope-intercept form.

> ### Slope-Intercept Form
>
> The equation of a line in **slope-intercept form** is
>
> $$y = mx + b,$$
>
> where m is the slope and $(0, b)$ is the y-intercept.

E X A M P L E 4

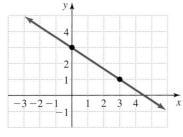

FIGURE 3.21

Writing an equation given its slope and y-intercept
Write the slope-intercept form of the equation of the line shown in Fig. 3.21.

Solution

From Fig. 3.21 we see that the y-intercept is $(0, 3)$. If we start at the y-intercept and move down 2 and 3 to the right, we get to another point on the line. So the slope is $-\frac{2}{3}$. The equation of this line in slope-intercept form is

$$y = -\frac{2}{3}x + 3. \quad \blacksquare$$

Study Tip

Get in the habit of checking your work and having confidence in your answers. The answers to the odd-numbered exercises are in the back of this book, but you should look in the answer section only after you have checked on your own. You will not always have an answer section available.

Standard Form

If x students paid $5 each and y adults paid $7 each to attend a play for which the ticket sales totaled $1900, then we can write the equation $5x + 7y = 1900$. This form of a linear equation is common in applications. It is called standard form.

> **Standard Form**
>
> The equation of a line in **standard form** is
> $$Ax + By = C,$$
> where A, B, and C are real numbers with A and B not both zero.

The numbers A, B, and C in standard form can be any real numbers, but it is a common practice to write standard form using only integers and a positive coefficient for x.

E X A M P L E   5

Changing to standard form

Write the equation $y = \frac{1}{2}x - \frac{3}{4}$ in standard form using only integers and a positive coefficient for x.

Helpful Hint

Solve $Ax + By = C$ for y, to get
$$y = \frac{-A}{B}x + \frac{C}{B}.$$
So the slope of $Ax + By = C$ is $-\frac{A}{B}$. This fact can be used in checking standard form. The slope of $2x - 4y = 3$ in Example 5 is $\frac{-2}{-4}$ or $\frac{1}{2}$, which is the slope of the original equation.

Solution

Use the properties of equality to get the equation in the form $Ax + By = C$:

$$y = \frac{1}{2}x - \frac{3}{4} \quad \text{Original equation}$$

$$-\frac{1}{2}x + y = -\frac{3}{4} \quad \text{Subtract } \tfrac{1}{2}x \text{ from each side.}$$

$$4\left(-\frac{1}{2}x + y\right) = 4\left(-\frac{3}{4}\right) \quad \text{Multiply each side by 4 to get integral coefficients.}$$

$$-2x + 4y = -3 \quad \text{Distributive property}$$

$$2x - 4y = 3 \quad \text{Multiply by } -1 \text{ to make the coefficient of } x \text{ positive.}$$

To find the slope and y-intercept of a line written in standard form, we convert the equation to slope-intercept form.

E X A M P L E   6

Changing to slope-intercept form

Find the slope and y-intercept of the line $3x - 2y = 5$.

Helpful Hint

Note that every term in a linear equation in two variables is either a constant or a multiple of a variable. That is why equations in one variable of the form $ax + b = 0$ were called linear equations in Chapter 2.

Solution

Solve for y to get slope-intercept form:

$$3x - 2y = 5 \quad \text{Original equation}$$

$$-2y = -3x + 5 \quad \text{Subtract } 3x \text{ from each side.}$$

$$y = \frac{3}{2}x - \frac{5}{2} \quad \text{Divide each side by } -2.$$

The slope is $\frac{3}{2}$, and the y-intercept is $\left(0, -\frac{5}{2}\right)$.

You learned in Section 3.1 that the graph of the equation $x = 4$ is a vertical line. Because slope is undefined for vertical lines, the equation of this line cannot be written in slope-intercept form or point-slope form. Only nonvertical lines can be written in those forms. However, a vertical line can be written in standard form. For example,

$$x = 4$$

can be written as

$$1 \cdot x + 0 \cdot y = 4.$$

Every line has an equation in standard form.

E X A M P L E   7

Finding the equation of a line

Write an equation in standard form with integral coefficients for the line l through $(2, 5)$ that is perpendicular to the line $2x + 3y = 1$.

Solution

First solve the equation $2x + 3y = 1$ for y to find its slope:

$$2x + 3y = 1$$
$$3y = -2x + 1$$
$$y = -\frac{2}{3}x + \frac{1}{3} \qquad \text{The slope is } -\frac{2}{3}.$$

The slope of line l is the opposite of the reciprocal of $-\frac{2}{3}$. So line l has slope $\frac{3}{2}$ and goes through $(2, 5)$. Now use the point-slope form to write the equation:

$$y - 5 = \frac{3}{2}(x - 2) \qquad \text{Point-slope form}$$

$$y - 5 = \frac{3}{2}x - 3 \qquad \text{Distributive property}$$

$$y = \frac{3}{2}x + 2$$

$$-\frac{3}{2}x + y = 2$$

$$3x - 2y = -4 \qquad \text{Multiply each side by } -2.$$

So $3x - 2y = -4$ is the standard form of the equation of the line through $(2, 5)$ that is perpendicular to $2x + 3y = 1$. ∎

Using Slope-Intercept Form for Graphing

In the slope-intercept form, a point on the line (the y-intercept) and the slope are readily available. To graph a line, we can start at the y-intercept and count off the rise and run to get a second point on the line.

E X A M P L E   8

Using slope and y-intercept to graph

Graph the line $2x - 3y = -3$.

Solution

First write the equation in slope-intercept form:

$$2x - 3y = -3$$
$$-3y = -2x - 3$$
$$y = \frac{2}{3}x + 1$$

Calculator Close-Up

Graph $y_1 = \left(-\frac{2}{3}\right)x + \frac{1}{3}$ and $y_2 = \left(\frac{3}{2}\right)x + 2$ to check that y_2 is perpendicular to y_1 and that y_2 goes through $(2, 5)$. The lines will look perpendicular only if the same unit length is used on both axes.

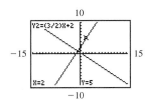

Some calculators have a feature that adjusts the window to get the same unit length on both axes.

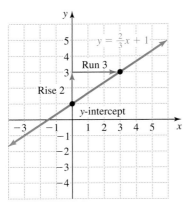

FIGURE 3.22

The slope is $\frac{2}{3}$, and the y-intercept is $(0, 1)$. Start at $(0, 1)$ on the y-axis, then rise 2 and run 3 to locate a second point on the line. Because there is only one line containing any two given points, these two points determine the line. See Fig. 3.22. ■

The three methods that we used for graphing linear equations are summarized as follows.

Methods for Graphing a Linear Equation

1. Arbitrarily select some points that satisfy the equation, and draw a line through them.

2. Find the x- and y-intercepts (provided that they are not the origin), and draw a line through them.

3. Start at the y-intercept and use the slope to locate a second point, then draw a line through the two points.

If the y-coordinate of the y-intercept is an integer and the slope is a rational number, then it is usually the easiest to use the y-intercept and slope.

Applications

The linear equation $y = mx + b$ with $m \neq 0$ is a formula that expresses y in terms of x. In Example 9, we use the point-slope formula to write Fahrenheit temperature in terms of Celsius temperature.

E X A M P L E   9

Writing a linear equation given two points

The equation that expresses Fahrenheit temperature F in terms of Celsius temperature C is linear. Water freezes at 0°C or 32°F and boils at 100°C or 212°F. Find the linear equation.

Solution

We want the equation of the line that contains the points $(0, 32)$ and $(100, 212)$ as shown in Fig. 3.23. Use C as the independent variable (x) and F as the dependent variable (y). The slope of the line is

$$m = \frac{F_2 - F_1}{C_2 - C_1} = \frac{212 - 32}{100 - 0} = \frac{180}{100} = \frac{9}{5}.$$

FIGURE 3.23

Using a slope of $\frac{9}{5}$ and the point $(100, 212)$ in the point-slope formula, we get

$$F - 212 = \frac{9}{5}(C - 100).$$

We can solve this equation for F to get the familiar formula relating Celsius and Fahrenheit temperature:

$$F = \frac{9}{5}C + 32$$

Because we knew the intercept $(0, 32)$, we could have used it and the slope $\frac{9}{5}$ in slope-intercept form to write $F = \frac{9}{5}C + 32$.   ■

WARM-UPS

True or false? Explain your answer.

1. There is exactly one line through a given point with a given slope.
2. The line $y - a = m(x - b)$ goes through (a, b) and has slope m.
3. The equation of the line through (a, b) with slope m is $y = mx + b$.
4. The x-coordinate of the y-intercept of a nonvertical line is 0.
5. The y-coordinate of the x-intercept of a nonhorizontal line is 0.
6. Every line in the xy-plane has an equation in slope-intercept form.
7. The line $2y + 3x = 7$ has slope $-\frac{3}{2}$.
8. The line $y = 3x - 1$ is perpendicular to the line $y = \frac{1}{3}x - 1$.
9. The line $2y = 3x + 5$ has a y-intercept of $(0, 5)$.
10. Every line in the xy-plane has an equation in standard form.

3.3   EXERCISES

Reading and Writing   *After reading this section, write out the answers to these questions. Use complete sentences.*

1. What is point-slope form?

2. What is slope-intercept form?

3. What two bits of information must you have to write the equation of a line from a description of the line?

4. What is standard form?

5. How do you find the slope of a line when its equation is given in standard form?

6. How do you graph a line when its equation is given in slope-intercept form?

Find the equation of line l in each case and solve it for y. See Examples 1–3.

7. Line *l* goes through $(2, -3)$ and has slope 2.

8. Line *l* goes through $(-3, -1)$ and has slope 6.

9. Line *l* goes through $(-2, 3)$ and has slope $-\frac{1}{2}$.

10. Line *l* goes through $(3, 5)$ and has slope $\frac{2}{3}$.

11. Line *l* goes through $(-2, -1)$ and $(3, -6)$.

12. Line *l* goes through $(-1, -5)$ and $(2, 1)$.

13. Line *l* goes through $(2, 2)$ and $(-1, 1)$.

14. Line *l* goes through $(2, 3)$ and $(-5, 6)$.

15. Line *l* goes through $(-1, -12)$ and is perpendicular to the line through $(-3, 1)$ and $(5, -1)$.

16. Line *l* goes through $(0, 0)$ and is perpendicular to the line through $(0, 6)$ and $(-5, 0)$.

17. Line *l* goes through $(0, 0)$ and is parallel to the line through $(9, -3)$ and $(-3, 6)$.

18. Line *l* goes through $(2, -4)$ and is parallel to the line through $(6, 2)$ and $(-2, 6)$.

In Exercises 19–30, write an equation in slope-intercept form (if possible) for each of the lines shown. See Example 4.

19.

20.

21.

22.

23.

24.

25.

26.

27.

28.

29.

30.

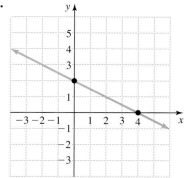

Write each equation in standard form using only integers and a positive coefficient for x. See Example 5.

31. $y = \dfrac{1}{3}x - 2$

32. $y = \dfrac{1}{2}x + 7$

33. $y - 5 = \dfrac{1}{2}(x + 3)$

34. $y - 1 = \dfrac{1}{4}(x - 6)$

35. $y + \dfrac{1}{2} = \dfrac{1}{3}(x - 4)$

36. $y + \dfrac{1}{3} = \dfrac{1}{4}(x - 3)$

37. $0.05x + 0.06y - 8.9 = 0$

38. $0.03x - 0.07y = 2$

Write each equation in slope-intercept form, and identify the slope and y-intercept. See Example 6.

39. $2x + 5y = 1$

40. $3x - 3y = 2$

41. $3x - y - 2 = 0$

42. $5 - x - 2y = 0$

43. $y + 3 = 5$

44. $y - 9 = 0$

45. $y - 2 = 3(x - 1)$

46. $y + 4 = -2(x - 5)$

47. $\dfrac{y - 5}{x + 4} = \dfrac{3}{2}$

48. $\dfrac{y - 6}{x - 2} = -\dfrac{3}{5}$

49. $y - \dfrac{1}{2} = \dfrac{1}{3}\left(x + \dfrac{1}{4}\right)$

50. $y - \dfrac{1}{3} = -\dfrac{1}{2}\left(x - \dfrac{1}{4}\right)$

51. $y - 6000 = 0.01(x + 5700)$

52. $y - 5000 = 0.05(x - 1990)$

Find the equation of line l in each case and then write it in standard form with integral coefficients. See Example 7.

53. Line l has slope $\frac{1}{2}$ and goes through $(0, 5)$.

54. Line l has slope 5 and goes through $\left(0, \frac{1}{2}\right)$.

55. Line l has x-intercept $(2, 0)$ and y-intercept $(0, 4)$.

56. Line l has y-intercept $(0, 5)$ and x-intercept $(4, 0)$.

57. Line l goes through $(-3, -1)$ and is parallel to $y = 2x + 6$.

58. Line l goes through $(1, -3)$ and is parallel to $y = -3x - 5$.

59. Line l is parallel to $2x + 4y = 1$ and goes through $(-3, 5)$.

60. Line l is parallel to $3x - 5y = -7$ and goes through $(-8, -2)$.

61. Line l goes through $(1, 1)$ and is perpendicular to $y = \frac{1}{2}x - 3$.

62. Line l goes through $(-1, -2)$ and is perpendicular to $y = -3x + 7$.

63. Line l goes through $(-4, -3)$ and is perpendicular to $x + 3y = 4$.

64. Line l is perpendicular to $2y + 5 - 3x = 0$ and goes through $(2, 7)$.

65. Line l goes through $(2, 5)$ and is parallel to the x-axis.

66. Line l goes through $(-1, 6)$ and is parallel to the y-axis.

Graph each line. Use the slope and y-intercept when possible. See Example 8.

67. $y = \dfrac{1}{2}x$

68. $y = -\dfrac{2}{3}x$

69. $y = 2x - 3$

70. $y = -x + 1$

71. $y = -\dfrac{2}{3}x + 2$

72. $y = 3x - 4$

73. $3y + x = 0$

74. $4y - x = 0$

81. $y = \dfrac{3}{4}x + 3$

$y = -\dfrac{4}{3}x + 1$

82. $y = \dfrac{2}{3}x + 1$

$y = -\dfrac{3}{2}x + 3$

Graph each pair of lines in the same coordinate system using the slope and y-intercept.

75. $y = x + 3$
$y = x + 2$

76. $y = -x + 2$
$y = -x - 2$

Determine whether each pair of lines is parallel, perpendicular, or neither.

83. $y = 3x - 8, x + 3y = 7$

84. $y = \dfrac{1}{2}x - 4, \dfrac{1}{2}x + \dfrac{1}{4}y = 1$

85. $2x - 4y = 9, \dfrac{1}{3}x = \dfrac{2}{3}y - 8$

86. $\dfrac{1}{4}x - \dfrac{1}{6}y = \dfrac{1}{3}, \dfrac{1}{3}y = \dfrac{1}{2}x - 2$

87. $2y = x + 6, y - 2x = 4$

88. $y - 3x = 5, 3x + y = 7$

77. $y = 3x + 1$
$y = -\dfrac{1}{3}x + 1$

78. $y = 2x + 3$
$y = -\dfrac{1}{2}x + 3$

89. $x - 6 = 9, y - 4 = 12$

90. $9 - x = 3, \dfrac{1}{2}x = 8$

Solve each problem. See Example 9.

91. *Heating water.* There is a linear equation that expresses the temperature, t, of a cup of water in terms of the number of seconds, s, that it is in the microwave. If the temperature at $s = 0$ second is $t = 60°F$ and the temperature at $s = 120$ seconds is $200°F$, find the linear equation that expresses t in terms of s. What should the temperature be after 30 seconds? (*Hint:* Write the equation of the line containing the points $(0, 60)$ and $(120, 200)$ in the form $t = ms + b$.) Draw a graph of this linear equation.

79. $y = \dfrac{2}{3}x - 1$
$y = \dfrac{2}{3}x + 1$

80. $y = -2x + 4$
$y = -2x + 2$

92. *Making circuit boards.* There is a linear equation that expresses the cost C per week in dollars for making circuit boards in terms of the number n of circuit boards per week. If $C = \$1500$ when $n = 1000$, and $C = \$2000$ when $n = 2000$, find the linear equation that expresses C in terms of n. What is the cost if only one circuit board is produced in a week? Draw a graph of this linear equation.

93. *Carbon dioxide emission.* Worldwide emission of carbon dioxide (CO_2) increased from 14 billion tons in 1970 to 26 billion tons in 2000 (World Resources Institute, www.wri.org).
a) Find the equation of the line through (1970, 14) and (2000, 26).
b) Use the equation to predict the worldwide emission of CO_2 in 2010.

94. *World energy use.* Worldwide energy use in all forms increased from the equivalent of 3.5 billion tons of oil in 1970 to the equivalent of 6.5 billion tons of oil in 2000 (World Resources Institute, www.wri.org).
a) Find the equation of the line through (1970, 3.5) and (2000, 6.5).
b) Use the equation to predict the worldwide energy use in 2010.

95. *Depth and flow.* On April 15, 2002, the depth of the water in the Tangipahoa River at Robert, Louisiana, was

9.14 feet and the flow was 1230 cubic feet per second (ft^3/sec). On April 8, 2002, the depth was 7.84 feet and the flow was 826 ft^3/sec. (U.S. Geological Survey, www.usgs.gov). Let w represent the flow in cubic feet per second and d represent the depth in feet.
a) Write the equation of the line through (9.14, 1230) and (7.84, 826) and express w in terms of d. Round to two decimal places.
b) What is the flow when the depth is 8.25 ft?
c) Is the flow increasing or decreasing as the depth increases?

96. *Buying stock.* On April 15, 2002, a mutual fund manager spent $484,375 on x shares of Ford Motor Company Stock at $15.50 per share and y shares of General Motors stock at $62.50 per share.
a) Write a linear equation that models this situation.
b) If 10,000 shares of Ford were purchased, then how many shares of GM were purchased?
c) Find and interpret the intercepts of the graph of the linear equation.
d) As the number of shares of Ford increases, does the number of shares of GM increase or decrease?

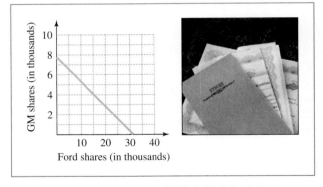

FIGURE FOR EXERCISE 96

GETTING MORE INVOLVED

97. *Exploration.* The **intercept form** for the equation of a line is

$$\frac{x}{a} + \frac{y}{b} = 1$$

where neither a nor b is zero.
a) Find the x- and y-intercepts for $\frac{x}{4} + \frac{y}{6} = 1$.
b) Find the x- and y-intercepts for $\frac{x}{a} + \frac{y}{b} = 1$.

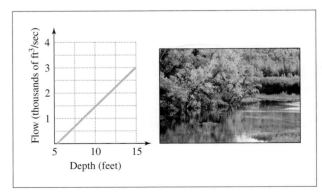

FIGURE FOR EXERCISE 95

c) Write the equation of the line through (0, 3) and (−5, 0) in intercept form.

d) Which lines cannot be written in intercept form?

GRAPHING CALCULATOR EXERCISES

98. Graph the equation $y = 0.5x - 1$ using the standard viewing window. Adjust the range of y-values so that the line goes from the lower left corner of your viewing window to the upper right corner.

99. Graph $y = x - 3000$, using a viewing window that shows both the x-intercept and the y-intercept.

100. Graph $y = 2x - 400$ and $y = -0.5x + 1$ on the same screen, using the viewing window $-500 \leq x \leq 500$ and $-1000 \leq y \leq 1000$. Should these lines be perpendicular? Explain.

101. The lines $y = 2x - 3$ and $y = 1.9x + 2$ are not parallel. Find a viewing window in which the lines intersect. Estimate the point of intersection.

In This Section

- Definition
- Graphing Linear Inequalities
- The Test Point Method
- Graphing Compound Inequalities
- Applications

3.4   LINEAR INEQUALITIES AND THEIR GRAPHS

In the first three sections of this chapter you studied linear equations. We now turn our attention to linear inequalities.

Definition

A linear inequality is a linear equation with the equal sign replaced by an inequality symbol.

> **Linear Inequality**
>
> If A, B, and C are real numbers with A and B not both zero, then
>
> $$Ax + By \leq C$$
>
> is called a **linear inequality.** In place of $\leq$, we can also use $\geq$, $<$, or $>$.

Graphing Linear Inequalities

Consider the inequality $-x + y > 1$. If we solve the inequality for y, we get

$$y > x + 1.$$

Which points in the xy-plane satisfy this inequality? We want the points where the y-coordinate is larger than the x-coordinate plus 1. If we locate a point on the line $y = x + 1$, say (2, 3), then the y-coordinate is equal to the x-coordinate plus 1. If we move upward from that point, to say (2, 4), the y-coordinate is larger than the x-coordinate plus 1. Because this argument can be made at every point on the line, all points above the line satisfy $y > x + 1$. Likewise, points below the line satisfy $y < x + 1$. The solution sets, or graphs, for the inequality $y > x + 1$ and the inequality $y < x + 1$ are the shaded regions shown in Figs. 3.24(a) and 3.24(b) on the next page. In each case the line $y = x + 1$ is dashed to indicate that points on the line do not satisfy the inequality and so are not in the solution set. If the inequality symbol is $\leq$ or $\geq$, then points on the boundary line also satisfy the inequality, and the line is drawn solid.

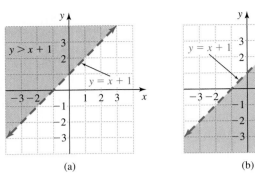

(a)   (b)

FIGURE 3.24

Every nonvertical line divides the xy-plane into two regions. One region is above the line, and the other is below the line. A vertical line also divides the plane into two regions, but one is on the left side of the line and the other is on the right side of the line. An inequality involving only x has a vertical boundary line, and its graph is one of those regions.

Graphing a Linear Inequality

1. Solve the inequality for y, then graph $y = mx + b$.

$\qquad$ $y > mx + b$ is satisfied above the line.

$\qquad$ $y = mx + b$ is satisfied on the line itself.

$\qquad$ $y < mx + b$ is satisfied below the line.

2. If the inequality involves x and not y, then graph the vertical line $x = k$.

$\qquad$ $x > k$ is satisfied to the right of the line.

$\qquad$ $x = k$ is satisfied on the line itself.

$\qquad$ $x < k$ is satisfied to the left of the line.

E X A M P L E   1

Graphing linear inequalities

Graph each inequality.

a) $y < \dfrac{1}{2}x - 1$ **b)** $y \geq -2x + 1$ **c)** $3x - 2y < 6$

Helpful Hint

Why do we keep drawing graphs? When we solve $2x + 1 = 7$, we don't bother to draw a graph showing 3 because the solution set is so simple. However, the solution set to a linear inequality is a very large set of ordered pairs. Graphing gives us a way to visualize the solution set.

Solution

a) The set of points satisfying this inequality is the region below the line $y = \frac{1}{2}x - 1$. To show this region, we first graph the boundary line $y = \frac{1}{2}x - 1$. The slope of the line is $\frac{1}{2}$, and the y-intercept is $(0, -1)$. Start at $(0, -1)$ on the y-axis, then rise 1 and run 2 to get a second point of the line. We draw the line dashed because points on the line do not satisfy this inequality. The solution set to the inequality is the shaded region shown in Fig. 3.25.

b) Because the inequality symbol is $\geq$, every point on or above the line $y = -2x + 1$ satisfies $y \geq -2x + 1$. To graph the line use y-intercept $(0, 1)$ and slope -2. Start at $(0, 1)$ and find a second point on the line using a rise of -2 and a run of 1. Draw a solid line through $(0, 1)$ and $(1, -1)$ to show that it is included in the solution set to the inequality. Shade above the line as in Fig. 3.26.

c) First solve for y:

$$3x - 2y < 6$$
$$-2y < -3x + 6$$
$$y > \frac{3}{2}x - 3 \qquad \text{Divide by } -2 \text{ and reverse the inequality.}$$

To graph this inequality, first graph the boundary $y = \frac{3}{2}x - 3$ using its y-intercept $(0, -3)$ and slope $\frac{3}{2}$ or graph the line using its intercepts $(0, -3)$ and $(2, 0)$. Use a dashed line for the boundary and shade the region above the line as in Fig. 3.27.

FIGURE 3.25

FIGURE 3.26

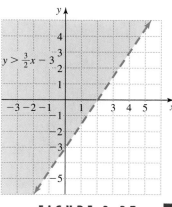

FIGURE 3.27 ■

CAUTION　In Example 1(c) we solved the inequality for y before graphing the line. We did that because $<$ corresponds to the region below the line and $>$ corresponds to the region above the line only when the inequality is solved for y.

E X A M P L E　2　**Inequalities with horizontal and vertical boundaries**

Graph the inequalities.

a) $y \leq 5$　　　　　　　　　　　**b)** $x > 4$

Solution

a) The line $y = 5$ is the horizontal line with y-intercept $(0, 5)$. Draw a solid horizontal line and shade below it as in Fig. 3.28.

b) The points that satisfy $x > 4$ lie to the right of the vertical line $x = 4$. The solution set is shown in Fig. 3.29.

FIGURE 3.28

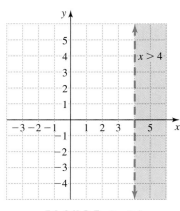

FIGURE 3.29 ■

The Test Point Method

The graph of any line $Ax + By = C$ separates the xy-plane into two regions. Every point on one side of the line satisfies the inequality $Ax + By < C$, and every point on the other side satisfies the inequality $Ax + By > C$. We can use these facts to graph an inequality by the **test point method:**

1. Graph the corresponding equation.
2. Choose any point *not* on the line.
3. Test to see whether the point satisfies the inequality.

If the point satisfies the inequality, then the solution set is the region containing the test point. If not, then the solution set is the other region. With this method, it is not necessary to solve the inequality for y.

EXAMPLE 3

Using the test point method
Graph the inequality $3x - 4y > 7$.

Study Tip

Students who have difficulty with algebra often schedule a class that meets one day per week so that they do not have to see it as often. However, students usually do better in classes that meet more often for shorter time periods.

Solution

First graph the equation $3x - 4y = 7$ using the x-intercept and the y-intercept. If $x = 0$, then $y = -\frac{7}{4}$. If $y = 0$, then $x = \frac{7}{3}$. Use the x-intercept $\left(\frac{7}{3}, 0\right)$ and the y-intercept $\left(0, -\frac{7}{4}\right)$ to graph the line as shown in Fig. 3.30(a). Select a point on one side of the line, say $(0, 1)$, to test in the inequality. Because

$$3(0) - 4(1) > 7$$

is false, the region on the other side of the line satisfies the inequality. The graph of $3x - 4y > 7$ is shown in Fig. 3.30(b).

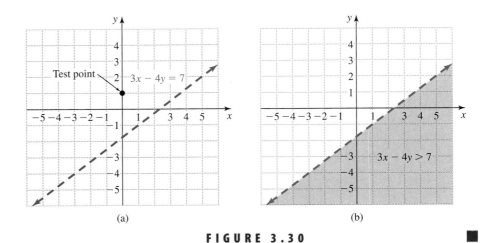

(a)   (b)

FIGURE 3.30

Graphing Compound Inequalities

We can write compound inequalities with two variables just as we do for one variable. For example,

$$y > x - 3 \quad \text{and} \quad y < -\frac{1}{2}x + 2$$

is a compound inequality. Because the inequalities are connected by the word *and*, a point is in the solution set to the compound inequality if and only if it is in the solution sets to *both* of the individual inequalities. So the graph of this compound inequality is the intersection of the solution sets to the individual inequalities.

E X A M P L E   4

Graphing a compound inequality with *and*

Graph the compound inequality $y > x - 3$ and $y < -\frac{1}{2}x + 2$.

Solution

We first graph the equations $y = x - 3$ and $y = -\frac{1}{2}x + 2$. These lines divide the plane into four regions as shown in Fig. 3.31(a). Now test one point of each region to determine which region satisfies the compound inequality. Test the points $(3, 3)$, $(0, 0)$, $(4, -5)$, and $(5, 0)$:

$$3 > 3 - 3 \qquad \text{and} \qquad 3 < -\frac{1}{2} \cdot 3 + 2 \qquad \text{Second inequality is incorrect.}$$

$$0 > 0 - 3 \qquad \text{and} \qquad 0 < -\frac{1}{2} \cdot 0 + 2 \qquad \text{Both inequalities are correct.}$$

$$-5 > 4 - 3 \qquad \text{and} \qquad -5 < -\frac{1}{2} \cdot 4 + 2 \qquad \text{First inequality is incorrect.}$$

$$0 > 5 - 3 \qquad \text{and} \qquad 5 < -\frac{1}{2} \cdot 0 + 2 \qquad \text{Both inequalities are incorrect.}$$

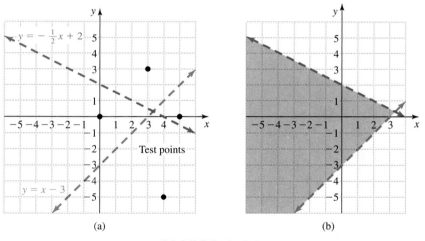

(a)   (b)

FIGURE 3.31

The only point that satisfies both inequalities is $(0, 0)$. So the solution set to the compound inequality consists of all points in the region containing $(0, 0)$. The graph of the compound inequality is shown in Fig. 3.31(b). ∎

Compound inequalities are also formed by connecting individual inequalities with the word *or*. A point satisfies a compound inequality connected by *or* if and only if it satisfies one or the other or both of the individual inequalities. The graph is the union of the graphs of the individual inequalities.

E X A M P L E   5

Graphing a compound inequality with *or*

Graph the compound inequality

$$2x - 3y \leq -6 \qquad \text{or} \qquad x + 2y \geq 4.$$

Helpful Hint

When graphing a compound in-equality connected with "or," shade the region that satisfies the first in-equality and then shade the region that satisfies the second inequality. If the inequalities are connected with "and," then you must be careful not to shade too much.

Solution

First graph the lines $2x - 3y = -6$ and $x + 2y = 4$. If we graph the lines using x- and y-intercepts, then we do not have to solve the equations for y. The lines are shown in Fig. 3.32(a). The graph of the compound inequality is the set of all points that satisfy either one inequality or the other (or both). Test the points $(0, 0)$, $(3, 2)$, $(0, 5)$, and $(-3, 2)$. You should verify that only $(0, 0)$ fails to satisfy at least one of the inequalities. So only the region containing the origin is left unshaded. The graph of the compound inequality is shown in Fig. 3.32(b).

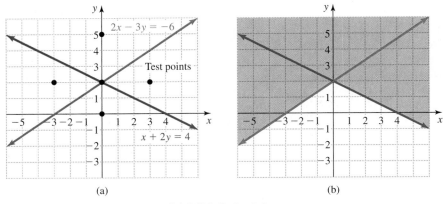

(a)   (b)

FIGURE 3.32

In Section 2.6 we learned that the absolute value inequality $|x| > 2$ is equivalent to the compound inequality $x < -2$ or $x > 2$. The absolute value inequality $|x| < 2$ is equivalent to the compound inequality $x > -2$ and $x < 2$. We can also write $|x| < 2$ as $-2 < x < 2$. We use these ideas with inequalities in two variables in Example 6.

E X A M P L E   6

Graphing absolute value inequalities

Graph each absolute value inequality.

a) $|y - 2x| \leq 3$ **b)** $|x - y| > 1$

Helpful Hint

Remember that absolute value of a quantity is its distance from 0 (Section 2.6). If $|w| < 3$, then w is less than 3 units from 0:

$$-3 < w < 3$$

If $|w| > 1$, then w is more than 1 unit away from 0:

$$w > 1 \quad \text{or} \quad w < -1$$

In Example 6 we are using an ex-pression in place of w.

Solution

a) The inequality $|y - 2x| \leq 3$ is equivalent to $-3 \leq y - 2x \leq 3$, which is equiv-alent to the compound inequality

$$y - 2x \leq 3 \qquad \text{and} \qquad y - 2x \geq -3.$$

First graph the lines $y - 2x = 3$ and $y - 2x = -3$ as shown in Fig. 3.33(a). These lines divide the plane into three regions. Test a point from each region in the original inequality, say $(-5, 0)$, $(0, 1)$, and $(5, 0)$:

$$|0 - 2(-5)| \leq 3 \qquad |1 - 2 \cdot 0| \leq 3 \qquad |0 - 2 \cdot 5| \leq 3$$
$$10 \leq 3 \qquad\qquad 1 \leq 3 \qquad\qquad 10 \leq 3$$

Only $(0, 1)$ satisfies the original inequality. So the region satisfying the absolute value inequality is the shaded region containing $(0, 1)$ as shown in Fig. 3.33(b). The boundary lines are solid because of the $\leq$ symbol.

b) The inequality $|x - y| > 1$ is equivalent to

$$x - y > 1 \quad \text{or} \quad x - y < -1.$$

(a)

(b)

FIGURE 3.33

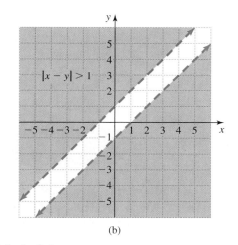

(a)

(b)

FIGURE 3.34

First graph the lines $x - y = 1$ and $x - y = -1$ as shown in Fig. 3.34(a). Test a point from each region in the original inequality, say $(-4, 0)$, $(0, 0)$, and $(4, 0)$:

$$|-4 - 0| > 1 \qquad |0 - 0| > 1 \qquad |4 - 0| > 1$$
$$4 > 1 \qquad\qquad 0 > 1 \qquad\qquad 4 > 1$$

Because $(-4, 0)$ and $(4, 0)$ satisfy the inequality, we shade those regions as shown in Fig. 3.34(b). The boundary lines are dashed because of the $>$ symbol. ∎

Applications

In real situations x and y often represent quantities or amounts, which cannot be negative. In this case our graphs are restricted to the first quadrant, where x and y are both nonnegative.

E X A M P L E   7   **Inequalities in business**

The manager of a furniture store can spend a maximum of $3000 on advertising per week. It costs $50 to run a 30-second ad on an AM radio station and $75 to run the ad on an FM station. Graph the region that shows the possible numbers of AM and FM ads that can be purchased and identify some possibilities.

Solution

If x represents the number of AM ads and y represents the number of FM ads, then x and y must satisfy the inequality $50x + 75y \leq 3000$. Because the number of ads cannot be negative, we also have $x \geq 0$ and $y \geq 0$. So we graph only points in the first quadrant that satisfy $50x + 75y \leq 3000$. The line $50x + 75y = 3000$ goes

FIGURE 3.35

MATH AT WORK

"We will return after these messages." We often hear these words on television and radio just before several minutes of commercials. Carolanne Johnson, Account Executive and Media Salesperson for WBOQ, a classical radio station, is involved in every step of creating such advertisements.

The first step is finding clients that are consistent with the station's image. Ms. Johnson generates her own leads from a number of sources, such as print ads and billboards. The next steps are sitting down with the client, gathering information about the product or service, assessing the competition, and finally determining how much of the client's advertising budget should be spent on radio. Typically, this can be 2% to 4% of the total budget.

MEDIA SALESPERSON

Radio ads usually run for 60 seconds, but reminder ads can be as short as 30 seconds. Some of the radio spots are time-sensitive and run 40 to 60 times a month for a specific month. Other clients are concerned with image building and may sponsor one particular broadcast every day for the whole year.

Ms. Johnson is concerned that the clients receive an adequate return on their investment. She is constantly reviewing the budget and making sure that the commercials present what the client wishes to project.

Example 7 and Exercise 77 of this section give problems that involve allocation of advertising dollars.

through (0, 40) and (60, 0). The inequality is satisfied below this line. The region showing the possible numbers of AM ads and FM ads is shown in Fig. 3.35. We shade the entire region in Fig. 3.35, but only points in the shaded region in which both coordinates are whole numbers actually satisfy the given condition. For example, 40 AM ads and 10 FM ads could be purchased. Other possibilities are 30 AM ads and 20 FM ads, or 10 AM ads and 10 FM ads.

WARM-UPS

True or false? Explain your answer.

1. The point $(2, -3)$ satisfies the inequality $y > -3x + 2$.
2. The graph of $3x - y > 2$ is the region above the line $3x - y = 2$.
3. The graph of $3x + y < 5$ is the region below the line $y = -3x + 5$.
4. The graph of $x < -3$ is the region to the left of the vertical line $x = 3$.
5. The graph of $y > x + 3$ and $y < 2x - 6$ is the intersection of two regions.

6. The graph of $y \leq 2x - 3$ or $y \geq 3x + 5$ is the union of two regions.
7. The ordered pair $(2, -5)$ satisfies $y > -3x + 5$ and $y < 2x - 3$.
8. The ordered pair $(-3, 2)$ satisfies $y \leq 3x - 6$ or $y \leq x + 5$.
9. The inequality $|2x - y| \leq 4$ is equivalent to $2x - y \leq 4$ and $2x + y \leq 4$.

10. The inequality $|x - y| > 3$ is equivalent to $x - y > 3$ or $x - y < -3$.

3.4   EXERCISES

Reading and Writing   *After reading this section, write out the answers to these questions. Use complete sentences.*

1. What is a linear inequality?

2. How do we usually illustrate the solution set to a linear inequality in two variables.

3. How do you know whether the line should be solid or dashed when graphing a linear inequality?

4. How do you know which side of the line to shade when graphing a linear inequality?

5. What is the test point method used for?

6. How do you graph a compound inequality?

Graph each linear inequality. See Examples 1 and 2.

7. $y < x + 2$ 8. $y < x - 1$

9. $y \leq -2x + 1$ 10. $y \geq -3x + 4$

11. $x + y > 3$

12. $x + y \leq -1$

21. $y < 3$

22. $y > -1$

13. $2x + 3y < 9$

14. $-3x + 2y > 6$

Graph each linear inequality by using a test point. See Example 3.

23. $2x - 3y < 5$

24. $5x - 4y > 3$

15. $3x - 4y \leq 8$

16. $4x - 5y > 10$

25. $x + y + 3 \geq 0$

26. $x - y - 6 \leq 0$

17. $x - y > 0$

18. $2x - y < 0$

27. $y - 2x \leq 0$

28. $2y - x > 0$

19. $x \geq 1$

20. $x < 0$

29. $3x - 2y > 0$

30. $6x - 2y \leq 0$

31. $\frac{1}{2}x + \frac{1}{3}y < 1$

32. $2 - \frac{2}{5}y > \frac{1}{2}x$

39. $x + y \le 5$ and
$x - y \le 3$

40. $2x - y < 3$ and
$3x - y > 0$

Graph each compound inequality. See Examples 4 and 5.

33. $y > x$ and $y > -2x + 3$　　**34.** $y < x$ and $y < -3x + 2$

41. $x - 2y \le 4$ or
$2x - 3y \le 6$

42. $4x - 3y \le 3$ or
$2x + y \ge 2$

35. $y < x + 3$ or
$y > -x + 2$

36. $y \ge x - 5$ or
$y \le -2x + 1$

43. $y > 2$ and $x < 3$

44. $x \le 5$ and $y \ge -1$

37. $x - 4y < 0$ and
$3x + 2y \ge 6$

38. $x \ge -2y$ and
$x - 3y < 6$

45. $y \ge x$ and $x \le 2$

46. $y < x$ and $y > 0$

47. $2x < y + 3$ or
$\quad\ y > 2 - x$

48. $3 - x < y + 2$ or
$\quad\ x > y + 5$

Graph the absolute value inequalities. See Example 6.

55. $|x + y| < 2$ **56.** $|2x + y| < 1$

49. $y > x - 1$ and
$\quad\ y < x + 3$

50. $y > x - 1$ and
$\quad\ y < 2x + 5$

57. $|2x + y| \geq 1$ **58.** $|x + 2y| \geq 6$

51. $0 \leq y \leq x$ and $x \leq 1$

52. $x \leq y \leq 1$ and $x \geq 0$

59. $|y - x| > 2$ **60.** $|2y - x| > 6$

53. $1 \leq x \leq 3$ and
$\quad\ 2 \leq y \leq 5$

54. $-1 < x < 1$ and
$\quad\ -1 < y < 1$

61. $|x - 2y| \leq 4$ **62.** $|x - 3y| \leq 6$

63. $|x| > 2$ **64.** $|x| \leq 3$

65. $|y| < 1$ **66.** $|y| \geq 2$

67. $|x| < 2$ and $|y| < 3$ **68.** $|x| \geq 3$ or $|y| \geq 1$

69. $|x - 3| < 1$ and   **70.** $|x - 2| \geq 3$ or
       $|y - 2| < 1$ $|y - 5| \geq 2$

Solve each problem. See Example 7.

71. *Budget planning.* The Highway Patrol can spend a maximum of $120,000 on new vehicles this year. They can get a fully equipped compact car for $15,000 or a fully equipped full-size car for $20,000. Graph the region that shows the number of cars of each type that could be purchased.

72. *Allocating resources.* A furniture maker has a shop that can employ 12 workers for 40 hours per week at its maximum capacity. The shop makes tables and chairs. It takes 16 hours of labor to make a table and 8 hours of labor to make a chair. Graph the region that shows the possibilities for the number of tables and chairs that could be made in one week.

73. *More restrictions.* In Exercise 71, add the condition that the number of full-size cars must be greater than or equal to the number of compact cars. Graph the region showing the possibilities for the number of cars of each type that could be purchased.

74. *Chairs per table.* In Exercise 72, add the condition that the number of chairs must be at least four times the number of tables and at most six times the number of tables. Graph the region showing the possibilities for the number of tables and chairs that could be made in one week.

75. **Building fitness.** To achieve cardiovascular fitness, you should exercise so that your target heart rate is between 70% and 85% of its maximum rate. Your target heart rate h depends on your age a. For building fitness, you should have $h \leq 187 - 0.85a$ and $h \geq 154 - 0.70a$ (NordicTrack brochure). Graph this compound inequality for $20 \leq a \leq 75$ to see the heart rate target zone for building fitness.

76. **Waist-to-hip ratio.** A study by Dr. Aaron R. Folsom concluded that waist-to-hip ratios are a better predictor of 5-year survival than more traditional height-to-weight ratios. Dr. Folsom concluded that for good health the waist size of a woman aged 50 to 69 should be less than or equal to 80% of her hip size, $w \leq 0.80h$. Make a graph showing possible waist and hip sizes for good health for women in this age group for which hip size is no more than 50 inches.

77. **Advertising dollars.** A restaurant manager can spend at most $9000 on advertising per month and has two choices for advertising. The manager can purchase an ad in the *Daily Chronicle* (a 7-day-per-week newspaper) for $300 per day or a 30-second ad on WBTU television for $1000 each time the ad is aired. Graph the region that shows the possible number of days that an ad can be run in the newspaper and the possible number of times that an ad can be aired on television.

78. **Shipping restrictions.** The accompanying graph shows all of the possibilities for the number of refrigerators and the number of TVs that will fit into an 18-wheeler.
   a) Write an inequality to describe this region.
   b) Will the truck hold 71 refrigerators and 118 TVs?
   c) Will the truck hold 51 refrigerators and 176 TVs?

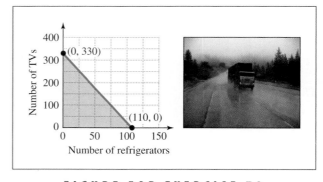

FIGURE FOR EXERCISE 78

GETTING MORE INVOLVED

79. **Writing.** Explain the difference between a compound inequality using the word *and* and a compound inequality using the word *or*.

80. **Discussion.** Explain how to write an absolute value inequality as a compound inequality.

3.5   FUNCTIONS AND RELATIONS

In this chapter we have been studying ordered pairs. In this section we will use ordered pairs in our study of functions and relations.

The Concept of a Function

If the value of the variable y is determined by the value of the variable x, then y **is a function of x.** So "is a function of" means "is uniquely determined by." But what does uniquely determined mean? According to the dictionary "determine" means "to settle conclusively." There can be no ambiguity. There is only one y for any x.

Consider all possible circles. Is the area of a circle A a function of the radius r? The well-known formula $A = \pi r^2$ tells us exactly how to determine the area from the radius. There is only one area for any given radius and A is a function of r.

Now consider all first-class letters mailed today in the United States. Is the weight W a function of the amount of postage P? That is, can W be determined from P? There are certainly letters that have the same amount of postage and different weights. So the weight cannot be determined from the postage and W is not a function of P. The weight cannot be determined conclusively if there is more than one weight for a given amount of postage.

E X A M P L E   1

Deciding if b is a function of a

In each situation decide whether b is a function of a.

a) Consider all students at Pasadena City College. Let b represent the weight of a student to the nearest pound and a represent the height of the same student to the nearest inch.

b) Consider all possible rectangles. Let b represent the area a rectangle and a represent the width.

c) Consider all cars sold at Bill Hood Ford this year where the sales tax rate is 9%. Let b represent the amount of sales tax and a represent the selling price of the car.

Solution

a) Can the weight of a student be determined from the height of the student? Imagine that we have a list containing weights and heights for all students. There will certainly be two 5 ft 9 in. students with different weights. So weight cannot be determined from the height and b is not a function of a.

b) Can the area of a rectangle be determined from the width? Among all possible rectangles there are infinitely many rectangles with width 1 ft and different areas. So the area is not determined by the width and b is not a function of a.

c) Can the amount of sales tax be determined from the price of the car? The formula $b = 0.09a$ is used to determine the amount of tax. For example, the tax on every $20,000 car is $1,800. So b is a function of a. ∎

Example 1 should help you understand the concept of function. However, answers to questions like those in Example 1 might vary depending on the interpretation of the situation. So we must have a mathematically precise definition of a function.

When discussing two variables, we can consider the set of all ordered pairs containing their possible values. If we are trying to decide whether weight is a function of height, then the ordered pairs have the form (height, weight). If we are considering whether p is a function of s, then the ordered pairs look like (s, p). The variable corresponding to the first coordinate is the **independent variable** and the variable corresponding to the second coordinate is the **dependent variable.** The dependent variable is a function of the independent variable if and only if the corresponding set of ordered pairs is a function according to the following definition.

Function—A Set of Ordered Pairs

A **function** is a set of ordered pairs in which no two ordered pairs have the same first coordinate and different second coordinates.

Note that in Example 1(a) we concluded that weight was not a function of height because there are certainly two students with the same height and different weights. There may be many more, but all it takes to fail to be a function is two ordered pairs with the same first coordinate and different second coordinates.

Identifying Functions

Any set of ordered pairs is called a **relation.** The ordered pairs of a relation may be given by a graph, list, or equation. In each case we can use the definition of function to decide whether the relation is a function.

If the ordered pairs of a relation are given by a graph, then we can use a simple visual test, the **vertical-line test,** to determine whether the relation is a function.

The Vertical-Line Test

A graph is the graph of a function if and only if there is no vertical line that crosses the graph more than once.

If there is a vertical line that crosses a graph twice (or more), then we have two points with the same *x*-coordinate and different *y*-coordinates, and the graph is not the graph of a function. If you mentally consider every possible vertical line and none of them crosses the graph more than once, then you can conclude that the graph is the graph of a function.

E X A M P L E   2   **Using the vertical-line test**
Which of these graphs are graphs of functions?

a)

b)

c)

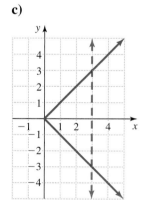

Solution

Neither (a) nor (c) is the graph of a function, since we can draw vertical lines that cross these graphs twice. The graph (b) is the graph of a function, since no vertical line crosses it more than once. ■

The vertical-line test illustrates the visual difference between a set of ordered pairs that is a function and one that is not. Because graphs are not precise, the vertical-line test might be inconclusive. When a relation is given as a list of ordered pairs we can decide conclusively whether the relation is a function, as in the next example.

E X A M P L E   3

Relations given as lists of ordered pairs

Determine whether each relation is a function.

a) $\{(1, 2), (1, 5), (3, 7)\}$

b) $\{(4, 5), (3, 5), (2, 6), (1, 7)\}$

Solution

a) This relation is not a function because $(1, 2)$ and $(1, 5)$ have the same first coordinate but different second coordinates.

b) This relation is a function. Note that the same second coordinate with different first coordinates is permitted in a function. ■

The solution set to any equation in x and y is the set of ordered pairs that satisfy the equation. Since any set of ordered pairs is called a relation, any equation in x and y is called a relation. If the solution set is a function, then the equation is also called a function.

E X A M P L E   4

Relations given as equations

Determine whether each relation is a function.

a) $x = y^2$ **b)** $y = 2x$ **c)** $x = |y|$

Solution

a) Is it possible to find two ordered pairs with the same first coordinate and different second coordinates that satisfy $x = y^2$? Since $(1, 1)$ and $(1, -1)$ both satisfy $x = y^2$, this relation is not a function.

b) The equation $y = 2x$ indicates that the y-coordinate is always twice the x-coordinate. Ordered pairs such as $(0, 0)$, $(2, 4)$, and $(3, 6)$ satisfy $y = 2x$. It is not possible to find two ordered pairs with the same first coordinate and different second coordinates. So $y = 2x$ is a function. Note that the graph of $y = 2x$ is a straight line with slope 2. Since no vertical line will cross that line more than once, we can also conclude that $y = 2x$ is a function by the vertical-line test.

c) The equation $x = |y|$ is satisfied by ordered pairs such as $(2, 2)$ and $(2, -2)$ because $2 = |2|$ and $2 = |-2|$ are both correct. So this relation is not a function. ■

Domain and Range

A relation or function is a set of ordered pairs. The **domain** of a relation or function is the set of first coordinates of the ordered pairs. The **range** is the set of second coordinates of the ordered pairs. If the ordered pairs are listed, then the domain and range can be simply read from the list. More often, a relation or function is given by an equation, with no domain stated. *When the domain is not stated we assume that the domain consists of all real numbers that, when substituted for the independent variable, produce real numbers for the dependent variable.*

E X A M P L E   5

Identifying the domain and range

Determine the domain and range of each relation.

a) $\{(2, 5), (2, 7), (4, 3)\}$ **b)** $y = 2x$ **c)** $y = \sqrt{x - 1}$

Solution

a) The domain is the set of first coordinates, $\{2, 4\}$. The range is the set of second coordinates, $\{3, 5, 7\}$.

b) Since any real number can be used in place of x in $y = 2x$, the domain is $(-\infty, \infty)$. Since any real number can be used in place of y in $y = 2x$, the range is also $(-\infty, \infty)$.

c) Since the square root of a negative number is not a real number, we must have $x - 1 \geq 0$ or $x \geq 1$. So the domain is the interval $[1, \infty)$. Since the square root of a nonnegative real number is a nonnegative real number, we must have $y \geq 0$. So the range is the interval $[0, \infty)$. ◼

Using domain and range we can write another definition of function that is equivalent to the ordered-pair definition that we have been using:

Function—A Rule

A **function** is a rule that assigns to each element of one set (the domain) exactly one element of another set (the range).

If a set of ordered pairs is a function, then the ordered pairs give us a rule for assigning each element of the domain with exactly one element of the range. Conversely, if we have a rule for assigning elements, then we could write all of the assignments as ordered pairs that satisfy the ordered-pair definition of function. So a function by one definition is also a function by the other definition.

Function Notation

If y is a function of x, we can use the notation $f(x)$ to represent y. The expression $f(x)$ is read as "f of x." The notation $f(x)$ is called **function notation.** So if x is the independent variable, then either y or $f(x)$ is the dependent variable. For example, the function $y = 2x + 3$ can be written as

$$f(x) = 2x + 3.$$

FIGURE 3.36

We use y and $f(x)$ interchangeably. We can think of f as the name of the function. We may use letters other than f. For example $g(x) = 2x + 3$ is the same function as $f(x) = 2x + 3$. The ordered pairs for each function are identical. Note that $f(x)$ does not mean f times x. The expression $f(x)$ represents the second coordinate when the first coordinate is x.

If $f(x) = 2x + 3$, then $f(4) = 2(4) + 3 = 11$. So the second coordinate is 11 if the first coordinate is 4. The ordered pair (4, 11) is an ordered pair in the function f. Figure 3.36 illustrates this situation.

EXAMPLE 6   **Using function notation**

Let $f(x) = 3x - 2$ and $g(x) = x^2 - x$. Evaluate each expression.

a) $f(-5)$ **b)** $g(-5)$ **c)** $f(0) + g(3)$

Solution

a) Replace x by -5 in the equation defining the function f:

$$f(x) = 3x - 2$$
$$f(-5) = 3(-5) - 2$$
$$= -17$$

So $f(-5) = -17$.

b) Replace x by -5 in the equation defining the function g:

$$g(x) = x^2 - x$$
$$g(-5) = (-5)^2 - (-5) = 30$$

So $g(-5) = 30$.

c) Since $f(0) = 3(0) - 2 = -2$ and $g(3) = 3^2 - 3 = 6$, we have $f(0) + g(3) = -2 + 6 = 4$. ∎

Linear Functions

A function of the form $f(x) = mx + b$ is called a **linear function** if $m \neq 0$ and a **constant function** if $m = 0$. So $f(x) = 3x - 1$ is a linear function and $f(x) = 5$ is a constant function. The graph of a linear function is a line with slope m and the graph of a constant function is a line with slope 0 (a horizontal line).

E X A M P L E   7   **Graphing linear and constant functions**

Graph each function.

a) $f(x) = 3x - 1$ **b)** $f(x) = 5$

Solution

a) The graph of $f(x) = 3x - 1$ is the same as the graph of $y = 3x - 1$, a line with y-intercept $(0, -1)$ and slope 3. See Fig. 3.37.

b) The graph of $f(x) = 5$ is the same as the graph of $y = 5$, a line with slope 0 and y-intercept $(0, 5)$. See Fig. 3.38.

FIGURE 3.37

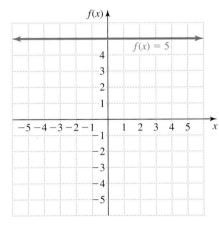

FIGURE 3.38 ∎

In Example 8 we see function notation with a linear function in an applied setting.

E X A M P L E   8   **Using function notation in applications**

To determine the cost of an in-home repair, a computer technician uses the linear function $C(n) = 40n + 30$, where n is the time in hours and $C(n)$ is the cost in dollars. Find $C(2)$ and $C(4)$.

Solution

Replace n with 2 to get

$$C(2) = 40(2) + 30 = 110.$$

Replace n with 4 to get

$$C(4) = 40(4) + 30 = 190.$$

So for 2 hours the cost is \$110 and for 4 hours the cost is \$190. ■

In this section we studied functions of one variable. However, a variable can be a function of another variable or a function of many other variables. For example, your grade on the next test is not a function of the number of hours that you study for it. Your grade is a function of many variables: study time, sleep time, work time, your mother's IQ, and so on. Even though study time alone does not determine your grade, it is the variable that has the most influence on your grade.

Calculator Close-Up

A graphing calculator has function notation built in. To find $C(2)$ and $C(4)$ with a graphing calculator, enter $y_1 = 40x + 30$ as shown here:

To find $C(2)$ and $C(4)$, enter $y_1(2)$ and $y_1(4)$ as shown here:

WARM-UPS

True or false? Explain your answer.

1. Any set of ordered pairs is a function.

2. The circumference of a circle is a function of the diameter.

3. The set $\{(1, 2), (3, 2), (5, 2)\}$ is a function.

4. The set $\{(1, 5), (3, 6), (1, 7)\}$ is a function.

5. The equation $y = x^2$ is a function.

6. Every relation is a function.

7. The domain of a relation is the set of first coordinates.

8. The domain of a function is the set of second coordinates.

9. The domain of $f(x) = \sqrt{x}$ is $[0, \infty)$.

10. If $h(x) = x^2 - 3$, then $h(-2) = 1$.

3.5   EXERCISES

Reading and Writing *After reading this section, write out the answers to these questions. Use complete sentences.*

1. What does it mean to say that *b* is a function of *a*?

2. What is a function?

3. What is a relation?

4. What is the domain of a relation?

5. What is the range of a relation?

6. What is function notation?

In each situation determine whether b is a function of a. Explain your answer. See Example 1.

7. Consider all gas stations in your area. Let *a* represent the price per gallon of regular unleaded gasoline and *b* represent the number of gallons that you can get for $10.

8. Consider all items at Sears. Let *a* represent the universal product code for an item and *b* represent the price of that item.

9. Consider all students taking algebra at your school. Let *a* represent the number of hours (to the nearest hour) a student spent studying for the first test and *b* represent the student's score on the test.

10. Consider all students taking algebra at your school. Let *a* represent a student's height to the nearest inch and *b* represent the student's IQ.

11. Consider the air temperature at noon today in every town in the United States. Let *a* represent the Celsius temperature for a town and *b* represent the Fahrenheit temperature.

12. Consider all first-class letters mailed within the United States today. Let *a* represent the weight of a letter and *b* represent the amount of postage on the letter.

13. Consider all items for sale at the nearest Wal-Mart. Let *a* represent the cost of an item and *b* represent the universal product code for the item.

14. Consider all packages shipped by UPS. Let *a* represent the weight of a package and *b* represent the cost of shipping that package.

Use the vertical-line test to determine which of the graphs are graphs of functions.

15.

16.

17.

18.

19.

20.

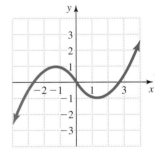

Determine whether each relation is a function. See Example 3.

21. $\{(2, 4), (3, 4), (4, 5)\}$

22. $\{(2, -5), (2, 5), (3, 10)\}$

23. $\{(-2, 4), (-2, 6), (3, 6)\}$

24. $\{(3, 6), (6, 3)\}$

25. $\{(\pi, -1), (\pi, 1)\}$

26. $\{(-0.3, -0.3), (-0.2, 0), (-0.3, 1)\}$

27. $\left\{\left(\dfrac{1}{2}, \dfrac{1}{2}\right)\right\}$

28. $\left\{\left(\dfrac{1}{3}, 7\right)\left(-\dfrac{1}{3}, 7\right)\left(\dfrac{1}{6}, 7\right)\right\}$

Find two ordered pairs that satisfy each equation and have the same x-coordinate but different y-coordinates. Answers may vary. See Example 4.

29. $x = 2y^2$ **30.** $x^2 = y^2$

31. $x = |2y|$ **32.** $|x| = |y|$

33. $x^2 + y^2 = 1$ **34.** $x^2 + y^2 = 4$

35. $x = y^4$ **36.** $x^4 = y^4$

37. $x - 2 = |y|$ **38.** $x + 5 = |y|$

Determine whether each relation is a function. See Example 4.

39. $y = x^2$ **40.** $y = x^2 + 3$

41. $x = |y| + 1$ **42.** $|x| = |y + 1|$

43. $y = x$ **44.** $x = y + 4$

45. $x = y^4 + 1$ **46.** $x^4 = y^2$

47. $y = \sqrt{x}$ **48.** $x = \sqrt{y}$

49. $|x| = |2y|$ **50.** $|4x| = |2y|$

51. $x^2 + y^2 = 9$ **52.** $x^2 + y^4 = 1$

53. $x = 2\sqrt{y}$ **54.** $y = \sqrt{x - 5}$

55. $x + 5 = |y|$ **56.** $x - 2 = |y|$

Determine the domain and range of each relation. See Example 5.

57. $\{(4, 1), (7, 1)\}$

58. $\{(0, 2), (3, 5)\}$

59. $\{(2, 3), (2, 5), (2, 7)\}$

60. $\{(3, 1), (5, 1), (4, 1)\}$

61. $y = x + 1$

62. $y = 3x + 1$

63. $y = 5 - x$

64. $y = -2x + 1$

65. $y = \sqrt{x - 2}$

66. $y = \sqrt{x + 4}$

67. $y = \sqrt{2x}$

68. $y = \sqrt{2x - 4}$

Let $f(x) = 3x - 2$, $g(x) = -x^2 + 3x - 2$, and $h(x) = |x + 2|$. Evaluate each expression.

69. $f(0)$ **70.** $f(1)$

71. $f(4)$ **72.** $f(100)$

73. $g(-2)$ **74.** $g(-3)$

75. $h(-3)$ **76.** $h(-19)$

77. $h(-4.236)$ **78.** $h(-1.99)$

79. $f(2) + g(3)$ **80.** $f(1) - g(0)$

81. $\dfrac{g(2)}{h(-3)}$ **82.** $\dfrac{h(-10)}{f(2)}$

83. $f(-1) \cdot h(-4)$ **84.** $h(0) \cdot g(0)$

Graph each function. See Example 7.

85. $f(x) = 2x - 3$ **86.** $f(x) = 4x - 4$

87. $f(x) = 5 - 2x$ **88.** $f(x) = 4 - 3x$

89. $f(x) = 3$ **90.** $f(x) = -2$

Solve each problem. See Example 8.

91. **Height.** If a ball is dropped from the top of a 256 ft building, then the formula

$$h(t) = 256 - 16t^2$$

expresses its height $h(t)$ in feet as a function of the time t in seconds.
a) Find $h(2)$, the height of the ball 2 seconds after it is dropped.
b) Find $h(4)$.

92. **Velocity.** If a ball is dropped from a height of 256 ft, then the formula

$$v(t) = -32t$$

expresses its velocity $v(t)$ in feet per second as a function of time t in seconds.
a) Find $v(0)$, the velocity of the ball at time $t = 0$.

b) Find $v(4)$.

93. **Area of a square.** Find a formula that expresses the area of a square A as a function of the length of its side s.

94. *Perimeter of a square.* Find a formula that expresses the perimeter of a square P as a function of the length of its side s.

95. *Cost of fabric.* If a certain fabric is priced at $3.98 per yard, express the cost $C(x)$ as a function of the number of yards x. Find $C(3)$.

96. *Earned income.* If Mildred earns $14.50 per hour, express her total pay $P(h)$ as a function of the number of hours worked h. Find $P(40)$.

97. *Cost of pizza.* A pizza parlor charges $14.95 for a pizza plus $0.50 for each topping. Express the total cost of a pizza $C(n)$ in dollars as a function of the number of toppings n. Find $C(6)$.

98. *Cost of gravel.* A gravel dealer charges $50 plus $30 per cubic yard for delivering a truckload of gravel. Express the total cost $C(n)$ in dollars as a function of the number of cubic yards delivered n. Find $C(12)$.

GETTING MORE INVOLVED

99. *Writing.* Consider $y = x + 2$ and $y > x + 2$. Explain why one of these relations is a function and the other is not.

100. *Writing.* Consider the graphs of $y = 2$ and $x = 3$ in the rectangular coordinate system. Explain why one of these relations is a function and the other is not.

COLLABORATIVE ACTIVITIES

Parallel and Perpendicular Explorations

In this activity you will take turns graphing lines and answering questions about the lines you have graphed. You will need graph paper.

1. Student A will graph the first line $3x - 5y = 15$ and label it line A_1. Label the x- and y-intercepts. Write the equation of the line in slope-intercept form.

2. Student B will graph the second line on the same coordinate system as line A_1. This line will have the same y-intercept as line A_1 and an x-intercept of $(-5, 0)$. Graph this line and label it B_1. Find the equation of line B_1 in both slope-intercept and standard form.

3. Together find the slopes of your lines. Are your lines perpendicular? How do you know?

4. Student A will graph a third line on the same coordinate system. This line must be parallel to line A_1 and pass through the x-intercept of line B_1. Starting at the x-intercept use the slope of A_1 to find a second point. Label your new line A_2. Find and label the y-intercept.

Grouping: Two students per group
Topic: Graphing linear equations

5. Student B will graph the fourth line on the same coordinate system. Starting at the y-intercept of line A_2 use the slope of line B_1 to find a second point. This line will be parallel to line B_1.

6. Together find the equations of lines A_2 and B_2. Write the equations in standard and slope-intercept form. How are the equations similar? How are they different? What geometric shape did your lines make?

7. On a new coordinate system draw a square such that $(0, -3)$ is one vertex of the square and the x- and y-axes are diagonals of the square. Find the equations and slopes of each line segment that forms your square. Verify that some lines are parallel and some are perpendicular.

8. A square is entirely contained in the first quadrant and one of its sides is a line segment with endpoints $(1, 3)$ and $(4, 1)$. What are the other two vertices of the square?

WRAP-UP   CHAPTER 3

SUMMARY

Rectangular Coordinate System

		Examples
x-intercept	The point where a nonhorizontal line intersects the x-axis	For the line $2x + y = 6$, the x-intercept is $(3, 0)$ and the
y-intercept	The point where a nonvertical line intersects the y-axis	y-intercept is $(0, 6)$.

Midpoint formula	The midpoint of the line segment with endpoints (x_1, y_1) and (x_2, y_2) is $$(\bar{x}, \bar{y}) = \left(\frac{x_1 + x_2}{2}, \frac{y_1 + y_2}{2}\right).$$	If $(x_1, y_1) = (1, -2)$ and $(x_2, y_2) = (7, 8)$, then $(\bar{x}, \bar{y}) = (4, 3)$.
Distance formula	The distance between (x_1, y_1) and (x_2, y_2) is $\sqrt{(x_2 - x_1)^2 + (y_2 - y_1)^2}$.	The distance between $(3, 5)$ and $(-2, 9)$ is $\sqrt{41}$.

Slope

Examples

Slope of a line	$$\text{Slope} = \frac{\text{change in } y\text{-coordinate}}{\text{change in } x\text{-coordinate}}$$ $$= \frac{\text{rise}}{\text{run}}$$	
Slope using coordinates	Slope of line through (x_1, y_1) and (x_2, y_2) is $m = \dfrac{y_2 - y_1}{x_2 - x_1}$, provided that $x_2 - x_1 \neq 0$.	If $(x_1, y_1) = (4, -2)$ and $(x_2, y_2) = (3, -6)$, then $$m = \frac{-6 - (-2)}{3 - 4} = 4.$$
Types of slope		
Perpendicular lines	The slope of one line is the negative of the reciprocal of the slope of the other line.	The lines $y = -\frac{1}{3}x + 5$ and $y = 3x - 9$ are perpendicular.
Parallel lines	Nonvertical parallel lines have equal slopes.	The lines $y = 2x - 3$ and $y = 2x + 7$ are parallel.

Forms of Linear Equations

Examples

Point-slope form	$y - y_1 = m(x - x_1)$ (x_1, y_1) is a point on the line, and m is the slope.	Line through $(5, -3)$ with slope 2: $y + 3 = 2(x - 5)$
Slope-intercept form	$y = mx + b$ m is the slope, $(0, b)$ is the y-intercept, and y is a linear function of x. We also write $f(x) = mx + b$.	Line through $(0, -3)$ with slope 2: $y = 2x - 3$ $f(x) = 2x - 3, f(4) = 5$
Standard form	$Ax + By = C$ A and B are not both 0.	$3x - 2y = 12$

| Vertical line | $x = k$, where k is any real number. Slope is undefined for vertical lines. | $x = 5$ |

| Horizontal line | $y = k$, where k is any real number. Slope is zero for horizontal lines. | $y = -2$ |

Graphing Linear Equations

Examples

| Point-plotting | Arbitrarily select some points that satisfy the equation, and draw a line through them. | For $y = 2x + 1$, draw a line through $(0, 1)$, $(1, 3)$, and $(2, 5)$. |

| Intercepts | Find the x- and y-intercepts (provided that they are not the origin), and draw a line through them. | For $x + y = 4$ the intercepts are $(0, 4)$ and $(4, 0)$. |

| y-intercept and slope | Start at the y-intercept and use the slope to locate a second point, then draw a line through the two points. | For $y = 3x - 2$ start at $(0, -2)$, rise 3 and run 1 to get to $(1, 1)$. Draw a line through the two points. |

Linear Inequalities

Examples

| Linear inequality | $Ax + By \leq C$, where A and B are not both zero. The symbols $<$, $>$, and $\geq$ are also used. | $2x - 3y \leq 7$ $x - y > 6$ |

| Graphing linear inequalities | Solve for y, then graph the line $y = mx + b$. $\quad y > mx + b$ is the region above the line. $\quad y < mx + b$ is the region below the line. | Graph of $y = x + 2$ is a line. $y > x + 2$ above $y = x + 2$. $y < x + 2$ below $y = x + 2$. |
| | For inequalities without y, graph $x = k$. $\quad x > k$ is the region to the right of $x = k$. $\quad x < k$ is the region to the left of $x = k$. | The graph of $x > 5$ is to the right of the vertical line $x = 5$, and the graph of $x < 5$ is to left of $x = 5$. |

| Test points | A linear inequality may also be graphed by graphing the corresponding line and then testing a point to determine which region satisfies the inequality. | |

| Compound inequalities | Simple inequalities connected by *and* or *or* For *and*, find the intersection of the regions. For *or*, find the union of the regions. | $x < 3$ and $y > x - 4$ $x + y \geq 1$ or $y \leq x - 1$ |

Relations and Functions

Examples

| Relation | Any set of ordered pairs of real numbers | $\{(1, 2), (1, 3)\}$ |

| Function | A relation in which no two ordered pairs have the same first coordinate and different second coordinates. | $\{(1, 2), (3, 5), (4, 5)\}$ |
| | If y is a function of x, then y is uniquely determined by x. A function may be defined by a table, a listing of ordered pairs, or an equation. | |

| Domain | The set of first coordinates of the ordered pairs | Function: $y = x^2$ Domain: $(-\infty, \infty)$ |

Range	The set of second coordinates of the ordered pairs. Range: $[0, \infty)$	
Function notation	If y is a function of x, the expression $f(x)$ is used in place of y.	$y = 2x + 3$ $f(x) = 2x + 3$
Vertical-line test	If a graph can be crossed more than once by a vertical line, then it is not the graph of a function.	
Linear function	A function of the form $f(x) = mx + b$ with $m \neq 0$	$f(x) = 3x - 7$ $f(x) = -2x + 5$
Constant function	A function of the form $f(x) = b$, where b is a real number	$f(x) = 2$

ENRICHING YOUR MATHEMATICAL WORD POWER

For each mathematical term, choose the correct meaning.

1. **graph of an equation**
   a. the Cartesian coordinate system
   b. two number lines that intersect at a right angle
   c. the x-axis and y-axis
   d. an illustration in the coordinate plane that shows all ordered pairs that satisfy an equation

2. **origin**
   a. the point of intersection of the x- and y-axes
   b. the beginning of algebra
   c. the number 0
   d. the x-axis

3. **x-coordinate**
   a. the first number in an ordered pair
   b. the second number in an ordered pair
   c. a point on the x-axis
   d. a point where a graph crosses the x-axis

4. **y-intercept**
   a. the second number in an ordered pair
   b. a point at which a graph intersects the y-axis
   c. any point on the y-axis
   d. the point where the y-axis intersects the x-axis

5. **coordinate plane**
   a. a matching plane
   b. when the x-axis is coordinated with the y-axis
   c. a plane with a rectangular coordinate system
   d. a coordinated system for graphs

6. **independent variable**
   a. the first coordinate of an ordered pair
   b. the second coordinate of an ordered pair
   c. the x-axis
   d. the y-axis

7. **dependent variable**
   a. the first coordinate of an ordered pair
   b. the second coordinate of an ordered pair

   c. the x-axis
   d. the y-axis

8. **slope**
   a. the change in x divided by the change in y
   b. a measure of the steepness of a line
   c. the run divided by the rise
   d. the slope of a line

9. **slope-intercept form**
   a. $y = mx + b$
   b. rise over run
   c. the point at which a line crosses the y-axis
   d. $y - y_1 = m(x - x_1)$

10. **point-slope form**
    a. $Ax + By = C$
    b. rise over run
    c. $y - y_1 = m(x - x_1)$
    d. the slope of a line at a single point

11. **standard form**
    a. $y = mx + b$
    b. $Ax + By = C$, where A and B are not both 0
    c. $y - y_1 = m(x - x_1)$
    d. the most common form

12. **linear inequality in two variables**
    a. when two lines are not equal
    b. line segments that are unequal in length
    c. an inequality of the form $Ax + By \geq C$ or with another symbol of inequality
    d. an inequality of the form $Ax^2 + By^2 < C^2$

13. **function**
    a. a set of ordered pairs of real numbers
    b. a set of ordered pairs of real numbers in which no two have the same first coordinates and different second coordinates

c.   a set of ordered pairs of real numbers in which no two have the same second coordinates and different first coordinates

d.   an equation

14.   relation

a.   a set of ordered pairs of real numbers

b.   a set of ordered pairs of real numbers in which no two have the same first coordinates and different second coordinates

c.   cousins and second cousins

d.   a fraction

15.   domain

a.   the range

b.   the set of second coordinates of a relation

c.   the independent variable

d.   the set of first coordinates of a relation

16.   function notation

a.   a notation where $f(x)$ is used as the independent variable

b.   a notation where $f(x)$ is used as the dependent variable

c.   the notation of algebra

d.   the notation of exponents

Study Tip

Note how the review exercises are arranged according to the sections in this chapter. If you are having trouble with a certain type of problem, refer back to the appropriate section for examples and explanations.

REVIEW EXERCISES

3.1 *For each point, name the quadrant in which it lies or the axis on which it lies.*

1. $(-3, -2)$

2. $(0, \pi)$

3. $(\pi, 0)$

4. $(-5, 4)$

5. $(0, -1)$

6. $\left(\dfrac{\pi}{2}, 1\right)$

7. $(\sqrt{2}, -3)$

8. $(6, -3)$

Find the midpoint and length of the line segment with the given endpoints.

9. $(8, -2)$ and $(2, 6)$

10. $(-9, 4)$ and $(-3, -4)$

11. $(2, -2)$ and $(3, 1)$

12. $(0, 3)$ and $(-1, -1)$

Complete the given ordered pairs so that each ordered pair satisfies the given equation.

13. $(0,\ ), (\ , 0), (4,\ ), (\ , -3), y = -3x + 2$

14. $(0,\ ), (\ , 0), (-6,\ ), (\ , 5), 2x + 3y = 5$

3.2 *Find the slope of the line through each pair of points.*

15. $(-5, 6), (-2, 9)$

16. $(-2, 7), (3, -4)$

17. $(4, 1), (-3, -2)$

18. $(6, 0), (0, -3)$

Solve each problem.

19. What is the slope of any line that is parallel to the line through $(-3, -4)$ and $(5, -1)$?

20. What is the slope of the line through $(4, 6)$ that is parallel to the line through $(-2, 1)$ and $(7, 1)$?

21. What is the slope of any line that is perpendicular to the line through $(-3, 5)$ and $(4, -6)$?

22. What is the slope of the line through $(1, 2)$ that is perpendicular to the line through $(5, 4)$ and $(5, -2)$?

3.3 *Find the slope and y-intercept for each line.*

23. $y = -3x + 4$

24. $2y - 3x + 1 = 0$

25. $y - 3 = \dfrac{2}{3}(x - 1)$

26. $y - 3 = 5$

Write each equation in standard form with integral coefficients.

27. $y = \dfrac{2}{3}x - 4$

28. $y = -0.05x + 0.26$

29. $y - 1 = \dfrac{1}{2}(x + 3)$

30. $\dfrac{1}{2}x - \dfrac{1}{3}y = \dfrac{1}{4}$

Write the equation of the line containing the given point and having the given slope. Rewrite each equation in standard form with integral coefficients.

31. $(1, -3), m = \dfrac{1}{2}$

32. $(0, 2), m = 3$

33. $(-2, 6), m = -\dfrac{3}{4}$

34. $\left(2, \dfrac{1}{2}\right), m = \dfrac{1}{4}$

35. $(3, 5), m = 0$

36. $(0, 0), m = -1$

Graph each equation.

37. $y = 2x - 3$

38. $y = \dfrac{2}{3}x + 1$

39. $3x - 2y = -6$

40. $4x + 5y = 10$

41. $y - 3 = 10$

42. $2x = 8$

43. $5x - 3y = 7$

44. $3x + 4y = -1$

45. $5x + 4y = 100$

46. $2x - y = 120$

47. $x - 80y = 400$

48. $75x + y = 300$

3.4 *Graph each linear inequality.*

49. $y > 3x - 2$

50. $y \leq 2x + 3$

51. $x - y \leq 5$

52. $2x + y > 1$

59. $5x - 2y < 9$

60. $3x + 4y \leq -1$

53. $3x > 2$

54. $x + 2 \leq 0$

Graph each compound or absolute value inequality.

61. $y > 3$ and
    $y - x < 5$

62. $x + y \leq 1$ or
    $y \leq 4$

55. $4y \leq 0$

56. $4y - 4 > 0$

63. $3x + 2y \geq 8$ or
    $3x - 2y \leq 6$

64. $x + 8y > 8$ and
    $x - 2y < 10$

57. $4x - 2y \geq 6$

58. $-5x - 3y > 6$

65. $|x + 2y| < 10$

66. $|x - 3y| \geq 9$

67. $|x| \le 5$

68. $|y| > 6$

69. $|y - x| > 2$

70. $|x - y| \le 1$

3.5 *Determine whether each relation is a function.*

71. $\{(5, 7), (5, 10), (5, 3)\}$

72. $\{(1, 3), (4, 7), (1, 6)\}$

73. $\{(1, 1), (2, 1), (3, 3)\}$

74. $\{(2, 4), (4, 6), (6, 8)\}$

75. $y = x^2$

76. $x^2 = 1 + y^2$

77. $x = y^4$

78. $y = \sqrt{x - 1}$

Determine the domain and range of each relation.

79. $\{(3, 5), (4, 9), (5, 1)\}$

80. $\{(2, 6), (6, 7), (8, 9)\}$

81. $y = x + 1$

82. $y = 2x - 3$

83. $y = \sqrt{x + 5}$

84. $y = \sqrt{x - 1}$

Let $f(x) = 2x - 5$ and $g(x) = x^2 + x - 6$. Evaluate each expression.

85. $f(0)$

86. $f(-3)$

87. $g(0)$

88. $g(-2)$

89. $g\left(\dfrac{1}{2}\right)$

90. $g\left(-\dfrac{1}{2}\right)$

MISCELLANEOUS

Write an equation in standard form with integral coefficients for each line described.

91. The line that crosses the x-axis at $(2, 0)$ and the y-axis at $(0, -6)$

92. The line with an x-intercept of $(4, 0)$ and slope $-\dfrac{1}{2}$

93. The line through $(-1, 4)$ with slope $-\dfrac{1}{2}$

94. The line through $(2, -3)$ with slope 0

95. The line through $(2, -6)$ and $(2, 5)$

96. The line through $(-3, 6)$ and $(4, 2)$

97. The line through $(0, 0)$ perpendicular to $x = 5$

98. The line through $(2, -3)$ perpendicular to $y = -3x + 5$

99. The line through $(-1, 4)$ parallel to $y = 2x + 1$

100. The line through $(2, 1)$ perpendicular to $y = 10$

For Exercises 101–104, write an equation in standard form with integral coefficients for each line.

101.

102.

103.

104.

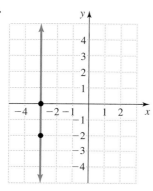

Use slope to solve each geometric problem.

105. Show that the points $(-5, -5)$, $(-3, -1)$, $(6, 2)$, and $(4, -2)$ are the vertices of a parallelogram.

106. Show that the points $(-5, -5)$, $(4, -2)$, and $(3, 1)$ are the vertices of a right triangle.

107. Show that the points $(-2, 2)$, $(0, 0)$, $(2, 6)$, and $(4, 4)$ are the vertices of a rectangle.

108. Determine whether the points $(2, 1)$, $(4, 7)$, and $(-3, -14)$ lie on a straight line.

Solve each problem.

109. *Maximum heart rate.* The maximum heart rate during exercise for a 20 year old is 200 beats per minute, and the maximum heart rate for a 70 year old is 150 (NordicTrack brochure) as shown in the accompanying figure.

a) Write the maximum heart rate h as a linear function of age a.

b) What is the maximum heart rate for a 40 year old?

c) Does your maximum heart rate increase or decrease as you get older?

110. *Resting heart rate.* A subject is given 3 milligrams (mg) of an experimental drug, and a resting heart rate of 82 is recorded. Another subject is given 5 mg of the same drug, and a resting heart rate of 89 is recorded. If we assume the heart rate, h, is a linear function of the dosage, d, find the linear equation expressing h in terms of d. If a subject is given 10 mg of the drug, what would be the expected heart rate?

111. *Rental costs.* The charge, C, in dollars, for renting an air hammer from the Tools Is Us Rental Company is determined from the formula $C = 26 + 17d$, where d is the number of days in the rental period. Graph this function for d from 1 to 30. If the air hammer is worth \$1080, then in how many days would the rental charge equal the value of the air hammer?

112. *Waist-to-hip ratio.* Dr. Aaron R. Folsom, from the University of Minnesota School of Public Health, has concluded that for a man aged 50 to 69 to be in good health, his waist size w should be less than or equal to

FIGURE FOR EXERCISE 109

FIGURE FOR EXERCISE 112

95% of his hip size h as shown in the figure on the previous page.

a) Write an inequality that describes the region shown in the figure.

b) Is a man in this group with a 36-inch waist and 37-inch hips in good health?

c) If a man in this group has a waist of 38 inches, then what is his minimum hip size for good health?

CHAPTER 3 TEST

Complete each ordered pair so that it satisfies the given equation.

1. $(0, \ )$, $(\ , 0)$, $(\ , -8)$, $2x + y = 5$

Solve each problem.

2. Find the slope of the line through $(-3, 7)$ and $(2, 1)$.

3. Find the midpoint and length of the line segment with endpoints $(2, 0)$ and $(-3, -1)$.

4. Determine the slope and y-intercept for the line $8x - 5y = -10$.

5. Show that $(-1, -2)$, $(0, 0)$, $(6, 2)$, and $(5, 0)$ are the vertices of a parallelogram.

6. Suppose the value, V, in dollars, of a boat is a linear function of its age, a, in years. If a boat was valued at \$22,000 brand new and it is worth \$16,000 when it is 3 years old, find the linear equation that expresses V in terms of a.

For each line described below, write its equation in standard form with integral coefficients.

7. The line with y-intercept $(0, 3)$ and slope $-\frac{1}{2}$

8. The line through $(-3, 5)$ with slope -4

9. The line through $(2, 3)$ that is perpendicular to $3x - 5y = 7$

10. The line shown in the graph:

FIGURE FOR EXERCISE 10

Sketch the graph of each equation in the rectangular coordinate system.

11. $y = 4$

12. $x = 3$

13. $3x + 4y = 12$

14. $y = \frac{2}{3}x - 2$

Sketch the graph of each inequality.

15. $y > -\dfrac{1}{2}x + 3$

16. $x > 2$ and $x + y > 0$

17. $|2x + y| \geq 3$

Study Tip

Solve each problem.

18. Determine whether $\{(0, 5), (9, 5), (4, 5)\}$ is a function.

19. Let $f(x) = -2x + 5$. Find $f(-3)$.

20. Find the domain and range of the function $y = \sqrt{x - 7}$.

21. A mail-order firm charges its customers a shipping and handling fee of $3.00 plus $0.50 per pound for each order shipped. Express the shipping and handling fee S as a function of the weight of the order n.

22. If a ball is tossed into the air from a height of 6 feet with a velocity of 32 feet per second, then its altitude at time t (in seconds) can be described by the function

$$A(t) = -16t^2 + 32t + 6.$$

Find the altitude of the ball at 2 seconds.

Graph Paper

Use these grids for graphing. Make as many copies of this page as you need.

Evaluate each expression.

1. $2^3 \cdot 4^2$

2. $2^7 - 2^6$

3. $3^2 - 4(5)(-2)$

4. $3 - 2 \,|\, 5 - 7 \cdot 3 \,|$

5. $\dfrac{2 - (-3)}{5 - 6}$

6. $\dfrac{-3 - 7}{-1 - (-3)}$

Simplify each expression.

7. $3t \cdot 4t$

8. $3t + 4t$

9. $\dfrac{4x + 8}{4}$

10. $\dfrac{-8y}{-4} - \dfrac{10y}{-2}$

11. $3(x - 4) - 4(5 - x)$

12. $-2(3x^2 - x) + 3(2x - 5x^2)$

Solve each equation.

13. $15(b - 27) = 0$

14. $0.05a - 0.04(a - 50) = 4$

15. $|\, 3v - 7 \,| = 0$

16. $|\, 3u - 7 \,| = 3$

17. $|\, 3x - 7 \,| = -77$

18. $|\, 3x - 7 \,| + 1 = 8$

Graph the solution set to each inequality or compound inequality in one variable on the number line.

19. $2x - 1 > 7$

20. $5 - 3x \le -1$

21. $x - 5 \le 4$ and $3x - 1 < 8$

22. $2x \le -6$ or $5 - 2x < -7$

23. $|\, x - 3 \,| < 2$

24. $|\, 1 - 2x \,| \ge 7$

Graph the solution set to each linear inequality or compound inequality in a rectangular coordinate system.

25. $y < 2x - 1$

26. $3x - y \le 2$

27. $y > x$ and $y < 5 - 3x$

28. $y \le 2$ or $x \ge -3$

Study Tip

Don't wait until the final exam to review material. Do some review on a regular basis. The Making Connections exercises on this page can be used to review, compare, and contrast different concepts that you have studied. A good time to work these exercises is between a test and the start of new material.

Solve this problem.

29. Social Security. A person retiring in the year 2005 who earned a lifetime average annual salary of $25,000 will

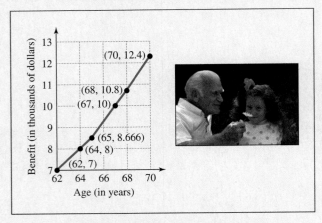

Benefit (in thousands of dollars) vs. Age (in years)

Points: (62, 7), (64, 8), (65, 8.666), (67, 10), (68, 10.8), (70, 12.4)

FIGURE FOR EXERCISE 29

receive a benefit based on age (Social Security Administration, www.ssa.gov). For ages 62 through 64 the benefit in dollars is determined by $b = 7,000 + 500(a - 62)$, for ages 65 through 67 the benefit is determined by $b = 10,000 + 667(a - 67)$, and for ages 68 through 70 the benefit is determined by $b = 10,000 + 800(a - 67)$.

a) Write each benefit formula in slope-intercept form.

b) What will be the annual Social Security benefit for a person who retires in 2005 at age 64?

c) If a person retires in 2005 and gets an $11,600 benefit, then what is the age of that person in 2005?

d) Find the slope of each line segment in the accompanying figure and interpret your results.

Systems of Linear Equations

I n his letter to M. Leroy in 1789 Benjamin Franklin said, "In this world nothing is certain but death and taxes." Since that time taxes have become not only inevitable, but also intricate and complex.

Each year the U.S. Congress revises parts of the Federal Income Tax Code. To help clarify these revisions, the Internal Revenue Service issues frequent revenue rulings. In addition, there are seven tax courts that further interpret changes and revisions, sometimes in entirely different ways. Is it any wonder that tax preparation has become complicated and few individuals actually prepare their own taxes? Both corporate and individual tax preparation is a growing business, and there are over 500,000 tax counselors helping more than 60 million taxpayers to file their returns correctly.

Everyone knows that doing taxes involves a lot of arithmetic, but not everyone knows that computing taxes can also involve algebra. In fact, to find state and federal taxes for certain corporations, you must solve a system of equations. You will see an example of using algebra to find amounts of income taxes in Exercises 61 and 62 of Section 4.1.

4.1   SOLVING SYSTEMS BY GRAPHING AND SUBSTITUTION

In Chapter 3 we studied linear equations in two variables, but we have usually considered only one equation at a time. In this chapter we will see problems that involve more than one equation. Any collection of two or more equations is called a **system** of equations. If the equations of a system involve two variables, then the set of ordered pairs that satisfy all of the equations is the **solution set of the system.** In this section we solve systems of linear equations in two variables and use systems to solve problems.

Solving a System by Graphing

Because the graph of each linear equation is a line, points that satisfy both equations lie on both lines. For some systems these points can be found by graphing.

E X A M P L E   1

A system with only one solution

Solve the system by graphing:

$$y = x + 2$$
$$x + y = 4$$

Solution

First write the equations in slope-intercept form:

$$y = x + 2$$
$$y = -x + 4$$

Use the y-intercept and the slope to graph each line. The graph of the system is shown in Fig. 4.1. From the graph it appears that these lines intersect at $(1, 3)$. To be certain, we can check that $(1, 3)$ satisfies both equations. Let $x = 1$ and $y = 3$ in $y = x + 2$ to get

$$3 = 1 + 2.$$

Let $x = 1$ and $y = 3$ in $x + y = 4$ to get

$$1 + 3 = 4.$$

Because $(1, 3)$ satisfies both equations, the solution set to the system is $\{(1, 3)\}$.

Calculator Close-Up

To check Example 1, graph

$$y_1 = x + 2$$

and

$$y_2 = -x + 4.$$

From the CALC menu, choose intersect to have the calculator locate the point of intersection of the two lines. After choosing intersect, you must indicate which two lines you want to intersect and then guess the point of intersection.

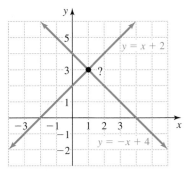

FIGURE 4.1

The graphs of the equations in Example 2 are parallel lines, and there is no point of intersection.

EXAMPLE 2

A system with no solution

Solve the system by graphing:

$$2x - 3y = 6$$
$$3y - 2x = 3$$

Solution

First write each equation in slope-intercept form:

$$2x - 3y = 6 \qquad\qquad 3y - 2x = 3$$
$$-3y = -2x + 6 \qquad\qquad 3y = 2x + 3$$
$$y = \frac{2}{3}x - 2 \qquad\qquad y = \frac{2}{3}x + 1$$

The graph of the system is shown in Fig. 4.2. Because the two lines in Fig. 4.2 are parallel, there is no ordered pair that satisfies both equations. The solution set to the system is the empty set, $\varnothing$.

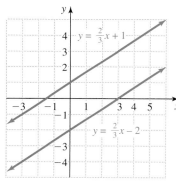

FIGURE 4.2   ■

The equations in Example 3 are two different equations for the same straight line.

EXAMPLE 3

A system with infinitely many solutions

Solve the system by graphing:

$$2(y + 2) = x$$
$$x - 2y = 4$$

Solution

Write each equation in slope-intercept form:

$$2(y + 2) = x \qquad\qquad x - 2y = 4$$
$$2y + 4 = x \qquad\qquad -2y = -x + 4$$
$$y = \frac{1}{2}x - 2 \qquad\qquad y = \frac{1}{2}x - 2$$

Because the equations have the same slope-intercept form, the original equations are equivalent. Their graphs are the same straight line as shown in Fig. 4.3. Every point on the line satisfies both equations of the system. There are infinitely many points in the solution set. The solution set is $\{(x, y) \mid x - 2y = 4\}$.   ■

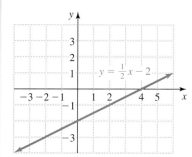

FIGURE 4.3

Independent, Inconsistent, and Dependent Equations

Our first three examples illustrate the three possible ways in which two lines can be positioned in a plane. In Example 1 the lines intersect in a single point. In this case we say that the equations are **independent** or the system is independent. If the two lines are parallel, as in Example 2, then there is no solution to the system, and the equations are **inconsistent** or the system is inconsistent. If the two equations of a system are equivalent, as in Example 3, the equations are **dependent** or the system is dependent. Figure 4.4 shows the types of graphs that correspond to independent, inconsistent, and dependent systems.

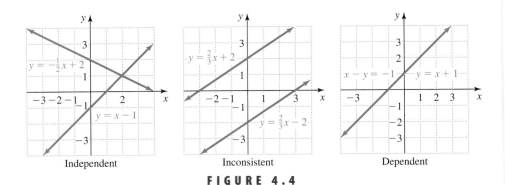

FIGURE 4.4

Solving by Substitution

Solving a system by graphing is certainly limited by the accuracy of the graph. If the lines intersect at a point whose coordinates are not integers, then it is difficult to determine those coordinates from the graph. The method of solving a system by **substitution** does not depend on a graph and is totally accurate. For substitution we replace a variable in one equation with an equivalent expression obtained from the other equation. Our intention in this substitution step is to eliminate a variable and to give us an equation involving only one variable.

EXAMPLE 4

An independent system solved by substitution

Solve the system by substitution:

$$2x + 3y = 8$$
$$y + 2x = 6$$

Solution

We can easily solve $y + 2x = 6$ for y to get $y = -2x + 6$. Now replace y in the first equation by $-2x + 6$:

$$2x + 3y = 8$$
$$2x + 3(-2x + 6) = 8 \quad \text{Substitute } -2x + 6 \text{ for } y.$$
$$2x - 6x + 18 = 8$$
$$-4x = -10$$
$$x = \frac{5}{2}$$

Calculator Close-Up

To check Example 4, graph
$$y_1 = (8 - 2x)/3$$
and
$$y_2 = -2x + 6.$$
From the CALC menu, choose intersect to have the calculator locate the point of intersection of the two lines.

To find y, we let $x = \frac{5}{2}$ in the equation $y = -2x + 6$:

$$y = -2\left(\frac{5}{2}\right) + 6 = -5 + 6 = 1$$

The next step is to check $x = \frac{5}{2}$ and $y = 1$ in each equation. If $x = \frac{5}{2}$ and $y = 1$ in $2x + 3y = 8$, we get

$$2\left(\frac{5}{2}\right) + 3(1) = 8.$$

If $x = \frac{5}{2}$ and $y = 1$ in $y + 2x = 6$, we get

$$1 + 2\left(\frac{5}{2}\right) = 6.$$

Because both of these equations are true, the solution set to the system is $\left\{\left(\frac{5}{2}, 1\right)\right\}$. The equations of this system are independent. ∎

E X A M P L E   5

An inconsistent system solved by substitution
Solve by substitution:

$$x - 2y = 3$$
$$2x - 4y = 7$$

Helpful Hint

The purpose of Example 5 is to show what happens when you try to solve an inconsistent system by substitution. If we had first written the equations in slope-intercept form, we would have known that the lines are parallel and the solution set is the empty set.

Solution

Solve the first equation for x to get $x = 2y + 3$. Substitute $2y + 3$ for x in the second equation:

$$2x - 4y = 7$$
$$2(2y + 3) - 4y = 7$$
$$4y + 6 - 4y = 7$$
$$6 = 7$$

Because $6 = 7$ is incorrect no matter what values are chosen for x and y, there is no solution to this system of equations. The equations are inconsistent. To check, we write each equation in slope-intercept form:

$$x - 2y = 3 \qquad\qquad 2x - 4y = 7$$
$$-2y = -x + 3 \qquad\qquad -4y = -2x + 7$$
$$y = \frac{1}{2}x - \frac{3}{2} \qquad\qquad y = \frac{1}{2}x - \frac{7}{4}$$

The graphs of these equations are parallel lines with different y-intercepts. The solution set to the system is the empty set, $\varnothing$. ∎

E X A M P L E   6

A dependent system solved by substitution
Solve by substitution:

$$2x + 3y = 5 + x + 4y$$
$$y = x - 5$$

Solution

Substitute $y = x - 5$ into the first equation:

$$2x + 3(x - 5) = 5 + x + 4(x - 5)$$
$$2x + 3x - 15 = 5 + x + 4x - 20$$
$$5x - 15 = 5x - 15$$

Because the last equation is an identity, any ordered pair that satisfies $y = x - 5$ will also satisfy $2x + 3y = 5 + x + 4y$. The equations of this system are dependent. The solution set to the system is the set of all points that satisfy $y = x - 5$. We write the solution set in set notation as

$$\{(x, y) \mid y = x - 5\}.$$

We can verify this result by writing $2x + 3y = 5 + x + 4y$ in slope-intercept form:

$$2x + 3y = 5 + x + 4y$$
$$3y = -x + 5 + 4y$$
$$-y = -x + 5$$
$$y = x - 5$$

Because this slope-intercept form is identical to the slope-intercept form of the other equation, they are two different equations for the same straight line.   ■

If a system is dependent, then an identity will result after the substitution. If the system is inconsistent, then an inconsistent equation will result after the substitution. The strategy for solving an independent system by substitution can be summarized as follows.

The Substitution Method

1. Solve one of the equations for one variable in terms of the other.
2. Substitute into the other equation to get an equation in one variable.
3. Solve for the remaining variable (if possible).
4. Insert the value just found into one of the original equations to find the value of the other variable.
5. Check the two values in both equations.

Applications

Many of the problems that we solved in previous chapters involved more than one unknown quantity. To solve them, we wrote expressions for all of the unknowns in terms of one variable. Now we can solve problems involving two unknowns by using two variables and writing a system of equations.

E X A M P L E   7   **Perimeter of a rectangle**

The length of a rectangular swimming pool is twice the width. If the perimeter is 120 feet, then what are the length and width?

FIGURE 4.5

Solution

Draw a diagram as shown in Fig. 4.5. If L represents the length and W represents the width, then we can write the following system.

$$L = 2W$$
$$2L + 2W = 120$$

Since $L = 2W$, we can replace L in $2L + 2W = 120$ with $2W$:

$$2(2W) + 2W = 120$$
$$4W + 2W = 120$$
$$6W = 120$$
$$W = 20$$

So the width is 20 feet and the length is 2(20) or 40 feet. ∎

E X A M P L E 8

Tale of two investments

Belinda had $20,000 to invest. She invested part of it at 10% and the remainder at 12%. If her income from the two investments was $2160, then how much did she invest at each rate?

Helpful Hint

In Chapter 2 we would have done Example 8 with one variable by letting x represent the amount invested at 10% and 20,000 $-x$ represent the amount invested at 12%.

Solution

Let x be the amount invested at 10% and y be the amount invested at 12%. We can summarize all of the given information in a table:

	Amount	Rate	Interest
First investment	x	10%	$0.10x$
Second investment	y	12%	$0.12y$

Calculator Close-Up

To check Example 8, graph
$$y_1 = 20,000 - x$$
and
$$y_2 = (2160 - 0.1x)/0.12.$$
The viewing window needs to be large enough to contain the point of intersection. Use the intersection feature to find the point of intersection.

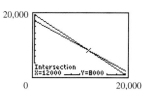

We can write one equation about the amounts invested and another about the interest from the investments:

$$x + y = 20,000 \quad \text{Total amount invested}$$
$$0.10x + 0.12y = 2,160 \quad \text{Total interest}$$

Solve the first equation for x to get $x = 20,000 - y$. Substitute $20,000 - y$ for x in the second equation:

$$0.10x + 0.12y = 2,160$$
$$0.10(20,000 - y) + 0.12y = 2,160 \quad \text{Replace } x \text{ by } 20,000 - y.$$
$$2,000 - 0.10y + 0.12y = 2,160 \quad \text{Solve for } y.$$
$$0.02y = 160$$
$$y = 8,000$$
$$x = 12,000 \quad \text{Because } x = 20,000 - y$$

To check this answer, find 10% of $12,000 and 12% of $8,000:

$$0.10(12,000) = 1,200$$
$$0.12(8,000) = 960$$

Because $1,200 + $960 = $2,160 and $8,000 + $12,000 = $20,000, we can be certain that Belinda invested $12,000 at 10% and $8,000 at 12%. ∎

MATH AT WORK

Accountants work with both people and numbers. When Maria L. Manning, an auditor at Deloitte & Touche LLP, is preparing for an audit, she studies the numbers on the balance sheet and income statement, comparing the current fiscal year to the prior one. The purpose of an independent audit is to give investors a realistic view of a company's finances. To determine that a company's financial statements are fairly stated in accordance with the General Accepted Accounting Procedures (GAAP), she first interviews the comptroller to get the story behind the numbers. Typical questions she could ask are: How productive was your year? Are there any new products? What was behind the big stories in the newspapers? Then Ms. Manning and members of the audit team test the financial statement in detail, closely examining accounts relating to unusual losses or profits.

ACCOUNTANT

Ms. Manning is responsible for both manufacturing and mutual fund companies. At a manufacturing company, accounts receivable and inventory are two key components of an audit. For example, to test inventory, Ms. Manning visits a company's warehouse and physically counts all the items for sale to verify a company's assets. For a mutual fund company the audit team pays close attention to current events, for they indirectly affect the financial industry.

In Exercises 63 and 64 of this section you will work problems that involve one aspect of cost accounting: calculating the amount of taxes and bonuses paid by a company.

WARM-UPS

True or false? Explain your answer.

1. The ordered pair (1, 2) is in the solution set to the equation $2x + y = 4$.

2. The ordered pair (1, 2) satisfies $2x + y = 4$ and $3x - y = 6$.

3. The ordered pair (2, 3) satisfies $4x - y = 5$ and $4x - y = -5$.

4. If two distinct straight lines in the coordinate plane are not parallel, then they intersect in exactly one point.

5. The substitution method is used to eliminate a variable.

6. No ordered pair satisfies $y = 3x - 5$ and $y = 3x + 1$.

7. The equations $y = 3x - 6$ and $y = 2x + 4$ are independent.

8. The equations $y = 2x + 7$ and $y = 2x + 8$ are inconsistent.

9. The graphs of dependent equations are the same.

10. The graphs of independent linear equations intersect at exactly one point.

Reading and Writing After reading this section, write out the answers to these questions. Use complete sentences.

1. How do we solve a system of linear equations by graphing?

2. How can you determine whether a system has no solution by graphing?

3. What is the major disadvantage to solving a system by graphing?

4. How do we solve systems by substitution?

5. How can you identify an inconsistent system when solving by substitution?

6. How can you identify a dependent system when solving by substitution?

Solve each system by graphing. See Examples 1–3.

7. $y = 2x$
   $y = -x + 3$

8. $y = x - 3$
   $y = -x + 1$

9. $y = 2x - 1$
   $2y = x - 2$

10. $y = 2x + 1$
    $x + y = -2$

11. $y = x - 3$
    $x - 2y = 4$

12. $y = -3x$
    $x + y = 2$

13. $2y - 2x = 2$
    $2y - 2x = 6$

14. $3y - 3x = 9$
    $x - y = 1$

15. $y = -\frac{1}{2}x + 4$
    $x + 2y = 8$

16. $2x - 3y = 6$
    $y = \frac{2}{3}x - 2$

17. $y = 2x + 4$
    $3x + y = -1$

18. $3x - 2y = 6$
    $3x + 2y = 6$

19. $y = -\frac{1}{4}x$
    $x + 4y = 8$

20. $y = -\frac{2}{3}x$
    $2x + 3y = 5$

The graphs of the following systems are given in (a) through (d). Match each system with the correct graph.

21. $5x + 4y = 7$
    $x - 3y = 9$

22. $3x - 5y = -9$
    $5x - 6y = -8$

23. $4x - 5y = -2$
    $3y - x = -3$

24. $4x + 5y = -2$
    $4y - x = 11$

a)

b)

c)

d)

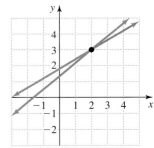

Solve each system by the substitution method. Determine whether the equations are independent, dependent, or inconsistent. See Examples 4–6.

25. $y = x - 5$
    $2x - 5y = 1$

26. $y = x + 4$
    $3y - 5x = 6$

27. $x = 2y - 7$
    $3x + 2y = -5$

28. $x = y + 3$
    $3x - 2y = 4$

29. $y = 2x - 30$
    $\frac{1}{5}x - \frac{1}{2}y = -1$

30. $3x - 5y = 4$
    $y = \frac{3}{4}x - 2$

31. $x - y = 5$
    $2x = 2y + 14$

32. $2x - y = 4$
    $2x - y = 3$

33. $y = 2x - 5$
    $y + 1 = 2(x - 2)$

34. $2x - y = 3$
    $2y = 4x - 6$

35. $2x + y = 9$
$2x - 5y = 15$

36. $3y - x = 0$
$x - 4y = -2$

37. $x - y = 0$
$2x + 3y = 35$

38. $2y = x + 6$
$-3x + 2y = -2$

39. $x + y = 40$
$0.2x + 0.8y = 23$

40. $x - y = 10$
$0.1x + 0.5y = 13$

41. $2x = 3y - 8$
$5y = 10x - 5$

42. $6x - 3y = 3$
$10x = y + 7$

43. $y = \dfrac{5}{7}x$

$x = -\dfrac{2}{3}y$

44. $y = \dfrac{5}{2}x$

$x + 3y = 3$

45. $x + y = 4$
$x - y = 5$

46. $3x - 6y = 5$
$2y = 4x - 6$

47. $3(y - 1) = 2(x - 3)$
$3y - 2x = -3$

48. $y = 3(x - 4)$
$3x - y = 12$

49. $y = 3x$
$y = 3x + 1$

50. $y = 2x - 3$
$y = 3x - 3$

51. $x - y = 0.1$
$2x - 3y = -0.5$

52. $y - 2x = -7.5$
$3x - 5y = 3.2$

In Exercises 53–66, write a system of two equations in two unknowns for each problem. Solve each system by substitution. See Examples 7 and 8.

53. Perimeter of a rectangle. The length of a rectangular swimming pool is 15 feet longer than the width. If the perimeter is 82 feet, then what are the length and width?

54. Household income. Alkena and Hsu together earn $84,326 per year. If Alkena earns $12,468 more per year than Hsu, then how much does each of them earn per year?

55. Different interest rates. Mrs. Brighton invested $30,000 and received a total of $2,300 in interest. If she invested part of the money at 10% and the remainder at 5%, then how much did she invest at each rate?

56. Different growth rates. The combined population of Marysville and Springfield was 25,000 in 1990. By 1995 the population of Marysville had increased by

10%, while Springfield had increased by 9%. If the total population increased by 2,380 people, then what was the population of each city in 1990?

57. Finding numbers. The sum of two numbers is 2, and their difference is 26. Find the numbers.

58. Finding more numbers. The sum of two numbers is -16, and their difference is 8. Find the numbers.

59. Toasters and vacations. During one week a land developer gave away Florida vacation coupons or toasters to 100 potential customers who listened to a sales presentation. It costs the developer $6 for a toaster and $24 for a Florida vacation coupon. If his bill for prizes that week was $708, then how many of each prize did he give away?

60. Ticket sales. Tickets for a concert were sold to adults for $3 and to students for $2. If the total receipts were $824 and twice as many adult tickets as student tickets were sold, then how many of each were sold?

61. Corporate taxes. According to Bruce Harrell, CPA, the amount of federal income tax for a class C corporation is deductible on the Louisiana state tax return, and the amount of state income tax for a class C corporation is deductible on the federal tax return. So for a state tax rate of 5% and a federal tax rate of 30%, we have

    state tax $= 0.05$(taxable income $-$ federal tax)

and

    federal tax $= 0.30$(taxable income $-$ state tax).

Find the amounts of state and federal income tax for a class C corporation that has a taxable income of $100,000.

62. More taxes. Use the information given in Exercise 61 to find the amounts of state and federal income tax for a class C corporation that has a taxable income of $300,000. Use a state tax rate of 6% and a federal tax rate of 40%.

63. Cost accounting. The problems presented in this exercise and the next are encountered in cost accounting. A company has agreed to distribute 20% of its net income N to its employees as a bonus; $B = 0.20N$. If the company has income of $120,000 before the bonus, the bonus B is deducted from the $120,000 as an expense to determine net income; $N = 120,000 - B$. Solve the system of two equations in N and B to find the amount of the bonus.

64. Bonus and taxes. A company has an income of $100,000 before paying taxes and a bonus. The bonus B is to be 20% of the income after deducting income taxes T but before deducting the bonus. So

$$B = 0.20(100,000 - T).$$

Because the bonus is a deductible expense, the amount of income tax T at a 40% rate is 40% of the income after deducting the bonus. So

$$T = 0.40(100,000 - B).$$

a) Use the accompanying graph to estimate the values of T and B that satisfy both equations.

b) Solve the system algebraically to find the bonus and the amount of tax.

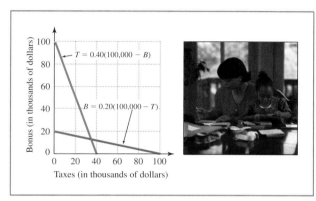

FIGURE FOR EXERCISE 64

65. Textbook case. The accompanying graph shows the cost of producing textbooks and the revenue from the sale of those textbooks.

a) What is the cost of producing 10,000 textbooks?

b) What is the revenue when 10,000 textbooks are sold?

c) For what number of textbooks is the cost equal to the revenue?

d) The cost of producing zero textbooks is called the *fixed cost*. Find the fixed cost.

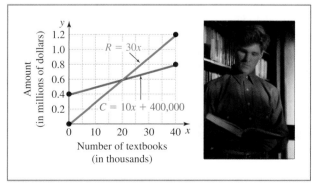

FIGURE FOR EXERCISE 65

66. Free market. The function $S = 5000 + 200x$ and $D = 9500 - 100x$ express the supply S and the demand D, respectively, for a popular compact disk brand as a function of its price x (in dollars).

a) Graph the functions on the same coordinate system.

b) What happens to the supply as the price increases?

c) What happens to the demand as the price increases?

d) The price at which supply and demand are equal is called the *equilibrium price*. What is the equilibrium price?

GETTING MORE INVOLVED

67. Discussion. Which of the following equations is not equivalent to $2x - 3y = 6$?

a) $3y - 2x = 6$

b) $y = \dfrac{2}{3}x - 2$

c) $x = \dfrac{3}{2}y + 3$

d) $2(x - 5) = 3y - 4$

68. Discussion. Which of the following equations is inconsistent with the equation $3x + 4y = 8$?

a) $y = \dfrac{3}{4}x + 2$

b) $6x + 8y = 16$

c) $y = -\dfrac{3}{4}x + 8$

d) $3x - 4y = 8$

GRAPHING CALCULATOR EXERCISES

69. Solve each system by graphing each pair of equations on a graphing calculator and using the trace feature or intersect feature to estimate the point of intersection. Find the coordinates of the intersection to the nearest tenth.

a) $y = 3.5x - 7.2$
   $y = -2.3x + 9.1$

b) $2.3x - 4.1y = 3.3$
   $3.4x + 9.2y = 1.3$

4.2 THE ADDITION METHOD

In Section 4.1 you used substitution to eliminate a variable in a system of equations. In this section we see another method for eliminating a variable in a system of equations.

The Addition Method

In the **addition method** we eliminate a variable by adding the equations.

E X A M P L E 1

An independent system solved by addition

Solve the system by the addition method:

$$3x - 5y = -9$$
$$4x + 5y = 23$$

Calculator Close-Up

To check Example 1, graph

$$y_1 = (-9 - 3x)/-5$$

and

$$y_2 = (23 - 4x)/5.$$

Use the intersect feature to find the point of intersection of the two lines.

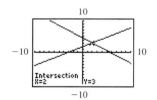

Solution

The addition property of equality allows us to add the same number to each side of an equation. We can also use the addition property of equality to add the two left sides and add the two right sides:

$$3x - 5y = -9$$
$$\underline{4x + 5y = 23}$$
$$7x \quad\quad = 14 \quad \text{Add.}$$
$$x = 2$$

The y-term was eliminated when we added the equations because the coefficients of the y-terms were opposites. Now use $x = 2$ in one of the original equations to find y. It does not matter which original equation we use. In this example we will use both equations to see that we get the same y in either case.

$$3x - 5y = -9 \qquad\qquad 4x + 5y = 23$$
$$3(2) - 5y = -9 \quad \text{Replace } x \text{ by 2.} \quad 4(2) + 5y = 23$$
$$6 - 5y = -9 \quad \text{Solve for } y. \quad 8 + 5y = 23$$
$$-5y = -15 \qquad\qquad\qquad 5y = 15$$
$$y = 3 \qquad\qquad\qquad\qquad y = 3$$

Because $3(2) - 5(3) = -9$ and $4(2) + 5(3) = 23$ are both true, $(2, 3)$ satisfies both equations. The solution set is $\{(2, 3)\}$. ■

Actually the addition method can be used to eliminate any variable whose coefficients are opposites. If neither variable has coefficients that are opposites, then we use the multiplication property of equality to change the coefficients of the variables, as shown in Examples 2 and 3.

E X A M P L E 2

Using multiplication and addition

Solve the system by the addition method:

$$2x - 3y = -13$$
$$5x - 12y = -46$$

Solution

If we multiply both sides of the first equation by -4, the coefficients of y will be 12 and -12, and y will be eliminated by addition.

$$(-4)(2x - 3y) = (-4)(-13) \quad \text{Multiply each side by } -4.$$
$$5x - 12y = -46$$

$$\begin{aligned} -8x + 12y &= 52 \\ \underline{5x - 12y} &= \underline{-46} \qquad \text{Add.} \\ -3x &= 6 \\ x &= -2 \end{aligned}$$

Replace x by -2 in one of the original equations to find y:

$$\begin{aligned} 2x - 3y &= -13 \\ 2(-2) - 3y &= -13 \\ -4 - 3y &= -13 \\ -3y &= -9 \\ y &= 3 \end{aligned}$$

Because $2(-2) - 3(3) = -13$ and $5(-2) - 12(3) = -46$ are both true, the solution set is $\{(-2, 3)\}$. ■

E X A M P L E   3

Multiplying both equations before adding

Solve the system by the addition method:

$$\begin{aligned} -2x + 3y &= 6 \\ 3x - 5y &= -11 \end{aligned}$$

Solution

To eliminate x, we multiply the first equation by 3 and the second by 2:

$$3(-2x + 3y) = 3(6) \qquad \text{Multiply each side by 3.}$$
$$2(3x - 5y) = 2(-11) \qquad \text{Multiply each side by 2.}$$

$$\begin{aligned} -6x + 9y &= 18 \\ \underline{6x - 10y} &= \underline{-22} \qquad \text{Add.} \\ -y &= -4 \\ y &= 4 \end{aligned}$$

Note that we could have eliminated y by multiplying by 5 and 3. Now insert $y = 4$ into one of the original equations to find x:

$$\begin{aligned} -2x + 3(4) &= 6 \qquad \text{Let } y = 4 \text{ in } -2x + 3y = 6. \\ -2x + 12 &= 6 \\ -2x &= -6 \\ x &= 3 \end{aligned}$$

Check that $(3, 4)$ satisfies both equations. The solution set is $\{(3, 4)\}$. ■

We can always use the addition method as long as the equations in a system are in the same form.

E X A M P L E   4

Using the addition method for an inconsistent system

Solve the system:

$$-4y = 5x + 7$$
$$4y = -5x + 12$$

Solution

If these equations are added, both variables are eliminated:

$$\begin{array}{rl} -4y = & 5x + 7 \\ 4y = & -5x + 12 \\ \hline 0 = & 19 \end{array}$$

Because this equation is inconsistent, the original equations are inconsistent. The solution set to the system is the empty set, $\varnothing$.   ■

Equations Involving Fractions or Decimals

When a system of equations involves fractions or decimals, we can use the multiplication property of equality to eliminate the fractions or decimals.

E X A M P L E   5

A system with fractions

Solve the system:

$$\frac{1}{2}x - \frac{2}{3}y = 7$$

$$\frac{2}{3}x - \frac{3}{4}y = 11$$

Solution

Multiply the first equation by 6 and the second equation by 12:

$$6\left(\frac{1}{2}x - \frac{2}{3}y\right) = 6(7) \qquad \rightarrow \qquad 3x - 4y = 42$$

$$12\left(\frac{2}{3}x - \frac{3}{4}y\right) = 12(11) \qquad \rightarrow \qquad 8x - 9y = 132$$

To eliminate x, multiply the first equation by -8 and the second by 3:

$$\begin{array}{rll} -8(3x - 4y) = -8(42) & \rightarrow & -24x + 32y = -336 \\ 3(8x - 9y) = 3(132) & \rightarrow & \underline{24x - 27y = 396} \\ & & 5y = 60 \\ & & y = 12 \end{array}$$

Substitute $y = 12$ into the first of the original equations:

$$\frac{1}{2}x - \frac{2}{3}(12) = 7$$

$$\frac{1}{2}x - 8 = 7$$

$$\frac{1}{2}x = 15$$

$$x = 30$$

Check $(30, 12)$ in the original system. The solution set is $\{(30, 12)\}$.   ■

E X A M P L E   6

A system with decimals

Solve the system:

$$0.05x + 0.7y = 40$$
$$x + 0.4y = 120$$

Solution

Multiply the first equation by 100 and the second by 10 to eliminate the decimals:

$$100(0.05x + 0.7y) = 100(40) \quad \rightarrow \quad 5x + 70y = 4000$$
$$10(x + 0.4y) = 10(120) \quad \rightarrow \quad 10x + 4y = 1200$$

To eliminate x by addition, multiply the first equation by -2:

$$-2(5x + 70y) = -2(4000) \quad \rightarrow \quad -10x - 140y = -8000$$
$$10x + 4y = 1200 \quad \rightarrow \quad \underline{10x + 4y = 1200}$$
$$-136y = -6800$$
$$y = 50$$

Use $y = 50$ in $x + 0.4y = 120$ to find x:

$$x + 0.4(50) = 120$$
$$x + 20 = 120$$
$$x = 100$$

Check (100, 50) in the original system. The solution set is $\{(100, 50)\}$. ■

The strategy for solving an independent system by addition is summarized as follows.

The Addition Method

1. Write both equations in the same form (usually $Ax + By = C$).
2. Multiply one or both of the equations by appropriate numbers (if necessary) so that one of the variables will be eliminated by addition.
3. Add the equations to get an equation in one variable.
4. Solve the equation in one variable.
5. Substitute the value obtained for one variable into one of the original equations to obtain the value of the other variable.
6. Check the two values in both of the original equations.

Applications

Any system of two linear equations in two variables can be solved by either the addition method or substitution. In applications we use whichever method appears to be the simpler for the problem at hand.

E X A M P L E   7

Fajitas and burritos

At the Cactus Cafe the total price for four fajita dinners and three burrito dinners is $48, and the total price for three fajita dinners and two burrito dinners is $34. What is the price of each type of dinner?

Solution

Let x represent the price (in dollars) of a fajita dinner, and let y represent the price (in dollars) of a burrito dinner. We can write two equations to describe the given information:

$$4x + 3y = 48$$
$$3x + 2y = 34$$

Because 12 is the least common multiple of 4 and 3 (the coefficients of x), we multiply the first equation by -3 and the second by 4:

$$-3(4x + 3y) = -3(48) \quad \text{Multiply each side by } -3.$$
$$4(3x + 2y) = 4(34) \quad \text{Multiply each side by } 4.$$

$$-12x - 9y = -144$$
$$\underline{12x + 8y = 136} \quad \text{Add.}$$
$$-y = -8$$
$$y = 8$$

To find x, use $y = 8$ in the first equation $4x + 3y = 48$:

$$4x + 3(8) = 48$$
$$4x + 24 = 48$$
$$4x = 24$$
$$x = 6$$

So the fajita dinners are $6 each, and the burrito dinners are $8 each. Check this solution in the original problem. ∎

EXAMPLE 8

Mixing cooking oil

Canola oil is 7% saturated fat, and corn oil is 14% saturated fat. Crisco sells a blend, Crisco Canola and Corn Oil, which is 11% saturated fat. How many gallons of each type of oil must be mixed to get 280 gallons of this blend?

Solution

Let x represent the number of gallons of canola oil, and let y represent the number of gallons of corn oil. Make a table to summarize all facts:

	Amount (gallons)	% fat	Amount of fat (gallons)
Canola oil	x	7	$0.07x$
Corn oil	y	14	$0.14y$
Canola and Corn Oil	280	11	$0.11(280)$ or 30.8

We can write two equations to express the following facts: (1) the total amount of oil is 280 gallons and (2) the total amount of fat is 30.8 gallons. Then we can use multiplication and addition to solve the system.

$$(1) \qquad x + y = 280 \qquad \text{Multiply by } -0.07. \quad -0.07x - 0.07y = -19.6$$
$$(2) \ 0.07x + 0.14y = 30.80 \qquad\qquad\qquad \underline{ 0.07x + 0.14y = 30.8}$$
$$0.07y = 11.2$$
$$y = \frac{11.2}{0.07} = 160$$

If $y = 160$ and $x + y = 280$, then $x = 120$. Check that $0.07(120) + 0.14(160) = 30.8$. So it takes 120 gallons of canola oil and 160 gallons of corn oil to make 280 gallons of Crisco Canola and Corn Oil. ∎

WARM-UPS

True or false? Explain your answer.

Exercises 1–6 refer to the following systems.

a) $3x - y = 9$ **b)** $4x - 2y = 20$ **c)** $x - y = 6$

    $2x + y = 6$ $-2x + y = -10$ $x - y = 7$

1. To solve system (a) by addition, we simply add the equations.

2. To solve system (a) by addition, we can multiply the first equation by 2 and the second by 3 and then add.

3. To solve system (b) by addition, we can multiply the second equation by 2 and then add.

4. Both $(0, -10)$ and $(5, 0)$ are in the solution set to system (b).

5. The solution set to system (b) is the set of all real numbers.

6. System (c) has no solution.

7. Both the addition method and substitution method are used to eliminate a variable from a system of two linear equations in two variables.

8. For the addition method, both equations must be in standard form.

9. To eliminate fractions in an equation, we multiply each side by the least common denominator of all fractions involved.

10. We can eliminate either variable by using the addition method.

4.2   EXERCISES

Reading and Writing   *After reading this section, write out the answers to these questions. Use complete sentences.*

1. What method is presented in this section for solving a system of linear equations?

2. What are we trying to accomplish by adding the equations?

3. What must we sometimes do before we add the equations?

4. How can you recognize an inconsistent system when solving by addition?

5. How can you recognize a dependent system when solving by addition?

6. For which systems is the addition method easier to use than substitution?

Solve each system by the addition method. See Examples 1–3.

7. $x + y = 7$
$x - y = 9$

8. $3x - 4y = 11$
$-3x + 2y = -7$

9. $x - y = 12$
$2x + y = 3$

10. $x - 2y = -1$
$-x + 5y = 4$

11. $3x - y = 5$
$5x + y = -2$

12. $-x + 2y = 4$
$x - 5y = 1$

13. $2x - y = -5$
$3x + 2y = 3$

14. $3x + 5y = -11$
$x - 2y = 11$

15. $-3x + 5y = 1$
$9x - 3y = 5$

16. $7x - 4y = -3$
$x + 2y = 3$

17. $2x - 5y = 13$
$3x + 4y = -15$

18. $3x + 4y = -5$
$5x + 6y = -7$

19. $2x = 3y + 11$
$7x - 4y = 6$

20. $2x = 2 - y$
$3x + y = -1$

21. $x + y = 48$
$12x + 14y = 628$

22. $x + y = 13$
$22x + 36y = 356$

Solve each system by the addition method. Determine whether the equations are independent, dependent, or inconsistent. See Example 4.

23. $3x - 4y = 9$
$-3x + 4y = 12$

24. $x - y = 3$
$-6x + 6y = 17$

25. $5x - y = 1$
$10x - 2y = 2$

26. $4x + 3y = 2$
$-12x - 9y = -6$

27. $2x - y = 5$
$2x + y = 5$

28. $-3x + 2y = 8$
$3x + 2y = 8$

Solve each system by the addition method. See Examples 5 and 6.

29. $\dfrac{1}{4}x + \dfrac{1}{3}y = 5$
$x - y = 6$

30. $\dfrac{3x}{2} - \dfrac{2y}{3} = 10$
$\dfrac{1}{2}x + \dfrac{1}{2}y = -1$

31. $\dfrac{x}{4} - \dfrac{y}{3} = -4$
$\dfrac{x}{8} + \dfrac{y}{6} = 0$

32. $\dfrac{x}{3} - \dfrac{y}{2} = -\dfrac{5}{6}$
$\dfrac{x}{5} - \dfrac{y}{3} = -\dfrac{3}{5}$

33. $\dfrac{1}{8}x + \dfrac{1}{4}y = 5$
$\dfrac{1}{16}x + \dfrac{1}{2}y = 7$

34. $\dfrac{3}{7}x + \dfrac{5}{9}y = 27$
$\dfrac{1}{9}x + \dfrac{2}{7}y = 7$

35. $\dfrac{1}{3}x + \dfrac{1}{2}y = \dfrac{1}{3}$
$\dfrac{5}{6}x - \dfrac{3}{4}y = \dfrac{1}{6}$

36. $\dfrac{2}{3}x + \dfrac{5}{6}y = \dfrac{1}{4}$
$\dfrac{1}{5}x - \dfrac{1}{10}y = -\dfrac{1}{10}$

37. $0.05x + 0.10y = 1.30$
$x + y = 19$

38. $0.1x + 0.06y = 9$
$0.09x + 0.5y = 52.7$

39. $x + y = 1200$
$0.12x + 0.09y = 120$

40. $x - y = 100$
$0.20x + 0.06y = 150$

41. $1.5x - 2y = -0.25$
$3x + 1.5y = 6.375$

42. $3x - 2.5y = 7.125$
$2.5x - 3y = 7.3125$

43. $0.24x + 0.6y = 0.58$
$0.8x - 0.12y = 0.52$

44. $0.18x + 0.27y = 0.09$
$0.06x - 0.54y = -0.04$

Solve each system by substitution or addition, whichever is easier.

45. $y = x + 1$
$2x - 5y = -20$

46. $y = 3x - 4$
$x + y = 32$

47. $x - y = 19$
$2x + y = -13$

48. $x + y = 3$
$7x - y = 29$

49. $2y = x + 2$
$x = y - 1$

50. $2y - x = 3$
$x = 3y - 5$

51. $2y - 3x = -1$
$5y + 3x = 29$

52. $y - 5 = 2x$
$y - 9 = -2x$

53. $6x + 3y = 4$

$y = \dfrac{2}{3}x$

54. $3x - 2y = 2$

$x = \dfrac{2}{9}y$

55. $y = 3x + 1$

$x = \dfrac{1}{3}y + 5$

56. $y = -\dfrac{2}{3}x - 3$

$x = -\dfrac{3}{2}y + 9$

57. $x - y = 0$

$x + y = 2x$

58. $5x - 4y = 9$

$8y - 10x = -18$

Write a system of two equations in two unknowns for each problem. Solve each system by the method of your choice. See Examples 7 and 8.

59. *Coffee and doughnuts.* On Monday, Archie paid $3.40 for three doughnuts and two coffees. On Tuesday he paid $3.60 for two doughnuts and three coffees. On Wednesday he was tired of paying the tab and went out for coffee by himself. What was his bill for one doughnut and one coffee?

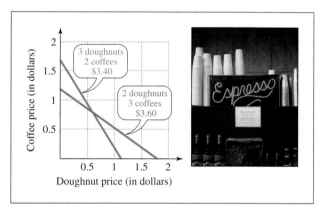

FIGURE FOR EXERCISE 59

60. *Books and magazines.* At Gwen's garage sale, all books were one price, and all magazines were another price. Harriet bought four books and three magazines for $1.45, and June bought two books and five magazines for $1.25. What was the price of a book and what was the price of a magazine?

61. *Boys and girls.* One-half of the boys and one-third of the girls of Freemont High attended the homecoming game, whereas one-third of the boys and one-half of the girls attended the homecoming dance. If there were 570 students at the game and 580 at the dance, then how many students are there at Freemont High?

62. *Girls and boys.* There are 385 surfers in Surf City. Two-thirds of the boys are surfers and one-twelfth of the girls are surfers. If there are two girls for every boy, then how many boys and how many girls are there in Surf City?

63. *Nickels and dimes.* Winborne has 35 coins consisting of dimes and nickels. If the value of his coins is $3.30, then how many of each type does he have?

64. *Pennies and nickels.* Wendy has 52 coins consisting of nickels and pennies. If the value of the coins is $1.20, then how many of each type does she have?

65. *Blending fudge.* The Chocolate Factory in Vancouver blends its double-dark-chocolate fudge, which is 35% fat, with its peanut butter fudge, which is 25% fat, to obtain double-dark-peanut fudge, which is 29% fat.
   a) Use the accompanying graph to estimate the number of pounds of each type that must be mixed to obtain 50 pounds of double-dark-peanut fudge.
   b) Write a system of equations and solve it algebraically to find the exact amount of each type that should be used to obtain 50 pounds of double-dark-peanut fudge.

FIGURE FOR EXERCISE 65

66. *Low-fat yogurt.* Ziggy's Famous Yogurt blends regular yogurt that is 3% fat with its no-fat yogurt to obtain low-fat yogurt that is 1% fat. How many pounds of regular yogurt and how many pounds of no-fat yogurt should be mixed to obtain 60 pounds of low-fat yogurt?

67. *Keystone state.* Judy averaged 42 miles per hour (mph) driving from Allentown to Harrisburg and 51 mph driving from Harrisburg to Pittsburgh. See the figure on the next page. If she drove a total of 288 miles in 6 hours, then how long did it take her to drive from Harrisburg to Pittsburgh?

FIGURE FOR EXERCISE 67

68. *Empire state.* Spike averaged 45 mph driving from Rochester to Syracuse and 49 mph driving from Syracuse to Albany. If he drove a total of 237 miles in 5 hours, then how far is it from Syracuse to Albany?

69. *Probability of rain.* The probability of rain tomorrow is four times the probability that it does not rain tomorrow. The probability that it rains plus the probability that it does not rain is 1. What is the probability that it rains tomorrow?

70. *Super Bowl contender.* The probability that San Francisco plays in the next Super Bowl is nine times the probability that they do not play in the next Super Bowl. The probability that San Francisco plays in the next Super Bowl plus the probability that they do not play is 1. What is the probability that San Francisco plays in the next Super Bowl?

71. *Rectangular lot.* The width of a rectangular lot is 75% of its length. If the perimeter is 700 meters, then what are the length and width?

72. *Fence painting.* Darren and Douglas must paint the 792-foot fence that encircles their family home. Because Darren is older, he has agreed to paint 20% more than Douglas. How much of the fence will each boy paint?

GETTING MORE INVOLVED

 73. *Discussion.* Explain how you decide whether it is easier to solve a system by substitution or addition.

 74. *Exploration.* **a)** Write a linear equation in two variables that is satisfied by $(-3, 5)$.
 b) Write another linear equation in two variables that is satisfied by $(-3, 5)$.
 c) Are your equations independent or dependent?
 d) Explain how to select the second equation so that it will be independent of the first.

 75. *Exploration.* **a)** Make up a system of two linear equations in two variables such that both $(-1, 2)$ and $(4, 5)$ are in the solution set.
 b) Are your equations independent or dependent?
 c) Is it possible to find an independent system that is satisfied by both ordered pairs? Explain.

In This Section

- Definition
- Solving a System by Elimination
- Graphs of Equations in Three Variables
- Applications

4.3

SYSTEMS OF LINEAR EQUATIONS IN THREE VARIABLES

The techniques that you learned in Section 4.2 can be extended to systems of equations in more than two variables. In this section we use elimination of variables to solve systems of equations in three variables.

Definition

The equation $5x - 4y = 7$ is called a linear equation in two variables because its graph is a straight line. The equation $2x + 3y - 4z = 12$ is similar in form, and so it is a linear equation in three variables. An equation in three variables is graphed in a three-dimensional coordinate system. The graph of a linear equation in three variables is a plane, not a line. We will not graph equations in three variables in this text, but we can solve systems without graphing. In general, we make the following definition.

Study Tip

Everyone knows that you must practice to be successful with musical instruments, foreign languages, and sports. Success in algebra also requires regular practice. Thus budget your time so that you have a regular practice period for algebra.

Linear Equation in Three Variables

If A, B, C, and D are real numbers, with A, B, and C not all zero, then

$$Ax + By + Cz = D$$

is called a **linear equation in three variables.**

Solving a System by Elimination

A solution to an equation in three variables is an **ordered triple** such as $(-2, 1, 5)$, where the first coordinate is the value of x, the second coordinate is the value of y, and the third coordinate is the value of z. There are infinitely many solutions to a linear equation in three variables.

The solution to a system of equations in three variables is the set of all ordered triples that satisfy all of the equations of the system. The techniques for solving a system of linear equations in three variables are similar to those used on systems of linear equations in two variables. We eliminate variables by either substitution or addition.

E X A M P L E   1

A linear system with a single solution

Solve the system:

$$
\begin{array}{ll}
(1) & x + y - z = -1 \\
(2) & 2x - 2y + 3z = 8 \\
(3) & 2x - y + 2z = 9
\end{array}
$$

Solution

We can eliminate y from Eqs. (1) and (2) by multiplying Eq. (1) by 2 and adding it to Eq. (2):

$$
\begin{array}{ll}
2x + 2y - 2z = -2 & \text{Eq. (1) multiplied by 2} \\
\underline{2x - 2y + 3z = 8} & \text{Eq. (2)} \\
(4) \quad 4x \qquad + z = 6 &
\end{array}
$$

Now we must eliminate the same variable, y, from another pair of equations. Eliminate y from Eqs. (1) and (3) by simply adding them:

$$
\begin{array}{ll}
x + y - z = -1 & \text{Eq. (1)} \\
\underline{2x - y + 2z = 9} & \text{Eq. (3)} \\
(5) \quad 3x \qquad + z = 8 &
\end{array}
$$

Equations (4) and (5) give us a system with two variables. We now solve this system. Eliminate z by multiplying Eq. (4) by -1 and adding the equations:

$$
\begin{array}{ll}
-4x - z = -6 & \text{Eq. (4) multiplied by } -1 \\
\underline{3x + z = 8} & \text{Eq. (5)} \\
-x \qquad = 2 & \\
x = -2 &
\end{array}
$$

Now that we have x, we can replace x by -2 in Eq. (5) to find y:

$$
\begin{array}{ll}
3x + z = 8 & \text{Eq. (5)} \\
3(-2) + z = 8 & \\
-6 + z = 8 & \\
z = 14 &
\end{array}
$$

Calculator Close-Up

You can use a calculator to check that $(-2, 15, 14)$ satisfies all three equations of the original system.

```
 -2+15-14
              -1
2*-2-2*15+3*14
              8
2*-2-15+2*14
              9
```

Now replace x by -2 and z by 14 in Eq. (1) to find y:

$$
\begin{array}{ll}
x + y - z = -1 & \text{Eq. (1)} \\
-2 + y - 14 = -1 & x = -2, z = 14 \\
y - 16 = -1 & \\
y = 15 &
\end{array}
$$

Check that $(-2, 15, 14)$ satisfies all three of the original equations. The solution set is $\{(-2, 15, 14)\}$. ■

Note that we could have eliminated any one of the three variables in Example 1 to get a system of two equations in two variables. We chose to eliminate y first because it was the easiest to eliminate. The strategy that we follow for solving a system of three linear equations in three variables is stated as follows:

Solving a System in Three Variables

1. Use substitution or addition to eliminate any one of the variables from a pair of equations of the system. Look for the easiest variable to eliminate.
2. Eliminate the same variable from another pair of equations of the system.
3. Solve the resulting system of two equations in two unknowns.
4. After you have found the values of two of the variables, substitute into one of the original equations to find the value of the third variable.
5. Check the three values in all of the original equations.

In Example 2 we use a combination of addition and substitution.

EXAMPLE 2

Using addition and substitution

Solve the system:

$$(1) \quad x + y \quad\quad = 4$$
$$(2) \quad 2x \quad\quad - 3z = 14$$
$$(3) \quad\quad 2y + z = 2$$

Helpful Hint

In Example 2 we chose to eliminate y first. Try solving Example 2 by first eliminating z. Write $z = 2 - 2y$ and then substitute $2 - 2y$ for z in Eqs. (1) and (2).

Solution

From Eq. (1) we get $y = 4 - x$. If we substitute $y = 4 - x$ into Eq. (3), then Eqs. (2) and (3) will be equations involving x and z only.

$$(3) \quad 2y + z = 2$$
$$2(4 - x) + z = 2 \quad \text{Replace } y \text{ by } 4 - x.$$
$$8 - 2x + z = 2 \quad \text{Simplify.}$$
$$(4) \quad -2x + z = -6$$

Now solve the system consisting of Eqs. (2) and (4) by addition:

$$2x - 3z = 14 \quad \text{Eq. (2)}$$
$$\underline{-2x + z = -6} \quad \text{Eq. (4)}$$
$$-2z = 8$$
$$z = -4$$

Use Eq. (3) to find y:

$$2y + z = 2 \quad \text{Eq. (3)}$$
$$2y + (-4) = 2 \quad \text{Let } z = -4.$$
$$2y = 6$$
$$y = 3$$

Use Eq. (1) to find x:

$$x + y = 4 \quad \text{Eq. (1)}$$
$$x + 3 = 4 \quad \text{Let } y = 3.$$
$$x = 1$$

Check that $(1, 3, -4)$ satisfies all three of the original equations. The solution set is $\{(1, 3, -4)\}$. ∎

CAUTION   In solving a system in three variables it is essential to keep your work organized and neat. Writing short notes that explain your steps (as was done in the examples) will allow you to go back and check your work.

Graphs of Equations in Three Variables

The graph of any equation in three variables can be drawn on a three-dimensional coordinate system. The graph of a linear equation in three variables is a plane. To solve a system of three linear equations in three variables by graphing, we would have to draw the three planes and then identify the points that lie on all three of them. This method would be difficult even when the points have simple coordinates. So we will not attempt to solve these systems by graphing.

By considering how three planes might intersect, we can better understand the different types of solutions to a system of three equations in three variables. Figure 4.6 shows some of the possibilities for the positioning of three planes in three-dimensional space. In most of the problems that we will solve the planes intersect at a single point as in Fig. 4.6(a). The solution set consists of one ordered triple. However, the system may include two equations corresponding to parallel planes that have no intersection. In this case the equations are said to be **inconsistent.** If the system has at least two inconsistent equations, then the solution set is the empty set [see Figs. 4.6(b) and 4.6(c)].

There are two ways in which the intersection of three planes can consist of infinitely many points. The intersection could be a line or a plane. To get a line, we can have either three different planes intersecting along a line, as in Fig. 4.6(d) or two equations for the same plane, with the third plane intersecting that plane. If all three equations are equations of the same plane, we get that plane for the intersection. We will not solve systems corresponding to all of the possible configurations described. The following examples illustrate two of these cases.

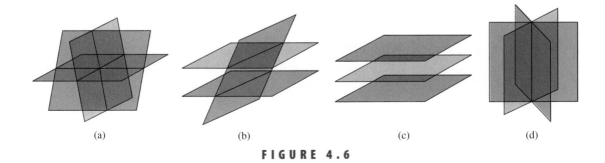

(a)   (b)   (c)   (d)

FIGURE 4.6

EXAMPLE 3   **An inconsistent system of three linear equations**
Solve the system:

$$
\begin{array}{ll}
(1) & x + y - z = 5 \\
(2) & 3x - 2y + z = 8 \\
(3) & 2x + 2y - 2z = 7
\end{array}
$$

Solution

We can eliminate the variable z from Eqs. (1) and (2) by adding them:

$$
\begin{array}{rl}
(1) & x + y - z = 5 \\
(2) & \underline{3x - 2y + z = 8} \\
& 4x - y = 13
\end{array}
$$

To eliminate z from Eqs. (1) and (3), multiply Eq. (1) by -2 and add the resulting equation to Eq. (3):

$$
\begin{array}{ll}
-2x - 2y + 2z = -10 & \text{Eq. (1) multiplied by } -2 \\
\underline{2x + 2y - 2z = 7} & \text{Eq. (3)} \\
 0 = -3 &
\end{array}
$$

Because the last equation is false, there are two inconsistent equations in the system. Therefore the solution set is the empty set. ■

EXAMPLE 4

A dependent system of three equations

Solve the system:

$$
\begin{array}{rl}
(1) & 2x - 3y - z = 4 \\
(2) & -6x + 9y + 3z = -12 \\
(3) & 4x - 6y - 2z = 8
\end{array}
$$

Solution

We will first eliminate x from Eqs. (1) and (2). Multiply Eq. (1) by 3 and add the resulting equation to Eq. (2):

$$
\begin{array}{ll}
6x - 9y - 3z = 12 & \text{Eq. (1) multiplied by 3} \\
\underline{-6x + 9y + 3z = -12} & \text{Eq. (2)} \\
 0 = 0 &
\end{array}
$$

The last statement is an identity. The identity occurred because Eq. (2) is a multiple of Eq. (1). In fact, Eq. (3) is also a multiple of Eq. (1). These equations are dependent. They are all equations for the same plane. The solution set is the set of all points on that plane,

$$\{(x, y, z) \mid 2x - 3y - z = 4\}.$$ ■

Applications

Problems involving three unknown quantities can often be solved by using a system of three equations in three variables.

EXAMPLE 5

Finding three unknown rents

Theresa took in a total of $1240 last week from the rental of three condominiums. She had to pay 10% of the rent from the one-bedroom condo for repairs, 20% of the rent from the two-bedroom condo for repairs, and 30% of the rent from the three-bedroom condo for repairs. If the three-bedroom condo rents for twice as much as the one-bedroom condo and her total repair bill was $276, then what is the rent for each condo?

Solution

Let x, y, and z represent the rent on the one-bedroom, two-bedroom, and three-bedroom condos, respectively. We can write one equation for the total rent, another

Helpful Hint

A problem involving two unknowns can often be solved with one variable as in Chapter 2. Likewise, you can often solve a problem with three unknowns using only two variables. Solve Example 5 by letting a, b, and $2a$ be the rent for a one-bedroom, two-bedroom, and a three-bedroom condo.

equation for the total repairs, and a third equation expressing the fact that the rent for the three-bedroom condo is twice that for the one-bedroom condo:

$$x + y + z = 1240$$
$$0.1x + 0.2y + 0.3z = 276$$
$$z = 2x$$

Substitute $z = 2x$ into both of the other equations to eliminate z:

$$x + y + 2x = 1240$$
$$0.1x + 0.2y + 0.3(2x) = 276$$

$$3x + \quad y = 1240$$
$$0.7x + 0.2y = 276$$

$$-2(3x + y) = -2(1240) \qquad \text{Multiply each side by } -2.$$
$$10(0.7x + 0.2y) = 10(276) \qquad \text{Multiply each side by } 10.$$

$$-6x - 2y = -2480$$
$$\underline{7x + 2y = 2760} \qquad \text{Add.}$$
$$x \qquad = 280$$

$$z = 2(280) = 560 \qquad\qquad \text{Because } z = 2x$$
$$280 + y + 560 = 1240 \qquad \text{Because } x + y + z = 1240$$
$$y = 400$$

Check that $(280, 400, 560)$ satisfies all three of the original equations. The condos rent for \$280, \$400, and \$560 per week.   ∎

WARM-UPS

True or false? Explain your answer.

1. The point $(1, -2, 3)$ is in the solution set to the equation $x + y - z = 4$.

2. The point $(4, 1, 1)$ is the only solution to the equation $x + y - z = 4$.

3. The ordered triple $(1, -1, 2)$ satisfies $x + y + z = 2$, $x - y - z = 0$, and $2x + y - z = -1$.

4. Substitution cannot be used on three equations in three variables.

5. Two distinct planes are either parallel or intersect in a single point.

6. The equations $x - y + 2z = 6$ and $x - y + 2z = 4$ are inconsistent.

7. The equations $3x + 2y - 6z = 4$ and $-6x - 4y + 12z = -8$ are dependent.

8. The graph of $y = 2x - 3z + 4$ is a straight line.

9. The value of x nickels, y dimes, and z quarters is $0.05x + 0.10y + 0.25z$ cents.

10. If $x = -2$, $z = 3$, and $x + y + z = 6$, then $y = 7$.

4.3   EXERCISES

Reading and Writing   *After reading this section, write out the answers to these questions. Use complete sentences.*

1. What is a linear equation in three variables?

2. What is an ordered triple?

3. What is a solution to a system of linear equations in three variables?

4. How do we solve systems of linear equations in three variables?

5. What does the graph of a linear equation in three variables look like?

6. How are the planes positioned when a system of linear equations in three variables is inconsistent?

Solve each system of equations. See Examples 1 and 2.

7. $x + y + z = 2$
$x + 2y - z = 6$
$2x + y - z = 5$

8. $2x - y + 3z = 14$
$x + y - 2z = -5$
$3x + y - z = 2$

9. $x - 2y + 4z = 3$
$x + 3y - 2z = 6$
$x - 4y + 3z = -5$

10. $2x + 3y + z = 13$
$-3x + 2y + z = -4$
$4x - 4y + z = 5$

11. $2x - y + z = 10$
$3x - 2y - 2z = 7$
$x - 3y - 2z = 10$

12. $x - 3y + 2z = -11$
$2x - 4y + 3z = -15$
$3x - 5y - 4z = 5$

13. $2x - 3y + z = -9$
$-2x + y - 3z = 7$
$x - y + 2z = -5$

14. $3x - 4y + z = 19$
$2x + 4y + z = 0$
$x - 2y + 5z = 17$

15. $2x - 5y + 2z = 16$
$3x + 2y - 3z = -19$
$4x - 3y + 4z = 18$

16. $-2x + 3y - 4z = 3$
$3x - 5y + 2z = 4$
$-4x + 2y - 3z = 0$

17. $x + y = 4$
$y - z = -2$
$x + y + z = 9$

18. $x + y - z = 0$
$x - y = -2$
$y + z = 10$

19. $x + y = 7$
$y - z = -1$
$x + 3z = 18$

20. $2x - y = -8$
$y + 3z = 22$
$x - z = -8$

Solve each system. See Examples 3 and 4.

21. $x - y + 2z = 3$
$2x + y - z = 5$
$3x - 3y + 6z = 4$

22. $2x - 4y + 6z = 12$
$6x - 12y + 18z = 36$
$-x + 2y - 3z = -6$

23. $3x - y + z = 5$
$9x - 3y + 3z = 15$
$-12x + 4y - 4z = -20$

24. $4x - 2y - 2z = 5$
$2x - y - z = 7$
$-4x + 2y + 2z = 6$

25. $x - y = 3$
$y + z = 8$
$2x + 2z = 7$

26. $2x - y = 6$
$2y + z = -4$
$8x + 2z = 3$

27. $0.10x + 0.08y - 0.04z = 3$
$5x + 4y - 2z = 150$
$0.3x + 0.24y - 0.12z = 9$

28. $0.06x - 0.04y + z = 6$
$3x - 2y + 50z = 300$
$0.03x - 0.02y + 0.5z = 3$

 Use a calculator to solve each system.

29. $3x + 2y - 0.4z = 0.1$
$3.7x - 0.2y + 0.05z = 0.41$
$-2x + 3.8y - 2.1z = -3.26$

30. $3x - 0.4y + 9z = 1.668$
$0.3x + 5y - 8z = -0.972$
$5x - 4y - 8z = 1.8$

Solve each problem by using a system of three equations in three unknowns. See Example 5.

31. ***Three cars.*** The town of Springfield purchased a Chevrolet, a Ford, and a Toyota for a total of $66,000. The Ford was $2,000 more than the Chevrolet and the Toyota was $2,000 more than the Ford. What was the price of each car?

32. *Buying texts.* Melissa purchased an English text, a math text, and a chemistry text for a total of $276. The English text was $20 more than the math text and the chemistry text was twice the price of the math text. What was the price of each text?

33. *Three-day drive.* In three days, Carter drove 2196 miles in 36 hours behind the wheel. The first day he averaged 64 mph, the second day 62 mph, and the third day 58 mph. If he drove 4 more hours on the third day than on the first day, then how many hours did he drive each day?

34. *Three-day trip.* In three days, Katy traveled 146 miles down the Mississippi River in her kayak with 30 hours of paddling. The first day she averaged 6 mph, the second day 5 mph, and the third day 4 mph. If her distance on the third day was equal to her distance on the first day, then for how many hours did she paddle each day?

35. *Diversification.* Ann invested a total of $12,000 in stocks, bonds, and a mutual fund. She received a 10% return on her stock investment, an 8% return on her bond investment, and a 12% return on her mutual fund. Her total return was $1,230. If the total investment in stocks and bonds equaled her mutual fund investment, then how much did she invest in each?

36. *Paranoia.* Fearful of a bank failure, Norman split his life savings of $60,000 among three banks. He received 5%, 6%, and 7% on the three deposits. In the account earning 7% interest, he deposited twice as much as in the account earning 5% interest. If his total earnings were $3,760, then how much did he deposit in each account?

37. *Weighing in.* Anna, Bob, and Chris will not disclose their weights but agree to be weighed in pairs. Anna and Bob together weigh 226 pounds. Bob and Chris together weigh 210 pounds. Anna and Chris together weigh 200 pounds. How much does each student weigh?

Anna & Bob   Bob & Chris   Anna & Chris

FIGURE FOR EXERCISE 37

38. *Big tipper.* On Monday Headley paid $1.70 for two cups of coffee and one doughnut, including the tip. On Tuesday he paid $1.65 for two doughnuts and a cup of coffee, including the tip. On Wednesday he paid $1.30 for one coffee and one doughnut, including the tip. If he always tips the same amount, then what is the amount of each item?

39. *Three coins.* Nelson paid $1.75 for his lunch with 13 coins, consisting of nickels, dimes, and quarters. If the number of dimes was twice the number of nickels, then how many of each type of coin did he use?

40. *Pocket change.* Harry has $2.25 in nickels, dimes, and quarters. If he had twice as many nickels, half as many dimes, and the same number of quarters, he would have $2.50. If he has 27 coins altogether, then how many of each does he have?

41. *Working overtime.* To make ends meet, Ms. Farnsby works three jobs. Her total income last year was $48,000. Her income from teaching was just $6,000 more than her income from house painting. Royalties from her textbook sales were one-seventh of the total money she received from teaching and house painting. How much did she make from each source last year?

42. *Lunch-box special.* Salvador's Fruit Mart sells variety packs. The small pack contains three bananas, two apples, and one orange for $1.80. The medium pack contains four bananas, three apples, and three oranges for $3.05. The family size contains six bananas, five apples, and four oranges for $4.65. What price should Salvador charge for his lunch-box special that consists of one banana, one apple, and one orange?

43. *Three generations.* Edwin, his father, and his grandfather have an average age of 53. One-half of his grandfather's age, plus one-third of his father's age, plus one-fourth of Edwin's age is 65. If 4 years ago, Edwin's grandfather was four times as old as Edwin, then how old are they all now?

44. *Three-digit number.* The sum of the digits of a three-digit number is 11. If the digits are reversed, the new number is 46 more than five times the old number. If the hundreds digit plus twice the tens digit is equal to the units digit, then what is the number?

GETTING MORE INVOLVED

45. *Exploration.* Draw diagrams showing the possible ways to position three planes in three-dimensional space.

46. *Discussion.* Make up a system of three linear equations in three variables for which the solution set is {(0, 0, 0)}. A system with this solution set is called a *homogeneous* system. Why do you think it is given that name?

4.4 SOLVING LINEAR SYSTEMS USING MATRICES

You solved linear systems in two variables by substitution and addition in Sections 4.1 and 4.2. Those methods are done differently on each system. In this section you will learn the Gauss-Jordan elimination method, which is related to the addition method. The Gauss-Jordan elimination method is performed in the same way on every system. We first need to introduce some new terminology.

Matrices

A **matrix** is a rectangular array of numbers. The **rows** of a matrix run horizontally, and the **columns** of a matrix run vertically. A matrix with m rows and n columns has **order** $m \times n$ (read "m by n"). Each number in a matrix is called an **element** or **entry** of the matrix.

E X A M P L E 1

Order of a matrix

Determine the order of each matrix.

a) $\begin{bmatrix} -1 & 2 \\ 5 & \sqrt{2} \\ 0 & 3 \end{bmatrix}$

b) $\begin{bmatrix} 2 & 3 \\ -1 & 5 \end{bmatrix}$

c) $\begin{bmatrix} 1 & 2 & 3 \\ 4 & 5 & 6 \\ -1 & 0 & 2 \end{bmatrix}$

d) $\begin{bmatrix} 1 & 3 & 6 \end{bmatrix}$

Study Tip

As soon as possible after class, find a quiet place and work on your homework. The longer you wait, the harder it is to remember what happened in class.

Solution

Because matrix (a) has 3 rows and 2 columns, its order is 3×2. Matrix (b) is a 2×2 matrix, matrix (c) is a 3×3 matrix, and matrix (d) is a 1×3 matrix. ■

The Augmented Matrix

The solution to a system of linear equations such as

$$x - 2y = -5$$
$$3x + y = 6$$

depends on the coefficients of x and y and the constants on the right-hand side of the equation. The matrix of coefficients for this system is the 2×2 matrix

$$\begin{bmatrix} 1 & -2 \\ 3 & 1 \end{bmatrix}.$$

If we insert the constants from the right-hand side of the system into the matrix of coefficients, we get the 2×3 matrix

$$\begin{bmatrix} 1 & -2 & | & -5 \\ 3 & 1 & | & 6 \end{bmatrix}.$$

We use a vertical line between the coefficients and the constants to represent the equal signs. This matrix is the **augmented matrix** of the system. Two systems of linear equations are **equivalent** if they have the same solution set. Two augmented matrices are **equivalent** if the systems they represent are equivalent.

E X A M P L E   2   **Writing the augmented matrix**

Write the augmented matrix for each system of equations.

a) $3x - 5y = 7$
$\quad\; x + y = 4$

b) $\;x + y - z = 5$
$\quad 2x \quad\; + z = 3$
$\quad 2x - y + 4z = 0$

c) $x + y \quad\quad = 1$
$\quad\quad y + z = 6$
$\quad\quad\quad z = -5$

Solution

a) $\begin{bmatrix} 3 & -5 & | & 7 \\ 1 & 1 & | & 4 \end{bmatrix}$

b) $\begin{bmatrix} 1 & 1 & -1 & | & 5 \\ 2 & 0 & 1 & | & 3 \\ 2 & -1 & 4 & | & 0 \end{bmatrix}$

c) $\begin{bmatrix} 1 & 1 & 0 & | & 1 \\ 0 & 1 & 1 & | & 6 \\ 0 & 0 & 1 & | & -5 \end{bmatrix}$ ■

E X A M P L E   3   **Writing the system**

Write the system of equations represented by each augmented matrix.

a) $\begin{bmatrix} 1 & 4 & | & -2 \\ 1 & -1 & | & 3 \end{bmatrix}$

b) $\begin{bmatrix} 1 & 0 & | & 5 \\ 0 & 1 & | & 1 \end{bmatrix}$

c) $\begin{bmatrix} 2 & 3 & 4 & | & 6 \\ -1 & 0 & 5 & | & -2 \\ 1 & -2 & 3 & | & 1 \end{bmatrix}$

Solution

a) Use the first two numbers in each row as the coefficients of x and y and the last number as the constant to get the following system:

$$x + 4y = -2$$
$$x - y = 3$$

b) Use the first two numbers in each row as the coefficients of x and y and the last number as the constant to get the following system:

$$x = 5$$
$$y = 1$$

c) Use the first three numbers in each row as the coefficients of x, y, and z and the last number as the constant to get the following system:

$$2x + 3y + 4z = 6$$
$$-x \quad\quad + 5z = -2$$
$$x - 2y + 3z = 1$$ ■

The Gauss-Jordan Elimination Method

When we solve a single equation, we write simpler and simpler equivalent equations to get an equation whose solution is obvious. In the **Gauss-Jordan elimination method** we write simpler and simpler equivalent augmented matrices until we get an augmented matrix [like the one in Example 3(b)] in which the solution to the corresponding system is obvious.

Because each row of an augmented matrix represents an equation, we can perform the operations on the rows of the augmented matrix. These **row operations**, which follow, correspond to the usual operations with equations used in the addition method.

Row Operations

The following row operations on an augmented matrix give an equivalent augmented matrix:

1. Interchange two rows of the matrix.
2. Multiply every element in a row by a nonzero real number.
3. Add to a row a multiple of another row.

In the Gauss-Jordan elimination method our goal is to use row operations to obtain an augmented matrix that has ones on the **diagonal** in its matrix of coefficients and zeros elsewhere:

$$\begin{bmatrix} 1 & 0 & | & a \\ 0 & 1 & | & b \end{bmatrix}$$

The system corresponding to this augmented matrix is $x = a$ and $y = b$. So the solution set to the system is $\{(a, b)\}$.

E X A M P L E   4   **Gauss-Jordan elimination with two equations in two variables**

Use the Gauss-Jordan elimination method to solve the system:

$$x - 3y = 11$$
$$2x + y = 1$$

Solution

Start with the augmented matrix:

$$\begin{bmatrix} 1 & -3 & | & 11 \\ 2 & 1 & | & 1 \end{bmatrix}$$

Multiply row 1 by -2 and add the result to row 2 (in symbols, $-2R_1 + R_2 \to R_2$). Because $-2R_1 = [-2, 6, -22]$ and $R_2 = [2, 1, 1]$, $-2R_1 + R_2 = [0, 7, -21]$. Note that the coefficient of x in the second equation is now 0. We get the following matrix:

$$\begin{bmatrix} 1 & -3 & | & 11 \\ 0 & 7 & | & -21 \end{bmatrix} \quad {\scriptstyle -2R_1 + R_2 \to R_2}$$

Multiply each element of row 2 by $\frac{1}{7}$ (in symbols, $\frac{1}{7}R_2 \to R_2$):

$$\begin{bmatrix} 1 & -3 & | & 11 \\ 0 & 1 & | & -3 \end{bmatrix} \quad {\scriptstyle \frac{1}{7}R_2 \to R_2}$$

Multiply row 2 by 3 and add the result to row 1. Because $3R_2 = [0, 3, -9]$ and $R_1 = [1, -3, 11]$, $3R_2 + R_1 = [1, 0, 2]$. Note that the coefficient of y in the first equation is now 0. We get the following matrix:

$$\begin{bmatrix} 1 & 0 & | & 2 \\ 0 & 1 & | & -3 \end{bmatrix} \quad {\scriptstyle 3R_2 + R_1 \to R_1}$$

This augmented matrix represents the system $x = 2$ and $y = -3$. So the solution set to the system is $\{(2, -3)\}$. Check in the original system.   ■

In Example 5 we use the row operations on the augmented matrix of a system of three linear equations in three variables.

E X A M P L E   5

Gauss-Jordan elimination with three equations in three variables

Use the Gauss-Jordan elimination method to solve the following system:

$$2x - y + z = -3$$
$$x + y - z = 6$$
$$3x - y - z = 4$$

Helpful Hint

It is not necessary to perform the row operations in exactly the same order as is shown in Example 5. As long as you use the legitimate row operations and get to the final form, you will get the solution to the system. Of course, you must double check your arithmetic at every step if you want to be successful at Gauss-Jordan elimination.

Solution

Start with the augmented matrix and interchange the first and second rows to get a 1 in the upper left position in the matrix:

$$\begin{bmatrix} 2 & -1 & 1 & | & -3 \\ 1 & 1 & -1 & | & 6 \\ 3 & -1 & -1 & | & 4 \end{bmatrix} \quad \text{The augmented matrix}$$

$$\begin{bmatrix} 1 & 1 & -1 & | & 6 \\ 2 & -1 & 1 & | & -3 \\ 3 & -1 & -1 & | & 4 \end{bmatrix} \quad R_1 \leftrightarrow R_2$$

Now multiply the first row by -2 and add the result onto the second row. Multiply the first row by -3 and add the result onto the third row. These two steps eliminate the variable x from the second and third rows:

$$\begin{bmatrix} 1 & 1 & -1 & | & 6 \\ 0 & -3 & 3 & | & -15 \\ 0 & -4 & 2 & | & -14 \end{bmatrix} \quad \begin{matrix} -2R_1 + R_2 \to R_2 \\ -3R_1 + R_3 \to R_3 \end{matrix}$$

Multiply the second row by $-\frac{1}{3}$ to get 1 in the second position on the diagonal:

$$\begin{bmatrix} 1 & 1 & -1 & | & 6 \\ 0 & 1 & -1 & | & 5 \\ 0 & -4 & 2 & | & -14 \end{bmatrix} \quad -\frac{1}{3}R_2 \to R_2$$

Use the second row to eliminate the variable y from the first and third rows:

$$\begin{bmatrix} 1 & 0 & 0 & | & 1 \\ 0 & 1 & -1 & | & 5 \\ 0 & 0 & -2 & | & 6 \end{bmatrix} \quad \begin{matrix} -1R_2 + R_1 \to R_1 \\ 4R_2 + R_3 \to R_3 \end{matrix}$$

Multiply the third row by $-\frac{1}{2}$ to get a 1 in the third position on the diagonal:

$$\begin{bmatrix} 1 & 0 & 0 & | & 1 \\ 0 & 1 & -1 & | & 5 \\ 0 & 0 & 1 & | & -3 \end{bmatrix} \quad -\frac{1}{2}R_3 \to R_3$$

Use the third row to eliminate the variable z from the second row:

$$\begin{bmatrix} 1 & 0 & 0 & | & 1 \\ 0 & 1 & 0 & | & 2 \\ 0 & 0 & 1 & | & -3 \end{bmatrix} \quad R_3 + R_2 \to R_2$$

This last augmented matrix represents the system $x = 1$, $y = 2$, and $z = -3$. So the solution set to the system is $\{(1, 2, -3)\}$. ∎

Inconsistent and Dependent Equations

Inconsistent and dependent equations are easily recognized in using the Gauss-Jordan elimination method.

EXAMPLE 6

Gauss-Jordan elimination with an inconsistent system

Solve the system:

$$x - y = 1$$
$$-3x + 3y = 4$$

Helpful Hint

The point of Example 6 is to recognize an inconsistent system with Gauss-Jordan elimination. We could also observe that -3 times the first equation yields

$$-3x + 3y = -3,$$

which is inconsistent with

$$-3x + 3y = 4.$$

Solution

Start with the augmented matrix:

$$\begin{bmatrix} 1 & -1 & | & 1 \\ -3 & 3 & | & 4 \end{bmatrix}$$

Multiply row 1 by 3 and add the result to row 2. We get the following matrix:

$$\begin{bmatrix} 1 & -1 & | & 1 \\ 0 & 0 & | & 7 \end{bmatrix} \quad 3R_1 + R_2 \rightarrow R_2$$

The second row of the augmented matrix corresponds to the equation $0 = 7$. So the equations are inconsistent, and there is no solution to the system. ∎

EXAMPLE 7

Gauss-Jordan elimination with a dependent system

Solve the system:

$$3x + y = 1$$
$$6x + 2y = 2$$

Solution

Start with the augmented matrix:

$$\begin{bmatrix} 3 & 1 & | & 1 \\ 6 & 2 & | & 2 \end{bmatrix}$$

Multiply row 1 by -2 and add the result to row 2. We get the following matrix:

$$\begin{bmatrix} 3 & 1 & | & 1 \\ 0 & 0 & | & 0 \end{bmatrix} \quad -2R_1 + R_2 \rightarrow R_2$$

In the second row of the augmented matrix we have the equation $0 = 0$. So the equations are dependent. Every ordered pair that satisfies the first equation satisfies both equations. The solution set is $\{(x, y) | 3x + y = 1\}$. ∎

The Gauss-Jordan elimination method may be applied to a system of n linear equations in n unknowns, where $n \geq 2$. However, it is a rather tedious method to perform when n is greater than 2, especially when fractions are involved. Computers are programmed to work with matrices, and the Gauss-Jordan elimination method is a popular method for computers.

WARM-UPS

True or false? Explain your answer.

Statements 1–7 refer to the following matrices:

a) $\begin{bmatrix} 1 & 3 & | & 5 \\ -1 & -3 & | & 2 \end{bmatrix}$ b) $\begin{bmatrix} 1 & 3 & | & 5 \\ 0 & 0 & | & 7 \end{bmatrix}$

c) $\begin{bmatrix} -1 & 2 & | & -3 \\ 2 & -4 & | & 3 \end{bmatrix}$ d) $\begin{bmatrix} 1 & 3 & | & 5 \\ 0 & 0 & | & 0 \end{bmatrix}$

1. The augmented matrix for $x + 3y = 5$ and $-x - 3y = 2$ is matrix (a).

2. The augmented matrix for $2y - x = -3$ and $2x - 4y = 3$ is matrix (c).

3. Matrix (a) is equivalent to matrix (b).

4. Matrix (c) is equivalent to matrix (d).

5. The system corresponding to matrix (b) is inconsistent.

6. The system corresponding to matrix (c) is dependent.

7. The system corresponding to matrix (d) is independent.

8. The augmented matrix for a system of two linear equations in two unknowns is a 2×2 matrix.

9. The notation $2R_1 + R_3 \rightarrow R_3$ means to replace R_3 by $2R_1 + R_3$.

10. The notation $R_1 \leftrightarrow R_2$ means to replace R_2 by R_1.

4.4   EXERCISES

Reading and Writing   *After reading this section, write out the answers to these questions. Use complete sentences.*

1. What is a matrix?

2. What is the difference between a row and a column of a matrix?

3. What is the order of a matrix?

4. What is an element of a matrix?

5. What is an augmented matrix?

6. What is the goal of Gauss-Jordan elimination?

Determine the order of each matrix. See Example 1.

7. $\begin{bmatrix} 5 & 0 \\ -2 & 3 \end{bmatrix}$

8. $\begin{bmatrix} 1 & 3 & 6 \\ -7 & 0 & 2 \end{bmatrix}$

9. $\begin{bmatrix} a & c \\ 0 & d \\ 3 & w \end{bmatrix}$

10. $\begin{bmatrix} 0 & a & b \\ 5 & 7 & -8 \\ a & b & 2 \end{bmatrix}$

11. $\begin{bmatrix} -\sqrt{3} \\ \pi \\ \frac{1}{2} \end{bmatrix}$

12. $[3 \quad 0 \quad 4]$

Write the augmented matrix for each system of equations. See Example 2.

13. $2x - 3y = 9$
     $-3x + y = -1$

14. $x - y = 4$
     $2x + y = 3$

15. $x - y + z = 1$
$x + y - 2z = 3$
$y - 3z = 4$

16. $x + y = 2$
$y - 3z = 5$
$-3x + 2z = 8$

Write the system of equations represented by each augmented matrix. See Example 3.

17. $\begin{bmatrix} 5 & 1 & | & -1 \\ 2 & -3 & | & 0 \end{bmatrix}$

18. $\begin{bmatrix} 1 & 0 & | & 4 \\ 0 & 1 & | & -3 \end{bmatrix}$

19. $\begin{bmatrix} 1 & 0 & 0 & | & 6 \\ -1 & 0 & 1 & | & -3 \\ 1 & 1 & 0 & | & 1 \end{bmatrix}$

20. $\begin{bmatrix} 1 & 0 & 4 & | & 3 \\ 0 & 2 & 1 & | & -1 \\ 1 & 1 & 1 & | & 1 \end{bmatrix}$

Determine the row operation that was used to convert each given augmented matrix into the equivalent augmented matrix that follows it. See Example 4.

21. $\begin{bmatrix} 3 & 2 & | & 12 \\ 1 & -1 & | & -1 \end{bmatrix}, \begin{bmatrix} 1 & -1 & | & -1 \\ 3 & 2 & | & 12 \end{bmatrix}$

22. $\begin{bmatrix} 1 & -1 & | & -1 \\ 3 & 2 & | & 12 \end{bmatrix}, \begin{bmatrix} 1 & -1 & | & -1 \\ 0 & 5 & | & 15 \end{bmatrix}$

23. $\begin{bmatrix} 1 & -1 & | & -1 \\ 0 & 5 & | & 15 \end{bmatrix}, \begin{bmatrix} 1 & -1 & | & -1 \\ 0 & 1 & | & 3 \end{bmatrix}$

24. $\begin{bmatrix} 1 & -1 & | & -1 \\ 0 & 1 & | & 3 \end{bmatrix}, \begin{bmatrix} 1 & 0 & | & 2 \\ 0 & 1 & | & 3 \end{bmatrix}$

Solve each system using the Gauss-Jordan elimination method. See Examples 4–7.

25. $x + y = 3$
$-3x + y = -1$

26. $x - y = -1$
$2x - y = 2$

27. $2x - y = 3$
$x + y = 9$

28. $3x - 4y = -1$
$x - y = 0$

29. $3x - y = 4$
$2x + y = 1$

30. $2x - y = -3$
$3x + y = -2$

31. $6x - 7y = 0$
$2x + y = 20$

32. $2x + y = 11$
$2x - y = 1$

33. $2x - 3y = 4$
$-2x + 3y = 5$

34. $x - 3y = 8$
$2x - 6y = 1$

35. $x + 2y = 1$
$3x + 6y = 3$

36. $2x - 3y = 1$
$-6x + 9y = -3$

37. $x + y + z = 6$
$x - y + z = 2$
$2y - z = 1$

38. $x - y - z = 0$
$-x - y + z = -4$
$-x + y - z = -2$

39. $2x + y + z = 4$
$x + y - z = 1$
$x - y + 2z = 2$

40. $3x - y = 1$
$x + y + z = 4$
$x + 2z = 3$

41. $2x - y + z = 0$
$x + y - 3z = 3$
$x - y + z = -1$

42. $x - y - z = 0$
$-x - y + 2z = -1$
$-x + y - 2z = -3$

43. $-x + 3y + z = 0$
$x - y - 4z = -3$
$x + y + 2z = 3$

44. $-x + z = -2$
$2x - y = 5$
$y + 3z = 9$

45. $x - y + z = 1$
$2x - 2y + 2z = 2$
$-3x + 3y - 3z = -3$

46. $4x - 2y + 2z = 2$
$2x - y + z = 1$
$-2x + y - z = -1$

47. $x + y - z = 2$
$2x - y + z = 1$
$3x + 3y - 3z = 8$

48. $x + y + z = 5$
$x - y - z = 8$
$-x + y + z = 2$

GETTING MORE INVOLVED

 49. *Cooperative learning.* Write a step-by-step procedure for solving any system of two linear equations in two variables by the Gauss-Jordan elimination method. Have a classmate evaluate your procedure by using it to solve a system.

 50. *Cooperative learning.* Repeat Exercise 49 for a system of three linear equations in three variables.

In This Section

- Determinants
- Cramer's Rule (2 × 2)
- Minors
- Evaluating a 3 × 3 Determinant
- Cramer's Rule (3 × 3)

 4.5

DETERMINANTS AND CRAMER'S RULE

The Gauss-Jordan elimination method of Section 4.4 can be performed the same way on every system. Another method that is applied the same way for every system is Cramer's rule, which we study in this section. Before you learn Cramer's rule, we need to introduce a new number associated with a matrix, called a **determinant**.

Determinants

The determinant of a square matrix is a real number corresponding to the matrix. For a 2×2 matrix the determinant is defined as follows.

Determinant of a 2 × 2 Matrix

The **determinant** of the matrix $\begin{bmatrix} a & b \\ c & d \end{bmatrix}$ is defined to be the real number $ad - bc$. We write

$$\begin{vmatrix} a & b \\ c & d \end{vmatrix} = ad - bc.$$

Note that the symbol for the determinant is a pair of vertical lines similar to the absolute value symbol, while a matrix is enclosed in brackets.

E X A M P L E   1

Using the definition of determinant

Find the determinant of each matrix.

a) $\begin{bmatrix} 1 & 3 \\ -2 & 5 \end{bmatrix}$

b) $\begin{bmatrix} 2 & 4 \\ 6 & 12 \end{bmatrix}$

Solution

a) $\begin{vmatrix} 1 & 3 \\ -2 & 5 \end{vmatrix} = 1 \cdot 5 - 3(-2)$

$$= 5 + 6$$
$$= 11$$

b) $\begin{vmatrix} 2 & 4 \\ 6 & 12 \end{vmatrix} = 2 \cdot 12 - 4 \cdot 6$

$$= 24 - 24$$
$$= 0 \qquad \blacksquare$$

Calculator Close-Up

With a graphing calculator you can define matrix A using MATRX EDIT.

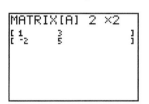

Then use the determinant function (det) found in MATRX MATH and the A from MATRX NAMES to find its determinant.

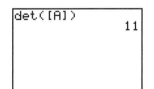

Cramer's Rule (2 × 2)

To understand Cramer's rule, we first solve a general system of two linear equations in two variables. Consider the system

$$(1) \qquad a_1 x + b_1 y = c_1$$
$$(2) \qquad a_2 x + b_2 y = c_2$$

where a_1, b_1, c_1, a_2, b_2, and c_2 represent real numbers. To eliminate y, we multiply Eq. (1) by b_2 and Eq. (2) by $-b_1$:

$$a_1 b_2 x + b_1 b_2 y = c_1 b_2 \qquad \text{Eq. (1) multiplied by } b_2$$
$$\underline{-a_2 b_1 x - b_1 b_2 y = -c_2 b_1} \qquad \text{Eq. (2) multiplied by } -b_1$$
$$a_1 b_2 x - a_2 b_1 x \qquad\qquad = c_1 b_2 - c_2 b_1 \qquad \text{Add.}$$
$$(a_1 b_2 - a_2 b_1)x = c_1 b_2 - c_2 b_1$$
$$x = \frac{c_1 b_2 - c_2 b_1}{a_1 b_2 - a_2 b_1} \qquad \text{Provided that } a_1 b_2 - a_2 b_1 \neq 0$$

Using similar steps to eliminate x from the system, we get

$$y = \frac{a_1 c_2 - a_2 c_1}{a_1 b_2 - a_2 b_1},$$

provided that $a_1 b_2 - a_2 b_1 \neq 0$. These formulas for x and y can be written by using determinants. In the determinant form they are known as **Cramer's rule.**

Cramer's Rule

The solution to the system

$$a_1x + b_1y = c_1$$
$$a_2x + b_2y = c_2$$

is given by $x = \dfrac{D_x}{D}$ and $y = \dfrac{D_y}{D}$, where

$$D = \begin{vmatrix} a_1 & b_1 \\ a_2 & b_2 \end{vmatrix}, \qquad D_x = \begin{vmatrix} c_1 & b_1 \\ c_2 & b_2 \end{vmatrix}, \qquad \text{and} \qquad D_y = \begin{vmatrix} a_1 & c_1 \\ a_2 & c_2 \end{vmatrix},$$

provided that $D \neq 0$.

Note that D is the determinant made up of the original coefficients of x and y. D is used in the denominator for both x and y. D_x is obtained by replacing the first (or x) column of D by the constants c_1 and c_2. D_y is found by replacing the second (or y) column of D by the constants c_1 and c_2.

E X A M P L E   2   **Solving an independent system with Cramer's rule**

Use Cramer's rule to solve the system:

$$3x - 2y = 4$$
$$2x + y = -3$$

Solution

First find the determinants D, D_x, and D_y:

$$D = \begin{vmatrix} 3 & -2 \\ 2 & 1 \end{vmatrix} = 3 - (-4) = 7$$

$$D_x = \begin{vmatrix} 4 & -2 \\ -3 & 1 \end{vmatrix} = 4 - 6 = -2, \qquad D_y = \begin{vmatrix} 3 & 4 \\ 2 & -3 \end{vmatrix} = -9 - 8 = -17$$

By Cramer's rule, we have

$$x = \frac{D_x}{D} = -\frac{2}{7} \qquad \text{and} \qquad y = \frac{D_y}{D} = -\frac{17}{7}.$$

Check in the original equations. The solution set is $\left\{ \left(-\frac{2}{7}, -\frac{17}{7} \right) \right\}$.   ■

C A U T I O N   Cramer's rule works *only* when the determinant D is *not* equal to zero. Cramer's rule solves only those systems that have a single point in their solution set. If $D = 0$, we use elimination to determine whether the solution set is empty or contains all points of a line.

Minors

To each element of a 3×3 matrix there corresponds a 2×2 matrix that is obtained by deleting the row and column of that element. The determinant of the 2×2 matrix is called the **minor** of that element.

E X A M P L E   3   **Finding minors**

Find the minors for the elements 2, 3, and -6 of the 3×3 matrix

$$\begin{bmatrix} 2 & -1 & -8 \\ 0 & -2 & 3 \\ 4 & -6 & 7 \end{bmatrix}.$$

Solution

To find the minor for 2, delete the first row and first column of the matrix:

$$\begin{bmatrix} 2 & -1 & -8 \\ 0 & -2 & 3 \\ 4 & -6 & 7 \end{bmatrix}$$

Now find the determinant of $\begin{bmatrix} -2 & 3 \\ -6 & 7 \end{bmatrix}$:

$$\begin{vmatrix} -2 & 3 \\ -6 & 7 \end{vmatrix} = (-2)(7) - (-6)(3) = 4$$

The minor for 2 is 4. To find the minor for 3, delete the second row and third column of the matrix:

$$\begin{bmatrix} 2 & -1 & -8 \\ 0 & -2 & 3 \\ 4 & -6 & 7 \end{bmatrix}$$

Now find the determinant of $\begin{bmatrix} 2 & -1 \\ 4 & -6 \end{bmatrix}$:

$$\begin{vmatrix} 2 & -1 \\ 4 & -6 \end{vmatrix} = (2)(-6) - (4)(-1) = -8$$

The minor for 3 is -8. To find the minor for -6, delete the third row and the second column of the matrix:

$$\begin{bmatrix} 2 & -1 & -8 \\ 0 & -2 & 3 \\ 4 & -6 & 7 \end{bmatrix}$$

Now find the determinant of $\begin{bmatrix} 2 & -8 \\ 0 & 3 \end{bmatrix}$:

$$\begin{vmatrix} 2 & -8 \\ 0 & 3 \end{vmatrix} = (2)(3) - (0)(-8) = 6$$

The minor for -6 is 6.   ■

Evaluating a 3 × 3 Determinant

The determinant of a 3×3 matrix is defined in terms of the determinants of minors.

Determinant of a 3 × 3 Matrix

The determinant of a 3 × 3 matrix is defined as follows:

$$\begin{vmatrix} a_1 & b_1 & c_1 \\ a_2 & b_2 & c_2 \\ a_3 & b_3 & c_3 \end{vmatrix} = a_1 \cdot \begin{vmatrix} b_2 & c_2 \\ b_3 & c_3 \end{vmatrix} - a_2 \cdot \begin{vmatrix} b_1 & c_1 \\ b_3 & c_3 \end{vmatrix} + a_3 \cdot \begin{vmatrix} b_1 & c_1 \\ b_2 & c_2 \end{vmatrix}$$

Note that the determinants following a_1, a_2, and a_3 are the minors for a_1, a_2, and a_3, respectively. Writing the determinant of a 3 × 3 matrix in terms of minors is called **expansion by minors.** In the definition we expanded by minors about the first column. Later we will see how to expand by minors using any row or column and get the same value for the determinant.

E X A M P L E   4   **Determinant of a 3 × 3 matrix**

Find the determinant of the matrix by expansion by minors about the first column.

$$\begin{bmatrix} 1 & 3 & -5 \\ -2 & 4 & 6 \\ 0 & -7 & 9 \end{bmatrix}$$

Solution

$$\begin{vmatrix} 1 & 3 & -5 \\ -2 & 4 & 6 \\ 0 & -7 & 9 \end{vmatrix} = 1 \cdot \begin{vmatrix} 4 & 6 \\ -7 & 9 \end{vmatrix} - (-2) \cdot \begin{vmatrix} 3 & -5 \\ -7 & 9 \end{vmatrix} + 0 \cdot \begin{vmatrix} 3 & -5 \\ 4 & 6 \end{vmatrix}$$

$$= 1 \cdot [36 - (-42)] + 2 \cdot (27 - 35) + 0 \cdot [18 - (-20)]$$

$$= 1 \cdot 78 + 2 \cdot (-8) + 0$$

$$= 78 - 16$$

$$= 62 \qquad \blacksquare$$

In Example 5 we evaluate a determinant using expansion by minors about the second row. In expanding about any row or column, the signs of the coefficients of the minors alternate according to the **sign array** that follows:

$$\begin{bmatrix} + & - & + \\ - & + & - \\ + & - & + \end{bmatrix}$$

The sign array is easily remembered by observing that there is a "+" sign in the upper left position and then alternating signs for all of the remaining positions.

E X A M P L E   5   **Determinant of a 3 × 3 matrix**

Evaluate the determinant of the matrix by expanding by minors about the second row.

$$\begin{bmatrix} 1 & 3 & -5 \\ -2 & 4 & 6 \\ 0 & -7 & 9 \end{bmatrix}$$

Solution

For expansion using the second row we prefix the signs "− + −" from the second row of the sign array to the corresponding numbers in the second row of the matrix, -2, 4, and 6. Note that the signs from the sign array are used in addition to any signs that occur on the numbers in the second row.

From the sign array, second row

$$\begin{vmatrix} 1 & 3 & -5 \\ -2 & 4 & 6 \\ 0 & -7 & 9 \end{vmatrix} = -(-2) \cdot \begin{vmatrix} 3 & -5 \\ -7 & 9 \end{vmatrix} + 4 \cdot \begin{vmatrix} 1 & -5 \\ 0 & 9 \end{vmatrix} - 6 \cdot \begin{vmatrix} 1 & 3 \\ 0 & -7 \end{vmatrix}$$

$$= 2(27 - 35) + 4(9 - 0) - 6(-7 - 0)$$
$$= 2(-8) + 4(9) - 6(-7)$$
$$= -16 + 36 + 42$$
$$= 62$$

Note that 62 is the same value that was obtained for this determinant in Example 4. ■

It can be shown that expanding by minors using any row or column prefixed by the corresponding signs from the sign array yields the same value for the determinant. Because we can use any row or column to evaluate a determinant of a 3×3 matrix, we can choose a row or column that makes the work easier. We can shorten the work considerably by picking a row or column with zeros in it.

Calculator Close-Up

A calculator is very useful for finding the determinant of a 3×3 matrix. Define A using MATRX EDIT.

Now use the determinant function from MATRX MATH and the A from MATRX NAMES to find the determinant.

E X A M P L E   6

Choosing the simplest row or column

Find the determinant of the matrix

$$\begin{bmatrix} 3 & -5 & 0 \\ 4 & -6 & 0 \\ 7 & 9 & 2 \end{bmatrix}.$$

Solution

We choose to expand by minors about the third column of the matrix because the third column contains two zeros. Prefix the third-column entries $0, 0, 2$ by the signs "$+ - +$" from the third column of the sign array:

$$\begin{vmatrix} 3 & -5 & 0 \\ 4 & -6 & 0 \\ 7 & 9 & 2 \end{vmatrix} = 0 \cdot \begin{vmatrix} 4 & -6 \\ 7 & 9 \end{vmatrix} - 0 \cdot \begin{vmatrix} 3 & -5 \\ 7 & 9 \end{vmatrix} + 2 \cdot \begin{vmatrix} 3 & -5 \\ 4 & -6 \end{vmatrix}$$

$$= 0 - 0 + 2[-18 - (-20)]$$
$$= 4$$
■

Cramer's Rule (3 × 3)

A system of three linear equations in three variables can be solved by using determinants and Cramer's rule.

Cramer's Rule for Three Equations in Three Unknowns

The solution to the system

$$a_1x + b_1y + c_1z = d_1$$
$$a_2x + b_2y + c_2z = d_2$$
$$a_3x + b_3y + c_3z = d_3$$

is given by $x = \dfrac{D_x}{D}$, $y = \dfrac{D_y}{D}$, and $z = \dfrac{D_z}{D}$, where

$$D = \begin{vmatrix} a_1 & b_1 & c_1 \\ a_2 & b_2 & c_2 \\ a_3 & b_3 & c_3 \end{vmatrix}, \qquad D_x = \begin{vmatrix} d_1 & b_1 & c_1 \\ d_2 & b_2 & c_2 \\ d_3 & b_3 & c_3 \end{vmatrix},$$

$$D_y = \begin{vmatrix} a_1 & d_1 & c_1 \\ a_2 & d_2 & c_2 \\ a_3 & d_3 & c_3 \end{vmatrix}, \qquad D_z = \begin{vmatrix} a_1 & b_1 & d_1 \\ a_2 & b_2 & d_2 \\ a_3 & b_3 & d_3 \end{vmatrix},$$

provided that $D \neq 0$.

Note that D_x, D_y, and D_z are obtained from D by replacing the x-, y-, or z-column with the constants d_1, d_2, and d_3.

E X A M P L E 7

Solving an independent system with Cramer's rule

Use Cramer's rule to solve the system:

$$x + y + z = 4$$
$$x - y = -3$$
$$x + 2y - z = 0$$

Solution

We first calculate D, D_x, D_y, and D_z. To calculate D, expand by minors about the third column because the third column has a zero in it:

$$D = \begin{vmatrix} 1 & 1 & 1 \\ 1 & -1 & 0 \\ 1 & 2 & -1 \end{vmatrix} = 1 \cdot \begin{vmatrix} 1 & -1 \\ 1 & 2 \end{vmatrix} - 0 \cdot \begin{vmatrix} 1 & 1 \\ 1 & 2 \end{vmatrix} + (-1) \cdot \begin{vmatrix} 1 & 1 \\ 1 & -1 \end{vmatrix}$$

$$= 1 \cdot [2 - (-1)] - 0 + (-1)[-1 - 1]$$
$$= 3 - 0 + 2$$
$$= 5$$

For D_x, expand by minors about the first column:

$$D_x = \begin{vmatrix} 4 & 1 & 1 \\ -3 & -1 & 0 \\ 0 & 2 & -1 \end{vmatrix} = 4 \cdot \begin{vmatrix} -1 & 0 \\ 2 & -1 \end{vmatrix} - (-3) \cdot \begin{vmatrix} 1 & 1 \\ 2 & -1 \end{vmatrix} + 0 \cdot \begin{vmatrix} 1 & 1 \\ -1 & 0 \end{vmatrix}$$

$$= 4 \cdot (1 - 0) + 3 \cdot (-1 - 2) + 0$$

$$= 4 - 9 + 0 = -5$$

For D_y, expand by minors about the third row:

$$D_y = \begin{vmatrix} 1 & 4 & 1 \\ 1 & -3 & 0 \\ 1 & 0 & -1 \end{vmatrix} = 1 \cdot \begin{vmatrix} 4 & 1 \\ -3 & 0 \end{vmatrix} - 0 \cdot \begin{vmatrix} 1 & 1 \\ 1 & 0 \end{vmatrix} + (-1) \cdot \begin{vmatrix} 1 & 4 \\ 1 & -3 \end{vmatrix}$$

$$= 1 \cdot 3 - 0 + (-1)(-7) = 10$$

To get D_z, expand by minors about the third row:

$$D_z = \begin{vmatrix} 1 & 1 & 4 \\ 1 & -1 & -3 \\ 1 & 2 & 0 \end{vmatrix} = 1 \cdot \begin{vmatrix} 1 & 4 \\ -1 & -3 \end{vmatrix} - 2 \cdot \begin{vmatrix} 1 & 4 \\ 1 & -3 \end{vmatrix} + 0 \cdot \begin{vmatrix} 1 & 1 \\ 1 & -1 \end{vmatrix}$$

$$= 1 \cdot 1 - 2(-7) + 0 = 15$$

Now, by Cramer's rule,

$$x = \frac{D_x}{D} = \frac{-5}{5} = -1, \qquad y = \frac{D_y}{D} = \frac{10}{5} = 2, \qquad \text{and} \qquad z = \frac{D_z}{D} = \frac{15}{5} = 3.$$

Check $(-1, 2, 3)$ in the original equations. The solution set is $\{(-1, 2, 3)\}$. ■

If $D = 0$, Cramer's rule does not apply. Cramer's rule provides the solution only to a system of three equations with three variables that has a single point in the solution set. If $D = 0$, then the solution set either is empty or consists of infinitely many points, and we can use the methods discussed in Sections 4.3 or 4.4 to find the solution.

WARM-UPS

True or false? Explain your answer.

1. $\begin{vmatrix} -1 & 2 \\ 3 & -5 \end{vmatrix} = -1$ **2.** $\begin{vmatrix} 2 & 4 \\ -4 & 8 \end{vmatrix} = 0$

3. Cramer's rule solves any system of two linear equations in two variables.

4. The determinant of a 2 × 2 matrix is a real number.

5. If $D = 0$, then there might be no solution to the system.

6. Cramer's rule is used to solve systems of linear equations only.

7. If the graphs of a pair of linear equations intersect at exactly one point, then this point can be found by using Cramer's rule.

8. The determinant of a 3 × 3 matrix is found by using minors.

9. Expansion by minors about any row or any column gives the same value for the determinant of a 3 × 3 matrix.

10. The sign array is used in evaluating the determinant of a 3 × 3 matrix.

Reading and Writing *After reading this section, write out the answers to these questions. Use complete sentences.*

1. What is a determinant?

2. What is Cramer's rule used for?

3. Which systems can be solved using Cramer's rule?

4. What is a minor?

5. How do you find the minor for an element of a 3×3 matrix?

6. What is the purpose of the sign array?

Find the value of each determinant. See Example 1.

7. $\begin{vmatrix} 2 & 5 \\ 3 & 7 \end{vmatrix}$

8. $\begin{vmatrix} -1 & 0 \\ 1 & 1 \end{vmatrix}$

9. $\begin{vmatrix} 0 & 3 \\ 1 & 5 \end{vmatrix}$

10. $\begin{vmatrix} 2 & 4 \\ 6 & 12 \end{vmatrix}$

11. $\begin{vmatrix} -3 & -2 \\ -4 & 2 \end{vmatrix}$

12. $\begin{vmatrix} -2 & 2 \\ -3 & -5 \end{vmatrix}$

13. $\begin{vmatrix} 0.05 & 0.06 \\ 10 & 20 \end{vmatrix}$

14. $\begin{vmatrix} 0.02 & -0.5 \\ 30 & 50 \end{vmatrix}$

Solve each system using Cramer's rule. See Example 2.

15. $2x - y = 5$
$3x + 2y = -3$

16. $3x + y = -1$
$x + 2y = 8$

17. $3x - 5y = -2$
$2x + 3y = 5$

18. $x - y = 1$
$3x - 2y = 0$

19. $4x - 3y = 5$
$2x + 5y = 7$

20. $2x - y = 2$
$3x - 2y = 1$

21. $0.5x + 0.2y = 8$
$0.4x - 0.6y = -5$

22. $0.6x + 0.5y = 18$
$0.5x - 0.25y = 7$

23. $\dfrac{1}{2}x + \dfrac{1}{4}y = 5$
$\dfrac{1}{3}x - \dfrac{1}{2}y = -1$

24. $\dfrac{1}{2}x + \dfrac{2}{3}y = 4$
$\dfrac{3}{4}x + \dfrac{1}{3}y = -2$

Find the indicated minors using the following matrix. See Example 3.

$$\begin{bmatrix} 3 & -2 & 5 \\ 4 & -3 & 7 \\ 0 & 1 & -6 \end{bmatrix}$$

25. Minor for 3

26. Minor for -2

27. Minor for 5

28. Minor for -3

29. Minor for 7

30. Minor for 0

31. Minor for 1

32. Minor for -6

Find the determinant of each 3×3 matrix by using expansion by minors about the first column. See Example 4.

33. $\begin{bmatrix} 1 & 1 & 2 \\ 2 & 3 & 1 \\ 3 & 1 & 5 \end{bmatrix}$

34. $\begin{bmatrix} 2 & 1 & 3 \\ 1 & 1 & 2 \\ 3 & 4 & 6 \end{bmatrix}$

35. $\begin{bmatrix} 2 & 1 & 0 \\ 1 & 0 & 1 \\ 3 & 1 & 2 \end{bmatrix}$

36. $\begin{bmatrix} 1 & 0 & 2 \\ 2 & 1 & 3 \\ 4 & 3 & 0 \end{bmatrix}$

37. $\begin{bmatrix} -2 & 1 & 2 \\ -3 & 3 & 1 \\ -5 & 4 & 0 \end{bmatrix}$

38. $\begin{bmatrix} -2 & 1 & 3 \\ -1 & 4 & 2 \\ 2 & 1 & 1 \end{bmatrix}$

39. $\begin{bmatrix} 1 & 1 & 5 \\ 0 & 3 & 2 \\ 0 & 2 & 3 \end{bmatrix}$

40. $\begin{bmatrix} 1 & 0 & 6 \\ 0 & 1 & 4 \\ 0 & 0 & 9 \end{bmatrix}$

Evaluate the determinant of each 3×3 matrix using expansion by minors about the row or column of your choice. See Examples 5 and 6.

41. $\begin{bmatrix} 3 & 1 & 5 \\ 2 & 0 & 6 \\ 4 & 0 & 1 \end{bmatrix}$

42. $\begin{bmatrix} 2 & 1 & 2 \\ 1 & 2 & 5 \\ 3 & 0 & 0 \end{bmatrix}$

43. $\begin{bmatrix} -2 & 1 & 3 \\ 0 & 1 & -1 \\ 2 & -4 & -3 \end{bmatrix}$

44. $\begin{bmatrix} -2 & 0 & 1 \\ -3 & 2 & -5 \\ 4 & -2 & 6 \end{bmatrix}$

45. $\begin{bmatrix} -2 & -3 & 0 \\ 4 & -1 & 0 \\ 0 & 3 & 5 \end{bmatrix}$

46. $\begin{bmatrix} -2 & 6 & 3 \\ 0 & 4 & 0 \\ -1 & -4 & 5 \end{bmatrix}$

47. $\begin{bmatrix} 2 & 1 & 1 \\ 0 & 0 & 5 \\ 5 & 0 & 4 \end{bmatrix}$

48. $\begin{bmatrix} 2 & 3 & 0 \\ 6 & 4 & 1 \\ 1 & 2 & 0 \end{bmatrix}$

Use Cramer's rule to solve each system. See Example 7.

49. $x + y + z = 6$
$x - y + z = 2$
$2x + y + z = 7$

50. $x + y + z = 2$
$x - y - 2z = -3$
$2x - y + z = 7$

51. $x - 3y + 2z = 0$
$x + y + z = 2$
$x - y + z = 0$

52. $3x + 2y + 2z = 0$
$x - y + z = 1$
$x + y - z = 3$

53. $x + y = -1$
$2y - z = 3$
$x + y + z = 0$

54. $x - y = 8$
$x - 2z = 0$
$x + y - z = 1$

55. $x + y - z = 0$
$2x + 2y + z = 6$
$x - 3y = 0$

56. $x + y + z = 1$
$5x - y = 0$
$3x + y + 2z = 0$

57. $x + y + z = 0$
$2y + 2z = 0$
$3x - y = -1$

58. $x + z = 0$
$x - 3y = 1$
$4y - 3z = 3$

Solve each problem by using two equations in two variables and Cramer's rule.

59. *Peas and beets.* One serving of canned peas contains 3 grams of protein and 11 grams of carbohydrates. One serving of canned beets contains 1 gram of protein and 8 grams of carbohydrates. A dietitian wants to determine the number of servings of each that would provide 38 grams of protein and 187 grams of carbohydrates.
a) Use the accompanying graph to estimate the number of servings of each.
b) Use Cramer's rule to find the number of servings of each.

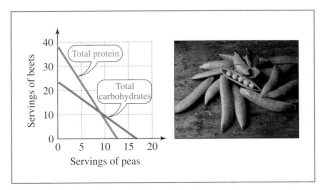

FIGURE FOR EXERCISE 59

60. *Protein and carbohydrates.* One serving of Cornies breakfast cereal contains 2 grams of protein and 25

grams of carbohydrates. One serving of Oaties breakfast cereal contains 4 grams of protein and 20 grams of carbohydrates. How many servings of each would provide exactly 24 grams of protein and 210 grams of carbohydrates?

61. *Milk and a magazine.* Althia bought a gallon of milk and a magazine for a total of $4.65, excluding tax. Including the tax, the bill was $4.95. If there is a 5% sales tax on milk and an 8% sales tax on magazines, then what was the price of each item?

62. *Washing machines and refrigerators.* A truck carrying 3600 cubic feet of cargo consisting of washing machines and refrigerators was hijacked. The washing machines are worth $300 each and are shipped in 36-cubic-foot cartons. The refrigerators are worth $900 each and are shipped in 45-cubic-foot cartons. If the total value of the cargo was $51,000, then how many of each were there on the truck?

63. *Singles and doubles.* Windy's Hamburger Palace sells singles and doubles. Toward the end of the evening, Windy himself noticed that he had on hand only 32 patties and 34 slices of tomatoes. If a single takes 1 patty and 2 slices, and a double takes 2 patties and 1 slice, then how many more singles and doubles must Windy sell to use up all of his patties and tomato slices?

64. *Valuable wrenches.* Carmen has a total of 28 wrenches, all of which are either box wrenches or open-end wrenches. For insurance purposes she values the box wrenches at $3.00 each and the open-end wrenches at $2.50 each. If the value of her wrench collection is $78, then how many of each type does she have?

65. *Gary and Harry.* Gary is 5 years older than Harry. Twenty-nine years ago, Gary was twice as old as Harry. How old are they now?

66. *Acute angles.* One acute angle of a right triangle is 3° more than twice the other acute angle. What are the sizes of the acute angles?

FIGURE FOR EXERCISE 66

67. *Equal perimeters.* A rope of length 80 feet is to be cut into two pieces. One piece will be used to form a square, and the other will be used to form an equilateral triangle. If the figures are to have equal perimeters, then what should be the length of a side of each?

FIGURE FOR EXERCISE 67

68. *Coffee and doughnuts.* For a cup of coffee and a doughnut, Thurrel spent $2.25, including a tip. Later he spent $4.00 for two coffees and three doughnuts, including a tip. If he always tips $1.00, then what is the price of a cup of coffee?

69. *Chlorine mixture.* A 10% chlorine solution is to be mixed with a 25% chlorine solution to obtain 30 gallons of 20% solution. How many gallons of each must be used?

70. *Safe drivers.* Emily and Camille started from the same city and drove in opposite directions on the freeway. After 3 hours they were 354 miles apart. If they had gone in the same direction, Emily would have been 18 miles ahead of Camille. How fast did each woman drive?

Write a system of three equations in three variables for each word problem. Use Cramer's rule to solve each system.

71. *Weighing dogs.* Cassandra wants to determine the weights of her two dogs, Mimi and Mitzi. However, neither dog will sit on the scale by herself. Cassandra, Mimi, and Mitzi altogether weigh 175 pounds. Cassandra and Mimi together weigh 143 pounds.

Cassandra   Cassandra   Cassandra
Mimi   Mimi   Mitzi
Mitzi

FIGURE FOR EXERCISE 71

Cassandra and Mitzi together weigh 139 pounds. How much does each weigh individually?

72. *Nickels, dimes, and quarters.* Bernard has 41 coins consisting of nickels, dimes, and quarters, and they are worth a total of $4.00. If the number of dimes plus the number of quarters is one more than the number of nickels, then how many of each does he have?

73. *Finding three angles.* If the two acute angles of a right triangle differ by 12°, then what are the measures of the three angles of this triangle?

74. *Two acute and one obtuse.* The obtuse angle of a triangle is twice as large as the sum of the two acute angles. If the smallest angle is only one-eighth as large as the sum of the other two, then what is the measure of each angle?

GETTING MORE INVOLVED

75. *Writing.* Explain what to do when you are trying to use Cramer's rule and $D = 0$.

76. *Exploration.* For what value of a does the system

$$ax - y = 3$$
$$x + 2y = 1$$

have a single solution?

77. *Exploration.* Can Cramer's rule be used to solve this system? Explain.

$$2x^2 - y = 3$$
$$3x^2 + 2y = 22$$

78. *Writing.* For what values of a, b, c, and d is the determinant of the matrix

$$\begin{bmatrix} a & b & 0 \\ c & d & 0 \\ b & a & 0 \end{bmatrix}$$

equal to zero? Explain your answer.

GRAPHING CALCULATOR EXERCISES

79. Use the determinant feature on your graphing calculator to find the determinants in Exercises 7–14 and 33–40 of this section.

80. Solve the systems in Exercises 15–24 and 49–58 of this section by using your graphing calculator to find the necessary determinants.

In This Section

- Graphing the Constraints
- Maximizing or Minimizing a Linear Function

4.6   LINEAR PROGRAMMING

In this section we graph the solution set to a system of several linear inequalities, much as we graphed compound linear inequalities in Chapter 3. We then use the solution set as the domain of a function for which we are seeking the maximum or minimum value. The method that we use is called **linear programming,** and it can be applied to problems such as finding maximum profit or minimum cost.

Graphing the Constraints

In linear programming we have two variables that must satisfy several linear inequalities. These inequalities are called the **constraints** because they restrict the variables to only certain values. A graph in the coordinate plane is used to indicate the points that satisfy all of the constraints.

E X A M P L E   1

Graphing the constraints

Graph the solution set to the system of inequalities and identify each vertex of the region:

$$x \geq 0, \quad y \geq 0$$
$$3x + 2y \leq 12$$
$$x + 2y \leq 8$$

Solution

The points on or to the right of the y-axis satisfy $x \geq 0$. The points on or above the x-axis satisfy $y \geq 0$. The points on or below the line $3x + 2y = 12$ satisfy $3x + 2y \leq 12$. The points on or below the line $x + 2y = 8$ satisfy $x + 2y \leq 8$. Graph each straight line and shade the region that satisfies all four inequalities as shown in Fig. 4.7. Three of the vertices are easily identified as (0, 0), (0, 4), and (4, 0). The fourth vertex is found by solving the system $3x + 2y = 12$ and $x + 2y = 8$. The fourth vertex is (2, 3).   ■

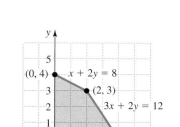

FIGURE 4.7

In linear programming the constraints usually come from physical limitations in some problem. In Example 2 we write the constraints and then graph the points in the coordinate plane that satisfy all of the constraints.

E X A M P L E   2

Writing the constraints

Jules is in the business of constructing dog houses. A small dog house requires 8 square feet (ft^2) of plywood and 6 ft^2 of insulation. A large dog house requires 16 ft^2 of plywood and 3 ft^2 of insulation. Jules has available only 48 ft^2 of plywood and 18 ft^2 of insulation. Write the constraints on the number of small and large dog houses that he can build with the available supplies and graph the solution set to the system of constraints.

Solution

Let x represent the number of small dog houses and y represent the number of large dog houses. We have two natural constraints $x \geq 0$ and $y \geq 0$ since he cannot build a negative number of dog houses. Since the total plywood available for use is at most 48 ft^2, $8x + 16y \leq 48$. Since the total insulation available is at most 18 ft^2,

FIGURE 4.8

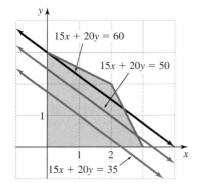

FIGURE 4.9

$6x + 3y \le 18$. Simplify the inequalities to get the following constraints:

$$x \ge 0, \quad y \ge 0$$
$$x + 2y \le 6$$
$$2x + y \le 6$$

The graph of the solution set to the system of inequalities is shown in Fig. 4.8. ■

Maximizing or Minimizing a Linear Function

In Example 2 any ordered pair within the region is a possible solution to the number of dog houses of each type that could be built. If a small dog house sells for $15 and a large dog house sells for $20, then the total revenue in dollars from x small and y large dog houses is $R = 15x + 20y$. Since the revenue is a function of x and y, we write $R(x, y) = 15x + 20y$. The function R is a linear function of x and y. The domain of R is the region graphed in Fig. 4.8.

Linear Function of Two Variables

A function of the form $f(x, y) = Ax + By + C$, where A, B, and C are real numbers, is called a **linear function of two variables.**

Naturally, we are interested in the maximum revenue subject to the constraints on x and y. To investigate some possible revenues, replace R in $R = 15x + 20y$ with, say 35, 50, and 60. The graphs of the parallel lines $15x + 20y = 35$, $15x + 20y = 50$, and $15x + 20y = 60$ are shown in Fig. 4.9. The revenue at any point on the line $15x + 20y = 35$ is $35. We get a larger revenue on a higher revenue line (and lower revenue on a lower line). The maximum revenue possible will be on the highest revenue line that still intersects the region. Because the sides of the region are straight-line segments, the intersection of the highest (or lowest) revenue line with the region must include a vertex of the region. This is the fundamental principle behind linear programming.

The Principle of Linear Programming

The maximum or minimum value of a linear function subject to linear constraints occurs at a vertex of the region determined by the constraints.

E X A M P L E   3   **Maximizing a linear function with linear constraints**

A small dog house requires 8 ft^2 of plywood and 6 ft^2 of insulation. A large dog house requires 16 ft^2 of plywood and 3 ft^2 of insulation. Only 48 ft^2 of plywood and 18 ft^2 of insulation are available. If a small dog house sells for $15 and a large dog house sells for $20, then how many dog houses of each type should be built to maximize the revenue and to satisfy the constraints?

Solution

Let x be the number of small dog houses and y be the number of large dog houses. We wrote and graphed the constraints for this problem in Example 2, so we will not repeat that here. The graph in Fig. 4.8 has four vertices: $(0, 0)$, $(0, 3)$, $(3, 0)$, and

(2, 2). The revenue function is $R(x, y) = 15x + 20y$. Since the maximum value of this function must occur at a vertex, we evaluate the function at each vertex:

$$R(0, 0) = 15(0) + 20(0) = \$0$$
$$R(0, 3) = 15(0) + 20(3) = \$60$$
$$R(3, 0) = 15(3) + 20(0) = \$45$$
$$R(2, 2) = 15(2) + 20(2) = \$70$$

From this list we can see that the maximum revenue is $70 when two small and two large dog houses are built. We also see that the minimum revenue is $0 when no dog houses of either type are built. ∎

We can summarize the procedure for solving linear programming problems with the following strategy.

Strategy for Linear Programming

Use the following steps to find the maximum or minimum value of a linear function subject to linear constraints.

1. Graph the region that satisfies all of the constraints.

2. Determine the coordinates of each vertex of the region.

3. Evaluate the function at each vertex of the region.

4. Identify which vertex gives the maximum or minimum value of the function.

In Example 4 we solve another linear programming problem.

E X A M P L E   4   **Minimizing a linear function with linear constraints**

One serving of food A contains 2 grams of protein and 6 grams of carbohydrates. One serving of food B contains 4 grams of protein and 3 grams of carbohydrates. A dietitian wants a meal that contains at least 12 grams of protein and at least 18 grams of carbohydrates. If the cost of food A is 9 cents per serving and the cost of food B is 20 cents per serving, then how many servings of each food would minimize the cost and satisfy the constraints?

Solution

Let x equal the number of servings of food A and y equal the number of servings of food B. If the meal is to contain at least 12 grams of protein, then $2x + 4y \geq 12$. If the meal is to contain at least 18 grams of carbohydrates, then $6x + 3y \geq 18$. Simplify each inequality and use the two natural constraints to get the following system:

$$x \geq 0, \quad y \geq 0$$
$$x + 2y \geq 6$$
$$2x + y \geq 6$$

The graph of the constraints is shown in Fig. 4.10. The vertices are (0, 6), (6, 0), and (2, 2). The cost in cents for x servings of A and y servings of B is $C(x, y) = 9x + 20y$. Evaluate the cost at each vertex:

$$C(0, 6) = 9(0) + 20(6) = 120 \text{ cents}$$
$$C(6, 0) = 9(6) + 20(0) = 54 \text{ cents}$$
$$C(2, 2) = 9(2) + 20(2) = 58 \text{ cents}$$

The minimum cost of 54 cents is attained by using six servings of food A and no servings of food B.

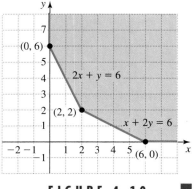

FIGURE 4.10

WARM-UPS

True or false? Explain your answer.

1. The graph of $x \geq 0$ in the coordinate plane consists of the points on or above the x-axis.
2. The graph of $y \geq 0$ in the coordinate plane consists of the points on or to the right of the y-axis.
3. The graph of $x + y \leq 6$ consists of the points below the line $x + y = 6$.
4. The graph of $2x + 3y = 30$ has x-intercept (0, 10) and y-intercept (15, 0).
5. The graph of a system of inequalities is a union of their individual solution sets.
6. In linear programming, constraints are inequalities that restrict the possible values that the variables can assume.
7. The function $F(x, y) = Ax^2 + By^2 + C$ is a linear function of x and y.
8. The value of $R(x, y) = 3x + 5y$ at the point (2, 4) is 26.
9. If $C(x, y) = 12x + 10y$, then $C(0, 5) = 62$.
10. In solving a linear programming problem, we must determine the vertices of the region defined by the constraints.

4.6   EXERCISES

Reading and Writing   *After reading this section, write out the answers to these questions. Use complete sentences.*

1. What is a constraint?
2. What is linear programming?
3. Where do the constraints come from in a linear programming problem?
4. What is a linear function of two variables?

5. Where does the maximum or minimum value of a linear function subject to linear constraints occur?

6. What is the strategy for solving a linear programming problem?

Graph the solution set to each system of inequalities and identify each vertex of the region. See Example 1.

7. $x \geq 0, y \geq 0$
   $x + y \leq 5$

8. $x \geq 0, y \geq 0$
   $y \leq 5, y \geq x$

9. $x \geq 0, y \geq 0$
   $2x + y \leq 4$
   $x + y \leq 3$

10. $x \geq 0, y \geq 0$
   $x + y \leq 4$
   $x + 2y \leq 6$

11. $x \geq 0, y \geq 0$
   $2x + y \geq 3$
   $x + y \geq 2$

12. $x \geq 0, y \geq 0$
   $3x + 2y \geq 12$
   $2x + y \geq 7$

13. $x \geq 0, y \geq 0$
   $x + 3y \leq 15$
   $2x + y \leq 10$

14. $x \geq 0, y \geq 0$
   $2x + 3y \leq 15$
   $x + y \leq 7$

15. $x \geq 0, y \geq 0$
   $x + y \geq 4$
   $3x + y \geq 6$

16. $x \geq 0, y \geq 0$
   $x + 3y \geq 6$
   $2x + y \geq 7$

Solve each problem. See Examples 2–4.

17. Phase I advertising. The publicity director for Mercy Hospital is planning to bolster the hospital's image by running a TV ad and a radio ad. Due to budgetary and other constraints, the number of times that she can run the TV ad, x, and the number of times that she can run the radio ad, y, must be in the region shown in the figure on the next page. The function

$$A = 9000x + 4000y$$

gives the total number of people reached by the ads.
a) Find the total number of people reached by the ads at each vertex of the region.
b) What mix of TV and radio ads maximizes the number of people reached?

18. Phase II advertising. Suppose the radio station in Exercise 17 starts playing country music and the function for the total number of people changes to

$$A = 9000x + 2000y.$$

a) Find A at each vertex of the region using this function.

b) What mix of TV and radio ads maximizes the number of people reached?

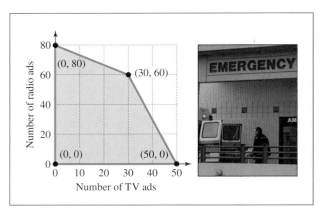

19. At Burger Heaven a double contains 2 meat patties and 6 pickles, whereas a triple contains 3 meat patties and 3 pickles. Near closing time one day, only 24 meat patties and 48 pickles are available. If a double burger sells for $1.20 and a triple burger sells for $1.50, then how many of each should be made to maximize the total revenue?

20. Sam and Doris manufacture rocking chairs and porch swings in the Ozarks. Each rocker requires 3 hours of work from Sam and 2 hours from Doris. Each swing requires 2 hours of work from Sam and 2 hours from Doris. Sam cannot work more than 48 hours per week, and Doris cannot work more than 40 hours per week. If a rocker sells for $160 and a swing sells for $100, then how many of each should be made per week to maximize the revenue?

21. If a double burger sells for $1.00 and a triple burger sells for $2.00, then how many of each should be made to maximize the total revenue subject to the constraints of Exercise 19?

22. If a rocker sells for $120 and a swing sells for $100, then how many of each should be made to maximize the total revenue subject to the constraints of Exercise 20?

23. One cup of Doggie Dinner contains 20 grams of protein and 40 grams of carbohydrates. One cup of Puppy Power contains 30 grams of protein and 20 grams of carbohydrates. Susan wants her dog to get at least 200 grams of protein and 180 grams of carbohydrates per

day. If Doggie Dinner costs 16 cents per cup and Puppy Power costs 20 cents per cup, then how many cups of each would satisfy the constraints and minimize the total cost?

24. Mammoth Muffler employs supervisors and helpers. According to the union contract, a supervisor does 2 brake jobs and 3 mufflers per day, whereas a helper does 6 brake jobs and 3 mufflers per day. The home office requires enough staff for at least 24 brake jobs and for at least 18 mufflers per day. If a supervisor makes $90 per day and a helper makes $100 per day, then how many of each should be employed to satisfy the constraints and to minimize the daily labor cost?

25. Suppose in Exercise 23 Doggie Dinner costs 4 cents per cup and Puppy Power costs 10 cents per cup. How many cups of each would satisfy the constraints and minimize the total cost?

26. Suppose in Exercise 24 the supervisor makes $110 per day and the helper makes $100 per day. How many of each should be employed to satisfy the constraints and to minimize the daily labor cost?

27. Anita has at most $24,000 to invest in her brother-in-law's laundromat and her nephew's car wash. Her brother-in-law has high blood pressure and heart disease but he will pay 18%, whereas her nephew is healthier but will pay only 12%. So the amount she will invest in the car wash will be at least twice the amount that she will invest in the laundromat but not more than three times as much. How much should she invest in each to maximize her total income from the two investments?

28. Herbert assembles computers in his shop. The parts for each economy model are shipped to him in a carton with a volume of 2 cubic feet (ft^3) and the parts for each deluxe model are shipped to him in a carton with a volume of 3 ft^3. After assembly, each economy model is shipped out in a carton with a volume of 4 ft^3, and each deluxe model is shipped out in a carton with a volume of 4 ft^3. The truck that delivers the parts has a maximum capacity of 180 ft^3, and the truck that takes out the completed computers has a maximum capacity of 280 ft^3. He can receive only one shipment of parts and send out one shipment of computers per week. If his profit on an economy model is $60 and his profit on a deluxe model is $100, then how many of each should he order per week to maximize his profit?

COLLABORATIVE ACTIVITIES

Types of Systems

Assign roles in your groups. Set up the system of equations for each scenario below and attempt to solve it. Analyze your results.

Part I: Talia's Tallitot. Talia plans to make tallitot (prayer shawls) and matching kipot (prayer hats) from a bolt of material. The fabric she plans to use is 250 yards long. She will need 2 yards of material for each tallit (prayer shawl) and $\frac{1}{6}$ of a yard for each kipah (prayer hat). She also plans to put tzitzit (fringes) on the tallit and will need 1 yard of cord for each tallit. The kipot will not have any fringes. She has 100 yards of cord to use for the tzitzit.

1. Write two equations to use to solve for how many kipot and tallitot she can make from the supplies on hand. Let t equal the number of tallitot made and k equal the number of kipot made.

2. Try to solve this system of equations. If you get a solution, state what it is. If not, describe what your result means.

Part II: Karif's Kerchiefs. Karif plans to make red and green kerchiefs in two sizes, medium and large. He has 60 yards of each color of material. He will need $\frac{1}{4}$ of a yard of the appropriate colored fabric for each medium kerchief and $\frac{1}{2}$ of a yard for each large kerchief. He also plans to trim each kerchief with the alternate color of ribbon. He has 240 yards of each color of ribbon. He will need 1 yard of ribbon for each medium kerchief and 2 yards for each large kerchief.

Grouping: Two to four students per group

Topic: Types of solutions to systems of equations

3. Let m equal the number of medium kerchiefs and l equal the number of large kerchiefs. Set up two equations to use to solve for the number of each color of kerchiefs Karif can make from the supplies on hand.

4. Try to solve this system of equations. If you get a solution, state what it is. If not, describe what your result means.

Part III: Maria's Mantillas. Maria plans to make two different kinds of mantillas (veils), some out of lace and some out of a sheer cotton fabric. She also plans to make two sizes of mantillas, one size for women and one size for young girls. She has 150 yards of the lace fabric and 200 yards of the cotton fabric. She will need 2 yards of either fabric for the smaller mantillas and $3\frac{1}{2}$ yards of either fabric for the larger mantillas.

5. Let w equal the number of mantillas for the women and y equal the number of mantillas for the young girls. Set up two equations to use to solve for the number of each mantilla Maria can make from each type of fabric.

6. Try to solve this system of equations. If you get a solution, state what it is. If not, describe what your result means.

Extension: Explain what you would need to do for the systems of equations you could not solve to make them solvable.

WRAP-UP CHAPTER 4

SUMMARY

Systems of Linear Equations

		Examples
Methods for solving systems in two variables	Graphing: Sketch the graphs to see the solution.	The graphs of $y = x - 1$ and $x + y = 3$ intersect at (2, 1).
	Substitution: Solve one equation for one variable in terms of the other, then substitute into the other equation.	Substitution: $x + (x - 1) = 3$
	Addition: Multiply each equation as necessary to eliminate a variable upon addition of the equations.	$\begin{array}{r} -x + y = -1 \\ x + y = 3 \\ \hline 2y = 2 \end{array}$

Types of linear systems in two variables	Independent: One point in solution set The lines intersect at one point.	$y = x - 5$ $y = 2x + 3$
	Inconsistent: Empty solution set The lines are parallel.	$2x + y = 1$ $2x + y = 5$
	Dependent: Infinite solution set The lines are the same.	$2x + 3y = 4$ $4x + 6y = 8$
Linear equation in three variables	$Ax + By + Cz = D$ In a three-dimensional coordinate system the graph is a plane.	$2x - y + 3z = 5$
Linear systems in three variables	Use substitution or addition to eliminate variables in the system. The solution set may be a single point, the empty set, or an infinite set of points.	$x + y - z = 3$ $2x - 3y + z = 2$ $x - y - 4z = 14$

Matrices and Determinants

Examples

Matrix	A rectangular array of real numbers An $n \times m$ matrix has n rows and m columns.	$\begin{bmatrix} 1 & -3 \\ 2 & 5 \end{bmatrix}, \begin{bmatrix} 1 & 0 & 1 \\ 2 & 1 & 4 \end{bmatrix}$
Augmented matrix	The matrix of coefficients and constants from a system of linear equations	$x - 3y = -7$ $2x + 5y = 19$ Augmented matrix: $\begin{bmatrix} 1 & -3 & -7 \\ 2 & 5 & 19 \end{bmatrix}$
Gauss-Jordan elimination method	Use the row operations to get ones on the diagonal and zeros elsewhere for the coefficients in the augmented matrix.	$\begin{bmatrix} 1 & 0 & 2 \\ 0 & 1 & 3 \end{bmatrix}$ $x = 2$ and $y = 3$
Determinant	A real number corresponding to a square matrix	
Determinant of a 2 × 2 matrix	$\begin{vmatrix} a_1 & b_1 \\ a_2 & b_2 \end{vmatrix} = a_1 b_2 - a_2 b_1$	$\begin{vmatrix} 1 & -3 \\ 2 & 5 \end{vmatrix} = 5 - (-6)$ $= 11$
Determinant of a 3 × 3 matrix	Expand by minors about any row or column, using signs from the sign array. $\begin{vmatrix} a_1 & b_1 & c_1 \\ a_2 & b_2 & c_2 \\ a_3 & b_3 & c_3 \end{vmatrix} = a_1 \cdot \begin{vmatrix} b_2 & c_2 \\ b_3 & c_3 \end{vmatrix} - a_2 \cdot \begin{vmatrix} b_1 & c_1 \\ b_3 & c_3 \end{vmatrix} + a_3 \cdot \begin{vmatrix} b_1 & c_1 \\ b_2 & c_2 \end{vmatrix}$	Sign array: $\begin{bmatrix} + & - & + \\ - & + & - \\ + & - & + \end{bmatrix}$

Cramer's Rules

Two linear equations in two variables

The solution to the system
$$a_1 x + b_1 y = c_1$$
$$a_2 x + b_2 y = c_2$$
is given by $x = \frac{D_x}{D}$ and $y = \frac{D_y}{D}$, where

$$D = \begin{vmatrix} a_1 & b_1 \\ a_2 & b_2 \end{vmatrix}, \qquad D_x = \begin{vmatrix} c_1 & b_1 \\ c_2 & b_2 \end{vmatrix}, \qquad \text{and} \qquad D_y = \begin{vmatrix} a_1 & c_1 \\ a_2 & c_2 \end{vmatrix}$$

provided that $D \neq 0$.

Three linear equations in three variables

The solution to the system

$$a_1x + b_1y + c_1z = d_1$$
$$a_2x + b_2y + c_2z = d_2$$
$$a_3x + b_3y + c_3z = d_3$$

is given by $x = \dfrac{D_x}{D}$, $y = \dfrac{D_y}{D}$, and $z = \dfrac{D_z}{D}$, where

$$D = \begin{vmatrix} a_1 & b_1 & c_1 \\ a_2 & b_2 & c_2 \\ a_3 & b_3 & c_3 \end{vmatrix}, \qquad D_x = \begin{vmatrix} d_1 & b_1 & c_1 \\ d_2 & b_2 & c_2 \\ d_3 & b_3 & c_3 \end{vmatrix},$$

$$D_y = \begin{vmatrix} a_1 & d_1 & c_1 \\ a_2 & d_2 & c_2 \\ a_3 & d_3 & c_3 \end{vmatrix}, \qquad D_z = \begin{vmatrix} a_1 & b_1 & d_1 \\ a_2 & b_2 & d_2 \\ a_3 & b_3 & d_3 \end{vmatrix},$$

provided that $D \neq 0$.

Linear Programming

Use the following steps to find the maximum or minimum value of a linear function subject to linear constraints.
1. Graph the region that satisfies all of the constraints.
2. Determine the coordinates of each vertex of the region.
3. Evaluate the function at each vertex of the region.
4. Identify which vertex gives the maximum or minimum value of the function.

ENRICHING YOUR MATHEMATICAL WORD POWER

For each mathematical term, choose the correct meaning.

1. system of equations
   a. a systematic method for classifying equations
   b. a method for solving an equation
   c. two or more equations
   d. the properties of equality

2. independent linear system
   a. a system with exactly one solution
   b. an equation that is satisfied by every real number
   c. equations that are identical
   d. a system of lines

3. inconsistent system
   a. a system with no solution
   b. a system of inconsistent equations
   c. a system that is incorrect
   d. a system that we are not sure how to solve

4. dependent system
   a. a system that is independent
   b. a system that depends on a variable
   c. a system that has no solution
   d. a system for which the graphs coincide

5. substitution method
   a. replacing the variables by the correct answer
   b. a method of eliminating a variable by substituting one equation into the other
   c. the replacement method
   d. any method of solving a system

6. addition method
   a. adding the same number to each side of an equation
   b. adding fractions
   c. eliminating a variable by adding two equations
   d. the sum of a number and its additive inverse is zero

7. linear equation in three variables
   a. $Ax + By + Cz = D$ with A, B, and C not all zero
   b. $Ax + By = C$ with A and B not both zero
   c. the equation of a line
   d. $A/x + B/y = C$ with A and B not both zero

8. matrix
   a. a television screen
   b. a maze
   c. a rectangular array of numbers
   d. coordinates in four dimensions

9. **augmented matrix**
   a. a matrix with a power booster
   b. a matrix with no solution
   c. a square matrix
   d. a matrix containing the coefficients and constants of a system of equations

10. **order**
   a. the length of a matrix
   b. the number of rows and columns in a matrix
   c. the highest power of a matrix
   d. the lowest power of a matrix

11. **determinant**
   a. a number corresponding to a square matrix
   b. a number that is determined by any matrix
   c. the first entry of a matrix
   d. a number that determines whether a matrix has a solution

12. **sign array**
   a. the signs of the entries of a matrix
   b. the sign of the determinant
   c. the signs of the answers
   d. a matrix of $+$ and $-$ signs used in computing a determinant

REVIEW EXERCISES

4.1 *Solve by graphing. Indicate whether each system is independent, inconsistent, or dependent.*

1. $y = 2x - 1$
   $x + y = 2$

2. $y = 3x - 4$
   $y = -2x + 1$

3. $x + 2y = 4$
   $y = -\frac{1}{2}x + 2$

4. $2x - 3y = 12$
   $3y - 2x = -12$

5. $y = -x$
   $y = -x + 3$

6. $3x - y = 4$
   $3x - y = 0$

Solve each system by the substitution method. Indicate whether each system is independent, inconsistent, or dependent.

7. $y = 3x + 11$
   $3x + 3y = 0$

8. $x - y = 3$
   $3x - 2y = 3$

9. $x = y + 5$
   $2x - 2y = 12$

10. $3y = x + 5$
    $3x - 9y = -10$

11. $2x - y = 3$
    $6x - 9 = 3y$

12. $y = \frac{1}{2}x - 9$
    $3x - 6y = 54$

13. $y = \frac{1}{2}x - 3$
    $y = \frac{1}{3}x + 2$

14. $x = \frac{1}{8}y - 1$
    $y = \frac{1}{4}x + 39$

15. $x + 2y = 1$
    $8x + 6y = 4$

16. $x - 5y = 4$
    $4x + 8y = -5$

4.2 *Solve each system by the addition method. Indicate whether each system is independent, inconsistent, or dependent.*

17. $5x - 3y = -20$
    $3x + 2y = 7$

18. $-3x + y = 3$
    $2x - 3y = 5$

19. $2(y - 5) + 4 = 3(x - 6)$
    $3x - 2y = 12$

20. $x + 3(y - 1) = 11$
    $2(x - y) + 8y = 28$

Study Tip

Note how the review exercises are arranged according to the sections in this chapter. If you are having trouble with a certain type of problem, refer back to the appropriate section for examples and explanations.

21. $3x - 4(y - 5) = x + 2$
    $2y - x = 7$

22. $4(1 - x) + y = 3$
    $3(1 - y) - 4x = -4y$

23. $\frac{1}{4}x + \frac{3}{8}y = \frac{3}{8}$
    $\frac{5}{2}x - 6y = 7$

24. $\frac{1}{3}x - \frac{1}{6}y = \frac{1}{3}$
    $\frac{1}{6}x + \frac{1}{4}y = 0$

25. $0.4x + 0.06y = 11.6$
    $0.8x - 0.05y = 13$

26. $0.08x + 0.7y = 37.4$
    $0.06x - 0.05y = -0.7$

4.3 *Solve each system by elimination of variables.*

27. $x - y + z = 4$
    $-x + 2y - z = 0$
    $-x + y - 3z = -16$

28. $2x - y + z = 5$
    $x + y - 2z = -4$
    $3x - y + 3z = 10$

29. $2x - y - z = 3$
$3x + y + 2z = 4$
$4x + 2y - z = -4$

30. $2x + 3y - 2z = -11$
$3x - 2y + 3z = 7$
$x - 4y + 4z = 14$

31. $x - 3y + z = 5$
$2x - 4y - z = 7$
$2x - 6y + 2z = 6$

32. $x - y + z = 1$
$2x - 2y + 2z = 2$
$-3x + 3y - 3z = -3$

4.4 *Solve each system by the Gauss-Jordan elimination method.*

33. $x + y = 7$
$-x + 2y = 5$

34. $-x + y = 1$
$2x - 3y = -7$

35. $2x + y = 0$
$x - 3y = 14$

36. $2x - y = 8$
$3x + 2y = -2$

37. $x + y - z = 0$
$x - y + 2z = 4$
$2x + y - z = 1$

38. $2x - y + 2z = 9$
$x + 3y = 5$
$3x + z = 9$

4.5 *Evaluate each determinant.*

39. $\begin{vmatrix} 1 & 3 \\ 0 & 2 \end{vmatrix}$

40. $\begin{vmatrix} -1 & 2 \\ -3 & 5 \end{vmatrix}$

41. $\begin{vmatrix} 0.01 & 0.02 \\ 50 & 80 \end{vmatrix}$

42. $\begin{vmatrix} \dfrac{1}{2} & \dfrac{1}{3} \\ \dfrac{1}{4} & \dfrac{1}{5} \end{vmatrix}$

Solve each system. Use Cramer's rule.

43. $2x - y = 0$
$3x + y = -5$

44. $3x - 2y = 14$
$2x + 3y = -8$

45. $y = 2x - 3$
$3x - 2y = 4$

46. $y = 2x - 5$
$y = 3x - 3y$

Evaluate each determinant.

47. $\begin{vmatrix} 2 & 3 & 1 \\ -1 & 2 & 4 \\ 6 & 1 & 1 \end{vmatrix}$

48. $\begin{vmatrix} 1 & -1 & 0 \\ -2 & 0 & 0 \\ 3 & 1 & 5 \end{vmatrix}$

49. $\begin{vmatrix} 2 & 3 & -2 \\ 2 & 0 & 4 \\ -1 & 0 & 3 \end{vmatrix}$

50. $\begin{vmatrix} 3 & -1 & 4 \\ 2 & -1 & 1 \\ -2 & 0 & 1 \end{vmatrix}$

Solve each system. Use Cramer's rule.

51. $x + y = 3$
$x + y + z = 0$
$x - y - z = 2$

52. $2x - y + z = 0$
$4x + 6y - 2z = 0$
$x - 2y - z = -9$

4.6 *Graph eac\h system of inequalities and identify each vertex of the region.*

53. $x \geq 0, y \geq 0$
$x + 2y \leq 6$
$x + y \leq 5$

54. $x \geq 0, y \geq 0$
$3x + 2y \geq 12$
$x + 2y \geq 8$

Solve each problem by linear programming.

55. Find the maximum value of the function $R(x, y) = 6x + 9y$ subject to the following constraints:

$$x \geq 0, y \geq 0$$
$$2x + y \leq 6$$
$$x + 2y \leq 6$$

56. Find the minimum value of the function $C(x, y) = 9x + 10y$ subject to the following constraints:

$$x \geq 0, y \geq 0$$
$$x + y \geq 4$$
$$3x + y \geq 6$$

MISCELLANEOUS

Use a system of equations in two or three variables to solve each word problem. Solve by the method of your choice.

57. *Two-digit number.* The sum of the digits in a two-digit number is 15. When the digits are reversed, the new number is 9 more than the original number. What is the original number?

58. *Two-digit number.* The sum of the digits in a two-digit number is 8. When the digits are reversed, the new number is 18 less than the original number. What is the original number?

59. *Traveling by boat.* Alonzo can travel from his camp downstream to the mouth of the river in 30 minutes. If it takes him 45 minutes to come back, then how long would it take him to go that same distance in the lake with no current?

Time with current = 30 min
Time against current = 45 min

FIGURE FOR EXERCISE 59

60. *Driving and dating.* In 4 years Gasper will be old enough to drive. His parents said that he must have a driver's license for 2 years before he can date. Three years ago, Gasper's age was only one-half of the age necessary to date. How old must Gasper be to drive, and how old is he now?

61. *Three solutions.* A chemist has three solutions of acid that must be mixed to obtain 20 liters of a solution that is 38% acid. Solution A is 30% acid, solution B is 20% acid, and solution C is 60% acid. Because of another chemical in these solutions, the chemist must keep the ratio of solution C to solution A at 2 to 1. How many liters of each should she mix together?

62. *Mixing investments.* Darlene invested a total of $20,000. The part that she invested in Dell Computer stock returned 70% and the part that she invested in U.S. Treasury bonds returned 5%. Her total return on these two investments was $9,580.
   a) Use the accompanying graph to estimate the amount that she put into each investment.
   b) Solve a system of equations to find the exact amount that she put into each investment.

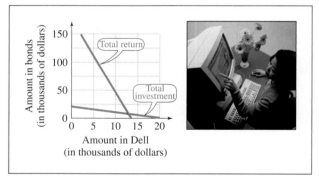

FIGURE FOR EXERCISE 62

63. *Beets and beans.* One serving of canned beets contains 1 gram of protein and 6 grams of carbohydrates. One serving of canned red beans contains 6 grams of protein and 20 grams of carbohydrates. How many servings of each would it take to get exactly 21 grams of protein and 78 grams of carbohydrates?

CHAPTER 4 TEST

Solve the system by graphing.

1. $x + y = 4$
$\quad y = 2x + 1$

Solve each system by substitution.

2. $y = 2x - 8$
$\quad 4x + 3y = 1$

3. $y = x - 5$
$\quad 3x - 4(y - 2) = 28 - x$

Solve each system by the addition method.

4. $3x + 2y = 3$
$\quad 4x - 3y = -13$

5. $\quad 3x - y = 5$
$\quad -6x + 2y = 1$

Determine whether each system is independent, inconsistent, or dependent.

6. $y = 3x - 5$
$\quad y = 3x + 2$

7. $2x + 2y = 8$
$\quad x + y = 4$

8. $y = 2x - 3$
$\quad y = 5x - 14$

Solve the following system by elimination of variables.

9. $x + y - z = 2$
$\quad 2x - y + 3z = -5$
$\quad x - 3y + z = 4$

Solve by the Gauss-Jordan elimination method.

10. $3x - y = 1$
$\quad x + 2y = 12$

11. $\quad x - y - z = 1$
$-x - y + 2z = -2$
$\quad -x - 3y + z = -5$

Evaluate each determinant.

12. $\begin{vmatrix} 2 & 3 \\ 4 & -3 \end{vmatrix}$

13. $\begin{vmatrix} 1 & -2 & -1 \\ 2 & 3 & 1 \\ 1 & 1 & 0 \end{vmatrix}$

Solve each system by using Cramer's rule.

14. $2x - y = -4$
$\quad 3x + y = -1$

15. $\quad x + y \qquad = 0$
$\quad x - y + 2z = 6$
$2x + y - z = 1$

Study Tip

Before you take an in-class exam on this chapter, work the sample test given here. Set aside one hour to work this test and use the answers in the back of this book to grade yourself. Even though your instructor might not ask exactly the same questions, you will get a good idea of your test readiness.

For each problem, write a system of equations in two or three variables. Use the method of your choice to solve each system.

16. One night the manager of the Sea Breeze Motel rented 5 singles and 12 doubles for a total of $390. The next night he rented 9 singles and 10 doubles for a total of $412. What is the rental charge for each type of room?

17. Jill, Karen, and Betsy studied a total of 93 hours last week. Jill's and Karen's study time totaled only one-half as much as Betsy's. If Jill studied 3 hours more than Karen, then how many hours did each one of the girls spend studying?

Solve the following problem by linear programming.

18. Find the maximum value of the function

$$P(x, y) = 8x + 10y$$

subject to the following constraints:

$$x \geq 0, y \geq 0$$
$$2x + 3y \leq 12$$
$$x + y \leq 5$$

Simplify each expression.

1. -3^4

2. $\dfrac{1}{3}(3) + 6$

3. $(-5)^2 - 4(-2)(6)$

4. $6 - (0.2)(0.3)$

5. $5(t - 3) - 6(t - 2)$

6. $0.1(x - 1) - (x - 1)$

7. $\dfrac{-9x^2 - 6x + 3}{-3}$

8. $\dfrac{4y - 6}{2} - \dfrac{3y - 9}{3}$

Solve each equation for y.

9. $3x - 5y = 7$

10. $Cx - Dy = W$

11. $Cy = Wy - K$

12. $A = \dfrac{1}{2}b(w - y)$

Solve each system.

13. $y = x - 5$
$2x + 3y = 5$

14. $0.05x + 0.06y = 67$
$x + y = 1200$

15. $3x - 15y = -51$
$x + 17 = 5y$

16. $0.07a + 0.3b = 6.70$
$7a + 30b = 67$

Find the equation of each line.

17. The line through $(0, 55)$ and $(-99, 0)$

18. The line through $(2, -3)$ and $(-4, 8)$

19. The line through $(-4, 6)$ that is parallel to $y = 5x$

20. The line through $(4, 7)$ that is perpendicular to
$y = -2x + 1$

21. The line through $(3, 5)$ that is parallel to the *x*-axis

22. The line through $(-7, 0)$ that is perpendicular to the *x*-axis

Study Tip

Don't wait until the final exam to review material. Do some review on a regular basis. The Making Connections exercises on this page can be used to review, compare, and contrast different concepts that you have studied. A good time to work these exercises is between a test and the start of new material.

Solve.

23. ***Comparing copiers.*** A self-employed consultant has prepared the accompanying graph to compare the total cost of purchasing and using two different copy machines.

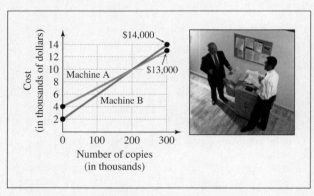

FIGURE FOR EXERCISE 23

a) Which machine has the larger purchase price?
b) What is the per copy cost for operating each machine, not including the purchase price?
c) Find the slope of each line and interpret your findings.
d) Find the equation of each line.
e) Find the number of copies for which the total cost is the same for both machines.

Exponents and Polynomials

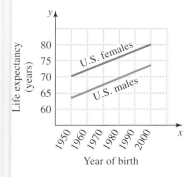

Year of birth

O ne statistic that can be used to measure the general health of a nation or group within a nation is life expectancy. This data is considered more accurate than many other statistics because it is easy to determine the precise number of years in a person's lifetime.

According to the National Center for Health Statistics, an American born in 2002 has a life expectancy of 77.5 years. However, an American male born in 2002 has a life expectancy of only 74.5 years, whereas a female can expect 80.3 years. A male who makes it to 65 can expect to live 15.9 more years, whereas a female who makes it to 65 can expect 17.8 more years. In the next few years, thanks in part to advances in health care and science, longevity is expected to increase significantly worldwide. In fact, the World Health Organization predicts that by 2025 no country will have a life expectancy of less than 50 years.

In this chapter we study algebraic expressions involving exponents. In Exercises 95 and 96 of Section 5.2 you will see how formulas involving exponents can be used to find the life expectancies of men and women.

5.1 INTEGRAL EXPONENTS AND SCIENTIFIC NOTATION

In Chapter 1 we defined positive integral exponents and learned to evaluate expressions involving exponents. In this section we will extend the definition of exponents to include all integers and to learn some rules for working with integral exponents. In Chapter 7 we will see that any rational number can be used as an exponent.

Positive and Negative Exponents

Positive integral exponents provide a convenient way to write repeated multiplication or very large numbers. For example,

$$2 \cdot 2 \cdot 2 = 2^3, \qquad y \cdot y \cdot y \cdot y = y^4, \qquad \text{and} \qquad 1{,}000{,}000{,}000 = 10^9.$$

We refer to 2^3 as "2 cubed," "2 raised to the third power," or "a power of 2."

Positive Integral Exponents

If a is a nonzero real number and n is a positive integer, then

$$a^n = \underbrace{a \cdot a \cdot a \cdot \ldots \cdot a.}_{n \text{ factors of } a}$$

In the **exponential expression** a^n, the **base** is a, and the **exponent** is n.

We use 2^{-3} to represent the reciprocal of 2^3. Because $2^3 = 8$, we have $2^{-3} = \frac{1}{8}$. In general, a^{-n} is defined as the reciprocal of a^n.

Negative Integral Exponents

If a is a nonzero real number and n is a positive integer, then

$$a^{-n} = \frac{1}{a^n}. \qquad \text{If } n \text{ is positive, } -n \text{ is negative.}$$

Helpful Hint

A negative exponent does not cause an expression to have a negative value. The negative exponent "causes" the reciprocal:

$$2^{-3} = \frac{1}{2^3} = \frac{1}{8},$$

$$(-3)^{-4} = \frac{1}{(-3)^4} = \frac{1}{81},$$

$$(-4)^{-3} = \frac{1}{(-4)^3} = -\frac{1}{64}.$$

To evaluate 2^{-3}, you can first cube 2 to get 8 and then find the reciprocal to get $\frac{1}{8}$, or you can first find the reciprocal of 2 $\left(\text{which is } \frac{1}{2}\right)$ and then cube $\frac{1}{2}$ to get $\frac{1}{8}$. So

$$2^{-3} = \frac{1}{2^3} = \left(\frac{1}{2}\right)^3 = \frac{1}{8}.$$

The power and the reciprocal can be found in either order. If the exponent is -1, we simply find the reciprocal. For example,

$$2^{-1} = \frac{1}{2}, \qquad \left(\frac{2}{3}\right)^{-1} = \frac{3}{2}, \qquad \text{and} \qquad \left(-\frac{1}{4}\right)^{-1} = -4.$$

If an expression with a negative exponent is a denominator, then we can rewrite the expression as follows:

$$\frac{1}{2^{-3}} = \frac{1}{\frac{1}{2^3}} = 1 \cdot \frac{2^3}{1} = 2^3.$$

So $2^{-3} = \dfrac{1}{2^3}$ and $\dfrac{1}{2^{-3}} = 2^3$. These examples illustrate the following rules.

Rules for Negative Exponents

If a and b are nonzero real numbers and n is a positive integer, then

$$\left(\frac{a}{b}\right)^{-n} = \left(\frac{b}{a}\right)^{n}, \qquad a^{-n} = \left(\frac{1}{a}\right)^{n}, \qquad a^{-1} = \frac{1}{a}, \qquad \text{and} \qquad \frac{1}{a^{-n}} = a^{n}.$$

E X A M P L E   1

Negative exponents

Evaluate each expression.

a) 3^{-2} b) $(-3)^{-2}$ c) -3^{-2} d) $\left(\dfrac{3}{4}\right)^{-3}$ e) $\dfrac{1}{5^{-3}}$

Calculator Close-Up

You can evaluate expressions with negative exponents using a graphing calculator. Use the fraction feature to get fractional answers.

```
3^-2►Frac
               1/9
(-3)^-2►Frac
               1/9
-3^-2►Frac
              -1/9
```

Solution

a) $3^{-2} = \dfrac{1}{3^2}$ Definition of negative exponent

$\phantom{3^{-2}} = \dfrac{1}{9}$ Since $3^2 = 9$

b) $(-3)^{-2} = \dfrac{1}{(-3)^2}$ Definition of negative exponent

$\phantom{(-3)^{-2}} = \dfrac{1}{9}$ Since $(-3)^2 = (-3)(-3) = 9$

c) $-3^{-2} = -\dfrac{1}{3^2}$ The negative exponent applies to 3 only.

$\phantom{-3^{-2}} = -\dfrac{1}{9}$ Since $3^2 = 9$

d) By the first rule of negative exponents we can find the reciprocal of $\dfrac{3}{4}$ and then cube:

$$\left(\frac{3}{4}\right)^{-3} = \left(\frac{4}{3}\right)^{3}$$

$$= \frac{64}{27}$$

e) Using the fourth rule for negative exponents we can simply write $\dfrac{1}{5^{-3}} = 5^3 = 125$. We could also evaluate as follows:

$$\frac{1}{5^{-3}} = \frac{1}{\dfrac{1}{5^3}}$$

$$= 1 \cdot \frac{5^3}{1}$$

$$= 125$$

■

CAUTION   In Chapter 1 we agreed to evaluate -3^2 by squaring 3 first and then taking the opposite. So $-3^2 = -9$, whereas $(-3)^2 = 9$. The same agreement also holds for negative exponents. That is why the answer to Example 1(c) is negative.

Product Rule

We can simplify an expression such as $2^3 \cdot 2^5$ using the definition of exponents.

$$2^3 \cdot 2^5 = \overbrace{(2 \cdot 2 \cdot 2)}^{\text{three 2's}}\overbrace{(2 \cdot 2 \cdot 2 \cdot 2 \cdot 2)}^{\text{five 2's}} = 2^8$$

$$\underbrace{}_{\text{eight 2's}}$$

Notice that the exponent 8 is the sum of the exponents 3 and 5. This example illustrates the **product rule for exponents.**

> ### Product Rule for Exponents
>
> If m and n are integers and $a \neq 0$, then
> $$a^m \cdot a^n = a^{m+n}.$$

EXAMPLE 2

Using the product rule

Simplify each expression. Write answers with positive exponents and assume all variables represent nonzero real numbers.

a) $3^4 \cdot 3^6$ **b)** $4x^{-3} \cdot 5x$ **c)** $-2y^{-3}(-5y^{-4})$

Solution

a) $3^4 \cdot 3^6 = 3^{4+6} = 3^{10}$ Product rule

b) $4x^{-3} \cdot 5x = 4 \cdot 5 \cdot x^{-3} \cdot x^1$

$\qquad\qquad = 20x^{-2}$ Product rule: $x^{-3} \cdot x^1 = x^{-3+1} = x^{-2}$

$\qquad\qquad = \dfrac{20}{x^2}$ Definition of negative exponent

c) $-2y^{-3}(-5y^{-4}) = (-2)(-5)y^{-3}y^{-4}$

$\qquad\qquad\qquad = 10y^{-7}$ Product rule: $-3 + (-4) = -7$

$\qquad\qquad\qquad = \dfrac{10}{y^7}$ Definition of negative exponent ∎

CAUTION The product rule cannot be applied to $2^3 \cdot 3^2$ because the bases are not identical. Even when the bases are identical, we do not multiply the bases. For example, $2^5 \cdot 2^4 \neq 4^9$. Using the rule correctly, we get $2^5 \cdot 2^4 = 2^9$.

Zero Exponent

We have used positive and negative integral exponents, but we have not yet seen the integer 0 used as an exponent. Note that the product rule was stated to hold for *any* integers m and n. If we use the product rule on $2^3 \cdot 2^{-3}$, we get

$$2^3 \cdot 2^{-3} = 2^0.$$

However, $2^3 \cdot 2^{-3} = 2^3 \cdot \dfrac{1}{2^3} = 8 \cdot \dfrac{1}{8} = 1$. So for consistency we define 2^0 and the zero power of any nonzero number to be 1.

> ### Zero Exponent
>
> If a is any nonzero real number, then $a^0 = 1$.

E X A M P L E   3

Using zero as an exponent

Simplify each expression. Write answers with positive exponents and assume all variables represent nonzero real numbers.

a) -3^0 b) $\left(\frac{1}{4} - \frac{3}{2}\right)^0$ c) $-2a^5b^{-6} \cdot 3a^{-5}b^2$

Helpful Hint

Defining a^0 to be 1 gives a consistent pattern to exponents:

$$3^{-2} = \frac{1}{9}$$

$$3^{-1} = \frac{1}{3}$$

$$3^0 = 1$$

$$3^1 = 3$$

$$3^2 = 9$$

If the exponent is increased by 1 (with base 3) the value of the expression is multiplied by 3.

Solution

a) To evaluate -3^0, we find 3^0 and then take the opposite. So $-3^0 = -1$.

b) $\left(\frac{1}{4} - \frac{3}{2}\right)^0 = 1$ Definition of zero exponent

c) $-2a^5b^{-6} \cdot 3a^{-5}b^2 = -6a^5 \cdot a^{-5} \cdot b^{-6} \cdot b^2$

$$= -6a^0b^{-4}$$ Product rule

$$= -\frac{6}{b^4}$$ Definitions of negative and zero exponent ■

Changing the Sign of an Exponent

Because a^{-n} and a^n are reciprocals of each other, we know that

$$a^{-n} = \frac{1}{a^n} \qquad \text{and} \qquad \frac{1}{a^{-n}} = a^n.$$

So a negative exponent in the numerator or denominator can be changed to positive by relocating the exponential expression. In Example 4 we use these facts to remove negative exponents from exponential expressions.

E X A M P L E   4

Simplifying expressions with negative exponents

Write each expression without negative exponents and simplify. All variables represent nonzero real numbers.

a) $\dfrac{5a^{-3}}{a^2 \cdot 2^{-2}}$ b) $\dfrac{-2x^{-3}}{y^{-2}z^3}$

Solution

a) $\dfrac{5a^{-3}}{a^2 \cdot 2^{-2}} = 5 \cdot a^{-3} \cdot \dfrac{1}{a^2} \cdot \dfrac{1}{2^{-2}}$ Rewrite division as multiplication.

$$= 5 \cdot \frac{1}{a^3} \cdot \frac{1}{a^2} \cdot 2^2$$ Change the signs of the negative exponents.

$$= \frac{20}{a^5}$$ Product rule: $a^3 \cdot a^2 = a^5$

Note that in $5a^{-3}$ the negative exponent applies only to a.

b) $\dfrac{-2x^{-3}}{y^{-2}z^3} = -2 \cdot x^{-3} \cdot \dfrac{1}{y^{-2}} \cdot \dfrac{1}{z^3}$ Rewrite as multiplication.

$$= -2 \cdot \frac{1}{x^3} \cdot y^2 \cdot \frac{1}{z^3}$$ Definition of negative exponent

$$= \frac{-2y^2}{x^3z^3}$$ Simplify. ■

In Example 4 we showed more steps than are necessary. For instance, in part (b) we could simply write

$$\frac{-2x^{-3}}{y^{-2}z^3} = \frac{-2y^2}{x^3z^3}.$$

Exponential expressions (that are factors) can be moved from numerator to denominator (or vice versa) as long as we change the sign of the exponent.

Calculator Close-Up

A graphing calculator cannot prove that the quotient rule is correct, but it can provide numerical support for the quotient rule.

```
2^15/2^5
            1024
2^10
            1024
```

C A U T I O N   If an exponential expression is *not* a factor, you *cannot* move it from numerator to denominator (or vice versa). For example,

$$\frac{2^{-1} + 1^{-1}}{1^{-1}} \neq \frac{1}{2 + 1}.$$

Because $2^{-1} = \frac{1}{2}$ and $1^{-1} = 1$, we get

$$\frac{2^{-1} + 1^{-1}}{1^{-1}} = \frac{\frac{1}{2} + 1}{1} = \frac{\frac{3}{2}}{1} = \frac{3}{2} \qquad \text{not} \qquad \frac{1}{2 + 1} = \frac{1}{3}.$$

Quotient Rule

We can use arithmetic to simplify the quotient of two exponential expressions. For example,

$$\frac{2^5}{2^3} = \frac{2 \cdot 2 \cdot 2 \cdot 2 \cdot 2}{2 \cdot 2 \cdot 2} = 2^2.$$

There are five 2's in the numerator and three 2's in the denominator. After dividing, two 2's remain. The exponent in 2^2 can be obtained by subtracting the exponents 3 and 5. This example illustrates the **quotient rule for exponents.**

Quotient Rule for Exponents

If m and n are any integers and $a \neq 0$, then

$$\frac{a^m}{a^n} = a^{m-n}.$$

C A U T I O N   Do not divide the bases when using the quotient rule. We cannot apply the quotient rule to $\frac{6^5}{2^4}$ even though 6 is divisible by 2.

E X A M P L E   5

Using the quotient rule

Simplify each expression. Write answers with positive exponents only. All variables represent nonzero real numbers.

a) $\dfrac{2^9}{2^4}$ 　　　　　　　**b)** $\dfrac{m^5}{m^{-3}}$ 　　　　　　　**c)** $\dfrac{y^{-4}}{y^{-2}}$

Solution

a) $\dfrac{2^9}{2^4} = 2^{9-4}$ 　　Quotient rule

$\phantom{\dfrac{2^9}{2^4}} = 2^5$ 　　Simplify the exponent.

b) $\dfrac{m^5}{m^{-3}} = m^{5-(-3)}$ Quotient rule

$\quad\quad = m^8$ Simplify the exponent.

c) $\dfrac{y^{-4}}{y^{-2}} = y^{-4-(-2)}$ Quotient rule

$\quad\quad = y^{-2}$ Simplify the exponent.

$\quad\quad = \dfrac{1}{y^2}$ Rewrite with a positive exponent.   ■

Example 6 further illustrates the rules of exponents. Remember that the bases must be identical for the quotient rule or the product rule.

E X A M P L E   6   **Using the product and quotient rules**

Use the rules of exponents to simplify each expression. Write answers with positive exponents only. All variables represent nonzero real numbers.

a) $\dfrac{2x^{-7}}{x^{-7}}$ **b)** $\dfrac{w(2w^{-4})}{3w^{-2}}$ **c)** $\dfrac{x^{-1}x^{-3}y^5}{x^{-2}y^2}$

Solution

a) $\dfrac{2x^{-7}}{x^{-7}} = 2x^0$ Quotient rule: $-7 - (-7) = 0$

$\quad\quad = 2$ Definition of zero exponent

b) $\dfrac{w(2w^{-4})}{3w^{-2}} = \dfrac{2w^{-3}}{3w^{-2}}$ Product rule: $w^1 \cdot w^{-4} = w^{-3}$

$\quad\quad = \dfrac{2w^{-1}}{3}$ Quotient rule: $-3 - (-2) = -1$

$\quad\quad = \dfrac{2}{3w}$ Definition of negative exponent

c) $\dfrac{x^{-1}x^{-3}y^5}{x^{-2}y^2} = \dfrac{x^{-4}y^5}{x^{-2}y^2}$ Product rule

$\quad\quad = x^{-2}y^3$ Quotient rule

$\quad\quad = \dfrac{y^3}{x^2}$ Rewrite x^{-2} with a positive exponent.   ■

Scientific Notation

Many of the numbers that are encountered in science are either very large or very small. For example, the distance from the earth to the sun is 93,000,000 miles, and a hydrogen atom weighs 0.00000000000000000000000017 gram. Scientific notation provides a convenient way of writing very large and very small numbers. In scientific notation the distance from the earth to the sun is 9.3×10^7 miles and a hydrogen atom weighs 1.7×10^{-24} gram. In scientific notation the times symbol, $\times$, is used to indicate multiplication. Converting a number from scientific notation to standard notation is simply a matter of multiplication.

EXAMPLE 7

Scientific notation to standard notation

Write each number using standard notation.

a) 7.62×10^5 **b)** 6.35×10^{-4}

Calculator Close-Up

In normal mode, display a number in scientific notation and press ENTER to convert to standard notation. You can use a power of 10 or the EE key to get the E for the built-in scientific notation.

```
7.62E5
           762000
7.62*10^5
           762000
```

Solution

a) Multiplying a number by 10^5 moves the decimal point five places to the right:

$$7.62 \times 10^5 = 762000. = 762,000$$

b) Multiplying a number by 10^{-4} or 0.0001 moves the decimal point four places to the left:

$$6.35 \times 10^{-4} = 0.000635 = 0.000635$$ ■

The procedure for converting a number from scientific notation to standard notation is summarized as follows.

> **Strategy for Converting from Scientific Notation to Standard Notation**
>
> 1. Determine the number of places to move the decimal point by examining the exponent on the 10.
> 2. Move to the right for a positive exponent and to the left for a negative exponent.

A positive number in scientific notation is written as a product of a number between 1 and 10, and a power of 10. Numbers in scientific notation are written with only one digit to the left of the decimal point. A number larger than 10 is written with a positive power of 10, and a positive number smaller than 1 is written with a negative power of 10. Note that 1000 (a power of 10) could be written as 1×10^3 or simply 10^3. Numbers between 1 and 10 are usually not written in scientific notation. To convert to scientific notation, we reverse the strategy for converting from scientific notation.

> **Strategy for Converting from Standard Notation to Scientific Notation**
>
> 1. Count the number of places (n) that the decimal point must be moved so that it will follow the first nonzero digit of the number.
> 2. If the original number was larger than 10, use 10^n.
> 3. If the original number was smaller than 1, use 10^{-n}.

EXAMPLE 8

Standard notation to scientific notation

Convert each number to scientific notation.

a) 934,000,000   **b)** 0.0000025

Calculator Close-Up

To convert standard notation to scientific notation, display the number with the calculator in scientific mode (Sci) and then press ENTER. In scientific mode all results are given in scientific notation.

Solution

a) In 934,000,000 the decimal point must be moved eight places to the left to get it to follow 9, the first nonzero digit.

$$934{,}000{,}000 = 9.34 \times 10^8 \quad \text{Use 8 because } 934{,}000{,}000 > 10.$$

b) The decimal point in 0.0000025 must be moved six places to the right to get the 2 to the left of the decimal point.

$$0.0000025 = 2.5 \times 10^{-6} \quad \text{Use } -6 \text{ because } 0.0000025 < 1. \quad \blacksquare$$

We can perform computations with numbers in scientific notation by using the rules of exponents on the powers of 10.

EXAMPLE 9

Using scientific notation in computations

Evaluate each expression without using a calculator. Express each answer in scientific notation.

a) $(2 \times 10^7)(6.3 \times 10^{-11})$ b) $\dfrac{7 \times 10^{13}}{2 \times 10^6}$ c) $\dfrac{(10{,}000)(0.000025)}{0.000005}$

Calculator Close-Up

If you use powers of 10 to perform the computation in Example 9, you will need parentheses as shown. If you use the built-in scientific notation you don't need parentheses.

```
1E4*2.5E-5/5E-6
            5E4
(1*10^4)*(2.5*10
^-5)/(5*10^-6)
            5E4
```

Solution

a) $(2 \times 10^7)(6.3 \times 10^{-11}) = 2 \cdot 6.3 \cdot 10^7 \cdot 10^{-11}$
$$= 12.6 \times 10^{-4}$$
$$= 1.26 \times 10^1 \times 10^{-4}$$
$$= 1.26 \times 10^{-3}$$

b) $\dfrac{7 \times 10^{13}}{2 \times 10^6} = \dfrac{7}{2} \cdot \dfrac{10^{13}}{10^6} = 3.5 \times 10^7$

c) $\dfrac{(10{,}000)(0.000025)}{0.000005} = \dfrac{(1 \times 10^4)(2.5 \times 10^{-5})}{5 \times 10^{-6}}$
$$= \dfrac{2.5}{5} \cdot \dfrac{10^4 \cdot 10^{-5}}{10^{-6}}$$
$$= 0.5 \times 10^5$$
$$= 5 \times 10^{-1} \times 10^5$$
$$= 5 \times 10^4 \quad \blacksquare$$

EXAMPLE 10

Counting hydrogen atoms

If the weight of hydrogen is 1.7×10^{-24} gram per atom, then how many hydrogen atoms are there in one kilogram of hydrogen?

Helpful Hint

You can divide 1×10^3 by 1.7×10^{-24} without a calculator by dividing 1 by 1.7 to get 0.59 and 10^3 by 10^{-24} to get 10^{27}. Then convert

$$0.59 \times 10^{27}$$

to

$$5.9 \times 10^{-1} \times 10^{27}$$

or

$$5.9 \times 10^{26}.$$

Solution

There are 1000 or 1×10^3 grams in one kilogram. So to find the number of hydrogen atoms in one kilogram of hydrogen, we divide 1×10^3 by 1.7×10^{-24}:

$$\dfrac{1 \times 10^3 \text{ g/kg}}{1.7 \times 10^{-24} \text{ g/atom}} \approx 5.9 \times 10^{26} \text{ atom per kilogram (atom/kg)}$$

To divide by grams per atom, we invert and multiply: $\frac{g}{kg} \cdot \frac{atom}{g} = \frac{atom}{kg}$. Keeping track of the units as we did here helps us to be sure that we performed the correct operation. So there are approximately 5.9×10^{26} hydrogen atoms in one kilogram of hydrogen. $\blacksquare$

WARM-UPS

True or false? Explain your answer. Assume that all variables represent nonzero real numbers.

1. $3^5 \cdot 3^4 = 3^9$

2. $2x^{-4} = \dfrac{1}{2x^4}$

3. $10^{-3} = 0.0001$

4. $\dfrac{x^5}{x^{-2}} = x^3$

5. $\dfrac{2^5}{2^{-2}} = 2^7$

6. $2^3 \cdot 5^2 = 10^5$

7. $-2^{-2} = -\dfrac{1}{4}$

8. $46.7 \times 10^5 = 4.67 \times 10^6$

9. $0.512 \times 10^{-3} = 5.12 \times 10^{-4}$

10. $\dfrac{8 \times 10^{30}}{2 \times 10^{-5}} = 4 \times 10^{25}$

5.1 EXERCISES

Reading and Writing *After reading this section, write out the answers to these questions. Use complete sentences.*

1. What is an exponential expression?

2. What is the meaning of a negative exponent?

3. What is the product rule?

4. What is the quotient rule?

5. How do you convert a number from scientific notation to standard notation?

6. How do you convert a number from standard notation to scientific notation?

For all exercises in this section, assume that the variables represent nonzero real numbers and use only positive exponents in your answers.

Evaluate each expression. See Example 1.

7. $2^2, -2^2, (-2)^2, 2^{-2}, -2^{-2}, (-2)^{-2}$

8. $3^2, -3^2, (-3)^2, 3^{-2}, -3^{-2}, (-3)^{-2}$

9. $2^3, -2^3, (-2)^3, 2^{-3}, -2^{-3}, (-2)^{-3}$

10. $4^3, -4^3, (-4)^3, 4^{-3}, -4^{-3}, (-4)^{-3}$

11. $\dfrac{1}{5^2}, \dfrac{1}{-5^2}, \dfrac{1}{(-5)^2}, \dfrac{1}{5^{-2}}, \dfrac{1}{-5^{-2}}, \dfrac{1}{(-5)^{-2}}$

12. $\dfrac{1}{4^2}, \dfrac{1}{-4^2}, \dfrac{1}{(-4)^2}, \dfrac{1}{4^{-2}}, \dfrac{1}{-4^{-2}}, \dfrac{1}{(-4)^{-2}}$

13. $7^1, -7^1, (-7)^1, 7^{-1}, -7^{-1}, (-7)^{-1}$

14. $\left(\dfrac{1}{6}\right)^1, \left(-\dfrac{1}{6}\right)^1, -\left(\dfrac{1}{6}\right)^1, \left(\dfrac{1}{6}\right)^{-1}, \left(-\dfrac{1}{6}\right)^{-1}, -\left(\dfrac{1}{6}\right)^{-1}$

15. $\left(\dfrac{1}{2}\right)^2, \left(-\dfrac{1}{2}\right)^2, -\left(\dfrac{1}{2}\right)^2, \left(\dfrac{1}{2}\right)^{-2}, \left(-\dfrac{1}{2}\right)^{-2}, -\left(\dfrac{1}{2}\right)^{-2}$

16. $\left(\dfrac{1}{3}\right)^2, \left(-\dfrac{1}{3}\right)^2, -\left(\dfrac{1}{3}\right)^2, \left(\dfrac{1}{3}\right)^{-2}, \left(-\dfrac{1}{3}\right)^{-2}, -\left(\dfrac{1}{3}\right)^{-2}$

17. $\left(\dfrac{2}{3}\right)^3, \left(-\dfrac{2}{3}\right)^3, -\left(\dfrac{2}{3}\right)^3, \left(\dfrac{2}{3}\right)^{-3}, \left(-\dfrac{2}{3}\right)^{-3}, -\left(\dfrac{2}{3}\right)^{-3}$

18. $\left(\dfrac{3}{5}\right)^3, \left(-\dfrac{3}{5}\right)^3, -\left(\dfrac{3}{5}\right)^3, \left(\dfrac{3}{5}\right)^{-3}, \left(-\dfrac{3}{5}\right)^{-3}, -\left(\dfrac{3}{5}\right)^{-3}$

Simplify. See Example 2.

19. $2^5 \cdot 2^{12}$ | **20.** $3^{15} \cdot 3^{-3}$

21. $-2x^{-7} \cdot 3x$ | **22.** $-5a \cdot 6a^{-12}$

23. $-7b^{-7}(-3b^{-3})$ | **24.** $-\dfrac{1}{2}w^{-4} \cdot (-6w^{-2})$

Simplify each expression. See Example 3.

25. $3^0, -3^0, (-3)^0, -(-3)^0$

26. $2a^0, -2a^0, (-2a)^0, -2(-a)^0$

27. $(2 + 3)^0, 2^0 + 3^0, (2^0 + 3)^0$

28. $(4 - 9)^0, 4^0 - 9^0, 4^0 - 9$

29. $3st^0, 3(st)^0, (3st)^0$

30. $-4xy^0, -4x^0y, -(4xy)^0$

31. $2w^{-3}(w^7 \cdot w^{-4})$

32. $5y^2z(y^{-3}z^{-1})$

Write each expression without negative exponents and simplify. See Example 4.

33. $\dfrac{2}{4^{-2}}$ | **34.** $\dfrac{5}{10^{-3}}$

35. $\dfrac{3^{-1}}{10^{-2}}$ | **36.** $\dfrac{2y^{-2}}{3^{-1}}$

37. $\dfrac{2x^{-3}(4x)}{5y^{-2}}$ | **38.** $\dfrac{5^{-2}xy^{-3}}{3x^{-2}}$

39. $\dfrac{4^{-2}x^3x^{-6}}{3x^{-3}x^2}$ | **40.** $\dfrac{3y^{-4}y^{-6}}{2^{-3}y^2y^{-7}}$

Simplify each expression. See Examples 5 and 6.

41. $\dfrac{x^5}{x^3}$ | **42.** $\dfrac{a^8}{a^3}$

43. $\dfrac{3^6}{3^{-2}}$ | **44.** $\dfrac{6^2}{6^{-5}}$

45. $\dfrac{4a^{-5}}{12a^{-2}}$ | **46.** $\dfrac{-3a^{-3}}{-21a^{-4}}$

47. $\dfrac{-6w^{-5}}{2w^3}$ | **48.** $\dfrac{10x^{-6}}{-2x^2}$

49. $\dfrac{3^3w^{-2}w^5}{3^{-5}w^{-3}}$ | **50.** $\dfrac{2^{-3}w^5}{2^5w^3w^{-7}}$

51. $\dfrac{3x^{-6} \cdot x^2y^{-1}}{6x^{-5}y^{-2}}$ | **52.** $\dfrac{2r^{-3}t^{-1}}{10r^5t^2 \cdot t^{-3}}$

Use the rules of exponents to simplify each expression.

53. $3^{-1}\left(\dfrac{1}{3}\right)^{-3}$ | **54.** $2^{-2}\left(\dfrac{1}{4}\right)^{-3}$

55. $-2^4 + \left(\dfrac{1}{2}\right)^{-1}$ | **56.** $-3^4 - (-3)^4$

57. $-(-2)^{-3} \cdot 2^{-1}$ | **58.** $-(-3)^{-1} \cdot 9^{-1}$

59. $7 \cdot 2^{-3} - 2 \cdot 4^{-1}$ | **60.** $5 \cdot 3^{-2} - 2 \cdot 5^0 \cdot 3^{-1}$

61. $(1 + 2^{-1})^{-2}$ | **62.** $(2^{-1} + 2^{-1})^{-2}$

63. $-5a^2 \cdot 3a^2$ | **64.** $2x^2 \cdot 5x^{-5}$

65. $5a \cdot a^2 + 3a^{-2} \cdot a^5$ | **66.** $2x^2 \cdot 5y^{-5}$

67. $\dfrac{-3a^5(-2a^{-1})}{6a^3}$ | **68.** $\dfrac{6a(-ab^{-2})}{-2a^2b^{-3}}$

69. $\dfrac{(-3x^3y^2)(-2xy^{-3})}{-9x^2y^{-5}}$

70. $\dfrac{(-2x^{-5}y)(-3xy^6)}{-6x^{-6}y^2}$

71. $\dfrac{2^{-1} + 3^{-1}}{2^{-1}}$ | **72.** $\dfrac{3^{-1} + 4^{-1}}{12^{-1}}$

For each equation, find the integer that can be used as the exponent to make the equation correct.

73. $8 = 2^?$ | **74.** $27 = 3^?$

75. $\dfrac{1}{4} = 2^?$ | **76.** $\dfrac{1}{125} = 5^?$

77. $16 = \left(\dfrac{1}{2}\right)^?$ | **78.** $81 = \left(\dfrac{1}{3}\right)^?$

79. $10^? = 0.001$ | **80.** $10^? = 10,000$

Write each number in standard notation. See Example 7.

81. 4.86×10^8 | **82.** 3.80×10^2

83. 2.37×10^{-6} | **84.** 1.62×10^{-3}

85. 4×10^6 | **86.** 496×10^3

87. 5×10^{-6} | **88.** 48×10^{-3}

Write each number in scientific notation. See Example 8.

89. 320,000 | **90.** 43,298,000

91. 0.00000071 | **92.** 0.00000894

93. 0.0000703 | **94.** 8,200,100

95. 205×10^5 | **96.** 0.403×10^{-9}

Evaluate each expression using scientific notation without a calculator. See Example 9.

97. $(4000)(5000)(0.0003)$

98. $(50,000)(0.00002)(100)$

99. $\dfrac{(5,000,000)(0.0003)}{2000}$

100. $\dfrac{(6000)(0.00004)}{(30,000)(0.002)}$

101. $\dfrac{6 \times 10^{40}}{2 \times 10^{18}}$

102. $\dfrac{4.6 \times 10^{12}}{2.3 \times 10^{5}}$

103. $\dfrac{(-4 \times 10^{5})(6 \times 10^{-9})}{2 \times 10^{-16}}$

104. $\dfrac{(4.8 \times 10^{-3})(5 \times 10^{-8})}{(1.2 \times 10^{-6})(2 \times 10^{12})}$

 Evaluate each expression using a calculator. Write answers in scientific notation. Round the decimal part to three decimal places. See Example 10.

105. $(4.3 \times 10^{9})(3.67 \times 10^{-5})$

106. $(2.34 \times 10^{6})(8.7 \times 10^{5})$

107. $(4.37 \times 10^{-6}) + (8.75 \times 10^{-5})$

108. $(6.72 \times 10^{5}) + (8.98 \times 10^{6})$

109. $\dfrac{(5.6 \times 10^{14})^{2}(3.2 \times 10^{-6})}{(6.4 \times 10^{-3})^{3}}$

110. $\dfrac{(3.51 \times 10^{-6})^{3}(4000)^{5}}{2\pi}$

Solve each problem.

111. *Distance to the sun.* The distance from the earth to the sun is 93 million miles. Express this distance in feet using scientific notation (1 mile = 5,280 feet).

FIGURE FOR EXERCISE 111

112. *Traveling time.* The speed of light is 9.83569×10^{8} feet per second. How long does it take light to get from the sun to the earth? (See Exercise 111.)

113. *Space travel.* How long does it take a spacecraft traveling 1.2×10^{5} kilometers per second to travel 4.6×10^{12} kilometers?

114. *Diameter of a dot.* If the circumference of a very small circle is 2.35×10^{-8} meter, then what is the diameter of the circle?

115. *Solid waste per person.* In 1960 the 1.80863×10^{8} people in the United States generated 8.71×10^{7} tons of municipal solid waste (Environmental Protection Agency, www.epa.gov). How many pounds per person per day were generated in 1960?

FIGURE FOR EXERCISES 115 AND 116

116. *An increasing problem.* According to the EPA, in 2002 the 2.86843×10^{8} people in the United States generated 4.8×10^{11} pounds of solid municipal waste.
a) How many pounds per person per day were generated in 2002?
b) Use the graph to predict the number of pounds per person per day that will be generated in the year 2010.

GETTING MORE INVOLVED

117. *Exploration.* a) Using pairs of integers, find values for m and n for which $2^{m} \cdot 3^{n} = 6^{m+n}$. b) For which values of m and n is it true that $2^{m} \cdot 3^{n} \neq 6^{m+n}$?

118. *Cooperative learning.* Work in a group to find the units digit of 3^{99} and explain how you found it.

119. *Discussion.* What is the difference between $-a^{n}$ and $(-a)^{n}$, where n is an integer? For which values of a and n do they have the same value, and for which values of a and n do they have different values?

120. *Exploration.* If $a + b = a$, then what can you conclude about b? Use scientific notation on your calculator to find $5 \times 10^{20} + 3 \times 10^{6}$. Explain why your calculator displays the answer that it gets.

5.2 THE POWER RULES

In Section 5.1 you learned some of the basic rules for working with exponents. All of the rules of exponents are designed to make it easier to work with exponential expressions. In this section we will extend our list of rules to include three new ones.

Raising an Exponential Expression to a Power

An expression such as $(x^3)^2$ consists of the exponential expression x^3 raised to the power 2. We can use known rules to simplify this expression.

$$(x^3)^2 = x^3 \cdot x^3 \qquad \text{Exponent 2 indicates two factors of } x^3.$$
$$= x^6 \qquad \text{Product rule: } 3 + 3 = 6$$

Note that the exponent 6 is the *product* of the exponents 2 and 3. This example illustrates the **power of a power rule.**

> **Power of a Power Rule**
>
> If m and n are any integers and $a \neq 0$, then
> $$(a^m)^n = a^{mn}.$$

E X A M P L E   1

Using the power of a power rule

Use the rules of exponents to simplify each expression. Write the answer with positive exponents only. Assume all variables represent nonzero real numbers.

a) $(2^3)^5$ **b)** $(x^2)^{-6}$ **c)** $3(y^{-3})^{-2}y^{-5}$ **d)** $\dfrac{(x^2)^{-1}}{(x^{-3})^3}$

Raising a Product to a Power

Consider how we would simplify a product raised to a positive power and a product raised to a negative power using known rules.

$$(2x)^3 = \overbrace{2x \cdot 2x \cdot 2x}^{\text{3 factors of } 2x} = 2^3 \cdot x^3 = 8x^3$$

$$(ay)^{-3} = \frac{1}{(ay)^3} = \frac{1}{(ay)(ay)(ay)} = \frac{1}{a^3y^3} = a^{-3}y^{-3}$$

In each of these cases the original exponent is applied to each factor of the product. These examples illustrate the **power of a product rule.**

> ### Power of a Product Rule
>
> If a and b are nonzero real numbers and n is any integer, then
>
> $$(ab)^n = a^n \cdot b^n.$$

E X A M P L E   2

Using the power of a product rule

Simplify. Assume the variables represent nonzero real numbers. Write the answers with positive exponents only.

a) $(-3x)^4$ b) $(-2x^2)^3$ c) $(3x^{-2}y^3)^{-2}$

Solution

a) $(-3x)^4 = (-3)^4x^4$ Power of a product rule

   $= 81x^4$

b) $(-2x^2)^3 = (-2)^3(x^2)^3$ Power of a product rule

   $= -8x^6$ Power of a power rule

c) $(3x^{-2}y^3)^{-2} = (3)^{-2}(x^{-2})^{-2}(y^3)^{-2}$ Power of a product rule

   $= \dfrac{1}{9}x^4y^{-6}$ Power of a power rule

   $= \dfrac{x^4}{9y^6}$ Rewrite y^{-6} with a positive exponent.   ∎

Calculator Close-Up

Raising a Quotient to a Power

Now consider an example of applying known rules to a power of a quotient:

$$\left(\frac{x}{5}\right)^3 = \frac{x}{5} \cdot \frac{x}{5} \cdot \frac{x}{5} = \frac{x^3}{5^3}$$

We get a similar result with a negative power:

$$\left(\frac{x}{5}\right)^{-3} = \left(\frac{5}{x}\right)^3 = \frac{5}{x} \cdot \frac{5}{x} \cdot \frac{5}{x} = \frac{5^3}{x^3} = \frac{x^{-3}}{5^{-3}}$$

In each of these cases the original exponent applies to both the numerator and denominator. These examples illustrate the **power of a quotient rule.**

> ### Power of a Quotient Rule
>
> If a and b are nonzero real numbers and n is any integer, then
>
> $$\left(\frac{a}{b}\right)^n = \frac{a^n}{b^n}.$$

E X A M P L E   3

Using the power of a quotient rule

Use the rules of exponents to simplify each expression. Write your answers with positive exponents only. Assume the variables are nonzero real numbers.

a) $\left(\dfrac{x}{2}\right)^3$ b) $\left(-\dfrac{2x^3}{3y^2}\right)^3$ c) $\left(\dfrac{x^{-2}}{2^3}\right)^{-1}$ d) $\left(-\dfrac{3}{4x^3}\right)^{-2}$

Helpful Hint

The exponent rules in this section apply to expressions that involve only multiplication and division. This is not too surprising since exponents, multiplication, and division are closely related. Recall that $a^3 = a \cdot a \cdot a$ and $a \div b = a \cdot b^{-1}$.

Solution

a) $\left(\dfrac{x}{2}\right)^3 = \dfrac{x^3}{2^3}$ Power of a quotient rule

$= \dfrac{x^3}{8}$

b) $\left(-\dfrac{2x^3}{3y^2}\right)^3 = \dfrac{(-2)^3 x^9}{3^3 y^6}$ Because $(x^3)^3 = x^9$ and $(y^2)^3 = y^6$

$= \dfrac{-8x^9}{27y^6}$

$= -\dfrac{8x^9}{27y^6}$

c) $\left(\dfrac{x^{-2}}{2^3}\right)^{-1} = \dfrac{x^2}{2^{-3}} = 8x^2$

d) $\left(-\dfrac{3}{4x^3}\right)^{-2} = \dfrac{(-3)^{-2}}{4^{-2}x^{-6}} = \dfrac{4^2 x^6}{(-3)^2} = \dfrac{16x^6}{9}$ ■

A fraction to a negative power can be simplified by using the power of a quotient rule as in Example 3. Another method is to find the reciprocal of the fraction first, then use the power of a quotient rule as shown in Example 4.

E X A M P L E   4

Negative powers of fractions

Simplify. Assume the variables are nonzero real numbers and write the answers with positive exponents only.

a) $\left(\dfrac{3}{4}\right)^{-3}$ **b)** $\left(\dfrac{x^2}{5}\right)^{-2}$ **c)** $\left(-\dfrac{2y^3}{3}\right)^{-2}$

Solution

a) $\left(\dfrac{3}{4}\right)^{-3} = \left(\dfrac{4}{3}\right)^3$ The reciprocal of $\dfrac{3}{4}$ is $\dfrac{4}{3}$.

$= \dfrac{4^3}{3^3}$ Power of a quotient rule

$= \dfrac{64}{27}$

b) $\left(\dfrac{x^2}{5}\right)^{-2} = \left(\dfrac{5}{x^2}\right)^2 = \dfrac{5^2}{(x^2)^2} = \dfrac{25}{x^4}$

c) $\left(-\dfrac{2y^3}{3}\right)^{-2} = \left(-\dfrac{3}{2y^3}\right)^2 = \dfrac{9}{4y^6}$ ■

Variable Exponents

So far, we have used the rules of exponents only on expressions with integral exponents. However, we can use the rules to simplify expressions having variable exponents that represent integers.

E X A M P L E   5

Expressions with variables as exponents

Simplify. Assume the variables represent integers.

a) $3^{4y} \cdot 3^{5y}$ **b)** $(5^{2x})^{3x}$ **c)** $\left(\dfrac{2^n}{3^m}\right)^{5n}$

Solution

a) $3^{4y} \cdot 3^{5y} = 3^{9y}$ Product rule: $4y + 5y = 9y$

b) $(5^{2x})^{3x} = 5^{6x^2}$ Power of a power rule: $2x \cdot 3x = 6x^2$

c) $\left(\dfrac{2^n}{3^m}\right)^{5n} = \dfrac{(2^n)^{5n}}{(3^m)^{5n}}$ Power of a quotient rule

$\qquad\qquad = \dfrac{2^{5n^2}}{3^{5mn}}$ Power of a power rule   ∎

Summary of the Rules

The definitions and rules that were introduced in the last two sections are summarized in the following box.

Rules for Integral Exponents

For these rules m and n are integers and a and b are nonzero real numbers.

1. $a^{-n} = \dfrac{1}{a^n}$ Definition of negative exponent

2. $a^{-n} = \left(\dfrac{1}{a}\right)^n$, $a^{-1} = \dfrac{1}{a}$, and $\dfrac{1}{a^{-n}} = a^n$ Negative exponent rules

3. $a^0 = 1$ Definition of zero exponent

4. $a^m a^n = a^{m+n}$ Product rule

5. $\dfrac{a^m}{a^n} = a^{m-n}$ Quotient rule

6. $(a^m)^n = a^{mn}$ Power of a power rule

7. $(ab)^n = a^n b^n$ Power of a product rule

8. $\left(\dfrac{a}{b}\right)^n = \dfrac{a^n}{b^n}$ Power of a quotient rule

---

Applications

Both positive and negative exponents occur in formulas used in investment situations. The amount of money invested is the **principal,** and the value of the principal after a certain time period is the **amount.** Interest rates are annual percentage rates.

Amount Formula

The amount A of an investment of P dollars with interest rate r compounded annually for n years is given by the formula

$$A = P(1 + r)^n.$$

E X A M P L E   6

Finding the amount

According to Fidelity Investments of Boston, U.S. common stocks have returned an average of 10% annually since 1926. If your great-grandfather had invested $100 in the stock market in 1926 and obtained the average increase each year, then how much would the investment be worth in the year 2006 after 80 years of growth?

Solution

Use $n = 80$, $P = \$100$, and $r = 0.10$ in the amount formula:

$$A = P(1 + r)^n$$
$$A = 100(1 + 0.10)^{80}$$
$$= 100(1.1)^{80}$$
$$= 204{,}840.02$$

So $100 invested in 1926 would have amounted to $204,840.02 in 2006.   ■

When we are interested in the principal that must be invested today to grow to a certain amount, the principal is called the **present value** of the investment. We can find a formula for present value by solving the amount formula for P:

$$A = P(1 + r)^n$$

$$P = \frac{A}{(1 + r)^n} \qquad \text{Divide each side by } (1 + r)^n.$$

$$P = A(1 + r)^{-n} \qquad \text{Definition of a negative exponent}$$

Present Value Formula

The present value P that will amount to A dollars after n years with interest compounded annually at annual interest rate r is given by

$$P = A(1 + r)^{-n}.$$

E X A M P L E   7

Finding the present value

If your great-grandfather wanted you to have $1,000,000 in 2006, then how much could he have invested in the stock market in 1926 to achieve this goal? Assume he could get the average annual return of 10% (from Example 6) for 80 years.

Solution

Use $r = 0.10$, $n = 80$, and $A = 1{,}000{,}000$ in the present value formula:

$$P = A(1 + r)^{-n}$$
$$P = 1{,}000{,}000(1 + 0.10)^{-80}$$
$$P = 1{,}000{,}000(1.1)^{-80} \qquad \text{Use a calculator with an exponent key.}$$
$$P = 488.19$$

A deposit of $488.19 in 1926 would have grown to $1,000,000 in 80 years at a rate of 10% compounded annually.   ■

WARM-UPS

True or false? Explain your answer. Assume all variables represent nonzero real numbers.

1. $(2^2)^3 = 2^5$ **2.** $(2^{-3})^{-1} = 8$ **3.** $(x^{-3})^3 = x^{-9}$

4. $2^3 \cdot 2^3 = (2^3)^3$ **5.** $(2x)^3 = 6x^3$ **6.** $(-3y^3)^2 = 9y^9$

7. $\left(\frac{2}{3}\right)^{-1} = \frac{3}{2}$ **8.** $\left(\frac{2}{3}\right)^3 = \frac{8}{27}$ **9.** $\left(\frac{x^2}{2}\right)^3 = \frac{x^6}{8}$

10. $\left(\frac{2}{x}\right)^{-2} = \frac{x^2}{4}$

5.2	**EXERCISES**

Reading and Writing *After reading this section, write out the answers to these questions. Use complete sentences.*

1. What is the power of a power rule?

2. What is the power of a product rule?

3. What is the power of a quotient rule?

4. What is principal?

5. What formula is used for computing the amount of an investment for which interest is compounded annually?

6. What formula is used for computing the present value of an amount in the future with interest compounded annually?

For all exercises in this section, assume the variables represent nonzero real numbers and use positive exponents only in your answers.

Use the rules of exponents to simplify each expression. See Example 1.

7. $(2^2)^3$

8. $(3^2)^2$

9. $(y^2)^5$

10. $(x^6)^2$

11. $(x^2)^{-4}$

12. $(x^{-2})^7$

13. $(m^{-3})^{-6}$

14. $(a^{-3})^{-3}$

15. $(x^{-2})^3(x^{-3})^{-2}$

16. $(m^{-3})^{-1}(m^2)^{-4}$

17. $\dfrac{(x^3)^{-4}}{(x^2)^{-5}}$

18. $\dfrac{(a^2)^{-3}}{(a^{-2})^4}$

Simplify. See Example 2.

19. $(-9y)^2$

20. $(-2a)^3$

21. $(-5w^3)^2$

22. $(-2w^{-5})^3$

23. $(x^3y^{-2})^3$

24. $(a^2b^{-3})^2$

25. $(3ab^{-1})^{-2}$

26. $(2x^{-1}y^2)^{-3}$

27. $\dfrac{2xy^{-2}}{(3x^2y)^{-1}}$

28. $\dfrac{3ab^{-1}}{(5ab^2)^{-1}}$

29. $\dfrac{(2ab)^{-2}}{2ab^2}$

30. $\dfrac{(3xy)^{-3}}{3xy^3}$

Simplify. See Example 3.

31. $\left(\dfrac{w}{2}\right)^3$

32. $\left(\dfrac{m}{5}\right)^2$

33. $\left(-\dfrac{3a}{4}\right)^3$

34. $\left(-\dfrac{2}{3b}\right)^4$

35. $\left(\dfrac{2x^{-1}}{y}\right)^{-2}$

36. $\left(\dfrac{2a^2b}{3}\right)^{-3}$

37. $\left(\dfrac{-3x^3}{y}\right)^{-2}$

38. $\left(\dfrac{-2y^2}{x}\right)^{-3}$

Simplify. See Example 4.

39. $\left(\dfrac{2}{5}\right)^{-2}$

40. $\left(\dfrac{3}{4}\right)^{-2}$

41. $\left(-\dfrac{1}{2}\right)^{-2}$

42. $\left(-\dfrac{2}{3}\right)^{-2}$

43. $\left(-\dfrac{2x}{3}\right)^{-3}$

44. $\left(-\dfrac{ab}{c}\right)^{-1}$

45. $\left(\dfrac{2x^2}{3y}\right)^{-3}$

46. $\left(\dfrac{ab^{-3}}{a^2b}\right)^{-2}$

Simplify each expression. Assume that the variables represent integers. See Example 5.

47. $5^{2t} \cdot 5^{4t}$

48. $3^{2n-3} \cdot 3^{4-2n}$

49. $(2^{-3w})^{-2w}$

50. $6^{8x} \cdot (6^{2x})^{-3}$

51. $\dfrac{7^{2m+6}}{7^{m+3}}$

52. $\dfrac{4^{-3p}}{4^{-4p}}$

53. $8^{2a-1} \cdot (8^{a+4})^3$

54. $(5^{4-3y})^3(5^{y-2})^2$

Use the rules of exponents to simplify each expression. If possible, write down only the answer.

55. $3x^4 \cdot 2x^5$

56. $(3x^4)^2$

57. $(-2x^2)^3$

58. $3x^2 \cdot 2x^{-4}$

59. $\dfrac{3x^{-2}y^{-1}}{z^{-1}}$

60. $\dfrac{2^{-1}x^2}{y^{-2}}$

61. $\left(\dfrac{-2}{3}\right)^{-1}$

62. $\left(\dfrac{-1}{5}\right)^{-1}$

63. $\left(\dfrac{2x^3}{3}\right)^2$

64. $\left(\dfrac{-2y^4}{x}\right)^3$

65. $(-2x^{-2})^{-1}$

66. $(-3x^{-2})^3$

Use the rules of exponents to simplify each expression.

67. $\left(\dfrac{2x^2y}{xy^2}\right)^{-3}$

68. $\left(\dfrac{2x^3y^2}{3xy^3}\right)^{-1}$

69. $\dfrac{(5a^{-1}b^2)^3}{(5ab^{-2})^4}$

70. $\dfrac{(2m^2n^{-3})^4}{mn^5}$

71. $\dfrac{(2x^{-2}y)^{-3}}{(2xy^{-1})^2}\,(2x^2y^{-7})$

72. $\dfrac{(3x^{-1}y^3)^{-2}}{(3xy^{-1})^3}\,(9x^{-9}y^5)$

73. $\left(\dfrac{6a^{-2}b^3}{2c^4}\right)^{-2}(3a^{-1}b^2)^3$

74. $(7xz^2)^{-4}\left(\dfrac{7xy^{-1}}{z}\right)^3$

Write each expression as 2 raised to a power. Assume that the variables represent integers.

75. $32 \cdot 64$ **76.** 8^{20} **77.** $81 \cdot 6^{-4}$

78. $10^{-6} \cdot 20^6$ **79.** 4^{3n} **80.** $6^{n-5} \cdot 3^{5-n}$

81. $\left(\dfrac{1}{16^{-m}}\right)^m$ **82.** $\dfrac{32^n}{128^{3n}}$

 Use a calculator to evaluate each expression. Round approximate answers to three decimal places.

83. $\dfrac{1}{5^{-2}}$ **84.** $\dfrac{(2.5)^{-3}}{(2.5)^{-5}}$

85. $2^{-1} + 2^{-2}$ **86.** $\left(\dfrac{2}{3}\right)^{-1} + 2^{-1}$

87. $(0.036)^{-2} + (4.29)^3$ **88.** $3(4.71)^2 - 5(0.471)^{-3}$

89. $\dfrac{(5.73)^{-1} + (4.29)^{-1}}{(3.762)^{-1}}$ **90.** $[5.29 + (0.374)^{-1}]^3$

Solve each problem. See Examples 6 and 7.

91. *Deeper in debt.* Melissa borrowed $40,000 at 12% compounded annually and made no payments for 3 years. How much did she owe the bank at the end of the 3 years? (Use the compound interest formula.)

92. *Comparing stocks and bonds.* Historically, the average annual return on stocks is 10%, whereas the average annual return on bonds is 7%.

a) If you had invested $10,000 in bonds in 2000 and achieved the average annual return, then what would you expect your investment to be worth in 2015?

b) How much more would your $10,000 investment be worth in 2015 if you had invested in stocks in 2000?

93. *Saving for college.* Mr. Watkins wants to have $10,000 in a savings account when his little Wanda is ready for college. How much must he deposit today in an account paying 7% compounded annually to have $10,000 in 18 years?

94. *Saving for retirement.* Wilma wants to have $2,000,000 when she retires in 45 years. Assuming that she can average 4.5% return annually in Treasury Bills, then how much must she invest now in Treasury Bills to achieve her goal?

95. *Life expectancy of white males.* Strange as it may seem, your life expectancy increases as you get older. The function

$$L = 72.2(1.002)^a$$

can be used to model life expectancy L for U.S. white males with present age a (National Center for Health Statistics, www.cdc.gov/nchswww).
a) To what age can a 20-year-old white male expect to live?
b) To what age can a 60-year-old white male expect to live? (See also Chapter Review Exercises 135 and 136.)

96. *Life expectancy of white females.* Life expectancy improved more for females than for males during the 1940s and 1950s due to a dramatic decrease in maternal mortality rates. The function

$$L = 78.5(1.001)^a$$

can be used to model life expectancy L for U.S. white females with present age a.
a) To what age can a 20-year-old white female expect to live?

FIGURE FOR EXERCISE 92

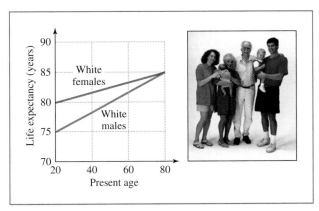

FIGURE FOR EXERCISES 95 AND 96

b) Bob, 30, and Ashley, 26, are an average white couple. How many years can Ashley expect to live as a widow?

c) Interpret the intersection of the life expectancy curves in the accompanying figure.

GETTING MORE INVOLVED

97. Discussion. For which values of a and b is it true that $(ab)^{-1} = a^{-1}b^{-1}$? Find a pair of nonzero values for a and b for which $(a + b)^{-1} \neq a^{-1} + b^{-1}$.

98. Writing. Explain how to evaluate $\left(-\frac{2}{3}\right)^{-3}$ in three different ways.

99. Discussion. Which of the following expressions has a value different from the others? Explain.

a) -1^{-1} b) -3^0 c) $-2^{-1} - 2^{-1}$
d) $(-1)^{-2}$ e) $(-1)^{-3}$

100. True or False? Explain your answer.

a) The square of a product is the product of the squares.

b) The square of a sum is the sum of the squares.

GRAPHING CALCULATOR EXERCISES

101. At 12% compounded annually the value of an investment of $10,000 after x years is given by

$$y = 10,000(1.12)^x.$$

a) Graph $y = 10,000(1.12)^x$ and the function $y = 20,000$ on a graphing calculator. Use a viewing window that shows the intersection of the two graphs.

b) Use the intersect feature of your calculator to find the point of intersection.

c) The x-coordinate of the point of intersection is the number of years that it will take for the $10,000 investment to double. What is that number of years?

102. The function $y = 72.2(1.002)^x$ gives the life expectancy y of a U.S. white male with present age x. (See Exercise 95.)

a) Graph $y = 72.2(1.002)^x$ and $y = 86$ on a graphing calculator. Use a viewing window that shows the intersection of the two graphs.

b) Use the intersect feature of your calculator to find the point of intersection.

c) What does the x-coordinate of the point of intersection tell you?

In This Section

- Polynomials
- Evaluating Polynomial Functions
- Addition and Subtraction of Polynomials
- Multiplication of Polynomials

5.3 POLYNOMIALS AND POLYNOMIAL FUNCTIONS

A polynomial is a particular type of algebraic expression that serves as a fundamental building block in algebra. We used polynomials in Chapters 1 and 2, but we did not identify them as polynomials. In this section you will learn to recognize polynomials and to add, subtract, and multiply them.

Polynomials

A **term** is a single number or the product of a number and one or more variables raised to whole number powers. For example, the expressions $3x^3$, $-15x^2$, $7x$, and -2 are terms. The number preceding the variable in each term is called the **coefficient** of that variable. The coefficient of x^3 is 3, the coefficient of x^2 is -15, and the coefficient of x is 7. In algebra a number is often referred to as a **constant,** and so the term -2 is called a **constant term.** A **polynomial** is defined as a single term or a sum of a finite number of terms. So the expression

$$3x^3 + (-15x^2) + 7x + (-2)$$

is a polynomial in one variable with four terms. For simplicity we will write this polynomial as $3x^3 - 15x^2 + 7x - 2$.

E X A M P L E   1

Identifying polynomials

Determine whether each algebraic expression is a polynomial.

a) -3 **b)** $3x + 2^{-1}$ **c)** $3x^{-2} + 4x^2$

d) $\dfrac{1}{x} + \dfrac{1}{x^2}$ **e)** $x^{49} - 8x^2 + 11x - 2$

Solution

a) The number -3 is a polynomial of one term, a constant term.

b) Since $3x + 2^{-1}$ can be written as $3x + \frac{1}{2}$, it is a polynomial of two terms.

c) The expression $3x^{-2} + 4x^2$ is not a polynomial because x has a negative exponent.

d) If this expression is rewritten as $x^{-1} + x^{-2}$, then it fails to be a polynomial because of the negative exponents. So a polynomial does not have variables in denominators, and

$$\frac{1}{x} + \frac{1}{x^2}$$

is not a polynomial.

e) The expression $x^{49} - 8x^2 + 11x - 2$ is a polynomial.   ■

For simplicity we usually write polynomials in one variable with the exponents in decreasing order from left to right. Thus we would write

$$3x^3 - 15x^2 + 7x - 2 \qquad \text{rather than} \qquad -15x^2 - 2 + 7x + 3x^3.$$

When a polynomial is written in decreasing order, the coefficient of the first term is called the **leading coefficient.**

Certain polynomials have special names depending on the number of terms. A **monomial** is a polynomial that has one term, a **binomial** is a polynomial that has two terms, and a **trinomial** is a polynomial that has three terms. The **degree** of a polynomial in one variable is the highest power of the variable in the polynomial. The number 0 is considered to be a monomial without degree because $0 = 0x^n$, where n could be any number.

E X A M P L E   2

Identifying coefficients and degree

State the degree of each polynomial and the coefficient of x^2. Determine whether the polynomial is monomial, binomial, or trinomial.

a) $\dfrac{x^2}{3} - 5x^3 + 7$ **b)** $x^{48} - x^2$ **c)** 6

Study Tip

Effective time management will allow adequate time for school, social life, and free time. However, at times you will have to sacrifice to do well.

Solution

a) The degree of this trinomial is 3, and the coefficient of x^2 is $\frac{1}{3}$.

b) The degree of this binomial is 48, and the coefficient of x^2 is -1.

c) Because $6 = 6x^0$, the number 6 is a monomial with degree 0. Because x^2 does not appear in this polynomial, the coefficient of x^2 is 0.   ■

Although we are mainly concerned here with polynomials in one variable, we will also encounter polynomials in more than one variable, such as

$$4x^2 - 5xy + 6y^2, \qquad x^2 + y^2 + z^2, \qquad \text{and} \qquad ab^2 - c^2.$$

In a term containing more than one variable, the coefficient of a variable consists of all other numbers and variables in the term. For example, the coefficient of x in $-5xy$ is $-5y$, and the coefficient of y is $-5x$. The degree of a term with more than one variable is the sum of the powers of the variables. So $-5xy$ has degree 2. The degree of a polynomial in more than one variable is equal to the highest degree of any of its terms. So $ab^2 - c^2$ has degree 3.

Evaluating Polynomial Functions

The formula $D = -16t^2 + v_0 t + s_0$ is used to model the effect of gravity on an object tossed straight upward with initial velocity v_0 feet per second from an initial height of s_0 feet. For example, if a ball is tossed into the air at 64 feet per second from a height of 4 feet, then $D = -16t^2 + 64t + 4$ gives the ball's distance above the ground in feet, t seconds after it is tossed. Because D is determined by t, we say that D is a function of t. The values of t range from $t = 0$ when the ball is tossed to the time when it hits the ground. To emphasize that the value of D depends on t, we can use the function notation introduced in Chapter 3 and write

$$D(t) = -16t^2 + 64t + 4.$$

We read $D(t)$ as "D of t." The expression $D(t)$ is the value of the polynomial at time t. To find the value when $t = 2$, replace t by 2:

$$\begin{aligned} D(2) &= -16 \cdot 2^2 + 64 \cdot 2 + 4 \\ &= -16 \cdot 4 + 128 + 4 \\ &= 68 \end{aligned}$$

The statement $D(2) = 68$ means that the ball is 68 feet above the ground 2 seconds after the ball was tossed upward. Note that $D(2)$ does not mean D times 2.

E X A M P L E   3   **Finding the value of a polynomial**
Suppose $Q(x) = 2x^3 - 3x^2 - 7x - 6$. Find $Q(3)$ and $Q(-1)$.

Solution
To find $Q(3)$, replace x by 3 in $Q(x) = 2x^3 - 3x^2 - 7x - 6$:

$$\begin{aligned} Q(3) &= 2 \cdot 3^3 - 3 \cdot 3^2 - 7 \cdot 3 - 6 \\ &= 54 - 27 - 21 - 6 \\ &= 0 \end{aligned}$$

To find $Q(-1)$, replace x by -1 in $Q(x) = 2x^3 - 3x^2 - 7x - 6$:

$$\begin{aligned} Q(-1) &= 2(-1)^3 - 3(-1)^2 - 7(-1) - 6 \\ &= -2 - 3 + 7 - 6 \\ &= -4 \end{aligned}$$

So $Q(3) = 0$ and $Q(-1) = -4$. ∎

Addition and Subtraction of Polynomials

In Section 1.6 we learned that like terms are terms that have the same variables with the same exponents. For example, $3x^2$ and $-5x^2$ are like terms. The distributive property allows us to add or subtract like terms. For example,

$$-5x^2 + 3x^2 = (-5 + 3)x^2 = -2x^2$$

and

$$-5x^2 - 3x^2 = (-5 - 3)x^2 = -8x^2.$$

To add two polynomials, we simply add the like terms.

E X A M P L E   4

Adding polynomials

Find the sums.

a) $(x^2 - 5x - 7) + (7x^2 - 4x + 10)$

b) $(3x^3 - 5x^2 - 7) + (4x^2 - 2x + 3)$

Helpful Hint

When we perform operations with polynomials and write the results as equations, those equations are identities. For example,

$(2x + 1) + (3x + 7) = 5x + 8$

is an identity.

Solution

a) $(x^2 - 5x - 7) + (7x^2 - 4x + 10) = 8x^2 - 9x + 3$ Combine like terms.

b) For illustration we will write this addition vertically:

$$
\begin{array}{r}
3x^3 - 5x^2 \qquad - 7 \\
\underline{4x^2 - 2x + 3} \quad \text{Line up like terms.} \\
3x^3 - x^2 - 2x - 4 \quad \text{Add.}
\end{array}
$$
∎

When we subtract polynomials, we subtract like terms. Because $a - b = a + (-b)$, we often perform subtraction by changing signs and adding.

E X A M P L E   5

Subtracting polynomials

Find the differences.

a) $(x^2 - 7x - 2) - (5x^2 + 6x - 4)$

b) $(6y^3z - 5yz + 7) - (4y^2z - 3yz - 9)$

Helpful Hint

For subtraction, write the original problem and then rewrite it as addition with the signs changed. Many students have trouble when they write the original problem and then overwrite the signs. Vertical subtraction is essential for performing long division of polynomials in Section 6.5.

Solution

a) We find the first difference horizontally:

$(x^2 - 7x - 2) - (5x^2 + 6x - 4) = x^2 - 7x - 2 - 5x^2 - 6x + 4$ Change signs.

$\qquad\qquad\qquad\qquad\qquad = -4x^2 - 13x + 2$ Combine like terms.

b) For illustration we write $(6y^3z - 5yz + 7) - (4y^2z - 3yz - 9)$ vertically:

$$
\begin{array}{r}
6y^3z \qquad - 5yz + 7 \\
\underline{-4y^2z + 3yz + 9} \quad \text{Change signs.} \\
6y^3z - 4y^2z - 2yz + 16 \quad \text{Add.}
\end{array}
$$
∎

It is certainly not necessary to write out all of the steps shown in Examples 4 and 5, but we must use the following rule.

Addition and Subtraction of Polynomials

To add two polynomials, add the like terms.
To subtract two polynomials, subtract the like terms.

Multiplication of Polynomials

We learned how to multiply monomials when we learned the product rule in Section 5.1. For example,

$$-2x^3 \cdot 4x^2 = -8x^5.$$

To multiply a monomial and a polynomial of two or more terms, we apply the distributive property. For example,

$$3x(x^3 - 5) = 3x^4 - 15x.$$

E X A M P L E 6   **Multiplying a monomial and a polynomial**

Find the products.

a) $2ab^2 \cdot 3a^2b$

b) $(-1)(5 - x)$

c) $(x^3 - 5x + 2)(-3x)$

Solution

a) $2ab^2 \cdot 3a^2b = 6a^3b^3$

b) $(-1)(5 - x) = -5 + x = x - 5$

c) Each term of $x^3 - 5x + 2$ is multiplied by $-3x$:

$$(x^3 - 5x + 2)(-3x) = -3x^4 + 15x^2 - 6x \qquad ■$$

Note what happened to the binomial in Example 6(b) when we multiplied it by -1. If we multiply any difference by -1, we get the same type of result:

$$-1(a - b) = -a + b = b - a.$$

Because multiplying by -1 is the same as taking the opposite, we can write this equation as

$$-(a - b) = b - a.$$

This equation says that $a - b$ and $b - a$ are opposites or additive inverses of each other. Note that the opposite of $a + b$ is $-a - b$, not $a - b$.

To multiply a binomial and a trinomial, we can use the distributive property or set it up like multiplication of whole numbers.

E X A M P L E 7   **Multiplying a binomial and a trinomial**

Find the product $(x + 2)(x^2 + 3x - 5)$.

Helpful Hint

Many students find vertical multiplication easier than applying the distributive property twice horizontally. However, you should learn both methods because horizontal multiplication will help you with factoring by grouping in Section 5.6.

Solution

We can find this product by applying the distributive property twice. First we multiply the binomial and each term of the trinomial:

$$(x + 2)(x^2 + 3x - 5) = (x + 2)x^2 + (x + 2)3x + (x + 2)(-5) \quad \text{Distributive property}$$

$$= x^3 + 2x^2 + 3x^2 + 6x - 5x - 10 \quad \text{Distributive property}$$

$$= x^3 + 5x^2 + x - 10 \quad \text{Combine like terms.}$$

We could have found this product vertically:

$$
\begin{array}{r}
x^2 + 3x - 5 \\
x + 2 \\
\hline
2x^2 + 6x - 10 \\
x^3 + 3x^2 - 5x \\
\hline
x^3 + 5x^2 + x - 10
\end{array}
$$

$2(x^2 + 3x - 5) = 2x^2 + 6x - 10$

$x(x^2 + 3x - 5) = x^3 + 3x^2 - 5x$

Add.

Multiplication of Polynomials

To multiply polynomials, multiply each term of the first polynomial by each term of the second polynomial and then combine like terms.

In Example 8 we multiply binomials.

E X A M P L E   8

Multiplying binomials
Find the products.

a) $(x + y)(z + 4)$ **b)** $(x - 3)(2x + 5)$

Solution

a) $(x + y)(z + 4) = (x + y)z + (x + y)4$ Distributive property

$\qquad\qquad\qquad\quad = xz + yz + 4x + 4y$ Distributive property

Notice that this product does not have any like terms to combine.

b) Multiply:

$$
\begin{array}{r}
x - 3 \\
2x + 5 \\
\hline
5x - 15 \\
2x^2 - 6x \\
\hline
2x^2 - x - 15
\end{array}
$$

WARM-UPS

True or false? Explain your answers.

1. The expression $3x^{-2} - 5x + 2$ is a trinomial.
2. In the polynomial $3x^2 - 5x + 3$ the coefficient of x is 5.
3. The degree of the polynomial $x^2 + 3x - 5x^3 + 4$ is 2.
4. If $C(x) = x^2 - 3$, then $C(5) = 22$.
5. If $P(t) = 30t + 10$, then $P(0) = 40$.
6. $(2x^2 - 3x + 5) + (x^2 + 5x - 7) = 3x^2 + 2x - 2$ for any value of x.
7. $(x^2 - 5x) - (x^2 - 3x) = -8x$ for any value of x.
8. $-2x(3x - 4x^2) = 8x^3 - 6x^2$ for any value of x.
9. $-(x - 7) = 7 - x$ for any value of x.
10. The opposite of $y + 5$ is $y - 5$ for any value of y.

5.3. EXERCISES

Reading and Writing   *After reading this section, write out the answers to these questions. Use complete sentences.*

1. What is a term of a polynomial?

2. What is a coefficient?

3. What is a constant?

4. What is a polynomial?

5. What is the degree of a polynomial?

6. What property is used when multiplying a binomial and a trinomial?

Determine whether each algebraic expression is a polynomial. See Example 1.

7. $3x$

8. -9

9. $x^{-1} + 4$

10. $3x^{-3} + 4x - 1$

11. $x^2 - 3x + \sqrt{5}$

12. $\dfrac{x^3}{3} - \dfrac{3x^2}{5} + 0.2x$

13. $\dfrac{1}{x} + x - 3$

14. $x^5 - \dfrac{9}{x^2}$

State the degree of each polynomial and the coefficient of x^3. Determine whether each polynomial is a monomial, binomial, or trinomial. See Example 2.

15. $x^4 - 8x^3$

16. $15 - x^3$

17. -8

18. 17

19. $\dfrac{x^7}{15}$

20. $5x^4$

21. $x^3 + 3x^4 - 5x^6$

22. $\dfrac{x^3}{2} + \dfrac{5x}{2} - 7$

For each given polynomial, find the indicated value of the polynomial. See Example 3.

23. $P(x) = x^4 - 1$, $P(3)$

24. $P(x) = x^2 - x - 2$, $P(-1)$

25. $M(x) = -3x^2 + 4x - 9$, $M(-2)$

26. $C(w) = 3w^2 - w$, $C(0)$

27. $R(x) = x^5 - x^4 + x^3 - x^2 + x - 1$, $R(1)$

28. $T(a) = a^7 + a^6$, $T(-1)$

Perform the indicated operations. See Examples 4 and 5.

29. $(2a - 3) + (a + 5)$

30. $(2w - 6) + (w + 5)$

31. $(7xy + 30) - (2xy + 5)$

32. $(5ab + 7) - (3ab + 6)$

33. $(x^2 - 3x) + (-x^2 + 5x - 9)$

34. $(2y^2 - 3y - 8) + (y^2 + 4y - 1)$

35. $(2x^3 - 4x - 3) - (x^2 - 2x + 5)$

36. $(2x - 5) - (x^2 - 3x + 2)$

Perform the indicated operations vertically. See Examples 4 and 5.

37. Add
$$\begin{array}{r} x^3 + 3x^2 - 5x - 2 \\ -x^3 + 8x^2 + 3x - 7 \\ \hline \end{array}$$

38. Add
$$\begin{array}{r} x^2 - 3x + 7 \\ -2x^2 - 5x + 2 \\ \hline \end{array}$$

39. Subtract
$$\begin{array}{r} 5x + 2 \\ 4x - 3 \\ \hline \end{array}$$

40. Subtract
$$\begin{array}{r} 4x + 3 \\ 2x - 6 \\ \hline \end{array}$$

41. Subtract
$$\begin{array}{r} -x^2 + 3x - 5 \\ 5x^2 - 2x - 7 \\ \hline \end{array}$$

42. Subtract
$$\begin{array}{r} -3x^2 + 5x - 2 \\ x^2 - 5x - 6 \\ \hline \end{array}$$

43. Add
$$\begin{array}{r} x - y \\ x + y \\ \hline \end{array}$$

44. Add
$$\begin{array}{r} -w + 4 \\ 2w - 3 \\ \hline \end{array}$$

Find each product. See Examples 6–8.

45. $-3x^2 \cdot 5x^4$

46. $(-ab^5)(-2a^2b)$

47. $-1(3x - 2)$

48. $-1(-x^2 + 3x - 9)$

49. $5x^2y^3(3x^2y - 4x)$

50. $3y^4z(8y^2z^2 - 3yz + 2y)$

51. $(x - 2)(x + 2)$

52. $(x - 1)(x + 1)$

53. $(x^2 + x + 2)(2x - 3)$

54. $(x^2 - 3x + 2)(x - 4)$

Find each product vertically. See Examples 6–8.

55. Multiply
$$\begin{array}{r} 2x - 3 \\ -5x \\ \hline \end{array}$$

56. Multiply
$$\begin{array}{r} 3a^3 - 5a^2 + 7 \\ -2a \\ \hline \end{array}$$

57. Multiply
$$\begin{array}{r} x + 5 \\ x + 5 \\ \hline \end{array}$$

58. Multiply
$$\begin{array}{r} a + b \\ a - b \\ \hline \end{array}$$

59. Multiply

$$x + 6$$
$$2x - 3$$

60. Multiply

$$3x^2 + 2$$
$$2x^2 - 5$$

61. Multiply

$$x^2 + xy + y^2$$
$$x - y$$

62. Multiply

$$a^2 - ab + b^2$$
$$a + b$$

Perform the indicated operations.

63. $(x - 7) + (2x - 3) + (5 - x)$

64. $(5x - 3) + (x^3 + 3x - 2) + (-2x - 3)$

65. $(a^2 - 5a + 3) + (3a^2 - 6a - 7)$

66. $(w^2 - 3w + 2) + (2w - 3 + w^2)$

67. $(w^2 - 7w - 2) - (w - 3w^2 + 5)$

68. $(a^3 - 3a) - (1 - a - 2a^2)$

69. $(x - 2)(x^2 + 2x + 4)$

70. $(a - 3)(a^2 + 3a + 9)$

71. $(x - w)(z + 2w)$

72. $(w^2 - a)(t^2 + 3)$

73. $(x^2 - x + 2)(x^2 + x - 2)$

74. $(a^2 + a + b)(a^2 - a - b)$

 Perform the following operations using a calculator.

75. $(2.31x - 5.4)(6.25x + 1.8)$

76. $(x - 0.28)(x^2 - 34.6x + 21.2)$

77. $(3.759x^2 - 4.71x + 2.85) + (11.61x^2 + 6.59x - 3.716)$

78. $(43.19x^3 - 3.7x^2 - 5.42x + 3.1)$
$- (62.7x^3 - 7.36x - 12.3)$

Perform the indicated operations.

79. $\left(\dfrac{1}{2}x + 2\right) + \left(\dfrac{1}{4}x - \dfrac{1}{2}\right)$

80. $\left(\dfrac{1}{3}x + 1\right) + \left(\dfrac{1}{3}x - \dfrac{3}{2}\right)$

81. $\left(\dfrac{1}{2}x^2 + \dfrac{1}{3}x - \dfrac{1}{5}\right) - \left(x^2 - \dfrac{2}{3}x - \dfrac{1}{5}\right)$

82. $\left(\dfrac{2}{3}x^2 - \dfrac{1}{3}x + \dfrac{1}{6}\right) - \left(-\dfrac{1}{3}x^2 + x + 1\right)$

83. $[x^2 - 3 - (x^2 + 5x - 4)] - [x - 3(x^2 - 5x)]$

84. $[x^3 - 4x(x^2 - 3x + 2) - 5x] + [x^2 - 5(4 - x^2) + 3]$

85. $[5x - 4(x - 3)][3x - 7(x + 2)]$

86. $[x^2 - (5x - 2)][x^2 + (5x - 2)]$

87. $[x^2 - (m + 2)][x^2 + (m + 2)]$

88. $[3x^2 - (x - 2)][3x^2 + (x + 2)]$

89. $2x(5x - 4) - 3x[5x^2 - 3x(x - 7)]$

90. $-3x(x - 2) - 5[2x - 4(x + 6)]$

Perform the indicated operations. A variable used in an exponent represents an integer; a variable used as a base represents a nonzero real number.

91. $(a^{2m} + 3a^m - 3) + (-5a^{2m} - 7a^m + 8)$

92. $(b^{3z} - 6) - (4b^{3z} - b^{2z} - 7)$

93. $(x^n - 1)(x^n + 3)$

94. $(2y^t - 3)(4y^t + 7)$

95. $z^{3w} - z^{2w}(z^{1-w} - 4z^w)$

96. $(w^p - 1)(w^{2p} + w^p + 1)$

97. $(x^{2r} + y)(x^{4r} - x^{2r}y + y^2)$

98. $(2x^a - z)(2x^a + z)$

Solve each problem.

99. *Cost of gravel.* The cost in dollars of x cubic yards of gravel is given by the formula

$$C(x) = 20x + 15.$$

Find $C(3)$, the cost of 3 cubic yards of gravel.

100. *Annual bonus.* Sheila's annual bonus in dollars for selling n life insurance policies is given by the formula

$$B(n) = 0.1n^2 + 3n + 50.$$

Find $B(20)$, her bonus for selling 20 policies.

101. *Marginal cost.* A company uses the formula $C(n) = 50n - 0.01n^4$ to find the daily cost in dollars of manufacturing n aluminum windows. The *marginal cost* of the nth window is the additional cost incurred for manufacturing that window. For example, the marginal cost of the third window is $C(3) - C(2)$. Find the marginal cost for manufacturing the third window. What is the marginal cost for manufacturing the tenth window?

102. *Marginal profit.* A company uses the formula $P(n) = 4n + 0.9n^3$ to estimate its daily profit in dollars for producing n automatic garage door openers. The *marginal profit* of the nth opener is the amount of additional profit made for that opener. For example, the marginal profit for the fourth opener is $P(4) - P(3)$. Find the marginal profit for the fourth opener. What is the marginal profit for the tenth opener? Use the bar graph, on the next page, to explain why the marginal profit increases as production goes up.

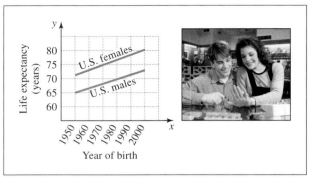

FIGURE FOR EXERCISE 102

FIGURE FOR EXERCISES 103 AND 104

103. *Male and female life expectancy.* Since 1950 the life expectancies of U.S. males and females born in year y can be modeled by the formulas

$$M(y) = 0.16252y - 251.91$$

and

$$F(y) = 0.18268y - 284.98,$$

respectively (National Center for Health Statistics, www.cdc.gov/nchswww).

a) How much greater was the life expectancy of a female born in 1950 than a male born in 1950?

b) Are the lines in the accompanying figure parallel?

c) In what year will female life expectancy be 8 years greater than male life expectancy?

104. *More life expectancy.* Use the functions from Exercise 103 for these questions.

a) A male born in 1975 does not want his future wife to outlive him. What should be the year of birth for his wife so that they both can be expected to die in the same year?

b) Find $\dfrac{M(y) + F(y)}{2}$ to get a formula for the life expectancy of a person born in year y.

GETTING MORE INVOLVED

105. *Discussion.* Is it possible for a binomial to have degree 4? If so, give an example.

106. *Discussion.* Give an example of two fourth-degree trinomials whose sum is a third-degree binomial.

107. *Cooperative learning.* Work in a group to find the product $(a + b)(c + d)$. How many terms does it have? Find the product $(a + b)(c + d)(e + f)$. How many terms does it have? How many terms are there in a product of four binomials in which there are no like terms to combine? How many terms are there in a product of n binomials in which there are no like terms?

In This Section

- The FOIL Method
- The Square of a Binomial
- Product of a Sum and a Difference

5.4   MULTIPLYING BINOMIALS

In Section 5.3 you learned to multiply polynomials. In this section you will learn rules to make multiplication of binomials simpler.

The FOIL Method

Consider how we find the product of two binomials $x + 3$ and $x + 5$ using the distributive property twice:

$$(x + 3)(x + 5) = (x + 3)x + (x + 3)5 \quad \text{Distributive property}$$
$$= x^2 + 3x + 5x + 15 \quad \text{Distributive property}$$
$$= x^2 + 8x + 15 \quad \text{Combine like terms.}$$

There are four terms in the product. The term x^2 is the product of the first term of each binomial. The term $5x$ is the product of the two outer terms, 5 and x. The term $3x$ is the product of the two inner terms, 3 and x. The term 15 is the product of the

Helpful Hint

The product of two binomials always has four terms before combining like terms. The product of two trinomials always has nine terms before combining like terms. How many terms are there in the product of a binomial and trinomial?

last two terms in each binomial, 3 and 5. It may be helpful to connect the terms multiplied by lines.

$(x + 3)(x + 5)$

F = First terms
O = Outer terms
I = Inner terms
L = Last terms

So instead of writing out all of the steps in using the distributive property, we can get the result by finding the products of the first, outer, inner, and last terms. This method is called the **FOIL method.**

For example, let's apply FOIL to the product $(x - 3)(x + 4)$:

$$(x - 3)(x + 4) = x^2 + 4x - 3x - 12 = x^2 + x - 12$$

If the outer and inner products are like terms, you can save a step by writing down only their sum.

E X A M P L E   1

Multiplying binomials

Use FOIL to find the products of the binomials.

a) $(2x - 3)(3x + 4)$ **b)** $(2x^3 + 5)(2x^3 - 5)$

c) $(m + w)(2m - w)$ **d)** $(a + b)(a - 3)$

Solution

a) $(2x - 3)(3x + 4) = 6x^2 + 8x - 9x - 12$
$$= 6x^2 - x - 12$$

b) $(2x^3 + 5)(2x^3 - 5) = 4x^6 - 10x^3 + 10x^3 - 25$
$$= 4x^6 - 25$$

c) $(m + w)(2m - w) = 2m^2 - mw + 2mw - w^2$
$$= 2m^2 + mw - w^2$$

d) $(a + b)(a - 3) = a^2 - 3a + ab - 3b$ There are no like terms. ■

Helpful Hint

To visualize the square of a sum, draw a square with sides of length $a + b$ as shown.

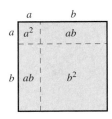

The area of the large square is $(a + b)^2$. It comes from four terms as stated in the rule for the square of a sum.

The Square of a Binomial

To find $(a + b)^2$, the square of a sum, we can use FOIL on $(a + b)(a + b)$:

$$(a + b)(a + b) = a^2 + ab + ab + b^2$$
$$= a^2 + 2ab + b^2$$

You can use the result $a^2 + 2ab + b^2$ that we obtained from FOIL to quickly find the square of *any* sum. *To square a sum, we square the first term* (a^2), *add twice the product of the two terms* $(2ab)$, *then add the square of the last term* (b^2).

Rule for the Square of a Sum

$$(a + b)^2 = a^2 + 2ab + b^2$$

In general, the square of a sum $(a + b)^2$ is not equal to the sum of the squares $a^2 + b^2$. The square of a sum has the middle term $2ab$.

E X A M P L E   2

Squaring a binomial

Square each sum, using the new rule.

a) $(x + 5)^2$ **b)** $(2w + 3)^2$ **c)** $(2y^4 + 3)^2$

Solution

a) $(x + 5)^2 = x^2 + 2(x)(5) + 5^2 = x^2 + 10x + 25$

$\uparrow$ $\uparrow$ $\uparrow$
Square   Twice   Square
of   the   of
first   product last

b) $(2w + 3)^2 = (2w)^2 + 2(2w)(3) + 3^2$
$= 4w^2 + 12w + 9$

c) $(2y^4 + 3)^2 = (2y^4)^2 + 2(2y^4)(3) + 3^2$
$= 4y^8 + 12y^4 + 9$ ■

C A U T I O N   Squaring $x + 5$ correctly, as in Example 2(a), gives us the identity

$$(x + 5)^2 = x^2 + 10x + 25,$$

which is satisfied by any x. If you forget the middle term and write $(x + 5)^2 = x^2 + 25$, then you have an equation that is satisfied only if $x = 0$.

To find $(a - b)^2$, the square of a difference, we can use FOIL:

$$(a - b)(a - b) = a^2 - ab - ab + b^2$$
$$= a^2 - 2ab + b^2$$

As in squaring a sum, it is simply better to remember the result of using FOIL. *To square a difference, square the first term, subtract twice the product of the two terms, and add the square of the last term.*

Rule for the Square of a Difference

$$(a - b)^2 = a^2 - 2ab + b^2$$

E X A M P L E   3

Squaring a binomial

Square each difference, using the new rule.

a) $(x - 6)^2$ **b)** $(3w - 5y)^2$
c) $(-4 - st)^2$ **d)** $(3 - 5a^3)^2$

Helpful Hint

Many students keep using FOIL to find the square of a sum or a difference. However, you will be greatly rewarded if you learn the new rules for squaring a sum or a difference.

Solution

a) $(x - 6)^2 = x^2 - 2(x)(6) + 6^2$ For the middle term, subtract twice
the product: $2(x)(6)$.

$= x^2 - 12x + 36$

b) $(3w - 5y)^2 = (3w)^2 - 2(3w)(5y) + (5y)^2$
$= 9w^2 - 30wy + 25y^2$

c) $(-4 - st)^2 = (-4)^2 - 2(-4)(st) + (st)^2$
$$= 16 + 8st + s^2t^2$$
d) $(3 - 5a^3)^2 = 3^2 - 2(3)(5a^3) + (5a^3)^2$
$$= 9 - 30a^3 + 25a^6$$ ■

Product of a Sum and a Difference

If we multiply the sum $a + b$ and the difference $a - b$ by using FOIL, we get
$$(a + b)(a - b) = a^2 - ab + ab - b^2$$
$$= a^2 - b^2.$$

The inner and outer products add up to zero, canceling each other out. So *the product of a sum and a difference is the difference of two squares,* as shown in the following rule.

Rule for the Product of a Sum and a Difference
$$(a + b)(a - b) = a^2 - b^2$$

E X A M P L E   4

Finding the product of a sum and a difference
Find the products.
a) $(x + 3)(x - 3)$ **b)** $(a^3 + 8)(a^3 - 8)$ **c)** $(3x^2 - y^3)(3x^2 + y^3)$

Solution
a) $(x + 3)(x - 3) = x^2 - 9$
b) $(a^3 + 8)(a^3 - 8) = a^6 - 64$
c) $(3x^2 - y^3)(3x^2 + y^3) = 9x^4 - y^6$ ■

The square of a sum, the square of a difference, and the product of a sum and a difference are referred to as **special products.** Although the special products can be found by using the distributive property or FOIL, they occur so frequently in algebra that it is essential to learn the new rules. In the next example we use the special product rules to multiply two trinomials and to square a trinomial.

E X A M P L E   5

Using special product rules to multiply trinomials
Find the products.
a) $[(x + y) + 3][(x + y) - 3]$ **b)** $[(m - n) + 5]^2$

Solution
a) Use the rule $(a + b)(a - b) = a^2 - b^2$ with $a = x + y$ and $b = 3$:
$$[(x + y) + 3][(x + y) - 3] = (x + y)^2 - 3^2$$
$$= x^2 + 2xy + y^2 - 9$$
b) Use the rule $(a + b)^2 = a^2 + 2ab + b^2$ with $a = m - n$ and $b = 5$:
$$[(m - n) + 5]^2 = (m - n)^2 + 2(m - n)5 + 5^2$$
$$= m^2 - 2mn + n^2 + 10m - 10n + 25$$ ■

WARM-UPS

True or false? Explain your answer.

1. $(x + 2)(x + 5) = x^2 + 7x + 10$ for any value of x.
2. $(2x - 3)(3x + 5) = 6x^2 + x - 15$ for any value of x.
3. $(2 + 3)^2 = 2^2 + 3^2$
4. $(x + 7)^2 = x^2 + 14x + 49$ for any value of x.
5. $(8 - 3)^2 = 64 - 9$
6. The product of a sum and a difference of the same two terms is equal to the difference of two squares.
7. $(60 - 1)(60 + 1) = 3600 - 1$
8. $(x - y)^2 = x^2 - 2xy + y^2$ for any values of x and y.
9. $(x - 3)^2 = x^2 - 3x + 9$ for any value of x.
10. The expression $3x \cdot 5x$ is a product of two binomials.

5.4   EXERCISES

Reading and Writing   *After reading this section, write out the answers to these questions. Use complete sentences.*

1. What property of the real numbers is used in multiplying two binomials?

2. What does FOIL stand for?

3. What is the purpose of the FOIL method?

4. How do you square a sum of two terms?

5. How do you square a difference of two terms?

6. How do you find the product of a sum and a difference?

7. Why is $(a + b)^2$ not equivalent to $a^2 + b^2$?

8. Why is $(a - b)^2$ not equivalent to $a^2 - b^2$?

Find each product. When possible, write down only the answer. See Example 1.

9. $(x - 2)(x + 4)$
10. $(x - 3)(x + 5)$

11. $(1 + 2x)(3 + x)$
12. $(3 + 2y)(y + 2)$
13. $(-2a - 3)(-a + 5)$
14. $(-3x - 5)(-x + 6)$
15. $(2x^2 - 7)(2x^2 + 7)$
16. $(3y^3 + 8)(3y^3 - 8)$
17. $(2x^3 - 1)(x^3 + 4)$
18. $(3t^2 - 4)(2t^2 + 3)$
19. $(6z + w)(w - z)$
20. $(4y + w)(w - 2y)$
21. $(3k - 2t)(4t + 3k)$
22. $(7a - 2x)(x + a)$
23. $(x - 3)(y + w)$
24. $(z - 1)(y + 2)$

Find the square of each sum or difference. When possible, write down only the answer. See Examples 2 and 3.

25. $(m + 3)^2$
26. $(a + 2)^2$
27. $(4 - a)^2$
28. $(3 - b)^2$
29. $(2w + 1)^2$
30. $(3m + 4)^2$
31. $(3t - 5u)^2$

32. $(3w - 2x)^2$

33. $(-x - 1)^2$

34. $(-d - 5)^2$

35. $(a - 3y^3)^2$

36. $(3m - 5n^3)^2$

Find each product. See Example 4.

37. $(w - 9)(w + 9)$

38. $(m - 4)(m + 4)$

39. $(w^3 + y)(w^3 - y)$

40. $(a^3 - x)(a^3 + x)$

41. $(7 - 2x)(7 + 2x)$

42. $(3 + 5x)(3 - 5x)$

43. $(3x^2 - 2)(3x^2 + 2)$

44. $(4y^2 + 1)(4y^2 - 1)$

45. $(5a^3 - 2b)(5a^3 + 2b)$

46. $(6w^4 + 5y^3)(6w^4 - 5y^3)$

Use the special product rules to find each product. See Example 5.

47. $[(m + t) + 5][(m + t) - 5]$

48. $[(2x + 3) - y][(2x + 3) + y]$

49. $[y - (r + 5)][y + (r + 5)]$

50. $[x + (3 - k)][x - (3 - k)]$

51. $[(2y - t) + 3]^2$

52. $[(u - 3v) - 4]^2$

53. $[3h + (k - 1)]^2$

54. $[2p - (3q + 6)]^2$

Perform the operations and simplify.

55. $(x - 6)(x + 9)$

56. $(2x^2 - 3)(3x^2 + 4)$

57. $(5 - x)(5 + x)$

58. $(4 - ab)(4 + ab)$

59. $(3x - 4a)(2x + 5a)$

60. $(x^5 + 2)(x^5 - 2)$

61. $(2t - 3)(t + w)$

62. $(5x - 9)(ax + b)$

63. $(3x^2 + 2y^3)^2$

64. $(5a^4 - 2b)^2$

65. $(2 + 2y)(3y - 5)$

66. $(3b - 3)(3 + 2b)$

67. $(2m - 7)^2$

68. $(5a + 4)^2$

69. $(3 + 7x)^2$

70. $(1 - pq)^2$

71. $4y\left(3y + \dfrac{1}{2}\right)^2$

72. $25y\left(2y - \dfrac{1}{5}\right)^2$

73. $(a + h)^2 - a^2$

74. $\dfrac{(x + h)^2 - x^2}{h}$

75. $(x + 2)(x + 2)^2$

76. $(a + 1)^2(a + 1)^2$

77. $(y + 3)^3$

78. $(2x - 3y)^3$

79. $4x - 3(x - 5)^2$

80. $2(x + 3)(x - 2) - (2x - 1)^2$

 Use a calculator to help you perform the following operations.

81. $(3.2x - 4.5)(5.1x + 3.9)$

82. $(5.3x - 9.2)^2$

83. $(3.6y + 4.4)^2$

84. $(3.3a - 7.9b)(3.3a + 7.9b)$

Find the products. Assume all variables are nonzero and variables used in exponents represent integers.

85. $(x^m + 2)(x^{2m} + 3)$

86. $(a^n - b)(a^n + b)$

87. $a^{n+1}(a^{2n} + a^n - 3)$

88. $x^{3b}(x^{-3b} + 3x^{-b} + 5)$

89. $(a^m + a^n)^2$

90. $(x^w - x^t)^2$

91. $(5y^m + 8z^k)(3y^{2m} + 4z^{3-k})$

92. $(4x^{a-1} + 3y^{b+5})(x^{2a-3} - 2y^{4-b})$

Solve each problem.

93. *Area of a room.* Suppose the length of a rectangular room is $x + 3$ meters and the width is $x + 1$ meters. Find a trinomial that can be used to represent the area of the room.

94. *House plans.* Barbie and Ken planned to build a square house with area x^2 square feet. Then they revised the plan so that one side was lengthened by 20 feet and the other side was shortened by 6 feet. (See the figure on the next page.) Find a trinomial that can be used to represent the area of the revised house.

FIGURE FOR EXERCISE 94

FIGURE FOR EXERCISE 97

95. *Available habitat.* A wild animal will generally stay more than x kilometers from the edge of a forest preserve. So the available habitat for the animal excludes an area of uniform width x on the edge of the rectangular forest preserve shown in the figure. The value of x depends on the animal. Find a trinomial in x that gives the area of the available habitat in square kilometers (km^2) for the forest preserve shown. What is the available habitat in this forest preserve for a bobcat for which $x = 0.4$ kilometers?

98. *Energy efficient.* A manufacturer of mobile homes makes a custom model that is x feet long, 12 feet wide, and 8 feet high (all inside dimensions). The insulation is 3 inches thick in the walls, 6 inches thick in the floor, and 8 inches thick in the ceiling. Given that the insulation costs the manufacturer 25 cents per cubic foot and doors and windows take up 80 square feet of wall space, find a polynomial in x that gives the cost in dollars for insulation in this model. State any assumptions that you are making to solve this problem.

FIGURE FOR EXERCISE 95

96. *Cubic coating.* A cubic metal box x inches on each side is designed for transporting frozen specimens. The box is surrounded on all sides by a 2-inch-thick layer of styrofoam insulation. Find a polynomial that represents the total volume of the cube and styrofoam.

97. *Overflow pan.* An air conditioning contractor makes an overflow pan for a condenser by cutting squares with side of length x feet from the corners of a 4 foot by 6 foot piece of galvanized sheet metal as shown in the figure. The sides are then folded up, and the corners are sealed. Find a polynomial that gives the volume of the pan in cubic feet (ft^3). What is the volume of the pan if $x = 4$ inches?

GETTING MORE INVOLVED

99. *Exploration.* **a)** Find $(a + b)^3$ by multiplying $(a + b)^2$ by $a + b$.
b) Next find $(a + b)^4$ and $(a + b)^5$.
c) How many terms are in each of these powers of $a + b$ after combining like terms?
d) Make a general statement about the number of terms in $(a + b)^n$.

100. *Cooperative learning.* Make a four-column table with columns for a, b, $(a + b)^2$, and $a^2 + b^2$. Work with a group to fill in the table with five pairs of numbers for a and b for which $(a + b)^2 \neq a^2 + b^2$. For what values of a and b does $(a + b)^2 = a^2 + b^2$?

101. *Discussion.* The area of the large square shown in the figure is $(a + b)^2$. Find the area of each of the four smaller regions in the figure, and then find the sum of those areas. What conclusion can you draw from these areas about $(a + b)^2$?

FIGURE FOR EXERCISE 101

5.5   FACTORING POLYNOMIALS

In Sections 5.3 and 5.4 we multiplied polynomials. In this section and Sections 5.6 and 5.7 we will learn to factor polynomials. Factoring will then be used for solving equations and problems in the last section of this chapter.

Factoring Out the Greatest Common Factor (GCF)

A natural number larger than 1 that has no factors other than itself and 1 is called a **prime number.** The numbers

$$2, 3, 5, 7, 11, 13, 17, 19, 23$$

are the first nine prime numbers. There are infinitely many prime numbers.

To factor a natural number **completely** means to write it as a product of prime numbers. In factoring 12 we might write $12 = 4 \cdot 3$. However, 12 is not factored completely as $4 \cdot 3$ because 4 is not a prime. To factor 12 completely, we write $12 = 2 \cdot 2 \cdot 3$ (or $2^2 \cdot 3$).

We use the distributive property to multiply a monomial and a binomial:

$$6x(2x - 1) = 12x^2 - 6x$$

If we start with $12x^2 - 6x$, we can use the distributive property to get

$$12x^2 - 6x = 6x(2x - 1).$$

We have **factored out** $6x$, which is a common factor of $12x^2$ and $-6x$. We could have factored out just 3 to get

$$12x^2 - 6x = 3(4x^2 - 2x),$$

but this would not be factoring out the *greatest* common factor. The **greatest common factor** (GCF) is a monomial that includes every number or variable that is a factor of all of the terms of the polynomial.

We can use the following strategy for finding the greatest common factor of a group of terms.

Strategy for Finding the Greatest Common Factor (GCF)

1. Factor each term completely.
2. Write a product using each factor that is common to all of the terms.
3. On each of these factors, use an exponent equal to the smallest exponent that appears on that factor in any of the terms.

E X A M P L E   1

The greatest common factor

Find the greatest common factor (GCF) for each group of terms.

a) $8x^2y, 20xy^3$ b) $30a^2, 45a^3b^2, 75a^4b$

Solution

a) First factor each term completely:

$$8x^2y = 2^3x^2y$$
$$20xy^3 = 2^2 \cdot 5xy^3$$

The factors common to both terms are 2, x, and y. In the GCF we use the smallest exponent that appears on each factor in either of the terms. So the GCF is 2^2xy or $4xy$.

b) First factor each term completely:

$$30a^2 = 2 \cdot 3 \cdot 5a^2$$
$$45a^3b^2 = 3^2 \cdot 5a^3b^2$$
$$75a^4b = 3 \cdot 5^2a^4b$$

The GCF is $3 \cdot 5a^2$ or $15a^2$.   ■

To factor out the GCF from a polynomial, find the GCF for the terms, then use the distributive property to factor it out.

E X A M P L E   2

Factoring out the greatest common factor
Factor each polynomial by factoring out the GCF.
a) $5x^4 - 10x^3 + 15x^2$ b) $8xy^2 + 20x^2y$ c) $60x^5 + 24x^3 + 36x^2$

Solution
a) First factor each term completely:

$$5x^4 = 5x^4, \qquad 10x^3 = 2 \cdot 5x^3, \qquad 15x^2 = 3 \cdot 5x^2.$$

The GCF of the three terms is $5x^2$. Now factor $5x^2$ out of each term:

$$5x^4 - 10x^3 + 15x^2 = 5x^2(x^2 - 2x + 3)$$

b) The GCF for $8xy^2$ and $20x^2y$ is $4xy$:

$$8xy^2 + 20x^2y = 4xy(2y + 5x)$$

c) First factor each coefficient in $60x^5 + 24x^3 + 36x^2$:

$$60 = 2^2 \cdot 3 \cdot 5, \qquad 24 = 2^3 \cdot 3, \qquad 36 = 2^2 \cdot 3^2.$$

The GCF of the three terms is $2^2 \cdot 3x^2$ or $12x^2$:

$$60x^5 + 24x^3 + 36x^2 = 12x^2(5x^3 + 2x + 3)$$ ■

In the next example the common factor in each term is a binomial.

E X A M P L E   3

Factoring out a binomial
Factor.
a) $(x + 3)w + (x + 3)a$ b) $x(x - 9) - 4(x - 9)$

Solution
a) We treat $x + 3$ like a common monomial when factoring:

$$(x + 3)w + (x + 3)a = (x + 3)(w + a)$$

b) Factor out the common binomial $x - 9$:

$$x(x - 9) - 4(x - 9) = (x - 4)(x - 9)$$ ■

Factoring Out the Opposite of the GCF

In Example 4 we factor each polynomial twice. First we factor out the greatest common factor. Then we factor out the opposite of the GCF.

E X A M P L E   4

Factoring out the opposite of the GCF

Factor out the GCF, then factor out the opposite of the GCF.

a) $5x - 5y$ **b)** $-x^2 - 3$ **c)** $-x^3 + 3x^2 - 5x$

Solution

a) $5x - 5y = 5(x - y)$ Factor out 5.

$\quad\quad\quad\quad = -5(-x + y)$ Factor out -5.

b) $-x^2 - 3 = 1(-x^2 - 3)$ The GCF is 1.

$\quad\quad\quad\quad = -1(x^2 + 3)$ Factor out -1.

c) $-x^3 + 3x^2 - 5x = x(-x^2 + 3x - 5)$ Factor out x.

$\quad\quad\quad\quad\quad\quad = -x(x^2 - 3x + 5)$ Factor out $-x$. ■

Factoring by Grouping

In Example 5 we factor a four-term polynomial by factoring out a common factor from the first group of two terms and a common factor from the last group of two terms. We then proceed to factor out a common binomial as in Example 3. This method is called **factoring by grouping.** To factor by grouping it is sometimes necessary to factor out the opposite of the greatest common factor as was shown in Example 4.

E X A M P L E   5

Factoring by grouping

Factor each four-term polynomial by grouping

a) $2x + 2y + ax + ay$ **b)** $wa - wb + a - b$

c) $4am - 4an - bm + bn$

Solution

a) The first group of two terms has 2 as a common factor and the second group of two terms has a as a common factor:

$$2x + 2y + ax + ay = 2(x + y) + a(x + y)$$
$$= (2 + a)(x + y)$$

b) Factor w out of the first two terms and 1 out of the last two terms:

$$wa - wb + a - b = w(a - b) + 1(a - b)$$
$$= (w + 1)(a - b)$$

c) Factor out $4a$ from the first two terms and $-b$ (the opposite of the greatest common factor) from the last two terms:

$$4am - 4an - bm + bn = 4a(m - n) - b(m - n)$$
$$= (4a - b)(m - n)$$ ■

Factoring the Difference of Two Squares

A first-degree polynomial in one variable, such as $3x - 5$, is called a linear polynomial. (The equation $3x - 5 = 0$ is a linear equation.)

Linear Polynomial

If a and b are real numbers with $a \neq 0$, then $ax + b$ is called a **linear polynomial.**

A second-degree polynomial such as $x^2 + 5x - 6$ is called a quadratic polynomial.

> **Quadratic Polynomial**
>
> If a, b, and c are real numbers with $a \neq 0$, then $ax^2 + bx + c$ is called a **quadratic polynomial.**

One of the main goals of this chapter is to write a quadratic polynomial (when possible) as a product of linear factors.

Consider the quadratic polynomial $x^2 - 25$. We recognize that $x^2 - 25$ is a difference of two squares, $x^2 - 5^2$. We recall that the product of a sum and a difference is a difference of two squares: $(a + b)(a - b) = a^2 - b^2$. If we reverse this special product rule, we get a rule for factoring the difference of two squares.

> **Factoring the Difference of Two Squares**
>
> $$a^2 - b^2 = (a + b)(a - b)$$

The difference of two squares factors as the product of a sum and a difference. To factor $x^2 - 25$, we replace a by x and b by 5 to get

$$x^2 - 25 = (x + 5)(x - 5).$$

This equation expresses a quadratic polynomial as a product of two linear factors.

E X A M P L E   6 **Factoring the difference of two squares**

Factor each polynomial.

a) $y^2 - 36$ 　　　　b) $9x^2 - 1$ 　　　　c) $4x^2 - y^2$

Helpful Hint

Using the power of a power rule, we can see that any even power is a perfect square:

$$x^{2n} = (x^n)^2$$

Solution

Each of these binomials is a difference of two squares. Each binomial factors into a product of a sum and a difference.

a) $y^2 - 36 = (y + 6)(y - 6)$ 　　We could also write $(y - 6)(y + 6)$ because the factors can be written in any order.

b) $9x^2 - 1 = (3x + 1)(3x - 1)$

c) $4x^2 - y^2 = (2x + y)(2x - y)$ ■

Factoring Perfect Square Trinomials

The trinomial that results from squaring a binomial is called a **perfect square trinomial.** We can reverse the rules from Section 5.4 for the square of a sum or a difference to get rules for factoring.

> **Factoring Perfect Square Trinomials**
>
> $$a^2 + 2ab + b^2 = (a + b)^2$$
> $$a^2 - 2ab + b^2 = (a - b)^2$$

Consider the polynomial $x^2 + 6x + 9$. If we recognize that

$$x^2 + 6x + 9 = x^2 + 2 \cdot x \cdot 3 + 3^2,$$

then we can see that it is a perfect square trinomial. It fits the rule if $a = x$ and $b = 3$:

$$x^2 + 6x + 9 = (x + 3)^2$$

Perfect square trinomials can be identified by using the following strategy.

> **Strategy for Identifying Perfect Square Trinomials**
>
> A trinomial is a perfect square trinomial if
> **1.** the first and last terms are of the form a^2 and b^2,
> **2.** the middle term is 2 or -2 times the product of a and b.

We use this strategy in Example 7.

EXAMPLE   7   **Factoring perfect square trinomials**
Factor each polynomial.
a) $x^2 - 8x + 16$ **b)** $a^2 + 14a + 49$ **c)** $4x^2 + 12x + 9$

Solution

a) Because the first term is x^2, the last is 4^2, and $-2(x)(4)$ is equal to the middle term $-8x$, the trinomial $x^2 - 8x + 16$ is a perfect square trinomial:

$$x^2 - 8x + 16 = (x - 4)^2$$

b) Because $49 = 7^2$ and $14a = 2(a)(7)$, we have a perfect square trinomial:

$$a^2 + 14a + 49 = (a + 7)^2$$

c) Because $4x^2 = (2x)^2$, $9 = 3^2$, and the middle term $12x$ is equal to $2(2x)(3)$, the trinomial $4x^2 + 12x + 9$ is a perfect square trinomial:

$$4x^2 + 12x + 9 = (2x + 3)^2$$ ∎

Factoring a Difference or Sum of Two Cubes

To factor $a^3 - b^3$, a difference of two cubes, examine the following product:

$$(a - b)(a^2 + ab + b^2) = a(a^2 + ab + b^2) - b(a^2 + ab + b^2)$$
$$= a^3 + a^2b + ab^2 - a^2b - ab^2 - b^3$$
$$= a^3 - b^3$$

To factor $a^3 + b^3$, a sum of two cubes, examine the following product:

$$(a + b)(a^2 - ab + b^2) = a(a^2 - ab + b^2) + b(a^2 - ab + b^2)$$
$$= a^3 - a^2b + ab^2 + a^2b - ab^2 + b^3$$
$$= a^3 + b^3$$

By finding these products, we have verified the following formulas for factoring $a^3 - b^3$ and $a^3 + b^3$.

> **Factoring a Difference or a Sum of Two Cubes**
>
> $$a^3 - b^3 = (a - b)(a^2 + ab + b^2)$$
> $$a^3 + b^3 = (a + b)(a^2 - ab + b^2)$$

EXAMPLE   8   **Factoring a difference or a sum of two cubes**
Factor each polynomial.
a) $x^3 - 8$ **b)** $y^3 + 1$ **c)** $8z^3 - 27$

Solution

a) Because $8 = 2^3$, we can use the formula for factoring the difference of two cubes. In the formula $a^3 - b^3 = (a - b)(a^2 + ab + b^2)$, let $a = x$ and $b = 2$:

$$x^3 - 8 = (x - 2)(x^2 + 2x + 4)$$

b) $y^3 + 1 = y^3 + 1^3$ Recognize a sum of two cubes.

$= (y + 1)(y^2 - y + 1)$ Let $a = y$ and $b = 1$ in the formula for the sum of two cubes.

c) $8z^3 - 27 = (2z)^3 - 3^3$ Recognize a difference of two cubes.

$= (2z - 3)(4z^2 + 6z + 9)$ Let $a = 2z$ and $b = 3$ in the formula for a difference of two cubes. ■

Factoring a Polynomial Completely

Polynomials that cannot be factored are called **prime polynomials.** Because binomials such as $x + 5$, $a - 6$, and $3x + 1$ cannot be factored, they are prime polynomials. A polynomial is **factored completely** when it is written as a product of prime polynomials. To factor completely, always factor out the GCF (or its opposite) first. Then continue to factor until all of the factors are prime.

E X A M P L E 9

Factoring completely

Factor each polynomial completely.

a) $5x^2 - 20$ **b)** $3a^3 - 30a^2 + 75a$ **c)** $-2b^4 + 16b$

Solution

a) $5x^2 - 20 = 5(x^2 - 4)$ Greatest common factor

$= 5(x - 2)(x + 2)$ Difference of two squares

b) $3a^3 - 30a^2 + 75a = 3a(a^2 - 10a + 25)$ Greatest common factor

$= 3a(a - 5)^2$ Perfect square trinomial

c) $-2b^4 + 16b = -2b(b^3 - 8)$ Factor out $-2b$ to make the next step easier.

$= -2b(b - 2)(b^2 + 2b + 4)$ Difference of two cubes ■

WARM-UPS

True or false? Explain your answer.

1. For the polynomial $3x^2y - 6xy^2$ we can factor out either $3xy$ or $-3xy$.

2. The greatest common factor for the polynomial $8a^3 - 15b^2$ is 1.

3. $2x - 4 = -2(2 - x)$ for any value of x.

4. $x^2 - 16 = (x - 4)(x + 4)$ for any value of x.

5. The polynomial $x^2 + 6x + 36$ is a perfect square trinomial.

6. The polynomial $y^2 + 16$ is a perfect square trinomial.

7. $9x^2 + 21x + 49 = (3x + 7)^2$ for any value of x.

8. The polynomial $x + 1$ is a factor of $x^3 + 1$.

9. $x^3 - 27 = (x - 3)(x^2 + 6x + 9)$ for any value of x.

10. $x^3 - 8 = (x - 2)^3$ for any value of x.

5.5   EXERCISES

Reading and Writing   *After reading this section, write out the answers to these questions. Use complete sentences.*

1. What is a prime number?

2. When is a natural number factored completely?

3. What is the greatest common factor for the terms of a polynomial?

4. What are the two ways to factor out the greatest common factor?

5. What is a linear polynomial?

6. What is a quadratic polynomial?

7. What is a prime polynomial?

8. When is a polynomial factored completely?

Find the greatest common factor for each group of terms. See Example 1.

9. $48, 36x$

10. $42a, 28a^2$

11. $9wx, 21wy, 15xy$

12. $70x^2, 84x, 42x^3$

13. $24x^2y, 42xy^2, 66xy^3$

14. $60a^2b^5, 140a^9b^2, 40a^3b^6$

Factor out the greatest common factor in each expression. See Examples 2 and 3.

15. $x^3 - 5x$

16. $10x^2 - 20y^3$

17. $48wx + 36wy$

18. $42wz + 28wa$

19. $2x^3 - 4x^2 + 6x$

20. $6x^3 - 12x^2 + 18x$

21. $36a^3b^6 - 24a^4b^2 + 60a^5b^3$

22. $44x^8y^6z - 110x^6y^9z^2$

23. $(x - 6)a + (x - 6)b$

24. $(y - 4)3 + (y - 4)b$

25. $(y - 1)^2y + (y - 1)^2z$

26. $(w - 2)^2 \cdot w + (w - 2)^2 \cdot 3$

Factor out the greatest common factor, then factor out the opposite of the greatest common factor. See Example 4.

27. $2x - 2y$

28. $-3x + 6$

29. $6x^2 - 3x$

30. $10x^2 + 5x$

31. $-w^3 + 3w^2$

32. $-2w^4 + 6w^3$

33. $-a^3 + a^2 - 7a$

34. $-2a^4 - 4a^3 + 6a^2$

Factor each polynomial by grouping. See Example 5.

35. $ax + ay + 3x + 3y$

36. $2a + 2b + wa + wb$

37. $xy - 3y + x - 3$

38. $2wt - 2wa + t - a$

39. $4a - 4b - ca + cb$

40. $pr - 2r - ap + 2a$

41. $xy - y - 6x + 6$

42. $-3a + 3 + ax - x$

Factor each polynomial. See Example 6.

43. $x^2 - 100$

44. $81 - y^2$

45. $4y^2 - 49$

46. $16b^2 - 1$

47. $9x^2 - 25a^2$

48. $121a^2 - b^2$

49. $144w^2z^2 - h^2$

50. $x^2y^2 - 9c^2$

Factor each polynomial. See Example 7.

51. $x^2 - 20x + 100$

52. $y^2 + 10y + 25$

53. $4m^2 - 4m + 1$

54. $9t^2 + 30t + 25$

55. $w^2 - 2wt + t^2$

56. $4r^2 + 20rt + 25t^2$

Factor. See Example 8.

57. $a^3 - 1$

58. $w^3 + 1$

59. $w^3 + 27$

60. $x^3 - 64$

61. $8x^3 - 1$

62. $27x^3 + 1$

63. $64x^3 + 125$

64. $27a^3 + 1000$

65. $8a^3 - 27b^3$

66. $27w^3 - 125y^3$

Factor each polynomial completely. See Example 9.

67. $2x^2 - 8$

68. $3x^3 - 27x$

69. $x^3 + 10x^2 + 25x$

70. $5a^4m - 45a^2m$

71. $4x^2 + 4x + 1$

72. $ax^2 - 8ax + 16a$

73. $(x + 3)x + (x + 3)7$

74. $(x - 2)x - (x - 2)5$

75. $6y^2 + 3y$

76. $4y^2 - y$

77. $4x^2 - 20x + 25$

78. $a^3x^3 - 6a^2x^2 + 9ax$

79. $2m^4 - 2mn^3$

80. $5x^3y^2 - y^5$

81. $(2x - 3)x - (2x - 3)2$

82. $(2x + 1)x + (2x + 1)3$

83. $9a^3 - aw^2$

84. $2bn^2 - 4b^2n + 2b^3$

85. $-5a^2 + 30a - 45$

86. $-2x^2 + 50$

87. $16 - 54x^3$

88. $27x^2y - 64x^2y^4$

89. $-3y^3 - 18y^2 - 27y$

90. $-2m^2n - 8mn - 8n$

91. $-7a^2b^2 + 7$

92. $-17a^2 - 17a$

93. $7x - 7h - hx + h^2$

94. $6a - 6y - ax + xy$

95. $a^2x + 3a^2 - 4x - 12$

96. $x^2y - 2x^2 - y + 2$

Replace k in each trinomial by a number that makes the trinomial a perfect square trinomial.

97. $x^2 + 6x + k$ **98.** $y^2 - 8y + k$

99. $4a^2 - ka + 25$

100. $9u^2 + kuv + 49v^2$

101. $km^2 - 24m + 9$ **102.** $kz^2 + 40z + 16$

103. $81y^2 - 180y + k$ **104.** $36a^2 + 60a + k$

Solve each problem.

105. ***Volume of a bird cage.*** A company makes rectangular shaped bird cages with height b inches and square

bottoms. The volume of these cages is given by the function

$$V = b^3 - 6b^2 + 9b.$$

a) Find an expression for the length of each side of the square bottom by factoring the expression on the right side of the function.

b) Use the function to find the volume of a cage with a height of 18 inches.

c) Use the accompanying graph to estimate the height of a cage for which the volume is 20,000 cubic inches.

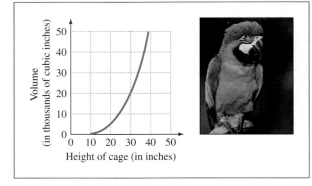

FIGURE FOR EXERCISE 105

106. ***Pyramid power.*** A powerful crystal pyramid has a square base and a volume of $3y^3 + 12y^2 + 12y$ cubic centimeters. If its height is y centimeters, then what polynomial represents the length of a side of the square base? (The volume of a pyramid with a square base of area a^2 and height h is given by $V = \frac{ha^2}{3}$.)

FIGURE FOR EXERCISE 106

GETTING MORE INVOLVED

107. ***Cooperative learning.*** List the perfect square trinomials corresponding to $(x + 1)^2$, $(x + 2)^2$, $(x + 3)^2$, ..., $(x + 12)^2$. Use your list to quiz a classmate. Read a perfect square trinomial at random from your list and ask your classmate to write its factored form. Repeat until both of you have mastered these 12 perfect square trinomials.

5.6   FACTORING $ax^2 + bx + c$

In Section 5.5 you learned to factor certain special polynomials. In this section you will learn to factor general quadratic polynomials. We first factor $ax^2 + bx + c$ with $a = 1$, and then we consider the case $a \neq 1$.

Factoring Trinomials with Leading Coefficient 1

Let's look closely at an example of finding the product of two binomials using the distributive property:

$$(x + 3)(x + 4) = (x + 3)x + (x + 3)4 \quad \text{Distributive property}$$
$$= x^2 + 3x + 4x + 12 \quad \text{Distributive property}$$
$$= x^2 + 7x + 12$$

To factor $x^2 + 7x + 12$, we need to reverse these steps. First observe that the coefficient 7 is the sum of two numbers that have a product of 12. The only numbers that have a product of 12 and a sum of 7 are 3 and 4. So write $7x$ as $3x + 4x$:

$$x^2 + 7x + 12 = x^2 + 3x + 4x + 12$$

Now factor the common factor x out of the first two terms and the common factor 4 out of the last two terms.

$$x^2 + 7x + 12 = \overbrace{x^2 + 3x}^{\text{Factor out } x} + \overbrace{4x + 12}^{\text{Factor out } 4} \quad \text{Rewrite } 7x \text{ as } 3x + 4x.$$
$$= (x + 3)x + (x + 3)4 \quad \text{Factor out common factors.}$$
$$= (x + 3)(x + 4) \quad \text{Factor out the common factor } x + 3.$$

EXAMPLE 1

Factoring $ax^2 + bx + c$ with $a = 1$ by grouping

Factor each trinomial by grouping.

a) $x^2 + 9x + 18$ b) $x^2 - 2x - 24$

Solution

a) We need to find two integers with a product of 18 and a sum of 9. For a product of 18 we could use 1 and 18, 2 and 9, or 3 and 6. Only 3 and 6 have a sum of 9. So we replace $9x$ with $3x + 6x$ and factor by grouping:

$$x^2 + 9x + 18 = x^2 + 3x + 6x + 18 \quad \text{Replace } 9x \text{ by } 3x + 6x.$$
$$= (x + 3)x + (x + 3)6 \quad \text{Factor out common factors.}$$
$$= (x + 3)(x + 6) \quad \text{Check by using FOIL.}$$

b) We need to find two integers with a product of -24 and a sum of -2. For a product of 24 we have 1 and 24, 2 and 12, 3 and 8, or 4 and 6. To get a product of -24 and a sum of -2, we must use 4 and -6:

$$x^2 - 2x - 24 = x^2 - 6x + 4x - 24 \quad \text{Replace } -2x \text{ with } -6x + 4x.$$
$$= (x - 6)x + (x - 6)4 \quad \text{Factor out common factors.}$$
$$= (x - 6)(x + 4) \quad \text{Check by using FOIL.} \quad\blacksquare$$

We factored the trinomials in Example 1 by grouping to show that we could reverse the steps in the multiplication of binomials. However, it is not necessary to write down all of the details shown in Example 1. In Example 2 we simply write the factors.

EXAMPLE 2

A simpler way to factor $ax^2 + bx + c$ with $a = 1$

Factor each quadratic polynomial.

a) $x^2 + 4x + 3$ **b)** $x^2 + 3x - 10$ **c)** $a^2 - 5a + 6$

Study Tip

Set short-term goals and reward yourself for accomplishing them. When you have solved 10 problems, take a short break and listen to your favorite music.

Solution

a) Two integers with a product of 3 and a sum of 4 are 1 and 3:
$$x^2 + 4x + 3 = (x + 1)(x + 3)$$
Check by using FOIL.

b) Two integers with a product of -10 and a sum of 3 are 5 and -2:
$$x^2 + 3x - 10 = (x + 5)(x - 2)$$
Check by using FOIL.

c) Two integers with a product of 6 and a sum of -5 are -3 and -2:
$$a^2 - 5a + 6 = (a - 3)(a - 2)$$

Check by using FOIL.   ■

Factoring Trinomials with Leading Coefficient Not 1

If the leading coefficient of $ax^2 + bx + c$ is not 1 there are two ways to proceed: the ac method or the trial-and-error method. The ac method is a slight variation of the grouping method shown in Example 1 and there is a definite procedure to follow. The trial-and-error method is not as definite. We write down possible factors. If they check you are done and if not you try again. We will present the ac method first.

Consider the trinomial $2x^2 + 11x + 12$, for which $a = 2$, $b = 11$, and $c = 12$. First find ac, the product of the leading coefficient and the constant term. In this case $ac = 2 \cdot 12 = 24$. Now find two integers with a product of 24 and a sum of 11. The pairs of integers with a product of 24 are 1 and 24, 2 and 12, 3 and 8, and 4 and 6. Only 3 and 8 have a product of 24 and a sum of 11. Now replace $11x$ by $3x + 8x$ and factor by grouping:

$$2x^2 + 11x + 12 = 2x^2 + 3x + 8x + 12$$
$$= (2x + 3)x + (2x + 3)4$$
$$= (2x + 3)(x + 4)$$

This strategy for factoring a quadratic trinomial, known as the ***ac* method,** is summarized in the following box. The ac method works also when $a = 1$.

Strategy for Factoring $ax^2 + bx + c$ by the *ac* Method

To factor the trinomial $ax^2 + bx + c$

1. find two integers that have a product equal to ac and a sum equal to b,

2. replace bx by two terms using the two new integers as coefficients,

3. then factor the resulting four-term polynomial by grouping.

EXAMPLE 3

Factoring $ax^2 + bx + c$ with $a \neq 1$

Factor each trinomial.

a) $2x^2 + 9x + 4$ **b)** $2x^2 + 5x - 12$ **c)** $6w^2 - w - 15$

Solution

a) Because $2 \cdot 4 = 8$, we need two numbers with a product of 8 and a sum of 9. The numbers are 1 and 8. Replace $9x$ by $x + 8x$ and factor by grouping:

$$2x^2 + 9x + 4 = 2x^2 + x + 8x + 4$$
$$= (2x + 1)x + (2x + 1)4$$
$$= (2x + 1)(x + 4) \quad \text{Check by FOIL.}$$

Note that if you start with $2x^2 + 8x + x + 4$, and factor by grouping, you get the same result.

b) Because $2(-12) = -24$, we need two numbers with a product of -24 and a sum of 5. The pairs of numbers with a product of 24 are 1 and 24, 2 and 12, 3 and 8, and 4 and 6. To get a product of -24, one of the numbers must be negative and the other positive. To get a sum of positive 5, we need -3 and 8:

$$2x^2 + 5x - 12 = 2x^2 - 3x + 8x - 12$$
$$= (2x - 3)x + (2x - 3)4$$
$$= (2x - 3)(x + 4) \quad \text{Check by FOIL.}$$

c) To factor $6w^2 - w - 15$ we first find that $ac = 6(-15) = -90$. Now we need two numbers that have a product of -90 and a sum of -1. The numbers are -10 and 9. Replace $-w$ with $-10w + 9w$ and factor by grouping:

$$6w^2 - w - 15 = 6w^2 - 10w + 9w - 15$$
$$= 2w(3w - 5) + 3(3w - 5)$$
$$= (2w + 3)(3w - 5) \quad \text{Check by FOIL.} \quad \blacksquare$$

Helpful Hint

The *ac* method has more written work and less guesswork than trial and error. However, many students enjoy the challenge of trying to write only the answer without any other written work.

Trial and Error

After we have gained some experience at factoring by grouping, we can often find the factors without going through the steps of grouping. Consider the polynomial

$$2x^2 - 7x + 6.$$

The factors of $2x^2$ can only be $2x$ and x. The factors of 6 could be 2 and 3 or 1 and 6. We can list all of the possibilities that give the correct first and last terms without putting in the signs:

$$(2x \quad 2)(x \quad 3) \qquad (2x \quad 6)(x \quad 1)$$
$$(2x \quad 3)(x \quad 2) \qquad (2x \quad 1)(x \quad 6)$$

Before actually trying these out, we make an important observation. If $(2x \quad 2)$ or $(2x \quad 6)$ were one of the factors, then there would be a common factor 2 in the original trinomial, but there is not. *If the original trinomial has no common factor, there can be no common factor in either of its linear factors.* Since 6 is positive and the middle term is $-7x$, both of the missing signs must be negative. So the only possibilities are $(2x - 1)(x - 6)$ and $(2x - 3)(x - 2)$. The middle term of the first product is $-13x$, and the middle term of the second product is $-7x$. So we have found the factors:

$$2x^2 - 7x + 6 = (2x - 3)(x - 2)$$

Even though there may be many possibilities in some factoring problems, often we find the correct factors without writing down every possibility. We can use a bit of guesswork in factoring trinomials. *Try* whichever possibility you think might work. *Check* it by multiplying. If it is not right, then *try again*. That is why this method is called **trial and error.**

E X A M P L E   4

Trial and error

Factor each quadratic trinomial using trial and error.

a) $2x^2 + 5x - 3$ **b)** $3x^2 - 11x + 6$ **c)** $6m^2 + 17m + 10$

Solution

a) Because $2x^2$ factors only as $2x \cdot x$ and 3 factors only as $1 \cdot 3$, there are only two possible ways to factor this trinomial to get the correct first and last terms:

$$(2x \quad 1)(x \quad 3) \qquad \text{and} \qquad (2x \quad 3)(x \quad 1)$$

Because the last term of the trinomial is negative, one of the missing signs must be $+$, and the other must be $-$. Now we try the various possibilities until we get the correct middle term:

$$(2x + 1)(x - 3) = 2x^2 - 5x - 3$$
$$(2x + 3)(x - 1) = 2x^2 + x - 3$$
$$(2x - 1)(x + 3) = 2x^2 + 5x - 3$$

Since the last product has the correct middle term, the trinomial is factored as

$$2x^2 + 5x - 3 = (2x - 1)(x + 3).$$

b) There are four possible ways to factor $3x^2 - 11x + 6$:

$$(3x \quad 1)(x \quad 6) \qquad (3x \quad 2)(x \quad 3)$$
$$(3x \quad 6)(x \quad 1) \qquad (3x \quad 3)(x \quad 2)$$

Because the last term is positive and the middle term is negative, both signs must be negative. Now try possible factors until we get the correct middle term:

$$(3x - 1)(x - 6) = 3x^2 - 19x + 6$$
$$(3x - 2)(x - 3) = 3x^2 - 11x + 6$$

The trinomial is factored correctly as

$$3x^2 - 11x + 6 = (3x - 2)(x - 3).$$

c) Because all of the signs in $6m^2 + 17m + 10$ are positive, all of the signs in the factors are positive. There are eight possible products that will start with $6m^2$ and end with 10:

$$(2m + 2)(3m + 5) \qquad (6m + 2)(m + 5)$$
$$(2m + 5)(3m + 2) \qquad (6m + 5)(m + 2)$$
$$(2m + 1)(3m + 10) \qquad (6m + 1)(m + 10)$$
$$(2m + 10)(3m + 1) \qquad (6m + 10)(m + 1)$$

Only $(6m + 5)(m + 2)$ has a middle term of $17m$. So

$$6m^2 + 17m + 10 = (6m + 5)(m + 2). \qquad \blacksquare$$

Factoring by Substitution

So far, the polynomials that we have factored, without common factors, have all been of degree 2 or 3. Some polynomials of higher degree can be factored by substituting a single variable for a variable with a higher power. After factoring, we replace the single variable by the higher-power variable. This method is called **substitution.**

E X A M P L E   5

Factoring by substitution

Factor each polynomial.

a) $x^4 - 9$

b) $y^8 - 14y^4 + 49$

Solution

a) We recognize $x^4 - 9$ as a difference of two squares in which $x^4 = (x^2)^2$ and $9 = 3^2$. If we let $w = x^2$, then $w^2 = x^4$. So we can replace x^4 by w^2 and factor:

$$x^4 - 9 = w^2 - 9 \qquad \text{Replace } x^4 \text{ by } w^2.$$
$$= (w + 3)(w - 3) \qquad \text{Difference of two squares}$$
$$= (x^2 + 3)(x^2 - 3) \qquad \text{Replace } w \text{ by } x^2.$$

b) We recognize $y^8 - 14y^4 + 49$ as a perfect square trinomial in which $y^8 = (y^4)^2$ and $49 = 7^2$. We let $w = y^4$ and $w^2 = y^8$:

$$y^8 - 14y^4 + 49 = w^2 - 14w + 49 \qquad \text{Replace } y^4 \text{ by } w \text{ and } y^8 \text{ by } w^2.$$
$$= (w - 7)^2 \qquad \text{Perfect square trinomial}$$
$$= (y^4 - 7)^2 \qquad \text{Replace } w \text{ by } y^4. \qquad ■$$

C A U T I O N   Polynomials that we factor by substitution must contain just the right exponents. We can factor $y^8 - 14y^4 + 49$ because y^8 is a perfect square: $y^8 = (y^4)^2$. Note that even powers such as x^4, y^{14}, and w^{20} are perfect squares, because $x^4 = (x^2)^2$, $y^{14} = (y^7)^2$, and $w^{20} = (w^{10})^2$.

In Example 6 we use substitution to factor polynomials that have variables as exponents.

E X A M P L E   6

Polynomials with variable exponents

Factor completely. The variables used in the exponents represent positive integers.

a) $x^{2m} - y^2$

b) $z^{2n+1} - 6z^{n+1} + 9z$

Solution

a) Notice that $x^{2m} = (x^m)^2$. So if we let $w = x^m$, then $w^2 = x^{2m}$:

$$x^{2m} - y^2 = w^2 - y^2 \qquad \text{Substitution}$$
$$= (w + y)(w - y) \qquad \text{Difference of two squares}$$
$$= (x^m + y)(x^m - y) \qquad \text{Replace } w \text{ by } x^m.$$

b) First factor out the common factor z:

$$z^{2n+1} - 6z^{n+1} + 9z = z(z^{2n} - 6z^n + 9)$$
$$= z(a^2 - 6a + 9) \qquad \text{Let } a = z^n.$$
$$= z(a - 3)^2 \qquad \text{Perfect square trinomial}$$
$$= z(z^n - 3)^2 \qquad \text{Replace } a \text{ by } z^n. \qquad ■$$

It is not absolutely necessary to use substitution in factoring polynomials with higher degrees or variable exponents as we did in Examples 5 and 6. In Example 7 we use trial and error to factor similar polynomials. Remember to always look for a common factor first.

E X A M P L E 7

Higher-degree and variable exponent trinomials

Factor each polynomial completely. Variables used as exponents represent positive integers.

a) $x^8 - 2x^4 - 15$ **b)** $-18y^7 + 21y^4 + 15y$ **c)** $2u^{2m} - 5u^m - 3$

Solution

a) To factor by trial and error, notice that $x^8 = x^4 \cdot x^4$. Now 15 is $3 \cdot 5$ or $1 \cdot 15$. Using 1 and 15 will not give the required -2 for the coefficient of the middle term. So choose 3 and -5 to get the -2 in the middle term:

$$x^8 - 2x^4 - 15 = (x^4 - 5)(x^4 + 3)$$

b) $-18y^7 + 21y^4 + 15y = -3y(6y^6 - 7y^3 - 5)$ Factor out the common factor $-3y$ first.

$$= -3y(2y^3 + 1)(3y^3 - 5)$$ Factor the trinomial by trial and error.

c) Notice that $2u^{2m} = 2u^m \cdot u^m$ and $3 = 3 \cdot 1$. Using trial and error, we get

$$2u^{2m} - 5u^m - 3 = (2u^m + 1)(u^m - 3). \qquad ■$$

W A R M - U P S

True or false? Answer true if the polynomial is factored correctly and false otherwise.

1. $x^2 + 9x + 18 = (x + 3)(x + 6)$

2. $y^2 + 2y - 35 = (y + 5)(y - 7)$

3. $x^2 + 4 = (x + 2)(x + 2)$

4. $x^2 - 5x - 6 = (x - 3)(x - 2)$

5. $x^2 - 4x - 12 = (x - 6)(x + 2)$

6. $x^2 + 15x + 36 = (x + 4)(x + 9)$

7. $3x^2 + 4x - 15 = (3x + 5)(x - 3)$

8. $4x^2 + 4x - 3 = (4x - 1)(x + 3)$

9. $4x^2 - 4x - 3 = (2x + 1)(2x - 3)$

10. $4x^2 + 8x + 3 = (2x + 1)(2x + 3)$

5.6   E X E R C I S E S

Reading and Writing   *After reading this section, write out the answers to these questions. Use complete sentences.*

1. How do we factor trinomials that have a leading coefficient of 1?

2. How do we factor trinomials in which the leading coefficient is not 1?

3. What is trial-and-error factoring?

4. What should you always first look for when factoring a polynomial?

Factor each polynomial. See Examples 1 and 2.

5. $x^2 + 4x + 3$ **6.** $y^2 + 5y + 6$

7. $a^2 + 15a + 50$ **8.** $t^2 + 11t + 24$

9. $y^2 - 5y - 14$ **10.** $x^2 - 3x - 18$

11. $x^2 - 6x + 8$ **12.** $y^2 - 13y + 30$

13. $a^2 - 12a + 27$

14. $x^2 - x - 30$

15. $a^2 + 7a - 30$

16. $w^2 + 29w - 30$

Factor each polynomial. See Example 3.

17. $6w^2 + 5w + 1$

18. $4x^2 + 11x + 6$

19. $2x^2 - 5x - 3$

20. $2a^2 + 3a - 2$

21. $4x^2 + 16x + 15$

22. $6y^2 + 17y + 12$

23. $6x^2 - 5x + 1$

24. $6m^2 - m - 12$

25. $12y^2 + y - 1$

26. $12x^2 + 5x - 2$

27. $6a^2 + a - 5$

28. $30b^2 - b - 3$

Factor each polynomial. See Example 4.

29. $2x^2 + 15x - 8$

30. $3a^2 + 20a + 12$

31. $3b^2 - 16b - 35$

32. $2y^2 - 17y + 21$

33. $6w^2 + w - 12$

34. $15x^2 - x - 6$

35. $4x^2 - 5x + 1$

36. $4x^2 + 7x + 3$

37. $5m^2 + 13m - 6$

38. $5t^2 - 9t - 2$

39. $6y^2 - 7y - 20$

40. $7u^2 + 11u - 6$

Factor each polynomial completely. See Example 5.

41. $x^{10} - 9$

42. $y^8 - 4$

43. $z^{12} - 6z^6 + 9$

44. $a^6 + 10a^3 + 25$

45. $2x^7 + 8x^4 + 8x$

46. $x^{13} - 6x^7 + 9x$

47. $4x^5 + 4x^3 + x$

48. $18x^6 + 24x^3 + 8$

49. $x^6 - 8$

50. $y^6 - 27$

Factor each polynomial completely. The variables used as exponents represent positive integers. See Example 6.

51. $a^{2n} - 1$

52. $b^{4n} - 9$

53. $a^{2r} + 6a^r + 9$

54. $u^{6n} - 4u^{3n} + 4$

55. $x^{3m} - 8$

56. $y^{3n} + 1$

57. $a^{3m} - b^3$

58. $r^{3m} + 8t^3$

59. $k^{2w+1} - 10k^{w+1} + 25k$

60. $4a^{2t+1} + 4a^{t+1} + a$

Factor each polynomial completely. See Example 7. The variables used in exponents represent positive integers.

61. $x^6 - 2x^3 - 35$

62. $x^4 + 7x^2 - 30$

63. $a^{20} - 20a^{10} + 100$

64. $b^{16} + 22b^8 + 121$

65. $-12a^5 - 10a^3 - 2a$

66. $-4b^7 + 4b^4 + 3b$

67. $x^{2a} + 2x^a - 15$

68. $y^{2b} + y^b - 20$

69. $x^{2a} - y^{2b}$

70. $w^{4m} - a^2$

71. $x^8 - x^4 - 6$

72. $m^{10} - 5m^5 - 6$

73. $x^{a+2} - x^a$

74. $y^{2a+1} - y$

75. $x^{2a} + 6x^a + 9$

76. $x^{2a} - 2x^a y^b + y^{2b}$

Factor each polynomial completely.

77. $2x^2 + 20x + 50$

78. $3a^2 + 6a + 3$

79. $a^3 - 36a$

80. $x^3 + 5x^2 - 6x$

81. $10a^2 + 55a - 30$

82. $6a^2 + 22a - 84$

83. $2x^2 - 128y^2$

84. $a^3 - 6a^2 + 9a$

85. $-9x^2 + 33x + 12$

86. $2xy^2 - 27xy + 70x$

87. $m^5 + 20m^4 + 100m^3$

88. $4a^2 - 16a + 16$

89. $6x^2 + 23x + 20$

90. $2y^2 - 13y + 6$

91. $9y^3 - 24y^2 + 16y$

92. $25m^3 - 10m^2 + m$

93. $r^2 - 6rs + 8s^2$

94. $7z^2 + 15zy + 2y^2$

95. $m^3 + 2m + 3m^2$

96. $7w^2 - 18w + w^3$

97. $6m^3 - m^2n - 2mn^2$

98. $3a^3 + 3a^2b - 18ab^2$

99. $9m^2 - 25n^2$

100. $m^2n^2 - 2mn^3 + n^4$

101. $5a^2 + 20a - 60$

102. $-3y^2 + 9y + 30$

103. $-2w^2 + 18w + 20$

104. $x^2z + 2xyz + y^2z$

105. $w^2x^2 - 100x^2$

106. $9x^2 + 30x + 25$

107. $81x^2 - 9$

108. $12w^2 - 38w - 72$

109. $8x^2 - 2x - 15$

110. $4w^2 + 12w + 9$

111. $3m^4 - 24m$
112. $6w^3z + 6z$

GETTING MORE INVOLVED

 113. *Discussion.* Which of the following is not a perfect square trinomial? Explain.
a) $4a^6 - 6a^3b^4 + 9b^8$ **b)** $1000x^2 + 200ax + a^2$
c) $900y^4 - 60y^2 + 1$ **d)** $36 - 36z^7 + 9z^{14}$

 114. *Discussion.* Which of the following is not a difference of two squares? Explain.
a) $16a^8y^4 - 25c^{12}$ **b)** $a^9 - b^4$
c) $t^{90} - 1$ **d)** $x^2 - 196$

 115. *Writing.* Factor each polynomial and explain how you decided which method to use.
a) $x^2 + 10x + 25$
b) $x^2 - 10x + 25$
c) $x^2 + 26x + 25$
d) $x^2 - 25$
e) $x^2 + 25$

 116. *Discussion.* On an exam, a student factored $2x^2 - 6x + 4$ as $(2x - 4)(x - 1)$. Even though the student carefully checked that

$$(2x - 4)(x - 1) = 2x^2 - 6x + 4,$$

the student lost some points. What went wrong?

In This Section

- Prime Polynomials
- Factoring Polynomials Completely
- Summary

 5.7 **FACTORING STRATEGY**

In previous sections we established the general idea of factoring and many special cases. In this section we will see that a polynomial can have as many factors as its degree, and we will factor higher-degree polynomials completely. We will also see a general strategy for factoring polynomials.

Prime Polynomials

A polynomial that cannot be factored is a prime polynomial. Binomials with no common factors, such as $2x + 1$ and $a - 3$, are prime polynomials. To determine whether a polynomial such as $x^2 + 1$ is a prime polynomial, we must try all possibilities for factoring it. If $x^2 + 1$ could be factored as a product of two binomials, the only possibilities that would give a first term of x^2 and a last term of 1 are $(x + 1)(x + 1)$ and $(x - 1)(x - 1)$. However,

$$(x + 1)(x + 1) = x^2 + 2x + 1 \quad \text{and} \quad (x - 1)(x - 1) = x^2 - 2x + 1.$$

Both products have an x-term. Of course, $(x + 1)(x - 1)$ has no x-term, but

$$(x + 1)(x - 1) = x^2 - 1.$$

Because none of these possibilities results in $x^2 + 1$, the polynomial $x^2 + 1$ is a prime polynomial. Note that $x^2 + 1$ is a sum of two squares. A sum of two squares of the form $a^2 + b^2$ is always a prime polynomial.

EXAMPLE 1 **Prime polynomials**
Determine whether the polynomial $x^2 + 3x + 4$ is a prime polynomial.

Solution

To factor $x^2 + 3x + 4$, we must find two integers with a product of 4 and a sum of 3. The only pairs of positive integers with a product of 4 are 1 and 4, and 2 and 2. Because the product is positive 4, both numbers must be negative or both positive. Under these conditions it is impossible to get a sum of positive 3. The polynomial is prime. ∎

Factoring Polynomials Completely

So far, a typical polynomial has been a product of two factors, with possibly a common factor removed first. However, it is possible that the factors can still be factored again. A polynomial in a single variable may have as many factors as its degree. We have factored a polynomial completely when all of the factors are prime polynomials.

E X A M P L E   2

Factoring higher-degree polynomials completely

Factor $x^4 + x^2 - 2$ completely.

Solution

Two numbers with a product of -2 and a sum of 1 are 2 and -1:

$$x^4 + x^2 - 2 = (x^2 + 2)(x^2 - 1)$$
$$= (x^2 + 2)(x - 1)(x + 1) \quad \text{Difference of two squares}$$

Since $x^2 + 2$, $x - 1$, and $x + 1$ are prime, the polynomial is factored completely. ∎

In Example 3 we factor a sixth-degree polynomial.

E X A M P L E   3

Study Tip

Find a clean, comfortable, well-lit place to study. But don't get too comfortable. Sitting at a desk is preferable to lying in bed. Where you study can influence your concentration and your study habits.

Factoring completely

Factor $3x^6 - 3$ completely.

Solution

To factor $3x^6 - 3$, we must first factor out the common factor 3 and then recognize that x^6 is a perfect square: $x^6 = (x^3)^2$:

$$3x^6 - 3 = 3(x^6 - 1) \qquad \text{Factor out the common factor.}$$
$$= 3((x^3)^2 - 1) \qquad \text{Write } x^6 \text{ as a perfect square.}$$
$$= 3(x^3 - 1)(x^3 + 1) \qquad \text{Difference of two squares}$$
$$= 3(x - 1)(x^2 + x + 1)(x + 1)(x^2 - x + 1) \qquad \text{Difference of two cubes and sum of two cubes}$$

Since $x^2 + x + 1$ and $x^2 - x + 1$ are prime, the polynomial is factored completely. ∎

In Example 3 we recognized $x^6 - 1$ as a difference of two squares. However, $x^6 - 1$ is also a difference of two cubes, and we can factor it using the rule for the difference of two cubes:

$$x^6 - 1 = (x^2)^3 - 1 = (x^2 - 1)(x^4 + x^2 + 1)$$

Now we can factor $x^2 - 1$, but it is difficult to see how to factor $x^4 + x^2 + 1$. (It is not prime.) Although x^6 can be thought of as a perfect square or a perfect cube, in this case thinking of it as a perfect square is better.

In Example 4 we use substitution to simplify the polynomial before factoring. This fourth-degree polynomial has four factors.

E X A M P L E   4

Using substitution to simplify

Factor $(w^2 - 1)^2 - 11(w^2 - 1) + 24$ completely.

Solution

Let $a = w^2 - 1$ to simplify the polynomial:

$$
\begin{aligned}
(w^2 - 1)^2 - 11(w^2 - 1) + 24 &= a^2 - 11a + 24 & \text{Replace } w^2 - 1 \text{ by } a.\\
&= (a - 8)(a - 3)\\
&= (w^2 - 1 - 8)(w^2 - 1 - 3) & \text{Replace } a \text{ by } w^2 - 1.\\
&= (w^2 - 9)(w^2 - 4)\\
&= (w + 3)(w - 3)(w + 2)(w - 2) & \blacksquare
\end{aligned}
$$

Example 5 shows two four-term polynomials that can be factored by grouping. In the first part, the terms must be rearranged before the polynomial can be factored by grouping. In the second part the polynomial is grouped in a new manner.

E X A M P L E   5

More factoring by grouping

Factor completely.

a) $x^2 - 3w - 3x + xw$

b) $x^2 - 6x + 9 - y^2$

Solution

a) Since the first two terms do not have a common factor, we rearrange the terms as follows:

$$
\begin{aligned}
x^2 - 3w - 3x + xw &= x^2 - 3x + xw - 3w\\
&= x(x - 3) + w(x - 3)\\
&= (x + w)(x - 3)
\end{aligned}
$$

b) We cannot factor this polynomial by grouping pairs of terms. However, $x^2 - 6x + 9$ is a perfect square, $(x - 3)^2$. So we can group the first three terms and then factor the difference of two squares:

$$
\begin{aligned}
x^2 - 6x + 9 - y^2 &= (x - 3)^2 - y^2 & \text{Perfect square trinomial}\\
&= (x - 3 + y)(x - 3 - y) & \text{Difference of two squares} \quad \blacksquare
\end{aligned}
$$

Summary

A strategy for factoring polynomials is given in the following box.

Strategy for Factoring Polynomials

1. If there are any common factors, factor them out first.

2. When factoring a binomial, look for the special cases: difference of two squares, difference of two cubes, and sum of two cubes. Remember that a sum of two squares $a^2 + b^2$ is prime.

3. When factoring a trinomial, check to see whether it is a perfect square trinomial.

4. When factoring a trinomial that is not a perfect square, use grouping or trial and error.

5. When factoring a polynomial of high degree, use substitution to get a polynomial of degree 2 or 3, or use trial and error.

6. If the polynomial has four terms, try factoring by grouping.

E X A M P L E   6

Using the factoring strategy

Factor each polynomial completely.

a) $3w^3 - 3w^2 - 18w$ **b)** $10x^2 + 160$

c) $16a^2b - 80ab + 100b$ **d)** $aw + mw + az + mz$

e) $a^4b + 125ab$ **f)** $12x^2y - 26xy - 30y$

Helpful Hint
_____

When factoring integers, we write $4 = 2 \cdot 2$. However, when factoring polynomials we usually do not factor any of the integers that appear. So we say that $4b(2a - 5)^2$ is factored completely.

Solution

a) The greatest common factor (GCF) for the three terms is $3w$:

$$3w^3 - 3w^2 - 18w = 3w(w^2 - w - 6) \quad \text{Factor out } 3w.$$
$$= 3w(w - 3)(w + 2) \quad \text{Factor completely.}$$

b) The GCF in $10x^2 + 160$ is 10:

$$10x^2 + 160 = 10(x^2 + 16)$$

Because $x^2 + 16$ is prime, the polynomial is factored completely.

c) The GCF in $16a^2b - 80ab + 100b$ is $4b$:

$$16a^2b - 80ab + 100b = 4b(4a^2 - 20a + 25)$$
$$= 4b(2a - 5)^2$$

d) The polynomial has four terms, and we can factor it by grouping:

$$aw + mw + az + mz = w(a + m) + z(a + m)$$
$$= (w + z)(a + m)$$

e) The GCF in $a^4b + 125ab$ is ab:

$$a^4b + 125ab = ab(a^3 + 125) \quad \text{Factor out } ab.$$
$$= ab(a + 5)(a^2 - 5a + 25) \quad \text{Factor the sum of two cubes.}$$

f) The GCF in $12x^2y - 26xy - 30y$ is $2y$:

$$12x^2y - 26xy - 30y = 2y(6x^2 - 13x - 15) \quad \text{Factor out } 2y.$$
$$= 2y(x - 3)(6x + 5) \quad \text{Trial and error} \quad \blacksquare$$

WARM-UPS

True or false? Explain your answer.

1. $x^2 - 9 = (x - 3)^2$ for any value of x.
2. The polynomial $4x^2 + 12x + 9$ is a perfect square trinomial.
3. The sum of two squares $a^2 + b^2$ is prime.
4. The polynomial $x^4 - 16$ is factored completely as $(x^2 - 4)(x^2 + 4)$.
5. $y^3 - 27 = (y + 3)(y^2 + 3y - 9)$ for any value of y.
6. The polynomial $y^6 - 1$ is a difference of two squares.
7. The polynomial $2x^2 + 2x - 12$ is factored completely as $(2x - 4)(x + 3)$.

8. The polynomial $x^2 - 4x - 4$ is a prime polynomial.
9. The polynomial $a^6 - 1$ is the difference of two cubes.
10. The polynomial $x^2 + 3x - ax + 3a$ can be factored by grouping.

5.7   EXERCISES ────────────────────────────────

Reading and Writing   *After reading this section, write out the answers to these questions. Use complete sentences.*

1. What should you do first when factoring a polynomial?

2. If you are factoring a binomial, then what should you look for?

3. When factoring a trinomial what should you look for?

4. What should you look for when factoring a four-term polynomial?

Determine whether each polynomial is a prime polynomial. See Example 1.

5. $y^2 + 100$

6. $3x^2 + 27$

7. $-9w^2 - 9$

8. $25y^2 + 36$

9. $x^2 - 2x - 3$

10. $x^2 - 2x + 3$

11. $x^2 + 2x + 3$

12. $x^2 + 4x + 3$

13. $x^2 - 4x - 3$

14. $x^2 + 4x - 3$

15. $6x^2 + 3x - 4$

16. $4x^2 - 5x - 3$

Factor each polynomial completely. See Examples 2–4.

17. $a^4 - 10a^2 + 25$

18. $9y^4 + 12y^2 + 4$

19. $x^4 - 6x^2 + 8$

20. $x^6 + 2x^3 - 3$

21. $(3x - 5)^2 - 1$

22. $(2x + 1)^2 - 4$

23. $2y^6 - 128$

24. $6 - 6y^6$

25. $32a^4 - 18$

26. $2a^4 - 32$

27. $x^4 - (x - 6)^2$

28. $y^4 - (2y + 1)^2$

29. $(m + 2)^2 + 2(m + 2) - 3$

30. $(2w - 3)^2 - 2(2w - 3) - 15$

31. $3(y - 1)^2 + 11(y - 1) - 20$

32. $2(w + 2)^2 + 5(w + 2) - 3$

33. $(y^2 - 3)^2 - 4(y^2 - 3) - 12$

34. $(m^2 - 8)^2 - 4(m^2 - 8) - 32$

Factor completely. See Example 5.

35. $x^2 - 2b - 2x + bx$

36. $y^2 - c - y + cy$

37. $x^2 - ay - xy + ax$

38. $ax - by + bx - ay$

39. $x^2 + 2x + 1 - a^2$

40. $x^2 + 10x + 25 - b^2$

41. $x^2 - 4x + 4 - w^2$

42. $x^2 - 8x + 16 - c^2$

43. $x^2 - z^2 + 4x + 4$

44. $x^2 + 36 - m^2 - 12x$

Use the factoring strategy to factor each polynomial completely. See Example 6.

45. $9x^2 - 24x + 16$

46. $-3x^2 + 18x + 48$

47. $12x^2 - 13x + 3$

48. $2x^2 - 3x - 6$

49. $3a^4 + 81a$

50. $-a^3 + 25a$

51. $32 + 2x^2$

52. $x^3 + 4x^2 + 4x$

53. $6x^2 - 5x + 12$

54. $x^4 + 2x^3 - x - 2$

55. $(x + y)^2 - 1$

56. $x^3 + 9x$

57. $a^3b - ab^3$

58. $2m^3 - 250n^3$

59. $x^4 + 2x^3 - 8x - 16$

60. $(x + 5)^2 - 4$

61. $m^2n + 2mn^2 + n^3$

62. $a^2b - 2ab^2 + b^3$

63. $2m + wn + 2n + wm$

64. $aw - 5b + bw - 5a$

65. $4w^2 + 4w - 3$

66. $4w^2 + 8w - 63$

67. $t^4 + 4t^2 - 21$

68. $m^4 + 5m^2 + 4$

69. $-a^3 - 7a^2 + 30a$

70. $2y^4 + 3y^3 - 20y^2$

71. $(y + 5)^2 - 2(y + 5) - 3$

72. $(2t - 1)^2 + 7(2t - 1) + 10$

73. $-2w^4 + 1250$

74. $5a^5 - 5a$

75. $4a^2 + 16$

76. $9w^2 + 81$

77. $8a^3 + 8a$

78. $awx + ax$

79. $(w + 5)^2 - 9$

80. $(a - 6)^2 - 1$

81. $4aw^2 - 12aw + 9a$

82. $9an^3 + 15an^2 - 14an$

83. $x^2 - 6xy + 9y^2$

84. $x^3 + 12x^2y + 36xy^2$

85. $3x^4 - 75x^2$

86. $3x^2 + 9x + 12$

87. $m^3n - n$

88. $m^4 + 16m^2$

89. $12x^2 + 2x - 30$

90. $90x^2 + 3x - 60$

91. $2a^3 - 32$

92. $12x^2 - 28x + 15$

Factor completely. Assume variables used as exponents represent positive integers.

93. $a^{3m} - 1$

94. $x^{6a} + 8$

95. $a^{3w} - b^{6n}$

96. $x^{2n} - 9$

97. $t^{4n} - 16$

98. $a^{3n+2} + a^2$

99. $a^{2n+1} - 2a^{n+1} - 15a$

100. $x^{3m} + x^{2m} - 6x^m$

101. $a^{2n} - 3a^n + a^nb - 3b$

102. $x^mz + 5z + x^{m+1} + 5x$

GETTING MORE INVOLVED

 103. *Cooperative learning.* Write down 10 trinomials of the form $ax^2 + bx + c$ "at random" using integers for a, b, and c. What percent of your 10 trinomials are prime? Would you say that prime trinomials are the exception or the rule? Compare your results with those of your classmates.

 104. *Writing.* The polynomial

$$x^3 + 5x^2 + 7x + 3$$

is a product of three factors of the form $x \pm n$, where n is a natural number smaller than 4. Factor this polynomial completely and explain your procedure.

In This Section

- The Zero Factor Property
- Applications

Helpful Hint

Note that the zero factor property is our second example of getting an equivalent equation without "doing the same thing to each side." What was the first?

 5.8

SOLVING EQUATIONS BY FACTORING

The techniques of factoring can be used to solve equations involving polynomials that cannot be solved by the other methods that you have learned. After you learn to solve equations by factoring, we will use this technique to solve some new applied problems in this section and in Chapters 6 and 8.

The Zero Factor Property

The equation $ab = 0$ indicates that the product of two unknown numbers is 0. But the product of two real numbers is zero only when one or the other of the numbers is 0. So even though we do not know exactly the values of a and b from $ab = 0$, we do know that $a = 0$ or $b = 0$. This idea is called the **zero factor property.**

> **Zero Factor Property**
>
> The equation $ab = 0$ is equivalent to the compound equation
>
> $$a = 0 \qquad \text{or} \qquad b = 0.$$

Example 1 shows how to use the zero factor property to solve an equation in one variable.

E X A M P L E   1   **Using the zero factor property**
Solve $x^2 + x - 12 = 0$.

Solution

We factor the left-hand side of the equation to get a product of two factors that are equal to 0. Then we write an equivalent equation using the zero factor property.

$$x^2 + x - 12 = 0$$

$$(x + 4)(x - 3) = 0 \quad \text{Factor the left-hand side.}$$

$$x + 4 = 0 \qquad \text{or} \qquad x - 3 = 0 \quad \text{Zero factor property}$$

$$x = -4 \qquad \text{or} \qquad x = 3 \quad \text{Solve each part of the compound equation.}$$

Check that both -4 and 3 satisfy $x^2 + x - 12 = 0$. If $x = -4$, we get

$$(-4)^2 + (-4) - 12 = 16 - 4 - 12 = 0.$$

If $x = 3$, we get

$$(3)^2 + 3 - 12 = 9 + 3 - 12 = 0.$$

So the solution set is $\{-4, 3\}$. ∎

   The zero factor property is used only in solving polynomial equations that have zero on one side and a polynomial that can be factored on the other side. The polynomials that we factored most often were the quadratic polynomials. The equations that we will solve most often using the zero factor property will be quadratic equations.

Quadratic Equation

If a, b, and c are real numbers, with $a \neq 0$, then the equation

$$ax^2 + bx + c = 0$$

is called a **quadratic equation.**

M A T H   A T   W O R K

Seamas Mercado, professional bodyboarder and 1988 National Champion, charges the waves off Hawaii, Tahiti, Indonesia, Mexico, and California. In choosing a board for competition and for the maneuvers he wants to perform, Mercado factors in his height and weight as well as the size, power, and temperature of the waves he will be riding. In colder water a softer, more flexible board is used; in warmer water a stiffer board is chosen. When waves crash on shore, the ride usually lasts 3 to 5 seconds, and a shorter board with a narrow tail is chosen for greater control. When waves break along a sand bar or reef, the ride can sometimes last as long as 2 minutes, and a straighter board with more surface area is chosen so that the board will move faster and allow the rider to pull off more maneuvers. Basic maneuvers include bottom turns, aerials, forward and reverse 360's, and el rollos.

BODYBOARD DESIGNER

   As one of the top 10 bodyboarders in the world, Mercado helps to design the boards he uses. "Performance levels are greatly increased with fine-tuned equipment and techniques," he says. In Exercise 75 of Section 5.8 you will find the dimensions of a given bodyboard.

In Chapter 8 we will study quadratic equations further and solve quadratic equations that cannot be solved by factoring. Keep the following strategy in mind when solving equations by factoring.

> **Strategy for Solving Equations by Factoring**
>
> 1. Write the equation with 0 on the right-hand side.
> 2. Factor the left-hand side.
> 3. Use the zero factor property to get simpler equations. (Set each factor equal to 0.)
> 4. Solve the simpler equations.
> 5. Check the answers in the original equation.

E X A M P L E   2

Solving a quadratic equation by factoring

Solve each equation.

a) $10x^2 = 5x$

b) $3x - 6x^2 = -9$

Solution

a) Use the steps in the strategy for solving equations by factoring:

$$10x^2 = 5x \qquad \text{Original equation}$$
$$10x^2 - 5x = 0 \qquad \text{Rewrite with zero on the right-hand side.}$$
$$5x(2x - 1) = 0 \qquad \text{Factor the left-hand side.}$$
$$5x = 0 \quad \text{or} \quad 2x - 1 = 0 \qquad \text{Zero factor property}$$
$$x = 0 \quad \text{or} \quad x = \frac{1}{2} \qquad \text{Solve for } x.$$

The solution set is $\left\{0, \frac{1}{2}\right\}$. Check each solution in the original equation.

b) First rewrite the equation with 0 on the right-hand side and the left-hand side in order of descending exponents:

$$3x - 6x^2 = -9 \qquad \text{Original equation}$$
$$-6x^2 + 3x + 9 = 0 \qquad \text{Add 9 to each side.}$$
$$2x^2 - x - 3 = 0 \qquad \text{Divide each side by } -3.$$
$$(2x - 3)(x + 1) = 0 \qquad \text{Factor.}$$
$$2x - 3 = 0 \quad \text{or} \quad x + 1 = 0 \qquad \text{Zero factor property}$$
$$x = \frac{3}{2} \quad \text{or} \quad x = -1 \qquad \text{Solve for } x.$$

The solution set is $\left\{-1, \frac{3}{2}\right\}$. Check each solution in the original equation.   ■

C A U T I O N   If we divide each side of $10x^2 = 5x$ by $5x$, we get $2x = 1$, or $x = \frac{1}{2}$. We do not get $x = 0$. By dividing by $5x$ we have lost one of the factors and one of the solutions.

In Example 3 there are more than two factors, but we can still write an equivalent equation by setting each factor equal to 0.

E X A M P L E   3

Solving a cubic equation by factoring

Solve $2x^3 - 3x^2 - 8x + 12 = 0$.

Solution

First notice that the first two terms have the common factor x^2 and the last two terms have the common factor -4.

$$x^2(2x - 3) - 4(2x - 3) = 0 \quad \text{Factor by grouping.}$$
$$(x^2 - 4)(2x - 3) = 0 \quad \text{Factor out } 2x - 3.$$
$$(x - 2)(x + 2)(2x - 3) = 0 \quad \text{Factor completely.}$$

$x - 2 = 0 \quad$ or $\quad x + 2 = 0 \quad$ or $\quad 2x - 3 = 0 \quad$ Set each factor equal to 0.

$x = 2 \quad$ or $\quad x = -2 \quad$ or $\quad x = \dfrac{3}{2}$

The solution set is $\left\{-2, \dfrac{3}{2}, 2\right\}$. Check each solution in the original equation. ■

The equation in the next example involves absolute value.

Calculator Close-Up

To check, use Y= to enter

$\quad y_1 = 2x^3 - 3x^2 - 8x + 12.$

Then use the variables feature (VARS) to find $y_1(-2)$, $y_1(3/2)$, and $y_1(2)$.

```
Y₁(-2)
              0
Y₁(3/2)
              0
Y₁(2)
              0
```

E X A M P L E   4

Solving an absolute value equation by factoring

Solve $|x^2 - 2x - 16| = 8$.

Solution

First write an equivalent compound equation without absolute value:

$$x^2 - 2x - 16 = 8 \qquad \text{or} \qquad x^2 - 2x - 16 = -8$$
$$x^2 - 2x - 24 = 0 \qquad \text{or} \qquad x^2 - 2x - 8 = 0$$
$$(x - 6)(x + 4) = 0 \qquad \text{or} \qquad (x - 4)(x + 2) = 0$$

$x - 6 = 0 \quad$ or $\quad x + 4 = 0 \quad$ or $\quad x - 4 = 0 \quad$ or $\quad x + 2 = 0$

$x = 6 \quad$ or $\quad x = -4 \quad$ or $\quad x = 4 \quad$ or $\quad x = -2$

The solution set is $\{-2, -4, 4, 6\}$. Check each solution. ■

Applications

Many applied problems can be solved by using equations such as those we have been solving.

E X A M P L E   5

Area of a room

Ronald's living room is 2 feet longer than it is wide, and its area is 168 square feet. What are the dimensions of the room?

Solution

Let x be the width and $x + 2$ be the length. See Fig. 5.1. Because the area of a rectangle is the length times the width, we can write the equation

$$x(x + 2) = 168.$$

We solve the equation by factoring:

$$x^2 + 2x - 168 = 0$$
$$(x - 12)(x + 14) = 0$$

$x - 12 = 0 \qquad$ or $\qquad x + 14 = 0$

$x = 12 \qquad$ or $\qquad x = -14$

Helpful Hint

To prove the Pythagorean theorem, draw two squares with sides of length $a + b$, and partition them as shown.

Erase the four triangles in each picture. Since we started with equal areas, we must have equal areas after erasing the triangles:

$$a^2 + b^2 = c^2$$

FIGURE 5.1

Because the width of a room is a positive number, we disregard the solution $x = -14$. We use $x = 12$ and get a width of 12 feet and a length of 14 feet. Check this answer by multiplying 12 and 14 to get 168. ∎

Applications involving quadratic equations often require a theorem called the **Pythagorean theorem.** This theorem states that *in any right triangle the sum of the squares of the lengths of the legs is equal to the length of the hypotenuse squared.*

The Pythagorean Theorem

The triangle shown is a right triangle if and only if

$$a^2 + b^2 = c^2.$$

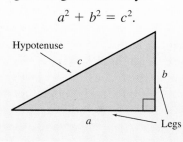

We use the Pythagorean theorem in Example 6.

EXAMPLE 6

Using the Pythagorean theorem

Shirley used 14 meters of fencing to enclose a rectangular region. To be sure that the region was a rectangle, she measured the diagonals and found that they were 5 meters each. (If the opposite sides of a quadrilateral are equal and the diagonals are equal, then the quadrilateral is a rectangle.) What are the length and width of the rectangle?

Solution

The perimeter of a rectangle is twice the length plus twice the width, $P = 2L + 2W$. Because the perimeter is 14 meters, the sum of one length and one width is 7 meters. If we let x represent the width, then $7 - x$ is the length. We use the Pythagorean theorem to get a relationship among the length, width, and diagonal. See Fig. 5.2.

$$x^2 + (7 - x)^2 = 5^2 \quad \text{Pythagorean theorem}$$
$$x^2 + 49 - 14x + x^2 = 25 \quad \text{Simplify.}$$
$$2x^2 - 14x + 24 = 0 \quad \text{Simplify.}$$
$$x^2 - 7x + 12 = 0 \quad \text{Divide each side by 2.}$$
$$(x - 3)(x - 4) = 0 \quad \text{Factor the left-hand side.}$$
$$x - 3 = 0 \quad \text{or} \quad x - 4 = 0 \quad \text{Zero factor property}$$
$$x = 3 \quad \text{or} \quad x = 4$$
$$7 - x = 4 \quad \text{or} \quad 7 - x = 3$$

FIGURE 5.2

Solving the equation gives two possible rectangles: a 3 by 4 rectangle or a 4 by 3 rectangle. However, those are identical rectangles. The rectangle is 3 meters by 4 meters. ∎

Example 7 involves a formula from physics for the height of a projectile where the only force acting on the object is gravity. If an object is projected upward at v_0 feet/sec from h_0 feet above the ground, then its height in feet at time t in seconds is given by $h(t) = -16t^2 + v_0 t + h_0$.

E X A M P L E   7

Height of a projectile

A construction worker accidentally fires a nail gun upward from a height of 144 feet. The nail is propelled upward at 128 feet/sec, as shown in Fig. 5.3. The height of the nail in feet at time t in seconds is given by the function $h(t) = -16t^2 + 128t + 144$. How long does it take for the nail to fall to the ground?

Solution

On the ground the height is 0 feet. So we want to solve the quadratic equation $-16t^2 + 128t + 144 = 0$:

$$-16t^2 + 128t + 144 = 0$$
$$-16(t^2 - 8t - 9) = 0 \quad \text{Factor out the GCF.}$$
$$-16(t - 9)(t + 1) = 0 \quad \text{Factor the trinomial.}$$
$$t - 9 = 0 \quad \text{or} \quad t + 1 = 0 \quad \text{Zero factor property}$$
$$t = 9 \quad \text{or} \quad t = -1$$

FIGURE 5.3

Since $t = -1$ does not make sense, the nail takes 9 seconds to fall to the ground. ∎

WARM-UPS

True or false? Explain your answer.

1. The equation $(x - 1)(x + 3) = 12$ is equivalent to $x - 1 = 3$ or $x + 3 = 4$.

2. Equations solved by factoring may have two solutions.

3. The equation $c \cdot d = 0$ is equivalent to $c = 0$ or $d = 0$.

4. The equation $|x^2 + 4| = 5$ is equivalent to the compound equation $x^2 + 4 = 5$ or $x^2 - 4 = 5$.

5. The solution set to the equation $(2x - 1)(3x + 4) = 0$ is $\left\{\frac{1}{2}, -\frac{4}{3}\right\}$.

6. The Pythagorean theorem states that the sum of the squares of any two sides of any triangle is equal to the square of the third side.

7. If the perimeter of a rectangular room is 38 feet, then the sum of the length and width is 19 feet.

8. Two numbers that have a sum of 8 can be represented by x and $8 - x$.

9. The solution set to the equation $x(x - 1)(x - 2) = 0$ is $\{1, 2\}$.

10. The solution set to the equation $3(x + 2)(x - 5) = 0$ is $\{3, -2, 5\}$.

5.8 EXERCISES

Reading and Writing *After reading this section, write out the answers to these questions. Use complete sentences.*

1. What is the zero factor property?

2. What is a quadratic equation?

3. Where is the hypotenuse in a right triangle?

4. Where are the legs in a right triangle?

5. What is the Pythagorean theorem?

6. Where is the diagonal of a rectangle?

Solve each equation. See Examples 1–3.

7. $(x - 5)(x + 4) = 0$

8. $(a - 6)(a + 5) = 0$

9. $(2x - 5)(3x + 4) = 0$

10. $(3k + 8)(4k - 3) = 0$

11. $4(x - 2)(x + 5) = 0$

12. $8(x - 9)(x + 9) = 0$

13. $x(x - 5)(x + 5) = 0$

14. $x(x - 4)(x + 7) = 0$

15. $w^2 + 5w - 14 = 0$

16. $t^2 - 6t - 27 = 0$

17. $m^2 - 7m = 0$

18. $h^2 - 5h = 0$

19. $a^2 - a = 20$

20. $p^2 - p = 42$

21. $2a^2 + 7a = 15$

22. $6p^2 + p = 1$

23. $10a^2 + 38a - 8 = 0$

24. $-48b^2 + 28b + 6 = 0$

25. $3x^2 - 3x - 36 = 0$

26. $-2x^2 - 16x - 24 = 0$

27. $z^2 + \dfrac{3}{2}z = 10$

28. $m^2 + \dfrac{11}{3}m = -2$

29. $x^3 - 4x = 0$

30. $16x - x^3 = 0$

31. $-4x^3 + x = 3x^2$

32. $2x - 11x^2 = 6x^3$

33. $w^3 + 4w^2 - 25w - 100 = 0$

34. $a^3 + 2a^2 - 16a - 32 = 0$

35. $n^3 - 2n^2 - n + 2 = 0$

36. $w^3 - w^2 - 25w + 25 = 0$

Solve each equation. See Example 4.

37. $|x^2 - 5| = 4$

38. $|x^2 - 17| = 8$

39. $|x^2 + 2x - 36| = 12$

40. $|x^2 + 2x - 19| = 16$

41. $|x^2 + 4x + 2| = 2$

42. $|x^2 + 8x + 8| = 8$

43. $|x^2 + 6x + 1| = 8$

44. $|x^2 - x - 21| = 9$

Solve each equation.

45. $2x^2 - x = 6$

46. $3x^2 + 14x = 5$

47. $|x^2 + 5x| = 6$

48. $|x^2 + 6x - 4| = 12$

49. $x^2 + 5x = 6$

50. $x + 5x = 6$

51. $(x + 2)(x + 1) = 12$

52. $(x + 2)(x + 3) = 20$

53. $y^3 + 9y^2 + 20y = 0$

54. $m^3 - 2m^2 - 3m = 0$

55. $5a^3 = 45a$

56. $5x^3 = 125x$

57. $(2x - 1)(x^2 - 9) = 0$

58. $(3x - 5)(25x^2 - 4)$

59. $(2x - 1)(3x + 1)(4x - 1) = 0$

60. $(x - 1)(x + 3)(x - 9) = 0$

61. $4x^2 - 12x + 9 = 0$

62. $16x^2 + 8x + 1 = 0$

Solve each equation for y. Assume a and b are positive numbers.

63. $y^2 + by = 0$

64. $y^2 + ay + by + ab = 0$

65. $a^2y^2 - b^2 = 0$

66. $9y^2 + 6ay + a^2 = 0$

67. $4y^2 + 4by + b^2 = 0$

68. $y^2 - b^2 = 0$

69. $ay^2 + 3y - ay = 3$

70. $a^2y^2 + 2aby + b^2 = 0$

Solve each problem. See Examples 5, 6, and 7.

71. *Color print.* The length of a new "super size" color print is 2 inches more than the width. If the area is 24 square inches, what are the length and width?

72. *Tennis court dimensions.* In singles competition, each player plays on a rectangular area of 117 square yards. Given that the length of that area is 4 yards greater than its width, find the length and width.

73. *Missing numbers.* The sum of two numbers is 13 and their product is 36. Find the numbers.

74. *More missing numbers.* The sum of two numbers is 6.5, and their product is 9. Find the numbers.

75. *Bodyboarding.* The Seamas Channel pro bodyboard shown in the figure has a length that is 21 inches greater than its width. Any rider weighing up to 200 pounds can use it because its surface area is 946 square inches. Assume that it is rectangular in shape and find the length and width.

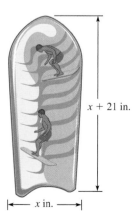

$x + 21$ in.

x in.

FIGURE FOR EXERCISE 75

76. *New dimensions in gardening.* Mary Gold has a rectangular flower bed that measures 4 feet by 6 feet. If she wants to increase the length and width by the same

amount to have a flower bed of 48 square feet, then what will be the new dimensions?

x ft

4 ft

6 ft

x ft

FIGURE FOR EXERCISE 76

77. *Shooting arrows.* An archer shoots an arrow straight upward at 64 feet per second. The height of the arrow $h(t)$ (in feet) at time t seconds is given by the function

$$h(t) = -16t^2 + 64t.$$

a) Use the accompanying graph to estimate the amount of time that the arrow is in the air.

b) Algebraically find the amount of time that the arrow is in the air.

c) Use the accompanying graph to estimate the maximum height reached by the arrow.

d) At what time does the arrow reach its maximum height?

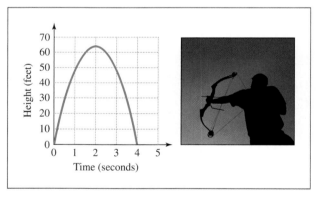

FIGURE FOR EXERCISE 77

78. *Time until impact.* If an object is dropped from a height of s_0 feet, then its altitude after t seconds is given by the formula $S = -16t^2 + s_0$. If a pack of emergency supplies is dropped from an airplane at a height of 1600 feet, then how long does it take for it to reach the ground?

79. *Firing an M-16.* If an M-16 is fired straight upward, then the height $h(t)$ of the bullet in feet at time t in seconds is given by

$$h(t) = -16t^2 + 325t.$$

a) What is the height of the bullet 5 seconds after it is fired?

b) How long does it take for the bullet to return to the earth?

80. *Firing a howitzer.* If an 8-in. (diameter) howitzer is fired straight into the air, then the height $h(t)$ of the projectile in feet at time t in seconds is given by

$$h(t) = -16t^2 + 1332t.$$

a) What is the height of the projectile 10 seconds after it is fired?

b) How long does it take for the projectile to return to the earth?

81. *Tossing a ball.* A boy tosses a ball upward at 32 feet per second from a window that is 48 feet above the ground. The height of the ball above the ground (in feet) at time t (in seconds) is given by

$$h(t) = -16t^2 + 32t + 48.$$

Find the time at which the ball strikes the ground.

82. *Firing a slingshot.* A girl uses a slingshot to propel a stone upward at 64 feet per second from a window that is 80 feet above the ground. The height of the stone above the ground (in feet) at time t (in seconds) is given by

$$h(t) = -16t^2 + 64t + 80.$$

Find the time at which the stone strikes the ground.

83. *Yolanda's closet.* The length of Yolanda's closet is 2 feet longer than twice its width. If the diagonal measures 13 feet, then what are the length and width?

FIGURE FOR EXERCISE 83

84. *Ski jump.* The base of a ski ramp forms a right triangle. One leg of the triangle is 2 meters longer than the other. If the hypotenuse is 10 meters, then what are the lengths of the legs?

FIGURE FOR EXERCISE 84

85. *Trimming a gate.* A total of 34 feet of 1×4 lumber is used around the perimeter of the gate shown in the figure. If the diagonal brace is 13 feet long, then what are the length and width of the gate?

FIGURE FOR EXERCISE 85

86. *Maria's kids.* The sum of the squares of the ages of Maria's two kids is 289. If the boy is seven years older than the girl, then what are their ages?

87. *Leaning ladder.* A 15-foot ladder is leaning against a wall. If the distance from the top of the ladder to the ground is 3 feet more than the distance from the bottom of the ladder to the wall, then what is the distance from the top of the ladder to the ground?

88. *Laying tile.* Lorinda is planning to redo the floor in her bedroom, which has an area of 192 square feet. If the width of the rectangular room is 4 feet less than the length, then what are its dimensions?

89. *Finding numbers.* If the square of a number decreased by the number is 12, then what is the number?

90. *Perimeter of a rectangle.* The perimeter of a rectangle is 28 inches, and the diagonal measures 10 inches. What are the length and width of the rectangle?

91. *Consecutive integers.* The sum of the squares of two consecutive integers is 25. Find the integers.

92. *Pete's garden.* Each row in Pete's garden is 3 feet wide. If the rows run north and south, he can have two more rows than if they run east and west. If the area of Pete's garden is 135 square feet, then what are the length and width?

93. *House plans.* In the plans for their dream house the Baileys have a master bedroom that is 240 square feet in area. If they increase the width by 3 feet, they must decrease the length by 4 feet to keep the original area. What are the original dimensions of the bedroom?

94. *Arranging the rows.* Mr. Converse has 112 students in his algebra class with an equal number in each row. If he arranges the desks so that he has one fewer rows, he will have two more students in each row. How many rows did he have originally?

GETTING MORE INVOLVED

95. *Writing.* If you divide each side of $x^2 = x$ by x, you get $x = 1$. If you subtract x from each side of $x^2 = x$, you get $x^2 - x = 0$, which has two solutions. Which method is correct? Explain.

96. *Cooperative learning.* Work with a group to examine the following solution to $x^2 - 2x = -1$:

$$x(x - 2) = -1$$

$$x = -1 \quad \text{or} \quad x - 2 = -1$$

$$x = -1 \quad \text{or} \quad x = 1$$

Is this method correct? Explain.

97. *Cooperative learning.* Work with a group to examine the following steps in the solution to $5x^2 - 5 = 0$

$$5(x^2 - 1) = 0$$

$$5(x - 1)(x + 1) = 0$$

$$x - 1 = 0 \quad \text{or} \quad x + 1 = 0$$

$$x = 1 \quad \text{or} \quad x = -1$$

What happened to the 5? Explain.

COLLABORATIVE ACTIVITIES

Magic Tricks

Jim and Sadar are talking one day after class.

Sadar: Jim, I have a trick for you. Think of a number between 1 and 10. I will ask you to do some things to this number. Then at the end tell me your result, and I will tell you your number.

Jim: Oh, yeah you probably rig it so the result is my number.

Sadar: Come on Jim, give it a try and see.

Jim: Okay, okay, I thought of a number.

Sadar: Good, now write it down, and don't let me see your paper. Now add x. Got that? Now multiply everything by 2.

Jim: Hey, I didn't know you were going to make me think! This is algebra!

Sadar: I know, now just do it. Okay, now square the polynomial. Got that? Now subtract $4x^2$.

Jim: How did you know I had a $4x^2$? I told you this was rigged!

Sadar: Of course it's rigged, or it wouldn't work. Do you want to finish or not?

Jim: Yeah, I guess so. Go ahead, what do I do next?

Sadar: Divide by 4. Okay, now subtract the x-term.

Grouping: Two students per group

Topic: Practice with exponent rules, multiplying polynomials

Jim: Just any old x-term? Got any particular coefficient in mind?

Sadar: Now stop teasing me. I know you only have one x-term left, so subtract it.

Jim: Ha, ha, I *could* give you a hint about the coefficient, but that wouldn't be fair, would it?

Sadar: Well you could, and then I could tell you your number, or you could just tell me the number you have left after subtracting.

Jim: Okay, the number I had left at the end was 25. Let's see if you can tell me what the coefficient of the x-term I subtracted is.

Sadar: Aha, then the number you chose at the beginning was 5, and the coefficient was 10!

Jim: Hey, you're right! How did you do that?

In your group, follow Sadar's instructions and determine why she knew Jim's number. Make up another set of instructions to use as a magic trick. Be sure to use variables and some of the exponent rules or rules for multiplying polynomials that you learned in this chapter. Exchange instructions with another group and see whether you can figure out how their trick works.

WRAP-UP

CHAPTER 5

SUMMARY

Definitions		Examples
Definition of negative integral exponents	If a is a nonzero real number and n is a positive integer, then $$a^{-n} = \frac{1}{a^n}.$$	$2^{-3} = \dfrac{1}{2^3} = \dfrac{1}{8}$

Definition of zero exponent	If a is any nonzero real number, then $a^0 = 1$. The expression 0^0 is undefined.	$3^0 = 1$

Rules of Exponents

Examples

If a and b are nonzero real numbers and m and n are integers, then the following rules hold.

Negative exponent rules	$a^{-n} = \left(\dfrac{1}{a}\right)^n, \quad a^{-1} = \dfrac{1}{a}, \quad$ and $\quad \dfrac{1}{a^{-n}} = a^n$	$5^{-1} = \dfrac{1}{5}, \dfrac{1}{5^{-3}} = 5^3$
	Find the power and reciprocal in either order.	$\left(\dfrac{2}{3}\right)^{-2} = \left(\dfrac{3}{2}\right)^2$
Product rule	$a^m \cdot a^n = a^{m+n}$	$3^5 \cdot 3^7 = 3^{12}, 2^{-3} \cdot 2^{10} = 2^7$
Quotient rule	$\dfrac{a^m}{a^n} = a^{m-n}$	$\dfrac{x^8}{x^5} = x^3, \dfrac{5^4}{5^{-7}} = 5^{11}$
Power of a power rule	$(a^m)^n = a^{mn}$	$(5^2)^3 = 5^6$
Power of a product rule	$(ab)^n = a^n b^n$	$(2x)^3 = 8x^3$ $(2x^3)^4 = 16x^{12}$
Power of a quotient rule	$\left(\dfrac{a}{b}\right)^n = \dfrac{a^n}{b^n}$	$\left(\dfrac{x}{3}\right)^2 = \dfrac{x^2}{9}$

Scientific Notation

Examples

Converting from scientific notation	1. Determine the number of places to move the decimal point by examining the exponent on the 10. 2. Move to the right for a positive exponent and to the left for a negative exponent.	$4 \times 10^3 = 4000$ $3 \times 10^{-4} = 0.0003$
Converting to scientific notation	1. Count the number of places (n) that the decimal point must be moved so that it will follow the first nonzero digit of the number. 2. If the original number was larger than 10, use 10^n. 3. If the original number was smaller than 1, use 10^{-n}.	 $67,000 = 6.7 \times 10^4$ $0.009 = 9 \times 10^{-3}$

Polynomials

Examples

Term of a polynomial	The product of a number (coefficient) and one or more variables raised to whole number powers	$3x^4, -2xy^2, 5$
Polynomial	A single term or a finite sum of terms	$x^5 - 3x^2 + 7$
Adding or subtracting polynomials	Add or subtract the like terms.	$(x + 3) + (x - 7) = 2x - 4$ $(x^2 - 2x) - (3x^2 - x) = -2x^2 - x$

Multiplying two polynomials	Multiply each term of the first polynomial by each term of the second polynomial, then combine like terms.	$(x^2 + 2x + 3)(x + 1)$ $= (x^2 + 2x + 3)x + (x^2 + 2x + 3)1$ $= x^3 + 2x^2 + 3x + x^2 + 2x + 3$ $= x^3 + 3x^2 + 5x + 3$

Shortcuts for Multiplying Two Binomials

Examples

FOIL	The product of two binomials can be found quickly by multiplying their **F**irst, **O**uter, **I**nner, and **L**ast terms.	$(x + 2)(x + 3) = x^2 + 5x + 6$
Square of a sum	$(a + b)^2 = a^2 + 2ab + b^2$	$(x + 5)^2 = x^2 + 10x + 25$
Square of a difference	$(a - b)^2 = a^2 - 2ab + b^2$	$(m - 3)^2 = m^2 - 6m + 9$
Product of a sum and a difference	$(a + b)(a - b) = a^2 - b^2$	$(x + 3)(x - 3) = x^2 - 9$

Factoring

Examples

Factoring a polynomial	Write a polynomial as a product of two or more polynomials. A polynomial is factored completely if it is a product of prime polynomials.	$3x^2 - 3 = 3(x^2 - 1)$ $= 3(x + 1)(x - 1)$
Common factors	Factor out the greatest common factor (GCF).	$2x^3 - 6x = 2x(x^2 - 3)$
Difference of two squares	$a^2 - b^2 = (a + b)(a - b)$ (The sum of two squares $a^2 + b^2$ is prime.)	$m^2 - 25 = (m + 5)(m - 5)$ $m^2 + 25$ is prime.
Perfect square trinomials	$a^2 + 2ab + b^2 = (a + b)^2$ $a^2 - 2ab + b^2 = (a - b)^2$	$x^2 + 10x + 25 = (x + 5)^2$ $x^2 - 6x + 9 = (x - 3)^2$
Difference of two cubes	$a^3 - b^3 = (a - b)(a^2 + ab + b^2)$	$x^3 - 8 = (x - 2)(x^2 + 2x + 4)$
Sum of two cubes	$a^3 + b^3 = (a + b)(a^2 - ab + b^2)$	$x^3 + 27 = (x + 3)(x^2 - 3x + 9)$
Grouping	Factor out common factors from groups of terms.	$3x + 3w + bx + bw$ $= 3(x + w) + b(x + w)$ $= (3 + b)(x + w)$
Factoring $ax^2 + bx + c$	By the *ac* method: 1. Find two numbers that have a product equal to *ac* and a sum equal to *b*. 2. Replace *bx* by two terms using the two new numbers as coefficients. 3. Factor the resulting four-term polynomial by grouping.	$2x^2 + 7x + 3$ $ac = 6, b = 7, 1 \cdot 6 = 6, 1 + 6 = 7$ $2x^2 + 7x + 3$ $= 2x^2 + x + 6x + 3$ $= (2x + 1)x + (2x + 1)3$ $= (2x + 1)(x + 3)$

By trial and error:
Try possibilities by considering factors of the first term and factors of the last term. Check them by FOIL.

$$12x^2 + 19x - 18$$
$$= (3x - 2)(4x + 9)$$

Substitution	Use substitution on higher-degree polynomials to reduce the degree to 2 or 3.	$x^4 - 3x^2 - 18$ Let $a = x^2$. $a^2 - 3a - 18$

Solving Equations by Factoring

Examples

Strategy
1. Write the equation with 0 on the right-hand side.
2. Factor the left-hand side.
3. Set each factor equal to 0.
4. Solve the simpler equations.
5. Check the answers in the original equation.

$$x^2 - 3x - 18 = 0$$
$$(x - 6)(x + 3) = 0$$
$$x - 6 = 0 \quad \text{or} \quad x + 3 = 0$$
$$x = 6 \quad \text{or} \qquad x = -3$$
$$6^2 - 3(6) - 18 = 0$$
$$(-3)^2 - 3(-3) - 18 = 0$$

ENRICHING YOUR MATHEMATICAL WORD POWER

For each mathematical term, choose the correct meaning.

1. **polynomial**
   a. four or more terms
   b. many numbers
   c. a sum of four or more numbers
   d. a single term or a finite sum of terms

2. **degree of a polynomial**
   a. the number of terms in a polynomial
   b. the highest degree of any of the terms of a polynomial
   c. the value of a polynomial when $x = 0$
   d. the largest coefficient of any of the terms of a polynomial

3. **leading coefficient**
   a. the first coefficient
   b. the largest coefficient
   c. the coefficient of the first term when a polynomial is written with decreasing exponents
   d. the most important coefficient

4. **monomial**
   a. a single polynomial
   b. one number
   c. an equation that has only one solution
   d. a polynomial that has one term

5. **FOIL**
   a. a method for adding polynomials
   b. first, outer, inner, last
   c. an equation with no solution
   d. a polynomial with five terms

6. **binomial**
   a. a polynomial with two terms
   b. any two numbers
   c. the two coordinates in an ordered pair
   d. an equation with two variables

7. **scientific notation**
   a. the notation of rational exponents
   b. the notation of algebra
   c. a notation for expressing large or small numbers with powers of 10
   d. radical notation

8. **trinomial**
   a. a polynomial with three terms
   b. an ordered triple of real numbers
   c. a sum of three numbers
   d. a product of three numbers

9. **factor**
   a. to write an expression as a product
   b. to multiply
   c. what two numbers have in common
   d. to FOIL

10. **prime number**
    a. a polynomial that cannot be factored
    b. a number with no divisors
    c. an integer between 1 and 10
    d. an integer larger than 1 that has no integral factors other than itself and 1

11. **greatest common factor**
    a. the least common multiple
    b. the least common denominator
    c. the largest integer that is a factor of two or more integers
    d. the largest number in a product

12. **prime polynomial**
    a. a polynomial that has no factors
    b. a product of prime numbers
    c. a first-degree polynomial
    d. a monomial

13. **factor completely**
    a. to factor by grouping
    b. to factor out a prime number
    c. to write as a product of primes
    d. to factor by trial-and-error

14. **sum of two cubes**
    a. $(a + b)^3$
    b. $a^3 + b^3$

c. $a^3 - b^3$
d. $a^3 b^3$

15. **quadratic equation**
    a. $ax + b = 0$, where $a \neq 0$
    b. $ax + b = cx + d$
    c. $ax^2 + bx + c = 0$, where $a \neq 0$
    d. any equation with four terms

16. **zero factor property**
    a. If $ab = 0$, then $a = 0$ or $b = 0$
    b. $a \cdot 0 = 0$ for any a
    c. $a = a + 0$ for any real number a
    d. $a + (-a) = 0$ for any real number a

17. **difference of two squares**
    a. $a^3 - b^3$
    b. $2a - 2b$
    c. $a^2 - b^2$
    d. $(a - b)^2$

REVIEW EXERCISES

5.1 *Simplify each expression. Assume all variables represent nonzero real numbers. Write your answers with positive exponents.*

1. $2 \cdot 2 \cdot 2^{-1}$
2. $5^{-1} \cdot 5$
3. $2^2 \cdot 3^2$
4. $3^2 \cdot 5^2$
5. $(-3)^{-3}$
6. $(-2)^{-2}$
7. $-(-1)^{-3}$
8. $3^4 \cdot 3^7$
9. $2x^3 \cdot 4x^{-6}$
10. $-3a^{-3} \cdot 4a^{-4}$
11. $\dfrac{y^{-5}}{y^{-3}}$
12. $\dfrac{w^3}{w^{-3}}$
13. $\dfrac{a^5 \cdot a^{-2}}{a^{-4}}$
14. $\dfrac{2m^3 \cdot m^6}{2m^{-2}}$
15. $\dfrac{6x^{-2}}{3x^2}$
16. $\dfrac{-5y^2 x^{-3}}{5y^{-2} x^7}$

Write each number in standard notation.

17. 8.36×10^6
18. 3.4×10^7
19. 5.7×10^{-4}
20. 4×10^{-3}

Write each number in scientific notation.

21. $8,070,000$
22. $90,000$
23. 0.000709
24. 0.0000005

Perform each computation without a calculator. Write the answer in scientific notation.

25. $\dfrac{(4,000,000,000)(0.0000006)}{(0.000012)(2,000,000)}$
26. $\dfrac{(1.2 \times 10^{32})(2 \times 10^{-5})}{4 \times 10^{-7}}$

5.2 *Simplify each expression. Assume all variables represent nonzero real numbers. Write your answers with positive exponents.*

27. $(a^{-3})^{-2} \cdot a^{-7}$
28. $(-3x^{-2}y)^{-4}$
29. $(m^2 n^3)^{-2}(m^{-3} n^2)^4$
30. $(w^{-3}xy)^{-1}(wx^{-3}y)^2$
31. $\left(\dfrac{2}{3}\right)^{-4}$
32. $\left(\dfrac{a^4}{3}\right)^{-2}$
33. $\left(\dfrac{1}{2} + \dfrac{1}{3}\right)^2$
34. $\left(\dfrac{1}{2} - \dfrac{1}{3}\right)^{-2}$
35. $\left(-\dfrac{3a}{4b^{-1}}\right)^{-1}$
36. $\left(-\dfrac{4x^5}{5y^{-3}}\right)^{-1}$
37. $\dfrac{(a^{-3}b)^4}{(ab^2)^{-5}}$
38. $\dfrac{(2x^3)^3}{(3x^2)^{-2}}$

Simplify each expression. Assume that the variables represent integers.

39. $5^{2w} \cdot 5^{4w} \cdot 5^{-1}$
40. $3^y (3^{2y})^3$
41. $\left(\dfrac{7^{3a}}{7^8}\right)^5$
42. $\left(\dfrac{2^{6-k}}{2^{2-3k}}\right)^3$

5.3 *Perform the indicated operations.*

43. $(2w - 3) + (6w + 5)$
44. $(3a - 2xy) + (5xy - 7a)$
45. $(x^2 - 3x - 4) - (x^2 + 3x - 7)$
46. $(7 - 2x - x^2) - (x^2 - 5x + 6)$
47. $(x^2 - 2x + 4)(x - 2)$

48. $(x + 5)(x^2 - 2x + 10)$
49. $xy + 7z - 5(xy - 3z)$
50. $7 - 4(x - 3)$
51. $m^2(5m^3 - m + 2)$
52. $(a + 2)^3$

5.4 *Perform the following computations mentally. Write down only the answers.*

53. $(x - 3)(x + 7)$ **54.** $(k - 5)(k + 4)$

55. $(z - 5y)(z + 5y)$ **56.** $(m - 3)(m + 3)$

57. $(m + 8)^2$ **58.** $(b + 2a)^2$

59. $(w - 6x)(w - 4x)$ **60.** $(2w - 3)(w + 6)$

61. $(k - 3)^2$ **62.** $(n - 5)^2$

63. $(m^2 - 5)(m^2 + 5)$ **64.** $(3k^2 - 5t)(2k^2 + 6t)$

5.5 *Complete the factoring by filling in the parentheses.*
65. $3x - 6 = 3(\qquad)$
66. $7x^2 - x = x(\qquad)$
67. $4a - 20 = -4(\qquad)$
68. $w^2 - w = -w(\qquad)$
69. $3w - w^2 = -w(\qquad)$
70. $3x - 6 = (\quad)(2 - x)$

Factor each polynomial.
71. $y^2 - 81$
72. $r^2t^2 - 9v^2$
73. $4x^2 + 28x + 49$
74. $y^2 - 20y + 100$
75. $t^2 - 18t + 81$
76. $4w^2 + 4ws + s^2$
77. $t^3 - 125$
78. $8y^3 + 1$

5.6 *Factor each polynomial.*
79. $x^2 - 7x - 30$
80. $y^2 + 4y - 32$
81. $w^2 - 3w - 28$
82. $6t^2 - 5t + 1$
83. $2m^2 + 5m - 7$

84. $12x^2 - 17x + 6$
85. $m^7 - 3m^4 - 10m$
86. $6w^5 - 7w^3 - 5w$

5.7 *Factor each polynomial completely.*
87. $5x^3 + 40$
88. $w^3 - 6w^2 + 9w$
89. $9x^2 + 9x + 2$
90. $ax^3 + a$
91. $x^3 + x^2 - x - 1$
92. $16x^2 - 4x - 2$
93. $-x^2y + 16y$
94. $-5m^2 + 5$
95. $-a^3b^2 + 2a^2b^2 - ab^2$
96. $-2w^2 - 16w - 32$
97. $x^3 - x^2 + 9x - 9$
98. $w^4 + 2w^2 - 3$
99. $x^4 - x^2 - 12$
100. $8x^3 - 1$
101. $a^6 - a^3$
102. $a^2 - ab + 2a - 2b$
103. $-8m^2 - 24m - 18$
104. $-3x^2 - 9x + 30$
105. $(2x - 3)^2 - 16$
106. $(m - 6)^2 - (m - 6) - 12$
107. $x^6 + 7x^3 - 8$
108. $32a^5 - 2a$
109. $(a^2 - 9)^2 - 5(a^2 - 9) + 6$
110. $x^3 - 9x + x^2 - 9$

Factor each polynomial completely. Variables used as exponents represent positive integers.
111. $x^{2k} - 49$
112. $x^{6k} - 1$
113. $m^{2a} - 2m^a - 3$
114. $2y^{2n} - 7y^n + 6$
115. $9z^{2k} - 12z^k + 4$
116. $25z^{6m} + 20z^{3m} + 4$
117. $y^{2a} - by^a + cy^a - bc$
118. $x^3y^b - xy^b + 2x^3 - 2x$

5.8 *Solve each equation.*

119. $x^3 - 5x^2 = 0$

120. $2m^2 + 10m + 12 = 0$

121. $(a - 2)(a - 3) = 6$

122. $(w - 2)(w + 3) = 50$

123. $2m^2 - 9m - 5 = 0$

124. $m^3 + 4m^2 - 9m - 36 = 0$

125. $w^3 + 5w^2 - w - 5 = 0$

126. $12x^2 + 5x - 3 = 0$

127. $|x^2 - 5| = 4$

128. $|x^2 - 3x - 7| = 3$

MISCELLANEOUS

Solve each problem.

129. *Roadrunner and the coyote.* The roadrunner has just taken a position atop a giant saguaro cactus. While positioning a 10-foot Acme ladder against the cactus, Wile E. Coyote notices a warning label on the ladder. For safety, Acme recommends that the distance from the ground to the top of the ladder, measured vertically along the cactus, must be 2 feet longer than the distance between the bottom of the ladder and the cactus. How far from the cactus should he place the bottom of this ladder?

130. *Three consecutive integers.* Find three consecutive integers such that the sum of their squares is 50.

131. *Playground dimensions.* It took 32 meters of fencing to enclose the rectangular playground at Kiddie Kare. If the area of the playground is 63 square meters, then what are its dimensions?

132. *Landscape design.* Rico is planting red tulips in a rectangular flower bed that is 2 feet longer than it is wide. He plans to surround the tulips with a border of daffodils that is 2 feet wide. If the total area is 224 square feet and he plants 36 daffodils per square foot, then how many daffodils does he need?

133. *Panoramic screen.* Engineers are designing a new 25-inch diagonal measure television. The new rectangular screen will have a length that is 17 inches larger than its width. What are the dimensions of the screen?

134. *Less panoramic.* The engineers are also experimenting with a 25-inch diagonal measure television that has a width that is 5 inches less than the length. What are the dimensions of this rectangular screen?

135. *Life expectancy of black males.* The age at which people die is precisely measured and provides an indication of the health of the population as a whole. The formula

$$L = 64.3(1.0033)^a$$

can be used to model life expectancy L for U.S. black males with present age a (National Center for Health Statistics, www.cdc.gov/nchswww).
a) To what age can a 20-year-old black male expect to live?
b) How many more years is a 20-year-old white male expected to live than a 20-year-old black male? (See Section 5.2 Exercise 95.)

136. *Life expectancy of black females.* The formula

$$L = 72.9(1.002)^a$$

can be used to model life expectancy for U.S. black females with present age a. How long can a 20-year-old black female expect to live?

137. *Golden years.* A person earning $80,000 per year should expect to receive 21% of her retirement income from Social Security and the rest from personal savings. To calculate the amount of regular savings, we use the formula

$$S = R \cdot \frac{(1 + i)^n - 1}{i},$$

where S is the amount at the end of n years of n investments of R dollars each year earning interest rate i compounded annually.
a) Use the accompanying graph to estimate the interest rate needed to get an investment of $1 per year for 20 years to amount to $100.
b) Use the formula to determine the annual savings for 20 years that would amount to $500,000 at 7% compounded annually.

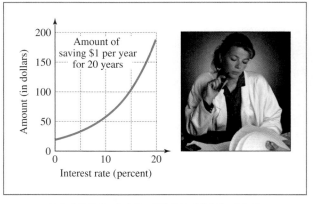

FIGURE FOR EXERCISE 137

138. *Costly education.* The cost of attending Tulane University for one year is approximately $35,414 (www.tulane.edu). Use the formula in Exercise 137 to find the annual savings for 18 years that would amount to $35,414 with an annual return of 8%.

CHAPTER 5 TEST

Simplify each expression. Assume all variables represent nonzero real numbers. Exponents in your answers should be positive exponents.

1. 3^{-2}

2. $\dfrac{1}{6^{-2}}$

3. $\left(\dfrac{1}{2}\right)^{-3}$

4. $3x^4 \cdot 4x^3$

5. $\dfrac{8y^9}{2y^{-3}}$

6. $(4a^2b)^3$

7. $\left(\dfrac{x^2}{3}\right)^{-3}$

8. $\dfrac{(2^{-1}a^2b)^{-3}}{4a^{-9}}$

Convert to standard notation.

9. 3.24×10^9

10. 8.673×10^{-4}

Perform each computation by converting each number to scientific notation. Give the answer in scientific notation.

11. $\dfrac{(80,000)(0.0006)}{2,000,000}$

12. $\dfrac{(0.00006)^2(500)}{(30,000)^2(0.01)}$

Perform the indicated operations.

13. $(3x^3 - x^2 + 6) + (4x^2 - 2x - 3)$

14. $(x^2 - 6x - 7) - (3x^2 + 2x - 4)$

15. $(x^2 - 3x + 7)(x - 2)$

16. $(x - 2)^3$

Find the products.

17. $(x - 7)(2x + 3)$

18. $(x - 6)^2$

19. $(2x + 5)^2$

20. $(3y^2 - 5)(3y^2 + 5)$

Factor completely.

21. $a^2 - 2a - 24$

22. $4x^2 + 28x + 49$

23. $3m^3 - 24$

24. $2x^2y - 32y$

25. $12m^2 + 28m + 15$

26. $2x^{10} + 5x^5 - 12$

27. $2xa + 3a - 10x - 15$

28. $x^4 + 3x^2 - 4$

Solve each equation.

29. $2m^2 + 7m - 15 = 0$

30. $x^3 - 4x = 0$

31. $|x^2 + x - 9| = 3$

Write a complete solution for each problem.

32. A portable television is advertised as having a 10-inch diagonal measure screen. If the width of the screen is 2 inches more than the height, then what are the dimensions of the screen?

33. The infant mortality rate for the United States, the number of deaths per 100,000 live births, has decreased dramatically since 1950. The formula

$$d = (1.8 \times 10^{28})(1.032)^{-y}$$

gives the infant mortality rate d as a function of the year y (National Center for Health Statistics, www.cdc.gov/nchswww). Find the infant mortality rates in 1950, 1990, and 2000.

34. If a boy uses a slingshot to propel a stone straight upward, then the height $h(t)$ of the stone in feet at time t in seconds is given by

$$h(t) = -16t^2 + 80t.$$

   a) What is the height of the stone at 2 seconds and at 3 seconds?

   b) For how long is the stone in the air?

35. **Room dimensions.** The perimeter of the den in the Bailey's house is 88 feet. If the area is 480 square feet, then what are the dimensions of this rectangular room?

Simplify each expression.

1. 4^2

2. $4(-2)$

3. 4^{-2}

4. $2^3 \cdot 4^{-1}$

5. $2^{-1} + 2^{-1}$

6. $2^{-1} \cdot 3^{-1}$

7. $3^{-1} - 2^{-2}$

8. $3^2 - 4(5)(-2)$

9. $2^7 - 2^6$

10. $0.08(32) + 0.08(68)$

11. $3 - 2|5 - 7 \cdot 3|$

12. $5^{-1} + 6^{-1}$

Solve each equation.

13. $0.05a - 0.04(a - 50) = 4$

14. $15b - 27 = 0$

15. $2c^2 + 15c - 27 = 0$

16. $2t^2 + 15t = 0$

17. $|15u - 27| = 3$

18. $|15v - 27| = 0$

19. $|15x - 27| = -78$

20. $|x^2 + x - 4| = 2$

21. $(2x - 1)(x + 5) = 0$

22. $|3x - 1| + 6 = 9$

23. $(1.5 \times 10^{-4})w - 5 \times 10^5 = 7 \times 10^6$

24. $(3 \times 10^7)(y - 5 \times 10^3) = 6 \times 10^{12}$

Solve each problem.

25. ***Negative income tax.*** In a negative income tax proposal, the function

$$D = 0.75E + 5000$$

is used to determine the disposable income D (the amount available for spending) for an earned income E (the amount earned). If $E > D$, then the difference is paid in federal taxes. If $D > E$, then the difference is paid to the wage earner by Uncle Sam.

a) Find the amount of tax paid by a person who earns $100,000.

b) Find the amount received from Uncle Sam by a person who earns $10,000.

c) The accompanying graph shows the lines $D = 0.75E + 5000$ and $D = E$. Find the intersection of these lines.

d) How much tax does a person pay whose earned income is at the intersection found in part (c)?

FIGURE FOR EXERCISE 25

Rational Expressions and Functions

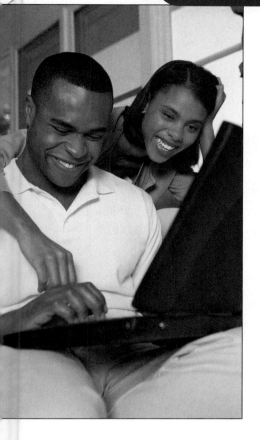

nformation is everywhere—in the newspapers and magazines we read, the televisions we watch, and the computers we use. And now people are talking about the Information Superhighway, which will deliver vast amounts of information directly to consumers' homes. In the future the combination of telephone, television, and computer will give us on-the-spot health care recommendations, video conferences, home shopping, and perhaps even electronic voting and driver's license renewal, to name just a few. There is even talk of 500 television channels!

Some experts are concerned that the consumer will give up privacy for this technology. Others worry about regulation, access, and content of the enormous international computer network.

Whatever the future of this technology, few people understand how all their electronic devices work. However, this vast array of electronics rests on physical principles, which are described by mathematical formulas. In Exercises 49 and 50 of Section 6.7 we will see that the formula governing resistance for receivers connected in parallel involves rational expressions, which are the subject of this chapter.

6.1 PROPERTIES OF RATIONAL EXPRESSIONS AND FUNCTIONS

A rational number is a quotient of two integers and a rational expression is a quotient of two polynomials. Rational expressions are as fundamental to algebra as rational numbers are to arithmetic. In this section we will see how the properties of rational numbers extend to properties of rational expressions.

Definition of Rational Expressions

A **rational expression** is the quotient or ratio of two polynomials with the denominator not equal to zero. For example,

$$\frac{2}{3}, \qquad 3a + 5, \qquad \frac{x - 3}{2x^2 - 2}, \qquad \frac{y + 2}{5y}, \qquad \text{and} \qquad \frac{x - 2}{x + 1}$$

are rational expressions. The rational number $\frac{2}{3}$ is a rational expression because 2 and 3 are monomials and $\frac{2}{3}$ is a ratio of two monomials. If the denominator of a rational expression is 1, it is usually omitted, as in the expression $3a + 5$.

Domain

Because division by zero is undefined, a rational expression is undefined for any real number that causes the denominator to be zero. So numbers that cause the denominator to have a value of zero cannot be used in place of the variable. The **domain** of a rational expression is the set of all real numbers that can be used in place of the variable. The domain of

$$\frac{x}{x + 5}$$

is the set of all real numbers excluding -5, because replacing x with -5 causes the denominator to be zero. In set-builder notation the domain is

$$\{x \mid x \neq -5\},$$

and in interval notation it is written as

$$(-\infty, -5) \cup (-5, \infty).$$

E X A M P L E   1   Domain

Find the domain of each rational expression.

a) $\dfrac{x - 2}{x + 9}$ **b)** $\dfrac{y + 2}{5y}$

c) $\dfrac{x - 3}{2x^2 - 2}$

Solution

a) The denominator is zero if $x + 9 = 0$ or $x = -9$. The domain is $\{x \mid x \neq -9\}$ or

$$(-\infty, -9) \cup (-9, \infty).$$

b) The denominator is zero if $5y = 0$ or $y = 0$. The domain is $\{y \mid y \neq 0\}$ or

$$(-\infty, 0) \cup (0, \infty).$$

c) The denominator is zero if $2x^2 - 2 = 0$. Solve this equation.

$$2x^2 - 2 = 0$$
$$2(x^2 - 1) = 0 \quad \text{Factor out 2.}$$
$$2(x + 1)(x - 1) = 0 \quad \text{Factor completely.}$$
$$x + 1 = 0 \quad \text{or} \quad x - 1 = 0 \quad \text{Zero factor property}$$
$$x = -1 \quad \text{or} \quad x = 1$$

The domain is the set of all real numbers except -1 and 1. This set is written as $\{x \mid x \neq -1 \text{ and } x \neq 1\}$, or in interval notation as

$$(-\infty, -1) \cup (-1, 1) \cup (1, \infty). \qquad \blacksquare$$

CAUTION   The numbers that you find when you set the denominator equal to zero and solve for x are *not* in the domain of the rational expression. The solutions to that equation are excluded from the domain.

Helpful Hint

Most students learn to convert $\frac{2}{3}$ into $\frac{4}{6}$ by dividing 3 into 6 to get 2 and then multiply 2 by 2 to get 4. In algebra it is better to do this conversion by multiplying the numerator and denominator of $\frac{2}{3}$ by 2 as shown here.

Reducing to Lowest Terms

Each rational number can be written in infinitely many equivalent forms. For example,

$$\frac{2}{3} = \frac{4}{6} = \frac{6}{9} = \frac{8}{12} = \frac{10}{15} = \cdots.$$

Each equivalent form of $\frac{2}{3}$ is obtained from $\frac{2}{3}$ by multiplying both numerator and denominator by the same nonzero number. For example,

$$\frac{2}{3} = \frac{2}{3} \cdot 1 = \frac{2}{3} \cdot \frac{2}{2} = \frac{4}{6} \quad \text{and} \quad \frac{2}{3} = \frac{2}{3} \cdot \frac{3}{3} = \frac{6}{9}.$$

Note that we are actually multiplying $\frac{2}{3}$ by equivalent forms of 1, the multiplicative identity.

If we start with $\frac{4}{6}$ and convert it into $\frac{2}{3}$, we are simplifying by *reducing* $\frac{4}{6}$ to its *lowest terms*. We can reduce as follows:

$$\frac{4}{6} = \frac{\cancel{2} \cdot 2}{\cancel{2} \cdot 3} = \frac{2}{3}.$$

A rational number is expressed in its lowest terms when the numerator and denominator have no common factors other than 1. In reducing $\frac{4}{6}$, we divide the numerator and denominator by the common factor 2, or "divide out" the common factor 2. We can multiply or divide both numerator and denominator of a rational number by the same nonzero number without changing the value of the rational number. This fact is called the **basic principle of rational numbers.**

Basic Principle of Rational Numbers

If $\frac{a}{b}$ is a rational number and c is a nonzero real number, then

$$\frac{a}{b} = \frac{ac}{bc}.$$

CAUTION   Although it is true that

$$\frac{5}{6} = \frac{2+3}{2+4},$$

we cannot divide out the 2's in this expression because the 2's are not factors. We can divide out only common *factors* when reducing fractions.

Just as a rational number has infinitely many equivalent forms, a rational expression also has infinitely many equivalent forms. To reduce rational expressions to lowest terms, we follow exactly the same procedure as we do for rational numbers: *Factor the numerator and denominator completely, then divide out all common factors.*

E X A M P L E   2

Reducing

Reduce each rational expression to its lowest terms.

a) $\dfrac{18}{42}$ b) $\dfrac{-2a^7 b}{a^2 b^3}$

Helpful Hint

A negative sign in a fraction can be placed in three locations:

$$\frac{-1}{2} = \frac{1}{-2} = -\frac{1}{2}$$

The same goes for rational expressions:

$$\frac{-3x^2}{5y} = \frac{3x^2}{-5y} = -\frac{3x^2}{5y}$$

Solution

a) Factor 18 as $2 \cdot 3^2$ and 42 as $2 \cdot 3 \cdot 7$:

$$\frac{18}{42} = \frac{2 \cdot 3^2}{2 \cdot 3 \cdot 7} \qquad \text{Factor.}$$

$$= \frac{3}{7} \qquad \text{Divide out the common factors.}$$

b) Because this expression is already factored, we use the quotient rule for exponents to reduce:

$$\frac{-2a^7 b}{a^2 b^3} = \frac{-2a^5}{b^2}$$ ■

In Example 3 we use the techniques for factoring polynomials that we learned in Chapter 5.

E X A M P L E   3

Reducing

Reduce each rational expression to its lowest terms.

a) $\dfrac{2x^2 - 18}{x^2 + x - 6}$ b) $\dfrac{w - 2}{2 - w}$ c) $\dfrac{2a^3 - 16}{16 - 4a^2}$

Solution

a) $\dfrac{2x^2 - 18}{x^2 + x - 6} = \dfrac{2(x^2 - 9)}{(x - 2)(x + 3)}$ $\quad$ Factor.

$$= \frac{2(x - 3)(x + 3)}{(x - 2)(x + 3)} \qquad \text{Factor completely.}$$

$$= \frac{2x - 6}{x - 2} \qquad \text{Divide out the common factors.}$$

b) Factor out -1 from the numerator to get a common factor:

$$\frac{w-2}{2-w} = \frac{-1(2-w)}{(2-w)} = -1$$

c) $\dfrac{2a^3 - 16}{16 - 4a^2} = \dfrac{2(a^3 - 8)}{-4(a^2 - 4)}$ Factoring out -4 will give the common factor $a - 2$.

$$= \frac{2(a-2)(a^2 + 2a + 4)}{-2 \cdot 2(a-2)(a+2)}$$ Difference of two cubes, difference of two squares

$$= -\frac{a^2 + 2a + 4}{2a + 4}$$ Divide out common factors.

■

The rational expressions in Example 3(a) are equivalent because they have the same value for any replacement of the variables, provided that the replacement is in the domain of both expressions. In other words, the equation

$$\frac{2x^2 - 18}{x^2 + x - 6} = \frac{2x - 6}{x - 2}$$

is an identity. It is true for any value of x except 2 and -3.

The main points to remember for reducing rational expressions are summarized as follows.

> ### Strategy for Reducing Rational Expressions
>
> 1. All reducing is done by dividing out common factors.
> 2. Factor the numerator and denominator completely to see the common factors.
> 3. Use the quotient rule to reduce a ratio of two monomials involving exponents.
> 4. We may have to factor out a common factor with a negative sign to get identical factors in the numerator and denominator.

Building Up the Denominator

In Section 6.3 we will see that only rational expressions with identical denominators can be added or subtracted. Fractions without identical denominators can be converted to equivalent fractions with a common denominator by reversing the procedure for reducing fractions to lowest terms. This procedure is called **building up the denominator.**

Consider converting the fraction $\frac{1}{3}$ into an equivalent fraction with a denominator of 51. Any fraction that is equivalent to $\frac{1}{3}$ can be obtained by multiplying the numerator and denominator of $\frac{1}{3}$ by the same nonzero number. Because $51 = 3 \cdot 17$, we multiply the numerator and denominator of $\frac{1}{3}$ by 17 to get an equivalent fraction with a denominator of 51:

$$\frac{1}{3} = \frac{1}{3} \cdot 1 = \frac{1}{3} \cdot \frac{17}{17} = \frac{17}{51}$$

E X A M P L E   4

Building up the denominator

Convert each rational expression into an equivalent rational expression that has the indicated denominator.

a) $\dfrac{2}{7}, \dfrac{?}{42}$

b) $\dfrac{5}{3a^2b}, \dfrac{?}{9a^3b^4}$

Helpful Hint

Notice that reducing and building up are exactly the opposite of each other. In reducing you remove a factor that is common to the numerator and denominator, and in building-up you put a common factor into the numerator and denominator.

Solution

a) Factor 42 as $42 = 2 \cdot 3 \cdot 7$, then multiply the numerator and denominator of $\dfrac{2}{7}$ by the missing factors, 2 and 3:

$$\frac{2}{7} = \frac{2 \cdot 2 \cdot 3}{7 \cdot 2 \cdot 3} = \frac{12}{42}$$

b) Because $9a^3b^4 = 3ab^3 \cdot 3a^2b$, we multiply the numerator and denominator by $3ab^3$:

$$\frac{5}{3a^2b} = \frac{5 \cdot 3ab^3}{3a^2b \cdot 3ab^3}$$

$$= \frac{15ab^3}{9a^3b^4}$$ ∎

When building up a denominator to match a more complicated denominator, we factor both denominators completely to see which factors are missing from the simpler denominator. Then we multiply the numerator and denominator of the simpler expression by the missing factors.

E X A M P L E   5

Building up the denominator

Convert each rational expression into an equivalent rational expression that has the indicated denominator.

a) $\dfrac{5}{2a - 2b}, \dfrac{?}{6b - 6a}$

b) $\dfrac{x + 2}{x + 3}, \dfrac{?}{x^2 + 7x + 12}$

Helpful Hint

Multiplying the numerator and denominator of a rational expression by -1 changes the appearance of the expression:

$$\frac{6 - x}{x - 7} = \frac{-1(6 - x)}{-1(x - 7)}$$

$$= \frac{x - 6}{7 - x}$$

$$\frac{y - 5}{-4 - y} = \frac{-1(y - 5)}{-1(-4 - y)}$$

$$= \frac{5 - y}{4 + y}$$

Solution

a) Factor both $2a - 2b$ and $6b - 6a$ to see which factor is missing in $2a - 2b$. Note that we factor out -6 from $6b - 6a$ to get the factor $a - b$:

$$2a - 2b = 2(a - b)$$
$$6b - 6a = -6(a - b) = -3 \cdot 2(a - b)$$

Now multiply the numerator and denominator by the missing factor, -3:

$$\frac{5}{2a - 2b} = \frac{5(-3)}{(2a - 2b)(-3)} = \frac{-15}{6b - 6a}$$

b) Because $x^2 + 7x + 12 = (x + 3)(x + 4)$, multiply the numerator and denominator by $x + 4$:

$$\frac{x + 2}{x + 3} = \frac{(x + 2)(x + 4)}{(x + 3)(x + 4)} = \frac{x^2 + 6x + 8}{x^2 + 7x + 12}$$ ∎

Rational Functions

A rational expression can be used to determine the value of a variable. For example, if

$$y = \frac{3x - 1}{x^2 - 4},$$

then we say that y is a **rational function** of x. We can also use function notation as shown in Example 6. The domain of a rational function is the same as the domain of the rational expression used to define the function.

EXAMPLE 6

Evaluating a rational function

Find $R(3)$, $R(-1)$, and $R(2)$ for the rational function

$$R(x) = \frac{3x - 1}{x^2 - 4}.$$

Calculator Close-Up

To check, use Y= to enter

$$y_1 = (3x - 1)/(x^2 - 4).$$

Then use the variables feature (VARS) to find $y_1(3)$ and $y_1(-1)$.

```
Y₁(3)▶Frac
             8/5
Y₁(-1)▶Frac
             4/3
```

Solution

To find $R(3)$, replace x by 3 in the formula:

$$R(3) = \frac{3 \cdot 3 - 1}{3^2 - 4} = \frac{8}{5}$$

To find $R(-1)$, replace x by -1 in the formula:

$$R(-1) = \frac{3(-1) - 1}{(-1)^2 - 4}$$

$$= \frac{-4}{-3} = \frac{4}{3}$$

We cannot find $R(2)$ because 2 is not in the domain of the rational expression. ■

Applications

A rational expression can occur in finding an average cost. The average cost of making a product is the total cost divided by the number of products made.

EXAMPLE 7

Average cost function

A car maker spent $700 million to develop a new SUV, which will sell for $40,000. If the cost of manufacturing the SUV is $30,000 each, then what rational function gives the average cost of developing and manufacturing x vehicles? Compare the average cost per vehicle for manufacturing levels of 10,000 vehicles and 100,000 vehicles.

Solution

The polynomial $30,000x + 700,000,000$ gives the cost in dollars of developing and manufacturing x vehicles. The average cost per vehicle is given by the rational function

$$AC(x) = \frac{30,000x + 700,000,000}{x}.$$

If $x = 10,000$, then

$$AC(10,000) = \frac{30,000(10,000) + 700,000,000}{10,000} = 100,000.$$

If $x = 100,000$, then

$$AC(100,000) = \frac{30,000(100,000) + 700,000,000}{100,000} = 37,000.$$

The average cost per vehicle when 10,000 vehicles are made is $100,000, whereas the average cost per vehicle when 100,000 vehicles are made is $37,000. ■

True or false? Explain.

1. A rational number is a rational expression.
2. The expression $\frac{2 + x}{x - 1}$ is a rational expression.
3. The domain of the rational expression $\frac{3}{x - 2}$ is {2}.
4. The domain of $\frac{2x + 5}{(x - 9)(2x + 1)}$ is $\left\{ x \mid x \neq 9 \text{ and } x \neq -\frac{1}{2} \right\}$.
5. The domain of $\frac{x - 1}{x + 2}$ is $(-\infty, -2) \cup (-2, 1) \cup (1, \infty)$.
6. The rational expression $\frac{5x + 2}{15}$ reduces to $\frac{x + 2}{3}$.
7. Multiplying the numerator and denominator of $\frac{x}{x - 1}$ by x yields $\frac{x^2}{x^2 - 1}$.
8. The expression $\frac{2}{3 - x}$ is equivalent to $\frac{-2}{x - 3}$.
9. The equation $\frac{4x^3}{6x} = \frac{2x^2}{3}$ is an identity.
10. The expression $\frac{x^2 - y^2}{x - y}$ reduced to its lowest terms is $x - y$.

6.1   EXERCISES

Reading and Writing   *After reading this section, write out the answers to these questions. Use complete sentences.*

1. What is a rational expression?

2. What is the domain of a rational expression?

3. What is the basic principle of rational numbers?

4. How do we reduce a rational expression to lowest terms?

5. How do you build up the denominator of a rational expression?

6. What is average cost?

Find the domain of each rational expression. See Example 1.

7. $\dfrac{3x}{x - 1}$

8. $\dfrac{x}{x + 5}$

9. $\dfrac{2z - 5}{7z}$

10. $\dfrac{z - 12}{4z}$

11. $\dfrac{5y - 1}{y^2 - 4}$

12. $\dfrac{2y - 1}{y^2 - 9}$

13. $\dfrac{2a - 3}{a^2 + 5a + 6}$

14. $\dfrac{3b + 1}{b^2 - 3b - 4}$

15. $\dfrac{x - 1}{x^2 + 4}$

16. $\dfrac{y + 5}{y^2 + 9}$

17. $\dfrac{x + 1}{x^3 + x^2 - 6x}$

18. $\dfrac{x^2 - 3x - 4}{2x^5 - 2x}$

Reduce each rational expression to its lowest terms. See Examples 2 and 3.

19. $\dfrac{6}{57}$

20. $\dfrac{14}{91}$

21. $\dfrac{42}{210}$

22. $\dfrac{242}{154}$

23. $\dfrac{2x + 2}{4}$

24. $\dfrac{3a + 3}{3}$

25. $\dfrac{3x - 6y}{10y - 5x}$

26. $\dfrac{5b - 10a}{2a - b}$

27. $\dfrac{ab^2}{a^3b}$

28. $\dfrac{36y^3z^8}{54y^2z^9}$

29. $\dfrac{-2w^2x^3y}{6wx^5y^2}$

30. $\dfrac{6a^3b^{12}c^5}{-8ab^4c^9}$

31. $\dfrac{a^3b^2}{a^3 + a^4}$

32. $\dfrac{b^8 - ab^5}{ab^5}$

33. $\dfrac{a - b}{2b - 2a}$

34. $\dfrac{2m - 2n}{4n - 4m}$

35. $\dfrac{3x + 6}{3x}$

36. $\dfrac{7x - 14}{7x}$

37. $\dfrac{a^3 - b^3}{a - b}$

38. $\dfrac{27x^3 + y^3}{6x + 2y}$

39. $\dfrac{4x^2 - 4}{4x^2 + 4}$

40. $\dfrac{2a^2 - 2b^2}{2a^2 + 2b^2}$

41. $\dfrac{12x^2 - 26x - 10}{4x^2 - 25}$

42. $\dfrac{9x^2 - 15x - 6}{81x^2 - 9}$

43. $\dfrac{x^3 + 7x^2 - 4x}{x^3 - 16x}$

44. $\dfrac{2x^4 - 32}{4x - 8}$

45. $\dfrac{2ab + 2by + 3a + 3y}{2b^2 - 7b - 15}$

46. $\dfrac{3m^2 + 3mn + m + n}{12m^2 - 5m - 3}$

47. $\dfrac{4x^2 - 10x - 6}{2x^2 + 11x + 5}$

48. $\dfrac{6x^2 + x - 1}{8x^2 - 2x - 3}$

49. $\dfrac{2a^2 + 5ab + 3b^2}{4a^2 + 12ab + 9b^2}$

50. $\dfrac{3x^2 + 2xy - y^2}{9x^2 - 6xy + y^2}$

Convert each rational expression into an equivalent rational expression that has the indicated denominator. See Examples 4 and 5.

51. $\dfrac{1}{5}, \dfrac{?}{50}$

52. $\dfrac{2}{3}, \dfrac{?}{9}$

53. $\dfrac{1}{xy}, \dfrac{?}{3x^2y^3}$

54. $\dfrac{3}{ab^2}, \dfrac{?}{a^3b^5}$

55. $\dfrac{5}{x - 1}, \dfrac{?}{x^2 - 2x + 1}$

56. $\dfrac{7}{2x + 1}, \dfrac{?}{4x^2 + 4x + 1}$

57. $\dfrac{3}{2x - 5}, \dfrac{?}{4x^2 - 25}$

58. $\dfrac{x}{x - 3}, \dfrac{?}{x^2 - 9}$

59. $\dfrac{1}{2x + 2}, \dfrac{?}{-6x - 6}$

60. $\dfrac{-2}{-3x + 4}, \dfrac{?}{15x - 20}$

61. $5, \dfrac{?}{a}$

62. $3, \dfrac{?}{a + 1}$

63. $\dfrac{x + 2}{x + 3}, \dfrac{?}{x^2 + 2x - 3}$

64. $\dfrac{x}{x - 5}, \dfrac{?}{x^2 - x - 20}$

65. $\dfrac{7}{x - 1}, \dfrac{?}{1 - x}$

66. $\dfrac{1}{a - b}, \dfrac{?}{2b - 2a}$

67. $\dfrac{3}{x + 2}, \dfrac{?}{x^3 + 8}$

68. $\dfrac{x}{x - 2}, \dfrac{?}{x^3 - 8}$

69. $\dfrac{x + 2}{3x - 1}, \dfrac{?}{6x^2 + 13x - 5}$ **70.** $\dfrac{a}{2a + 1}, \dfrac{?}{4a^2 - 16a - 9}$

91. $\dfrac{3a + 3}{3a} = \dfrac{?}{a}$ **92.** $\dfrac{x - 3}{x^2 - 9} = \dfrac{1}{?}$

93. $\dfrac{1}{x - 1} = \dfrac{?}{x^3 - 1}$ **94.** $\dfrac{x^2 + 2x + 4}{x + 2} = \dfrac{?}{x^2 - 4}$

Find the indicated value for each given rational expression, if possible. See Example 6.

71. $R(x) = \dfrac{3x - 5}{x + 4}$, $R(3)$

72. $T(x) = \dfrac{5 - x}{x - 5}$, $T(-9)$

73. $H(y) = \dfrac{y^2 - 5}{3y - 4}$, $H(-2)$

74. $G(a) = \dfrac{3 - 5a}{2a + 7}$, $G(5)$

75. $W(b) = \dfrac{4b^3 - 1}{b^2 - b - 6}$, $W(-2)$

76. $N(x) = \dfrac{x + 3}{x^3 - 2x^2 - 2x - 3}$, $N(3)$

Reduce each rational expression to its lowest terms. Variables used in exponents represent integers.

95. $\dfrac{x^{2a} - 4}{x^a + 2}$ **96.** $\dfrac{x^{2b} + 3x^b - 18}{x^{2b} - 36}$

97. $\dfrac{x^a + m + wx^a + wm}{x^{2a} - m^2}$ **98.** $\dfrac{x^{3a} - 8}{x^{2a} + 2x^a + 4}$

99. $\dfrac{x^{3b+1} - x}{x^{2b+1} - x}$ **100.** $\dfrac{2x^{2a+1} + 3x^{a+1} + x}{4x^{2a+1} - x}$

In place of each question mark in Exercises 77–94, put an expression that will make the rational expressions equivalent.

77. $\dfrac{1}{3} = \dfrac{?}{21}$ **78.** $4 = \dfrac{?}{3}$

79. $5 = \dfrac{10}{?}$ **80.** $\dfrac{3}{4} = \dfrac{12}{?}$

81. $\dfrac{3}{a} = \dfrac{?}{a^2}$ **82.** $\dfrac{5}{y} = \dfrac{10}{?}$

83. $\dfrac{2}{a - b} = \dfrac{?}{b - a}$ **84.** $\dfrac{3}{x - 4} = \dfrac{?}{4 - x}$

85. $\dfrac{2}{x - 1} = \dfrac{?}{x^2 - 1}$ **86.** $\dfrac{5}{x + 3} = \dfrac{?}{x^2 - 9}$

87. $\dfrac{2}{w - 3} = \dfrac{-2}{?}$ **88.** $\dfrac{-2}{5 - x} = \dfrac{2}{?}$

89. $\dfrac{2x + 4}{6} = \dfrac{?}{3}$ **90.** $\dfrac{2x - 3}{4x - 6} = \dfrac{1}{?}$

Solve each problem. See Example 7.

101. *Driving speed.* If Jeremy drives 500 miles in $2x$ hours, then what rational expression represents his speed in miles per hour (mph)?

102. *Filing suit.* If Marsha files 48 suits in $2x + 2$ work days, then what rational expression represents the rate (in suits per day) at which she is filing suits?

103. *Wedding bells.* Wheeler Printing Co. charges $45 plus $0.50 per invitation to print wedding invitations.
  a) Write a rational function that gives the average cost in dollars per invitation for printing n invitations.

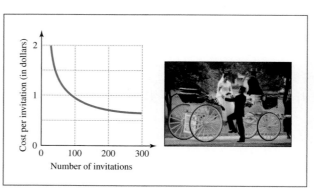

FIGURE FOR EXERCISE 103

b) How much less does it cost per invitation to print 300 invitations rather than 200 invitations?
c) As the number of invitations increases, does the average cost per invitation increase or decrease?
d) As the number of invitations increases, does the total cost of the invitations increase or decrease?

104. *Rose Bowl bound.* A travel agent offers a Rose Bowl package including hotel, tickets, and transportation. It costs the travel agent $50,000 plus $300 per person to charter the airplane. Find a rational function that gives the average cost in dollars per person for the charter flight. How much lower is the average cost per person when 200 people go compared to 100 people?

 105. *Solid waste recovery.* The amount of municipal solid waste generated in the United States in the year 1960 + n is given by the polynomial

$$3.43n + 87.24,$$

whereas the amount recycled is given by the polynomial

$$0.053n^2 - 0.64n + 6.71,$$

where the amounts are in millions of tons (U.S. Environmental Protection Agency, www.epa.gov).
a) Write a rational function $p(n)$ that gives the fraction of solid waste that is recovered in the year 1960 + n.
b) Find $p(0)$, $p(30)$, and $p(50)$.

 106. *Higher education.* The total number of degrees awarded in U.S. higher education in the year 1990 + n is given in thousands by the polynomial $41.7n + 1429$, whereas the number of bachelor's degrees awarded is given in thousands by the polynomial $25.2n + 1069$ (National Center for Education Statistics, www.nces.ed.gov).
a) Write a rational function $p(n)$ that gives the percentage of bachelor's degrees among the total number of degrees conferred for the year 1990 + n.
b) What percentage of the degrees awarded in 2010 will be bachelor's degrees?

GETTING MORE INVOLVED

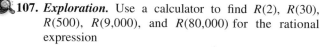 **107. *Exploration.*** Use a calculator to find $R(2)$, $R(30)$, $R(500)$, $R(9,000)$, and $R(80,000)$ for the rational expression

$$R(x) = \frac{x - 3}{2x + 1}.$$

Round answers to four decimal places. What can you conclude about the value of $R(x)$ as x gets larger and larger without bound?

 108. *Exploration.* Use a calculator to find $H(1,000)$, $H(100,000)$, $H(1,000,000)$, and $H(10,000,000)$ for the rational expression

$$H(x) = \frac{7x - 50}{3x + 91}.$$

Round answers to four decimal places. What can you conclude about the value of $H(x)$ as x gets larger and larger without bound?

In This Section

- Multiplying Rational Expressions
- Dividing $a - b$ by $b - a$
- Dividing Rational Expressions

6.2 **MULTIPLICATION AND DIVISION**

In Chapter 5 you learned to add, subtract, multiply, and divide polynomials. In this chapter you will learn to perform the same operations with rational expressions. We begin in this section with multiplication and division.

Multiplying Rational Expressions

We multiply two rational numbers by multiplying their numerators and multiplying their denominators. For example,

$$\frac{6}{7} \cdot \frac{14}{15} = \frac{84}{105} = \frac{21 \cdot 4}{21 \cdot 5} = \frac{4}{5}.$$

Instead of reducing the rational number after multiplying, it is often easier to reduce before multiplying. We first factor all terms, then divide out the common factors, then multiply:

$$\frac{6}{7} \cdot \frac{14}{15} = \frac{2 \cdot 3 \cdot 2 \cdot 7}{7 \cdot 3 \cdot 5} = \frac{4}{5}$$

When we multiply rational numbers, we use the following definition.

Multiplication of Rational Numbers

If $\frac{a}{b}$ and $\frac{c}{d}$ are rational numbers, then $\frac{a}{b} \cdot \frac{c}{d} = \frac{ac}{bd}$.

We multiply rational expressions in the same way that we multiply rational numbers: Factor all polynomials, divide out the common factors, then multiply the remaining factors.

EXAMPLE 1   **Multiplying rational expressions**

Find each product of rational expressions.

a) $\dfrac{3a^8b^3}{6b} \cdot \dfrac{10a}{a^2b^6}$

b) $\dfrac{x^2 + 7x + 12}{x^2 + 3x} \cdot \dfrac{x^2}{x^2 - 16}$

Solution

a) First factor the coefficients in each numerator and denominator:

$$\frac{3a^8b^3}{6b} \cdot \frac{10a}{a^2b^6} = \frac{3a^8b^3}{2 \cdot 3b} \cdot \frac{2 \cdot 5a}{a^2b^6} \quad \text{Factor.}$$

$$= \frac{5a^9b^3}{a^2b^7} \quad \text{Divide out the common factors.}$$

$$= \frac{5a^7}{b^4} \quad \text{Quotient rule}$$

b) $\dfrac{x^2 + 7x + 12}{x^2 + 3x} \cdot \dfrac{x^2}{x^2 - 16} = \dfrac{(x+3)(x+4)}{x(x+3)} \cdot \dfrac{x \cdot x}{(x-4)(x+4)} = \dfrac{x}{x-4}$ ■

CAUTION   Do not attempt to divide out the x in $\frac{x}{x-4}$. This expression cannot be reduced because x is not a factor of *both* terms in the denominator. Compare this expression to the following:

$$\frac{3x}{x - xy} = \frac{x \cdot 3}{x(1 - y)} = \frac{3}{1 - y}$$

In Example 2(a) we will multiply a rational expression and a polynomial. For Example 2(b) we will use the rule for factoring the difference of two cubes.

EXAMPLE 2   **Multiplying rational expressions**

Find each product.

a) $(a^2 - 1) \cdot \dfrac{6}{2a^2 + 4a + 2}$

b) $\dfrac{a^3 - b^3}{b - a} \cdot \dfrac{6}{2a^2 + 2ab + 2b^2}$

Solution

a) First factor the polynomials completely:

$$(a^2 - 1) \cdot \frac{6}{2a^2 + 4a + 2} = \frac{(a + 1)(a - 1)}{1} \cdot \frac{2 \cdot 3}{2(a + 1)(a + 1)}$$

$$= \frac{3(a - 1)}{a + 1} \qquad \text{Divide out the common factors.}$$

$$= \frac{3a - 3}{a + 1} \qquad \text{Multiply.}$$

b) First factor the polynomials completely:

$$\frac{a^3 - b^3}{b - a} \cdot \frac{6}{2a^2 + 2ab + 2b^2} = \frac{(a - b)(a^2 + ab + b^2)}{b - a} \cdot \frac{2 \cdot 3}{2(a^2 + ab + b^2)}$$

$$= \frac{(a - b)3}{b - a}$$

$$= \frac{-1(b - a)3}{b - a} \qquad \begin{array}{l}\text{Factor out } -1 \text{ to get} \\ \text{a common } b - a.\end{array}$$

$$= -3 \qquad\qquad\qquad\qquad\qquad \blacksquare$$

Dividing $a - b$ by $b - a$

Since $a - b = -1(b - a)$ we have $\frac{a-b}{b-a} = -1$. So instead of factoring out -1 as in Example 2(b) we can simply divide $a - b$ by $b - a$ to get -1 as shown in Example 3.

E X A M P L E   3   **Dividing $a - b$ by $b - a$**

Find the product:

$$\frac{m - 4}{3} \cdot \frac{6}{4 - m}$$

Solution

Instead of factoring out -1 from $m - 4$, we divide $m - 4$ by $4 - m$ to get -1:

$$\frac{m - 4}{3} \cdot \frac{6}{4 - m} = \frac{\overset{-1}{m - 4}}{3} \cdot \frac{\overset{2}{6}}{4 - m} \qquad \text{Note that } (m - 4) \div (4 - m) = -1.$$

$$= -2 \qquad\qquad\qquad\qquad\qquad \blacksquare$$

Dividing Rational Expressions

We divide rational numbers by multiplying by the reciprocal or multiplicative inverse of the divisor. For example,

$$\frac{3}{4} \div \frac{15}{2} = \frac{3}{4} \cdot \frac{2}{15} = \frac{3}{2 \cdot 2} \cdot \frac{2 \cdot 1}{3 \cdot 5} = \frac{1}{10}.$$

When we divide rational numbers, we use the following definition.

Division of Rational Numbers

If $\frac{a}{b}$ and $\frac{c}{d}$ are rational numbers with $\frac{c}{d} \neq 0$, then

$$\frac{a}{b} \div \frac{c}{d} = \frac{a}{b} \cdot \frac{d}{c}.$$

We use the same method to divide rational expressions: We invert the divisor and multiply.

E X A M P L E 4   **Dividing rational expressions**

Find each quotient.

a) $\dfrac{10}{3x} \div \dfrac{6}{5x}$

b) $\dfrac{5a^2b^8}{c^3} \div (4ab^3c)$

Solution

a) The reciprocal of the divisor $\frac{6}{5x}$ is $\frac{5x}{6}$.

$$\frac{10}{3x} \div \frac{6}{5x} = \frac{10}{3x} \cdot \frac{5x}{6} \qquad \text{Invert and multiply.}$$

$$= \frac{\cancel{2} \cdot 5}{3\cancel{x}} \cdot \frac{5\cancel{x}}{\cancel{2} \cdot 3} = \frac{25}{9}$$

b) The reciprocal of $4ab^3c$ is $\frac{1}{4ab^3c}$.

$$\frac{5a^2b^8}{c^3} \div (4ab^3c) = \frac{5a^2b^8}{c^3} \cdot \frac{1}{4ab^3c} = \frac{5ab^5}{4c^4} \qquad \text{Quotient rule} \qquad \blacksquare$$

In Example 5 we factor the polynomials in the rational expressions.

E X A M P L E 5   **Dividing rational expressions**

Find the quotient:

$$\frac{25 - x^2}{x^2 + x} \div \frac{x - 5}{x^2 - 1}$$

Solution

$$\frac{25 - x^2}{x^2 + x} \div \frac{x - 5}{x^2 - 1} = \frac{25 - x^2}{x^2 + x} \cdot \frac{x^2 - 1}{x - 5} \qquad \text{Invert and multiply.}$$

$$= \frac{\overset{-1}{\cancel{(5 - x)}}(5 + x)}{x\cancel{(x + 1)}} \cdot \frac{\cancel{(x + 1)}(x - 1)}{\cancel{x - 5}} \qquad (5 - x) \div (x - 5) = -1.$$

$$= \frac{-1(5 + x)(x - 1)}{x} \qquad \text{Divide out the common factors.}$$

$$= \frac{-x^2 - 4x + 5}{x} \qquad \text{Multiply the factors in the numerator.} \qquad \blacksquare$$

C A U T I O N   When dividing rational expressions, you can factor the polynomials at any time, but do not reduce until after you have inverted the divisor.

In Example 6 division is indicated by a fraction bar.

E X A M P L E 6   **Dividing rational expressions**

Perform the operations indicated.

a) $\dfrac{\dfrac{a + b}{3}}{\dfrac{1}{2}}$

b) $\dfrac{\dfrac{x^2 - 4}{2}}{\dfrac{x - 2}{3}}$

c) $\dfrac{\dfrac{m^2 + 1}{5}}{3}$

Solution

a) $\dfrac{\dfrac{a+b}{3}}{\dfrac{1}{2}} = \dfrac{a+b}{3} \div \dfrac{1}{2}$

$= \dfrac{a+b}{3} \cdot \dfrac{2}{1}$ Invert the divisor.

$= \dfrac{2a+2b}{3}$ Multiply.

b) $\dfrac{\dfrac{x^2-4}{2}}{\dfrac{x-2}{3}} = \dfrac{x^2-4}{2} \cdot \dfrac{3}{x-2}$ Invert and multiply.

$= \dfrac{(x-2)(x+2)}{2} \cdot \dfrac{3}{x-2}$ Factor.

$= \dfrac{3x+6}{2}$ Reduce.

c) $\dfrac{\dfrac{m^2+1}{5}}{3} = \dfrac{m^2+1}{5} \cdot \dfrac{1}{3} = \dfrac{m^2+1}{15}$ Multiply by $\frac{1}{3}$, the reciprocal of 3. ■

WARM-UPS

True or false? Explain.

1. We can multiply only fractions that have identical denominators.
2. $\frac{2}{7} \cdot \frac{3}{7} = \frac{6}{7}$
3. To divide rational expressions, invert the divisor and multiply.
4. $a \div b = \frac{1}{a} \cdot b$ for any nonzero a and b.
5. $\frac{1}{2x} \cdot 8x^2 = 4x$ for any nonzero real number x.
6. One-half of one-third is one-sixth.
7. One-third divided by one-half is two-thirds.
8. The quotient of $w - z$ divided by $z - w$ is -1, provided that $z - w \neq 0$.
9. $\frac{x}{3} \div 2 = \frac{x}{6}$ for any real number x.
10. $\frac{a}{b} \div \frac{b}{a} = 1$ for any nonzero real numbers a and b.

6.2   EXERCISES

Reading and Writing   *After reading this section, write out the answers to these questions. Use complete sentences.*

1. How do you multiply rational numbers?

2. What is the procedure for multiplying rational expressions?

3. What is the relationship between $a - b$ and $b - a$?

4. How do we divide rational numbers?

In Exercises 5–20, perform the indicated operations. See Examples 1–3.

5. $\dfrac{12}{42} \cdot \dfrac{35}{22}$

6. $\dfrac{3}{8} \cdot \dfrac{20}{21}$

7. $\dfrac{3a}{10b} \cdot \dfrac{5b^2}{6}$

8. $\dfrac{3x}{7y} \cdot \dfrac{14y^2}{9x}$

9. $\dfrac{3x - 3}{6} \cdot \dfrac{x}{x^2 - x}$

10. $\dfrac{-2x - 4}{2} \cdot \dfrac{6}{3x + 6}$

11. $\dfrac{10x + 5}{5x^2 + 5} \cdot \dfrac{2x^2 + x - 1}{4x^2 - 1}$

12. $\dfrac{x^3 + x}{5} \cdot \dfrac{5x - 5}{x^3 - x}$

13. $\dfrac{ax + aw + bx + bw}{x^2 - w^2} \cdot \dfrac{x - w}{a^2 - b^2}$

14. $\dfrac{3a - 3y}{3a - 3y - ab + by} \cdot \dfrac{b^2 - 9}{6b + 18}$

15. $\dfrac{a^2 - 2a + 4}{a^3 + 8} \cdot \dfrac{(a + 2)^3}{2a + 4}$

16. $\dfrac{w^3 - 1}{(w - 1)^2} \cdot \dfrac{w^2 - 1}{w^2 + w + 1}$

17. $\dfrac{x - 9}{12y} \cdot \dfrac{8y}{9 - x}$

18. $\dfrac{19x^2}{12y - 1} \cdot \dfrac{1 - 12y}{3x}$

19. $(a^2 - 4) \cdot \dfrac{7}{2 - a}$

20. $\dfrac{10x - 4x^2}{4x^2 - 20x + 25} \cdot (2x^3 - 5x^2)$

21. $\dfrac{(3x + 1)^3}{2x - 1} \cdot \dfrac{4x^2 - 4x + 1}{9x^2 + 6x + 1}$

22. $\dfrac{a^2 - 2ab + b^2}{a - b} \cdot \dfrac{(a + b)^3}{a^2 + 2ab + b^2}$

Perform the indicated operations. See Examples 4 and 5.

23. $\dfrac{15}{17} \div \dfrac{10}{17}$

24. $\dfrac{3}{4} \div \dfrac{1}{8}$

25. $\dfrac{36x}{5y} \div \dfrac{20x}{35y}$

26. $\dfrac{18a^3b^4}{c^9} \div \dfrac{12ab^6}{7c^2}$

27. $\dfrac{24a^5b^2}{5c^3} \div (4a^5bc^5)$

28. $\dfrac{60x^9y^2}{z} \div (48x^4y^3)$

29. $(w + 1) \div \dfrac{w^2 - 1}{w}$

30. $(a - 3) \div \dfrac{9 - a^2}{4}$

31. $\dfrac{x - y}{5} \div \dfrac{x^2 - 2xy + y^2}{10}$

32. $\dfrac{x^2 + 6x + 9}{18} \div \dfrac{(x + 3)^2}{36}$

33. $\dfrac{4x - 2}{x^2 - 5x} \div \dfrac{2x^2 + 9x - 5}{x^2 - 25}$

34. $\dfrac{2x^2 - 5x - 12}{6 + 4x} \div \dfrac{x^2 - 16}{2}$

Perform the indicated operations. See Example 6.

35. $\dfrac{\dfrac{x - y}{3}}{\dfrac{1}{6}}$

36. $\dfrac{\dfrac{2a - b}{10}}{\dfrac{1}{5}}$

37. $\dfrac{\dfrac{x^2 - 25}{3}}{\dfrac{x - 5}{6}}$

38. $\dfrac{\dfrac{3x^2 + 3}{5}}{\dfrac{3x + 3}{5}}$

39. $\dfrac{\dfrac{a - b}{2}}{3}$

40. $\dfrac{\dfrac{10}{a + b}}{5}$

41. $\dfrac{\dfrac{a^2 - b^2}{a + b}}{3}$

42. $\dfrac{\dfrac{x^2 + 5x + 6}{x + 2}}{x + 3}$

Perform the indicated operations. When possible write down only the answer.

43. $\dfrac{5x}{2} \div 3$

44. $\dfrac{x}{a} \div 2$

45. $\dfrac{3}{4} \div \dfrac{1}{4}$

46. $\dfrac{1}{4} \div \dfrac{1}{2}$

47. One-half of $\dfrac{1}{6}$

48. One-half of $\dfrac{b}{a}$

49. One-half of $\dfrac{4x}{3}$

50. One-third of $\dfrac{6x}{y}$

51. $(a - b) \div (b - a)$

52. $(a - b) \div (-1)$

53. $\dfrac{x-y}{3} \cdot \dfrac{6}{y-x}$

54. $\dfrac{5x-5y}{x} \cdot \dfrac{1}{x-y}$

55. $\dfrac{2a+2b}{a} \cdot \dfrac{1}{2}$

56. $\dfrac{x-y}{y-x} \cdot \dfrac{1}{2}$

57. $-1\left(\dfrac{9-x}{2}\right)$

58. $\dfrac{-1}{x-1} \cdot \dfrac{1-x}{2}$

59. $\dfrac{4}{y-7} \div \dfrac{2}{7-y}$

60. $\dfrac{1}{3-m} \div \dfrac{1}{2m-6}$

61. $\dfrac{a+b}{\dfrac{1}{2}}$

62. $\dfrac{x+3}{\dfrac{1}{3}}$

63. $\dfrac{\dfrac{3x}{5}}{y}$

64. $\dfrac{\dfrac{b^2-4a}{2}}{a}$

65. $\dfrac{\dfrac{3a}{5b}}{2}$

66. $\dfrac{\dfrac{6x}{a}}{x}$

Perform the indicated operations.

67. $\dfrac{3x^2+13x-10}{x} \cdot \dfrac{x^3}{9x^2-4} \cdot \dfrac{7x-35}{x^2-25}$

68. $\dfrac{x^2+5x+6}{x} \cdot \dfrac{x^2}{3x+6} \cdot \dfrac{9}{x^2-4}$

69. $\dfrac{(a^2b^3c)^2}{(-2ab^2c)^3} \cdot \dfrac{(a^3b^2c)^3}{(abc)^4}$

70. $\dfrac{(-wy^2)^3}{3w^2y} \cdot \dfrac{(2wy)^2}{4wy^3}$

71. $\dfrac{(2mn)^3}{6mn^2} \div \dfrac{2m^2n^3}{(m^2n)^4}$

72. $\dfrac{(rt)^3}{rt^4} \div \dfrac{(rt^2)^3}{r^2t^3}$

73. $\dfrac{2x^2+7x-15}{4x^2-100} \cdot \dfrac{2x^2-9x-5}{4x^2-1}$

74. $\dfrac{x^3+1}{x^2-1} \cdot \dfrac{3x-3}{x^3-x^2+x}$

75. $\dfrac{2h^2-5h-3}{5h^2-4h-1} \div \dfrac{2h^2+7h+3}{h^2+2h-3}$

76. $\dfrac{9w^2-64}{3w^2-5w-8} \cdot \dfrac{5w^2+3w-2}{25w^2-4}$

77. $\dfrac{9a-3}{1-9a^2} \cdot \dfrac{9a^2+6a+1}{6}$

78. $\dfrac{5-10k}{k^2-2k} \div \dfrac{2k^2+7k-4}{k^2+2k-8}$

79. $\dfrac{k^2+2km+m^2}{k^2-2km+m^2} \cdot \dfrac{m^2+3m-mk-3k}{m^2+mk+3m+3k}$

80. $\dfrac{a^2+2ab+b^2}{ac+bc-ad-bd} \div \dfrac{ac+ad-bc-bd}{c^2-d^2}$

Perform the indicated operations. Variables in exponents represent integers.

81. $\dfrac{x^a}{y^2} \cdot \dfrac{y^{b+2}}{x^{2a}}$

82. $\dfrac{x^{3a+1}}{y^{2b-3}} \cdot \dfrac{y^{3b+4}}{x^{2a-1}}$

83. $\dfrac{x^{2a}+x^a-6}{x^{2a}+6x^a+9} \div \dfrac{x^{2a}-4}{x^{2a}+2x^a-3}$

84. $\dfrac{w^{2b}+2w^b-8}{w^{2b}+3w^b-4} \div \dfrac{w^{2b}-w^b-2}{w^{2b}-1}$

85. $\dfrac{m^kv^k+3v^k-2m^k-6}{m^{2k}-9} \cdot \dfrac{m^{2k}-2m^k-3}{v^km^k-2m^k+2v^k-4}$

86. $\dfrac{m^{3k}-1}{m^{3k}+1} \cdot \dfrac{m^{2k+1}-m^{k+1}+m}{m^{3k}+m^{2k}+m^k}$

Solve each problem.

87. *School enrollment.* In 2005, $\frac{1}{50}$ of the children enrolled in U.S. schools will be enrolled in private secondary schools (National Center for Education Statistics, www.nces.ed.gov). Use the accompanying figure to determine the percentage of secondary school children who will be in private schools in 2005.

2005 distribution of students in U.S. schools

Secondary schools $\frac{7}{25}$

Elementary schools $\frac{18}{25}$

FIGURE FOR EXERCISE 87

88. *The golden state.* In 2000, $\frac{3}{25}$ of the U.S. population was living in California (U.S. Census Bureau). Use the figure on the next page to determine the percentage of the population of the western region living in California in 2000.

Distribution of U.S. Population in 2000

West $\dfrac{2}{9}$ East $\dfrac{7}{9}$

FIGURE FOR EXERCISE 88

250 miles in the same amount of time. Write a rational expression for her speed after lunch.

GETTING MORE INVOLVED

91. *Discussion.* Which of the following expressions is not equivalent to $x \div \frac{y}{z}$? Explain.

a) $x \cdot \dfrac{z}{y}$ b) $\dfrac{x}{y} \cdot z$ c) $zx \cdot \dfrac{1}{y}$

d) $\dfrac{x}{\frac{y}{z}}$ e) $\dfrac{xy}{z}$

92. *Discussion.* Which of the following equations is not an identity? Explain.

a) $\dfrac{x^2 - 1}{2} \cdot \dfrac{2}{x - 1} = x + 1$

b) $\dfrac{x - 1}{x^2 - 1} = x + 1$

c) $x^2 - 1 = (x - 1)(x + 1)$

d) $\dfrac{1}{x^2 - 1} \div \dfrac{1}{x + 1} = \dfrac{1}{x - 1}$

89. *Distance traveled.* Bonita drove 100 miles in x hours. Assuming she continued to drive at the same speed, write a rational expression for the distance that she traveled in the next $\frac{3}{4}$ of an hour.

90. *Increasing speed.* Before lunch Avonda drove 200 miles at x miles per hour (mph). After lunch she drove

---

In This Section

- Adding and Subtracting with Identical Denominators
- Least Common Denominator
- Adding and Subtracting with Different Denominators
- Shortcuts
- Applications

6.3   **ADDITION AND SUBTRACTION**

We can multiply or divide any rational expressions, but we add or subtract only rational expressions with identical denominators. So when the denominators are not the same, we must find equivalent forms of the expressions that have identical denominators. In this section we will review the idea of the least common denominator and will learn to use it for addition and subtraction of rational expressions.

Adding and Subtracting with Identical Denominators

It is easy to add or subtract fractions with identical denominators. For example,

$$\frac{1}{7} + \frac{3}{7} = \frac{4}{7} \quad \text{and} \quad \frac{3}{5} - \frac{2}{5} = \frac{1}{5}.$$

In general, we have the following definition.

Addition and Subtraction of Rational Numbers

If $b \neq 0$, then

$$\frac{a}{b} + \frac{c}{b} = \frac{a + c}{b} \quad \text{and} \quad \frac{a}{b} - \frac{c}{b} = \frac{a - c}{b}.$$

Rational expressions with identical denominators are added or subtracted in the same manner as fractions.

EXAMPLE 1   **Identical denominators**

Perform the indicated operations.

a) $\dfrac{3}{2x} + \dfrac{5}{2x}$

b) $\dfrac{5x-3}{x-1} + \dfrac{5-7x}{x-1}$

c) $\dfrac{x^2+4x+7}{x^2-1} - \dfrac{x^2-2x+1}{x^2-1}$

Helpful Hint

You can remind yourself of the difference between addition and multiplication of fractions with a simple example: If you and your spouse each own 1/7 of Microsoft, then together you own 2/7 of Microsoft. If you own 1/7 of Microsoft, and give 1/7 of your stock to your child, then your child owns 1/49 of Microsoft.

Study Tip

Studying in an environment similar to the one in which you will be tested can increase your chances of recalling information. When possible, review for a test in the classroom in which you will take the test.

Solution

a) $\dfrac{3}{2x} + \dfrac{5}{2x} = \dfrac{8}{2x}$ Add the numerators.

$= \dfrac{4}{x}$ Reduce.

b) $\dfrac{5x-3}{x-1} + \dfrac{5-7x}{x-1} = \dfrac{5x-3+5-7x}{x-1}$ Add the numerators.

$= \dfrac{-2x+2}{x-1}$ Combine like terms.

$= \dfrac{-2(x-1)}{x-1}$ Factor.

$= -2$ Reduce to lowest terms.

c) The polynomials in the numerators are treated as if they were in parentheses:

$\dfrac{x^2+4x+7}{x^2-1} - \dfrac{x^2-2x+1}{x^2-1} = \dfrac{x^2+4x+7-(x^2-2x+1)}{x^2-1}$

$= \dfrac{x^2+4x+7-x^2+2x-1}{x^2-1}$

$= \dfrac{6x+6}{x^2-1}$

$= \dfrac{6(x+1)}{(x+1)(x-1)} = \dfrac{6}{x-1}$ ∎

Least Common Denominator

To add fractions with denominators that are not identical, we use the basic principle of rational numbers to build up the denominators to the **least common denominator (LCD)**. For example,

$$\dfrac{1}{4} + \dfrac{1}{6} = \dfrac{1 \cdot 3}{4 \cdot 3} + \dfrac{1 \cdot 2}{6 \cdot 2} = \dfrac{3}{12} + \dfrac{2}{12} = \dfrac{5}{12}.$$

The LCD 12 is the **least common multiple (LCM)** of the numbers 4 and 6.

Finding the LCM for a pair of large numbers such as 24 and 126 will help you to understand the procedure for finding the LCM for any polynomials. First factor the numbers completely:

$$24 = 2^3 \cdot 3$$
$$126 = 2 \cdot 3^2 \cdot 7$$

Helpful Hint
___

The product of 24 and 126 is 3024 and 3024 is a common multiple but not the least common multiple of 24 and 126. If you divide 3024 by 6, the greatest common factor of 24 and 126, you get 504.

Any number that is a multiple of both 24 and 126 must have all of the factors of 24 and all of the factors of 126 in its factored form. So in the LCM we use the factors 2, 3, and 7, and for each factor we use the highest power that appears on that factor. The highest power of 2 is 3, the highest power of 3 is 2, and the highest power of 7 is 1. So the LCM is $2^3 \cdot 3^2 \cdot 7$. If we write this product without exponents, we can see clearly that it is a multiple of both 24 and 126:

$$\underbrace{2 \cdot 2 \cdot \overbrace{2 \cdot 3}^{126} \cdot 3 \cdot 7}_{24} = 504 \quad \begin{array}{l} 504 = 126 \cdot 4 \\ 504 = 24 \cdot 21 \end{array}$$

The strategy for finding the LCM for a group of polynomials can be stated as follows.

Strategy for Finding the LCM for Polynomials

1. Factor each polynomial completely. Use exponents to express repeated factors.
2. Write the product of all of the different factors that appear in the polynomials.
3. For each factor, use the highest power of that factor in any of the polynomials.

E X A M P L E 2

Finding the LCM

Find the least common multiple for each group of polynomials.

a) $4x^2y$, $6y$ 　　　　　　　**b)** a^2bc, ab^3c^2, a^3bc

c) $x^2 + 5x + 6$, $x^2 + 6x + 9$

Solution

a) Factor $4x^2y$ and $6y$ as follows:

$$4x^2y = 2^2 \cdot x^2y, \qquad 6y = 2 \cdot 3y$$

To get the LCM, we use 2, 3, x, and y the maximum number of times that each appears in either of the expressions. The LCM is $2^2 \cdot 3 \cdot x^2y$, or $12x^2y$.

b) The expressions a^2bc, ab^3c^2, and a^3bc are already factored. To get the LCM, we use a, b, and c the maximum number of times that each appears in any of the expressions. The LCM is $a^3b^3c^2$.

c) Factor $x^2 + 5x + 6$ and $x^2 + 6x + 9$ completely:

$$x^2 + 5x + 6 = (x + 2)(x + 3), \qquad x^2 + 6x + 9 = (x + 3)^2$$

The LCM is $(x + 2)(x + 3)^2$. ■

Adding and Subtracting with Different Denominators

To add or subtract rational expressions with different denominators, we must build up each rational expression to equivalent forms with identical denominators, as we did in Section 6.1. Of course, it is most efficient to use the LCD as in the following examples.

E X A M P L E   3   **Different denominators**

Perform the indicated operations.

a) $\dfrac{3}{a^2b} + \dfrac{5}{ab^3}$

b) $\dfrac{x+1}{6} - \dfrac{2x-3}{4}$

Solution

a) The LCD for a^2b and ab^3 is a^2b^3. To build up each denominator to a^2b^3, multiply the numerator and denominator of the first expression by b^2, and multiply the numerator and denominator of the second expression by a:

$$\dfrac{3}{a^2b} + \dfrac{5}{ab^3} = \dfrac{3(b^2)}{a^2b(b^2)} + \dfrac{5(a)}{ab^3(a)} \qquad \text{Build up each denominator to the LCD.}$$

$$= \dfrac{3b^2}{a^2b^3} + \dfrac{5a}{a^2b^3}$$

$$= \dfrac{3b^2 + 5a}{a^2b^3} \qquad \text{Add the numerators.}$$

b) $\dfrac{x+1}{6} - \dfrac{2x-3}{4} = \dfrac{(x+1)(2)}{6(2)} - \dfrac{(2x-3)(3)}{4(3)} \qquad \begin{array}{l}\text{Build up each denominator}\\\text{to the LCD 12.}\end{array}$

$$= \dfrac{2x+2}{12} - \dfrac{6x-9}{12} \qquad \text{Distributive property}$$

$$= \dfrac{2x+2-(6x-9)}{12} \qquad \begin{array}{l}\text{Subtract the numerators.}\\\text{Note that } 6x-9 \text{ is put in}\\\text{parentheses.}\end{array}$$

$$= \dfrac{2x+2-6x+9}{12} \qquad \text{Remove the parentheses.}$$

$$= \dfrac{-4x+11}{12} \qquad \text{Combine like terms.} \qquad \blacksquare$$

CAUTION   Before you add or subtract rational expressions, they must be written with identical denominators. For multiplication and division it is not necessary to have identical denominators.

In Example 4 we must first factor polynomials to find the LCD.

E X A M P L E   4   **Different denominators**

Perform the indicated operations.

a) $\dfrac{1}{x^2-1} + \dfrac{2}{x^2+x}$

b) $\dfrac{5}{a-2} - \dfrac{3}{2-a}$

Helpful Hint

It is not actually necessary to identify the LCD. Once the denominators are factored, simply look at each denominator and ask, "What factor does the other denominator have that is missing from this one?" Then use the missing factor to build up the denominator and you will obtain the LCD.

Solution

a) Because $x^2 - 1 = (x + 1)(x - 1)$ and $x^2 + x = x(x + 1)$, the LCD is $x(x - 1)(x + 1)$. The first denominator is missing the factor x, and the second denominator is missing the factor $x - 1$.

$$\underbrace{\frac{1}{x^2 - 1}}_{\text{Missing } x} + \underbrace{\frac{2}{x^2 + x}}_{} = \underbrace{\frac{1}{(x - 1)(x + 1)}}_{\text{Missing } x} + \underbrace{\frac{2}{x(x + 1)}}_{\text{Missing } x - 1} \qquad \text{The LCD is } x(x - 1)(x + 1).$$

$$= \frac{1(x)}{(x - 1)(x + 1)(x)} + \frac{2(x - 1)}{x(x + 1)(x - 1)} \qquad \begin{array}{l}\text{Build up the}\\\text{denominators to}\\\text{the LCD.}\end{array}$$

$$= \frac{x}{x(x - 1)(x + 1)} + \frac{2x - 2}{x(x - 1)(x + 1)}$$

$$= \frac{3x - 2}{x(x - 1)(x + 1)} \qquad \begin{array}{l}\text{Add the}\\\text{numerators.}\end{array}$$

For this type of answer we usually leave the denominator in factored form. That way, if we need to work with the expression further, we do not have to factor the denominator again.

b) Because $-1(2 - a) = a - 2$, we can convert the denominator $2 - a$ to $a - 2$.

$$\frac{5}{a - 2} - \frac{3}{2 - a} = \frac{5}{a - 2} - \frac{3(-1)}{(2 - a)(-1)}$$

$$= \frac{5}{a - 2} - \frac{-3}{a - 2} \qquad \text{The LCD is } a - 2.$$

$$= \frac{5 - (-3)}{a - 2} \qquad \text{Subtract the numerators.}$$

$$= \frac{8}{a - 2} \qquad \text{Simplify.}$$

Note that we get an equivalent answer if we multiply the numerator and denominator by -1:

$$\frac{8}{a - 2} = \frac{8(-1)}{(a - 2)(-1)} = \frac{-8}{2 - a}$$

This is the answer that we would have gotten if we had used $2 - a$ as the common denominator in the beginning.   ■

If the rational expressions in a sum or difference are not in lowest terms, then they should be reduced before finding the least common denominator.

E X A M P L E   5   **Reducing before finding the LCD**

Perform the indicated operations.

a) $\dfrac{2xy}{4x} + \dfrac{x^2}{xy}$

b) $\dfrac{8x - 8}{4x^2 - 4} - \dfrac{9x}{3x^2 - 3x - 6}$

Solution

a) Notice that the rational expressions can be reduced:

$$\frac{2xy}{4x} + \frac{x^2}{xy} = \frac{y}{2} + \frac{x}{y} \qquad \text{Reduce each rational expression.}$$

$$= \frac{y \cdot y}{2 \cdot y} + \frac{x \cdot 2}{y \cdot 2} \qquad \text{Build up each denominator to } 2y.$$

$$= \frac{y^2 + 2x}{2y} \qquad \text{Add the rational expressions.}$$

b) Notice that $3x^2 - 3x - 6 = 3(x^2 - x - 2) = 3(x - 2)(x + 1)$ and $4x^2 - 4 = 4(x^2 - 1) = 4(x - 1)(x + 1)$:

$$\frac{8x - 8}{4x^2 - 4} - \frac{9x}{3x^2 - 3x - 6}$$

$$= \frac{8(x - 1)}{4(x - 1)(x + 1)} - \frac{9x}{3(x - 2)(x + 1)} \qquad \text{Factor.}$$

$$= \frac{2}{x + 1} - \frac{3x}{(x - 2)(x + 1)} \qquad \text{Reduce.}$$

$$= \frac{2(x - 2)}{(x + 1)(x - 2)} - \frac{3x}{(x - 2)(x + 1)} \qquad \text{Build up to get the LCD.}$$

$$= \frac{2x - 4 - 3x}{(x + 1)(x - 2)} \qquad \text{Subtract the expressions.}$$

$$= \frac{-x - 4}{(x + 1)(x - 2)} \qquad \text{Simplify. Leave denominator factored.}$$

■

Shortcuts

Consider the following addition:

$$\frac{a}{b} + \frac{c}{d} = \frac{a(d)}{b(d)} + \frac{c(b)}{d(b)} = \frac{ad + bc}{bd} \qquad \text{The LCD is } bd.$$

We can use this result as a rule for adding simple fractions in which the LCD is the product of the denominators. A similar rule works for subtraction.

Adding or Subtracting Simple Fractions

If $b \neq 0$ and $d \neq 0$, then

$$\frac{a}{b} + \frac{c}{d} = \frac{ad + bc}{bd} \qquad \text{and} \qquad \frac{a}{b} - \frac{c}{d} = \frac{ad - bc}{bd}.$$

E X A M P L E   6

Adding and subtracting simple fractions

Use the rules for adding and subtracting simple fractions to find the sums and differences.

a) $\dfrac{1}{2} + \dfrac{1}{3}$

b) $\dfrac{1}{a} - \dfrac{1}{x}$

c) $\dfrac{a}{5} + \dfrac{a}{3}$

d) $x - \dfrac{2}{3}$

Solution

a) For the numerator, compute $ad + bc = 1 \cdot 3 + 2 \cdot 1 = 5$. Use $2 \cdot 3$ or 6 for the denominator:

$$\frac{1}{2} + \frac{1}{3} = \frac{5}{6}$$

b) $\dfrac{1}{a} - \dfrac{1}{x} = \dfrac{1 \cdot x - 1 \cdot a}{ax} = \dfrac{x - a}{ax}$

c) $\dfrac{a}{5} + \dfrac{a}{3} = \dfrac{3a + 5a}{15} = \dfrac{8a}{15}$

d) $x - \dfrac{2}{3} = \dfrac{x}{1} - \dfrac{2}{3} = \dfrac{3x - 2}{3}$ ∎

CAUTION   The rules for adding or subtracting simple fractions can be applied to any rational expressions, but they work best when the LCD is the product of the two denominators. Always make sure that the answer is in its lowest terms. If the product of the two denominators is too large, these rules are not helpful because then reducing can be difficult.

Applications

Rational expressions occur often in expressing rates. For example, if you can process one application in 2 hours, then you are working at the rate of $\frac{1}{2}$ of an application per hour. If you can complete one task in x hours, then you are working at the rate of $\frac{1}{x}$ task per hour.

E X A M P L E 7   **Work rates**

Susan takes an average of x hours to process a mortgage application, whereas Betty's average is 1 hour longer. Write a rational expression for the number of applications that they can process in 40 hours.

Solution

The number of applications processed by Susan is the product of her rate and her time:

$$\frac{1 \text{ application}}{x \quad \text{hr}} \cdot 40 \text{ hr} = \frac{40}{x} \text{ applications}$$

The number of applications processed by Betty is the product of her rate and her time:

$$\frac{1}{x + 1} \frac{\text{application}}{\text{hr}} \cdot 40 \text{ hr} = \frac{40}{x + 1} \text{ applications}$$

Find the sum of the rational expressions:

$$\frac{40}{x} + \frac{40}{x + 1} = \frac{40x + 40 + 40x}{x(x + 1)} = \frac{80x + 40}{x(x + 1)}$$

So together in 40 hours they process $\frac{80x + 40}{x(x + 1)}$ applications.   ∎

WARM-UPS

True or false? Explain.

1. The LCM of 6 and 10 is 60.
2. The LCM of $6a^2b$ and $8ab^3$ is $24ab$.
3. The LCM of $x^2 - 1$ and $x - 1$ is $x^2 - 1$.
4. The LCD for the rational expressions $\frac{5}{x}$ and $\frac{x-3}{x+1}$ is $x + 1$.
5. $\dfrac{1}{2} + \dfrac{2}{3} = \dfrac{3}{5}$
6. $5 + \dfrac{1}{x} = \dfrac{6}{x}$ for any nonzero real number x.
7. $\dfrac{7}{a} + 3 = \dfrac{7 + 3a}{a}$ for any $a \neq 0$.
8. $\dfrac{c}{3} - \dfrac{d}{5} = \dfrac{5c - 3d}{15}$ for any real numbers c and d.
9. $\dfrac{2}{3} + \dfrac{3}{4} = \dfrac{17}{12}$
10. If Jamal uses x reams of paper in one day, then he uses $\frac{1}{x}$ ream per day.

6.3   EXERCISES

Reading and Writing *After reading this section, write out the answers to these questions. Use complete sentences.*

1. How do you add rational numbers?

2. What is the least common denominator (LCD)?

3. What is the least common multiple?

4. How do we find the LCM for a group of polynomials?

5. How do we add or subtract rational expressions with different denominators?

6. For which operations with rational expressions is it not necessary to have identical denominators?

Perform the indicated operations. Reduce answers to their lowest terms. See Example 1.

7. $\dfrac{3x}{2} + \dfrac{5x}{2}$

8. $\dfrac{5x^2}{3} + \dfrac{4x^2}{3}$

9. $\dfrac{x-3}{2x} - \dfrac{3x-5}{2x}$

10. $\dfrac{9-4y}{3y} - \dfrac{6-y}{3y}$

11. $\dfrac{3x-4}{2x-4} + \dfrac{2x-6}{2x-4}$

12. $\dfrac{a^3}{a+b} + \dfrac{b^3}{a+b}$

13. $\dfrac{x^2+4x-6}{x^2-9} - \dfrac{x^2+2x-12}{x^2-9}$

14. $\dfrac{x^2+3x-3}{x-4} - \dfrac{x^2+4x-7}{x-4}$

15. $\dfrac{2x^2-8x-4}{2x^2+7x+3} + \dfrac{4x^2+x-1}{2x^2+7x+3}$

16. $\dfrac{5x^2-2x-5}{2x^2+3x-2} - \dfrac{x^2-9x-3}{2x^2+3x-2}$

Find the least common multiple for each group of polynomials. See Example 2.

17. 24, 20

18. 12, 18, 22

19. $10x^3y$, $15x$

20. $12a^3b^2$, $18ab^5$

21. a^3b, ab^4c, ab^5c^2

22. x^2yz, xy^2z^3, xy^6

23. x, $x + 2$, $x - 2$

24. y, $y - 5$, $y + 2$

25. $4a + 8$, $6a + 12$

26. $4a - 6$, $2a^2 - 3a$

27. $x^2 - 1$, $x^2 + 2x + 1$

28. $y^2 - 2y - 15$, $y^2 + 6y + 9$

29. $x^2 - 4x$, $x^2 - 16$, $x^2 + 6x + 8$

30. $z^2 - 25$, $5z - 25$, $5z + 25$

31. $6x^2 + 17x + 12$, $9x^2 - 16$

32. $16x^2 - 8x - 3$, $4x^2 - 7x + 3$

Perform the indicated operations. Reduce answers to lowest terms. See Examples 3, 4, and 5.

33. $\dfrac{1}{28} + \dfrac{3}{35}$

34. $\dfrac{7}{24} - \dfrac{4}{15}$

35. $\dfrac{7}{48} - \dfrac{5}{36}$

36. $\dfrac{7}{52} + \dfrac{3}{40}$

37. $\dfrac{3}{wz^2} + \dfrac{5}{w^2z}$

38. $\dfrac{2}{a^2b} - \dfrac{3}{ab^2}$

39. $\dfrac{2x - 3}{8} - \dfrac{x - 2}{6}$

40. $\dfrac{a - 5}{10} + \dfrac{3 - 2a}{15}$

41. $\dfrac{xa^3}{2a^4} + \dfrac{21x^2}{35ax}$

42. $\dfrac{5x^2}{30xy} - \dfrac{30x}{80y}$

43. $\dfrac{9}{4y} - x$

44. $\dfrac{b^2}{4a} - c$

45. $\dfrac{5}{a + 2} - \dfrac{7}{a}$

46. $\dfrac{2}{x + 1} - \dfrac{3}{x}$

47. $\dfrac{1}{a - b} + \dfrac{2}{a + b}$

48. $\dfrac{5}{x + 2} + \dfrac{3}{x - 2}$

49. $\dfrac{2x^2}{2x^3 - 18x} + \dfrac{15}{5x - 15}$

50. $\dfrac{5x}{5x^2 - 125} + \dfrac{5x - 5}{x^2 - 6x + 5}$

51. $\dfrac{1}{a - b} + \dfrac{1}{b - a}$

52. $\dfrac{3}{x - 5} + \dfrac{7}{5 - x}$

53. $\dfrac{10}{4x - 8} - \dfrac{15}{10 - 5x}$

54. $\dfrac{8}{6x - 18} - \dfrac{14}{6 - 2x}$

55. $\dfrac{5}{x^2 + x - 2} - \dfrac{6}{x^2 + 2x - 3}$

56. $\dfrac{2}{x^2 - 4} - \dfrac{5}{x^2 - 3x - 10}$

57. $\dfrac{x}{2x^2 + x - 1} + \dfrac{3}{3x^2 + 2x - 1}$

58. $\dfrac{x + 1}{3x^2 - 2x - 1} + \dfrac{x - 1}{3x^2 + 4x + 1}$

59. $\dfrac{1}{x} + \dfrac{2}{x - 1} - \dfrac{3}{x + 2}$

60. $\dfrac{2}{a} - \dfrac{3}{a + 1} + \dfrac{5}{a - 1}$

Perform the following operations. Write down only the answer. See Example 6.

61. $\dfrac{1}{3} + \dfrac{1}{4}$

62. $\dfrac{3}{5} + \dfrac{1}{4}$

63. $\dfrac{1}{8} - \dfrac{3}{5}$

64. $\dfrac{a}{2} + \dfrac{5}{3}$

65. $\dfrac{x}{3} + \dfrac{x}{2}$

66. $\dfrac{y}{4} - \dfrac{y}{3}$

67. $\dfrac{a}{b} - \dfrac{2}{3}$

68. $\dfrac{3}{x} + \dfrac{1}{9}$

69. $a + \dfrac{2}{3}$

70. $\dfrac{m}{3} + y$

71. $\dfrac{3}{a} + 1$

72. $\dfrac{1}{x} + 1$

73. $\dfrac{3+x}{x} - 1$ **74.** $\dfrac{a+2}{a} + 3$

75. $\dfrac{2}{3} + \dfrac{1}{4x}$ **76.** $\dfrac{1}{5} + \dfrac{1}{5x}$

Perform the indicated operations.

77. $\dfrac{w^2 - 3w + 6}{w - 5} + \dfrac{9 - w^2}{w - 5}$

78. $\dfrac{2z^2 - 3z + 6}{z^2 - 1} - \dfrac{z^2 - 5z + 9}{z^2 - 1}$

79. $\dfrac{1}{3x - 6} - \dfrac{6}{5x - 10}$

80. $\dfrac{3}{6x^2 - 4x} - \dfrac{x - 2}{9x - 6}$

81. $\dfrac{x - 1}{2x^2 + 3x + 1} - \dfrac{x + 1}{2x^2 - x - 1}$

82. $\dfrac{2x + 1}{6x^2 - 5x + 1} + \dfrac{2x - 1}{6x^2 + x - 1}$

83. $\dfrac{(a^2b^3)^4}{(ab^4)^3} \cdot \dfrac{(ab)^3}{(a^4b)^2}$

84. $\dfrac{(ab)^2}{(a + b)^2} \cdot \dfrac{(a + b)^3}{(ab)^3}$

85. $\dfrac{x^2 + 4}{25x^2 - 20x + 4} + \dfrac{10x + 4}{25x^2 - 4}$

86. $\dfrac{8a}{2a^2 + 4a + 2} - \dfrac{3a - 3}{a^2 - 1}$

87. $\dfrac{4x^2 + 9}{4x^2 - 9} \cdot \dfrac{4x^2 + 12x + 9}{2x^2 + 3x}$

88. $\dfrac{3a^2 - 2a - 16}{2a^2 + 3a - 2} \cdot \dfrac{6a + 16}{9a^2 - 64}$

89. $\dfrac{w^2 - 3}{3w^3 + 81} - \dfrac{2}{6w + 18} - \dfrac{w - 4}{w^2 - 3w + 9}$

90. $\dfrac{a - 3}{a^3 + 8} - \dfrac{2}{a + 2} - \dfrac{a - 3}{a^2 - 2a + 4}$

91. $\dfrac{a^2 - 6a + 9}{a^3 - 8} \div \dfrac{a^2 - a - 6}{a^2 - 4}$

92. $\dfrac{1}{z^2 + 4} \div \dfrac{z^3 - 8}{z^4 - 16}$

93. $\dfrac{w^2 + 3}{w^3 - 8} - \dfrac{2w}{w^2 - 4}$

94. $\dfrac{x + 5}{x^3 + 27} - \dfrac{x - 1}{x^2 - 9}$

95. $\dfrac{1}{x^3 - 1} - \dfrac{1}{x^2 - 1} + \dfrac{1}{x - 1}$

96. $\dfrac{x - 4}{x^3 - 1} + \dfrac{x - 2}{x^2 - 1}$

In Exercises 97–102, solve each problem. See Example 7.

97. *Processing.* Joe takes x hours on the average to process a claim, whereas Ellen averages $x + 1$ hours to process a claim. Write a rational expression for the number of claims that they will process while working together for an 8-hour shift.

98. *Roofing.* Bill attaches one bundle of shingles in an average of x minutes using a hammer, whereas Julio can attach one bundle in an average of $x - 6$ minutes using a pneumatic stapler. Write a rational expression for the number of bundles that they can attach while working together for 10 hours.

FIGURE FOR EXERCISE 98

99. *Selling.* George sells one magazine subscription every 20 minutes, whereas Theresa sells one every x minutes. Write a rational expression for the number of magazine subscriptions that they will sell when working together for one hour.

100. *Painting.* Harry can paint his house by himself in 6 days. His wife Judy can paint the house by herself in x days. Write a rational expression for the portion of the house that they paint when working together for 2 days.

101. *Driving.* Joan drove for 100 miles at one speed and then increased her speed by 5 miles per hour and drove 200 additional miles. Write a rational expression for her total travel time.

102. *Running.* Willard jogged for 3 miles at one speed and then doubled his speed for an additional mile. Write a rational expression for his total running time.

GETTING MORE INVOLVED

103. *Discussion.* Explain why fractions must have common denominators for addition but not for multiplication.

104. *Discussion.* Find each "infinite sum" and explain your answer.

a) $\dfrac{3}{10} + \dfrac{3}{10^2} + \dfrac{3}{10^3} + \dfrac{3}{10^4} + \cdots$

b) $\dfrac{9}{10} + \dfrac{9}{10^2} + \dfrac{9}{10^3} + \dfrac{9}{10^4} + \cdots$

In This Section

- Simplifying Complex Fractions
- Simplifying Expressions with Negative Exponents
- Applications

6.4   COMPLEX FRACTIONS

In this section we will use the techniques of Section 6.3 to simplify complex fractions. As their name suggests, complex fractions are rather messy-looking expressions.

Simplifying Complex Fractions

A **complex fraction** is a fraction that has rational expressions in the numerator, the denominator, or both. For example,

$$\frac{\dfrac{1}{2} + \dfrac{1}{3}}{\dfrac{1}{4} + \dfrac{1}{5}}, \qquad \frac{3 - \dfrac{2}{x}}{\dfrac{1}{x^2} - \dfrac{1}{4}}, \qquad \text{and} \qquad \frac{\dfrac{x+2}{x^2-9}}{\dfrac{x}{x^2-6x+9} + \dfrac{4}{x-3}}$$

are complex fractions. In the next example we show two methods for simplifying a complex fraction.

E X A M P L E   1

A complex fraction without variables

Simplify $\dfrac{\dfrac{1}{2} + \dfrac{1}{3}}{\dfrac{1}{4} + \dfrac{1}{5}}$.

Calculator Close-Up

You can use a calculator to find the value of a complex fraction.

Solution

Method A   For this method we perform the computations of the numerator and denominator separately and then divide:

$$\frac{\dfrac{1}{2} + \dfrac{1}{3}}{\dfrac{1}{4} + \dfrac{1}{5}} = \frac{\dfrac{5}{6}}{\dfrac{9}{20}} = \frac{5}{6} \div \frac{9}{20} = \frac{5}{6} \cdot \frac{20}{9} = \frac{5 \cdot 2 \cdot 10}{2 \cdot 3 \cdot 9} = \frac{50}{27}$$

Method B   For this method we find the LCD for all of the fractions in the complex fraction. Then we multiply the numerator and denominator of the complex fraction by the LCD. The LCD for the denominators 2, 3, 4, and 5 is 60. So we multiply the numerator and denominator of the complex fraction by 60:

$$\frac{\dfrac{1}{2} + \dfrac{1}{3}}{\dfrac{1}{4} + \dfrac{1}{5}} = \frac{\left(\dfrac{1}{2} + \dfrac{1}{3}\right)60}{\left(\dfrac{1}{4} + \dfrac{1}{5}\right)60} = \frac{30 + 20}{15 + 12} = \frac{50}{27} \qquad \begin{array}{l} \dfrac{1}{2} \cdot 60 = 30, \dfrac{1}{3} \cdot 60 = 20 \\[2mm] \dfrac{1}{4} \cdot 60 = 15, \dfrac{1}{5} \cdot 60 = 12 \end{array}$$ ∎

In most cases Method B of Example 1 is the faster method for simplifying complex fractions, and we will continue to use it.

EXAMPLE   2

A complex fraction with variables

Simplify $\dfrac{3 - \dfrac{2}{x}}{\dfrac{1}{x^2} - \dfrac{1}{4}}$.

Helpful Hint

When students see addition or subtraction in a complex fraction, they often convert all of the fractions to the same denominator. This is not wrong, but it is not necessary. Simply multiplying every fraction by the LCD eliminates the denominators of the original fractions.

Solution

The LCD of x, x^2, and 4 is $4x^2$. Multiply the numerator and denominator by $4x^2$:

$$\frac{3 - \dfrac{2}{x}}{\dfrac{1}{x^2} - \dfrac{1}{4}} = \frac{\left(3 - \dfrac{2}{x}\right)(4x^2)}{\left(\dfrac{1}{x^2} - \dfrac{1}{4}\right)(4x^2)}$$

$$= \frac{3(4x^2) - \dfrac{2}{x}(4x^2)}{\dfrac{1}{x^2}(4x^2) - \dfrac{1}{4}(4x^2)} \qquad \text{Distributive property}$$

$$= \frac{12x^2 - 8x}{4 - x^2}$$ ∎

EXAMPLE   3

More complicated denominators

Simplify $\dfrac{\dfrac{x+2}{x^2 - 9}}{\dfrac{x}{x^2 - 6x + 9} + \dfrac{4}{x - 3}}$.

Study Tip

Your mood for studying should match the mood in which you are tested. Being too relaxed during studying will not match the increased level of activation you attain during a test. Likewise, if you get too tensed-up during a test, you will not do well because your test-taking mood will not match your studying mood.

Solution

Because $x^2 - 9 = (x - 3)(x + 3)$ and $x^2 - 6x + 9 = (x - 3)^2$, the LCD is $(x - 3)^2(x + 3)$. Multiply the numerator and denominator by the LCD:

$$\frac{\dfrac{x+2}{x^2 - 9}}{\dfrac{x}{x^2 - 6x + 9} + \dfrac{4}{x - 3}} = \frac{\dfrac{x+2}{(x - 3)(x + 3)}(x - 3)^2(x + 3)}{\dfrac{x}{(x - 3)^2}(x - 3)^2(x + 3) + \dfrac{4}{x - 3}(x - 3)^2(x + 3)}$$

$$= \frac{(x + 2)(x - 3)}{x(x + 3) + 4(x - 3)(x + 3)} \qquad \text{Simplify.}$$

$$= \frac{(x + 2)(x - 3)}{(x + 3)[x + 4(x - 3)]} \qquad \text{Factor out } x + 3.$$

$$= \frac{(x + 2)(x - 3)}{(x + 3)(5x - 12)}$$ ∎

Simplifying Expressions with Negative Exponents

Consider the expression

$$\frac{3a^{-1} - 2^{-1}}{1 - b^{-1}}.$$

Using the definition of negative exponents, we can rewrite this expression as a complex fraction:

$$\frac{3a^{-1} - 2^{-1}}{1 - b^{-1}} = \frac{\dfrac{3}{a} - \dfrac{1}{2}}{1 - \dfrac{1}{b}}$$

The LCD for the complex fraction is $2ab$. Note that $2ab$ could be obtained from a^{-1}, 2^{-1}, and b^{-1} in the original expression. To simplify the complex fraction we can multiply the numerator and denominator of either of the above expressions by $2ab$. To gain more experience with negative exponents, we will work with the first expression in Example 4.

E X A M P L E   4

A complex fraction with negative exponents

Simplify the complex fraction $\frac{3a^{-1} - 2^{-1}}{1 - b^{-1}}$.

Solution

Multiply the numerator and denominator by $2ab$, the LCD of the fractions. Remember that $a^{-1} \cdot a = a^0 = 1$.

$$\frac{3a^{-1} - 2^{-1}}{1 - b^{-1}} = \frac{(3a^{-1} - 2^{-1})2ab}{(1 - b^{-1})2ab}$$

$$= \frac{3a^{-1}(2ab) - 2^{-1}(2ab)}{1(2ab) - b^{-1}(2ab)} \qquad \text{Distributive property}$$

$$= \frac{6b - ab}{2ab - 2a} \qquad\qquad\qquad ■$$

E X A M P L E   5

A complex fraction with negative exponents

Simplify the complex fraction $\frac{a^{-1} + b^{-2}}{ab^{-2} + ba^{-3}}$.

Solution

If we rewrote a^{-1}, b^{-2}, b^{-2}, and a^{-3}, then the denominators would be a, b^2, b^2, and a^3. So the LCD is a^3b^2. If we multiply the numerator and denominator by a^3b^2, the negative exponents will be eliminated:

$$\frac{a^{-1} + b^{-2}}{ab^{-2} + ba^{-3}} = \frac{(a^{-1} + b^{-2})a^3b^2}{(ab^{-2} + ba^{-3})a^3b^2}$$

$$= \frac{a^{-1} \cdot a^3b^2 + b^{-2} \cdot a^3b^2}{ab^{-2} \cdot a^3b^2 + ba^{-3} \cdot a^3b^2} \qquad \text{Distributive property}$$

$$= \frac{a^2b^2 + a^3}{a^4 + b^3} \qquad \begin{array}{l} b^{-2}b^2 = b^0 = 1 \\ a^{-3}a^3 = a^0 = 1 \end{array}$$

Note that the positive exponents of a^3b^2 are just large enough to eliminate all of the negative exponents when we multiply. ■

Example 6 is not exactly a complex fraction, but we can use the same technique as in the previous example.

EXAMPLE 6

More negative exponents

Eliminate negative exponents and simplify $p + p^{-1}q^{-2}$.

Solution

If we multiply the numerator and denominator by pq^2, we will eliminate the negative exponents:

$$p + p^{-1}q^{-2} = \frac{(p + p^{-1}q^{-2})}{1} \cdot \frac{pq^2}{pq^2}$$

$$= \frac{p^2q^2 + 1}{pq^2} \quad \begin{array}{l} p \cdot pq^2 = p^2q^2 \\ p^{-1}q^{-2} \cdot pq^2 = 1 \end{array}$$

Applications

Example 7 illustrates how complex fractions can occur in a problem.

EXAMPLE 7

An application of complex fractions

Eastside Elementary has the same number of students as Westside Elementary. One-half of the students at Eastside ride buses to school, and two-thirds of the students at Westside ride buses to school. One-sixth of the students at Eastside are female, and one-third of the students at Westside are female. If all of the female students ride the buses, then what percentage of the students who ride the buses are female?

Solution

To find the required percentage, we must divide the number of females who ride the buses by the total number of students who ride the buses. Let

$$x = \text{the number of students at Eastside.}$$

Because the number of students at Westside is also x, we have

$$\frac{1}{2}x + \frac{2}{3}x = \text{the total number of students who ride the buses}$$

and

$$\frac{1}{6}x + \frac{1}{3}x = \text{the total number of female students.}$$

Because all of the female students ride the buses, we can express the percentage of riders who are female by the following rational expression:

$$\frac{\dfrac{1}{6}x + \dfrac{1}{3}x}{\dfrac{1}{2}x + \dfrac{2}{3}x}$$

Multiply the numerator and denominator by 6, the LCD for 2, 3, and 6:

$$\frac{\left(\dfrac{1}{6}x + \dfrac{1}{3}x\right)6}{\left(\dfrac{1}{2}x + \dfrac{2}{3}x\right)6} = \frac{x + 2x}{3x + 4x} = \frac{3x}{7x} = \frac{3}{7} \approx 0.43 = 43\%$$

So 43% of the students who ride the buses are female.

WARM-UPS

True or false? Explain.

1. The LCM for 2, x, 6, and x^2 is $6x^3$.

2. The LCM for $a - b$, $2b - 2a$, and 6 is $6a - 6b$.

3. The LCD is the LCM of the denominators.

4. $\dfrac{\dfrac{1}{2} + \dfrac{1}{3}}{1 + \dfrac{1}{2}} = \dfrac{5}{6} \div \dfrac{3}{2}$

5. $2^{-1} + 3^{-1} = (2 + 3)^{-1}$

6. $(2^{-1} + 3^{-1})^{-1} = 2 + 3$

7. $2 + 3^{-1} = 5^{-1}$

8. $x + 2^{-1} = \dfrac{x}{2}$ for any real number x.

9. To simplify $\dfrac{a^{-1} - b^{-1}}{a - b}$, multiply the numerator and denominator by ab.

10. To simplify $\dfrac{ab^{-2} + a^{-5}b^2}{a^{-3}b - a^5b^{-1}}$, multiply the numerator and denominator by a^5b^2.

6.4 EXERCISES

Reading and Writing *After reading this section, write out the answers to these questions. Use complete sentences.*

1. What is a complex fraction?

2. What are the two methods for simplifying complex fractions?

Simplify each complex fraction. Use either method. See Example 1.

3. $\dfrac{\dfrac{1}{2} - \dfrac{1}{3}}{\dfrac{1}{4} - \dfrac{1}{5}}$

4. $\dfrac{\dfrac{1}{3} + \dfrac{1}{4}}{\dfrac{1}{5} + \dfrac{1}{6}}$

5. $\dfrac{\dfrac{2}{3} + \dfrac{5}{6} - \dfrac{1}{2}}{\dfrac{1}{8} - \dfrac{1}{3} + \dfrac{1}{12}}$

6. $\dfrac{\dfrac{2}{5} - \dfrac{x}{9} - \dfrac{1}{3}}{\dfrac{1}{3} + \dfrac{x}{5} + \dfrac{2}{15}}$

Simplify the complex fractions. Use Method B. See Example 2.

7. $\dfrac{\dfrac{a + b}{b}}{\dfrac{a - b}{ab}}$

8. $\dfrac{\dfrac{m - n}{m^2}}{\dfrac{m - 3}{mn^3}}$

9. $\dfrac{a + \dfrac{3}{b}}{\dfrac{b}{a} + \dfrac{1}{b}}$

10. $\dfrac{m - \dfrac{2}{n}}{\dfrac{1}{m} - \dfrac{3}{n}}$

11. $\dfrac{\dfrac{x - 3y}{xy}}{\dfrac{1}{x} + \dfrac{1}{y}}$

12. $\dfrac{\dfrac{2}{w} + \dfrac{3}{t}}{\dfrac{w - t}{4wt}}$

13. $\dfrac{3 - \dfrac{m - 2}{6}}{\dfrac{4}{9} + \dfrac{2}{m}}$

14. $\dfrac{6 - \dfrac{2 - z}{z}}{\dfrac{1}{3z} - \dfrac{1}{6}}$

15. $\dfrac{\dfrac{a^2 - b^2}{a^2b^3}}{\dfrac{a + b}{a^3b}}$

16. $\dfrac{\dfrac{4x^2 - 1}{x^2y}}{\dfrac{4x - 2}{xy^2}}$

17. $\dfrac{\dfrac{1}{x^2y^2} + \dfrac{1}{xy^3}}{\dfrac{1}{x^3y} - \dfrac{1}{xy}}$

18. $\dfrac{\dfrac{1}{2a^3b} - \dfrac{1}{ab^4}}{\dfrac{1}{6a^2b^2} + \dfrac{1}{3a^4b}}$

Simplify each complex fraction. See Examples 1–3.

19. $\dfrac{x + \dfrac{4}{x + 4}}{x - \dfrac{4x + 4}{x + 4}}$

20. $\dfrac{x - \dfrac{x + 6}{x + 2}}{x - \dfrac{4x + 15}{x + 2}}$

21. $\dfrac{1 - \dfrac{1}{y - 1}}{3 + \dfrac{1}{y + 1}}$

22. $\dfrac{2 - \dfrac{3}{a - 2}}{4 - \dfrac{1}{a + 2}}$

23. $\dfrac{\dfrac{2}{3 - x} - 4}{\dfrac{1}{x - 3} - 1}$

24. $\dfrac{\dfrac{x}{x - 5} - 2}{\dfrac{2x}{5 - x} - 1}$

25. $\dfrac{\dfrac{w + 2}{w - 1} - \dfrac{w - 3}{w}}{\dfrac{w + 4}{w} + \dfrac{w - 2}{w - 1}}$

26. $\dfrac{\dfrac{x - 1}{x + 2} - \dfrac{x - 2}{x + 3}}{\dfrac{x - 3}{x + 3} + \dfrac{x + 1}{x + 2}}$

27. $\dfrac{\dfrac{1}{a - b} - \dfrac{3}{a + b}}{\dfrac{2}{b - a} + \dfrac{4}{b + a}}$

28. $\dfrac{\dfrac{3}{2 + x} - \dfrac{4}{2 - x}}{\dfrac{1}{x + 2} - \dfrac{3}{x - 2}}$

29. $\dfrac{\dfrac{4}{y} - \dfrac{y + 4}{y - 3}}{\dfrac{2}{y - 3} + \dfrac{y + 1}{y}}$

30. $\dfrac{\dfrac{x + 4}{x + 1} + \dfrac{4}{x}}{\dfrac{x + 1}{x} - \dfrac{1}{x + 1}}$

31. $\dfrac{3 - \dfrac{4}{a - 1}}{5 - \dfrac{3}{1 - a}}$

32. $\dfrac{\dfrac{x}{3} - \dfrac{x - 1}{9 - x}}{\dfrac{x}{6} - \dfrac{2 - x}{x - 9}}$

33. $\dfrac{\dfrac{2}{m - 3} + \dfrac{4}{m}}{\dfrac{3}{m - 2} + \dfrac{1}{m}}$

34. $\dfrac{\dfrac{1}{y + 2} - \dfrac{4}{3y}}{\dfrac{3}{y} - \dfrac{2}{y + 3}}$

35. $\dfrac{\dfrac{3}{x^2 - 1} - \dfrac{x - 2}{x^3 - 1}}{\dfrac{3}{x^2 + x + 1} + \dfrac{x - 3}{x^3 - 1}}$

36. $\dfrac{\dfrac{2}{a^3 + 8} - \dfrac{3}{a^2 - 2a + 4}}{\dfrac{4}{a^2 - 4} + \dfrac{a - 3}{a^3 + 8}}$

Simplify. See Examples 4–6.

37. $\dfrac{w^{-1} + y^{-1}}{z^{-1} + y^{-1}}$

38. $\dfrac{a^{-1} - b^{-1}}{a^{-1} + b^{-1}}$

39. $\dfrac{1 - x^{-1}}{1 - x^{-2}}$

40. $\dfrac{4 - a^{-2}}{2 - a^{-1}}$

41. $\dfrac{a^{-2} + b^{-2}}{a^{-1}b}$

42. $\dfrac{m^{-3} + n^{-3}}{mn^{-2}}$

43. $1 - a^{-1}$

44. $m^{-1} - a^{-1}$

45. $\dfrac{x^{-1} + x^{-2}}{x + x^{-2}}$

46. $\dfrac{x - x^{-2}}{1 - x^{-2}}$

47. $\dfrac{2m^{-1} - 3m^{-2}}{m^{-2}}$

48. $\dfrac{4x^{-3} - 6x^{-5}}{2x^{-5}}$

49. $\dfrac{a^{-1} - b^{-1}}{a - b}$

50. $\dfrac{a^2 - b^2}{a^{-2} - b^{-2}}$

51. $\dfrac{x^3 - y^3}{x^{-3} - y^{-3}}$

52. $\dfrac{(a - b)^2}{a^{-2} - b^{-2}}$

53. $\dfrac{1 - 8x^{-3}}{x^{-1} + 2x^{-2} + 4x^{-3}}$

54. $\dfrac{a + 27a^{-2}}{1 - 3a^{-1} + 9a^{-2}}$

55. $(x^{-1} + y^{-1})^{-1}$

56. $(a^{-1} - b^{-1})^{-2}$

Use a calculator to evaluate each complex fraction. Round answers to four decimal places. If your calculator does fractions, then also find the fractional answer.

57. $\dfrac{\dfrac{5}{3} - \dfrac{4}{5}}{\dfrac{1}{3} - \dfrac{5}{6}}$

58. $\dfrac{\dfrac{1}{12} + \dfrac{1}{2} - \dfrac{3}{4}}{\dfrac{3}{5} + \dfrac{5}{6}}$

59. $\dfrac{4^{-1} - 9^{-1}}{2^{-1} + 3^{-1}}$

60. $\dfrac{2^{-1} + 3^{-1} - 6^{-1}}{3^{-1} - 5^{-1} + 4^{-1}}$

Solve each problem. See Example 7.

61. *Racial balance.* Clarksville has three elementary schools. Northside has one-half as many students as Central, and Southside has two-thirds as many students as Central. One-third of the students at Northside are African-American, three-fourths of the students at Central are African-American, and one-sixth of the students at Southside are African-American. What percent of the city's elementary students are African-American?

62. *Explosive situation.* All of the employees at Acme Explosives are in either development, manufacturing, or sales. One-fifth of the employees in development are women, one-third of the employees in manufacturing are women, and one-half of the employees in sales are women. Use the accompanying figure to determine the percentage of workers at Acme who are women. What percent of the women at Acme are in sales?

FIGURE FOR EXERCISE 62

63. *Average speed.* Mary drove from Clarksville to Leesville at 45 miles per hour (mph). At Leesville she discovered that she had forgotten her purse. She immediately returned to Clarksville at 55 mph. What was her average speed for the entire trip? (The answer is *not* 50 mph.)

64. *Average price.* On her way to New York, Jenny spent the same amount for gasoline each time she stopped for gas. She paid 139.9 cents per gallon the first time, 149.9 cents per gallon the second time, and 159.9 cents per gallon the third time. What was the average price per gallon to the nearest tenth of a cent for the gasoline that she bought?

FIGURE FOR EXERCISE 64

GETTING MORE INVOLVED

65. *Cooperative learning.* Write a step-by-step strategy for simplifying complex fractions with negative exponents. Have a classmate use your strategy to simplify some complex fractions from Exercises 37–56.

66. *Discussion.* **a)** Find the exact value of each expression.

i) $\dfrac{1}{1 + \dfrac{1}{1 + \dfrac{1}{1 + \dfrac{1}{2}}}}$

ii) $\dfrac{1}{1 + \dfrac{1}{1 + \dfrac{1}{1 + \dfrac{1}{1 + \dfrac{1}{3}}}}}$

b) Explain why in each case the exact value must be less than 1.

67. *Cooperative learning.* Work with a group to simplify the complex fraction. For what values of x is the complex fraction undefined?

$$\dfrac{1}{1 + \dfrac{1}{1 + \dfrac{1}{1 + \dfrac{1}{x}}}}$$

6.5   DIVISION OF POLYNOMIALS

We began our study of polynomials in Section 5.3 by learning how to add, subtract, and multiply polynomials. In this section we will study division of polynomials.

Dividing a Polynomial by a Monomial

You learned how to divide monomials in Section 5.1. For example,

$$6x^3 \div (3x) = \frac{6x^3}{3x} = 2x^2.$$

We check by multiplying. Because $2x^2 \cdot 3x = 6x^3$, this answer is correct. Recall that $a \div b = c$ if and only if $c \cdot b = a$. We call a the **dividend,** b the **divisor,** and c the **quotient.** We may also refer to $a \div b$ and $\frac{a}{b}$ as quotients.

We can use the distributive property to find that

$$3x(2x^2 + 5x - 4) = 6x^3 + 15x^2 - 12x.$$

So if we divide $6x^3 + 15x^2 - 12x$ by the monomial $3x$, we must get $2x^2 + 5x - 4$. We can perform this division by dividing $3x$ into *each term* of $6x^3 + 15x^2 - 12x$:

$$\frac{6x^3 + 15x^2 - 12x}{3x} = \frac{6x^3}{3x} + \frac{15x^2}{3x} - \frac{12x}{3x}$$

$$= 2x^2 + 5x - 4$$

In this case the divisor is $3x$, the dividend is $6x^3 + 15x^2 - 12x$, and the quotient is $2x^2 + 5x - 4$.

E X A M P L E   1

Dividing a polynomial by a monomial

Find the quotient.

a) $-12x^5 \div (2x^3)$

b) $(-20x^6 + 8x^4 - 4x^2) \div (4x^2)$

Helpful Hint

Recall that the order of operations gives multiplication and division an equal ranking and says to do them in order from left to right. So without parentheses,

$$-12x^5 \div 2x^3$$

actually means

$$\frac{-12x^5}{2} \cdot x^3.$$

Solution

a) When dividing x^5 by x^3, we subtract the exponents:

$$-12x^5 \div (2x^3) = \frac{-12x^5}{2x^3} = -6x^2$$

The quotient is $-6x^2$. Check:

$$-6x^2 \cdot 2x^3 = -12x^5$$

b) Divide each term of $-20x^6 + 8x^4 - 4x^2$ by $4x^2$:

$$\frac{-20x^6 + 8x^4 - 4x^2}{4x^2} = \frac{-20x^6}{4x^2} + \frac{8x^4}{4x^2} - \frac{4x^2}{4x^2}$$

$$= -5x^4 + 2x^2 - 1$$

The quotient is $-5x^4 + 2x^2 - 1$. Check:

$$4x^2(-5x^4 + 2x^2 - 1) = -20x^6 + 8x^4 - 4x^2$$

In Example 1 we found the quotient of a polynomial and a monomial and the remainder was zero. If the remainder is zero, then the dividend is equal to the divisor times the quotient. If the remainder is not zero, then the degree of the remainder must be less than the degree of the divisor and

$$\textbf{dividend} = (\textbf{divisor})(\textbf{quotient}) + (\textbf{remainder}).$$

If we divide each side of this equation by the divisor, we get

$$\frac{\textbf{dividend}}{\textbf{divisor}} = \textbf{quotient} + \frac{\textbf{remainder}}{\textbf{divisor}}.$$

The remainder in Example 1 was zero, because the degree of the monomial denominator was less than or equal to the degree of every term in the numerator. If the degree of the monomial denominator is larger than the degree of at least one term in the numerator, then there will be a remainder, as shown in Example 2.

E X A M P L E   2   **Dividing a polynomial by a monomial (remainder ≠ 0)**

Find the quotient and remainder.

a) $\dfrac{6x - 1}{2x}$

b) $\dfrac{x^3 - 4x^2 + 5x - 3}{2x^2}$

Solution

a) Divide each term of $6x - 1$ by $2x$:

$$\frac{6x - 1}{2x} = \frac{6x}{2x} + \frac{-1}{2x} = 3 + \frac{-1}{2x}$$

Now $3 + \dfrac{-1}{2x}$ has the form quotient + $\frac{\text{remainder}}{\text{divisor}}$. So the quotient is 3 and the remainder is -1. Check that (divisor)(quotient) + remainder = dividend:

$$(2x)(3) + (-1) = 6x - 1$$

b) The first two terms in the numerator have a degree that is greater than or equal to the degree of the denominator. So divide the first two terms of the numerator by the monomial denominator:

$$\frac{x^3 - 4x^2 + 5x - 3}{2x^2} = \frac{x^3}{2x^2} - \frac{4x^2}{2x^2} + \frac{5x - 3}{2x^2}$$

$$= \frac{1}{2}x - 2 + \frac{5x - 3}{2x^2}$$

The last expression has the form quotient + $\frac{\text{remainder}}{\text{divisor}}$. So the quotient is $\frac{1}{2}x - 2$ and the remainder is $5x - 3$. Check that

$$(2x^2)\left(\frac{1}{2}x - 2\right) + 5x - 3 = x^3 - 4x^2 + 5x - 3. \qquad ■$$

Dividing a Polynomial by a Binomial

We can multiply $x - 2$ and $x + 5$ to get

$$(x - 2)(x + 5) = x^2 + 3x - 10.$$

So if we divide $x^2 + 3x - 10$ by the factor $x - 2$, we should get the other factor $x + 5$. This division is not done like division by a monomial; it is done like long division of whole numbers. We get the first term of the quotient by dividing the first term of $x - 2$ into the first term of $x^2 + 3x - 10$. Divide x^2 by x to get x.

$$
\begin{array}{r}
x \\
x - 2 \overline{)x^2 + 3x - 10} \\
\underline{x^2 - 2x} \\
5x
\end{array}
$$

$x^2 \div x = x$

Multiply: $x(x - 2) = x^2 - 2x.$

Subtract: $3x - (-2x) = 5x.$

Now bring down -10. We get the second term of the quotient (below) by dividing the first term of $x - 2$ into the first term of $5x - 10$. Divide $5x$ by x to get 5.

$$
\begin{array}{r}
x + 5 \\
x - 2 \overline{)x^2 + 3x - 10} \\
\underline{x^2 - 2x} \\
5x - 10 \\
\underline{5x - 10} \\
0
\end{array}
$$

$5x \div x = 5$

Multiply: $5(x - 2) = 5x - 10.$

Subtract: $-10 - (-10) = 0.$

So the quotient is $x + 5$ and the remainder is 0.

When dividing polynomials, we must write the terms of the divisor and the dividend in descending order of the exponents. If any terms are missing, as in Example 3, we insert terms with a coefficient of 0 as placeholders. When dividing polynomials, we stop the process when the degree of the remainder is smaller than the degree of the divisor.

E X A M P L E   3

Dividing polynomials

Find the quotient and remainder for $(3x^4 - 2 - 5x) \div (x^2 - 3x)$.

Helpful Hint

Students usually have the most difficulty with the subtraction part of long division. So pay particular attention to that step and double check your work.

Solution

Rearrange $3x^4 - 2 - 5x$ as $3x^4 - 5x - 2$ and insert the terms $0x^3$ and $0x^2$:

$$
\begin{array}{r}
3x^2 + 9x + 27 \\
x^2 - 3x \overline{)3x^4 + 0x^3 + 0x^2 - 5x - 2} \\
\underline{3x^4 - 9x^3} \\
9x^3 + 0x^2 \\
\underline{9x^3 - 27x^2} \\
27x^2 - 5x \\
\underline{27x^2 - 81x} \\
76x - 2
\end{array}
$$

$0x^3 - (-9x^3) = 9x^3$

The quotient is $3x^2 + 9x + 27$, and the remainder is $76x - 2$. Note that the degree of the remainder is 1, and the degree of the divisor is 2. To check, verify that

$$(x^2 - 3x)(3x^2 + 9x + 27) + 76x - 2 = 3x^4 - 5x - 2. \quad \blacksquare$$

E X A M P L E   4

Rewriting a ratio of two polynomials

Write $\frac{4x^3 - x - 9}{2x - 3}$ in the form

$$\text{quotient} + \frac{\text{remainder}}{\text{divisor}}.$$

Solution

Divide $4x^3 - x - 9$ by $2x - 3$. Insert $0 \cdot x^2$ for the missing term.

$$
\begin{array}{r}
2x^2 + 3x + 4 \\
2x - 3 \overline{)4x^3 + 0x^2 - x - 9} \\
\underline{4x^3 - 6x^2} \\
6x^2 - x \\
\underline{6x^2 - 9x} \\
8x - 9 \\
\underline{8x - 12} \\
3
\end{array}
$$

$4x^3 \div (2x) = 2x^2$

$0x^2 - (-6x^2) = 6x^2$

$-x - (-9x) = 8x$

$-9 - (-12) = 3$

Since the quotient is $2x^2 + 3x + 4$ and the remainder is 3, we have

$$\frac{4x^3 - x - 9}{2x - 3} = 2x^2 + 3x + 4 + \frac{3}{2x - 3}.$$

To check the answer, we must verify that

$$(2x - 3)(2x^2 + 3x + 4) + 3 = 4x^3 - x - 9.$$

Synthetic Division

When dividing a polynomial by a binomial of the form $x - c$, we can use **synthetic division** to speed up the process. For synthetic division we write only the essential parts of ordinary division. For example, to divide $x^3 - 5x^2 + 4x - 3$ by $x - 2$, we write only the coefficients of the dividend 1, -5, 4, and -3 in order of descending exponents. From the divisor $x - 2$ we use 2 and start with the following arrangement:

$$
2 \,\big|\; 1 \;\; -5 \;\; 4 \;\; -3 \qquad {\scriptstyle (1 \cdot x^3 - 5x^2 + 4x - 3) \div (x - 2)}
$$

Next we bring the first coefficient, 1, straight down:

$$
\begin{array}{c}
2 \,\big|\; 1 \;\; -5 \;\; 4 \;\; -3 \\
\downarrow \;\; \text{Bring down} \\
1
\end{array}
$$

We then multiply the 1 by the 2 from the divisor, place the answer under the -5, and then add that column. Using 2 for $x - 2$ allows us to add the column rather than subtract as in ordinary division:

$$
\begin{array}{c}
2 \,\big|\; 1 \;\; -5 \;\; 4 \;\; -3 \\
 2 \;\;\; \text{Add} \\
\text{Multiply} \;\; 1 \;\; -3
\end{array}
$$

We then repeat the multiply-and-add step for each of the remaining columns:

$$
\begin{array}{c}
2 \,\big|\; 1 \;\; -5 \;\;\; 4 \;\; -3 \\
 2 \;\; -6 \;\; -4 \\
\text{Multiply} \;\; 1 \;\; -3 \;\; -2 \;\; -7 \quad \leftarrow \text{Remainder} \\
\underbrace{}_{\text{Quotient}}
\end{array}
$$

From the bottom row we can read the quotient and remainder. Since the degree of the quotient is one less than the degree of the dividend, the quotient is $1x^2 - 3x - 2$. The remainder is -7.

The strategy for getting the quotient $Q(x)$ and remainder R by synthetic division can be stated as follows.

Strategy for Using Synthetic Division

1. List the coefficients of the polynomial (the dividend).
2. Be sure to include zeros for any missing terms in the dividend.
3. For dividing by $x - c$, place c to the left.
4. Bring the first coefficient down.
5. Multiply by c and add for each column.
6. Read $Q(x)$ and R from the bottom row.

CAUTION Synthetic division is used only for dividing a polynomial by the binomial $x - c$, where c is a constant. If the binomial is $x - 7$, then $c = 7$. For the binomial $x + 7$ we have $x + 7 = x - (-7)$ and $c = -7$.

E X A M P L E   5   **Using synthetic division**

Find the quotient and remainder when $2x^4 - 5x^2 + 6x - 9$ is divided by $x + 2$.

Solution

Since $x + 2 = x - (-2)$, we use -2 for the divisor. Because x^3 is missing in the dividend, use a zero for the coefficient of x^3:

$$
\begin{array}{r|rrrrr}
-2 & 2 & 0 & -5 & 6 & -9 \\
   &   & -4 & 8 & -6 & 0 \\
\hline
   & 2 & -4 & 3 & 0 & -9
\end{array}
$$

$\leftarrow 2x^4 + 0 \cdot x^3 - 5x^2 + 6x - 9$

$\leftarrow$ Quotient and remainder

Because the degree of the dividend is 4, the degree of the quotient is 3. The quotient is $2x^3 - 4x^2 + 3x$, and the remainder is -9. We can also express the results of this division in the form quotient $+ \frac{\text{remainder}}{\text{divisor}}$:

$$\frac{2x^4 - 5x^2 + 6x - 9}{x + 2} = 2x^3 - 4x^2 + 3x + \frac{-9}{x + 2}$$

■

Division and Factoring

To **factor** a polynomial means to write it as a product of two or more simpler polynomials. If we divide two polynomials and get 0 remainder, then we can write

$$\text{dividend} = (\text{divisor})(\text{quotient})$$

and we have factored the dividend. *The dividend factors as the divisor times the quotient if and only if the remainder is* 0. We can use division to help us discover factors of polynomials. To use this idea, however, we must know a factor or a possible factor to use as the divisor.

E X A M P L E   6   **Using synthetic division to determine factors**

Is $x - 1$ a factor of $6x^3 - 5x^2 - 4x + 3$?

Solution

We can use synthetic division to divide $6x^3 - 5x^2 - 4x + 3$ by $x - 1$:

$$
\begin{array}{r|rrrr}
1 & 6 & -5 & -4 & 3 \\
  & \downarrow & 6 & 1 & -3 \\
\hline
  & 6 & 1 & -3 & 0
\end{array}
$$

Because the remainder is 0, $x - 1$ is a factor, and

$$6x^3 - 5x^2 - 4x + 3 = (x - 1)(6x^2 + x - 3).$$ ■

The Remainder Theorem

If a polynomial $P(x)$ is divided by $x - c$ we get a quotient and a remainder that satisfy

$$P(x) = (x - c)(\text{quotient}) + \text{remainder}$$

Now replace x by c:

$$
\begin{aligned}
P(c) &= (c - c)(\text{quotient}) + \text{remainder} \\
&= 0(\text{quotient}) + \text{remainder} \\
&= \text{remainder}
\end{aligned}
$$

This computation proves the remainder theorem.

> **The Remainder Theorem**
>
> If the polynomial $P(x)$ is divided by $x - c$, then the remainder is equal to $P(c)$.

The remainder theorem gives us a new way to evaluate a polynomial. Note that we could use long division or synthetic division to find the remainder, but it easier to use synthetic division.

E X A M P L E   7   **Using synthetic division to evaluate a polynomial**

Use synthetic division to find $P(2)$ when $P(x) = 4x^3 - 5x^2 + 6x - 7$.

Solution

Find the remainder when $P(x)$ is divided by $x - 2$:

$$
\begin{array}{r|rrrr}
2 & 4 & -5 & 6 & -7 \\
  & \downarrow & 8 & 6 & 24 \\
\hline
  & 4 & 3 & 12 & 17
\end{array}
$$

Since 17 is the remainder, $P(2) = 17$. Check by replacing x with 2 in $P(x)$:

$$
\begin{aligned}
P(2) &= 4 \cdot 2^3 - 5 \cdot 2^2 + 6 \cdot 2 - 7 \\
&= 32 - 20 + 12 - 7 \\
&= 17
\end{aligned}
$$ ■

WARM-UPS

True or false? Explain your answer.

  1. If $a \div b = c$, then c is the dividend.
  2. The quotient times the dividend plus the remainder equals the divisor.
  3. $(x + 2)(x + 3) + 1 = x^2 + 5x + 7$ is true for any value of x.
  4. The quotient of $(x^2 + 5x + 7) \div (x + 3)$ is $x + 2$.
  5. If $x^2 + 5x + 7$ is divided by $x + 2$, the remainder is 1.
  6. To divide $x^3 - 4x + 1$ by $x - 3$, we use -3 in synthetic division.
  7. We can use synthetic division to divide $x^3 - 4x^2 - 6$ by $x^2 - 5$.
  8. If $3x^5 - 4x^2 - 3$ is divided by $x + 2$, the quotient has degree 4.
  9. If the remainder is zero, then the divisor is a factor of the dividend.
  10. If the remainder is zero, then the quotient is a factor of the dividend.

6.5   EXERCISES

Reading and Writing   *After reading this section, write out the answers to these questions. Use complete sentences.*

  1. What are the dividend, divisor, and quotient?

  2. In what form should polynomials be written for long division?

  3. What do you do about missing terms when dividing polynomials?

  4. When do you stop the long division process for dividing polynomials?

  5. What is synthetic division used for?

  6. What is the relationship between division of polynomials and factoring polynomials?

Find the quotient. See Example 1.

  7. $36x^7 \div (3x^3)$
  8. $-30x^3 \div (-5x)$
  9. $16x^2 \div (-8x^2)$
  10. $-22a^3 \div (11a^2)$
  11. $(6b - 9) \div 3$

  12. $(8x^2 - 6x) \div 2$
  13. $(3x^2 + 3x) \div (3x)$
  14. $(5x^3 - 10x^2 - 5x) \div (5x)$
  15. $(10x^4 - 8x^3 + 6x^2) \div (-2x^2)$
  16. $(-9x^3 + 6x^2 - 12x) \div (-3x)$

  17. $(7x^3 - 4x^2) \div (2x)$

  18. $(6x^3 - 5x^2) \div (4x^2)$

Find the quotient and remainder. See Example 2.
  19. $(8x - 3) \div (4x)$
  20. $(9x - 5) \div (3x)$

  21. $(2x^3 + x^2 + 4x - 3) \div (3x^2)$

  22. $(5x^3 - 6x^2 + 4x - 1) \div (5x^2)$

  23. $(-10x^4 - 5x^3 - 6x - 7) \div (-5x^2)$
  24. $(-12x^5 - 8x^4 - 6x^2 + x - 4) \div (3x^3)$

Find the quotient and remainder as in Example 3. Check by using the formula

$$dividend = (divisor)(quotient) + remainder.$$

  25. $(x^2 + 8x + 13) \div (x + 3)$
  26. $(x^2 + 5x + 7) \div (x + 3)$
  27. $(x^2 - 2x) \div (x + 2)$
  28. $(3x) \div (x - 1)$
  29. $(x^3 + 8) \div (x + 2)$
  30. $(y^3 - 1) \div (y - 1)$

31. $(a^3 + 4a - 5) \div (a - 2)$

32. $(w^3 + w^2 - 3) \div (w - 2)$

33. $(x^3 - x^2 + x - 3) \div (x + 1)$

34. $(a^3 - a^2 + a - 4) \div (a + 2)$

35. $(x^4 - x + x^3 - 1) \div (x - 2)$

36. $(3x^4 + 6 - x^2 + 3x) \div (x + 2)$

37. $(5x^2 - 3x^4 + x - 2) \div (x^2 - 2)$

38. $(x^4 - 2 + x^3) \div (x^2 + 3)$

39. $(6x^2 + x - 16) \div (2x - 3)$

40. $(12x^2 - x - 9) \div (3x + 2)$

41. $(10b^2 - 17b - 22) \div (5b + 4)$

42. $(20a^2 + 2a - 7) \div (4a - 2)$

43. $(2x^3 + 3x^2 - 3x - 2) \div (2x + 1)$

44. $(6x^3 - 7x^2 + 5x + 6) \div (3x - 2)$

45. $(x^3 - 4x^2 - 3x - 10) \div (x^2 + x + 2)$

46. $(2x^3 - 3x^2 + 7x - 3) \div (x^2 - x + 3)$

Write each expression in the form

$$quotient + \frac{remainder}{divisor}.$$

See Example 4.

47. $\dfrac{2x}{x - 5}$

48. $\dfrac{x}{x - 1}$

49. $\dfrac{2x^2 - x}{2x + 1}$

50. $\dfrac{8x^2 - 3}{4x - 6}$

51. $\dfrac{x^3}{x + 2}$

52. $\dfrac{x^3 - 1}{x - 2}$

53. $\dfrac{x^3 + 2x}{x^2}$

54. $\dfrac{2x^2 + 3}{2x}$

55. $\dfrac{2x^2 - 11x - 4}{2x + 1}$

56. $\dfrac{5x^2 - 13x + 13}{5x - 3}$

57. $\dfrac{3x^3 - 4x^2 + 7}{x - 1}$

58. $\dfrac{-2x^3 + x^2 - 3}{x + 2}$

59. $\dfrac{6x^3 - 4x + 5}{x - 2}$

60. $\dfrac{-x^3 - x + 2}{x + 3}$

61. $\dfrac{x^3 + x}{x + 1}$

62. $\dfrac{x^3 - x}{x - 3}$

Use synthetic division to find the quotient and remainder when the first polynomial is divided by the second. See Example 5.

63. $x^3 - 5x^2 + 6x - 3, \quad x - 2$

64. $x^3 + 6x^2 - 3x - 5, \quad x - 3$

65. $2x^2 - 4x + 5, \quad x + 1$

66. $3x^2 - 7x + 4, \quad x + 2$

67. $3x^4 - 15x^2 + 7x - 9, \quad x - 3$

68. $-2x^4 + 3x^2 - 5, \quad x - 2$

69. $x^5 - 1, \quad x - 1$

70. $x^6 - 1, \quad x + 1$

71. $x^3 - 5x + 6, \quad x + 2$

72. $x^3 - 3x - 7, \quad x - 4$

73. $x^3 - 3x^2 + 5, \quad x - 5$

74. $3x^3 + 20x^2 + 2, \quad x + 7$

For each pair of polynomials, use division to determine whether the first polynomial is a factor of the second. Use synthetic division when possible. If the first polynomial is a factor, then factor the second polynomial. See Example 6.

75. $x + 4, x^3 + x^2 - 11x + 8$

76. $x - 1, x^3 + 3x^2 - 5x$

77. $x - 4, x^2 - 6x + 8$

78. $x + 8, x^2 + 3x - 40$

79. $w - 3, w^3 - 27$

80. $w + 5, w^3 + 125$

81. $2x - 3, 2x^3 - 3x^2 - 4x + 7$

82. $3x - 5, 3x^3 + x^2 - 7x + 6$

83. $y - 2, y^3 - 4y^2 + 6y - 4$

84. $z + 1, 2z^3 + 5z + 7$

Use synthetic division and the remainder theorem to find $P(c)$ for the given polynomial and given value of c. See Example 7.

85. $P(x) = x^2 - 5x - 9, c = 3$

86. $P(x) = x^3 + 3x^2 - 7x + 2, c = 2$

87. $P(y) = 4y^3 - 6y + 7, c = -1$

88. $P(y) = 2y^3 - y^2 - 1, c = -4$

89. $P(w) = -w^3 + 5w^2 + 3w, c = 4$

90. $P(w) = -2w^3 - w^2 - 15, c = -3$

Solve each problem.

91. *Average cost.* The total cost in dollars for manufacturing x professional racing bicycles in one week is given by the polynomial function

$$C(x) = 0.03x^2 + 300x.$$

The average cost per bicycle is given by

$$AC(x) = \frac{C(x)}{x}.$$

a) Find a formula for $AC(x)$.

b) Is $AC(x)$ a constant function?

c) Why does the average cost look constant in the accompanying figure?

FIGURE FOR EXERCISE 91

92. *Average profit.* The weekly profit in dollars for manufacturing x bicycles is given by the polynomial $P(x) = 100x + 2x^2$. The average profit per bicycle is given by $AP(x) = \frac{P(x)}{x}$. Find $AP(x)$. Find the average profit per bicycle when 12 bicycles are manufactured.

93. *Area of a poster.* The area of a rectangular poster advertising a Pearl Jam concert is $x^2 - 1$ square feet. If the length is $x + 1$ feet, then what is the width?

94. *Volume of a box.* The volume of a shipping crate is $h^3 + 5h^2 + 6h$. If the height is h and the length is $h + 2$, then what is the width?

FIGURE FOR EXERCISE 94

95. *Volume of a pyramid.* Ancient Egyptian pyramid builders knew that the volume of the truncated pyramid shown in the figure is given by

$$V = \frac{H(a^3 - b^3)}{3(a - b)},$$

where a^2 is the area of the square base, b^2 is the area of the square top, and H is the distance from the base to the top. Find the volume of a truncated pyramid that has a base of 900 square meters, a top of 400 square meters, and a height H of 10 meters.

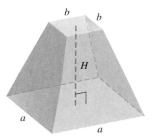

FIGURE FOR EXERCISE 95

96. *Egyptian pyramid formula.* Simplify the expression in Exercise 95.

GETTING MORE INVOLVED

97. *Discussion.* On a test a student divided $3x^3 - 5x^2 - 3x + 7$ by $x - 3$ and got a quotient of $3x^2 + 4x$ and remainder $9x + 7$. Verify that the divisor times the quotient plus the remainder is equal to the dividend. Why was the student's answer incorrect?

98. *Exploration.* Use synthetic division to find the quotient when $x^5 - 1$ is divided by $x - 1$ and the quotient when $x^6 - 1$ is divided by $x - 1$. Observe the pattern in the first two quotients and then write the quotient for $x^9 - 1$ divided by $x - 1$ without dividing.

6.6   SOLVING EQUATIONS INVOLVING RATIONAL EXPRESSIONS

Many problems in algebra are modeled by equations involving rational expressions. In this section you will learn how to solve equations that have rational expressions, and in Section 6.7 we will solve problems using these equations.

Multiplying by the LCD

To solve equations having rational expressions, we multiply each side of the equation by the LCD of the rational expressions.

E X A M P L E   1

An equation with rational expressions

Solve $\frac{1}{x} + \frac{1}{4} = \frac{1}{6}$.

Helpful Hint

Note that it is not necessary to convert each fraction into an equivalent fraction with a common denominator here. Since we can multiply both sides of an equation by any expression we choose, we choose to multiply by the LCD. This tactic eliminates the fractions in one step and that is good.

Solution

The LCD for the denominators 4, 6, and x is $12x$:

$$12x\left(\frac{1}{x} + \frac{1}{4}\right) = 12x\left(\frac{1}{6}\right) \qquad \text{Multiply each side by } 12x.$$

$$12x \cdot \frac{1}{x} + \overset{3}{12x} \cdot \frac{1}{4} = \overset{2}{12x} \cdot \frac{1}{6} \qquad \text{Distributive property}$$

$$12 + 3x = 2x \qquad \text{Divide out the common factors.}$$

$$12 + x = 0$$

$$x = -12$$

Check -12 in the original equation. The solution set is $\{-12\}$. ■

E X A M P L E   2

An equation with rational expressions

Solve $\frac{1}{x} + \frac{2}{3x} = \frac{1}{5}$.

Solution

Multiply each side by $15x$, the LCD for x, $3x$, and 5:

$$15x\left(\frac{1}{x} + \frac{2}{3x}\right) = 15x\left(\frac{1}{5}\right)$$

$$15x \cdot \frac{1}{x} + 15x \cdot \frac{2}{3x} = 3x$$

$$15 + 10 = 3x$$

$$25 = 3x$$

$$\frac{25}{3} = x$$

Check $\frac{25}{3}$ in the original equation. The solution set is $\left\{\frac{25}{3}\right\}$. ■

CAUTION   To solve an equation with rational expressions, we do *not* convert the rational expressions to ones with a common denominator. Instead, we multiply each side by the LCD to *eliminate* the denominators.

E X A M P L E   3

An equation with two solutions

Solve $\frac{200}{x} + \frac{300}{x + 20} = 10$.

Solution

$$x(x + 20)\left(\frac{200}{x} + \frac{300}{x + 20}\right) = x(x + 20)10 \qquad \text{Multiply each side by } x(x + 20).$$

$$x(x + 20)\frac{200}{x} + x(x + 20)\frac{300}{x + 20} = x(x + 20)10 \qquad \text{Distributive property}$$

$$(x + 20)200 + x(300) = (x^2 + 20x)10 \qquad \text{Simplify.}$$

$$200x + 4000 + 300x = 10x^2 + 200x$$

$$4000 + 300x = 10x^2 \qquad \text{Combine like terms.}$$

$$400 + 30x = x^2 \qquad \text{Divide each side by 10.}$$

$$0 = x^2 - 30x - 400$$

$$0 = (x - 40)(x + 10) \qquad \text{Factor.}$$

$$x - 40 = 0 \quad \text{or} \quad x + 10 = 0 \qquad \text{Set each factor equal to 0.}$$

$$x = 40 \quad \text{or} \qquad x = -10$$

> ### Study Tip
>
> To get the "big picture," survey the chapter that you are studying. Read the headings to get the general idea of the chapter content. Read the chapter summary to see what is important in the chapter. Repeat this survey procedure several times while you are working in a chapter.

Check these values in the original equation. The solution set is $\{-10, 40\}$.   ■

Extraneous Roots

Because equations involving rational expressions have variables in denominators, a root to the equation might cause a 0 to appear in a denominator. In this case the root does not satisfy the original equation, and so it is called an **extraneous root.**

E X A M P L E   4

An equation with an extraneous root

Solve $\frac{3}{x} + \frac{6}{x - 2} = \frac{12}{x^2 - 2x}$.

Solution

Because $x^2 - 2x = x(x - 2)$, the LCD for x, $x - 2$, and $x^2 - 2x$ is $x(x - 2)$.

$$x(x - 2)\frac{3}{x} + x(x - 2)\frac{6}{x - 2} = x(x - 2)\frac{12}{x(x - 2)} \qquad \text{Multiply each side by } x(x - 2).$$

$$3(x - 2) + 6x = 12$$

$$3x - 6 + 6x = 12$$

$$9x - 6 = 12$$

$$9x = 18$$

$$x = 2$$

Neither 0 nor 2 could be a solution because replacing x by either 0 or 2 would cause 0 to appear in a denominator in the original equation. So 2 is an extraneous root and the solution set is the empty set, $\varnothing$.   ■

EXAMPLE 5

An equation with an extraneous root

Solve $x + 2 + \dfrac{x}{x-2} = \dfrac{2}{x-2}$.

Solution

Because the LCD is $x - 2$, we multiply each side by $x - 2$:

$$(x-2)(x+2) + (x-2)\frac{x}{x-2} = (x-2)\frac{2}{x-2}$$

$$x^2 - 4 + x = 2$$

$$x^2 + x - 6 = 0$$

$$(x+3)(x-2) = 0$$

$$x + 3 = 0 \quad \text{or} \quad x - 2 = 0$$

$$x = -3 \quad \text{or} \quad x = 2$$

Replacing x by 2 in the original equation would cause 0 to appear in a denominator. So 2 is an extraneous root. Check that the original equation is satisfied if $x = -3$. The solution set is $\{-3\}$.   ■

Proportions

An equation that expresses the equality of two rational expressions is called a **proportion.** The equation

$$\frac{a}{b} = \frac{c}{d}$$

is a proportion. The terms in the position of b and c are called the **means.** The terms in the position of a and d are called the **extremes.** If we multiply this proportion by the LCD, bd, we get

$$bd \cdot \frac{a}{b} = bd \cdot \frac{c}{d}$$

or

$$ad = bc.$$

The equation $ad = bc$ says that *the product of the extremes is equal to the product of the means.* When solving a proportion, we can omit multiplication by the LCD and just remember the result, $ad = bc$, as the **extremes-means property.**

Helpful Hint

The extremes-means property is often referred to as *cross-multiplying.* Whatever you call it, remember that it is nothing new. You can accomplish the same thing by multiplying each side of the equation by the LCD.

Extremes-Means Property

If $\dfrac{a}{b} = \dfrac{c}{d}$, then $ad = bc$.

The extremes-means property makes it easier to solve proportions.

EXAMPLE 6

A proportion with one solution

Solve $\dfrac{20}{x} = \dfrac{30}{x+20}$.

Solution

Rather than multiplying by the LCD, we use the extremes-means property to eliminate the denominators:

$$\frac{20}{x} = \frac{30}{x + 20}$$

$$20(x + 20) = 30x \qquad \text{Extremes-means property}$$

$$20x + 400 = 30x$$

$$400 = 10x$$

$$40 = x$$

Check 40 in the original equation. The solution set is {40}.   ■

E X A M P L E   7   **A proportion with two solutions**

Solve $\frac{2}{x} = \frac{x + 3}{5}$.

Solution

Use the extremes-means property to write an equivalent equation:

$$x(x + 3) = 2 \cdot 5 \qquad \text{Extremes-means property}$$

$$x^2 + 3x = 10$$

$$x^2 + 3x - 10 = 0$$

$$(x + 5)(x - 2) = 0 \qquad \text{Factor.}$$

$$x + 5 = 0 \quad \text{or} \quad x - 2 = 0 \qquad \text{Zero factor property}$$

$$x = -5 \quad \text{or} \quad x = 2$$

Both -5 and 2 satisfy the original equation. The solution set is $\{-5, 2\}$.   ■

> **CAUTION**   Use the extremes-means property only when solving a *proportion*. It cannot be used on an equation such as
>
> $$\frac{3}{x} = \frac{2}{x + 1} + 5.$$

E X A M P L E   8   **Ratios and proportions**

The ratio of men to women at a football game was 4 to 3. If there were 12,000 more men than women in attendance, then how many men and how many women were in attendance?

Solution

Let x represent the number of men in attendance and $x - 12,000$ represent the number of women in attendance. Because the ratio of men to women was 4 to 3, we can write the following proportion:

$$\frac{4}{3} = \frac{x}{x - 12,000}$$

$$4x - 48,000 = 3x$$

$$x = 48,000$$

So there were 48,000 men and 36,000 women at the game.   ■

M A T H   A T   W O R K

Cargo has been lost, or the hull of a ship has been damaged. What is the amount of money that should be paid to the insured party? Lisa M. Paccione, Ocean Marine Claim Representative for the St. Paul Insurance Company, investigates, evaluates, resolves, and pays these types of claims. Ms. Paccione does this by gathering data, occasionally doing a visual inspection, interviewing witnesses, and negotiating with attorneys.

**M A R I N E
I N S U R A N C E
A G E N T**

Decisions about losses are based on the insured party's individual policy as well as traditional marine practices and maritime law. When consignees suffer a cargo loss, they not only are compensated for the actual amount of the damaged goods, but also receive an additional "advance" in the settlement. Customarily, the advance is 10% over the value of the goods. The amount that St. Paul pays the insured party for a valid claim is computed by using a proportion. In Exercises 73 and 74 of this section you will solve problems involving this proportion.

WARM-UPS

True or false? Explain.

1. In solving an equation involving rational expressions, multiply each side by the LCD for all of the denominators.

2. To solve $\frac{1}{x} + \frac{1}{2x} = \frac{1}{3}$, first change each rational expression to an equivalent rational expression with a denominator of $6x$.

3. Extraneous roots are not real numbers.

4. To solve $\frac{1}{x-2} + 3 = \frac{1}{x+2}$, multiply each side by $x^2 - 4$.

5. The solution set to $\frac{x}{3x+4} - \frac{6}{2x+1} = \frac{7}{5}$ is $\left\{-\frac{4}{3}, -\frac{1}{2}\right\}$.

6. The solution set to $\frac{3}{x} = \frac{2}{5}$ is $\left\{\frac{15}{2}\right\}$.

7. We should use the extremes-means property to solve $\frac{x-2}{x+3} + 1 = \frac{1}{x}$.

8. The equation $x^2 = x$ is equivalent to the equation $x = 0$.

9. The solution set to $(2x - 3)(3x + 4) = 0$ is $\left\{\frac{3}{2}, \frac{4}{3}\right\}$.

10. The equation $\frac{2}{x+1} = \frac{x-1}{4}$ is equivalent to $x^2 - 1 = 8$.

6.6   EXERCISES

Reading and Writing   *After reading this section, write out the answers to these questions. Use complete sentences.*

1. What is the usual first step in solving an equation involving rational expressions?

2. How can an equation involving rational expressions have an extraneous root?

3. What is a proportion?

4. What are the means?

5. What are the extremes?

6. What is the extremes-means property?

Find the solution set to each equation. See Examples 1–5.

7. $\dfrac{1}{x} + \dfrac{1}{6} = \dfrac{1}{8}$

8. $\dfrac{3}{x} + \dfrac{1}{5} = \dfrac{1}{2}$

9. $\dfrac{2}{3x} + \dfrac{1}{15x} = \dfrac{1}{2}$

10. $\dfrac{5}{6x} - \dfrac{1}{8x} = \dfrac{17}{24}$

11. $\dfrac{3}{x-2} + \dfrac{5}{x} = \dfrac{10}{x}$

12. $\dfrac{5}{x-1} + \dfrac{1}{2x} = \dfrac{1}{x}$

13. $\dfrac{x}{x-2} + \dfrac{3}{x} = 2$

14. $\dfrac{x}{x-5} + \dfrac{5}{x} = \dfrac{11}{6}$

15. $\dfrac{100}{x} = \dfrac{150}{x+5} - 1$

16. $\dfrac{30}{x} = \dfrac{50}{x+10} + \dfrac{1}{2}$

17. $\dfrac{3x-5}{x-1} = 2 - \dfrac{2x}{x-1}$

18. $\dfrac{x-3}{x+2} = 3 - \dfrac{1-2x}{x+2}$

19. $x + 1 + \dfrac{2x-5}{x-5} = \dfrac{x}{x-5}$

20. $\dfrac{x-3}{2} - \dfrac{1}{x-3} = \dfrac{8-3x}{x-3}$

21. $5 + \dfrac{9}{x-2} = 2 + \dfrac{x+7}{x-2}$

22. $3 + \dfrac{x+1}{x-3} = 2 - \dfrac{5-3x}{x-3}$

23. $\dfrac{2}{x+2} + \dfrac{x}{x-3} + \dfrac{1}{x^2-x-6} = 0$

24. $\dfrac{x-4}{x^2+2x-15} = 2 - \dfrac{2}{x-3}$

Find the solution set to each equation. See Examples 6 and 7.

25. $\dfrac{2}{x} = \dfrac{3}{4}$

26. $\dfrac{5}{x} = \dfrac{7}{9}$

27. $\dfrac{a}{3} = \dfrac{-1}{4}$

28. $\dfrac{b}{5} = \dfrac{-3}{7}$

29. $-\dfrac{5}{7} = \dfrac{2}{x}$

30. $-\dfrac{3}{8} = \dfrac{5}{x}$

31. $\dfrac{10}{x} = \dfrac{20}{x+20}$

32. $\dfrac{x}{5} = \dfrac{x+2}{3}$

33. $\dfrac{2}{x+1} = \dfrac{x-1}{4}$

34. $\dfrac{3}{x-2} = \dfrac{x+2}{7}$

35. $\dfrac{x}{6} = \dfrac{5}{x-1}$

36. $\dfrac{x+5}{2} = \dfrac{3}{x}$

37. $\dfrac{x+7}{x+4} = \dfrac{x+1}{x-2}$

38. $\dfrac{x+1}{x-5} = \dfrac{x+2}{x-4}$

39. $\dfrac{x-2}{x-3} = \dfrac{x+5}{x+2}$

40. $\dfrac{a-5}{a+6} = \dfrac{a-7}{a+8}$

41. $\dfrac{3w}{3w-5} = \dfrac{w}{w+2}$

42. $\dfrac{x}{x+5} = \dfrac{x}{x-2}$

Solve each equation.

43. $\dfrac{a}{9} = \dfrac{4}{a}$

44. $\dfrac{y}{3} = \dfrac{27}{y}$

45. $\dfrac{1}{2x-4} + \dfrac{1}{x-2} = \dfrac{1}{4}$

46. $\dfrac{7}{3x-9} - \dfrac{1}{x-3} = \dfrac{4}{9}$

47. $\dfrac{x-2}{4} = \dfrac{x-2}{x}$

48. $\dfrac{y+5}{2} = \dfrac{y+5}{y}$

49. $\dfrac{5}{2x+4} - \dfrac{1}{x-1} = \dfrac{3}{x+2}$

50. $\dfrac{5}{2w+6} - \dfrac{1}{w-1} = \dfrac{1}{w+3}$

51. $\dfrac{5}{x-3} = \dfrac{x}{x-3}$

52. $\dfrac{6}{a+2} = \dfrac{a}{a+2}$

53. $\dfrac{w}{6} = \dfrac{3}{2w}$

54. $\dfrac{2m}{5} = \dfrac{10}{m}$

55. $\dfrac{5}{4x-2} - \dfrac{1}{1-2x} = \dfrac{7}{3x+6}$

56. $\dfrac{5}{x+1} - \dfrac{1}{1-x} = \dfrac{1}{x^2-1}$

57. $\dfrac{5}{x} = \dfrac{2}{5}$

58. $\dfrac{-3}{2x} = \dfrac{1}{-5}$

59. $\dfrac{x}{x-2} - \dfrac{x+2}{x^2-2x} = \dfrac{1}{x}$

60. $\dfrac{x-2}{x-6} - \dfrac{4}{x} = \dfrac{24}{x^2-6x}$

61. $\dfrac{5}{x^2-9} + \dfrac{2}{x+3} = \dfrac{1}{x-3}$

62. $\dfrac{1}{x-2} - \dfrac{2}{x+3} = \dfrac{11}{x^2+x-6}$

63. $\dfrac{9}{x^3-1} - \dfrac{1}{x-1} = \dfrac{2}{x^2+x+1}$

64. $\dfrac{x+4}{x^3+8} + \dfrac{x+2}{x^2-2x+4} = \dfrac{11}{2x+4}$

Either solve the given equation or perform the indicated operation(s), whichever is appropriate.

65. $\dfrac{4}{x} = \dfrac{3}{4}$

66. $\dfrac{5}{h} = \dfrac{h}{5}$

67. $\dfrac{4}{x} + \dfrac{3}{4}$

68. $\dfrac{5}{h} - \dfrac{h}{5}$

69. $\dfrac{2}{x} - \dfrac{3}{4} = \dfrac{1}{2}$

70. $\dfrac{1}{2x} - \dfrac{5}{3x} = \dfrac{1}{4}$

71. $\dfrac{2}{x} - \dfrac{3}{4} - \dfrac{1}{2}$

72. $\dfrac{1}{2x} - \dfrac{5}{3x} + \dfrac{1}{4}$

In Exercises 73–82, solve each problem. See Example 8.

73. *Maritime losses.* The amount paid to an insured party by the American Insurance Company is computed by using the proportion

$$\frac{\text{value shipped}}{\text{amount of loss}} = \frac{\text{amount of declared premium}}{\text{amount insured party gets paid}}.$$

If the value shipped was $300,000, the amount of loss was $250,000, and the amount of declared premium was $200,000, then what amount is paid to the insured party?

74. *Maritime losses.* Suppose the value shipped was $400,000, the amount of loss was $300,000, and the amount that the insured party got paid was $150,000. Use the proportion of Exercise 73 to find the amount of declared premium.

75. *Capture-recapture method.* To estimate the size of the grizzly bear population in a national park, rangers tagged and released 12 bears. Later it was observed that in 23 sightings of grizzly bears, only two had been tagged. Assuming the proportion of tagged bears in the later sightings is the same as the proportion of tagged bears in the population, estimate the number of bears in the population.

76. *Please rewind.* In a sample of 24 returned videotapes, it was found that only 3 were rewound as requested. If 872 videos are returned in a day, then how many of them would you expect to find that are not rewound?

77. *Pleasing painting.* The ancient Greeks often used the ratio of length to width for a rectangle as 7 to 6 to give the rectangle a pleasing shape. If the length of a pleasantly shaped Greek painting is 22 centimeters (cm) longer than its width, then what are its length and width?

78. *Pickups and cars.* The ratio of pickups to cars sold at a dealership is 2 to 3. If the dealership sold 142 more cars than pickups in 1999, then how many of each did it sell?

79. *Cleaning up the river.* Pollution in the Tickfaw River has been blamed primarily on pesticide runoff from area farms. The formula

$$C = \frac{4{,}000{,}000p}{100 - p}$$

FIGURE FOR EXERCISE 79

has been used to model the cost in dollars for removing $p\%$ of the pollution in the river. If the state gets a $1 million federal grant for cleaning up the river, then what percentage of the pollution can be removed? Use the bar graph to estimate the percentage that can be cleaned up with a $100 million grant.

80. *Campaigning for governor.* A campaign manager for a gubernatorial candidate estimates that the cost in dollars for an advertising campaign that will get his candidate $p\%$ of the votes is given by

$$C = \frac{1{,}000{,}000 + 2{,}000{,}000p}{100 - p}.$$

If the candidate can spend only $2 million for advertising, then what percentage of the votes can she expect to receive? Use the bar graph to estimate the percentage of votes expected if $4 million is spent.

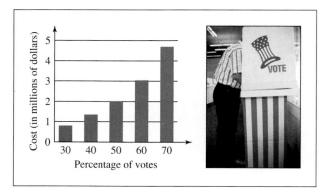

FIGURE FOR EXERCISE 80

81. *Wealth-building portfolio.* Misty decided to invest her annual bonus in a wealth-building portfolio as shown in the figure on the next page *(Fidelity Investments, Boston)*.

a) If the amount that she invested in stocks was $20,000 greater than her investment in bonds, then how much did she invest in bonds?

b) What was the amount of her annual bonus?

Designing a retirement portfolio

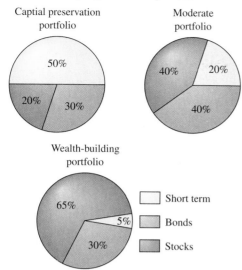

Captial preservation portfolio

Moderate portfolio

Wealth-building portfolio

☐ Short term

▨ Bonds

▧ Stocks

FIGURE FOR EXERCISE 81

82. *Estimating weapons.* When intelligence agents obtain enemy weapons marked with serial numbers, they use the formula $N = (1 + 1/C)B - 1$ to estimate the total number of such weapons N that the enemy has produced. B is the biggest serial number obtained and C is the number of weapons obtained. It is assumed the weapons are numbered 1 through N.

a) Find N if agents obtain five nerve gas containers numbered 45, 143, 258, 301, and 465.

b) Find C if agents estimate that the enemy has 255 tanks from a group of captured tanks on which the biggest serial number is 224.

GETTING MORE INVOLVED

 83. *Writing.* In this chapter the LCD is used to add rational expressions and to solve equations. Explain the difference between using the LCD to solve the equation

$$\frac{3}{x - 2} + \frac{7}{x + 2} = 2$$

and using the LCD to find the sum

$$\frac{3}{x - 2} + \frac{7}{x + 2}.$$

 84. *Discussion.* For each equation, find the values for x that *cannot* be solutions to the equation. Do not solve the equations.

a) $\dfrac{1}{x} + \dfrac{1}{x - 1} = \dfrac{1}{2}$ **b)** $\dfrac{x}{x - 1} = \dfrac{1}{2}$

c) $\dfrac{1}{x^2 + 1} = \dfrac{1}{x + 1}$

In This Section

- Formulas
- Uniform Motion Problems
- Work Problems
- Miscellaneous Problems

6.7 APPLICATIONS

In this section we will use the techniques of Section 6.6 to rewrite formulas involving rational expressions and to solve some problems.

Formulas

Rewriting formulas having rational expressions is similar to solving equations having rational expressions. Generally, the first step is to multiply each side by the LCD for the rational expressions.

EXAMPLE 1   **Solving a formula**

In Chapter 3, we wrote the equation of a line by starting with an equation involving a rational expression:

$$\frac{y - y_1}{x - x_1} = m$$

Solve the equation for y.

Solution

$$(x - x_1)\frac{y - y_1}{x - x_1} = (x - x_1)m \quad \text{Multiply each side by the denominator } x - x_1.$$

$$y - y_1 = (x - x_1)m \quad \text{Reduce.}$$

$$y = (x - x_1)m + y_1$$

In Example 2 we solve for a variable that occurs twice in the original formula. Remember that when a formula is solved for a certain variable, that variable must appear only once in the final formula.

E X A M P L E 2 **Solving for a variable**

The formula

$$\frac{P}{P_W} = \frac{2L}{2L + d}$$

is used in physics to find the relative density of a substance. Since P_W has subscript W, we treat P and P_W as two different variables. Solve the formula for L.

Solution

$$\frac{P}{P_W} = \frac{2L}{2L + d}$$

$$P(2L + d) = P_W(2L) \quad \text{The extremes-means property}$$

$$2PL + Pd = 2LP_W \quad \text{Simplify.}$$

$$Pd = 2LP_W - 2PL \quad \text{Get all terms involving } L \text{ onto the same side.}$$

$$Pd = (2P_W - 2P)L \quad \text{Factor out } L.$$

$$\frac{Pd}{2P_W - 2P} = L$$

In Example 3 we find the value of one variable when given the values of the remaining variables.

E X A M P L E 3 **Evaluating a formula**

Find x if $x_1 = 2$, $y_1 = -3$, $y = -1$, $m = \frac{1}{2}$, and

$$\frac{y - y_1}{x - x_1} = m.$$

Solution

Substitute all of the values into the formula and solve for x:

$$\frac{-1 - (-3)}{x - 2} = \frac{1}{2} \quad \text{Substitute.}$$

$$\frac{2}{x - 2} = \frac{1}{2}$$

$$x - 2 = 4 \quad \text{Extremes-means property}$$

$$x = 6 \quad \text{Check in the original formula.}$$

Uniform Motion Problems

The uniform motion problems here are similar to those of Chapter 2, but in this chapter the equations have rational expressions.

E X A M P L E   4

Uniform motion

300 mi
Speed = x mph

300 mi
Speed = $x - 10$ mph

F I G U R E   6 . 1

Michele drove her empty rig 300 miles to Salina to pick up a load of cattle. When her rig was fully loaded, her average speed was 10 miles per hour less than when the rig was empty. If the return trip took her 1 hour longer, then what was her average speed with the rig empty? (See Fig. 6.1.)

Solution

Let x be Michele's average speed empty and let $x - 10$ be her average speed full. Because the time can be determined from the distance and the rate, $T = \dfrac{D}{R}$, we can make the following table.

	Rate	Time	Distance
Empty	$x \dfrac{\text{mi}}{\text{hr}}$	$\dfrac{300}{x}$ hr	300 mi
Full	$x - 10 \dfrac{\text{mi}}{\text{hr}}$	$\dfrac{300}{x - 10}$ hr	300 mi

We now write an equation expressing the fact that her time empty was 1 hour less than her time full:

$$\frac{300}{x} = \frac{300}{x - 10} - 1$$

$$x(x - 10)\frac{300}{x} = x(x - 10)\frac{300}{x - 10} - x(x - 10)1 \quad \text{Multiply each side by } x(x - 10).$$

$$300x - 3000 = 300x - x^2 + 10x \quad \text{Reduce.}$$

$$-3000 = -x^2 + 10x$$

$$x^2 - 10x - 3000 = 0 \quad \text{Get 0 on one side.}$$

$$(x + 50)(x - 60) = 0 \quad \text{Factor.}$$

$$x + 50 = 0 \quad \text{or} \quad x - 60 = 0 \quad \text{Zero factor property}$$

$$x = -50 \quad \text{or} \quad x = 60$$

The equation is satisfied if $x = -50$, but because -50 is negative, it cannot be the speed of the truck. Michele's average speed empty was 60 miles per hour (mph). Checking this answer, we find that if she traveled 300 miles at 60 mph, it would take her 5 hours. If she traveled 300 miles at 50 mph with the loaded rig, it would take her 6 hours. Because Michele's time with the empty rig was 1 hour less than her time with the loaded rig, 60 mph is the correct answer. ∎

Work Problems

Problems involving different rates for completing a task are referred to as **work problems.** We did not solve work problems earlier because they usually require equations with rational expressions. Work problems are similar to uniform motion problems in which $RT = D$. The product of a person's time and rate is the amount of work completed. For example, if your puppy gains 1 pound every 3 days, then he is growing at the rate of $\frac{1}{3}$ pound per day. If he grows at the rate of $\frac{1}{3}$ pound per day for a period of 30 days, then he gains 10 pounds.

EXAMPLE 5

Working together

Linda can mow a certain lawn with her riding lawn mower in 4 hours. When Linda uses the riding mower and Rebecca operates the push mower, it takes them 3 hours to mow the lawn. How long would it take Rebecca to mow the lawn by herself using the push mower?

Solution

If x is the number of hours it takes for Rebecca to complete the lawn alone, then her rate is $\frac{1}{x}$ of the lawn per hour. Because Linda can mow the entire lawn in 4 hours, her rate is $\frac{1}{4}$ of the lawn per hour. In the 3 hours that they work together, Rebecca completes $\frac{3}{x}$ of the lawn while Linda completes $\frac{3}{4}$ of the lawn. We can classify all of the necessary information in a table that looks a lot like the one we used in Example 4.

	Rate	Time	Amount of Work
Linda	$\frac{1}{4}\frac{\text{lawn}}{\text{hr}}$	3 hr	$\frac{3}{4}$ lawn
Rebecca	$\frac{1}{x}\frac{\text{lawn}}{\text{hr}}$	3 hr	$\frac{3}{x}$ lawn

Because the lawn is finished in 3 hours, the two portions of the lawn (in the work column) mowed by each girl have a sum of 1:

$$\frac{3}{4} + \frac{3}{x} = 1$$

$$4x \cdot \frac{3}{4} + 4x \cdot \frac{3}{x} = 4x \cdot 1 \quad \text{Multiply each side by } 4x.$$

$$3x + 12 = 4x$$

$$12 = x$$

If $x = 12$, then in the 3 hours that they work together, Rebecca does $\frac{3}{12}$ or $\frac{1}{4}$ of the job while Linda does $\frac{3}{4}$ of the job. So it would take Rebecca 12 hours to mow the lawn by herself using the push mower. ∎

The methods in Examples 4 and 5 are the same. One table uses $RT = D$ and the other uses $RT = W$. Making a table will help you understand a problem. Another method for solving Example 5 is to use only the rates. Since Linda's rate is $\frac{1}{4}$ lawn/hr and Rebecca's rate is $\frac{1}{x}$ lawn/hr, together their rate is $\left(\frac{1}{4} + \frac{1}{x}\right)$ lawn/hr. Since their rate together is $\frac{1}{3}$ lawn/hr, we have $\frac{1}{4} + \frac{1}{x} = \frac{1}{3}$. Solving this equation also yields $x = 12$.

Miscellaneous Problems

EXAMPLE 6

Hamburger and steak

Patrick bought 50 pounds of meat consisting of hamburger and steak. Steak costs twice as much per pound as hamburger. If he bought $30 worth of hamburger and $90 worth of steak, then how many pounds of each did he buy?

Solution

Let x be the number of pounds of hamburger and $50 - x$ be the number of pounds of steak. Because Patrick got x pounds of hamburger for \$30, he paid $\frac{30}{x}$ dollars per pound for the hamburger. We can classify all of the given information in a table.

	Price per pound	Amount	Total price
Hamburger	$\frac{30}{x}$ $\frac{\text{dollars}}{\text{lb}}$	x lb	30 dollars
Steak	$\frac{90}{50-x}$ $\frac{\text{dollars}}{\text{lb}}$	$50 - x$ lb	90 dollars

Because the price per pound of steak is twice that of hamburger, we can write the following equation:

$$2\left(\frac{30}{x}\right) = \frac{90}{50 - x}$$

$$\frac{60}{x} = \frac{90}{50 - x}$$

$$90x = 3000 - 60x \quad \text{The extremes-means property}$$

$$150x = 3000$$

$$x = 20$$

$$50 - x = 30$$

Patrick purchased 20 pounds of hamburger and 30 pounds of steak. Check this answer. ■

WARM-UPS

True or false? Explain.

1. The formula $w = \frac{1-t}{t}$, solved for t, is $t = \frac{1-t}{w}$.

2. To solve $\frac{1}{p} + \frac{1}{q} = \frac{1}{s}$ for s, multiply each side by pqs.

3. If 50 pounds of steak cost x dollars, then the price is $\frac{50}{x}$ dollars per pound.

4. If Claudia drives x miles in 3 hours, then her rate is $\frac{x}{3}$ miles per hour.

5. If Takenori mows his entire lawn in $x + 2$ hours, then he mows $\frac{1}{x+2}$ of the lawn per hour.

6. If Kareem drives 200 nails in 12 hours, then he is driving $\frac{200}{12}$ nails per hour.

7. If x hours is 1 hour less than y hours, then $x - 1 = y$.

8. If $A = \frac{mv^2}{B}$ and m and B are nonzero, then $v^2 = \frac{AB}{m}$.

9. If a and y are nonzero and $a = \frac{x}{y}$, then $y = ax$.

10. If x hours is 3 hours more than y hours, then $x + 3 = y$.

6.7 EXERCISES

Solve each equation for y. See Example 1.

1. $\dfrac{y-3}{x-2} = 5$

2. $\dfrac{y-4}{x-7} = -6$

3. $\dfrac{y+1}{x-6} = -\dfrac{1}{3}$

4. $\dfrac{y+7}{x-2} = \dfrac{-2}{3}$

5. $\dfrac{y-a}{x-b} = m$

6. $\dfrac{y-h}{x-k} = a$

7. $\dfrac{y-2}{x+5} = -\dfrac{7}{3}$

8. $\dfrac{y-3}{x+1} = -\dfrac{9}{4}$

Solve each formula for the indicated variable. See Example 2.

9. $M = \dfrac{F}{f}$ for f

10. $P = \dfrac{A}{1+rt}$ for A

11. $A = \dfrac{\pi}{4} \cdot D^2$ for D^2

12. $V = \pi r^2 h$ for r^2

13. $F = k\dfrac{m_1 m_2}{r^2}$ for m_1

14. $F = \dfrac{mv^2}{r}$ for v^2

15. $\dfrac{1}{p} + \dfrac{1}{q} = \dfrac{1}{f}$ for q

16. $\dfrac{1}{R} = \dfrac{1}{R_1} + \dfrac{1}{R_2}$ for R_1

17. $e^2 = 1 - \dfrac{b^2}{a^2}$ for a^2

18. $e^2 = 1 - \dfrac{b^2}{a^2}$ for b^2

19. $\dfrac{P_1 V_1}{T_1} = \dfrac{P_2 V_2}{T_2}$ for T_1

20. $\dfrac{P_1 V_1}{T_1} = \dfrac{P_2 V_2}{T_2}$ for P_2

21. $V = \dfrac{4}{3}\pi r^2 h$ for h

22. $h = \dfrac{S - 2\pi r^2}{2\pi r}$ for S

Use the formula from the indicated exercise to find the value of the indicated variable. See Example 3. For calculator problems, round answers to three decimal places.

23. If $M = 10$ and $F = 5$ in Exercise 9, find f.

24. If $A = 550$, $P = 500$, and $t = 2$ in Exercise 10, find r.

25. If $A = 6\pi$ in Exercise 11, find D^2.

26. If $V = 12\pi$ and $r = 3$ in Exercise 12, find h.

27. If $F = 32$, $r = 4$, $m_1 = 6$, and $m_2 = 8$ in Exercise 13, find k.

28. If $F = 10$, $m = 8$, and $v = 6$ in Exercise 14, find r.

29. If $f = 2.3$ and $q = 1.7$ in Exercise 15, find p.

30. If $R = 1.29$ and $R_1 = 0.045$ in Exercise 16, find R_2.

31. If $e = 0.62$ and $b = 3.5$ in Exercise 17, find a^2.

32. If $a = 3.61$ and $e = 2.4$ in Exercise 18, find b^2.

33. If $V = 25.6$ and $h = 3.2$ in Exercise 21, find r^2.

34. If $h = 3.6$ and $r = 2.45$ in Exercise 22, find S.

Solve each problem. See Examples 4–6.

35. *Walking and riding.* Karen can ride her bike from home to school in the same amount of time as she can walk from home to the post office. She rides 10 miles per hour (mph) faster than she walks. The distance from her home to school is 7 miles, and the distance from her home to the post office is 2 miles. How fast does Karen walk?

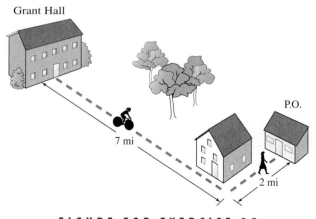

Grant Hall

P.O.

7 mi

2 mi

FIGURE FOR EXERCISE 35

36. *Fast driving.* Beverly can drive 600 miles in the same time as it takes Susan to drive 500 miles. If Beverly drives 10 mph faster than Susan, then how fast does Beverly drive?

37. Faster driving. Patrick drives 40 miles to work, and Guy drives 60 miles to work. Guy claims that he drives at the same speed as Patrick, but it takes him only 12 minutes longer to get to work. If this is true, then how long does it take each of them to get to work? What are their speeds? Do you think that Guy's claim is correct?

38. Route drivers. David and Keith are route drivers for a fast-photo company. David's route is 80 miles, and Keith's is 100 miles. Keith averages 10 mph more than David and finishes his route 10 minutes before David. What is David's speed?

39. Physically fit. Every morning, Yong Yi runs 5 miles, then walks one mile. He runs 6 mph faster than he walks. If his total time yesterday was 45 minutes, then how fast did he run?

40. Row, row, row your boat. Norma can row her boat 12 miles in the same time as it takes Marietta to cover 36 miles in her motorboat. If Marietta's boat travels 15 mph faster than Norma's boat, then how fast is Norma rowing her boat?

41. Pumping out the pool. A large pump can drain an 80,000-gallon pool in 3 hours. With a smaller pump also operating, the job takes only 2 hours. How long would it take the smaller pump to drain the pool by itself?

42. Trimming hedges. Lourdes can trim the hedges around her property in 8 hours by using an electric hedge trimmer. Rafael can do the same job in 15 hours by using a manual trimmer. How long would it take them to trim the hedges working together?

43. Filling the tub. It takes 10 minutes to fill Alisha's bathtub and 12 minutes to drain the water out. How long would it take to fill it with the drain accidentally left open?

FIGURE FOR EXERCISE 43

44. Eating machine. Charles can empty the cookie jar in $1\frac{1}{2}$ hours. It takes his mother 2 hours to bake enough cookies to fill it. If the cookie jar is full when Charles comes home from school, and his mother continues baking and

restocking the cookie jar, then how long will it take him to empty the cookie jar?

45. Filing the invoices. It takes Gina 90 minutes to file the monthly invoices. If Hilda files twice as fast as Gina does, how long will it take them working together?

46. Painting alone. Julie can paint a fence by herself in 12 hours. With Betsy's help, it takes only 5 hours. How long would it take Betsy by herself?

47. Buying fruit. Molly bought $5.28 worth of oranges and $8.80 worth of apples. She bought 2 more pounds of oranges than apples. If apples cost twice as much per pound as oranges, then how many pounds of each did she buy?

48. Raising rabbits. Luke raises rabbits and raccoons to sell for meat. The price of raccoon meat is three times the price of rabbit meat. One day Luke sold 160 pounds of meat, $72 worth of each type. What is the price per pound of each type of meat?

49. Total resistance. If two receivers with resistances R_1 and R_2 are connected in parallel, then the formula

$$\frac{1}{R} = \frac{1}{R_1} + \frac{1}{R_2}$$

relates the total resistance for the circuit R with R_1 and R_2. Given that R_1 is 3 ohms and R is 2 ohms, find R_2.

FIGURE FOR EXERCISE 49

50. More resistance. Use the formula from Exercise 49 to find R_1 and R_2 given that the total resistance is 1.2 ohms and R_1 is 1 ohm larger than R_2.

51. Las Vegas vacation. Brenda of Horizon Travel has arranged for a group of gamblers to share the $24,000 cost of a charter flight to Las Vegas. If Brenda can get 40 more people to share the cost, then the cost per person will decrease by $100. See the figure on the next page.
a) How many people were in the original group?
b) Write the cost per person as a function of the number of people sharing the cost.

FIGURE FOR EXERCISE 51

52. White-water rafting. Adventures, Inc. has a $1500 group rate for an overnight rafting trip on the Colorado River. For the last trip five people failed to show, causing the price per person to increase by $25. How many were originally scheduled for the trip?

53. Doggie bag. Muffy can eat a 25-pound bag of dog food in 28 days, whereas Missy eats a 25-pound bag in 23 days. How many days would it take them together to finish a 50-pound bag of dog food.

54. Rodent food. A pest control specialist has found that 6 rats can eat an entire box of sugar-coated breakfast cereal in 13.6 minutes, and it takes a dozen mice 34.7 minutes to devour the same size box of cereal. How long would it take all 18 rodents, in a cooperative manner, to finish off a box of cereal?

COLLABORATIVE ACTIVITIES

Beorg's Business

In manufacturing or other businesses in which time is money and tasks are easily shared, problems involving work appear. An owner or manager who wants to know how to bid a job often develops a table of times needed to complete the job as determined by how much work is required and who could be assigned to the job.

Beorg owns a kaleidoscope-manufacturing company with two employees, Scott and Salina. It takes Scott one hour to make one kaleidoscope, and it takes Salina $\frac{1}{2}$ hour to make one kaleidoscope. Beorg wants to know how long it would take to complete a certain number of kaleidoscopes. Using the information given and answering the questions below, fill in the following table for Beorg.

Name of Employee	Time for one kaleidoscope	Time for 20 kaleidoscopes
Scott	1 hr	
Salina	$\frac{1}{2}$ hr	
Scott & Salina		
Sammy		
Scott & Sammy	$\frac{3}{4}$ hr	
Salina & Sammy		
Scott, Salina, & Sammy		

Grouping: Four students per group

Topic: Applications of work problems

1. How long will it take Scott and Salina working together to make one kaleidoscope?

2. Beorg hires a third person, Sammy, and has him and Scott make one kaleidoscope. Working together, it takes them $\frac{3}{4}$ hour to make one kaleidoscope. How long would it take Sammy by himself to make one kaleidoscope?

3. How long would it take Salina and Sammy working together to make one kaleidoscope? How long would it take for all three working together?

Now Beorg wants to finish his time table. He would like to have 20 kaleidoscopes completed each day.

4. Finish the preceding table, and find the best combination or combinations of employees to use to have 20 kaleidoscopes at the end of an 8-hour day.

Extension: Is Sammy in the combination or combinations you found in the last question? Is it worth having Sammy work? Remember that when someone is starting a new job, he or she may work more slowly until he or she learns how to do the job more efficiently. Find out how fast Sammy would need to work for production to double (40 kaleidoscopes in an 8-hour day).

WRAP-UP   CHAPTER 6

SUMMARY

Rational Expressions

		Examples
Rational expression	The ratio of two polynomials with the denominator not equal to zero	$\dfrac{x^2 - 1}{2x - 3}$
Domain of a rational expression	The set of all possible numbers that can be used as replacements for the variable	$D = \left\{ x \mid x \neq \dfrac{3}{2} \right\}$

Operations with Rational Expressions

		Examples
Basic principle of rational numbers	If $\dfrac{a}{b}$ is a rational number and c is a nonzero real number, then $$\frac{a}{b} = \frac{ac}{bc}.$$	Used for reducing: $$\frac{14}{16} = \frac{2 \cdot 7}{2 \cdot 8} = \frac{7}{8}$$ Used for building: $$\frac{2}{x} = \frac{2 \cdot 3}{x \cdot 3} = \frac{6}{3x}$$
Multiplication of rational numbers	If $\dfrac{a}{b}$ and $\dfrac{c}{d}$ are rational numbers, then $$\frac{a}{b} \cdot \frac{c}{d} = \frac{ac}{bd}.$$	$$\frac{3}{x} \cdot \frac{6}{x^2} = \frac{18}{x^3}$$
Division of rational numbers	If $\dfrac{a}{b}$ and $\dfrac{c}{d}$ are rational numbers with $\dfrac{c}{d} \neq 0$, then $$\frac{a}{b} \div \frac{c}{d} = \frac{a}{b} \cdot \frac{d}{c}. \quad \text{(Invert and multiply.)}$$	$$\frac{a}{x} \div \frac{5}{4x} = \frac{a}{x} \cdot \frac{4x}{5} = \frac{4a}{5}$$
Least common multiple	The LCM is the product of all of the different factors that appear in the polynomials. The exponent on each factor is the highest power that occurs on that factor in any of the polynomials.	$4a^3b, \; 6ab^2$ $\text{LCM} = 12a^3b^2$
Least common denominator	The LCD for a group of denominators is the LCM of the denominators.	$\dfrac{1}{4a^3b} + \dfrac{1}{6ab^2}$ $\text{LCD} = 12a^3b^2$

Addition and subtraction	If $b \neq 0$, then $$\frac{a}{b} + \frac{c}{b} = \frac{a+c}{b} \quad \text{and} \quad \frac{a}{b} - \frac{c}{b} = \frac{a-c}{b}.$$ If the denominators are not identical, we must build up each fraction to an equivalent fraction with the LCD as denominator.	$$\frac{2x}{x-3} + \frac{7x}{x-3} = \frac{9x}{x-3}$$ $$\frac{1}{2} + \frac{1}{x} = \frac{x}{2x} + \frac{2}{2x} = \frac{x+2}{2x}$$
Rules for adding and subtracting simple fractions	If $b \neq 0$ and $d \neq 0$, then $$\frac{a}{b} + \frac{c}{d} = \frac{ad+bc}{bd}$$ and $$\frac{a}{b} - \frac{c}{d} = \frac{ad-bc}{bd}.$$	$$\frac{1}{2} + \frac{1}{3} = \frac{5}{6}$$ $$\frac{2}{5} - \frac{3}{7} = \frac{-1}{35}$$
Simplifying complex fractions	Multiply the numerator and denominator by the LCD.	$$\frac{\left(\frac{1}{2} + \frac{1}{x}\right)6x}{\left(\frac{1}{x} - \frac{1}{3}\right)6x} = \frac{3x+6}{6-2x}$$

Division of Polynomials

Ordinary or long division	dividend = (quotient)(divisor) + remainder $$\frac{\text{dividend}}{\text{divisor}} = \text{quotient} + \frac{\text{remainder}}{\text{divisor}}$$	$$\begin{array}{r} x - 7 \\ x+2\overline{)x^2 - 5x - 14} \\ \underline{x^2 + 2x} \\ -7x - 14 \\ \underline{-7x - 14} \\ 0 \end{array}$$
Synthetic division	A condensed version of long division, used only for dividing by a polynomial of the form $x - c$	$$\begin{array}{r} -2 \,\rfloor\; 1 \;\; -5 \;\; -14 \\ -2 \;\;\;\; 14 \\ \hline 1 \;\; -7 \;\;\;\; 0 \end{array}$$
	If the remainder is 0, then the dividend factors as dividend = (quotient)(divisor).	$$x^2 - 5x - 14 = (x-7)(x+2)$$
Remainder Theorem	If the polynomial $P(x)$ is divided by $x - c$, then the remainder is equal to $P(c)$.	$$P(x) = x^2 - 2x + 7$$ $$\begin{array}{r} 3 \,\rfloor\; 1 \;\; -2 \;\;\; 7 \\ 3 \;\;\; 3 \\ \hline 1 \;\;\; 1 \;\; 10 \end{array}$$ $$P(3) = 10$$

Equations with Rational Expressions

Solving equations with rational expressions	Multiply each side by the LCD to eliminate all denominators.

Examples

$$\frac{1}{x} - \frac{1}{3} = \frac{1}{2x} - \frac{1}{6}$$

$$6x\left(\frac{1}{x} - \frac{1}{3}\right) = 6x\left(\frac{1}{2x} - \frac{1}{6}\right)$$

$$6 - 2x = 3 - x$$

Solving proportions by the extremes-means property	If $\frac{a}{b} = \frac{c}{d}$, then $ad = bc$.

$$\frac{2}{x-3} = \frac{5}{6}$$

$$12 = 5x - 15$$

ENRICHING YOUR MATHEMATICAL WORD POWER

For each mathematical term, choose the correct meaning.

1. **rational expression**
   a. a ratio of integers
   b. a ratio of two polynomials with the denominator not equal to zero
   c. an expression involving fractions
   d. a fraction in which the numerator and denominator contain fractions

2. **domain of a rational expression**
   a. all real numbers
   b. the denominator of the rational expression
   c. the set of all real numbers that cannot be used in place of the variable
   d. the set of all real numbers that can be used in place of the variable

3. **lowest terms**
   a. the numerator is smaller than the denominator
   b. no common factors
   c. the best interest rate
   d. when the numerator is 1

4. **reducing**
   a. less than
   b. losing weight
   c. making equivalent
   d. dividing out common factors

5. **equivalent fractions**
   a. identical fractions
   b. fractions that represent the same number
   c. fractions with the same denominator
   d. fractions with the same numerator

6. **complex fraction**
   a. a fraction having rational expressions in the numerator, denominator, or both
   b. a fraction with a large denominator
   c. the sum of two fractions
   d. a fraction with a variable in the denominator

7. **building up the denominator**
   a. the opposite of reducing a fraction
   b. finding the least common denominator
   c. adding the same number to the numerator and denominator
   d. writing a fraction larger

8. **least common denominator**
   a. the largest number that is a multiple of all denominators
   b. the sum of the denominators
   c. the product of the denominators
   d. the smallest number that is a multiple of all denominators

9. **extraneous root**
   a. a number that appears to be a solution to an equation but does not satisfy the equation
   b. an extra solution to an equation
   c. the second solution
   d. a nonreal solution

10. **ratio of *a* to *b***
    a. b/a
    b. a/b
    c. $a/(a+b)$
    d. ab

11. **synthetic division**
    a. division of nonreal numbers
    b. division by zero
    c. multiplication that looks like division
    d. a quick method for dividing by $x - c$

12. **proportion**
    a. a ratio
    b. two ratios
    c. the product of the means equals the product of the extremes
    d. a statement expressing the equality of two rational expressions

13. **extremes**
  a. a and d in $a/b = c/d$
  b. b and c in $a/b = c/d$
  c. the extremes-means property
  d. if $a/b = c/d$, then $ad = bc$
14. **means**
  a. the average of a, b, c, and d
  b. a and d in $a/b = c/d$

c. b and c in $a/b = c/d$
d. if $a/b = c/d$, then $(a + b)/2 = (c + d)/2$

15. **extremes-means property**
  a. $ab = ba$ for any real numbers a and b
  b. $(a - b)^2 = (b - a)^2$ for any real numbers a and b
  c. if $a/b = c/d$, then $ab = cd$
  d. if $a/b = c/d$, then $ad = bc$

REVIEW EXERCISES

6.1 *State the domain of each rational expression.*

1. $\dfrac{5 - x}{3x - 3}$

2. $\dfrac{x - 4}{x^2 - 25}$

3. $\dfrac{x}{x^2 - x - 2}$

4. $\dfrac{1}{x^3 - x^2}$

Reduce each rational expression to its lowest terms.

5. $\dfrac{a^3bc^3}{a^5b^2c}$

6. $\dfrac{x^4 - 1}{3x^2 - 3}$

7. $\dfrac{68x^3}{51xy}$

8. $\dfrac{5x^2 - 15x + 10}{5x - 10}$

6.2 *Perform the indicated operations.*

9. $\dfrac{a^3b^2}{b^3a} \cdot \dfrac{ab - b^2}{ab - a^2}$

10. $\dfrac{x^3 - 1}{3x} \cdot \dfrac{6x^2}{x - 1}$

11. $\dfrac{w - 4}{3w} \div \dfrac{2w - 8}{9w}$

12. $\dfrac{x^3 - xy^2}{y} \div \dfrac{x^3 + 2x^2y + xy^2}{3y}$

6.3 *Find the least common multiple for each group of polynomials.*

13. $6x$, $3x - 6$, $x^2 - 2x$

14. $x^3 - 8$, $x^2 - 4$, $2x + 4$

15. $6ab^3$, $4a^5b^2$

16. $4x^2 - 9$, $4x^2 + 12x + 9$

Perform the indicated operations.

17. $\dfrac{3}{2x - 6} + \dfrac{1}{x^2 - 9}$

18. $\dfrac{3}{x - 3} - \dfrac{5}{x + 4}$

19. $\dfrac{w}{ab^2} - \dfrac{5}{a^2b}$

20. $\dfrac{x}{x - 1} + \dfrac{3x}{x^2 - 1}$

6.4 *Simplify the complex fractions.*

21. $\dfrac{\dfrac{3}{2x} - \dfrac{4}{5x}}{\dfrac{1}{3} - \dfrac{2}{x}}$

22. $\dfrac{\dfrac{5}{x - 2} - \dfrac{4}{4 - x^2}}{\dfrac{3}{x + 2} - \dfrac{1}{2 - x}}$

23. $\dfrac{\dfrac{1}{y - 2} - 3}{\dfrac{5}{y - 2} + 4}$

24. $\dfrac{\dfrac{a}{b^2} - \dfrac{b}{a^3}}{\dfrac{a}{b} + \dfrac{b}{a^2}}$

25. $\dfrac{a^{-2} - b^{-3}}{a^{-1}b^{-2}}$

26. $p^{-1} + pq^{-2}$

6.5 *Find the quotient and remainder.*

27. $(x^3 + x^2 - 11x + 10) \div (x - 2)$

28. $(2x^3 + 5x^2 + 9) \div (x + 3)$

29. $(m^4 - 1) \div (m + 1)$

30. $(x^4 - 1) \div (x - 1)$

31. $(a^9 - 8) \div (a^3 - 2)$

32. $(a^2 - b^2) \div (a - b)$

33. $(3m^3 + 6m^2 - 18m) \div (3m)$

34. $(w - 3) \div (3 - w)$

Rewrite each expression in the form

$$quotient + \frac{remainder}{divisor}.$$

Use synthetic division.

35. $\dfrac{x^2 - 5}{x - 1}$

36. $\dfrac{x^2 + 3x + 2}{x + 3}$

37. $\dfrac{3x}{x - 2}$

38. $\dfrac{4x}{x - 5}$

Use division to determine whether the first polynomial is a factor of the second. Use synthetic division when possible.

39. $x + 2$, $x^3 - 2x^2 + 3x + 22$

40. $x - 2$, $x^3 + x - 10$

41. $x - 5$, $x^3 - x - 120$

42. $x + 3$, $x^3 + 2x + 15$

43. $x - 1$, $x^3 + x^2 - 3$

44. $x - 1$, $x^3 + 1$

45. $x^2 + 2$, $x^4 + x^3 + 5x^2 + 2x + 6$

46. $x^2 + 1$, $x^4 - 1$

6.6 Solve each equation.

47. $\dfrac{-3}{8} = \dfrac{2}{x}$

48. $\dfrac{2}{x} + \dfrac{5}{2x} = 1$

49. $5 + \dfrac{x + 1}{x - 1} = 3 + \dfrac{5x - 3}{x - 1}$

50. $2 + \dfrac{7}{x - 5} = 3 + \dfrac{x + 2}{x - 5}$

51. $\dfrac{15}{a^2 - 25} + \dfrac{1}{a - 5} = \dfrac{6}{a + 5}$

52. $2 + \dfrac{3}{x - 5} = \dfrac{x - 1}{x - 5}$

6.7 Solve each formula for the indicated variable.

53. $\dfrac{y - b}{m} = x$ for y

54. $\dfrac{2A}{h} = b_1 + b_2$ for A

55. $F = \dfrac{mv^2}{r}$ for m

56. $P = \dfrac{A}{1 + rt}$ for r

57. $A = \dfrac{2}{3}\pi rh$ for r

58. $\dfrac{a}{w^2} = \dfrac{2}{b}$ for b

59. $\dfrac{y + 3}{x - 7} = 2$ for y

60. $\dfrac{y - 5}{x + 4} = \dfrac{-1}{2}$ for y

MISCELLANEOUS

Either perform the indicated operation or solve the equation, whichever is appropriate.

61. $\dfrac{5x}{3x^2y} + \dfrac{7a^2}{6a^2x}$

62. $\dfrac{4}{2x - 4} - \dfrac{15}{5x}$

63. $\dfrac{5}{a - 5} - \dfrac{3}{-a - 5}$

64. $\dfrac{2}{x - 2} - \dfrac{3}{x} = \dfrac{-1}{5x}$

65. $\dfrac{1}{x - 2} - \dfrac{1}{x + 2} = \dfrac{1}{15}$

66. $\dfrac{2}{x - 3} \cdot \dfrac{6x - 18}{30}$

67. $\dfrac{-3}{x + 2} \cdot \dfrac{5x + 10}{10}$

68. $\dfrac{x}{10} = \dfrac{10}{x}$

69. $\dfrac{x}{-3} = \dfrac{-27}{x}$

70. $\dfrac{x^2 - 4}{x} \div \dfrac{x^3 - 8}{x}$

71. $\dfrac{wx + wm + 3x + 3m}{w^2 - 9} \div \dfrac{x^2 - m^2}{w - 3}$

72. $\dfrac{-5}{7} = \dfrac{3}{x}$

73. $\dfrac{5}{a^2 - 25} + \dfrac{3}{a^2 - 4a - 5}$

74. $\dfrac{3}{w^2 - 1} + \dfrac{2}{2w + 2}$

75. $\dfrac{-7}{2a^2 - 18} - \dfrac{4}{a^2 + 5a + 6}$

76. $\dfrac{-5}{3a^2 - 12} - \dfrac{1}{a^2 - 3a + 2}$

77. $\dfrac{7}{a^2 - 1} + \dfrac{2}{1 - a} = \dfrac{1}{a + 1}$

78. $2 + \dfrac{4}{x - 1} = \dfrac{3x + 1}{x - 1}$

79. $\dfrac{2x}{x - 3} + \dfrac{3}{x - 2} = \dfrac{6}{(x - 2)(x - 3)}$

80. $\dfrac{a-3}{a+3} \div \dfrac{9-a^2}{3}$

81. $\dfrac{x-2}{6} \div \dfrac{2-x}{2}$

82. $\dfrac{x}{x+4} - \dfrac{2}{x+1} = \dfrac{-2}{(x+1)(x+4)}$

83. $\dfrac{x-3}{x^2+3x+2} \cdot \dfrac{x^2-4}{3x-9}$

84. $\dfrac{x^2-1}{x^2+2x+1} \cdot \dfrac{x^3+1}{2x-2}$

85. $\dfrac{a+4}{a^3-8} - \dfrac{3}{2-a}$

86. $\dfrac{x+2}{5} = \dfrac{3}{x}$

87. $\dfrac{x^3-9x}{1-x^2} \div \dfrac{x^3+6x^2+9x}{x-1}$

88. $\dfrac{x+3}{2x+3} = \dfrac{x-3}{x-1}$

89. $\dfrac{a^2+3a+3w+aw}{a^2+6a+8} \cdot \dfrac{a^2-aw-2w+2a}{a^2+3a-3w-aw}$

90. $\dfrac{3}{4-2y} + \dfrac{6}{y^2-4} + \dfrac{3}{2+y}$

91. $\dfrac{5}{x} - \dfrac{4}{x+2} = \dfrac{1}{5} + \dfrac{1}{5x}$

92. $\dfrac{1}{x} + \dfrac{1}{x-5} = \dfrac{2x+1}{x^2-25} + \dfrac{9}{x^2+5x}$

Replace each question mark by an expression that makes the equation an identity.

93. $\dfrac{6}{x} = \dfrac{?}{3x}$

94. $\dfrac{?}{a} = \dfrac{8}{4a}$

95. $\dfrac{3}{a-b} = \dfrac{?}{b-a}$

96. $\dfrac{-2}{a-x} = \dfrac{2}{?}$

97. $4 = \dfrac{?}{x}$

98. $5a = \dfrac{?}{b}$

99. $5x \div \dfrac{1}{2} = ?$

100. $3a \div \dfrac{1}{a} = ?$

101. $4a \div ? = 12a$

102. $14x \div ? = 28x^2$

103. $\dfrac{a-3}{a^2-9} = \dfrac{1}{?}$

104. $\dfrac{?}{x^2-4} = \dfrac{1}{x-2}$

105. $\dfrac{1}{2} - \dfrac{1}{5} = ?$

106. $\dfrac{1}{4} - \dfrac{1}{5} = ?$

107. $\dfrac{a}{3} + \dfrac{a}{2} = ?$

108. $\dfrac{x}{5} + \dfrac{x}{3} = ?$

Solve each problem.

109. *AIDS by gender.* The ratio of new reported male AIDS cases to female AIDS cases in 2002 was 7 to 3 (Center for Disease Control, www.cdc.gov). See the accompanying

figure. If there were 16,000 more male AIDS cases than female AIDS cases, then how many reported male AIDS cases were there in 2002?

Distribution of new AIDS cases

FIGURE FOR EXERCISE 109

110. *Aggressive portfolio.* In an aggressive portfolio the ratio of money invested in stocks to money invested in bonds should be 5 to 1. If Halle has an aggressive portfolio with $20,972 more invested in stocks than bonds, then how much does she have in her portfolio?

111. *Just passing through.* Nikita drove 310 miles on his way to Louisville in the same amount of time that he drove 360 miles after passing through Louisville. If his average speed after passing Louisville was 10 miles per hour (mph) more than his average speed on his way to Louisville, then for how many hours did he drive?

310 mi
Average speed = x mph

Louisville

360 mi
Average speed = $x + 10$ mph

FIGURE FOR EXERCISE 111

112. *Pushing a barge.* A tug can push a barge 144 miles down the Mississippi River in the same time that it takes to push the barge 84 miles in the Gulf of Mexico. If the tug's speed

FIGURE FOR EXERCISE 112

is 5 mph greater going down the river, then what is its speed in the Gulf of Mexico?

113. *Quilting bee.* Debbie can make a hand-sewn quilt in 2,000 hours, and Rosalina can make an identical quilt in 1,000 hours. If Cheryl works just as fast as Rosalina, then how long will it take all three of them working together to make one quilt?

114. *Blood out of a turnip.* A small pump can pump all of the blood out of an average turnip in 30 minutes. A larger pump can pump all of the blood from the same turnip in 20 minutes. If both pumps are hooked to the turnip, then how long would it take to get all of the blood out?

CHAPTER 6 TEST

State the domain of each rational expression.

1. $\dfrac{5}{4 - 3x}$

2. $\dfrac{2x - 1}{x^2 - 9}$

3. $\dfrac{17}{x^2 + 9}$

Reduce to lowest terms.

4. $\dfrac{12a^9b^8}{(2a^2b^3)^3}$

5. $\dfrac{y^2 - x^2}{2x^2 - 4xy + 2y^2}$

Perform the indicated operations. Write answers in lowest terms.

6. $\dfrac{5y}{12y} - \dfrac{4x}{9x}$

7. $\dfrac{3}{y} + 7y$

8. $\dfrac{4}{a - 9} - \dfrac{1}{9 - a}$

9. $\dfrac{1}{6ab^2} + \dfrac{1}{8a^2b}$

10. $\dfrac{3a^3b}{20ab} \cdot \dfrac{2a^2b}{9ab^3}$

11. $\dfrac{a - b}{7} \div \dfrac{b^2 - a^2}{21}$

12. $\dfrac{x - 3}{x - 1} \div (x^2 - 2x - 3)$

13. $\dfrac{2}{x^2 - 4} - \dfrac{6}{x^2 - 3x - 10}$

14. $\dfrac{m^3 - 1}{(m - 1)^2} \cdot \dfrac{m^2 - 1}{3m^2 + 3m + 3}$

Find the solution set to each equation.

15. $\dfrac{3}{x} = \dfrac{7}{4}$

16. $\dfrac{x}{x - 2} - \dfrac{5}{x} = \dfrac{3}{4}$

17. $\dfrac{3m}{2} = \dfrac{6}{m}$

Solve each formula for the indicated variable.

18. $W = \dfrac{a^2}{t}$ for t

19. $\dfrac{1}{a} + \dfrac{1}{b} = \dfrac{1}{2}$ for b

Simplify.

20. $\dfrac{\dfrac{1}{x} + \dfrac{1}{3x}}{\dfrac{3}{4x} - \dfrac{1}{2}}$

21. $\dfrac{m^{-2} - w^{-2}}{m^{-2}w^{-1} + m^{-1}w^{-2}}$

22. $\dfrac{\dfrac{a^2b^3}{4a}}{\dfrac{ab^3}{6a^2}}$

Find the quotient and remainder.

23. $(6x^2 + 7x - 6) \div (2x + 1)$

24. $(x - 3) \div (3 - x)$

Rewrite each expression in the form

$$\text{quotient} + \frac{\text{remainder}}{\text{divisor}}.$$

Use synthetic division.

25. $\dfrac{5x}{x + 3}$

26. $\dfrac{x^2 + 3x - 6}{x - 2}$

Solve each problem.

27. When Jane's wading pool was new, it could be filled in 6 minutes with water from the hose. Now that the pool has several leaks, it takes only 8 minutes for all of the water to leak out of a full pool. How long does it take to fill the leaky pool?

28. Milton and Bonnie are hiking the Appalachian Trail together. Milton averages 4 miles per hour (mph), and Bonnie averages 3 mph. If they start out together in the morning, but Milton gets to camp 2 hours and 30 minutes ahead of Bonnie, then how many miles did they hike that day?

29. A group of sailors plans to share equally the cost and use of a $72,000 boat. If they can get three more sailors to join their group, then the cost per person will be reduced by $2,000. How many sailors are in the original group?

Find the solution set to each equation.

1. $\dfrac{3}{x} = \dfrac{4}{5}$

2. $\dfrac{2}{x} = \dfrac{x}{8}$

3. $\dfrac{x}{3} = \dfrac{4}{5}$

4. $\dfrac{3}{x} = \dfrac{x+3}{6}$

5. $\dfrac{1}{x} = 4$

6. $\dfrac{2}{3}x = 4$

7. $2x + 3 = 4$

8. $2x + 3 = 4x$

9. $\dfrac{2a}{3} = \dfrac{6}{a}$

10. $\dfrac{12}{x} - \dfrac{14}{x+1} = \dfrac{1}{2}$

11. $|\,6x - 3\,| = 1$

12. $\dfrac{x}{2x+9} = \dfrac{3}{x}$

13. $4(6x - 3)(2x + 9) = 0$

14. $\dfrac{x-1}{x+2} - \dfrac{1}{5(x+2)} = 1$

Solve each equation for y. Assume A, B, and C are constants for which all expressions are defined.

15. $Ax + By = C$

16. $\dfrac{y-3}{x+5} = -\dfrac{1}{3}$

17. $Ay = By + C$

18. $\dfrac{A}{y} = \dfrac{y}{A}$

19. $\dfrac{A}{y} - \dfrac{1}{2} = \dfrac{B}{y}$

20. $\dfrac{A}{y} - \dfrac{1}{2} = \dfrac{B}{C}$

21. $3x - 4y = 6$

22. $y^2 - 2y - Ay + 2A = 0$

23. $A = \dfrac{1}{2}B(C + y)$

24. $y^2 + Cy = BC + By$

Simplify each expression.

25. $3x^5 \cdot 4x^8$

26. $3x^2(x^3 + 5x^6)$

27. $(5x^6)^2$

28. $(3a^3b^2)^3$

29. $\dfrac{12a^9b^4}{-3a^3b^{-2}}$

30. $\left(\dfrac{x^{-2}}{2}\right)^5$

31. $\left(\dfrac{2x^{-4}}{3y^5}\right)^{-3}$

32. $(-2a^{-1}b^3c)^{-2}$

33. $\dfrac{a^{-1} + b^3}{a^{-2} + b^{-1}}$

34. $\dfrac{(a+b)^{-1}}{(a+b)^{-2}}$

Solve.

35. ***Basic energy requirement.*** Clinical dietitians must design diets that meet patients' energy requirements and are suitable for the condition of their health (*Snapshots of Applications in Mathematics*). The basic energy requirement B (in calories) for a male is a function of three variables,

$$B = 655 + 9.56W + 1.85H - 4.68A,$$

where W is the patient's weight in kilograms, H is the height in centimeters, and A is the age in years.

a) Find the basic energy requirement for Chicago Bulls' center Luc Longley. Longley is 30 years old, has a height of 7 ft 2 in., and weight of 292 pounds (www.nba.com). (1 in. ≈ 2.54 cm, 1 kg ≈ 2.2 lb.)

b) The accompanying graph shows the basic energy requirement for a 7 ft 2 in. male at age 30 as a function of his weight. As the weight increases, does the basic energy requirement increase or decrease?

c) What is the equation for the line in the accompanying figure?

d) Write the basic energy requirement for Luc Longley as a function of his age and graph this function for $20 \le A \le 70$. Assume his size stays fixed.

FIGURE FOR EXERCISE 35

Radicals and Rational Exponents

Just how cold is it in Fargo, North Dakota, in winter? According to local meteorologists, the mercury hit a low of −33°F on January 18, 1994. But air temperature alone is not always a reliable indicator of how cold you feel. On the same date the average wind velocity was 13.8 miles per hour. This dramatically affected how cold people felt when they stepped outside. High winds along with cold temperatures make exposed skin feel colder because the wind significantly speeds up the loss of body heat. Meteorologists use the terms "wind chill factor," "wind chill index," and "wind chill temperature" to take into account both air temperature and wind velocity.

Through experimentation in Antarctica, Paul A. Siple developed a formula in the 1940s that measures the wind chill from the velocity of the wind and the air temperature. His complex formula involving the square root of the velocity of the wind is still used today to calculate wind chill temperatures. Siple's formula is unlike most scientific formulas in that it is not based on theory. Siple experimented with various formulas involving wind velocity and temperature until he found a formula that seemed to predict how cold the air felt. His formula is stated and used in Exercises 107 and 108 of Section 7.1.

Wind velocity (mph)

7.1 RADICALS

In Section 5.1 you learned the basic facts about powers. In this section you will study roots and see how powers and roots are related.

Roots

We use the idea of roots to reverse powers. Because $3^2 = 9$ and $(-3)^2 = 9$, both 3 and -3 are square roots of 9. Because $2^4 = 16$ and $(-2)^4 = 16$, both 2 and -2 are fourth roots of 16. Because $2^3 = 8$ and $(-2)^3 = -8$, there is only one real cube root of 8 and only one real cube root of -8. The cube root of 8 is 2 and the cube root of -8 is -2.

> **nth Roots**
>
> If $a = b^n$ for a positive integer n, then b is an **nth root of a.** If $a = b^2$, then b is a **square root** of a. If $a = b^3$, then b is the **cube root** of a.

If n is a positive even integer and a is positive, then there are two real nth roots of a. We call these roots **even roots.** The positive even root of a positive number is called the **principal root.** The principal square root of 9 is 3 and the principal fourth root of 16 is 2 and these roots are even roots.

If n is a positive odd integer and a is any real number, there is only one real nth root of a. We call that root an **odd root.** Because $2^5 = 32$, the fifth root of 32 is 2 and 2 is an odd root.

We use the **radical symbol** $\sqrt{}$ to signify roots.

$$\sqrt[n]{a}$$

If n is a positive *even* integer and a is positive, then $\sqrt[n]{a}$ denotes the *principal nth root of a.*
If n is a positive *odd* integer, then $\sqrt[n]{a}$ denotes the nth root of a.
If n is any positive integer, then $\sqrt[n]{0} = 0$.

We read $\sqrt[n]{a}$ as "the nth root of a." In the notation $\sqrt[n]{a}$, n is the **index of the radical** and a is the **radicand.** For square roots the index is omitted, and we simply write $\sqrt{a}$.

EXAMPLE 1

Evaluating radical expressions
Find the following roots:

a) $\sqrt{25}$ b) $\sqrt[3]{-27}$ c) $\sqrt[6]{64}$ d) $-\sqrt{4}$

Solution

a) Because $5^2 = 25$, $\sqrt{25} = 5$.
b) Because $(-3)^3 = -27$, $\sqrt[3]{-27} = -3$.
c) Because $2^6 = 64$, $\sqrt[6]{64} = 2$.
d) Because $\sqrt{4} = 2$, $-\sqrt{4} = -(\sqrt{4}) = -2$.   ■

> **CAUTION**   In radical notation, $\sqrt{4}$ represents the *principal square root of 4*, so $\sqrt{4} = 2$. Note that -2 is also a square root of 4, but $\sqrt{4} \neq -2$.

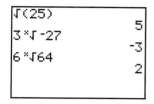

Note that even roots of negative numbers are omitted from the definition of nth roots because even powers of real numbers are never negative. So no real number can be an even root of a negative number. Expressions such as

$$\sqrt{-9}, \quad \sqrt[4]{-81}, \quad \text{and} \quad \sqrt[6]{-64}$$

are not real numbers. Square roots of negative numbers will be discussed in Section 7.6 when we discuss the imaginary numbers.

Roots and Variables

Consider the result of squaring a power of x:

$$(x^1)^2 = x^2, \quad (x^2)^2 = x^4, \quad (x^3)^2 = x^6, \quad \text{and} \quad (x^4)^2 = x^8.$$

When a power of x is squared, the exponent is multiplied by 2. So any even power of x is a perfect square.

Perfect Squares

The following expressions are perfect squares:

$$x^2, \quad x^4, \quad x^6, \quad x^8, \quad x^{10}, \quad x^{12}, \quad \ldots$$

Since taking a square root reverses the operation of squaring, the square root of an even power of x is found by dividing the exponent by 2. Provided x is nonnegative (see Caution below), we have:

$$\sqrt{x^2} = x^1 = x, \quad \sqrt{x^4} = x^2, \quad \sqrt{x^6} = x^3, \quad \text{and} \quad \sqrt{x^8} = x^4.$$

CAUTION   If x is negative, equations like $\sqrt{x^2} = x$ and $\sqrt{x^6} = x^3$ are not correct because the radical represents the nonnegative square root but x and x^3 are negative. That is why we assume x is nonnegative.

If a power of x is cubed, the exponent is multiplied by 3:

$$(x^1)^3 = x^3, \quad (x^2)^3 = x^6, \quad (x^3)^3 = x^9, \quad \text{and} \quad (x^4)^3 = x^{12}.$$

So if the exponent is a multiple of 3, we have a perfect cube.

Perfect Cubes

The following expressions are perfect cubes:

$$x^3, \quad x^6, \quad x^9, \quad x^{12}, \quad x^{15}, \quad \ldots$$

Since the cube root reverses the operation of cubing, the cube root of any of these perfect cubes is found by dividing the exponent by 3:

$$\sqrt[3]{x^3} = x^1 = x, \quad \sqrt[3]{x^6} = x^2, \quad \sqrt[3]{x^9} = x^3, \quad \text{and} \quad \sqrt[3]{x^{12}} = x^4.$$

If the exponent is divisible by 4, we have a perfect fourth power, and so on.

E X A M P L E   2

Roots of exponential expressions

Find each root. Assume that all variables represent nonnegative real numbers.

a) $\sqrt{x^{22}}$ b) $\sqrt[3]{t^{18}}$ c) $\sqrt[5]{s^{30}}$

Solution

a) $\sqrt{x^{22}} = x^{11}$ because $(x^{11})^2 = x^{22}$.

b) $\sqrt[3]{t^{18}} = t^6$ because $(t^6)^3 = t^{18}$.

c) $\sqrt[5]{s^{30}} = s^6$ because one-fifth of 30 is 6. ■

Calculator Close-Up

You can illustrate the product rule for radicals with a calculator.

```
√(2)*√(3)
          2.449489743
√(6)
          2.449489743
```

Product Rule for Radicals

Consider the expression $\sqrt{2} \cdot \sqrt{3}$. If we square this product, we get

$$(\sqrt{2} \cdot \sqrt{3})^2 = (\sqrt{2})^2(\sqrt{3})^2 \quad \text{Power of a product rule}$$
$$= 2 \cdot 3 \quad\quad (\sqrt{2})^2 = 2 \text{ and } (\sqrt{3})^2 = 3$$
$$= 6.$$

The number $\sqrt{6}$ is the unique positive number whose square is 6. Because we squared $\sqrt{2} \cdot \sqrt{3}$ and obtained 6, we must have $\sqrt{6} = \sqrt{2} \cdot \sqrt{3}$. This example illustrates the product rule for radicals.

> **Product Rule for Radicals**
>
> The *n*th root of a product is equal to the product of the *n*th roots. In symbols,
> $$\sqrt[n]{ab} = \sqrt[n]{a} \cdot \sqrt[n]{b},$$
> provided all of these roots are real numbers.

E X A M P L E   3   **Using the product rule for radicals to simplify**

Simplify each radical. Assume that all variables represent positive real numbers.

a) $\sqrt{4y}$ b) $\sqrt{3y^8}$ c) $\sqrt[3]{125w^2}$

Solution

a) $\sqrt{4y} = \sqrt{4} \cdot \sqrt{y}$ Product rule for radicals

       $= 2\sqrt{y}$ Simplify.

b) $\sqrt{3y^8} = \sqrt{3} \cdot \sqrt{y^8}$ Product rule for radicals

       $= \sqrt{3} \cdot y^4$ Simplify.

       $= y^4\sqrt{3}$ A radical is usually written last in a product.

c) $\sqrt[3]{125w^2} = \sqrt[3]{125} \cdot \sqrt[3]{w^2} = 5\sqrt[3]{w^2}$ ■

In Example 4 we simplify by factoring the radicand before applying the product rule.

E X A M P L E   4   **Using the product rule to simplify**

Simplify each radical.

a) $\sqrt{12}$ b) $\sqrt[3]{54}$ c) $\sqrt[4]{80}$ d) $\sqrt[5]{64}$

Solution

a) Since $12 = 4 \cdot 3$ and 4 is a perfect square, we can factor and then apply the product rule:

$$\sqrt{12} = \sqrt{4 \cdot 3} = \sqrt{4} \cdot \sqrt{3} = 2\sqrt{3}$$

b) Since $54 = 27 \cdot 2$ and 27 is a perfect cube, we can factor and then apply the product rule:

$$\sqrt[3]{54} = \sqrt[3]{27 \cdot 2} = \sqrt[3]{27} \cdot \sqrt[3]{2} = 3\sqrt[3]{2}$$

c) Since $80 = 16 \cdot 5$ and 16 is a perfect fourth power, we can factor and then apply the product rule:

$$\sqrt[4]{80} = \sqrt[4]{16 \cdot 5} = \sqrt[4]{16} \cdot \sqrt[4]{5} = 2\sqrt[4]{5}$$

d) $\sqrt[5]{64} = \sqrt[5]{32 \cdot 2} = \sqrt[5]{32} \cdot \sqrt[5]{2} = 2\sqrt[5]{32}$ ∎

In general, we simplify radical expressions of index n by using the product rule to remove any perfect nth powers from the radicand. In Example 5 we use the product rule to simplify more radicals involving variables. Remember x^n is a perfect square if n is divisible by 2, a perfect cube if n is divisible by 3, and so on.

E X A M P L E   5

Using the product rule to simplify

Simplify each radical. Assume that all variables represent positive real numbers.

a) $\sqrt{20x^3}$ **b)** $\sqrt[3]{40a^8}$

c) $\sqrt[4]{48a^4b^{11}}$ **d)** $\sqrt[5]{w^7}$

Solution

a) Factor $20x^3$ so that all possible perfect squares are inside one radical:

$$\sqrt{20x^3} = \sqrt{4x^2 \cdot 5x} \qquad \text{Factor out perfect squares.}$$
$$= \sqrt{4x^2} \cdot \sqrt{5x} \qquad \text{Product rule}$$
$$= 2x\sqrt{5x} \qquad \text{Simplify.}$$

b) Factor $40a^8$ so that all possible perfect cubes are inside one radical:

$$\sqrt[3]{40a^8} = \sqrt[3]{8a^6 \cdot 5a^2} \qquad \text{Factor out perfect cubes.}$$
$$= \sqrt[3]{8a^6} \cdot \sqrt[3]{5a^2} \qquad \text{Product rule}$$
$$= 3a^2\sqrt[3]{5a^2} \qquad \text{Simplify.}$$

c) Factor $48a^4b^{11}$ so that all possible perfect fourth powers are inside one radical:

$$\sqrt[4]{48a^4b^{11}} = \sqrt[4]{16a^4b^8 \cdot 3b^3} \qquad \text{Factor out perfect fourth powers.}$$
$$= \sqrt[4]{16a^4b^8} \cdot \sqrt[4]{3b^3} \qquad \text{Product rule}$$
$$= 2ab^2\sqrt[4]{3b^3} \qquad \text{Simplify.}$$

Calculator Close-Up

You can illustrate the quotient rule for radicals with a calculator.

d) $\sqrt[5]{w^7} = \sqrt[5]{w^5 \cdot w^2} = \sqrt[5]{w^5} \cdot \sqrt[5]{w^2} = w\sqrt[5]{w^2}$ ∎

Quotient Rule for Radicals

Because $\sqrt{2} \cdot \sqrt{3} = \sqrt{6}$, we have $\sqrt{6} \div \sqrt{3} = \sqrt{2}$, or

$$\sqrt{2} = \sqrt{\frac{6}{3}} = \frac{\sqrt{6}}{\sqrt{3}}.$$

This example illustrates the quotient rule for radicals.

Quotient Rule for Radicals

The nth root of a quotient is equal to the quotient of the nth roots. In symbols,

$$\sqrt[n]{\frac{a}{b}} = \frac{\sqrt[n]{a}}{\sqrt[n]{b}},$$

provided that all of these roots are real numbers and $b \neq 0$.

E X A M P L E 6   **Using the quotient rule for radicals**

Simplify each radical. Assume that all variables represent positive real numbers.

a) $\sqrt{\dfrac{25}{9}}$ b) $\dfrac{\sqrt{15}}{\sqrt{3}}$ c) $\sqrt[3]{\dfrac{b}{125}}$ d) $\sqrt[3]{\dfrac{x^{21}}{y^6}}$

Solution

a) $\sqrt{\dfrac{25}{9}} = \dfrac{\sqrt{25}}{\sqrt{9}}$ Quotient rule for radicals

$\qquad = \dfrac{5}{3}$ Simplify.

b) $\dfrac{\sqrt{15}}{\sqrt{3}} = \sqrt{\dfrac{15}{3}}$ Quotient rule for radicals

$\qquad = \sqrt{5}$ Simplify.

c) $\sqrt[3]{\dfrac{b}{125}} = \dfrac{\sqrt[3]{b}}{\sqrt[3]{125}} = \dfrac{\sqrt[3]{b}}{5}$

d) $\sqrt[3]{\dfrac{x^{21}}{y^6}} = \dfrac{\sqrt[3]{x^{21}}}{\sqrt[3]{y^6}} = \dfrac{x^7}{y^2}$ ■

In Example 7 we use the product and quotient rule to simplify radical expressions.

E X A M P L E 7   **Using the product and quotient rules for radicals**

Simplify each radical. Assume that all variables represent positive real numbers.

a) $\sqrt{\dfrac{50}{49}}$ b) $\sqrt[3]{\dfrac{x^5}{8}}$ c) $\sqrt[4]{\dfrac{a^5}{b^8}}$

Solution

a) $\sqrt{\dfrac{50}{49}} = \dfrac{\sqrt{25} \cdot \sqrt{2}}{\sqrt{49}}$ Product and quotient rules for radicals

$\qquad = \dfrac{5\sqrt{2}}{7}$ Simplify.

b) $\sqrt[3]{\dfrac{x^5}{8}} = \dfrac{\sqrt[3]{x^3} \cdot \sqrt[3]{x^2}}{\sqrt[3]{8}} = \dfrac{x\sqrt[3]{x^2}}{2}$

c) $\sqrt[4]{\dfrac{a^5}{b^8}} = \dfrac{\sqrt[4]{a^4} \cdot \sqrt[4]{a}}{\sqrt[4]{b^8}} = \dfrac{a\sqrt[4]{a}}{b^2}$ ■

Radical Functions

Functions such as $f(x) = \sqrt{x - 5}$ and $g(x) = \sqrt[3]{x}$ that are defined by radicals are called **radical functions.** The radicand in an odd root can be any real number but in an even root the radicand must be nonnegative. So the domain for g is all real numbers, $(-\infty, \infty)$. For $f(x) = \sqrt{x - 5}$ we must have $x - 5 \geq 0$, or $x \geq 5$. So the domain of f is $[5, \infty)$.

E X A M P L E   8   **Finding the domain of a square root function**

For each function find $f(2)$ and the domain of the function.

a) $f(x) = \sqrt{2x + 12}$ **b)** $f(x) = \sqrt{x - 7}$

Solution

a) Let $x = 2$ in $f(x) = \sqrt{2x + 12}$ to get $f(x) = \sqrt{2(2) + 12} = 4$. Find the domain using the fact that $2x + 12$ must be nonnegative:

$$2x + 12 \geq 0$$
$$2x \geq -12$$
$$x \geq -6$$

So $f(2) = 4$ and the domain is the interval $[-6, \infty)$.

b) Let $x = 2$ to get $f(2) = \sqrt{2 - 7} = \sqrt{-5}$, which is not a real number. So 2 is not in the domain of the function and $f(2)$ does not exist. We must have $x - 7 \geq 0$, or $x \geq 7$. So the domain is the interval $[7, \infty)$. ■

M A T H   A T   W O R K

Ernie Godshalk, avid sailor and owner of the sloop *Golden Eye,* has competed in races all over the world. He has learned that success in a race depends on the winds, a good crew, lots of skill, and knowing what makes his boat go fast.

Because of its shape and hull design, the maximum speed (in knots) of a sailboat can be calculated by finding the value 1.3 times the square root of her waterline (in feet). Thus Godshalk knows the maximum possible speed of the *Golden Eye.* But decisions made while she is

Y A C H T S M A N

under sail make the difference between attaining her maximum speed and only approaching it. For example, Godshalk knows that the pressure on the sails is what makes the boat move at a certain speed. It is especially important to sail where the wind is the strongest. This means that choosing the correct tack, as well as "going where the wind is" can make the difference between coming in first and just finishing the race. In Exercise 111 of this section you will calculate the maximum speed of the *Golden Eye.*

WARM-UPS

True or false? Explain your answer.

1. $\sqrt{2} \cdot \sqrt{2} = 2$
2. $\sqrt[3]{2} \cdot \sqrt[3]{2} = 2$
3. $\sqrt[3]{-27} = -3$
4. $\sqrt{-25} = -5$
5. $\sqrt[4]{16} = 2$
6. $\sqrt{9} = \pm 3$
7. $\sqrt{2^9} = 2^3$
8. $\dfrac{\sqrt{10}}{2} = \sqrt{5}$
9. $\sqrt{\dfrac{1}{4}} = \dfrac{1}{2}$
10. $\dfrac{\sqrt{6}}{\sqrt{3}} = \sqrt{2}$

7.1 EXERCISES

Reading and Writing *After reading this section, write out the answers to these questions. Use complete sentences.*

1. How do you know if b is an nth root of a?

2. What is a principal root?

3. What is the difference between an even root and an odd root?

4. What symbol is used to indicate an nth root?

5. What is the product rule for radicals?

6. What is the quotient rule for radicals?

For all of the exercises in this section assume that all variables represent positive real numbers.

Find each root. See Example 1.

7. $\sqrt{36}$
8. $\sqrt{49}$
9. $\sqrt{100}$
10. $\sqrt{81}$
11. $-\sqrt{9}$
12. $-\sqrt{25}$
13. $\sqrt[3]{8}$
14. $\sqrt[3]{27}$
15. $\sqrt[3]{-8}$
16. $\sqrt[3]{-1}$
17. $\sqrt[5]{32}$
18. $\sqrt[4]{81}$
19. $\sqrt[3]{1000}$
20. $\sqrt[4]{16}$
21. $\sqrt[4]{-16}$
22. $\sqrt{-1}$
23. $\sqrt[5]{-32}$
24. $\sqrt[3]{-125}$

Find each root. See Example 2.

25. $\sqrt{m^2}$
26. $\sqrt{m^6}$
27. $\sqrt{x^{16}}$
28. $\sqrt{y^{36}}$
29. $\sqrt[5]{y^{15}}$
30. $\sqrt[4]{m^8}$
31. $\sqrt[3]{y^{15}}$
32. $\sqrt{m^8}$
33. $\sqrt[3]{m^3}$
34. $\sqrt[4]{x^4}$
35. $\sqrt[4]{w^{12}}$
36. $\sqrt[5]{a^{30}}$

Use the product rule for radicals to simplify each expression. See Example 3.

37. $\sqrt{9y}$
38. $\sqrt{16n}$
39. $\sqrt{4a^2}$
40. $\sqrt{36n^2}$
41. $\sqrt{x^4 y^2}$
42. $\sqrt{w^6 t^2}$
43. $\sqrt{5m^{12}}$
44. $\sqrt{7z^{16}}$
45. $\sqrt[3]{8y}$
46. $\sqrt[3]{27z^2}$
47. $\sqrt[3]{3a^6}$
48. $\sqrt[3]{5b^9}$

Use the product rule to simplify. See Example 4.

49. $\sqrt{20}$
50. $\sqrt{18}$
51. $\sqrt{50}$
52. $\sqrt{45}$
53. $\sqrt{72}$
54. $\sqrt{98}$
55. $\sqrt[3]{40}$
56. $\sqrt[3]{24}$
57. $\sqrt[3]{81}$
58. $\sqrt[3]{250}$
59. $\sqrt[4]{48}$
60. $\sqrt[4]{32}$
61. $\sqrt[5]{96}$
62. $\sqrt[5]{2430}$

Use the product rule to simplify. See Example 5.

63. $\sqrt{a^3}$
64. $\sqrt{b^5}$
65. $\sqrt{18a^6}$
66. $\sqrt{12x^8}$
67. $\sqrt{20x^5 y}$
68. $\sqrt{8w^3 y^3}$
69. $\sqrt[3]{24m^4}$
70. $\sqrt[3]{54ab^5}$
71. $\sqrt[4]{32a^5}$
72. $\sqrt[4]{162b^4}$

73. $\sqrt[5]{64x^6}$

74. $\sqrt[5]{96a^8}$

75. $\sqrt{48x^3y^8z^7}$

76. $\sqrt[3]{48x^3y^8z^7}$

Simplify each radical. See Example 6.

77. $\sqrt{\dfrac{t}{4}}$

78. $\sqrt{\dfrac{w}{36}}$

79. $\sqrt{\dfrac{625}{16}}$

80. $\sqrt{\dfrac{9}{144}}$

81. $\dfrac{\sqrt{30}}{\sqrt{3}}$

82. $\dfrac{\sqrt{50}}{\sqrt{2}}$

83. $\sqrt[3]{\dfrac{t}{8}}$

84. $\sqrt[3]{\dfrac{a}{27}}$

85. $\sqrt[3]{\dfrac{-8x^6}{y^3}}$

86. $\sqrt[3]{\dfrac{-27y^{36}}{1000}}$

87. $\sqrt{\dfrac{4a^6}{9}}$

88. $\sqrt{\dfrac{9a^2}{49b^4}}$

Use the product and quotient rules to simplify. See Example 7.

89. $\sqrt{\dfrac{12}{25}}$

90. $\sqrt{\dfrac{8}{81}}$

91. $\sqrt{\dfrac{27}{16}}$

92. $\sqrt{\dfrac{98}{9}}$

93. $\sqrt[3]{\dfrac{a^4}{125}}$

94. $\sqrt[3]{\dfrac{b^7}{1000}}$

95. $\sqrt[3]{\dfrac{81}{8b^3}}$

96. $\sqrt[3]{\dfrac{a^3b^4}{125}}$

97. $\sqrt[4]{\dfrac{x^7}{y^8}}$

98. $\sqrt[4]{\dfrac{x^5y^4}{z^{12}}}$

99. $\sqrt[4]{\dfrac{a^5}{16b^{12}}}$

100. $\sqrt[4]{\dfrac{a^7b}{81c^{16}}}$

For each function find f(3) and the domain of the function.

101. $f(x) = \sqrt{x-2}$

102. $f(x) = \sqrt{x+6}$

103. $f(x) = \sqrt{2x+8}$

104. $f(x) = \sqrt{3x-2}$

105. $f(x) = \sqrt{3-3x}$

106. $f(x) = \sqrt{4-2x}$

In Exercises 107–114, solve each problem.

107. *Factoring in the wind.* Through experimentation in Antarctica, Paul Siple developed the formula

$$W = 91.4 - \dfrac{(10.5 + 6.7\sqrt{v} - 0.45v)(457 - 5t)}{110}$$

to calculate the wind chill temperature W (in degrees Fahrenheit) from the wind velocity v [in miles per hour (mph)] and the air temperature t (in degrees Fahrenheit). Find the wind chill temperature when the air temperature is 25°F and the wind velocity is 20 mph. Use the accompanying graph to estimate the wind chill temperature when the air temperature is 25°F and the wind velocity is 30 mph.

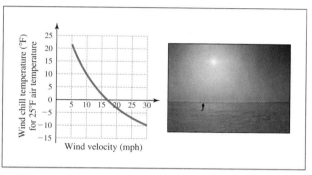

FIGURE FOR EXERCISE 107

108. *Comparing wind chills.* Use the formula from Exercise 107 to determine who will feel colder: a person in Minneapolis at 10°F with a 15-mph wind or a person in Chicago at 20°F with a 25-mph wind.

109. *Diving time.* The time t (in seconds) that it takes for a cliff diver to reach the water is a function of the height h (in feet) from which he dives:

$$t = \sqrt{\dfrac{h}{16}}$$

a) Use the properties of radicals to simplify this formula.

b) Find the exact time (according to the formula) that it takes for a diver to hit the water when diving from a height of 40 feet.

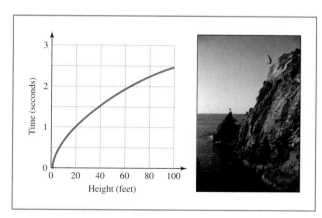

FIGURE FOR EXERCISE 109

c) Use the graph on page 401 to estimate the height if a diver takes 2.5 seconds to reach the water?

110. *Sky diving.* The formula in Exercise 109 accounts for the effect of gravity only on a falling object. According to that formula, how long would it take a sky diver to reach the earth when jumping from 17,000 feet? (A sky diver can actually get about twice as much falling time by spreading out and using the air to slow the fall.)

 111. *Maximum sailing speed.* To find the maximum possible speed in knots (nautical miles per hour) for a sailboat, sailors use the function $M = 1.3\sqrt{w}$, where w is the length of the waterline in feet. If the waterline for the sloop *Golden Eye* is 20 feet, then what is the maximum speed of the *Golden Eye*?

112. *America's Cup.* Since 1988 basic yacht dimensions for the America's Cup competition have satisfied the inequality

$$L + 1.25\sqrt{S} - 9.8\sqrt[3]{D} \le 16.296,$$

where L is the boat's length in meters (m), S is the sail area in square meters, and D is the displacement in cubic meters (www.sailing.com). A team of naval architects is planning to build a boat with a displacement of 21.44 cubic meters (m³), a sail area of 320.13 square meters (m²), and a length of 21.22 m. Does this boat satisfy the inequality? If the length and displacement of this boat cannot be changed, then how many square meters of sail area must be removed so that the boat satisfies the inequality?

113. *Landing a Piper Cheyenne.* Aircraft design engineers determine the proper landing speed V [in feet per second (ft/sec)] for an airplane from the formula

$$V = \sqrt{\frac{841L}{CS}},$$

where L is the gross weight of the aircraft in pounds (lb), C is the coefficient of lift, and S is the wing

surface area in square feet. According to Piper Aircraft of Vero Beach, Florida, the Piper Cheyenne has a gross weight of 8700 lb, a coefficient of lift of 2.81, and a wing surface area of 200 ft². Find the proper landing speed for this plane. What is the landing speed in miles per hour (mph)?

 114. *Landing speed and weight.* Because the gross weight of the Piper Cheyenne depends on how much fuel and cargo are on board, the proper landing speed (from Exercise 113) is not always the same. The function $V = \sqrt{1.496L}$ gives the landing speed as a function of the gross weight only.
a) Find the landing speed if the gross weight is 7000 lb.
b) What gross weight corresponds to a landing speed of 115 ft/sec?

GETTING MORE INVOLVED

 115. *Cooperative learning.* Work in a group to determine whether each equation is an identity. Explain your answers.
a) $\sqrt{x^2} = |x|$ b) $\sqrt[3]{x^3} = |x|$
c) $\sqrt{x^4} = x^2$ d) $\sqrt[4]{x^4} = |x|$

For which values of n is $\sqrt[n]{x^n} = x$ an identity?

116. *Cooperative learning.* Work in a group to determine whether each inequality is correct.
a) $\sqrt{0.9} > 0.9$ b) $\sqrt{1.01} > 1.01$
c) $\sqrt[3]{0.99} > 0.99$ d) $\sqrt[3]{1.001} > 1.001$

For which values of x and n is $\sqrt[n]{x} > x$?

117. *Discussion.* If your test scores are 80 and 100, then the arithmetic mean of your scores is 90. The geometric mean of the scores is a number h such that

$$\frac{80}{h} = \frac{h}{100}.$$

Are you better off with the arithmetic mean or the geometric mean?

In This Section

- Rational Exponents
- Using the Rules of Exponents
- Simplifying Expressions Involving Variables

7.2 RATIONAL EXPONENTS

You have learned how to use exponents to express powers of numbers and radicals to express roots. In this section you will see that roots can be expressed with exponents also. The advantage of using exponents to express roots is that the rules of exponents can be applied to the expressions.

Rational Exponents

The nth root of a number can be expressed by using radical notation or the exponent $1/n$. For example, $8^{1/3}$ and $\sqrt[3]{8}$ both represent the cube root of 8, and we have

$$8^{1/3} = \sqrt[3]{8} = 2.$$

Definition of $a^{1/n}$

If n is any positive integer, then

$$a^{1/n} = \sqrt[n]{a},$$

provided that $\sqrt[n]{a}$ is a real number.

Later in this section we will see that using exponent $1/n$ for nth root is compatible with the rules for integral exponents that we already know.

E X A M P L E   1

Radicals or exponents

Write each radical expression using exponent notation and each exponential expression using radical notation.

a) $\sqrt[3]{35}$

b) $\sqrt[4]{xy}$

c) $5^{1/2}$

d) $a^{1/5}$

Solution

a) $\sqrt[3]{35} = 35^{1/3}$

b) $\sqrt[4]{xy} = (xy)^{1/4}$

c) $5^{1/2} = \sqrt{5}$

d) $a^{1/5} = \sqrt[5]{a}$ ■

In the next example we evaluate some exponential expressions.

E X A M P L E   2

Finding roots

Evaluate each expression.

a) $4^{1/2}$

b) $(-8)^{1/3}$

c) $81^{1/4}$

d) $(-9)^{1/2}$

e) $-9^{1/2}$

Solution

a) $4^{1/2} = \sqrt{4} = 2$

b) $(-8)^{1/3} = \sqrt[3]{-8} = -2$

c) $81^{1/4} = \sqrt[4]{81} = 3$

d) Because $(-9)^{1/2}$ or $\sqrt{-9}$ is an even root of a negative number, it is not a real number.

e) Because the exponent in $-a^n$ is applied only to the base a (Section 1.4), we have $-9^{1/2} = -\sqrt{9} = -3$. ■

We now extend the definition of exponent $1/n$ to include any rational number as an exponent. The numerator of the rational number indicates the power, and the denominator indicates the root. For example, the expression

$$8^{2/3} \quad \begin{array}{l} \longleftarrow \text{Power} \\ \longleftarrow \text{Root} \end{array}$$

represents the square of the cube root of 8. So we have

$$8^{2/3} = (8^{1/3})^2 = (2)^2 = 4.$$

Helpful Hint

Note that in $a^{m/n}$ we do not require m/n to be reduced. As long as the nth root of a is real, then the value of $a^{m/n}$ is the same whether or not m/n is in lowest terms.

Definition of $a^{m/n}$

If m and n are positive integers and $a^{1/n}$ is a real number, then

$$a^{m/n} = (a^{1/n})^m.$$

Using radical notation, $a^{m/n} = (\sqrt[n]{a})^m$.

By definition $a^{m/n}$ is the mth power of the nth root of a. However, $a^{m/n}$ is also equal to the nth root of the mth power of a. For example,

$$8^{2/3} = (8^2)^{1/3} = 64^{1/3} = 4.$$

Evaluating $a^{m/n}$ in Either Order

If m and n are positive integers and $a^{1/n}$ is a real number, then

$$a^{m/n} = (a^{1/n})^m = (a^m)^{1/n}.$$

Using radical notation, $a^{m/n} = (\sqrt[n]{a})^m = \sqrt[n]{a^m}$.

A negative rational exponent indicates a reciprocal:

Definition of $a^{-m/n}$

If m and n are positive integers, $a \neq 0$, and $a^{1/n}$ is a real number, then

$$a^{-m/n} = \frac{1}{a^{m/n}}.$$

Using radical notation, $a^{-m/n} = \dfrac{1}{(\sqrt[n]{a})^m}$.

E X A M P L E   3   **Radicals or exponents**

Write each radical expression using exponent notation and each exponential expression using radical notation.

a) $\sqrt[3]{x^2}$ b) $\dfrac{1}{\sqrt[4]{m^3}}$ c) $5^{2/3}$ d) $a^{-2/5}$

Solution

a) $\sqrt[3]{x^2} = x^{2/3}$ b) $\dfrac{1}{\sqrt[4]{m^3}} = \dfrac{1}{m^{3/4}} = m^{-3/4}$

c) $5^{2/3} = \sqrt[3]{5^2}$ d) $a^{-2/5} = \dfrac{1}{\sqrt[5]{a^2}}$ ■

To evaluate an expression with a negative rational exponent, remember that the denominator indicates root, the numerator indicates power, and the negative sign indicates reciprocal:

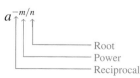

The root, power, and reciprocal can be evaluated in any order. However, to evaluate $a^{-m/n}$ mentally it is usually simplest to use the following strategy.

> **Strategy for Evaluating $a^{-m/n}$ Mentally**
>
> 1. Find the nth root of a.
> 2. Raise your result to the mth power.
> 3. Find the reciprocal.

For example, to evaluate $8^{-2/3}$ mentally, we find the cube root of 8 (which is 2), square 2 to get 4, then find the reciprocal of 4 to get $\frac{1}{4}$. In print $8^{-2/3}$ could be written for evaluation as $((8^{1/3})^2)^{-1}$ or $\frac{1}{(8^{1/3})^2}$.

E X A M P L E   4

Rational exponents

Evaluate each expression.

a) $27^{2/3}$ b) $4^{-3/2}$

c) $81^{-3/4}$ d) $(-8)^{-5/3}$

Calculator Close-Up

A negative fractional exponent indicates a reciprocal, a root, and a power. To find $4^{-3/2}$ you can find the reciprocal first, the square root first, or the third power first as shown here.

```
(1/4)^(3/2)
            .125
(√(4))^-3
            .125
(4³)^(-1/2)
            .125
```

Solution

a) Because the exponent is $2/3$, we find the cube root of 27 and then square it:
$$27^{2/3} = (27^{1/3})^2 = 3^2 = 9$$

b) Because the exponent is $-3/2$, we find the square root of 4, cube it, and find the reciprocal:
$$4^{-3/2} = \frac{1}{(4^{1/2})^3} = \frac{1}{2^3} = \frac{1}{8}$$

c) Because the exponent is $-3/4$, we find the fourth root of 81, cube it, and find the reciprocal:
$$81^{-3/4} = \frac{1}{(81^{1/4})^3} = \frac{1}{3^3} = \frac{1}{27} \quad \text{Definition of negative exponent}$$

d) $(-8)^{-5/3} = \frac{1}{((-8)^{1/3})^5} = \frac{1}{(-2)^5} = \frac{1}{-32} = -\frac{1}{32}$

CAUTION An expression with a negative base and a negative exponent can have a positive or a negative value. For example,
$$(-8)^{-5/3} = -\frac{1}{32} \quad \text{and} \quad (-8)^{-2/3} = \frac{1}{4}.$$

Using the Rules of Exponents

All of the rules for exponents hold for rational exponents as well as integral exponents. Of course, we cannot apply the rules of exponents to expressions that are not real numbers.

Rules for Rational Exponents

The following rules hold for any nonzero real numbers a and b and rational numbers r and s for which the expressions represent real numbers.

1. $a^r a^s = a^{r+s}$ Product rule

2. $\dfrac{a^r}{a^s} = a^{r-s}$ Quotient rule

3. $(a^r)^s = a^{rs}$ Power of a power rule

4. $(ab)^r = a^r b^r$ Power of a product rule

5. $\left(\dfrac{a}{b}\right)^r = \dfrac{a^r}{b^r}$ Power of a quotient rule

We can use the product rule to add rational exponents. For example,

$$16^{1/4} \cdot 16^{1/4} = 16^{2/4}.$$

The fourth root of 16 is 2, and 2 squared is 4. So $16^{2/4} = 4$. Because we also have $16^{1/2} = 4$, we see that a rational exponent can be reduced to its lowest terms. If an exponent can be reduced, it is usually simpler to reduce the exponent before we evaluate the expression. We can simplify $16^{1/4} \cdot 16^{1/4}$ as follows:

$$16^{1/4} \cdot 16^{1/4} = 16^{2/4} = 16^{1/2} = 4$$

E X A M P L E   5

Using the product and quotient rules with rational exponents

Simplify each expression.

a) $27^{1/6} \cdot 27^{1/2}$ **b)** $\dfrac{5^{3/4}}{5^{1/4}}$

Solution

a) $27^{1/6} \cdot 27^{1/2} = 27^{1/6+1/2}$ Product rule for exponents

$$= 27^{2/3}$$

$$= 9$$

b) $\dfrac{5^{3/4}}{5^{1/4}} = 5^{3/4-1/4} = 5^{2/4} = 5^{1/2} = \sqrt{5}$ We used the quotient rule to subtract the exponents.

E X A M P L E   6

Using the power rules with rational exponents

Simplify each expression.

a) $3^{1/2} \cdot 12^{1/2}$ **b)** $(3^{10})^{1/2}$ **c)** $\left(\dfrac{2^6}{3^9}\right)^{-1/3}$

Solution

a) Because the bases 3 and 12 are different, we cannot use the product rule to add the exponents. Instead, we use the power of a product rule to place the 1/2 power outside the parentheses:

$$3^{1/2} \cdot 12^{1/2} = (3 \cdot 12)^{1/2} = 36^{1/2} = 6$$

b) Use the power of a power rule to multiply the exponents:

$$(3^{10})^{1/2} = 3^5$$

c) $\left(\dfrac{2^6}{3^9}\right)^{-1/3} = \dfrac{(2^6)^{-1/3}}{(3^9)^{-1/3}}$ Power of a quotient rule

$$= \dfrac{2^{-2}}{3^{-3}}$$ Power of a power rule

$$= \dfrac{3^3}{2^2}$$ Definition of negative exponent

$$= \dfrac{27}{4}$$ ∎

Helpful Hint

We usually think of squaring and taking a square root as inverse operations, which they are as long as we stick to positive numbers. We can square 3 to get 9, and then find the square root of 9 to get 3—what we started with. We don't get back to where we began if we start with −3.

Simplifying Expressions Involving Variables

When simplifying expressions involving rational exponents and variables, we must be careful to write equivalent expressions. For example, in the equation

$$(x^2)^{1/2} = x$$

it looks as if we are correctly applying the power of a power rule. However, this statement is false if x is negative because the $1/2$ power on the left-hand side indicates the positive square root of x^2. For example, if $x = -3$, we get

$$[(-3)^2]^{1/2} = 9^{1/2} = 3,$$

which is not equal to -3. To write a simpler equivalent expression for $(x^2)^{1/2}$, we use absolute value as follows.

> **Square Root of x^2**
>
> $$(x^2)^{1/2} = |x| \text{ for any real number } x.$$

Note that $(x^2)^{1/2} = |x|$ is also written as $\sqrt{x^2} = |x|$. Both of these equations are identities.

It is also necessary to use absolute value when writing identities for other even roots of expressions involving variables.

EXAMPLE 7

Using absolute value symbols with roots

Simplify each expression. Assume the variables represent any real numbers and use absolute value symbols as necessary.

a) $(x^8 y^4)^{1/4}$
b) $\left(\dfrac{x^9}{8}\right)^{1/3}$

Solution

a) Apply the power of a product rule to get the equation $(x^8 y^4)^{1/4} = x^2 y$. The left-hand side is nonnegative for any choices of x and y, but the right-hand side is negative when y is negative. So for any real values of x and y we have

$$(x^8 y^4)^{1/4} = x^2 \,|y|.$$

b) Using the power of a quotient rule, we get

$$\left(\frac{x^9}{8}\right)^{1/3} = \frac{x^3}{2}.$$

This equation is valid for every real number x, so no absolute value signs are used. ∎

Because there are no real even roots of negative numbers, the expressions

$$a^{1/2}, \quad x^{-3/4}, \quad \text{and} \quad y^{1/6}$$

are not real numbers if the variables have negative values. To simplify matters, we sometimes assume the variables represent only positive numbers when we are working with expressions involving variables with rational exponents. That way we do not have to be concerned with undefined expressions and absolute value.

E X A M P L E   8

Expressions involving variables with rational exponents

Use the rules of exponents to simplify the following. Write your answers with positive exponents. Assume all variables represent *positive* real numbers.

a) $x^{2/3}x^{4/3}$

b) $\dfrac{a^{1/2}}{a^{1/4}}$

c) $(x^{1/2}y^{-3})^{1/2}$

d) $\left(\dfrac{x^2}{y^{1/3}}\right)^{-1/2}$

Solution

a) $x^{2/3}x^{4/3} = x^{6/3}$ Use the product rule to add the exponents.

         $= x^2$ Reduce the exponent.

b) $\dfrac{a^{1/2}}{a^{1/4}} = a^{1/2-1/4}$ Use the quotient rule to subtract the exponents.

        $= a^{1/4}$ Simplify.

c) $(x^{1/2}y^{-3})^{1/2} = (x^{1/2})^{1/2}(y^{-3})^{1/2}$ Power of a product rule

         $= x^{1/4}y^{-3/2}$ Power of a power rule

         $= \dfrac{x^{1/4}}{y^{3/2}}$ Definition of negative exponent

d) Because this expression is a negative power of a quotient, we can first find the reciprocal of the quotient, then apply the power of a power rule:

$$\left(\frac{x^2}{y^{1/3}}\right)^{-1/2} = \left(\frac{y^{1/3}}{x^2}\right)^{1/2} = \frac{y^{1/6}}{x} \quad \frac{1}{3} \cdot \frac{1}{2} = \frac{1}{6}$$ ∎

WARM-UPS

True or false? Explain your answer.

1. $9^{1/3} = \sqrt[3]{9}$

2. $8^{5/3} = \sqrt[5]{8^3}$

3. $(-16)^{1/2} = -16^{1/2}$

4. $9^{-3/2} = \dfrac{1}{27}$

5. $6^{-1/2} = \dfrac{\sqrt{6}}{6}$

6. $\dfrac{2}{2^{1/2}} = 2^{1/2}$

7. $2^{1/2} \cdot 2^{1/2} = 4^{1/2}$

8. $16^{-1/4} = -2$

9. $6^{1/6} \cdot 6^{1/6} = 6^{1/3}$

10. $(2^8)^{3/4} = 2^6$

7.2 EXERCISES

Reading and Writing *After reading this section, write out the answers to these questions. Use complete sentences.*

1. How do we indicate an *n*th root using exponents?

2. How do we indicate the *m*th power of the *n*th root using exponents?

3. What is the meaning of a negative rational exponent?

4. Which rules of exponents hold for rational exponents?

5. In what order must you perform the operations indicated by a negative rational exponent?

6. When is $a^{-m/n}$ a real number?

Write each radical expression using exponent notation. See Example 1.

7. $\sqrt[4]{7}$

8. $\sqrt[5]{cbs}$

9. $\sqrt{5x}$

10. $\sqrt{3y}$

Write each exponential expression using radical notation. See Example 1.

11. $9^{1/5}$

12. $3^{1/2}$

13. $a^{1/2}$

14. $(-b)^{1/5}$

Evaluate each expression. See Example 2.

15. $25^{1/2}$

16. $16^{1/2}$

17. $(-125)^{1/3}$

18. $(-32)^{1/5}$

19. $16^{1/4}$

20. $8^{1/3}$

21. $(-4)^{1/2}$

22. $(-16)^{1/4}$

Write each radical expression using exponent notation and each exponential expression using radical notation. See Example 3.

23. $\sqrt[3]{w^7}$

24. $\sqrt{a^5}$

25. $\dfrac{1}{\sqrt[3]{2^{10}}}$

26. $\sqrt[3]{\dfrac{1}{a^2}}$

27. $w^{-3/4}$

28. $6^{-5/3}$

29. $(ab)^{3/2}$

30. $(3m)^{-1/5}$

Evaluate each expression. See Example 4.

31. $125^{2/3}$

32. $1000^{2/3}$

33. $25^{3/2}$

34. $16^{3/2}$

35. $27^{-4/3}$

36. $16^{-3/4}$

37. $16^{-3/2}$

38. $25^{-3/2}$

39. $(-27)^{-1/3}$

40. $(-8)^{-4/3}$

41. $(-16)^{-1/4}$

42. $(-100)^{-3/2}$

Use the rules of exponents to simplify each expression. See Examples 5 and 6.

43. $3^{1/3}3^{1/4}$

44. $2^{1/2}\,2^{1/3}$

45. $3^{1/3}3^{-1/3}$

46. $5^{1/4}5^{-1/4}$

47. $\dfrac{8^{1/3}}{8^{2/3}}$

48. $\dfrac{27^{-2/3}}{27^{-1/3}}$

49. $4^{3/4} \div 4^{1/4}$

50. $9^{1/4} \div 9^{3/4}$

51. $18^{1/2}2^{1/2}$

52. $8^{1/2}2^{1/2}$

53. $(2^6)^{1/3}$

54. $(3^{10})^{1/5}$

55. $(3^8)^{1/2}$

56. $(3^{-6})^{1/3}$

57. $(2^{-4})^{1/2}$

58. $(5^4)^{1/2}$

59. $\left(\dfrac{3^4}{2^6}\right)^{1/2}$

60. $\left(\dfrac{5^4}{3^6}\right)^{1/2}$

Simplify each expression. Assume the variables represent any real numbers and use absolute value as necessary. See Example 7.

61. $(x^4)^{1/4}$

62. $(y^6)^{1/6}$

63. $(a^8)^{1/2}$

64. $(b^{10})^{1/2}$

65. $(y^3)^{1/3}$

66. $(w^9)^{1/3}$

67. $(9x^6y^2)^{1/2}$

68. $(16a^8b^4)^{1/4}$

69. $\left(\dfrac{81x^{12}}{y^{20}}\right)^{1/4}$

70. $\left(\dfrac{144a^8}{9y^{18}}\right)^{1/2}$

Simplify. Assume all variables represent positive numbers. Write answers with positive exponents only. See Example 8.

71. $x^{1/2}x^{1/4}$

72. $y^{1/3}y^{1/3}$

73. $(x^{1/2}y)(x^{-3/4}y^{1/2})$

74. $(a^{1/2}b^{-1/3})(ab)$

75. $\dfrac{w^{1/3}}{w^3}$

76. $\dfrac{a^{1/2}}{a^2}$

77. $(144x^{16})^{1/2}$

78. $(125a^8)^{1/3}$

79. $\left(\dfrac{a^{-1/2}}{b^{-1/4}}\right)^{-4}$

80. $\left(\dfrac{2a^{1/2}}{b^{1/3}}\right)^{6}$

81. $\left(\dfrac{2w^{1/3}}{w^{-3/4}}\right)^{3}$

82. $\left(\dfrac{a^{-1/2}}{3a^{2/3}}\right)^{-3}$

83. $\dfrac{9^{1/4}h^{1/2}k^{3/2}}{9^{3/4}h^{1/3}k^2}$

84. $\dfrac{4^{1/4}s^{1/3}t^{-1/2}}{(4s^2t^{-3})^{-1/4}}$

Simplify each expression. Write your answers with positive exponents. Assume that all variables represent positive real numbers.

85. $(9^2)^{1/2}$

86. $(4^{16})^{1/2}$

87. $-16^{-3/4}$

88. $-25^{-3/2}$

89. $125^{-4/3}$

90. $27^{-2/3}$

91. $2^{1/2}2^{-1/4}$

92. $9^{-1}9^{1/2}$

93. $3^{0.26}3^{0.74}$

94. $2^{1.5}2^{0.5}$

95. $3^{1/4}27^{1/4}$

96. $3^{2/3}9^{2/3}$

97. $\left(-\dfrac{8}{27}\right)^{2/3}$

98. $\left(-\dfrac{8}{27}\right)^{-1/3}$

99. $\left(-\dfrac{1}{16}\right)^{-3/4}$

100. $\left(-\dfrac{5}{9}\right)^{-7/2}$

101. $\left(\dfrac{9}{16}\right)^{-1/2}$

102. $\left(\dfrac{16}{81}\right)^{-1/4}$

103. $-\left(\dfrac{25}{36}\right)^{-3/2}$

104. $\left(-\dfrac{27}{8}\right)^{-4/3}$

105. $(9x^9)^{1/2}$

106. $(-27x^9)^{1/3}$

107. $(3a^{-2/3})^{-3}$

108. $(5x^{-1/2})^{-2}$

109. $(a^{1/2}b)^{1/2}(ab^{1/2})$

110. $(m^{1/4}n^{1/2})^2(m^2n^3)^{1/2}$

111. $(km^{1/2})^3(k^3m^5)^{1/2}$

112. $(tv^{1/3})^2(t^2v^{-3})^{-1/2}$

 Use a scientific calculator with a power key (x^y) to find the decimal value of each expression. Round answers to four decimal places.

113. $2^{1/3}$

114. $5^{1/2}$

115. $-2^{1/2}$

116. $(-3)^{1/3}$

117. $1024^{1/10}$

118. $7776^{0.2}$

119. $\left(\dfrac{64}{15,625}\right)^{-1/6}$

120. $\left(\dfrac{32}{243}\right)^{-3/5}$

Simplify each expression. Assume a and b are positive real numbers and m and n are rational numbers.

121. $a^{m/2} \cdot a^{m/4}$

122. $b^{n/2} \cdot b^{-n/3}$

123. $\dfrac{a^{-m/5}}{a^{-m/3}}$

124. $\dfrac{b^{-n/4}}{b^{-n/3}}$

125. $(a^{-1/m}b^{-1/n})^{-mn}$

126. $(a^{-m/2}b^{-n/3})^{-6}$

127. $\left(\dfrac{a^{-3m}b^{-6n}}{a^{9m}}\right)^{-1/3}$

128. $\left(\dfrac{a^{-3/m}b^{6/n}}{a^{-6/m}b^{9/n}}\right)^{-1/3}$

In Exercises 129–136, solve each problem.

129. Diagonal of a box. The length of the diagonal of a box can be found from the formula

$$D = (L^2 + W^2 + H^2)^{1/2},$$

where L, W, and H represent the length, width, and height of the box, respectively. If the box is 12 inches long, 4 inches wide, and 3 inches high, then what is the length of the diagonal?

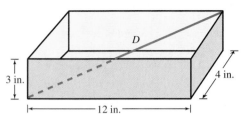

FIGURE FOR EXERCISE 129

130. Radius of a sphere. The radius of a sphere is a function of its volume, given by the formula

$$r = \left(\dfrac{0.75V}{\pi}\right)^{1/3}.$$

Find the radius of a spherical tank that has a volume of $\dfrac{32\pi}{3}$ cubic meters.

FIGURE FOR EXERCISE 130

131. Maximum sail area. According to the new International America's Cup Class Rules, the maximum sail area in square meters for a yacht in the America's Cup race is given by

$$S = (13.0368 + 7.84D^{1/3} - 0.8L)^2,$$

where D is the displacement in cubic meters (m^3), and L is the length in meters (m). (www.sailing.com).

Find the maximum sail area for a boat that has a displacement of 18.42 m³ and a length of 21.45 m.

FIGURE FOR EXERCISE 131

132. *Orbits of the planets.* According to Kepler's third law of planetary motion, the average radius R of the orbit of a planet around the sun is determined by $R = T^{2/3}$, where T is the number of years for one orbit and R is measured in astronomical units or AUs (Windows to the Universe, www.windows.umich.edu).
  a) It takes Mars 1.881 years to make one orbit of the sun. What is the average radius (in AUs) of the orbit of Mars?
  b) The average radius of the orbit of Saturn is 9.05 AU. Use the accompanying graph to estimate the number of years it takes Saturn to make one orbit of the sun.

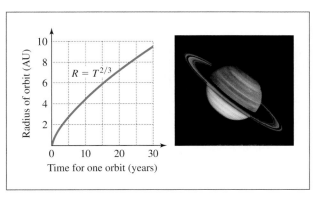

FIGURE FOR EXERCISE 132

133. *Top stock fund.* The average annual return r for an investment is given by the formula

$$r = \left(\frac{S}{P}\right)^{1/n} - 1,$$

where P is the initial investment and S is the amount it is worth after n years. An investment of $10,000 in 1999 in the Shroeder Ultra Investors Fund was worth $20,130 in 2002 (www.money.com). Find the 3-year average annual return.

134. *Top bond fund.* An investment of $10,000 in 1997 in the Spartan Investment Grade Bond Fund grew to $14,309.61 in 2002 (www.fidelity.com). Use the formula from the previous exercise to find the 5-year average annual return.

135. *Overdue loan payment.* In 1777 a wealthy Pennsylvania merchant, Jacob DeHaven, lent $450,000 to the Continental Congress to rescue the troops at Valley Forge. The loan was not repaid. In 1990 DeHaven's descendants filed suit for $141.6 billion (*New York Times,* May 27, 1990). What average annual rate of return were they using to calculate the value of the debt after 213 years? (See Exercise 133.)

136. *California growin'.* The population of California grew from 19.9 million in 1970 to 32.5 million in 2000 (U.S. Census Bureau, www.census.gov). Find the average annual rate of growth for that time period. (Use the formula from Exercise 133 with P being the initial population and S being the population n years later.)

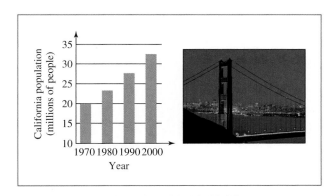

FIGURE FOR EXERCISE 136

GETTING MORE INVOLVED

137. *Discussion.* If we use the product rule to simplify $(-1)^{1/2} \cdot (-1)^{1/2}$, we get

$$(-1)^{1/2} \cdot (-1)^{1/2} = (-1)^1 = -1.$$

If we use the power of a product rule, we get

$$(-1)^{1/2} \cdot (-1)^{1/2} = (-1 \cdot -1)^{1/2} = 1^{1/2} = 1.$$

Which of these computations is incorrect? Explain your answer.

138. *Discussion.* Determine whether each equation is an identity. Explain.
  a) $(w^2 x^2)^{1/2} = |w| \cdot |x|$
  b) $(w^2 x^2)^{1/2} = |wx|$
  c) $(w^2 x^2)^{1/2} = w|x|$

7.3 OPERATIONS WITH RADICALS

In this section we will use the ideas of Section 7.1 in performing arithmetic operations with radical expressions.

Adding and Subtracting Radicals

To find the sum of $\sqrt{2}$ and $\sqrt{3}$, we can use a calculator to get $\sqrt{2} \approx 1.414$ and $\sqrt{3} \approx 1.732$. (The symbol $\approx$ means "is approximately equal to.") We can then add the decimal numbers and get

$$\sqrt{2} + \sqrt{3} \approx 1.414 + 1.732 = 3.146.$$

We cannot write an exact decimal form for $\sqrt{2} + \sqrt{3}$; the number 3.146 is an approximation of $\sqrt{2} + \sqrt{3}$. To represent the exact value of $\sqrt{2} + \sqrt{3}$, we just use the form $\sqrt{2} + \sqrt{3}$. This form cannot be simplified any further. However, a sum of like radicals can be simplified. **Like radicals** are radicals that have the same index and the same radicand.

To simplify the sum $3\sqrt{2} + 5\sqrt{2}$, we can use the fact that $3x + 5x = 8x$ is true for any value of x. Substituting $\sqrt{2}$ for x gives us $3\sqrt{2} + 5\sqrt{2} = 8\sqrt{2}$. So like radicals can be combined just as like terms are combined.

EXAMPLE 1   **Adding and subtracting like radicals**

Simplify the following expressions. Assume the variables represent positive numbers.

a) $3\sqrt{5} + 4\sqrt{5}$

b) $\sqrt[4]{w} - 6\sqrt[4]{w}$

c) $\sqrt{3} + \sqrt{5} - 4\sqrt{3} + 6\sqrt{5}$

d) $3\sqrt[3]{6x} + 2\sqrt[3]{x} + \sqrt[3]{6x} + \sqrt[3]{x}$

Solution

a) $3\sqrt{5} + 4\sqrt{5} = 7\sqrt{5}$

b) $\sqrt[4]{w} - 6\sqrt[4]{w} = -5\sqrt[4]{w}$

c) $\sqrt{3} + \sqrt{5} - 4\sqrt{3} + 6\sqrt{5} = -3\sqrt{3} + 7\sqrt{5}$ Only like radicals are combined.

d) $3\sqrt[3]{6x} + 2\sqrt[3]{x} + \sqrt[3]{6x} + \sqrt[3]{x} = 4\sqrt[3]{6x} + 3\sqrt[3]{x}$ ■

Remember that *only radicals with the same index and same radicand can be combined by addition or subtraction.* If the radicals are not in simplified form, then they must be simplified before you can determine whether they can be combined.

EXAMPLE 2   **Simplifying radicals before combining**

Perform the indicated operations. Assume the variables represent positive numbers.

a) $\sqrt{8} + \sqrt{18}$

b) $\sqrt{2x^3} - \sqrt{4x^2} + 5\sqrt{18x^3}$

c) $\sqrt[3]{16x^4y^3} - \sqrt[3]{54x^4y^3}$

Solution

a) $\sqrt{8} + \sqrt{18} = \sqrt{4} \cdot \sqrt{2} + \sqrt{9} \cdot \sqrt{2}$

$= 2\sqrt{2} + 3\sqrt{2}$ Simplify each radical.

$= 5\sqrt{2}$ Add like radicals.

Note that $\sqrt{8} + \sqrt{18} \neq \sqrt{26}$.

Calculator Close-Up

Check that

$$\sqrt{8} + \sqrt{18} = 5\sqrt{2}.$$

```
√(8)+√(18)
         7.071067812
5√(2)
         7.071067812
```

b) $\sqrt{2x^3} - \sqrt{4x^2} + 5\sqrt{18x^3} = \sqrt{x^2} \cdot \sqrt{2x} - 2x + 5 \cdot \sqrt{9x^2} \cdot \sqrt{2x}$

$$= x\sqrt{2x} - 2x + 15x\sqrt{2x} \quad \text{Simplify each radical.}$$

$$= 16x\sqrt{2x} - 2x \qquad\qquad \text{Add like radicals only.}$$

c) $\sqrt[3]{16x^4y^3} - \sqrt[3]{54x^4y^3} = \sqrt[3]{8x^3y^3} \cdot \sqrt[3]{2x} - \sqrt[3]{27x^3y^3} \cdot \sqrt[3]{2x}$

$$= 2xy\sqrt[3]{2x} - 3xy\sqrt[3]{2x} \quad \text{Simplify each radical.}$$

$$= -xy\sqrt[3]{2x} \qquad\qquad\qquad \blacksquare$$

Multiplying Radicals

The product rule for radicals, $\sqrt[n]{a} \cdot \sqrt[n]{b} = \sqrt[n]{ab}$, allows multiplication of radicals with the same index, such as

$$\sqrt{5} \cdot \sqrt{3} = \sqrt{15}, \qquad \sqrt[3]{2} \cdot \sqrt[3]{5} = \sqrt[3]{10}, \qquad \text{and} \qquad \sqrt[5]{x^2} \cdot \sqrt[5]{x} = \sqrt[5]{x^3}.$$

C A U T I O N   The product rule does not allow multiplication of radicals that have different indices. We cannot use the product rule to multiply $\sqrt{2}$ and $\sqrt[3]{5}$.

E X A M P L E   3

Multiplying radicals with the same index

Multiply and simplify the following expressions. Assume the variables represent positive numbers.

a) $5\sqrt{6} \cdot 4\sqrt{3}$

b) $\sqrt{3a^2} \cdot \sqrt{6a}$

c) $\sqrt[3]{4} \cdot \sqrt[3]{4}$

d) $\sqrt[4]{\dfrac{x^3}{2}} \cdot \sqrt[4]{\dfrac{x^2}{8}}$

Helpful Hint

Students often write

$$\sqrt{15} \cdot \sqrt{15} = \sqrt{225} = 15.$$

Although this is correct, you should get used to the idea that

$$\sqrt{15} \cdot \sqrt{15} = 15.$$

Because of the definition of a square root, $\sqrt{a} \cdot \sqrt{a} = a$ for any positive number a.

Solution

a) $5\sqrt{6} \cdot 4\sqrt{3} = 5 \cdot 4 \cdot \sqrt{6} \cdot \sqrt{3}$

$$= 20\sqrt{18} \qquad \text{Product rule for radicals}$$

$$= 20 \cdot 3\sqrt{2} \quad \sqrt{18} = \sqrt{9} \cdot \sqrt{2} = 3\sqrt{2}$$

$$= 60\sqrt{2}$$

b) $\sqrt{3a^2} \cdot \sqrt{6a} = \sqrt{18a^3} \quad \text{Product rule for radicals}$

$$= \sqrt{9a^2} \cdot \sqrt{2a}$$

$$= 3a\sqrt{2a} \quad \text{Simplify.}$$

c) $\sqrt[3]{4} \cdot \sqrt[3]{4} = \sqrt[3]{16}$

$$= \sqrt[3]{8} \cdot \sqrt[3]{2} \quad \text{Simplify.}$$

$$= 2\sqrt[3]{2}$$

d) $\sqrt[4]{\dfrac{x^3}{2}} \cdot \sqrt[4]{\dfrac{x^2}{8}} = \sqrt[4]{\dfrac{x^5}{16}} \qquad \text{Product rule for radicals}$

$$= \dfrac{\sqrt[4]{x^4} \cdot \sqrt[4]{x}}{\sqrt[4]{16}} \quad \text{Product and quotient rules for radicals}$$

$$= \dfrac{x\sqrt[4]{x}}{2} \qquad\qquad \text{Simplify.} \qquad\qquad \blacksquare$$

We find a product such as $3\sqrt{2}(4\sqrt{2} - \sqrt{3})$ by using the distributive property as we do when multiplying a monomial and a binomial. A product such as $(2\sqrt{3} + \sqrt{5})(3\sqrt{3} - 2\sqrt{5})$ can be found by using FOIL as we do for the product of two binomials.

E X A M P L E   4

Multiplying radicals

Multiply and simplify.

a) $3\sqrt{2}\,(4\sqrt{2} - \sqrt{3})$ **b)** $\sqrt[3]{a}\,(\sqrt[3]{a} - \sqrt[3]{a^2})$

c) $(2\sqrt{3} + \sqrt{5})(3\sqrt{3} - 2\sqrt{5})$ **d)** $(3 + \sqrt{x - 9})^2$

Solution

a) $3\sqrt{2}(4\sqrt{2} - \sqrt{3}) = 3\sqrt{2} \cdot 4\sqrt{2} - 3\sqrt{2} \cdot \sqrt{3}$ Distributive property

$\qquad\qquad\qquad = 12 \cdot 2 - 3\sqrt{6}$ Because $\sqrt{2} \cdot \sqrt{2} = 2$ and $\sqrt{2} \cdot \sqrt{3} = \sqrt{6}$

$\qquad\qquad\qquad = 24 - 3\sqrt{6}$

b) $\sqrt[3]{a}\,(\sqrt[3]{a} - \sqrt[3]{a^2}) = \sqrt[3]{a^2} - \sqrt[3]{a^3}$ Distributive property

$\qquad\qquad\qquad = \sqrt[3]{a^2} - a$

c) $(2\sqrt{3} + \sqrt{5})(3\sqrt{3} - 2\sqrt{5})$

$$= \overbrace{2\sqrt{3} \cdot 3\sqrt{3}}^{F} - \overbrace{2\sqrt{3} \cdot 2\sqrt{5}}^{O} + \overbrace{\sqrt{5} \cdot 3\sqrt{3}}^{I} - \overbrace{\sqrt{5} \cdot 2\sqrt{5}}^{L}$$

$\qquad = 18 - 4\sqrt{15} + 3\sqrt{15} - 10$

$\qquad = 8 - \sqrt{15}$ Combine like radicals.

d) To square a sum, we use $(a + b)^2 = a^2 + 2ab + b^2$:

$$(3 + \sqrt{x - 9})^2 = 3^2 + 2 \cdot 3\sqrt{x - 9} + (\sqrt{x - 9})^2$$

$\qquad\qquad\qquad = 9 + 6\sqrt{x - 9} + x - 9$

$\qquad\qquad\qquad = x + 6\sqrt{x - 9}$ ■

In the next example we multiply radicals that have different indices.

E X A M P L E   5

Multiplying radicals with different indices

Write each product as a single radical expression.

a) $\sqrt[3]{2} \cdot \sqrt[4]{2}$ **b)** $\sqrt[3]{2} \cdot \sqrt{3}$

Solution

a) $\sqrt[3]{2} \cdot \sqrt[4]{2} = 2^{1/3} \cdot 2^{1/4}$ Write in exponential notation.

$\qquad\qquad = 2^{7/12}$ Product rule for exponents: $\frac{1}{3} + \frac{1}{4} = \frac{7}{12}$

$\qquad\qquad = \sqrt[12]{2^7}$ Write in radical notation.

$\qquad\qquad = \sqrt[12]{128}$

b) $\sqrt[3]{2} \cdot \sqrt{3} = 2^{1/3} \cdot 3^{1/2}$ Write in exponential notation.

$\qquad\qquad = 2^{2/6} \cdot 3^{3/6}$ Write the exponents with the LCD of 6.

$\qquad\qquad = \sqrt[6]{2^2} \cdot \sqrt[6]{3^3}$ Write in radical notation.

$\qquad\qquad = \sqrt[6]{2^2 \cdot 3^3}$ Product rule for radicals

$\qquad\qquad = \sqrt[6]{108}$ $2^2 \cdot 3^3 = 4 \cdot 27 = 108$ ■

CAUTION   Because the bases in $2^{1/3} \cdot 2^{1/4}$ are identical, we can add the exponents [Example 5(a)]. Because the bases in $2^{2/6} \cdot 3^{3/6}$ are not the same, we cannot add the exponents [Example 5(b)]. Instead, we write each factor as a sixth root and use the product rule for radicals.

Helpful Hint

The word "conjugate" is used in many contexts in mathematics. According to the dictionary, conjugate means joined together, especially as in a pair.

Conjugates

Recall the special product rule $(a + b)(a - b) = a^2 - b^2$. The product of the sum $4 + \sqrt{3}$ and the difference $4 - \sqrt{3}$ can be found by using this rule:

$$(4 + \sqrt{3})(4 - \sqrt{3}) = 4^2 - (\sqrt{3})^2 = 16 - 3 = 13$$

The product of the irrational number $4 + \sqrt{3}$ and the irrational number $4 - \sqrt{3}$ is the rational number 13. For this reason the expressions $4 + \sqrt{3}$ and $4 - \sqrt{3}$ are called **conjugates** of one another. We will use conjugates in Section 7.4 to rationalize some denominators.

E X A M P L E   6

Multiplying conjugates

Find the products. Assume the variables represent positive real numbers.

a) $(2 + 3\sqrt{5})(2 - 3\sqrt{5})$
b) $(\sqrt{3} - \sqrt{2})(\sqrt{3} + \sqrt{2})$
c) $(\sqrt{2x} - \sqrt{y})(\sqrt{2x} + \sqrt{y})$

Solution

a) $(2 + 3\sqrt{5})(2 - 3\sqrt{5}) = 2^2 - (3\sqrt{5})^2$ $(a + b)(a - b) = a^2 - b^2$

$$= 4 - 45 \qquad (3\sqrt{5})^2 = 9 \cdot 5 = 45$$

$$= -41$$

b) $(\sqrt{3} - \sqrt{2})(\sqrt{3} + \sqrt{2}) = 3 - 2$

$$= 1$$

c) $(\sqrt{2x} - \sqrt{y})(\sqrt{2x} + \sqrt{y}) = 2x - y$ ■

WARM-UPS

True or false? Explain your answer.

1. $\sqrt{3} + \sqrt{3} = \sqrt{6}$
2. $\sqrt{8} + \sqrt{2} = 3\sqrt{2}$
3. $2\sqrt{3} \cdot 3\sqrt{3} = 6\sqrt{3}$
4. $\sqrt[3]{2} \cdot \sqrt[3]{2} = 2$
5. $2\sqrt{5} \cdot 3\sqrt{2} = 6\sqrt{10}$
6. $2\sqrt{5} + 3\sqrt{5} = 5\sqrt{10}$
7. $\sqrt{2}(\sqrt{3} - \sqrt{2}) = \sqrt{6} - 2$
8. $\sqrt{12} = 2\sqrt{6}$
9. $(\sqrt{2} + \sqrt{3})^2 = 2 + 3$
10. $(\sqrt{3} - \sqrt{2})(\sqrt{3} + \sqrt{2}) = 1$

```
7.3    EXERCISES
```

Reading and Writing After reading this section, write out the answers to these questions. Use complete sentences.

1. What are like radicals?

2. How do we combine like radicals?

3. Does the product rule allow multiplication of unlike radicals?

4. How do we multiply radicals of different indices?

All variables in the following exercises represent positive numbers.

Simplify the sums and differences. Give exact answers. See Example 1.

5. $\sqrt{3} - 2\sqrt{3}$

6. $\sqrt{5} - 3\sqrt{5}$

7. $5\sqrt{7x} + 4\sqrt{7x}$

8. $3\sqrt{6a} + 7\sqrt{6a}$

9. $2\sqrt[3]{2} + 3\sqrt[3]{2}$

10. $\sqrt[3]{4} + 4\sqrt[3]{4}$

11. $\sqrt{3} - \sqrt{5} + 3\sqrt{3} - \sqrt{5}$

12. $\sqrt{2} - 5\sqrt{3} - 7\sqrt{2} + 9\sqrt{3}$

13. $\sqrt[3]{2} + \sqrt[3]{x} - \sqrt[3]{2} + 4\sqrt[3]{x}$

14. $\sqrt[3]{5y} - 4\sqrt[3]{5y} + \sqrt[3]{x} + \sqrt[3]{x}$

15. $\sqrt[3]{x} - \sqrt[3]{2x} + \sqrt[3]{x}$

16. $\sqrt[3]{ab} + \sqrt{a} + 5\sqrt{a} + \sqrt[3]{ab}$

Simplify each expression. Give exact answers. See Example 2.

17. $\sqrt{8} + \sqrt{28}$

18. $\sqrt{12} + \sqrt{24}$

19. $\sqrt{8} + \sqrt{18}$

20. $\sqrt{12} + \sqrt{27}$

21. $2\sqrt{45} - 3\sqrt{20}$

22. $3\sqrt{50} - 2\sqrt{32}$

23. $\sqrt{2} - \sqrt{8}$

24. $\sqrt{20} - \sqrt{125}$

25. $\sqrt{45x^3} - \sqrt{18x^2} + \sqrt{50x^2} - \sqrt{20x^3}$

26. $\sqrt{12x^5} - \sqrt{18x} - \sqrt{300x^5} + \sqrt{98x}$

27. $2\sqrt[3]{24} + \sqrt[3]{81}$

28. $5\sqrt[3]{24} + 2\sqrt[3]{375}$

29. $\sqrt[4]{48} - 2\sqrt[4]{243}$

30. $\sqrt[5]{64} + 7\sqrt[5]{2}$

31. $\sqrt[3]{54t^4y^3} - \sqrt[3]{16t^4y^3}$

32. $\sqrt[3]{2000w^2z^5} - \sqrt[3]{16w^2z^5}$

Simplify the products. Give exact answers. See Examples 3 and 4.

33. $\sqrt{3} \cdot \sqrt{5}$

34. $\sqrt{5} \cdot \sqrt{7}$

35. $2\sqrt{5} \cdot 3\sqrt{10}$

36. $(3\sqrt{2})(-4\sqrt{10})$

37. $2\sqrt{7a} \cdot 3\sqrt{2a}$

38. $2\sqrt{5c} \cdot 5\sqrt{5}$

39. $\sqrt[4]{9} \cdot \sqrt[4]{27}$

40. $\sqrt[3]{5} \cdot \sqrt[3]{100}$

41. $(2\sqrt{3})^2$

42. $(-4\sqrt{2})^2$

43. $2\sqrt{3}(\sqrt{6} + 3\sqrt{3})$

44. $2\sqrt{5}(\sqrt{3} + 3\sqrt{5})$

45. $\sqrt{5}(\sqrt{10} - 2)$

46. $\sqrt{6}(\sqrt{15} - 1)$

47. $\sqrt[3]{3t}(\sqrt[3]{9t} - \sqrt[3]{t^2})$

48. $\sqrt[3]{2}(\sqrt[3]{12x} - \sqrt[3]{2x})$

49. $(\sqrt{3} + 2)(\sqrt{3} - 5)$

50. $(\sqrt{5} + 2)(\sqrt{5} - 6)$

51. $(\sqrt{11} - 3)(\sqrt{11} + 3)$

52. $(\sqrt{2} + 5)(\sqrt{2} + 5)$

53. $(2\sqrt{5} - 7)(2\sqrt{5} + 4)$

54. $(2\sqrt{6} - 3)(2\sqrt{6} + 4)$

55. $(2\sqrt{3} - \sqrt{6})(\sqrt{3} + 2\sqrt{6})$

56. $(3\sqrt{3} - \sqrt{2})(\sqrt{2} + \sqrt{3})$

Write each product as a single radical expression. See Example 5.

57. $\sqrt[3]{3} \cdot \sqrt{3}$

58. $\sqrt{3} \cdot \sqrt[4]{3}$

59. $\sqrt[3]{5} \cdot \sqrt[4]{5}$

60. $\sqrt[3]{2} \cdot \sqrt[5]{2}$

61. $\sqrt[3]{2} \cdot \sqrt{5}$

62. $\sqrt{6} \cdot \sqrt[3]{2}$

63. $\sqrt[3]{2} \cdot \sqrt[4]{3}$

64. $\sqrt[3]{3} \cdot \sqrt[4]{2}$

Find the product of each pair of conjugates. See Example 6.

65. $(\sqrt{3} - 2)(\sqrt{3} + 2)$

66. $(7 - \sqrt{3})(7 + \sqrt{3})$

67. $(\sqrt{5} + \sqrt{2})(\sqrt{5} - \sqrt{2})$

68. $(\sqrt{6} + \sqrt{5})(\sqrt{6} - \sqrt{5})$

69. $(2\sqrt{5} + 1)(2\sqrt{5} - 1)$

70. $(3\sqrt{2} - 4)(3\sqrt{2} + 4)$

71. $(3\sqrt{2} + \sqrt{5})(3\sqrt{2} - \sqrt{5})$

72. $(2\sqrt{3} - \sqrt{7})(2\sqrt{3} + \sqrt{7})$

73. $(5 - 3\sqrt{x})(5 + 3\sqrt{x})$

74. $(4\sqrt{y} + 3\sqrt{z})(4\sqrt{y} - 3\sqrt{z})$

Simplify each expression.

75. $\sqrt{300} + \sqrt{3}$

76. $\sqrt{50} + \sqrt{2}$

77. $2\sqrt{5} \cdot 5\sqrt{6}$

78. $3\sqrt{6} \cdot 5\sqrt{10}$

79. $(3 + 2\sqrt{7})(\sqrt{7} - 2)$

80. $(2 + \sqrt{7})(\sqrt{7} - 2)$

81. $4\sqrt{w} \cdot 4\sqrt{w}$

82. $3\sqrt{m} \cdot 5\sqrt{m}$

83. $\sqrt{3x^3} \cdot \sqrt{6x^2}$

84. $\sqrt{2t^5} \cdot \sqrt{10t^4}$

85. $(2\sqrt{5} + \sqrt{2})(3\sqrt{5} - \sqrt{2})$

86. $(3\sqrt{2} - \sqrt{3})(2\sqrt{2} + 3\sqrt{3})$

87. $\dfrac{\sqrt{2}}{3} + \dfrac{\sqrt{2}}{5}$

88. $\dfrac{\sqrt{2}}{4} + \dfrac{\sqrt{3}}{5}$

89. $(5 + 2\sqrt{2})(5 - 2\sqrt{2})$

90. $(3 - 2\sqrt{7})(3 + 2\sqrt{7})$

91. $(3 + \sqrt{x})^2$

92. $(1 - \sqrt{x})^2$

93. $(5\sqrt{x} - 3)^2$

94. $(3\sqrt{a} + 2)^2$

95. $(1 + \sqrt{x + 2})^2$

96. $(\sqrt{x - 1} + 1)^2$

97. $\sqrt{4w} - \sqrt{9w}$

98. $10\sqrt{m} - \sqrt{16m}$

99. $2\sqrt{a^3} + 3\sqrt{a^3} - 2a\sqrt{4a}$

100. $5\sqrt{w^2y} - 7\sqrt{w^2y} + 6\sqrt{w^2y}$

101. $\sqrt{x^5} + 2x\sqrt{x^3}$

102. $\sqrt{8x^3} + \sqrt{50x^3} - x\sqrt{2x}$

103. $\sqrt[3]{-16x^4} + 5x\sqrt[3]{54x}$

104. $\sqrt[3]{3x^5y^7} - \sqrt[3]{24x^5y^7}$

105. $\sqrt[3]{2x} \cdot \sqrt{2x}$

106. $\sqrt[3]{2m} \cdot \sqrt[4]{2n}$

In Exercises 107–110, solve each problem.

107. *Area of a rectangle.* Find the exact area of a rectangle that has a length of $\sqrt{6}$ feet and a width of $\sqrt{3}$ feet.

108. *Volume of a cube.* Find the exact volume of a cube with sides of length $\sqrt{3}$ meters.

FIGURE FOR EXERCISE 108

109. *Area of a trapezoid.* Find the exact area of a trapezoid with a height of $\sqrt{6}$ feet and bases of $\sqrt{3}$ feet and $\sqrt{12}$ feet.

FIGURE FOR EXERCISE 109

110. *Area of a triangle.* Find the exact area of a triangle with a base of $\sqrt{30}$ meters and a height of $\sqrt{6}$ meters.

FIGURE FOR EXERCISE 110

GETTING MORE INVOLVED

111. *Discussion.* Is $\sqrt{a} + \sqrt{b} = \sqrt{a + b}$ for all values of a and b?

112. *Discussion.* Which of the following equations are identities? Explain your answers.

a) $\sqrt{9x} = 3\sqrt{x}$

b) $\sqrt{9 + x} = 3 + \sqrt{x}$

c) $\sqrt{x - 4} = \sqrt{x} - 2$

d) $\sqrt{\dfrac{x}{4}} = \dfrac{\sqrt{x}}{2}$

113. *Exploration.* Because 3 is the square of $\sqrt{3}$, a binomial such as $y^2 - 3$ is a difference of two squares.

a) Factor $y^2 - 3$ and $2a^2 - 7$ using radicals.

b) Use factoring with radicals to solve the equation $x^2 - 8 = 0$.

c) Assuming a is a positive real number, solve the equation $x^2 - a = 0$.

7.4 QUOTIENTS, POWERS, AND RATIONALIZING DENOMINATORS

In this section we will continue studying operations with radicals. We will first learn how to rationalize denominators, then we will find quotients and powers with radicals.

Rationalizing the Denominator

Square roots such as $\sqrt{2}$, $\sqrt{3}$, and $\sqrt{5}$ are irrational numbers. If roots of this type appear in the denominator of a fraction, it is customary to rewrite the fraction with a rational number in the denominator, or **rationalize** it. We rationalize a denominator by multiplying both the numerator and denominator by another radical that makes the denominator rational.

You can find products of radicals in two ways. By definition, $\sqrt{2}$ is the positive number that you multiply by itself to get 2. So

$$\sqrt{2} \cdot \sqrt{2} = 2.$$

By the product rule, $\sqrt{2} \cdot \sqrt{2} = \sqrt{4} = 2$. Note that $\sqrt[3]{2} \cdot \sqrt[3]{2} = \sqrt[3]{4}$ by the product rule, but $\sqrt[3]{4} \neq 2$. By definition of a cube root,

$$\sqrt[3]{2} \cdot \sqrt[3]{2} \cdot \sqrt[3]{2} = 2.$$

EXAMPLE 1

Rationalizing the denominator

Rewrite each expression with a rational denominator.

a) $\dfrac{\sqrt{3}}{\sqrt{5}}$

b) $\dfrac{3}{\sqrt[3]{2}}$

Solution

a) Because $\sqrt{5} \cdot \sqrt{5} = 5$, multiplying both the numerator and denominator by $\sqrt{5}$ will rationalize the denominator:

$$\frac{\sqrt{3}}{\sqrt{5}} = \frac{\sqrt{3}}{\sqrt{5}} \cdot \frac{\sqrt{5}}{\sqrt{5}} = \frac{\sqrt{15}}{5} \quad \text{By the product rule, } \sqrt{3} \cdot \sqrt{5} = \sqrt{15}.$$

b) We must build up the denominator to be the cube root of a perfect cube. So we multiply by $\sqrt[3]{4}$ to get $\sqrt[3]{4} \cdot \sqrt[3]{2} = \sqrt[3]{8}$:

$$\frac{3}{\sqrt[3]{2}} = \frac{3}{\sqrt[3]{2}} \cdot \frac{\sqrt[3]{4}}{\sqrt[3]{4}} = \frac{3\sqrt[3]{4}}{\sqrt[3]{8}} = \frac{3\sqrt[3]{4}}{2} \qquad ■$$

CAUTION To rationalize a denominator with a single square root, you simply multiply by that square root. If the denominator has a cube root, you build the denominator to a cube root of a perfect cube, as in Example 1(b). For a fourth root you build to a fourth root of a perfect fourth power, and so on.

Simplifying Radicals

When simplifying a radical expression, we have three specific conditions to satisfy. First, we use the product rule to factor out perfect nth powers from the radicand in nth roots. That is, we factor out perfect squares in square roots, perfect cubes in cube roots, and so on. For example,

$$\sqrt{72} = \sqrt{36} \cdot \sqrt{2} = 6\sqrt{2} \qquad \text{and} \qquad \sqrt[3]{24} = \sqrt[3]{8} \cdot \sqrt[3]{3} = 2\sqrt[3]{3}.$$

Second, we use the quotient rule to remove all fractions from inside a radical. For example,

$$\sqrt{\frac{2}{3}} = \frac{\sqrt{2}}{\sqrt{3}}.$$

Third, we remove radicals from denominators by rationalizing the denominator:

$$\sqrt{\frac{2}{3}} = \frac{\sqrt{2} \cdot \sqrt{3}}{\sqrt{3} \cdot \sqrt{3}} = \frac{\sqrt{6}}{3}.$$

A radical expression that satisfies the three conditions is in *simplified radical form.*

Simplified Radical Form for Radicals of Index *n*

A radical expression of index *n* is in **simplified radical form** if it has
1. *no* perfect *n*th powers as factors of the radicand,
2. *no* fractions inside the radical, and
3. *no* radicals in the denominator.

E X A M P L E   2   **Writing radical expressions in simplified radical form**
Simplify.

a) $\dfrac{\sqrt{10}}{\sqrt{6}}$

b) $\sqrt[3]{\dfrac{5}{9}}$

Solution

a) To rationalize the denominator, multiply the numerator and denominator by $\sqrt{6}$:

$$\frac{\sqrt{10}}{\sqrt{6}} = \frac{\sqrt{10}}{\sqrt{6}} \cdot \frac{\sqrt{6}}{\sqrt{6}} \qquad \text{Rationalize the denominator.}$$

$$= \frac{\sqrt{60}}{6}$$

$$= \frac{\sqrt{4}\sqrt{15}}{6} \qquad \text{Remove the perfect square from } \sqrt{60}.$$

$$= \frac{2\sqrt{15}}{6}$$

$$= \frac{\sqrt{15}}{3} \qquad \text{Reduce } \frac{2}{6} \text{ to } \frac{1}{3}. \text{ Note that } \sqrt{15} \div 3 \neq \sqrt{5}.$$

b) To rationalize the denominator, build up the denominator to a cube root of a perfect cube. Because $\sqrt[3]{9} \cdot \sqrt[3]{3} = \sqrt[3]{27} = 3$, we multiply by $\sqrt[3]{3}$:

$$\sqrt[3]{\frac{5}{9}} = \frac{\sqrt[3]{5}}{\sqrt[3]{9}} \qquad \text{Quotient rule for radicals}$$

$$= \frac{\sqrt[3]{5}}{\sqrt[3]{9}} \cdot \frac{\sqrt[3]{3}}{\sqrt[3]{3}} \qquad \text{Rationalize the denominator.}$$

$$= \frac{\sqrt[3]{15}}{\sqrt[3]{27}}$$

$$= \frac{\sqrt[3]{15}}{3}$$

E X A M P L E 3

Rationalizing the denominator with variables

Simplify each expression. Assume all variables represent positive real numbers.

a) $\sqrt{\dfrac{a}{b}}$

b) $\sqrt{\dfrac{x^3}{y^5}}$

c) $\sqrt[3]{\dfrac{x}{y}}$

Solution

a) $\sqrt{\dfrac{a}{b}} = \dfrac{\sqrt{a}}{\sqrt{b}}$ Quotient rule for radicals

$\phantom{\sqrt{\dfrac{a}{b}}} = \dfrac{\sqrt{a} \cdot \sqrt{b}}{\sqrt{b} \cdot \sqrt{b}}$ Rationalize the denominator.

$\phantom{\sqrt{\dfrac{a}{b}}} = \dfrac{\sqrt{ab}}{b}$

b) $\sqrt{\dfrac{x^3}{y^5}} = \dfrac{\sqrt{x^3}}{\sqrt{y^5}}$ Quotient rule for radicals

$\phantom{\sqrt{\dfrac{x^3}{y^5}}} = \dfrac{\sqrt{x^2} \cdot \sqrt{x}}{\sqrt{y^4} \cdot \sqrt{y}}$ Product rule for radicals

$\phantom{\sqrt{\dfrac{x^3}{y^5}}} = \dfrac{x\sqrt{x}}{y^2\sqrt{y}}$ Simplify.

$\phantom{\sqrt{\dfrac{x^3}{y^5}}} = \dfrac{x\sqrt{x} \cdot \sqrt{y}}{y^2\sqrt{y} \cdot \sqrt{y}}$ Rationalize the denominator.

$\phantom{\sqrt{\dfrac{x^3}{y^5}}} = \dfrac{x\sqrt{xy}}{y^2 \cdot y} = \dfrac{x\sqrt{xy}}{y^3}$

c) Multiply by $\sqrt[3]{y^2}$ to rationalize the denominator:

$$\sqrt[3]{\dfrac{x}{y}} = \dfrac{\sqrt[3]{x}}{\sqrt[3]{y}} = \dfrac{\sqrt[3]{x}}{\sqrt[3]{y}} \cdot \dfrac{\sqrt[3]{y^2}}{\sqrt[3]{y^2}} = \dfrac{\sqrt[3]{xy^2}}{\sqrt[3]{y^3}} = \dfrac{\sqrt[3]{xy^2}}{y}$$

Dividing Radicals

In Section 7.3 you learned how to add, subtract, and multiply radical expressions. To divide two radical expressions, simply write the quotient as a ratio and then simplify. In general, we have

$$\sqrt[n]{a} \div \sqrt[n]{b} = \dfrac{\sqrt[n]{a}}{\sqrt[n]{b}} = \sqrt[n]{\dfrac{a}{b}},$$

provided that all expressions represent real numbers. Note that the quotient rule is applied only to radicals that have the same index.

E X A M P L E 4

Dividing radicals with the same index

Divide and simplify. Assume the variables represent positive numbers.

a) $\sqrt{10} \div \sqrt{5}$

b) $(3\sqrt{2}) \div (2\sqrt{3})$

c) $\sqrt[3]{10x^2} \div \sqrt[3]{5x}$

Solution

a) $\sqrt{10} \div \sqrt{5} = \dfrac{\sqrt{10}}{\sqrt{5}}$ $a \div b = \dfrac{a}{b}$, provided that $b \neq 0$.

$\qquad\qquad = \sqrt{\dfrac{10}{5}}$ Quotient rule for radicals

$\qquad\qquad = \sqrt{2}$ Reduce.

b) $(3\sqrt{2}) \div (2\sqrt{3}) = \dfrac{3\sqrt{2}}{2\sqrt{3}}$

$\qquad\qquad\qquad = \dfrac{3\sqrt{2}}{2\sqrt{3}} \cdot \dfrac{\sqrt{3}}{\sqrt{3}}$ Rationalize the denominator.

$\qquad\qquad\qquad = \dfrac{3\sqrt{6}}{2 \cdot 3}$

$\qquad\qquad\qquad = \dfrac{\sqrt{6}}{2}$ Note that $\sqrt{6} \div 2 \neq \sqrt{3}$.

c) $\sqrt[3]{10x^2} \div \sqrt[3]{5x} = \dfrac{\sqrt[3]{10x^2}}{\sqrt[3]{5x}}$

$\qquad\qquad\qquad = \sqrt[3]{\dfrac{10x^2}{5x}}$ Quotient rule for radicals

$\qquad\qquad\qquad = \sqrt[3]{2x}$ Reduce.   ∎

Note that in Example 4(a) we applied the quotient rule to get $\sqrt{10} \div \sqrt{5} = \sqrt{2}$. In Example 4(b) we did not use the quotient rule because 2 is not evenly divisible by 3. Instead, we rationalized the denominator to get the result in simplified form.

When working with radicals it is usually best to write them in simplified radical form before doing any operations with the radicals.

E X A M P L E   5   **Simplifying before dividing**

Divide and simplify. Assume the variables represent positive numbers.

a) $\sqrt{12} \div \sqrt{72x}$ **b)** $\sqrt[4]{16a} \div \sqrt[4]{a^5}$

Solution

a) $\sqrt{12} \div \sqrt{72x} = \dfrac{\sqrt{4} \cdot \sqrt{3}}{\sqrt{36} \cdot \sqrt{2x}}$ Factor out perfect squares.

$\qquad\qquad\qquad = \dfrac{2\sqrt{3}}{6\sqrt{2x}}$ Simplify.

$\qquad\qquad\qquad = \dfrac{\sqrt{3} \cdot \sqrt{2x}}{3\sqrt{2x} \cdot \sqrt{2x}}$ Reduce $\dfrac{2}{6}$ to $\dfrac{1}{3}$ and rationalize.

$\qquad\qquad\qquad = \dfrac{\sqrt{6x}}{6x}$ Multiply the radicals.

b) $\sqrt[4]{16a} \div \sqrt[4]{a^5} = \dfrac{\sqrt[4]{16} \cdot \sqrt[4]{a}}{\sqrt[4]{a^4} \cdot \sqrt[4]{a}}$ Factor out perfect fourth powers.

$\qquad\qquad\qquad = \dfrac{\sqrt[4]{16}}{\sqrt[4]{a^4}}$ Reduce.

$\qquad\qquad\qquad = \dfrac{2}{a}$ Simplify the radicals.   ∎

In Chapter 8 it will be necessary to simplify expressions of the type found in Example 6.

E X A M P L E 6

Simplifying radical expressions

Simplify.

a) $\dfrac{4 - \sqrt{12}}{4}$

b) $\dfrac{-6 + \sqrt{20}}{-2}$

Solution

a) First write $\sqrt{12}$ in simplified form. Then simplify the expression.

$$\frac{4 - \sqrt{12}}{4} = \frac{4 - 2\sqrt{3}}{4} \qquad \text{Simplify } \sqrt{12}.$$

$$= \frac{\cancel{2}(2 - \sqrt{3})}{\cancel{2} \cdot 2} \qquad \text{Factor.}$$

$$= \frac{2 - \sqrt{3}}{2} \qquad \text{Divide out the common factor.}$$

b) $\dfrac{-6 + \sqrt{20}}{-2} = \dfrac{-6 + 2\sqrt{5}}{-2}$

$$= \frac{-\cancel{2}(3 - \sqrt{5})}{-\cancel{2}}$$

$$= 3 - \sqrt{5} \qquad\blacksquare$$

C A U T I O N To simplify the expressions in Example 6, you must simplify the radical, factor the numerator, and then divide out the common factors. You cannot simply "cancel" the 4's in $\dfrac{4 - \sqrt{12}}{4}$ or the 2's in $\dfrac{2 - \sqrt{3}}{2}$ because they are not common factors.

Rationalizing Denominators Using Conjugates

A simplified expression involving radicals does not have radicals in the denominator. If an expression such as $4 - \sqrt{3}$ appears in a denominator, we can multiply both the numerator and denominator by its conjugate $4 + \sqrt{3}$ to get a rational number in the denominator.

E X A M P L E 7

Rationalizing the denominator using conjugates

Write in simplified form.

a) $\dfrac{2 + \sqrt{3}}{4 - \sqrt{3}}$

b) $\dfrac{\sqrt{5}}{\sqrt{6} + \sqrt{2}}$

Solution

a) $\dfrac{2 + \sqrt{3}}{4 - \sqrt{3}} = \dfrac{(2 + \sqrt{3})(4 + \sqrt{3})}{(4 - \sqrt{3})(4 + \sqrt{3})}$ Multiply the numerator and denominator by $4 + \sqrt{3}$.

$$= \frac{8 + 6\sqrt{3} + 3}{13} \qquad (4 - \sqrt{3})(4 + \sqrt{3}) = 16 - 3 = 13$$

$$= \frac{11 + 6\sqrt{3}}{13} \qquad \text{Simplify.}$$

b) $\dfrac{\sqrt{5}}{\sqrt{6} + \sqrt{2}} = \dfrac{\sqrt{5}(\sqrt{6} - \sqrt{2})}{(\sqrt{6} + \sqrt{2})(\sqrt{6} - \sqrt{2})}$ Multiply the numerator and denominator by $\sqrt{6} - \sqrt{2}$.

$\qquad\qquad\quad = \dfrac{\sqrt{30} - \sqrt{10}}{4}$ $(\sqrt{6} + \sqrt{2})(\sqrt{6} - \sqrt{2}) = 6 - 2 = 4$ ∎

Powers of Radical Expressions

In Example 8 we use the power of a product rule $((ab)^n = a^n b^n)$ and the power of a power rule $((a^m)^n = a^{mn})$ with radical expressions. We also use the fact that a root and a power can be found in either order. That is, $(\sqrt[n]{a})^m = \sqrt[n]{a^m}$.

E X A M P L E   8   **Finding powers of rational expressions**

Simplify. Assume the variables represent positive numbers.

a) $(5\sqrt{2})^3$ **b)** $(2\sqrt{x^3})^4$ **c)** $(3w\sqrt[3]{2w})^3$ **d)** $(2t\sqrt[4]{3t})^3$

Solution

a) $(5\sqrt{2})^3 = 5^3(\sqrt{2})^3$ Power of a product rule

$\qquad\qquad = 125\sqrt{8}$ $(\sqrt{2})^3 = \sqrt{2^3} = \sqrt{8}$

$\qquad\qquad = 125 \cdot 2\sqrt{2}$ $\sqrt{8} = \sqrt{4}\sqrt{2} = 2\sqrt{2}$

$\qquad\qquad = 250\sqrt{2}$

b) $(2\sqrt{x^3})^4 = 2^4(\sqrt{x^3})^4$ Power of a product rule

$\qquad\qquad = 2^4\sqrt{(x^3)^4}$ $(\sqrt[n]{a})^m = \sqrt[n]{a^m}$

$\qquad\qquad = 16\sqrt{x^{12}}$ $(a^m)^n = a^{mn}$

$\qquad\qquad = 16x^6$

c) $(3w\sqrt[3]{2w})^3 = 3^3 w^3(\sqrt[3]{2w})^3$

$\qquad\qquad = 27w^3(2w)$

$\qquad\qquad = 54w^4$

d) $(2t\sqrt[4]{3t})^3 = 2^3 t^3(\sqrt[4]{3t})^3 = 8t^3\sqrt[4]{27t^3}$ ∎

True or false? Explain your answer.

1. $\dfrac{\sqrt{6}}{\sqrt{2}} = \sqrt{3}$ **2.** $\dfrac{2}{\sqrt{2}} = \sqrt{2}$

3. $\dfrac{4 - \sqrt{10}}{2} = 2 - \sqrt{10}$ **4.** $\dfrac{1}{\sqrt{3}} = \dfrac{\sqrt{3}}{3}$

5. $\dfrac{8\sqrt{7}}{2\sqrt{7}} = 4\sqrt{7}$ **6.** $\dfrac{2(2 + \sqrt{3})}{(2 - \sqrt{3})(2 + \sqrt{3})} = 4 + 2\sqrt{3}$

7. $\dfrac{\sqrt{12}}{3} = \sqrt{4}$ **8.** $\dfrac{\sqrt{20}}{\sqrt{5}} = 2$

9. $(2\sqrt{4})^2 = 16$ **10.** $(3\sqrt{5})^3 = 27\sqrt{125}$

7.4   EXERCISES

All variables in the following exercises represent positive numbers.

Rewrite each expression with a rational denominator. See Example 1.

1. $\dfrac{2}{\sqrt{5}}$

2. $\dfrac{5}{\sqrt{3}}$

3. $\dfrac{\sqrt{3}}{\sqrt{7}}$

4. $\dfrac{\sqrt{6}}{\sqrt{5}}$

5. $\dfrac{1}{\sqrt[3]{4}}$

6. $\dfrac{7}{\sqrt[3]{3}}$

7. $\dfrac{\sqrt[3]{6}}{\sqrt[3]{5}}$

8. $\dfrac{\sqrt[4]{2}}{\sqrt[4]{27}}$

Write each radical expression in simplified radical form. See Example 2.

9. $\dfrac{\sqrt{5}}{\sqrt{12}}$

10. $\dfrac{\sqrt{7}}{\sqrt{18}}$

11. $\dfrac{\sqrt{3}}{\sqrt{12}}$

12. $\dfrac{\sqrt{2}}{\sqrt{18}}$

13. $\sqrt{\dfrac{1}{2}}$

14. $\sqrt{\dfrac{3}{8}}$

15. $\sqrt[3]{\dfrac{2}{3}}$

16. $\sqrt[3]{\dfrac{3}{5}}$

17. $\sqrt[3]{\dfrac{7}{4}}$

18. $\sqrt[4]{\dfrac{1}{5}}$

Simplify. See Example 3.

19. $\sqrt{\dfrac{x}{y}}$

20. $\sqrt{\dfrac{x^2}{a}}$

21. $\sqrt{\dfrac{a^3}{b^7}}$

22. $\sqrt{\dfrac{w^5}{y^3}}$

23. $\sqrt{\dfrac{a}{3b}}$

24. $\sqrt{\dfrac{5x}{2y}}$

25. $\sqrt[3]{\dfrac{a}{b}}$

26. $\sqrt[3]{\dfrac{4a}{b}}$

27. $\sqrt[3]{\dfrac{5}{2b^2}}$

28. $\sqrt[3]{\dfrac{3}{4a^2}}$

Divide and Simplify. See Examples 4 and 5.

29. $\sqrt{15} \div \sqrt{5}$

30. $\sqrt{14} \div \sqrt{7}$

31. $\sqrt{3} \div \sqrt{5}$

32. $\sqrt{5} \div \sqrt{7}$

33. $(3\sqrt{3}) \div (5\sqrt{6})$

34. $(2\sqrt{2}) \div (4\sqrt{10})$

35. $(2\sqrt{3}) \div (3\sqrt{6})$

36. $(5\sqrt{12}) \div (4\sqrt{6})$

37. $\sqrt{24a^2} \div \sqrt{72a}$

38. $\sqrt{32x^3} \div \sqrt{48x^2}$

39. $\sqrt[3]{20} \div \sqrt[3]{2}$

40. $\sqrt[3]{8x^7} \div \sqrt[3]{2x}$

41. $\sqrt[4]{48} \div \sqrt[4]{3}$

42. $\sqrt[4]{4a^{10}} \div \sqrt[4]{2a^2}$

43. $\sqrt[4]{16w} \div \sqrt[4]{w^5}$

44. $\sqrt[4]{81b^5} \div \sqrt[4]{b}$

Simplify. See Example 6.

45. $\dfrac{6 + \sqrt{45}}{3}$

46. $\dfrac{10 + \sqrt{50}}{5}$

47. $\dfrac{-2 + \sqrt{12}}{-2}$

48. $\dfrac{-6 + \sqrt{72}}{-6}$

Simplify each expression by rationalizing the denominator. See Example 7.

49. $\dfrac{4}{2 + \sqrt{8}}$

50. $\dfrac{6}{3 - \sqrt{18}}$

51. $\dfrac{3}{\sqrt{11} - \sqrt{5}}$

52. $\dfrac{6}{\sqrt{5} - \sqrt{14}}$

53. $\dfrac{1 + \sqrt{2}}{\sqrt{3} - 1}$

54. $\dfrac{2 - \sqrt{3}}{\sqrt{2} + \sqrt{6}}$

55. $\dfrac{\sqrt{2}}{\sqrt{6} + \sqrt{3}}$

56. $\dfrac{5}{\sqrt{7} - \sqrt{5}}$

57. $\dfrac{2\sqrt{3}}{3\sqrt{2} - \sqrt{5}}$

58. $\dfrac{3\sqrt{5}}{5\sqrt{2} + \sqrt{6}}$

Simplify. See Example 8.

59. $(2\sqrt{2})^5$

60. $(3\sqrt{3})^4$

61. $(\sqrt{x})^5$

62. $(2\sqrt{y})^3$

63. $(-3\sqrt{x^3})^3$

64. $(-2\sqrt{x^3})^4$

65. $(2x\sqrt[3]{x^2})^3$

66. $(2y\sqrt[3]{4y})^3$

67. $(-2\sqrt[3]{5})^2$

68. $(-3\sqrt[3]{4})^2$

69. $(\sqrt[3]{x^2})^6$

70. $(2\sqrt[4]{y^3})^3$

Simplify.

71. $\dfrac{\sqrt{3}}{\sqrt{2}} + \dfrac{2}{\sqrt{2}}$

72. $\dfrac{2}{\sqrt{7}} + \dfrac{5}{\sqrt{7}}$

73. $\dfrac{\sqrt{3}}{\sqrt{2}} + \dfrac{3\sqrt{6}}{2}$

74. $\dfrac{\sqrt{3}}{2\sqrt{2}} + \dfrac{\sqrt{5}}{3\sqrt{2}}$

75. $\dfrac{\sqrt{6}}{2} \cdot \dfrac{1}{\sqrt{3}}$

76. $\dfrac{\sqrt{6}}{\sqrt{7}} \cdot \dfrac{\sqrt{14}}{\sqrt{3}}$

77. $(2\sqrt{w}) \div (3\sqrt{w})$

78. $2 \div (3\sqrt{a})$

79. $\dfrac{8 - \sqrt{32}}{20}$

80. $\dfrac{4 - \sqrt{28}}{6}$

81. $\dfrac{5 + \sqrt{75}}{10}$

82. $\dfrac{3 + \sqrt{18}}{6}$

83. $\sqrt{a}(\sqrt{a} - 3)$

84. $3\sqrt{m}(2\sqrt{m} - 6)$

85. $4\sqrt{a}(a + \sqrt{a})$

86. $\sqrt{3ab}(\sqrt{3a} + \sqrt{3})$

87. $(2\sqrt{3m})^2$

88. $(-3\sqrt{4y})^2$

89. $(-2\sqrt{xy^2z})^2$

90. $(5a\sqrt{ab})^2$

91. $\sqrt[3]{m}(\sqrt[3]{m^2} - \sqrt[3]{m^5})$

92. $\sqrt[4]{w}(\sqrt[4]{w^3} - \sqrt[4]{w^7})$

93. $\sqrt[3]{8x^4} + \sqrt[3]{27x^4}$

94. $\sqrt[3]{16a^4} + a\sqrt[3]{2a}$

95. $(2m\sqrt[4]{2m^2})^3$

96. $(-2t\sqrt[6]{2t^2})^5$

97. $\dfrac{x - 9}{\sqrt{x} - 3}$

98. $\dfrac{x - y}{\sqrt{x} - \sqrt{y}}$

99. $\dfrac{3\sqrt{k}}{\sqrt{k} + \sqrt{7}}$

100. $\dfrac{\sqrt{hk}}{\sqrt{h} + 3\sqrt{k}}$

101. $\dfrac{5}{\sqrt{2} - 1} + \dfrac{3}{\sqrt{2} + 1}$

102. $\dfrac{\sqrt{3}}{\sqrt{6} - 1} - \dfrac{\sqrt{3}}{\sqrt{6} + 1}$

103. $\dfrac{1}{\sqrt{2}} + \dfrac{1}{\sqrt{3}}$

104. $\dfrac{4}{2\sqrt{3}} + \dfrac{1}{\sqrt{5}}$

105. $\dfrac{3}{\sqrt{2} - 1} + \dfrac{4}{\sqrt{2} + 1}$

106. $\dfrac{3}{\sqrt{5} - \sqrt{3}} - \dfrac{2}{\sqrt{5} + \sqrt{3}}$

107. $\dfrac{\sqrt{x}}{\sqrt{x} + 2} + \dfrac{3\sqrt{x}}{\sqrt{x} - 2}$

108. $\dfrac{\sqrt{5}}{3 - \sqrt{y}} - \dfrac{\sqrt{5y}}{3 + \sqrt{y}}$

109. $\dfrac{1}{\sqrt{x}} + \dfrac{1}{1 - \sqrt{x}}$

110. $\dfrac{\sqrt{x}}{\sqrt{x} - 3} + \dfrac{5}{\sqrt{x}}$

GETTING MORE INVOLVED

111. *Exploration.* A polynomial is prime if it cannot be factored by using integers, but many prime polynomials can be factored if we use radicals.

a) Find the product $(x - \sqrt[3]{2})(x^2 + \sqrt[3]{2}x + \sqrt[3]{4})$.

b) Factor $x^3 + 5$ using radicals.

c) Find the product
$$(\sqrt[3]{5} - \sqrt[3]{2})(\sqrt[3]{25} + \sqrt[3]{10} + \sqrt[3]{4}).$$

d) Use radicals to factor $a + b$ as a sum of two cubes and $a - b$ as a difference of two cubes.

112. *Discussion.* Which one of the following expressions is not equivalent to the others?

a) $(\sqrt[3]{x})^4$ **b)** $\sqrt[4]{x^3}$ **c)** $\sqrt[3]{x^4}$

d) $x^{4/3}$ **e)** $(x^{1/3})^4$

7.5 SOLVING EQUATIONS WITH RADICALS AND EXPONENTS

One of our goals in algebra is to keep increasing our knowledge of solving equations because the solutions to equations can give us the answers to various applied questions. In this section we will apply our knowledge of radicals and exponents to solving some new types of equations.

The Odd-Root Property

Because $(-2)^3 = -8$ and $2^3 = 8$, the equation $x^3 = 8$ is equivalent to $x = 2$. The equation $x^3 = -8$ is equivalent to $x = -2$. Because there is only one real odd root of each real number, there is a simple rule for writing an equivalent equation in this situation.

> **Odd-Root Property**
>
> If n is an odd positive integer,
>
> $$x^n = k \qquad \text{is equivalent to} \qquad x = \sqrt[n]{k}$$
>
> for any real number k.

EXAMPLE 1   **Using the odd-root property**

Solve each equation.

a) $x^3 = 27$ **b)** $x^5 + 32 = 0$ **c)** $(x - 2)^3 = 24$

Solution

a) $x^3 = 27$

$\qquad x = \sqrt[3]{27}$ Odd-root property

$\qquad x = 3$

Check 3 in the original equation. The solution set is $\{3\}$.

b) $x^5 + 32 = 0$

$\qquad\qquad x^5 = -32$ Isolate the variable.

$\qquad\qquad x = \sqrt[5]{-32}$ Odd-root property

$\qquad\qquad x = -2$

Check -2 in the original equation. The solution set is $\{-2\}$.

c) $(x - 2)^3 = 24$

$\qquad\quad x - 2 = \sqrt[3]{24}$ Odd-root property

$\qquad\qquad\quad x = 2 + 2\sqrt[3]{3}$ $\sqrt[3]{24} = \sqrt[3]{8} \cdot \sqrt[3]{3} = 2\sqrt[3]{3}$

Check. The solution set is $\{2 + 2\sqrt[3]{3}\}$.   ■

The Even-Root Property

In solving the equation $x^2 = 4$, you might be tempted to write $x = 2$ as an equivalent equation. But $x = 2$ is not equivalent to $x^2 = 4$ because $2^2 = 4$ and $(-2)^2 = 4$. So the solution set to $x^2 = 4$ is $\{-2, 2\}$. The equation $x^2 = 4$ is equivalent to the compound sentence $x = 2$ or $x = -2$, which we can abbreviate as $x = \pm 2$. The equation $x = \pm 2$ is read "x equals positive or negative 2."

Equations involving other even powers are handled like the squares. Because $2^4 = 16$ and $(-2)^4 = 16$, the equation $x^4 = 16$ is equivalent to $x = \pm 2$. So $x^4 = 16$ has two real solutions. Note that $x^4 = -16$ has no real solutions. The equation $x^6 = 5$ is equivalent to $x = \pm\sqrt[6]{5}$. We can now state a general rule.

> **Even-Root Property**
>
> Suppose n is a positive even integer.
> If $k > 0$, then $x^n = k$ is equivalent to $x = \pm\sqrt[n]{k}$.
> If $k = 0$, then $x^n = k$ is equivalent to $x = 0$.
> If $k < 0$, then $x^n = k$ has no real solution.

E X A M P L E   2   **Using the even-root property**
Solve each equation.

a) $x^2 = 10$ b) $w^8 = 0$ c) $x^4 = -4$

Solution

a) $x^2 = 10$

$\qquad x = \pm\sqrt{10}$ <small>Even-root property</small>

$\qquad$ The solution set is $\{-\sqrt{10}, \sqrt{10}\}$, or $\{\pm\sqrt{10}\}$.

b) $w^8 = 0$

$\qquad w = 0$ <small>Even-root property</small>

$\qquad$ The solution set is $\{0\}$.

c) By the even-root property, $x^4 = -4$ has no real solution. (The fourth power of any real number is nonnegative.) ∎

> ### Helpful Hint
>
> We do not say, "take the square root of each side." We are not doing the same thing to each side of $x^2 = 9$ when we write $x = \pm 3$. This is the third time that we have seen a rule for obtaining an equivalent equation without "doing the same thing to each side." (What were the other two?) Because there is only one odd root of every real number, you can actually take an odd root of each side.

Whether an equation has a solution depends on the domain of the variable. For example, $2x = 5$ has no solution in the set of integers and $x^2 = -9$ has no solution in the set of real numbers. We can say that the solution set to both of these equations is the empty set, $\varnothing$, as long as the domain of the variable is clear. In the next section we introduce a new set of numbers, the *imaginary numbers,* in which $x^2 = -9$ will have two solutions. So in this section it is best to say that $x^2 = -9$ has no real solution, because in the next section its solution set will *not* be $\varnothing$. An equation such as $x = x + 1$ never has a solution and so saying that its solution set is $\varnothing$ is clear.

In Example 3 the even-root property is used to solve some equations that are a bit more complicated than those of Example 2.

E X A M P L E   3   **Using the even-root property**
Solve each equation.

a) $(x - 3)^2 = 4$ b) $2(x - 5)^2 - 7 = 0$ c) $x^4 - 1 = 80$

Solution

a) $(x - 3)^2 = 4$

$\qquad x - 3 = 2 \quad$ or $\quad x - 3 = -2$ <small>Even-root property</small>

$\qquad\qquad x = 5 \quad$ or $\qquad\quad x = 1$ <small>Add 3 to each side.</small>

The solution set is $\{1, 5\}$.

Study Tip

Review, review, review! Don't wait until the end of a chapter to review. Do a little review every time you study for this course.

b) $2(x-5)^2 - 7 = 0$

$2(x-5)^2 = 7$ Add 7 to each side.

$(x-5)^2 = \dfrac{7}{2}$ Divide each side by 2.

$x - 5 = \sqrt{\dfrac{7}{2}}$ or $x - 5 = -\sqrt{\dfrac{7}{2}}$ Even-root property

$x = 5 + \dfrac{\sqrt{14}}{2}$ or $x = 5 - \dfrac{\sqrt{14}}{2}$ $\sqrt{\dfrac{7}{2}} = \dfrac{\sqrt{7}\cdot\sqrt{2}}{\sqrt{2}\cdot\sqrt{2}} = \dfrac{\sqrt{14}}{2}$

$x = \dfrac{10 + \sqrt{14}}{2}$ or $x = \dfrac{10 - \sqrt{14}}{2}$

The solution set is $\left\{\dfrac{10+\sqrt{14}}{2}, \dfrac{10-\sqrt{14}}{2}\right\}$.

c) $x^4 - 1 = 80$

$x^4 = 81$

$x = \pm\sqrt[4]{81} = \pm 3$

The solution set is $\{-3, 3\}$. ■

In Chapter 5 we solved quadratic equations by factoring. The quadratic equations that we encounter in this chapter can be solved by using the even-root property as in parts (a) and (b) of Example 3. In Chapter 8 you will learn general methods for solving any quadratic equation.

Equations Involving Radicals

If we start with the equation $x = 3$ and square both sides, we get $x^2 = 9$. The solution set to $x^2 = 9$ is $\{-3, 3\}$; the solution set to the original equation is $\{3\}$. Squaring both sides of an equation might produce a *nonequivalent* equation that has more solutions than the original equation. We call these additional solutions **extraneous solutions.** However, any solution of the original must be among the solutions to the new equation.

> **CAUTION**   When you solve an equation by raising each side to a power, you must check your answers. Raising each side to an odd power will always give an equivalent equation; raising each side to an even power might not.

E X A M P L E 4   **Raising each side to a power to eliminate radicals**

Solve each equation.

a) $\sqrt{2x-3} - 5 = 0$ **b)** $\sqrt[3]{3x+5} = \sqrt[3]{x-1}$ **c)** $\sqrt{3x+18} = x$

Solution

a) Eliminate the square root by raising each side to the power 2:

$\sqrt{2x-3} - 5 = 0$ Original equation

$\sqrt{2x-3} = 5$ Isolate the radical.

$(\sqrt{2x-3})^2 = 5^2$ Square both sides.

$2x - 3 = 25$

$2x = 28$

$x = 14$

Check by evaluating $x = 14$ in the original equation:

$$\sqrt{2(14) - 3} - 5 = 0$$
$$\sqrt{28 - 3} - 5 = 0$$
$$\sqrt{25} - 5 = 0$$
$$0 = 0$$

The solution set is $\{14\}$.

b)

$$\sqrt[3]{3x + 5} = \sqrt[3]{x - 1} \qquad \text{Original equation}$$
$$(\sqrt[3]{3x + 5})^3 = (\sqrt[3]{x - 1})^3 \qquad \text{Cube each side.}$$
$$3x + 5 = x - 1$$
$$2x = -6$$
$$x = -3$$

Check $x = -3$ in the original equation:

$$\sqrt[3]{3(-3) + 5} = \sqrt[3]{-3 - 1}$$
$$\sqrt[3]{-4} = \sqrt[3]{-4}$$

Note that $\sqrt[3]{-4}$ is a real number. The solution set is $\{-3\}$. In this example we checked for arithmetic mistakes. There was no possibility of extraneous solutions here because we raised each side to an odd power.

c)

$$\sqrt{3x + 18} = x \qquad\qquad\qquad \text{Original equation}$$
$$(\sqrt{3x + 18})^2 = x^2 \qquad\qquad\quad \text{Square both sides.}$$
$$3x + 18 = x^2 \qquad\qquad\qquad \text{Simplify.}$$
$$-x^2 + 3x + 18 = 0 \qquad\qquad\quad \begin{array}{l}\text{Subtract } x^2 \text{ from each side} \\ \text{to get zero on one side.}\end{array}$$
$$x^2 - 3x - 18 = 0 \qquad\qquad\quad \begin{array}{l}\text{Multiply each side by } -1 \\ \text{for easier factoring.}\end{array}$$
$$(x - 6)(x + 3) = 0 \qquad\qquad\quad \text{Factor.}$$
$$x - 6 = 0 \quad \text{or} \quad x + 3 = 0 \qquad \text{Zero factor property}$$
$$x = 6 \quad \text{or} \qquad x = -3$$

Because we squared both sides, we must check for extraneous solutions. If $x = -3$ in the original equation $\sqrt{3x + 18} = x$, we get

$$\sqrt{3(-3) + 18} = -3$$
$$\sqrt{9} = -3$$
$$3 = -3,$$

which is not correct. If $x = 6$ in the original equation, we get

$$\sqrt{3(6) + 18} = 6,$$

which is correct. The solution set is $\{6\}$. ■

In Example 5 the radicals are not eliminated after squaring both sides of the equation. In this case we must square both sides a second time. Note that we square the side with two terms the same way we square a binomial.

E X A M P L E 5

Squaring both sides twice

Solve $\sqrt{5x - 1} - \sqrt{x + 2} = 1$.

Solution

It is easier to square both sides if the two radicals are not on the same side.

$$\sqrt{5x - 1} - \sqrt{x + 2} = 1 \qquad \text{Original equation}$$

$$\sqrt{5x - 1} = 1 + \sqrt{x + 2} \qquad \text{Add } \sqrt{x + 2} \text{ to each side.}$$

$$(\sqrt{5x - 1})^2 = (1 + \sqrt{x + 2})^2 \qquad \text{Square both sides.}$$

$$5x - 1 = 1 + 2\sqrt{x + 2} + x + 2 \qquad \begin{array}{l}\text{Square the right side like}\\ \text{a binomial.}\end{array}$$

$$5x - 1 = 3 + x + 2\sqrt{x + 2} \qquad \begin{array}{l}\text{Combine like terms on}\\ \text{the right side.}\end{array}$$

$$4x - 4 = 2\sqrt{x + 2} \qquad \text{Isolate the square root.}$$

$$2x - 2 = \sqrt{x + 2} \qquad \text{Divide each side by 2.}$$

$$(2x - 2)^2 = (\sqrt{x + 2})^2 \qquad \text{Square both sides.}$$

$$4x^2 - 8x + 4 = x + 2 \qquad \begin{array}{l}\text{Square the binomial on}\\ \text{the left side.}\end{array}$$

$$4x^2 - 9x + 2 = 0$$

$$(4x - 1)(x - 2) = 0$$

$$4x - 1 = 0 \qquad \text{or} \qquad x - 2 = 0$$

$$x = \frac{1}{4} \qquad \text{or} \qquad x = 2$$

Check to see whether $\sqrt{5x - 1} - \sqrt{x + 2} = 1$ for $x = \frac{1}{4}$ and for $x = 2$:

$$\sqrt{5 \cdot \frac{1}{4} - 1} - \sqrt{\frac{1}{4} + 2} = \sqrt{\frac{1}{4}} - \sqrt{\frac{9}{4}} = \frac{1}{2} - \frac{3}{2} = -1$$

$$\sqrt{5 \cdot 2 - 1} - \sqrt{2 + 2} = \sqrt{9} - \sqrt{4} = 3 - 2 = 1$$

Because $\frac{1}{4}$ does not satisfy the original equation, the solution set is $\{2\}$. ■

Equations Involving Rational Exponents

Equations involving rational exponents can be solved by combining the methods that you just learned for eliminating radicals and integral exponents. For equations involving rational exponents, always eliminate the root first and the power second.

E X A M P L E 6

Helpful Hint

Note how we eliminate the root first by raising each side to an integer power, and then apply the even-root property to get two solutions in Example 6(a). A common mistake is to raise each side to the 3/2 power and get $x = 4^{3/2} = 8$. If you do not use the even-root property you can easily miss the solution -8.

Eliminating the root, then the power

Solve each equation.

a) $x^{2/3} = 4$

b) $(w - 1)^{-2/5} = 4$

Solution

a) Because the exponent 2/3 indicates a cube root, raise each side to the power 3:

$$x^{2/3} = 4 \qquad \text{Original equation}$$

$$(x^{2/3})^3 = 4^3 \qquad \text{Cube each side.}$$

$$x^2 = 64 \qquad \text{Multiply the exponents: } \frac{2}{3} \cdot 3 = 2.$$

$$x = 8 \qquad \text{or} \qquad x = -8 \qquad \text{Even-root property}$$

All of the equations are equivalent. Check 8 and -8 in the original equation. The solution set is $\{-8, 8\}$.

b)

$$(w - 1)^{-2/5} = 4 \qquad \text{Original equation}$$

$$[(w - 1)^{-2/5}]^{-5} = 4^{-5} \qquad \text{Raise each side to the power } -5 \text{ to eliminate the negative exponent.}$$

$$(w - 1)^2 = \frac{1}{1024} \qquad \text{Multiply the exponents: } -\frac{2}{5}(-5) = 2.$$

$$w - 1 = \pm\sqrt{\frac{1}{1024}} \qquad \text{Even-root property}$$

$$w - 1 = \frac{1}{32} \quad \text{or} \quad w - 1 = -\frac{1}{32}$$

$$w = \frac{33}{32} \quad \text{or} \quad w = \frac{31}{32}$$

Check the values in the original equation. The solution set is $\left\{\frac{31}{32}, \frac{33}{32}\right\}$. ■

An equation with a rational exponent might not have a real solution because all even powers of real numbers are nonnegative.

E X A M P L E   7

An equation with no solution

Solve $(2t - 3)^{-2/3} = -1$.

Solution

Raise each side to the power -3 to eliminate the root and the negative sign in the exponent:

$$(2t - 3)^{-2/3} = -1 \qquad \text{Original equation}$$

$$[(2t - 3)^{-2/3}]^{-3} = (-1)^{-3} \qquad \text{Raise each side to the } -3 \text{ power.}$$

$$(2t - 3)^2 = -1 \qquad \text{Multiply the exponents: } -\frac{2}{3}(-3) = 2.$$

By the even-root property this equation has no real solution. The square of every real number is nonnegative. ■

Summary of Methods

The three most important rules for solving equations with exponents and radicals are restated here.

> ### Strategy for Solving Equations with Exponents and Radicals
>
> 1. In raising each side of an equation to an even power, we can create an equation that gives extraneous solutions. We must check all possible solutions in the original equation.
> 2. When applying the even-root property, remember that there is a positive and a negative even root for any positive real number.
> 3. For equations with rational exponents, raise each side to a positive or negative integral power first, then apply the even- or odd-root property. (Positive fraction—raise to a positive power; negative fraction—raise to a negative power.)

Applications

The square of the hypotenuse of any right triangle is equal to the sum of the squares of the legs (the Pythagorean theorem). In Example 8 we use this fact and the even-root property to find a distance on a baseball diamond.

E X A M P L E   8   **Diagonal of a baseball diamond**

A baseball diamond is actually a square, 90 feet on each side. What is the distance from third base to first base?

Solution

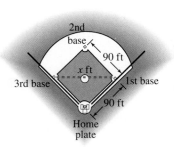

FIGURE 7.1

First make a sketch as in Fig. 7.1. The distance x from third base to first base is the length of the diagonal of the square shown in Fig. 7.1. The Pythagorean theorem can be applied to the right triangle formed from the diagonal and two sides of the square. The sum of the squares of the sides is equal to the diagonal squared:

$$x^2 = 90^2 + 90^2$$
$$x^2 = 8100 + 8100$$
$$x^2 = 16{,}200$$
$$x = \pm\sqrt{16{,}200} = \pm 90\sqrt{2}$$

The length of the diagonal of a square must be positive, so we disregard the negative solution. Checking the answer in the original equation verifies that the *exact* length of the diagonal is $90\sqrt{2}$ feet.   ■

WARM-UPS

True or false? Explain your answer.

1. The equations $x^2 = 4$ and $x = 2$ are equivalent.
2. The equation $x^2 = -25$ has no real solution.
3. There is no solution to the equation $x^2 = 0$.
4. The equation $x^3 = 8$ is equivalent to $x = \pm 2$.
5. The equation $-\sqrt{x} = 16$ has no real solution.
6. To solve $\sqrt{x - 3} = \sqrt{2x + 5}$, first apply the even-root property.
7. Extraneous solutions are solutions that cannot be found.
8. Squaring both sides of $\sqrt{x} = -7$ yields an equation with an extraneous solution.
9. The equations $x^2 - 6 = 0$ and $x = \pm\sqrt{6}$ are equivalent.
10. Cubing each side of an equation will not produce an extraneous solution.

7.5   EXERCISES

Reading and Writing   *After reading this section, write out the answers to these questions. Use complete sentences.*

1. What is the odd-root property?

2. What is the even-root property?

3. What is an extraneous solution?

4. Why can raising each side to a power produce an extraneous solution?

Solve each equation. See Example 1.

5. $x^3 = -1000$

6. $y^3 = 125$

7. $32m^5 - 1 = 0$

8. $243a^5 + 1 = 0$

9. $(y - 3)^3 = -8$

10. $(x - 1)^3 = -1$

11. $\dfrac{1}{2}x^3 + 4 = 0$

12. $3(x - 9)^7 = 0$

Find all real solutions to each equation. See Examples 2 and 3.

13. $x^2 = 25$

14. $x^2 = 36$

15. $x^2 - 20 = 0$

16. $a^2 - 40 = 0$

17. $x^2 + 9 = 0$

18. $w^2 + 49 = 0$

19. $(x - 3)^2 = 16$

20. $(a - 2)^2 = 25$

21. $(x + 1)^2 - 8 = 0$

22. $(w + 3)^2 - 12 = 0$

23. $\dfrac{1}{2}x^2 = 5$

24. $\dfrac{1}{3}x^2 = 6$

25. $(y - 3)^4 = 0$

26. $(2x - 3)^6 = 0$

27. $2x^6 = 128$

28. $3y^4 = 48$

Solve each equation and check for extraneous solutions. See Example 4.

29. $\sqrt{x - 3} - 3 = 4$

30. $\sqrt{a - 1} - 5 = 1$

31. $2\sqrt{w + 4} = 5$

32. $3\sqrt{w + 1} = 6$

33. $\sqrt[3]{2x + 3} = \sqrt[3]{x + 12}$

34. $\sqrt[3]{a + 3} = \sqrt[3]{2a - 7}$

35. $\sqrt{2t - 4} = \sqrt{t - 1}$

36. $\sqrt{w - 3} = \sqrt{4w - 15}$

37. $\sqrt{4x^2 + x - 3} = 2x$

38. $\sqrt{x^2 - 5x + 2} = x$

39. $\sqrt{x^2 + 2x - 6} = 3$

40. $\sqrt{x^2 - x - 4} = 4$

41. $\sqrt{2x^2 - 1} = x$

42. $\sqrt{2x^2 - 3x - 10} = x$

43. $\sqrt{2x^2 + 5x + 6} = x$

44. $\sqrt{2x^2 + 6x + 9} = x$

Solve each equation and check for extraneous solutions. See Example 5.

45. $\sqrt{x} + \sqrt{x - 3} = 3$

46. $\sqrt{x} + \sqrt{x + 3} = 3$

47. $\sqrt{x + 2} + \sqrt{x - 1} = 3$

48. $\sqrt{x} + \sqrt{x - 5} = 5$

49. $\sqrt{x + 3} - \sqrt{x - 2} = 1$

50. $\sqrt{2x + 1} - \sqrt{x} = 1$

51. $\sqrt{2x + 2} - \sqrt{x - 3} = 2$

52. $\sqrt{3x} - \sqrt{x - 2} = 4$

53. $\sqrt{4 - x} - \sqrt{x + 6} = 2$

54. $\sqrt{6 - x} - \sqrt{x - 2} = 2$

55. $\sqrt{x - 5} - \sqrt{x} = 3$

56. $\sqrt{2x} - \sqrt{2x - 12} = 6$

57. $\sqrt{3x + 1} + \sqrt{2x + 4} = 3$

58. $\sqrt{2x + 5} + \sqrt{x + 2} = 1$

Solve each equation. See Examples 6 and 7.

59. $x^{2/3} = 3$

60. $a^{2/3} = 2$

61. $y^{-2/3} = 9$

62. $w^{-2/3} = 4$

63. $w^{1/3} = 8$

64. $a^{1/3} = 27$

65. $t^{-1/2} = 9$

66. $w^{-1/4} = \dfrac{1}{2}$

67. $(3a - 1)^{-2/5} = 1$ **68.** $(r - 1)^{-2/3} = 1$

69. $(t - 1)^{-2/3} = 2$ **70.** $(w + 3)^{-1/3} = \dfrac{1}{3}$

71. $(x - 3)^{2/3} = -4$ **72.** $(x + 2)^{3/2} = -1$

Solve each equation.

73. $2x^2 + 3 = 7$

74. $3x^2 - 5 = 16$

75. $\sqrt[3]{2w + 3} = \sqrt[3]{w - 2}$

76. $\sqrt[3]{2 - w} = \sqrt[3]{2w - 28}$

77. $(w + 1)^{2/3} = -3$

78. $(x - 2)^{4/3} = -2$

79. $(a + 1)^{1/3} = -2$

80. $(a - 1)^{1/3} = -3$

81. $(4y - 5)^7 = 0$

82. $(5x)^9 = 0$

83. $\sqrt{5x^2 + 4x + 1} - x = 0$

84. $3 + \sqrt{x^2 - 8x} = 0$

85. $\sqrt{4x^2} = x + 2$

86. $\sqrt{9x^2} = x + 6$

87. $(t + 2)^4 = 32$

88. $(w + 1)^4 = 48$

89. $\sqrt{x^2 - 3x} = x$

90. $\sqrt[4]{4x^4 - 48} = -x$

91. $x^{-3} = 8$

92. $x^{-2} = 4$

Solve each problem by writing an equation and solving it. Find the exact answer and simplify it using the rules for radicals. See Example 8.

93. *Side of a square.* Find the length of the side of a square whose diagonal is 8 feet.

94. *Diagonal of a patio.* Find the length of the diagonal of a square patio with an area of 40 square meters.

95. *Side of a sign.* Find the length of the side of a square sign whose area is 50 square feet.

96. *Side of a cube.* Find the length of the side of a cubic box whose volume is 80 cubic feet.

97. *Diagonal of a rectangle.* If the sides of a rectangle are 30 feet and 40 feet in length, find the length of the diagonal of the rectangle.

98. *Diagonal of a sign.* What is the length of the diagonal of a rectangular billboard whose sides are 5 meters and 12 meters?

99. *Sailboat stability.* To be considered safe for ocean sailing, the capsize screening value C should be less than 2 (www.sailing.com). For a boat with a beam (or width) b in feet and displacement d in pounds, C is determined by the formula

$$C = 4d^{-1/3}b.$$

a) Find the capsize screening value for the Tartan 4100, which has a displacement of 23,245 pounds and a beam of 13.5 feet.

b) Solve this formula for d.

c) The accompanying graph shows C as a function of d for the Tartan 4100 ($b = 13.5$). For what displacement is the Tartan 4100 safe for ocean sailing?

FIGURE FOR EXERCISE 99

100. Sailboat speed. The sail area-displacement ratio S provides a measure of the sail power available to drive a boat. For a boat with a displacement of d pounds and a sail area of A square feet

$$S = 16Ad^{-2/3}.$$

a) Find S for the Tartan 4100, which has a sail area of 810 square feet and a displacement of 23,245 pounds.

b) Solve the formula for d.

101. Diagonal of a side. Find the length of the diagonal of a side of a cubic packing crate whose volume is 2 cubic meters.

102. Volume of a cube. Find the volume of a cube on which the diagonal of a side measures 2 feet.

103. Length of a road. An architect designs a public park in the shape of a trapezoid. Find the length of the diagonal road marked a in the figure.

104. Length of a boundary. Find the length of the border of the park marked b in the trapezoid shown in the figure.

FIGURE FOR EXERCISES 103 AND 104

105. Average annual return. The formula

$$r = \left(\frac{S}{P}\right)^{1/n} - 1$$

was used to find the average annual return on an investment in Exercise 133 in Section 7.2. Solve the formula for S (the amount). Solve it for P (the original principal).

106. Surface area of a cube. The formula $A = 6V^{2/3}$ gives the surface area of a cube in terms of its volume V. What is the volume of a cube with surface area 12 square feet?

 107. Kepler's third law. According to Kepler's third law of planetary motion, the ratio $\frac{T^2}{R^3}$ has the same value for every planet in our solar system. R is the average radius of the orbit of the planet measured in astronomical units (AU), and T is the number of years it takes for one complete orbit of the sun. Jupiter orbits the sun in 11.86 years with an average radius of 5.2 AU, whereas Saturn orbits the sun in 29.46 years. Find the average radius of the orbit of Saturn. (One AU is the distance from the earth to the sun.)

FIGURE FOR EXERCISE 107

 108. Orbit of Venus. If the average radius of the orbit of Venus is 0.723 AU, then how many years does it take for Venus to complete one orbit of the sun? Use the information in Exercise 107.

 Use a calculator to find approximate solutions to the following equations. Round your answers to three decimal places.

109. $x^2 = 3.24$

110. $(x + 4)^3 = 7.51$

111. $\sqrt{x - 2} = 1.73$

112. $\sqrt[3]{x - 5} = 3.7$

113. $x^{2/3} = 8.86$

114. $(x - 1)^{-3/4} = 7.065$

GETTING MORE INVOLVED

 115. Cooperative learning. Work in a small group to write a formula that gives the side of a cube in terms of the volume of the cube and explain the formula to the other groups.

116. Cooperative learning. Work in a small group to write a formula that gives the side of a square in terms of the diagonal of the square and explain the formula to the other groups.

7.6   COMPLEX NUMBERS

In Chapter 1 we discussed the real numbers and the various subsets of the real numbers. In this section we define a set of numbers that has the real numbers as a subset.

Definition

The equation $2x = 1$ has no solution in the set of integers, but in the set of rational numbers, $2x = 1$ has a solution. The situation is similar for the equation $x^2 = -4$. It has no solution in the set of real numbers because the square of every real number is nonnegative. However, in the set of complex numbers $x^2 = -4$ has two solutions. The complex numbers were developed so that equations such as $x^2 = -4$ would have solutions.

The complex numbers are based on the symbol $\sqrt{-1}$. In the real number system this symbol has no meaning. In the set of complex numbers this symbol is given meaning. We call it i. We make the definition that

$$i = \sqrt{-1} \quad \text{and} \quad i^2 = -1.$$

> **Complex Numbers**
>
> The set of **complex numbers** is the set of all numbers of the form
> $$a + bi,$$
> where a and b are real numbers, $i = \sqrt{-1}$, and $i^2 = -1$.

In the complex number $a + bi$, a is called the **real part** and b is called the **imaginary part.** If $b \neq 0$, the number $a + bi$ is called an **imaginary number.**

In dealing with complex numbers, we treat $a + bi$ as if it were a binomial, with i being a variable. Thus we would write $2 + (-3)i$ as $2 - 3i$. We agree that $2 + i3$, $3i + 2$, and $i3 + 2$ are just different ways of writing $2 + 3i$ (the standard form). Some examples of complex numbers are

$$-3 - 5i, \quad \frac{2}{3} - \frac{3}{4}i, \quad 1 + i\sqrt{2}, \quad 9 + 0i, \quad \text{and} \quad 0 + 7i.$$

For simplicity we write only $7i$ for $0 + 7i$. The complex number $9 + 0i$ is the real number 9, and $0 + 0i$ is the real number 0. Any complex number with $b = 0$ is a real number. For any real number a,

$$a + 0i = a.$$

The set of real numbers is a subset of the set of complex numbers. See Fig. 7.2.

Complex numbers	
Real numbers	Imaginary numbers
$3, \pi, \frac{5}{2}, 0, -9, \sqrt{2}$	$i, 2 + 3i, \sqrt{-5}, -3 - 8i$

FIGURE 7.2

Addition, Subtraction, and Multiplication

Addition and subtraction of complex numbers are performed as if the complex numbers were algebraic expressions with i being a variable.

E X A M P L E   1

Addition and subtraction of complex numbers

Find the sums and differences.

a) $(2 + 3i) + (6 + i)$ **b)** $(-2 + 3i) + (-2 - 5i)$

c) $(3 + 5i) - (1 + 2i)$ **d)** $(-2 - 3i) - (1 - i)$

Solution

a) $(2 + 3i) + (6 + i) = 8 + 4i$

b) $(-2 + 3i) + (-2 - 5i) = -4 - 2i$

c) $(3 + 5i) - (1 + 2i) = 2 + 3i$

d) $(-2 - 3i) - (1 - i) = -3 - 2i$ ■

We can give a symbolic definition of addition and subtraction as follows.

> **Addition and Subtraction of Complex Numbers**
>
> The sum and difference of $a + bi$ and $c + di$ are defined as follows:
>
> $$(a + bi) + (c + di) = (a + c) + (b + d)i$$
> $$(a + bi) - (c + di) = (a - c) + (b - d)i$$

Complex numbers are multiplied as if they were algebraic expressions. Whenever i^2 appears, we replace it by -1.

E X A M P L E   2

Products of complex numbers

Find each product.

a) $2i(1 + i)$ **b)** $(2 + 3i)(4 + 5i)$

c) $(3 + i)(3 - i)$

Calculator Close-Up

Many graphing calculators can perform operations with complex numbers.

```
2i(1+i)
               -2+2i
(2+3i)(4+5i)
               -7+22i
(3+i)(3-i)
                  10
```

Solution

a) $2i(1 + i) = 2i + 2i^2$ Distributive property

$= 2i + 2(-1)$ $i^2 = -1$

$= -2 + 2i$

b) Use the FOIL method to find the product:

$$(2 + 3i)(4 + 5i) = 8 + 10i + 12i + 15i^2$$
$$= 8 + 22i + 15(-1) \quad \text{Replace } i^2 \text{ by } -1.$$
$$= 8 + 22i - 15$$
$$= -7 + 22i$$

c) This product is the product of a sum and a difference.

$$(3 + i)(3 - i) = 9 - 3i + 3i - i^2$$
$$= 9 - (-1) \quad i^2 = -1$$
$$= 10 \qquad\qquad ■$$

We can find powers of i using the fact that $i^2 = -1$. For example,

$$i^3 = i^2 \cdot i = -1 \cdot i = -i.$$

The value of i^4 is found from the value of i^3:

$$i^4 = i^3 \cdot i = -i \cdot i = -i^2 = 1.$$

In Example 3 we find more powers of imaginary numbers.

E X A M P L E   3   **Powers of imaginary numbers**

Write each expression in the form $a + bi$.

a) $(2i)^2$ b) $(-2i)^2$ c) i^6

Solution

a) $(2i)^2 = 2^2 \cdot i^2 = 4(-1) = -4$

b) $(-2i)^2 = (-2)^2 \cdot i^2 = 4i^2 = 4(-1) = -4$

c) $i^6 = i^2 \cdot i^4 = -1 \cdot 1 = -1$ ■

For completeness we give the following symbolic definition of multiplication of complex numbers. However, it is simpler to find products as we did in Examples 2 and 3 than to use this definition.

Multiplication of Complex Numbers

The complex numbers $a + bi$ and $c + di$ are multiplied as follows:

$$(a + bi)(c + di) = (ac - bd) + (ad + bc)i$$

Division of Complex Numbers

To divide a complex number by a real number, divide each term by the real number, just as we would divide a binomial by a number. For example,

$$\frac{4 + 6i}{2} = \frac{2(2 + 3i)}{2}$$
$$= 2 + 3i.$$

Helpful Hint

Here is that word "conjugate" again. It is generally used to refer to two things that go together in some way.

To understand division by a complex number, we first look at imaginary numbers that have a real product. The product of the two imaginary numbers in Example 2(c) is a real number:

$$(3 + i)(3 - i) = 10$$

We say that $3 + i$ and $3 - i$ are complex conjugates of each other.

Complex Conjugates

The complex numbers $a + bi$ and $a - bi$ are called **complex conjugates** of one another. Their product is the real number $a^2 + b^2$.

E X A M P L E   4   **Products of conjugates**

Find the product of the given complex number and its conjugate.

a) $2 + 3i$ b) $5 - 4i$

Solution

a) The conjugate of $2 + 3i$ is $2 - 3i$.

$$(2 + 3i)(2 - 3i) = 4 - 9i^2$$
$$= 4 + 9$$
$$= 13$$

b) The conjugate of $5 - 4i$ is $5 + 4i$.

$$(5 - 4i)(5 + 4i) = 25 + 16$$
$$= 41$$ ∎

We use the idea of complex conjugates to divide complex numbers. The process is similar to rationalizing the denominator. Multiply the numerator and denominator of the quotient by the complex conjugate of the denominator.

E X A M P L E   5

Dividing complex numbers

Find each quotient. Write the answer in the form $a + bi$.

a) $\dfrac{5}{3 - 4i}$ **b)** $\dfrac{3 - i}{2 + i}$

c) $\dfrac{3 + 2i}{i}$

Solution

a) Multiply the numerator and denominator by $3 + 4i$, the conjugate of $3 - 4i$:

$$\frac{5}{3 - 4i} = \frac{5(3 + 4i)}{(3 - 4i)(3 + 4i)}$$

$$= \frac{15 + 20i}{9 - 16i^2}$$

$$= \frac{15 + 20i}{25} \qquad 9 - 16i^2 = 9 - 16(-1) = 25$$

$$= \frac{15}{25} + \frac{20}{25}i$$

$$= \frac{3}{5} + \frac{4}{5}i.$$

b) Multiply the numerator and denominator by $2 - i$, the conjugate of $2 + i$:

$$\frac{3 - i}{2 + i} = \frac{(3 - i)(2 - i)}{(2 + i)(2 - i)}$$

$$= \frac{6 - 5i + i^2}{4 - i^2}$$

$$= \frac{6 - 5i - 1}{4 - (-1)}$$

$$= \frac{5 - 5i}{5}$$

$$= 1 - i$$

c) Multiply the numerator and denominator by $-i$, the conjugate of i:

$$\frac{3+2i}{i} = \frac{(3+2i)(-i)}{i(-i)}$$

$$= \frac{-3i-2i^2}{-i^2}$$

$$= \frac{-3i+2}{1}$$

$$= 2-3i \qquad \blacksquare$$

The symbolic definition of division of complex numbers follows.

Division of Complex Numbers

We divide the complex number $a+bi$ by the complex number $c+di$ as follows:

$$\frac{a+bi}{c+di} = \frac{(a+bi)(c-di)}{(c+di)(c-di)}$$

Square Roots of Negative Numbers

In Examples 3(a) and 3(b) we saw that both

$$(2i)^2 = -4 \quad \text{and} \quad (-2i)^2 = -4.$$

Because the square of each of these complex numbers is -4, both $2i$ and $-2i$ are square roots of -4. We write $\sqrt{-4} = 2i$. In the complex number system the square root of any negative number is an imaginary number.

Square Root of a Negative Number

For any positive real number b,

$$\sqrt{-b} = i\sqrt{b}.$$

For example, $\sqrt{-9} = i\sqrt{9} = 3i$ and $\sqrt{-7} = i\sqrt{7}$. Note that the expression $\sqrt{7}i$ could easily be mistaken for the expression $\sqrt{7i}$, where i is under the radical. For this reason, when the coefficient of i is a radical, we write i preceding the radical.

Note that the product rule $(\sqrt{a} \cdot \sqrt{b} = \sqrt{ab})$ does not apply to negative numbers. For example $\sqrt{-2} \cdot \sqrt{-3} \neq \sqrt{6}$:

$$\sqrt{-2} \cdot \sqrt{-3} = i\sqrt{2} \cdot i\sqrt{3} = i^2\sqrt{6} = -\sqrt{6}$$

Square roots of negative numbers must written in terms of i before operations are performed.

EXAMPLE 6 **Square roots of negative numbers**

Write each expression in the form $a+bi$, where a and b are real numbers.

a) $3+\sqrt{-9}$ **b)** $\sqrt{-12}+\sqrt{-27}$

c) $\dfrac{-1-\sqrt{-18}}{3}$ **d)** $\sqrt{-4} \cdot \sqrt{-9}$

Solution

a) $3 + \sqrt{-9} = 3 + i\sqrt{9}$

$\qquad\qquad\quad = 3 + 3i$

b) $\sqrt{-12} + \sqrt{-27} = i\sqrt{12} + i\sqrt{27}$

$\qquad\qquad\qquad\quad = 2i\sqrt{3} + 3i\sqrt{3}$ $\begin{array}{l}\sqrt{12} = \sqrt{4}\,\sqrt{3} = 2\sqrt{3} \\ \sqrt{27} = \sqrt{9}\,\sqrt{3} = 3\sqrt{3}\end{array}$

$\qquad\qquad\qquad\quad = 5i\sqrt{3}$

c) $\dfrac{-1 - \sqrt{-18}}{3} = \dfrac{-1 - i\sqrt{18}}{3}$

$\qquad\qquad\qquad = \dfrac{-1 - 3i\sqrt{2}}{3}$

$\qquad\qquad\qquad = -\dfrac{1}{3} - i\sqrt{2}$

d) $\sqrt{-4} \cdot \sqrt{-9} = i\sqrt{4} \cdot i\sqrt{9} = 2i \cdot 3i = 6i^2 = -6$ ■

Imaginary Solutions to Equations

In the complex number system the even-root property can be restated so that $x^2 = k$ is equivalent to $x = \pm\sqrt{k}$ for any $k \neq 0$. So an equation such as $x^2 = -9$ that has no real solutions has two imaginary solutions in the complex numbers.

E X A M P L E   7

Complex solutions to equations

Find the complex solutions to each equation.

a) $x^2 = -9$ b) $3x^2 + 2 = 0$

Solution

a) First apply the even-root property:

$$x^2 = -9$$

$$x = \pm\sqrt{-9} \quad \text{Even-root property}$$

$$= \pm i\sqrt{9}$$

$$= \pm 3i$$

Check these solutions in the original equation:

$$(3i)^2 = 9i^2 = 9(-1) = -9$$

$$(-3i)^2 = 9i^2 = -9$$

The solution set is $\{\pm 3i\}$.

b) First solve the equation for x^2:

$$3x^2 + 2 = 0$$

$$x^2 = -\frac{2}{3}$$

$$x = \pm\sqrt{-\frac{2}{3}} = \pm i\sqrt{\frac{2}{3}} = \pm i\frac{\sqrt{6}}{3}$$

Check these solutions in the original equation. The solution set is $\left\{\pm i\dfrac{\sqrt{6}}{3}\right\}$.   ■

The basic facts about complex numbers are listed in the following box.

Complex Numbers

1. Definition of i: $i = \sqrt{-1}$, and $i^2 = -1$.
2. A complex number has the form $a + bi$, where a and b are real numbers.
3. The complex number $a + 0i$ is the real number a.
4. If b is a positive real number, then $\sqrt{-b} = i\sqrt{b}$.
5. The numbers $a + bi$ and $a - bi$ are called complex conjugates of each other. Their product is the real number $a^2 + b^2$.
6. Add, subtract, and multiply complex numbers as if they were algebraic expressions with i being the variable, and replace i^2 by -1.
7. Divide complex numbers by multiplying the numerator and denominator by the conjugate of the denominator.
8. In the complex number system $x^2 = k$ for any real number k is equivalent to $x = \pm\sqrt{k}$.

WARM-UPS

True or false? Explain your answer.

1. The set of real numbers is a subset of the set of complex numbers.
2. $2 - \sqrt{-6} = 2 - 6i$ 3. $\sqrt{-9} = \pm 3i$
4. The solution set to the equation $x^2 = -9$ is $\{\pm 3i\}$.
5. $2 - 3i - (4 - 2i) = -2 - i$
6. $i^4 = 1$ 7. $(2 - i)(2 + i) = 5$
8. $i^3 = i$ 9. $i^{48} = 1$
10. The equation $x^2 = k$ has two complex solutions for any real number k.

7.6 EXERCISES

Reading and Writing After reading this section, write out the answers to these questions. Use complete sentences.
1. What are complex numbers?

2. What is an imaginary number?

3. What is the relationship among the real numbers, the imaginary numbers, and the complex numbers?

4. How do we add, subtract, and multiply complex numbers?

5. What is the conjugate of a complex number?

6. How do we divide complex numbers?

Find the indicated sums and differences of complex numbers. See Example 1.
7. $(2 + 3i) + (-4 + 5i)$ 8. $(-1 + 6i) + (5 - 4i)$

9. $(2 - 3i) - (6 - 7i)$ 10. $(2 - 3i) - (6 - 2i)$

11. $(-1 + i) + (-1 - i)$ 12. $(-5 + i) + (-5 - i)$

13. $(-2 - 3i) - (6 - i)$ 14. $(-6 + 4i) - (2 - i)$

Find each product. Express each answer in the form a + bi.
See Example 2.

15. $3(2 + 5i)$ **16.** $4(1 - 3i)$ **17.** $2i(i - 5)$

18. $3i(2 - 6i)$ **19.** $-4i(3 - i)$ **20.** $-5i(2 + 3i)$

21. $(2 + 3i)(4 + 6i)$ **22.** $(2 + i)(3 + 4i)$

23. $(-1 + i)(2 - i)$ **24.** $(3 - 2i)(2 - 5i)$

25. $(-1 - 2i)(2 + i)$ **26.** $(1 - 3i)(1 + 3i)$

27. $(5 - 2i)(5 + 2i)$ **28.** $(4 + 3i)(4 + 3i)$

29. $(1 - i)(1 + i)$ **30.** $(2 + 6i)(2 - 6i)$

31. $(4 + 2i)(4 - 2i)$ **32.** $(4 - i)(4 + i)$

Find the indicated powers of complex numbers. See
Example 3.

33. $(3i)^2$ **34.** $(5i)^2$ **35.** $(-5i)^2$
36. $(-9i)^2$ **37.** $(2i)^4$ **38.** $(-2i)^3$
39. i^9 **40.** i^{12}

Find the product of the given complex number and its con-
jugate. See Example 4.

41. $3 + 5i$ **42.** $3 + i$ **43.** $1 - 2i$
44. $4 - 6i$ **45.** $-2 + i$ **46.** $-3 - 2i$
47. $2 - i\sqrt{3}$ **48.** $\sqrt{5} - 4i$

Find each quotient. Express each answer in the form a + bi.
See Example 5.

49. $\dfrac{3}{4 + i}$ **50.** $\dfrac{6}{7 - 2i}$

51. $\dfrac{2 + i}{3 - 2i}$ **52.** $\dfrac{3 + 5i}{2 - i}$

53. $\dfrac{4 + 3i}{i}$ **54.** $\dfrac{5 - 6i}{3i}$

55. $\dfrac{2 + 6i}{2}$ **56.** $\dfrac{9 - 3i}{-6}$

57. $\dfrac{1 + i}{3i - 2}$ **58.** $\dfrac{2 + i}{i + 5}$

59. $\dfrac{6}{3i}$ **60.** $\dfrac{8}{-2i}$

Write each expression in the form a + bi, where a and b are
real numbers. See Example 6.

61. $2 + \sqrt{-4}$ **62.** $3 + \sqrt{-9}$ **63.** $2\sqrt{-9} + 5$

64. $3\sqrt{-16} + 2$ **65.** $7 - \sqrt{-6}$ **66.** $\sqrt{-5} + 3$

67. $\sqrt{-8} + \sqrt{-18}$ **68.** $2\sqrt{-20} - \sqrt{-45}$

69. $\dfrac{2 + \sqrt{-12}}{2}$ **70.** $\dfrac{-6 - \sqrt{-18}}{3}$

71. $\dfrac{-4 - \sqrt{-24}}{4}$ **72.** $\dfrac{8 + \sqrt{-20}}{-4}$

73. $\sqrt{-2} \cdot \sqrt{-6}$ **74.** $\sqrt{-3} \cdot \sqrt{-15}$
75. $\sqrt{-3} \cdot \sqrt{-27}$ **76.** $\sqrt{-3} \cdot \sqrt{-7}$
77. $\dfrac{\sqrt{8}}{\sqrt{-4}}$ **78.** $\dfrac{\sqrt{6}}{\sqrt{-2}}$

Find the complex solutions to each equation. See Example 7.

79. $x^2 = -36$ **80.** $x^2 + 4 = 0$
81. $x^2 = -12$ **82.** $x^2 = -25$

83. $2x^2 + 5 = 0$ **84.** $3x^2 + 4 = 0$

85. $3x^2 + 6 = 0$ **86.** $x^2 + 1 = 0$

Write each expression in the form a + bi, where a and b
are real numbers.

87. $(2 - 3i)(3 + 4i)$ **88.** $(2 - 3i)(2 + 3i)$

89. $(2 - 3i) + (3 + 4i)$ **90.** $(3 - 5i) - (2 - 7i)$

91. $\dfrac{2 - 3i}{3 + 4i}$ **92.** $\dfrac{-3i}{3 - 6i}$

93. $i(2 - 3i)$ **94.** $-3i(4i - 1)$
95. $(-3i)^2$ **96.** $(-2i)^6$
97. $\sqrt{-12} + \sqrt{-3}$ **98.** $\sqrt{-49} - \sqrt{-25}$
99. $(2 - 3i)^2$ **100.** $(5 + 3i)^2$
101. $\dfrac{-4 + \sqrt{-32}}{2}$ **102.** $\dfrac{-2 - \sqrt{-27}}{-6}$

GETTING MORE INVOLVED

103. *Writing.* Explain why $2 - i$ is a solution to
$$x^2 - 4x + 5 = 0.$$

104. *Cooperative learning.* Work with a group to verify
that $-1 + i\sqrt{3}$ and $-1 - i\sqrt{3}$ satisfy the equation
$$x^3 - 8 = 0.$$
In the complex number system there are three cube
roots of 8. What are they?

105. *Discussion.* What is wrong with using the product
rule for radicals to get
$$\sqrt{-4} \cdot \sqrt{-4} = \sqrt{(-4)(-4)} = \sqrt{16} = 4?$$
What is the correct product?

COLLABORATIVE ACTIVITIES

Laws of Falling Bodies

Jaki Sena is a private investigator working on a case. Her client is accused of killing a woman who had lived in the same apartment building as he did. She pulls over the file of notes from across her desk and looks through it yet again.

"Okay, so my client said he was on the roof of the building just before 4:00 A.M., dropping blocks over into the alleyway. He dropped the last block just as the clock tower began striking the hour. I wonder how high the building is," Jaki says to herself.

During her initial investigation of the crime scene Jaki had asked the building manager whether he knew the height of the five-story building. He had been very condescending and had told her nothing. Another tenant of the building, some sort of math instructor at the city college, had told her about an experiment he had done with shadows and a climbing rope. He had given her a drawing.

Jaki looked through the file until she found the following drawing.

63.5 ft

21 ft
shadow

Grouping: 2 to 4 students per group

Topic: Applications of formulas with square roots

She pulled out a blank piece of paper, and using a calculator, she soon had a number.

"Now I can find out how long it took the block to fall!" Jaki exclaimed. "Okay, now the witness who saw my client on the top of the building also swears he saw the woman walking past the steps next door as the clock tower started to chime 4:00," Jaki said out loud as she got up from her desk and looked out the window. "I have no idea how fast the woman was walking. That may be a hard one to answer. But I do know the steps begin about $9\frac{1}{2}$ feet from where the block fell." Jaki turned back to the file of notes on her desk. She soon found another piece of paper with measurements on it.

"And I do know the woman was 5 feet tall!" Jaki exclaimed, taking out her calculator again.

1. Working in your groups, find the height of the building from the information on Jaki's paper. Round your answer to the nearest tenth of a foot.

2. Find out how many seconds it would take the block to fall from the top of the building to hit the woman on the head. Round your answer to the nearest tenth of a second. (*Hint:* You may need to look in other chapters of the book to find the formulas you need here.)

3. How fast would the woman have to walk to have been hit on the head by the block? Round your answer to the nearest tenth of a foot per second.

4. Could Jaki's client have "done it?" Give a reason for your answer.

WRAP-UP   CHAPTER 7

SUMMARY

Powers and Roots

		Examples
*n*th roots	If $a = b^n$ for a positive integer n, then b is an *n*th root of a.	2 and -2 are fourth roots of 16.
Principal root	The positive even root of a positive number.	The principal fourth root of 16 is 2.
Radical notation	If n is a positive even integer and a is positive, then the symbol $\sqrt[n]{a}$ denotes the principal *n*th root of a.	$\sqrt[4]{16} = 2$ $\sqrt[4]{16} \neq -2$

| | If n is a positive odd integer, then the symbol $\sqrt[n]{a}$ denotes the nth root of a. | $\sqrt[3]{-8} = -2, \sqrt[3]{8} = 2$ |
| | If n is any positive integer, then $\sqrt[n]{0} = 0$. | $\sqrt[5]{0} = 0, \sqrt[6]{0} = 0$ |

| Definition of $a^{1/n}$ | If n is any positive integer, then $a^{1/n} = \sqrt[n]{a}$, provided that $\sqrt[n]{a}$ is a real number. | $8^{1/3} = \sqrt[3]{8} = 2$
$(-4)^{1/2}$ is not real. |

| Definition of $a^{m/n}$ | If m and n are positive integers, then $a^{m/n} = (a^{1/n})^m$, provided that $a^{1/n}$ is a real number. | $8^{2/3} = (8^{1/3})^2 = 2^2 = 4$
$(-16)^{3/4}$ is not real. |

| Definition of $a^{-m/n}$ | If m and n are positive integers and $a \neq 0$, then $a^{-m/n} = \frac{1}{a^{m/n}}$, provided that $a^{1/n}$ is a real number. | $8^{-2/3} = \frac{1}{8^{2/3}} = \frac{1}{4}$ |

Rules for Radicals

Examples

| Product rule for radicals | Provided that all roots are real,
$\sqrt[n]{ab} = \sqrt[n]{a} \cdot \sqrt[n]{b}$. | $\sqrt{2} \cdot \sqrt{3} = \sqrt{6}$
$\sqrt{4x} = 2\sqrt{x}$ |

| Quotient rule for radicals | Provided that all roots are real and $b \neq 0$,
$$\sqrt[n]{\frac{a}{b}} = \frac{\sqrt[n]{a}}{\sqrt[n]{b}}.$$ | $\sqrt{\frac{5}{9}} = \frac{\sqrt{5}}{3}$
$\sqrt{10} \div \sqrt{5} = \sqrt{2}$ |

| Simplified radical form for radicals of index n | A simplified radical of index n has
1. *no* perfect nth powers as factors of the radicand,
2. *no* fractions inside the radical, and

3. *no* radicals in the denominator. | $\sqrt{20} = \sqrt{4 \cdot 5} = 2\sqrt{5}$
$\sqrt{\frac{3}{2}} = \frac{\sqrt{3}}{\sqrt{2}}$
$\frac{\sqrt{3}}{\sqrt{2}} = \frac{\sqrt{3}}{\sqrt{2}} \cdot \frac{\sqrt{2}}{\sqrt{2}} = \frac{\sqrt{6}}{2}$ |

Rules for Rational Exponents

Examples

If a and b are nonzero real numbers and r and s are rational numbers, then the following rules hold, provided all expressions represent real numbers.

| Product rule | $a^r \cdot a^s = a^{r+s}$ | $3^{1/4} \cdot 3^{1/2} = 3^{3/4}$ |

| Quotient rule | $\dfrac{a^r}{a^s} = a^{r-s}$ | $\dfrac{x^{3/4}}{x^{1/4}} = x^{1/2}$ |

| Power of a power rule | $(a^r)^s = a^{rs}$ | $(2^{1/2})^{-1/2} = 2^{-1/4}$
$(x^{3/4})^4 = x^3$ |

Power of a product rule	$(ab)^r = a^r b^r$	$(a^2 b^6)^{1/2} = ab^3$
Power of a quotient rule	$\left(\dfrac{a}{b}\right)^r = \dfrac{a^r}{b^r}$	$\left(\dfrac{8}{x^6}\right)^{2/3} = \dfrac{4}{x^4}$

Equations		**Examples**
Equations with radicals and exponents	1. In raising each side of an equation to an even power, we can create an equation that gives extraneous solutions. We must check.	$\sqrt{x} = -3$ $x = 9$
	2. When applying the even-root property, remember that there is a positive and a negative root.	$x^2 = 36$ $x = \pm 6$
	3. For equations with rational exponents, raise each side to a positive or a negative power first, then apply the even- or odd-root property.	$x^{-2/3} = 4$ $(x^{-2/3})^{-3} = 4^{-3}$ $x^2 = \dfrac{1}{64}$ $x = \pm\dfrac{1}{8}$

Complex Numbers		**Examples**
Complex numbers	Numbers of form $a + bi$, where a and b are real numbers: $i = \sqrt{-1},\ i^2 = -1$	$2 + 3i$ $-6i$ $\sqrt{2} + i$
Complex conjugates	Complex numbers of the form $a + bi$ and $a - bi$: Their product is the real number $a^2 + b^2$.	$(2 + 3i)(2 - 3i) = 2^2 + 3^2$ $= 13$
Complex number operations	Add, subtract, and multiply as algebraic expressions with i being the variable. Simplify using $i^2 = -1$.	$(2 + 5i) + (4 - 2i) = 6 + 3i$ $(2 + 5i) - (4 - 2i) = -2 + 7i$ $(2 + 5i)(4 - 2i) = 18 + 16i$
	Divide complex numbers by multiplying numerator and denominator by the conjugate of the denominator.	$(2 + 5i) \div (4 - 2i)$ $= \dfrac{(2 + 5i)(4 + 2i)}{(4 - 2i)(4 + 2i)}$ $= \dfrac{-2 + 24i}{20} = -\dfrac{1}{10} + \dfrac{6}{5}i$
Square root of a negative number	For any positive real number b, $\sqrt{-b} = i\sqrt{b}$.	$\sqrt{-9} = i\sqrt{9} = 3i$
Imaginary solutions to equations	In the complex number system, $x^2 = k$ for any real k is equivalent to $x = \pm\sqrt{k}$.	$x^2 = -25$ $x = \pm\sqrt{-25} = \pm 5i$

ENRICHING YOUR MATHEMATICAL WORD POWER

For each mathematical term, choose the correct meaning.

1. ***n*th root of *a***
   a. a square root
   b. the root of a^n
   c. a number b such that $a^n = b$
   d. a number b such that $b^n = a$

2. **square of *a***
   a. a number b such that $b^2 = a$
   b. a^2
   c. $|a|$
   d. $\sqrt{a}$

3. **cube root of *a***
   a. a^3
   b. a number b such that $b^3 = a$
   c. $a/3$
   d. a number b such that $b = a^3$

4. **principal root**
   a. the main root
   b. the positive even root of a positive number
   c. the positive odd root of a negative number
   d. the negative odd root of a negative number

5. **odd root of *a***
   a. the number b such that $b^n = a$, where a is an odd number
   b. the opposite of the even root of a
   c. the nth root of a
   d. the number b such that $b^n = a$, where n is an odd number

6. **index of a radical**
   a. the number n in $n\sqrt{a}$
   b. the number n in $\sqrt[n]{a}$
   c. the number n in a^n
   d. the number n in $\sqrt{a^n}$

7. **like radicals**
   a. radicals with the same index
   b. radicals with the same radicand
   c. radicals with the same radicand and the same index
   d. radicals with even indices

8. **integral exponent**
   a. an exponent that is an integer
   b. a positive exponent
   c. a rational exponent
   d. a fractional exponent

9. **rational exponent**
   a. an exponent that produces a rational number
   b. an integral exponent
   c. an exponent that is a real number
   d. an exponent that is a rational number

10. **radicand**
    a. the expression $\sqrt[n]{a}$
    b. the expression $\sqrt{a}$
    c. the number a in $\sqrt[n]{a}$
    d. the number n in $\sqrt[n]{a}$

11. **complex numbers**
    a. $a + bi$, where a and b are real
    b. irrational numbers
    c. imaginary numbers
    d. $\sqrt{-1}$

12. **imaginary unit**
    a. 1
    b. -1
    c. i
    d. $\sqrt{1}$

13. **imaginary number**
    a. $a + bi$, where a and b are real
    b. i
    c. a complex number
    d. a complex number in which $b \neq 0$

14. **complex conjugates**
    a. i and $\sqrt{-1}$
    b. $a + bi$ and $a - bi$
    c. $(a + b)(a - b)$
    d. i and -1

REVIEW EXERCISES

7.1 *Simplify each radical expression. Assume all variables represent positive real numbers.*

1. $\sqrt[5]{32}$
2. $\sqrt[3]{-27}$
3. $\sqrt[3]{1000}$
4. $\sqrt{100}$
5. $\sqrt{72}$
6. $\sqrt{48}$
7. $\sqrt{x^{12}}$
8. $\sqrt{a^{10}}$
9. $\sqrt[3]{x^6}$
10. $\sqrt[3]{a^9}$
11. $\sqrt{2x^9}$
12. $\sqrt{3a^7}$
13. $\sqrt{8w^5}$
14. $\sqrt{20n^{25}}$
15. $\sqrt[3]{16x^4}$
16. $\sqrt[3]{54b^5}$

17. $\sqrt[4]{a^9 b^5}$
18. $\sqrt[4]{32m^{11}}$
19. $\sqrt{\dfrac{x^3}{16}}$
20. $\sqrt{\dfrac{12a^3}{25}}$

7.2 *Simplify the expressions involving rational exponents. Assume all variables represent positive real numbers. Write your answers with positive exponents.*

21. $(-27)^{-2/3}$
22. $-25^{3/2}$
23. $(2^6)^{1/3}$
24. $(5^2)^{1/2}$

25. $100^{-3/2}$

26. $1000^{-2/3}$

27. $\dfrac{3x^{-1/2}}{3^{-2}x^{-1}}$

28. $\dfrac{(x^2y^{-3}z)^{1/2}}{x^{1/2}yz^{-1/2}}$

29. $(a^{1/2}b)^3(ab^{1/4})^2$

30. $(t^{-1/2})^{-2}(t^{-2}v^2)$

31. $(x^{1/2}y^{1/4})(x^{1/4}y)$

32. $(a^{1/3}b^{1/6})^2(a^{1/3}b^{2/3})$

7.3 *Perform the operations and simplify. Assume the variables represent positive real numbers.*

33. $\sqrt{13} \cdot \sqrt{13}$

34. $\sqrt[3]{14} \cdot \sqrt[3]{14} \cdot \sqrt[3]{14}$

35. $\sqrt{27} + \sqrt{45} - \sqrt{75}$

36. $\sqrt{12} - \sqrt{50} + \sqrt{72}$

37. $3\sqrt{2}(5\sqrt{2} - 7\sqrt{3})$

38. $-2\sqrt{a}(\sqrt{a} - \sqrt{ab^6})$

39. $(2 - \sqrt{3})(3 + \sqrt{2})$

40. $(2\sqrt{x} - \sqrt{y})(\sqrt{x} + \sqrt{y})$

7.4 *Perform the operations and simplify.*

41. $5 \div \sqrt{2}$

42. $(10\sqrt{6}) \div (2\sqrt{2})$

43. $\sqrt{\dfrac{2}{5}}$

44. $\sqrt{\dfrac{1}{6}}$

45. $\sqrt[3]{\dfrac{2}{3}}$

46. $\sqrt[3]{\dfrac{1}{9}}$

47. $\dfrac{2}{\sqrt{3x}}$

48. $\dfrac{3}{\sqrt{2y}}$

49. $\dfrac{\sqrt{10y^3}}{\sqrt{6}}$

50. $\dfrac{\sqrt{5x^5}}{\sqrt{8}}$

51. $\dfrac{3}{\sqrt[3]{2a}}$

52. $\dfrac{a}{\sqrt[3]{a^2}}$

53. $\dfrac{5}{\sqrt[4]{3x^2}}$

54. $\dfrac{b}{\sqrt[4]{a^2b^3}}$

55. $(\sqrt{3})^4$

56. $(-2\sqrt{x})^9$

57. $\dfrac{2 - \sqrt{8}}{2}$

58. $\dfrac{-3 - \sqrt{18}}{-6}$

59. $\dfrac{\sqrt{6}}{1 - \sqrt{3}}$

60. $\dfrac{\sqrt{15}}{2 + \sqrt{5}}$

61. $\dfrac{2\sqrt{3}}{3\sqrt{6} - \sqrt{12}}$

62. $\dfrac{-\sqrt{xy}}{3\sqrt{x} + \sqrt{xy}}$

63. $(2w\sqrt[3]{2w^2})^6$

64. $(m\sqrt[4]{m^3})^8$

7.5 *Find all real solutions to each equation.*

65. $x^2 = 16$

66. $w^2 = 100$

67. $(a - 5)^2 = 4$

68. $(m - 7)^2 = 25$

69. $(a + 1)^2 = 5$

70. $(x + 5)^2 = 3$

71. $(m + 1)^2 = -8$

72. $(w + 4)^2 = 16$

73. $\sqrt{m - 1} = 3$

74. $3\sqrt{x + 5} = 12$

75. $\sqrt[3]{2x + 9} = 3$

76. $\sqrt[4]{2x - 1} = 2$

77. $w^{2/3} = 4$

78. $m^{-4/3} = 16$

79. $(m + 1)^{1/3} = 5$

80. $(w - 3)^{-2/3} = 4$

81. $\sqrt{x - 3} = \sqrt{x + 2} - 1$

82. $\sqrt{x^2 + 3x + 6} = 4$

83. $\sqrt{5x - x^2} = \sqrt{6}$

84. $\sqrt{x + 4} - 2\sqrt{x - 1} = -1$

85. $\sqrt{x + 7} - 2\sqrt{x} = -2$

86. $\sqrt{x} - \sqrt{x - 1} = 1$

87. $2\sqrt{x} - \sqrt{x - 3} = 3$

88. $1 + \sqrt{x + 7} = \sqrt{2x + 7}$

7.6 *Perform the indicated operations. Write answers in the form $a + bi$.*

89. $(2 - 3i)(-5 + 5i)$

90. $(2 + i)(5 - 2i)$

91. $(2 + i) + (5 - 4i)$

92. $(2 + i) + (3 - 6i)$

93. $(1 - i) - (2 - 3i)$

94. $(3 - 2i) - (1 - i)$

95. $\dfrac{6 + 3i}{3}$

96. $\dfrac{8 + 12i}{4}$

97. $\dfrac{4 - \sqrt{-12}}{2}$

98. $\dfrac{6 + \sqrt{-18}}{3}$

99. $\dfrac{2 - 3i}{4 + i}$

100. $\dfrac{3 + i}{2 - 3i}$

Find the imaginary solutions to each equation.

101. $x^2 + 100 = 0$

102. $25a^2 + 3 = 0$

103. $2b^2 + 9 = 0$

104. $3y^2 + 8 = 0$

MISCELLANEOUS

Determine whether each equation is true or false and explain your answer. An equation involving variables should be marked true only if it is an identity. Do not use a calculator.

105. $2^3 \cdot 3^2 = 6^5$

106. $16^{1/4} = 4^{1/2}$

107. $(\sqrt{2})^3 = 2\sqrt{2}$

108. $\sqrt[3]{9} = 3$

109. $8^{200} \cdot 8^{200} = 64^{200}$

110. $\sqrt{295} \cdot \sqrt{295} = 295$

111. $4^{1/2} = \sqrt{2}$

112. $\sqrt{a^2} = |a|$

113. $5^2 \cdot 5^2 = 25^4$

114. $\sqrt{6} \div \sqrt{2} = \sqrt{3}$

115. $\sqrt{w^{10}} = w^5$

116. $\sqrt{a^{16}} = a^4$

117. $\sqrt{x^6} = x^3$

118. $\sqrt[6]{16} = \sqrt[3]{4}$

119. $\sqrt{x^8} = x^4$

120. $\sqrt[9]{2^6} = 2^{2/3}$

121. $\sqrt{16} = 2$

122. $2^{1/2} \cdot 2^{1/4} = 2^{3/4}$

123. $2^{600} = 4^{300}$

124. $\sqrt{2} \cdot \sqrt[4]{2} = \sqrt[6]{2}$

125. $\dfrac{2 + \sqrt{6}}{2} = 1 + \sqrt{6}$

126. $\dfrac{4 + 2\sqrt{3}}{2} = 2 + \sqrt{3}$

127. $\sqrt{\dfrac{4}{6}} = \dfrac{2}{3}$

128. $8^{200} \cdot 8^{200} = 8^{400}$

129. $81^{2/4} = 81^{1/2}$

130. $(-64)^{2/6} = (-64)^{1/3}$

131. $(a^4b^2)^{1/2} = |a^2b|$

132. $\left(\dfrac{a^2}{b^6}\right)^{1/2} = \dfrac{|a|}{b^3}$

In Exercises 133–136, solve each problem.

133. *Falling objects.* If we neglect air resistance, the number of feet s that an object falls from rest during t seconds is given by the equation $s = 16t^2$. How long would it take the landing gear of an airplane to reach the earth if it fell off the airplane at 12,000 feet?

134. *Timber.* Anne is pulling on a 60-foot rope attached to the top of a 48-foot tree while Walter is cutting the tree at its base. How far from the base of the tree is Anne standing?

60 ft   **48 ft**

— x ft —

FIGURE FOR EXERCISE 134

135. *Guy wire.* If a guy wire of length 40 feet is attached to an antenna at a height of 30 feet, then how far from the base of the antenna is the wire attached to the ground?

40 ft   **30 ft**

— x ft —

FIGURE FOR EXERCISE 135

136. *Touchdown.* Suppose at the kickoff of a football game, the receiver catches the football at the left side of the goal line and runs for a touchdown diagonally across the field. How many yards would he run? (A football field is 100 yards long and 160 feet wide.)

137. Long guy wires. The manufacturer of an antenna recommends that guy wires from the top of the antenna to the ground be attached to the ground at a distance from the base equal to the height of the antenna. How long would the guy wires be for a 200-foot antenna?

138. Height of a post. Betty observed that the lamp post in front of her house casts a shadow of length 8 feet when the angle of inclination of the sun is 60 degrees. How tall is the lamp post? (In a 30-60-90 right triangle, the side opposite 30 is one-half the length of the hypotenuse.)

FIGURE FOR EXERCISE 138

139. Manufacturing a box. A cubic box has a volume of 40 cubic feet. The amount of recycled cardboard that it takes to make the six-sided box is 10% larger than the surface area of the box. Find the exact amount of recycled cardboard used in manufacturing the box.

140. Shipping parts. A cubic box with a volume of 32 cubic feet is to be used to ship some machine parts. All of the parts are small except for a long, straight steel connecting rod. What is the maximum length of a connecting rod that will fit into this box?

141. Health care costs. Total annual cost of health care in the United States grew from $993.3 billion in 1995 to $1392.7 billion in 2002 (Statistical Abstract of the United States, www.census.gov).

a) Find the average annual rate of growth r for that period by solving $1392.7 = 993.3(1 + r)^7$.

b) Estimate the total annual cost of health care in 2005 by reading the accompanying graph.

142. Population growth rate. The formula $P = P_0(1 + r)^n$ gives the population P at the end of an n-year time period, where P_0 is the initial population and r is the average annual growth rate. The U.S. population grew from 248.7 million in 1990 to 287.1 million in 2002 (U.S. Census Bureau). Find the average annual rate of growth for the U.S. population for that period.

FIGURE FOR EXERCISE 141

143. Landing speed. Aircraft engineers determine the proper landing speed V (in feet per second) for an airplane from the formula

$$V = \sqrt{\frac{841L}{CS}},$$

where L is the gross weight of the aircraft in pounds, C is the coefficient of lift, and S is the wing surface area in square feet. Rewrite the formula so that the expression on the right-hand side is in simplified radical form.

144. Spillway capacity. Civil engineers use the formula

$$Q = 3.32LH^{3/2}$$

to find the maximum discharge that the dam (a broad-crested weir) shown in the figure can pass before the water breaches its abutments (Standard Handbook for Civil Engineers, 1968). In the formula Q is the discharge in cubic feet per second, L is the length of the spillway in feet, and H is the depth of the spillway. Find Q given that $L = 60$ feet and $H = 5$ feet. Find H given that $Q = 3000$ cubic feet per second and $L = 70$ feet.

FIGURE FOR EXERCISE 144

CHAPTER 7 TEST

Simplify each expression. Assume all variables represent positive numbers.

1. $8^{2/3}$

2. $4^{-3/2}$

3. $\sqrt{21} \div \sqrt{7}$

4. $2\sqrt{5} \cdot 3\sqrt{5}$

5. $\sqrt{20} + \sqrt{5}$

6. $\sqrt{5} + \dfrac{1}{\sqrt{5}}$

7. $2^{1/2} \cdot 2^{1/2}$

8. $\sqrt{72}$

9. $\sqrt{\dfrac{5}{12}}$

10. $\dfrac{6 + \sqrt{18}}{6}$

11. $(2\sqrt{3} + 1)(\sqrt{3} - 2)$

12. $\sqrt[4]{32a^5y^8}$

13. $\dfrac{1}{\sqrt[3]{2x^2}}$

14. $\sqrt{\dfrac{8a^9}{b^3}}$

15. $\sqrt[3]{-27x^9}$

16. $\sqrt{20m^3}$

17. $x^{1/2} \cdot x^{1/4}$

18. $(9y^4x^{1/2})^{1/2}$

19. $\sqrt[3]{40x^7}$

20. $(4 + \sqrt{3})^2$

Rationalize the denominator and simplify.

21. $\dfrac{2}{5 - \sqrt{3}}$

22. $\dfrac{\sqrt{6}}{4\sqrt{3} + \sqrt{2}}$

Write each expression in the form a + bi.

23. $(3 - 2i)(4 + 5i)$

24. $i^4 - i^5$

25. $\dfrac{3 - i}{1 + 2i}$

26. $\dfrac{-6 + \sqrt{-12}}{8}$

Find all real or imaginary solutions to each equation.

27. $(x - 2)^2 = 49$

28. $2\sqrt{x + 4} = 3$

29. $w^{2/3} = 4$

30. $9y^2 + 16 = 0$

31. $\sqrt{2x^2 + x - 12} = x$

32. $\sqrt{x - 1} + \sqrt{x + 4} = 5$

Show a complete solution to each problem.

33. Find the exact length of the side of a square whose diagonal is 3 feet.

34. Two positive numbers differ by 11, and their square roots differ by 1. Find the numbers.

35. If the perimeter of a rectangle is 20 feet and the diagonal is $2\sqrt{13}$ feet, then what are the length and width?

36. The average radius R of the orbit of a planet around the sun is determined by $R = T^{2/3}$, where T is the number of years for one orbit and R is measured in astronomical units (AU). If it takes Pluto 248.530 years to make one orbit of the sun, then what is the average radius of the orbit of Pluto? If the average radius of the orbit of Neptune is 30.08 AU, then how many years does it take Neptune to complete one orbit of the sun?

Find all real solutions to each equation or inequality. For the inequalities, also sketch the graph of the solution set.

1. $3(x - 2) + 5 = 7 - 4(x + 3)$

2. $\sqrt{6x + 7} = 4$

3. $|2x + 5| > 1$

4. $8x^3 - 27 = 0$

5. $2x - 3 > 3x - 4$

6. $\sqrt{2x - 3} - \sqrt{3x + 4} = 0$

7. $\dfrac{w}{3} + \dfrac{w - 4}{2} = \dfrac{11}{2}$

8. $2(x + 7) - 4 = x - (10 - x)$

9. $(x + 7)^2 = 25$

10. $a^{-1/2} = 4$

11. $x - 3 > 2$ or $x < 2x + 6$

12. $a^{-2/3} = 16$ 13. $3x^2 - 1 = 0$

14. $5 - 2(x - 2) = 3x - 5(x - 2) - 1$

15. $|3x - 4| < 5$

16. $3x - 1 = 0$ 17. $\sqrt{y - 1} = 9$

18. $|5(x - 2) + 1| = 3$

19. $0.06x - 0.04(x - 20) = 2.8$

20. $|3x - 1| > -2$ 21. $\dfrac{3\sqrt{2}}{x} = \dfrac{\sqrt{3}}{4\sqrt{5}}$

22. $\dfrac{\sqrt{x} - 4}{x} = \dfrac{1}{\sqrt{x} + 5}$

23. $\dfrac{3\sqrt{2} + 4}{\sqrt{2}} = \dfrac{x\sqrt{18}}{3\sqrt{2} + 2}$

24. $\dfrac{x}{2\sqrt{5} - \sqrt{2}} = \dfrac{2\sqrt{5} + \sqrt{2}}{x}$

25. $\dfrac{\sqrt{2x} - 5}{x} = \dfrac{-3}{\sqrt{2x} + 5}$

26. $\dfrac{\sqrt{6} + 2}{x} = \dfrac{2}{\sqrt{6} + 4}$

27. $\dfrac{x - 1}{\sqrt{6}} = \dfrac{\sqrt{6}}{x}$ 28. $\dfrac{x + 3}{\sqrt{10}} = \dfrac{\sqrt{10}}{x}$

29. $\dfrac{1}{x} - \dfrac{1}{x - 1} = -\dfrac{1}{6}$

30. $\dfrac{1}{x^2 - 2x} + \dfrac{1}{x} = \dfrac{2}{3}$

The expression $\dfrac{-b + \sqrt{b^2 - 4ac}}{2a}$ will be used in Chapter 8 to solve quadratic equations. Evaluate it for the given values of a, b, and c.

31. $a = 1, b = 2, c = -15$ 32. $a = 1, b = 8, c = 12$

33. $a = 2, b = 5, c = -3$ 34. $a = 6, b = 7, c = -3$

Solve each problem.

35. **Popping corn.** If 1 gram of popcorn with moisture content $x\%$ is popped in a hot-air popper, then the volume of popped corn v (in cubic centimeters) that results is modeled by the formula

$$v = -94.8 + 21.4x - 0.761x^2.$$

a) Use the formula to find the volume that results when 1 gram of popcorn with moisture content 11% is popped.

b) Use the accompanying graph to estimate the moisture content that will produce the maximum volume of popped corn.

c) Use the graph to estimate the maximum possible volume for popping 1 gram of popcorn in a hot-air popper.

FIGURE FOR EXERCISE 35

CHAPTER

8

Quadratic Equations, Functions, and Inequalities

I s it possible to measure beauty? For thousands of years artists and
philosophers have been challenged to answer this question. The
seventeenth-century philosopher John Locke said, "Beauty consists of a certain composition of color and figure causing delight in
the beholder." Over the centuries many architects, sculptors, and painters
have searched for beauty in their work by exploring numerical patterns in
various art forms.

Today many artists and architects still use the concepts of beauty
given to us by the ancient Greeks. One principle, called the Golden Rectangle, concerns the most pleasing proportions of a rectangle. The
Golden Rectangle appears in nature as well as in many cultures. Examples of it can be seen in Leonardo da Vinci's *Proportions of the Human
Figure* as well as in Indonesian temples and Chinese pagodas. Perhaps one of the best-known examples of the Golden Rectangle is
in the façade and floor plan of the Parthenon, built in Athens in the
fifth century B.C. In Exercise 63 of Section 8.4 we will see that
the principle of the Golden Rectangle is based on a proportion that we can solve using the quadratic formula.

8.1   FACTORING AND COMPLETING THE SQUARE

Factoring and the even-root property were used to solve quadratic equations in Chapters 5, 6, and 7. In this section we first review those methods. Then you will learn the method of completing the square, which can be used to solve any quadratic equation.

Review of Factoring

A quadratic equation has the form $ax^2 + bx + c = 0$, where a, b, and c are real numbers with $a \neq 0$. In Section 5.8 we solved quadratic equations by factoring and then applying the zero factor property.

> **Zero Factor Property**
>
> The equation $ab = 0$ is equivalent to the compound equation
> $$a = 0 \quad \text{or} \quad b = 0.$$

Of course we can only use the factoring method when we can factor the quadratic polynomial. To solve a quadratic equation by factoring we use the following strategy.

> **Strategy for Solving Quadratic Equations by Factoring**
>
> 1. Write the equation with 0 on one side.
> 2. Factor the other side.
> 3. Use the zero factor property to set each factor equal to zero.
> 4. Solve the simpler equations.
> 5. Check the answers in the original equation.

E X A M P L E   1

Helpful Hint

After you have factored the quadratic polynomial, use FOIL to check that you have factored correctly before proceeding to the next step.

Solving a quadratic equation by factoring

Solve $3x^2 - 4x = 15$ by factoring.

Solution

Subtract 15 from each side to get 0 on the right-hand side:

$$3x^2 - 4x - 15 = 0$$
$$(3x + 5)(x - 3) = 0 \quad \text{Factor the left-hand side.}$$
$$3x + 5 = 0 \quad \text{or} \quad x - 3 = 0 \quad \text{Zero factor property}$$
$$3x = -5 \quad \text{or} \quad x = 3$$
$$x = -\frac{5}{3}$$

The solution set is $\left\{-\frac{5}{3}, 3\right\}$. Check the solutions in the original equation. ■

Review of the Even-Root Property

In Chapter 7 we solved some simple quadratic equations by using the even-root property, which we restate as follows:

Even-Root Property

Suppose n is a positive even integer.

If $k > 0$, then $x^n = k$ is equivalent to $x = \pm\sqrt[n]{k}$.
If $k = 0$, then $x^n = k$ is equivalent to $x = 0$.
If $k < 0$, then $x^n = k$ has no real solution.

By the even-root property $x^2 = 4$ is equivalent to $x = \pm 2$, $x^2 = 0$ is equivalent to $x = 0$, and $x^2 = -4$ has no real solutions.

E X A M P L E   2   **Solving a quadratic equation by the even-root property**
Solve $(a - 1)^2 = 9$.

Solution

By the even-root property $x^2 = k$ is equivalent to $x = \pm\sqrt{k}$.

$$(a - 1)^2 = 9$$
$$a - 1 = \pm\sqrt{9} \quad \text{Even-root property}$$

$$a - 1 = 3 \quad \text{or} \quad a - 1 = -3$$
$$a = 4 \quad \text{or} \quad a = -2$$

Check these solutions in the original equation. The solution set is $\{-2, 4\}$. ■

Completing the Square

We cannot solve every quadratic by factoring because not all quadratic polynomials can be factored. However, we can write any quadratic equation in the form of Example 2 and then apply the even-root property to solve it. This method is called **completing the square.**

The essential part of completing the square is to recognize a perfect square trinomial when given its first two terms. For example, if we are given $x^2 + 6x$, how do we recognize that these are the first two terms of the perfect square trinomial $x^2 + 6x + 9$? To answer this question, recall that $x^2 + 6x + 9$ is a perfect square trinomial because it is the square of the binomial $x + 3$:

$$(x + 3)^2 = x^2 + 2 \cdot 3x + 3^2 = x^2 + 6x + 9$$

Notice that the 6 comes from multiplying 3 by 2 and the 9 comes from squaring the 3. So to find the missing 9 in $x^2 + 6x$, divide 6 by 2 to get 3, then square 3 to get 9. This procedure can be used to find the last term in any perfect square trinomial in which the coefficient of x^2 is 1.

Rule for Finding the Last Term

The last term of a perfect square trinomial is the square of one-half of the coefficient of the middle term. In symbols, the perfect square trinomial whose first two terms are $x^2 + bx$ is $x^2 + bx + \left(\dfrac{b}{2}\right)^2$.

Helpful Hint

The area of an x by x square and two x by 3 rectangles is $x^2 + 6x$. The area needed to "complete the square" in this figure is 9:

E X A M P L E   3

Finding the last term

Find the perfect square trinomial whose first two terms are given.

a) $x^2 + 8x$ **b)** $x^2 - 5x$ **c)** $x^2 + \dfrac{4}{7}x$ **d)** $x^2 - \dfrac{3}{2}x$

Study Tip

Most instructors believe that what they do in class is important. If you miss class, then you miss what is important to your instructor and what is most likely to appear on the test.

Solution

a) One-half of 8 is 4, and 4 squared is 16. So the perfect square trinomial is

$$x^2 + 8x + 16.$$

b) One-half of -5 is $-\dfrac{5}{2}$, and $-\dfrac{5}{2}$ squared is $\dfrac{25}{4}$. So the perfect square trinomial is $x^2 - 5x + \dfrac{25}{4}$.

c) Since $\dfrac{1}{2} \cdot \dfrac{4}{7} = \dfrac{2}{7}$ and $\dfrac{2}{7}$ squared is $\dfrac{4}{49}$, the perfect square trinomial is

$$x^2 + \dfrac{4}{7}x + \dfrac{4}{49}.$$

d) Since $\dfrac{1}{2}\left(-\dfrac{3}{2}\right) = -\dfrac{3}{4}$ and $\left(-\dfrac{3}{4}\right)^2 = \dfrac{9}{16}$, the perfect square trinomial is

$$x^2 - \dfrac{3}{2}x + \dfrac{9}{16}.$$

∎

Another essential step in completing the square is to write the perfect square trinomial as the square of a binomial. Recall that

$$a^2 + 2ab + b^2 = (a + b)^2$$

and

$$a^2 - 2ab + b^2 = (a - b)^2.$$

E X A M P L E   4

Factoring perfect square trinomials

Factor each trinomial.

a) $x^2 + 12x + 36$ **b)** $y^2 - 7y + \dfrac{49}{4}$ **c)** $z^2 - \dfrac{4}{3}z + \dfrac{4}{9}$

Helpful Hint

To square a binomial use the following rule (not FOIL):
• Square the first term.
• Add twice the product of the terms.
• Add the square of the last term.

Solution

a) The trinomial $x^2 + 12x + 36$ is of the form $a^2 + 2ab + b^2$ with $a = x$ and $b = 6$. So

$$x^2 + 12x + 36 = (x + 6)^2.$$

Check by squaring $x + 6$.

b) The trinomial $y^2 - 7y + \dfrac{49}{4}$ is of the form $a^2 - 2ab + b^2$ with $a = y$ and $b = \dfrac{7}{2}$. So

$$y^2 - 7y + \dfrac{49}{4} = \left(y - \dfrac{7}{2}\right)^2.$$

Check by squaring $y - \dfrac{7}{2}$.

c) The trinomial $z^2 - \dfrac{4}{3}z + \dfrac{4}{9}$ is of the form $a^2 - 2ab + b^2$ with $a = z$ and $b = -\dfrac{2}{3}$. So

$$z^2 - \dfrac{4}{3}z + \dfrac{4}{9} = \left(z - \dfrac{2}{3}\right)^2.$$

∎

In Example 5 we use the skills that we practiced in Examples 2, 3, and 4 to solve the quadratic equation $ax^2 + bx + c = 0$ with $a = 1$ by the method of completing the square.

E X A M P L E   5

Completing the square with $a = 1$

Solve $x^2 + 6x + 5 = 0$ by completing the square.

Solution

The perfect square trinomial whose first two terms are $x^2 + 6x$ is

$$x^2 + 6x + 9.$$

So we move 5 to the right-hand side of the equation, then add 9 to each side to create a perfect square on the left side:

$$x^2 + 6x \qquad\quad = -5 \qquad \text{Subtract 5 from each side.}$$

$$x^2 + 6x + 9 = -5 + 9 \qquad \begin{matrix}\text{Add 9 to each side to get}\\\text{a perfect square trinomial.}\end{matrix}$$

$$(x + 3)^2 = 4 \qquad \text{Factor the left-hand side.}$$

$$x + 3 = \pm\sqrt{4} \qquad \text{Even-root property}$$

$$x + 3 = 2 \qquad \text{or} \qquad x + 3 = -2$$

$$x = -1 \qquad \text{or} \qquad x = -5$$

Check in the original equation:

$$(-1)^2 + 6(-1) + 5 = 0$$

and

$$(-5)^2 + 6(-5) + 5 = 0$$

The solution set is $\{-1, -5\}$. ∎

Calculator Close-Up

The solutions to

$$x^2 + 6x + 5 = 0$$

correspond to the x-intercepts for the graph of the function

$$y = x^2 + 6x + 5.$$

So we can check our solutions by graphing the function and using the TRACE feature as shown here.

CAUTION All of the perfect square trinomials that we have used so far had a leading coefficient of 1. If $a \neq 1$, then we must divide each side of the equation by a to get an equation with a leading coefficient of 1.

The strategy for solving a quadratic equation by completing the square is stated in the following box.

Strategy for Solving Quadratic Equations by Completing the Square

1. If $a \neq 1$, then divide each side of the equation by a.
2. Get only the x^2 and the x terms on the left-hand side.
3. Add to each side the square of $\frac{1}{2}$ the coefficient of x.
4. Factor the left-hand side as the square of a binomial.
5. Apply the even-root property.
6. Solve for x.
7. Simplify.

E X A M P L E   6

Completing the square with $a \neq 1$

Solve $2x^2 + 3x - 2 = 0$ by completing the square.

Solution

For completing the square, the coefficient of x^2 must be 1. So we first divide each side of the equation by 2:

$$\frac{2x^2 + 3x - 2}{2} = \frac{0}{2} \qquad \text{Divide each side by 2.}$$

$$x^2 + \frac{3}{2}x - 1 = 0 \qquad \text{Simplify.}$$

$$x^2 + \frac{3}{2}x = 1 \qquad \begin{array}{l}\text{Get only } x^2 \text{ and } x \text{ terms on the}\\ \text{left-hand side.}\end{array}$$

$$x^2 + \frac{3}{2}x + \frac{9}{16} = 1 + \frac{9}{16} \qquad \text{One-half of } \frac{3}{2} \text{ is } \frac{3}{4}, \text{ and } \left(\frac{3}{4}\right)^2 = \frac{9}{16}.$$

$$\left(x + \frac{3}{4}\right)^2 = \frac{25}{16} \qquad \text{Factor the left-hand side.}$$

$$x + \frac{3}{4} = \pm\sqrt{\frac{25}{16}} \qquad \text{Even-root property}$$

$$x + \frac{3}{4} = \frac{5}{4} \qquad \text{or} \qquad x + \frac{3}{4} = -\frac{5}{4}$$

$$x = \frac{2}{4} = \frac{1}{2} \qquad \text{or} \qquad x = -\frac{8}{4} = -2$$

Check these values in the original equation. The solution set is $\left\{-2, \frac{1}{2}\right\}$. ■

In Examples 5 and 6 the solutions were rational numbers, and the equations could have been solved by factoring. In Example 7 the solutions are irrational numbers, and factoring will not work.

Calculator Close-Up

Note that the x-intercepts for the graph of the function:

$$y = 2x^2 + 3x - 2$$

are $(-2, 0)$ and $\left(\frac{1}{2}, 0\right)$:

E X A M P L E   7

A quadratic equation with irrational solutions

Solve $x^2 - 3x - 6 = 0$ by completing the square.

Solution

Because $a = 1$, we first get the x^2 and x terms on the left-hand side:

$$x^2 - 3x - 6 = 0$$

$$x^2 - 3x = 6 \qquad \text{Add 6 to each side.}$$

$$x^2 - 3x + \frac{9}{4} = 6 + \frac{9}{4} \qquad \text{One-half of } -3 \text{ is } -\frac{3}{2}, \text{ and } \left(-\frac{3}{2}\right)^2 = \frac{9}{4}.$$

$$\left(x - \frac{3}{2}\right)^2 = \frac{33}{4} \qquad 6 + \frac{9}{4} = \frac{24}{4} + \frac{9}{4} = \frac{33}{4}$$

$$x - \frac{3}{2} = \pm\sqrt{\frac{33}{4}} \qquad \text{Even-root property}$$

$$x = \frac{3}{2} \pm \frac{\sqrt{33}}{2} \qquad \text{Add } \frac{3}{2} \text{ to each side.}$$

$$x = \frac{3 \pm \sqrt{33}}{2}$$

The solution set is $\left\{\dfrac{3 + \sqrt{33}}{2}, \dfrac{3 - \sqrt{33}}{2}\right\}$. ■

Miscellaneous Equations

Examples 8 and 9 show equations that are not originally in the form of quadratic equations. However, after simplifying these equations, we get quadratic equations. Even though completing the square can be used on any quadratic equation, factoring and the square root property are usually easier and we can use them when applicable. In Examples 8 and 9 we will use the most appropriate method.

E X A M P L E 8

An equation containing a radical

Solve $x + 3 = \sqrt{153 - x}$.

Solution

Square both sides of the equation to eliminate the radical:

$$x + 3 = \sqrt{153 - x} \qquad \text{The original equation}$$
$$(x + 3)^2 = (\sqrt{153 - x})^2 \qquad \text{Square each side.}$$
$$x^2 + 6x + 9 = 153 - x \qquad \text{Simplify.}$$
$$x^2 + 7x - 144 = 0$$
$$(x - 9)(x + 16) = 0 \qquad \text{Factor.}$$
$$x - 9 = 0 \quad \text{or} \quad x + 16 = 0 \qquad \text{Zero factor property}$$
$$x = 9 \quad \text{or} \quad x = -16$$

Because we squared each side of the original equation, we must check for extraneous roots. Let $x = 9$ in the original equation:

$$9 + 3 = \sqrt{153 - 9}$$
$$12 = \sqrt{144} \qquad \text{Correct}$$

Let $x = -16$ in the original equation:

$$-16 + 3 = \sqrt{153 - (-16)}$$
$$-13 = \sqrt{169} \qquad \text{Incorrect because } \sqrt{169} = 13$$

Because -16 is an extraneous root, the solution set is $\{9\}$. ■

E X A M P L E 9

An equation containing rational expressions

Solve $\dfrac{1}{x} + \dfrac{3}{x - 2} = \dfrac{5}{8}$.

Solution

The least common denominator (LCD) for x, $x - 2$, and 8 is $8x(x - 2)$.

$$\frac{1}{x} + \frac{3}{x - 2} = \frac{5}{8}$$
$$8x(x - 2)\frac{1}{x} + 8x(x - 2)\frac{3}{x - 2} = 8x(x - 2)\frac{5}{8} \qquad \text{Multiply each side by the LCD.}$$
$$8x - 16 + 24x = 5x^2 - 10x$$
$$32x - 16 = 5x^2 - 10x$$
$$-5x^2 + 42x - 16 = 0$$
$$5x^2 - 42x + 16 = 0 \qquad \begin{array}{l}\text{Multiply each side by } -1 \\ \text{for easier factoring.}\end{array}$$
$$(5x - 2)(x - 8) = 0 \qquad \text{Factor.}$$
$$5x - 2 = 0 \quad \text{or} \quad x - 8 = 0$$
$$x = \frac{2}{5} \quad \text{or} \quad x = 8$$

Check these values in the original equation. The solution set is $\left\{\frac{2}{5}, 8\right\}$. ■

Imaginary Solutions

In Chapter 7 we found imaginary solutions to quadratic equations using the even-root property. We can get imaginary solutions also by completing the square.

E X A M P L E 10

An equation with imaginary solutions

Find the complex solutions to $x^2 - 4x + 12 = 0$.

Calculator Close-Up

The answer key (ANS) can be used to check imaginary answers as shown here.

```
2+2i√(2)
      2+2.828427125i
Ans²-4Ans+12
              0
```

Solution

Because the quadratic polynomial cannot be factored, we solve the equation by completing the square.

$$x^2 - 4x + 12 = 0 \qquad \text{The original equation}$$
$$x^2 - 4x = -12 \qquad \text{Subtract 12 from each side.}$$
$$x^2 - 4x + 4 = -12 + 4 \qquad \text{One-half of } -4 \text{ is } -2, \text{ and } (-2)^2 = 4.$$
$$(x - 2)^2 = -8$$
$$x - 2 = \pm\sqrt{-8} \qquad \text{Even-root property}$$
$$x = 2 \pm i\sqrt{8}$$
$$= 2 \pm 2i\sqrt{2}$$

Check these values in the original equation. The solution set is $\{2 \pm 2i\sqrt{2}\}$. ■

WARM-UPS

True or false? Explain your answer.

1. Completing the square means drawing the fourth side.
2. The equation $(x - 3)^2 = 12$ is equivalent to $x - 3 = 2\sqrt{3}$.
3. Every quadratic equation can be solved by factoring.
4. The trinomial $x^2 + \frac{4}{3}x + \frac{16}{9}$ is a perfect square trinomial.
5. Every quadratic equation can be solved by completing the square.
6. To complete the square for $2x^2 + 6x = 4$, add 9 to each side.
7. $(2x - 3)(3x + 5) = 0$ is equivalent to $x = \frac{3}{2}$ or $x = \frac{5}{3}$.
8. In completing the square for $x^2 - 3x = 4$, add $\frac{9}{4}$ to each side.
9. The equation $x^2 = -8$ is equivalent to $x = \pm2\sqrt{2}$.
10. All quadratic equations have two distinct complex solutions.

8.1 EXERCISES

Reading and Writing *After reading this section, write out the answers to these questions. Use complete sentences.*

1. What are the three methods discussed in this section for solving a quadratic equation?

2. Which quadratic equations can be solved by the even-root property?

3. How do you find the last term for a perfect square trinomial when completing the square?

4. How do you complete the square when the leading coefficient is not 1?

Solve by factoring. See Example 1.

5. $x^2 - x - 6 = 0$

6. $x^2 + 6x + 8 = 0$

7. $a^2 + 2a = 15$

8. $w^2 - 2w = 15$

9. $2x^2 - x - 3 = 0$

10. $6x^2 - x - 15 = 0$

11. $y^2 + 14y + 49 = 0$

12. $a^2 - 6a + 9 = 0$

13. $a^2 - 16 = 0$

14. $4w^2 - 25 = 0$

Use the even-root property to solve each equation. See Example 2.

15. $x^2 = 81$

16. $x^2 = \dfrac{9}{4}$

17. $x^2 = \dfrac{16}{9}$

18. $a^2 = 32$

19. $(x - 3)^2 = 16$

20. $(x + 5)^2 = 4$

21. $(z + 1)^2 = 5$

22. $(a - 2)^2 = 8$

23. $\left(w - \dfrac{3}{2}\right)^2 = \dfrac{7}{4}$

24. $\left(w + \dfrac{2}{3}\right)^2 = \dfrac{5}{9}$

Find the perfect square trinomial whose first two terms are given. See Example 3.

25. $x^2 + 2x$

26. $m^2 + 14m$

27. $x^2 - 3x$

28. $w^2 - 5w$

29. $y^2 + \dfrac{1}{4}y$

30. $z^2 + \dfrac{3}{2}z$

31. $x^2 + \dfrac{2}{3}x$

32. $p^2 + \dfrac{6}{5}p$

Factor each perfect square trinomial. See Example 4.

33. $x^2 + 8x + 16$

34. $x^2 - 10x + 25$

35. $y^2 - 5y + \dfrac{25}{4}$

36. $w^2 + w + \dfrac{1}{4}$

37. $z^2 - \dfrac{4}{7}z + \dfrac{4}{49}$

38. $m^2 - \dfrac{6}{5}m + \dfrac{9}{25}$

39. $t^2 + \dfrac{3}{5}t + \dfrac{9}{100}$

40. $h^2 + \dfrac{3}{2}h + \dfrac{9}{16}$

Solve by completing the square. See Examples 5–7. Use your calculator to check.

41. $x^2 - 2x - 15 = 0$

42. $x^2 - 6x - 7 = 0$

43. $2x^2 - 4x = 70$

44. $3x^2 - 6x = 24$

45. $w^2 - w - 20 = 0$

46. $y^2 - 3y - 10 = 0$

47. $q^2 + 5q = 14$

48. $z^2 + z = 2$

49. $2h^2 - h - 3 = 0$

50. $2m^2 - m - 15 = 0$

51. $x^2 + 4x = 6$

52. $x^2 + 6x - 8 = 0$

53. $x^2 + 8x - 4 = 0$

54. $x^2 + 10x - 3 = 0$

55. $4x^2 - 4x - 1 = 0$

56. $4x^2 + 4x - 2 = 0$

57. $2x^2 + 3x - 4 = 0$

58. $2x^2 + 5x - 1 = 0$

Solve each equation by an appropriate method. See Examples 8 and 9.

59. $\sqrt{2x + 1} = x - 1$

60. $\sqrt{2x - 4} = x - 14$

61. $w = \dfrac{\sqrt{w+1}}{2}$

62. $y - 1 = \dfrac{\sqrt{y+1}}{2}$

63. $\dfrac{t}{t-2} = \dfrac{2t-3}{t}$

64. $\dfrac{z}{z+3} = \dfrac{3z}{5z-1}$

65. $\dfrac{2}{x^2} + \dfrac{4}{x} + 1 = 0$

66. $\dfrac{1}{x^2} + \dfrac{3}{x} + 1 = 0$

Use completing the square to find the imaginary solutions to each equation. See Example 10.

67. $x^2 + 2x + 5 = 0$

68. $x^2 + 4x + 5 = 0$

69. $x^2 - 6x + 11 = 0$

70. $x^2 - 8x + 19 = 0$

71. $x^2 = -\dfrac{1}{2}$

72. $x^2 = -\dfrac{1}{8}$

73. $x^2 + 12 = 0$

74. $-3x^2 - 21 = 0$

75. $5z^2 - 4z + 1 = 0$

76. $2w^2 - 3w + 2 = 0$

Find all real or imaginary solutions to each equation. Use the method of your choice.

77. $x^2 = -121$

78. $w^2 = -225$

79. $4x^2 + 25 = 0$

80. $5w^2 - 3 = 0$

81. $\left(p + \dfrac{1}{2}\right)^2 = \dfrac{9}{4}$

82. $\left(y - \dfrac{2}{3}\right)^2 = \dfrac{4}{9}$

83. $5t^2 + 4t - 3 = 0$

84. $3v^2 + 4v - 1 = 0$

85. $m^2 + 2m - 24 = 0$

86. $q^2 + 6q - 7 = 0$

87. $(x - 2)^2 = -9$

88. $(2x - 1)^2 = -4$

89. $-x^2 + x + 6 = 0$

90. $-x^2 + x + 12 = 0$

91. $x^2 - 6x + 10 = 0$

92. $x^2 - 8x + 17 = 0$

93. $2x - 5 = \sqrt{7x + 7}$

94. $\sqrt{7x + 29} = x + 3$

95. $\dfrac{1}{x} + \dfrac{1}{x-1} = \dfrac{1}{4}$

96. $\dfrac{1}{x} - \dfrac{2}{1-x} = \dfrac{1}{2}$

If the solution to an equation is imaginary or irrational, it takes a bit more effort to check. Replace x by each given number to verify each statement.

97. Both $2 + \sqrt{3}$ and $2 - \sqrt{3}$ satisfy $x^2 - 4x + 1 = 0$.

98. Both $1 + \sqrt{2}$ and $1 - \sqrt{2}$ satisfy $x^2 - 2x - 1 = 0$.

99. Both $1 + i$ and $1 - i$ satisfy $x^2 - 2x + 2 = 0$.

100. Both $2 + 3i$ and $2 - 3i$ satisfy $x^2 - 4x + 13 = 0$.

Solve each problem.

101. *Approach speed.* The formula $1211.1L = CA^2S$ is used to determine the approach speed for landing an aircraft, where L is the gross weight of the aircraft in pounds, C is the coefficient of lift, S is the surface area of the wings in square feet (ft^2), and A is approach speed in feet per second. Find A for the Piper Cheyenne, which has a gross weight of 8700 lbs, a coefficient of lift of 2.81, and wing surface area of 200 ft^2.

102. *Time to swing.* The period T (time in seconds for one complete cycle) of a simple pendulum is related to the length L (in feet) of the pendulum by the formula $8T^2 = \pi^2 L$. If a child is on a swing with a 10-foot chain, then how long does it take to complete one cycle of the swing?

103. *Time for a swim.* Tropical Pools figures that its monthly revenue in dollars on the sale of x above-ground pools is given by $R = 1500x - 3x^2$, where x is less than 25. What number of pools sold would provide a revenue of $17,568?

104. *Pole vaulting.* In 1981 Vladimir Poliakov (USSR) set a world record of 19 ft $\frac{3}{4}$ in. for the pole vault (www.polevault.com). To reach that height, Poliakov obtained a speed of approximately 36 feet per second on the runway. The function $h = -16t^2 + 36t$ gives his height t seconds after leaving the ground.

   a) Use the formula to find the exact values of t for which his height was 18 feet.

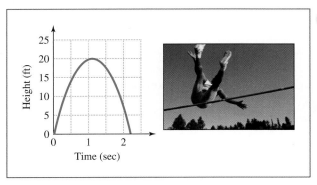

FIGURE FOR EXERCISE 104

b) Use the accompanying graph to estimate the value of t for which he was at his maximum height.

c) Approximately how long was he in the air?

GETTING MORE INVOLVED

 105. ***Discussion.*** Which of the following equations is not a quadratic equation? Explain your answer.

a) $\pi x^2 - \sqrt{5}x - 1 = 0$ **b)** $3x^2 - 1 = 0$
c) $4x + 5 = 0$ **d)** $0.009x^2 = 0$

106. ***Exploration.*** Solve $x^2 - 4x + k = 0$ for $k = 0, 4, 5,$ and 10.

a) When does the equation have only one solution?
b) For what values of k are the solutions real?
c) For what values of k are the solutions imaginary?

107. ***Cooperative learning.*** Write a quadratic equation of each of the following types, then trade your equations with those of a classmate. Solve the equations and verify that they are of the required types.

a) a single rational solution
b) two rational solutions
c) two irrational solutions
d) two imaginary solutions

108. ***Exploration.*** In the next section we will solve $ax^2 + bx + c = 0$ for x by completing the square. Try it now without looking ahead.

GRAPHING CALCULATOR EXERCISES

For each equation, find approximate solutions rounded to two decimal places.

109. $x^2 - 7.3x + 12.5 = 0$
110. $1.2x^2 - \pi x + \sqrt{2} = 0$
111. $2x - 3 = \sqrt{20 - x}$
112. $x^2 - 1.3x = 22.3 - x^2$

 8.2   **THE QUADRATIC FORMULA**

In This Section

- Developing the Formula
- Using the Formula
- Number of Solutions
- Applications

Completing the square from Section 8.1 can be used to solve any quadratic equation. Here we apply this method to the general quadratic equation to get a formula for the solutions to any quadratic equation.

Developing the Formula

Start with the general form of the quadratic equation,

$$ax^2 + bx + c = 0.$$

Assume a is positive for now, and divide each side by a:

$$\frac{ax^2 + bx + c}{a} = \frac{0}{a}$$

$$x^2 + \frac{b}{a}x + \frac{c}{a} = 0$$

$$x^2 + \frac{b}{a}x = -\frac{c}{a} \qquad \text{Subtract } \frac{c}{a} \text{ from each side.}$$

One-half of $\frac{b}{a}$ is $\frac{b}{2a}$, and $\frac{b}{2a}$ squared is $\frac{b^2}{4a^2}$:

$$x^2 + \frac{b}{a}x + \frac{b^2}{4a^2} = -\frac{c}{a} + \frac{b^2}{4a^2}$$

Factor the left-hand side and get a common denominator for the right-hand side:

$$\left(x + \frac{b}{2a}\right)^2 = \frac{b^2}{4a^2} - \frac{4ac}{4a^2} \qquad\qquad \frac{c(4a)}{a(4a)} = \frac{4ac}{4a^2}$$

$$\left(x + \frac{b}{2a}\right)^2 = \frac{b^2 - 4ac}{4a^2}$$

$$x + \frac{b}{2a} = \pm\sqrt{\frac{b^2 - 4ac}{4a^2}} \qquad\qquad \text{Even-root property}$$

$$x = \frac{-b}{2a} \pm \frac{\sqrt{b^2 - 4ac}}{2a} \qquad\qquad \text{Because } a > 0, \sqrt{4a^2} = 2a.$$

$$x = \frac{-b \pm \sqrt{b^2 - 4ac}}{2a}$$

We assumed a was positive so that $\sqrt{4a^2} = 2a$ would be correct. If a is negative, then $\sqrt{4a^2} = -2a$, and we get

$$x = \frac{-b}{2a} \pm \frac{\sqrt{b^2 - 4ac}}{-2a}.$$

However, the negative sign can be omitted in $-2a$ because of the $\pm$ symbol preceding it. For example, the results of $5 \pm (-3)$ and 5 ± 3 are the same. So when a is negative, we get the same formula as when a is positive. It is called the **quadratic formula.**

> **The Quadratic Formula**
>
> The solution to $ax^2 + bx + c = 0$, with $a \neq 0$, is given by the formula
>
> $$x = \frac{-b \pm \sqrt{b^2 - 4ac}}{2a}.$$

Using the Formula

The quadratic formula solves any quadratic equation. Simply identify a, b, and c and insert those numbers into the formula. Note that if b is positive then $-b$ (the opposite of b) is a negative number. If b is negative, then $-b$ is a *positive* number.

E X A M P L E   1   **Two rational solutions**

Solve $x^2 + 2x - 15 = 0$ using the quadratic formula.

Solution

To use the formula, we first identify the values of a, b, and c:

$$1x^2 + 2x - 15 = 0$$
$$\uparrow \qquad \uparrow \qquad \uparrow$$
$$a \qquad b \qquad c$$

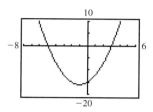

The coefficient of x^2 is 1, so $a = 1$. The coefficient of $2x$ is 2, so $b = 2$. The constant term is -15, so $c = -15$. Substitute these values into the quadratic formula:

$$x = \frac{-2 \pm \sqrt{2^2 - 4(1)(-15)}}{2(1)}$$

$$= \frac{-2 \pm \sqrt{4 + 60}}{2}$$

$$= \frac{-2 \pm \sqrt{64}}{2}$$

$$= \frac{-2 \pm 8}{2}$$

$$x = \frac{-2 + 8}{2} = 3 \qquad \text{or} \qquad x = \frac{-2 - 8}{2} = -5$$

Check 3 and -5 in the original equation. The solution set is $\{-5, 3\}$.   ■

CAUTION   To identify a, b, and c for the quadratic formula, the equation must be in the standard form $ax^2 + bx + c = 0$. If it is not in that form, then you must first rewrite the equation.

E X A M P L E   2

One rational solution

Solve $4x^2 = 12x - 9$ by using the quadratic formula.

Solution

Rewrite the equation in the form $ax^2 + bx + c = 0$ before identifying a, b, and c:

$$4x^2 - 12x + 9 = 0$$

In this form we get $a = 4$, $b = -12$, and $c = 9$.

$$x = \frac{12 \pm \sqrt{(-12)^2 - 4(4)(9)}}{2(4)} \qquad \text{Because } b = -12,\ -b = 12.$$

$$= \frac{12 \pm \sqrt{144 - 144}}{8}$$

$$= \frac{12 \pm 0}{8}$$

$$= \frac{12}{8}$$

$$= \frac{3}{2}$$

Check $\frac{3}{2}$ in the original equation. The solution set is $\left\{\frac{3}{2}\right\}$.   ■

Because the solutions to the equations in Examples 1 and 2 were rational numbers, these equations could have been solved by factoring. In Example 3 the solutions are irrational.

E X A M P L E   3

Two irrational solutions
Solve $2x^2 + 6x + 3 = 0$.

Calculator Close-Up

The two irrational solutions to
$$2x^2 + 6x + 3 = 0$$
correspond to the two x-intercepts
for the graph of
$$y = 2x^2 + 6x + 3.$$

Solution

Let $a = 2$, $b = 6$, and $c = 3$ in the quadratic formula:

$$x = \frac{-6 \pm \sqrt{(6)^2 - 4(2)(3)}}{2(2)}$$

$$= \frac{-6 \pm \sqrt{36 - 24}}{4}$$

$$= \frac{-6 \pm \sqrt{12}}{4}$$

$$= \frac{-6 \pm 2\sqrt{3}}{4}$$

$$= \frac{2(-3 \pm \sqrt{3})}{2 \cdot 2}$$

$$= \frac{-3 \pm \sqrt{3}}{2}$$

Check these values in the original equation. The solution set is $\left\{\dfrac{-3 \pm \sqrt{3}}{2}\right\}$.   ■

E X A M P L E   4

Two imaginary solutions, no real solutions
Find the complex solutions to $x^2 + x + 5 = 0$.

Calculator Close-Up

Because $x^2 + x + 5 = 0$ has no
real solutions, the graph of
$$y = x^2 + x + 5$$
has no x-intercepts.

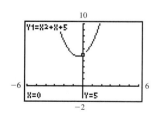

Solution

Let $a = 1$, $b = 1$, and $c = 5$ in the quadratic formula:

$$x = \frac{-1 \pm \sqrt{(1)^2 - 4(1)(5)}}{2(1)}$$

$$= \frac{-1 \pm \sqrt{-19}}{2}$$

$$= \frac{-1 \pm i\sqrt{19}}{2}$$

Check these values in the original equation. The solution set is $\left\{\dfrac{-1 \pm i\sqrt{19}}{2}\right\}$. There are no real solutions to the equation.   ■

You have learned to solve quadratic equations by four different methods: the even-root property, factoring, completing the square, and the quadratic formula. The even-root property and factoring are limited to certain special equations, but you should use those methods when possible. Any quadratic equation can be solved by completing the square or using the quadratic formula. Because the quadratic formula is usually faster, it is used more often than completing the square. However, completing the square is an important skill to learn. It will be used in the study of conic sections later in this text.

MATH AT WORK

$x + |x + 1|^2 = 5^2$

Remodeling a kitchen can be an expensive under-taking. Choosing the correct style of cabinets, doors, and floor covering is just a small part of the process. Joe Prendergast, designer for Lee Kimball Kitchens, is involved in every step of creating a new kitchen for a client.

KITCHEN DESIGNER

The process begins with customers visiting the store to see what products are available. Once the client has decided on material and style, he or she fills out an extensive questionnaire so that Prendergast can get a sense of the client's lifestyle. Design plans are drawn using a scale of $\frac{1}{2}$ inch to 1 foot. Consideration is given to traffic patterns, doorways, and especially work areas where the cook would want to work unencumbered. Storage areas are a big consideration, as are lighting and color.

A new kitchen can take anywhere from 5 weeks to a few months or more, depending on how complicated the design and construction is. In Exercise 87 of this section we will find the dimensions of a border around a countertop.

Methods for Solving $ax^2 + bx + c = 0$

Method	Comments	Examples
Even-root property	Use when $b = 0$.	$(x - 2)^2 = 8$ $x - 2 = \pm\sqrt{8}$
Factoring	Use when the polynomial can be factored.	$x^2 + 5x + 6 = 0$ $(x + 2)(x + 3) = 0$
Quadratic formula	Solves any quadratic equation	$x^2 + 5x + 3 = 0$ $x = \dfrac{-5 \pm \sqrt{25 - 4(3)}}{2}$
Completing the square	Solves any quadratic equation, but quadratic formula is faster	$x^2 - 6x + 7 = 0$ $x^2 - 6x + 9 = -7 + 9$ $(x - 3)^2 = 2$

Number of Solutions

The quadratic equations in Examples 1 and 3 had two real solutions each. In each of those examples the value of $b^2 - 4ac$ was positive. In Example 2 the quadratic equation had only one solution because the value of $b^2 - 4ac$ was zero. In Example 4 the quadratic equation had no real solutions because $b^2 - 4ac$ was negative. Because $b^2 - 4ac$ determines the kind and number of solutions to a quadratic equation, it is called the **discriminant.**

Number of Solutions to a Quadratic Equation

The quadratic equation $ax^2 + bx + c = 0$ with $a \neq 0$ has
two real solutions if $b^2 - 4ac > 0$,
one real solution if $b^2 - 4ac = 0$, and
no real solutions (two imaginary solutions) if $b^2 - 4ac < 0$.

E X A M P L E   5

Using the discriminant

Use the discriminant to determine the number of real solutions to each quadratic equation.

a) $x^2 - 3x - 5 = 0$ **b)** $x^2 = 3x - 9$

c) $4x^2 - 12x + 9 = 0$

Solution

a) For $x^2 - 3x - 5 = 0$, use $a = 1$, $b = -3$, and $c = -5$ in $b^2 - 4ac$:

$$b^2 - 4ac = (-3)^2 - 4(1)(-5) = 9 + 20 = 29$$

Because the discriminant is positive, there are two real solutions to this quadratic equation.

b) For $x^2 - 3x + 9 = 0$, use $a = 1$, $b = -3$, and $c = 9$ in $b^2 - 4ac$:

$$b^2 - 4ac = (-3)^2 - 4(1)(9) = 9 - 36 = -27$$

Because the discriminant is negative, the equation has no real solutions. It has two imaginary solutions.

c) For $4x^2 - 12x + 9 = 0$, use $a = 4$, $b = -12$, and $c = 9$ in $b^2 - 4ac$:

$$b^2 - 4ac = (-12)^2 - 4(4)(9) = 144 - 144 = 0$$

Because the discriminant is zero, there is only one real solution to this quadratic equation. ∎

Applications

With the quadratic formula we can easily solve problems whose solutions are irrational numbers. When the solutions are irrational numbers, we usually use a calculator to find rational approximations and to check.

E X A M P L E   6

Area of a tabletop

The area of a rectangular tabletop is 6 square feet. If the width is 2 feet shorter than the length, then what are the dimensions?

Solution

Let x be the length and $x - 2$ be the width, as shown in Fig. 8.1. Because the area is 6 square feet and $A = LW$, we can write the equation

$$x(x - 2) = 6$$

or

$$x^2 - 2x - 6 = 0.$$

FIGURE 8.1

Because this equation cannot be factored, we use the quadratic formula with $a = 1$, $b = -2$, and $c = -6$:

$$x = \frac{2 \pm \sqrt{(-2)^2 - 4(1)(-6)}}{2(1)}$$

$$= \frac{2 \pm \sqrt{28}}{2} = \frac{2 \pm 2\sqrt{7}}{2} = 1 \pm \sqrt{7}$$

Because $1 - \sqrt{7}$ is a negative number, it cannot be the length of a tabletop. If $x = 1 + \sqrt{7}$, then $x - 2 = 1 + \sqrt{7} - 2 = \sqrt{7} - 1$. Checking the product of $\sqrt{7} + 1$ and $\sqrt{7} - 1$, we get

$$(\sqrt{7} + 1)(\sqrt{7} - 1) = 7 - 1 = 6.$$

The exact length is $\sqrt{7} + 1$ feet, and the width is $\sqrt{7} - 1$ feet. Using a calculator, we find that the approximate length is 3.65 feet and the approximate width is 1.65 feet. ■

WARM-UPS

True or false? Explain.

1. Completing the square is used to develop the quadratic formula.
2. For the equation $3x^2 = 4x - 7$, we have $a = 3$, $b = 4$, and $c = -7$.
3. If $dx^2 + ex + f = 0$ and $d \neq 0$, then $x = \frac{-e \pm \sqrt{e^2 - 4df}}{2d}$.
4. The quadratic formula will not work on the equation $x^2 - 3 = 0$.
5. If $a = 2$, $b = -3$, and $c = -4$, then $b^2 - 4ac = 41$.
6. If the discriminant is zero, then there are no imaginary solutions.
7. If $b^2 - 4ac > 0$, then $ax^2 + bx + c = 0$ has two real solutions.
8. To solve $2x - x^2 = 0$ by the quadratic formula, let $a = -1$, $b = 2$, and $c = 0$.
9. Two numbers that have a sum of 6 can be represented by x and $x + 6$.
10. Some quadratic equations have one real and one imaginary solution.

8.2 EXERCISES

Reading and Writing After reading this section, write out the answers to these questions. Use complete sentences.

1. What is the quadratic formula used for?

2. When do you use the even-root property to solve a quadratic equation?

3. When do you use factoring to solve a quadratic equation?

4. When do you use the quadratic formula to solve a quadratic equation?

5. What is the discriminant?

6. How many solutions are there to any quadratic equation in the complex number system?

Solve each equation by using the quadratic formula. See Example 1.

7. $x^2 + 5x + 6 = 0$ **8.** $x^2 - 7x + 12 = 0$

9. $y^2 + y = 6$ **10.** $m^2 + 2m = 8$

11. $-6z^2 + 7z + 3 = 0$ **12.** $-8q^2 - 2q + 1 = 0$

Solve each equation by using the quadratic formula. See Example 2.

13. $4x^2 - 4x + 1 = 0$ **14.** $4x^2 - 12x + 9 = 0$

15. $-9x^2 + 6x - 1 = 0$ **16.** $-9x^2 + 24x - 16 = 0$

17. $9 + 24x + 16x^2 = 0$ **18.** $4 + 20x = -25x^2$

Solve each equation by using the quadratic formula. See Example 3.

19. $v^2 + 8v + 6 = 0$ **20.** $p^2 + 6p + 4 = 0$

21. $-x^2 - 5x + 1 = 0$ **22.** $-x^2 - 3x + 5 = 0$

23. $2t^2 - 6t + 1 = 0$ **24.** $3z^2 - 8z + 2 = 0$

Solve each equation by using the quadratic formula. See Example 4.

25. $2t^2 - 6t + 5 = 0$ **26.** $2y^2 + 1 = 2y$

27. $-2x^2 + 3x = 6$ **28.** $-3x^2 - 2x - 5 = 0$

29. $\frac{1}{2}x^2 + 13 = 5x$ **30.** $\frac{1}{4}x^2 + \frac{17}{4} = 2x$

Find $b^2 - 4ac$ and the number of real solutions to each equation. See Example 5.

31. $x^2 - 6x + 2 = 0$ **32.** $x^2 + 6x + 9 = 0$

33. $-2x^2 + 5x - 6 = 0$ **34.** $-x^2 + 3x - 4 = 0$

35. $4m^2 + 25 = 20m$ **36.** $v^2 = 3v + 5$

37. $y^2 - \frac{1}{2}y + \frac{1}{4} = 0$ **38.** $\frac{1}{2}w^2 - \frac{1}{3}w + \frac{1}{4} = 0$

39. $-3t^2 + 5t + 6 = 0$ **40.** $9m^2 + 16 = 24m$

41. $9 - 24z + 16z^2 = 0$ **42.** $12 - 7x + x^2 = 0$

43. $5x^2 - 7 = 0$ **44.** $-6x^2 - 5 = 0$

45. $x^2 = x$ **46.** $-3x^2 + 7x = 0$

Solve each equation by the method of your choice.

47. $\frac{1}{4}y^2 + y = 1$ **48.** $\frac{1}{2}x^2 + x = 1$

49. $\frac{1}{3}x^2 + \frac{1}{2}x = \frac{1}{3}$ **50.** $\frac{4}{9}w^2 + 1 = \frac{5}{3}w$

51. $3y^2 + 2y - 4 = 0$ **52.** $2y^2 - 3y - 6 = 0$

53. $\frac{w}{w - 2} = \frac{w}{w - 3}$ **54.** $\frac{y}{3y - 4} = \frac{2}{y + 4}$

55. $\frac{9(3x - 5)^2}{4} = 1$ **56.** $\frac{25(2x + 1)^2}{9} = 0$

57. $25 - \frac{1}{3}x^2 = 0$ **58.** $\frac{49}{2} - \frac{1}{4}x^2 = 0$

59. $1 + \frac{20}{x^2} = \frac{8}{x}$ **60.** $\frac{34}{x^2} = \frac{6}{x} - 1$

61. $(x - 8)(x + 4) = -42$
62. $(x - 10)(x - 2) = -20$

63. $y = \frac{3(2y + 5)}{8(y - 1)}$ **64.** $z = \frac{7z - 4}{12(z - 1)}$

 Use the quadratic formula and a calculator to solve each equation. Round answers to three decimal places and check your answers.

65. $x^2 + 3.2x - 5.7 = 0$

66. $x^2 + 7.15x + 3.24 = 0$

67. $x^2 - 7.4x + 13.69 = 0$

68. $1.44x^2 + 5.52x + 5.29 = 0$

69. $1.85x^2 + 6.72x + 3.6 = 0$

70. $3.67x^2 + 4.35x - 2.13 = 0$

71. $3x^2 + 14,379x + 243 = 0$

72. $x^2 + 12,347x + 6741 = 0$

73. $x^2 + 0.00075x - 0.0062 = 0$

74. $4.3x^2 - 9.86x - 3.75 = 0$

Find the exact solution(s) to each problem. If the solution(s) are irrational, then also find approximate solution(s) to the nearest tenth. See Example 6.

75. *Missing numbers.* Find two positive real numbers that differ by 1 and have a product of 16.

76. *Missing numbers.* Find two positive real numbers that differ by 2 and have a product of 10.

77. *More missing numbers.* Find two real numbers that have a sum of 6 and a product of 4.

78. *More missing numbers.* Find two real numbers that have a sum of 8 and a product of 2.

79. *Bulletin board.* The length of a bulletin board is one foot more than the width. The diagonal has a length of $\sqrt{3}$ feet (ft). Find the length and width of the bulletin board.

80. *Diagonal brace.* The width of a rectangular gate is 2 meters (m) larger than its height. The diagonal brace measures $\sqrt{6}$ m. Find the width and height.

FIGURE FOR EXERCISE 80

81. *Area of a rectangle.* The length of a rectangle is 4 ft longer than the width, and its area is 10 square feet (ft²). Find the length and width.

82. *Diagonal of a square.* The diagonal of a square is 2 m longer than a side. Find the length of a side.

If an object is given an initial velocity of v_0 feet per second from a height of s_0 feet, then its height S after t seconds is given by the formula $S = -16t^2 + v_0 t + s_0$.

83. *Projected pine cone.* If a pine cone is projected upward at a velocity of 16 ft/sec from the top of a 96-foot pine tree, then how long does it take to reach the earth?

84. *Falling pine cone.* If a pine cone falls from the top of a 96-foot pine tree, then how long does it take to reach the earth?

85. *Penny tossing.* If a penny is thrown downward at 30 ft/sec from the bridge at Royal Gorge, Colorado, how long does it take to reach the Arkansas River 1000 ft below?

86. *Foul ball.* Suppose Charlie O'Brian of the Braves hits a baseball straight upward at 150 ft/sec from a height of 5 ft.

a) Use the formula to determine how long it takes the ball to return to the earth.

b) Use the accompanying graph to estimate the maximum height reached by the ball.

FIGURE FOR EXERCISE 86

In Exercises 87–90, solve each problem.

87. *Kitchen countertop.* A 30 in. by 40 in. countertop for a work island is to be covered with green ceramic tiles, except for a border of uniform width as shown in the figure. If the area covered by the green tiles is 704 square inches (in.²), then how wide is the border?

FIGURE FOR EXERCISE 87

88. *Recovering an investment.* The manager at Cream of the Crop bought a load of watermelons for $200. She priced the melons so that she would make $1.50 profit on each melon. When all but 30 had been sold, the manager had recovered her initial investment. How many did she buy originally?

89. Baby shower. A group of office workers plans to share equally the $100 cost of giving a baby shower for a coworker. If they can get six more people to share the cost then the cost per person will decrease by $15. How many people are in the original group?

90. Sharing cost. The members of a flying club plan to share equally the cost of a $200,000 airplane. The members want to find five more people to join the club so that the cost per person will decrease by $2000. How many members are currently in the club?

GETTING MORE INVOLVED

 91. Discussion. Find the solutions to $6x^2 + 5x - 4 = 0$. Is the sum of your solutions equal to $-\frac{b}{a}$? Explain why the sum of the solutions to any quadratic equation is $-\frac{b}{a}$. (*Hint:* Use the quadratic formula.)

 92. Discussion. Use the result of Exercise 91 to check whether $\left\{\frac{2}{3}, \frac{1}{3}\right\}$ is the solution set to $9x^2 - 3x - 2 = 0$. If

this solution set is not correct, then what is the correct solution set?

 93. Discussion. What is the product of the two solutions to $6x^2 + 5x - 4 = 0$? Explain why the product of the solutions to any quadratic equation is $\frac{c}{a}$.

 94. Discussion. Use the result of the previous exercise to check whether $\left\{\frac{9}{2}, -2\right\}$ is the solution set to $2x^2 - 13x + 18 = 0$. If this solution set is not correct, then what is the correct solution set?

 ## GRAPHING CALCULATOR EXERCISES

Determine the number of real solutions to each equation by examining the calculator graph of the corresponding function. Use the discriminant to check your conclusions.

95. $x^2 - 6.33x + 3.7 = 0$

96. $1.8x^2 + 2.4x - 895 = 0$

97. $4x^2 - 67.1x + 344 = 0$

98. $-2x^2 - 403 = 0$

99. $-x^2 + 30x - 226 = 0$

100. $16x^2 - 648x + 6562 = 0$

8.3 QUADRATIC FUNCTIONS AND THEIR GRAPHS

In This Section

- Definition
- Graphing Quadratic Functions
- The Vertex and Intercepts
- Applications

We have seen *quadratic functions* on several occasions in this text, but we have not yet defined the term. In this section we study quadratic functions and their graphs.

Definition

If y is determined from x by a formula involving a quadratic polynomial, then we say that y is a *quadratic function of x*. Recall that we can use $f(x)$ or y for the dependent variable.

> **Quadratic Function**
>
> A **quadratic function** is a function of the form
>
> $$f(x) = ax^2 + bx + c,$$
>
> where a, b, and c are real numbers and $a \neq 0$.

Without the term ax^2, this function would be a linear function. That is why we specify that $a \neq 0$.

E X A M P L E   1   **Finding ordered pairs of a quadratic function**

Complete each ordered pair so that it satisfies the given equation.

a) $f(x) = x^2 - x - 6$; (2,   ), (, 0)

b) $s = -16t^2 + 48t + 84$; (0,   ), (, 20)

Solution

a) If $x = 2$, then $f(2) = 2^2 - 2 - 6 = -4$. So the ordered pair is $(2, -4)$. To find x when $y = 0$, replace $f(x)$ by 0 and solve the resulting quadratic equation:

$$x^2 - x - 6 = 0$$
$$(x - 3)(x + 2) = 0$$
$$x - 3 = 0 \quad \text{or} \quad x + 2 = 0$$
$$x = 3 \quad \text{or} \quad x = -2$$

The ordered pairs are $(-2, 0)$ and $(3, 0)$.

b) If $t = 0$, then $s = -16 \cdot 0^2 + 48 \cdot 0 + 84 = 84$. The ordered pair is $(0, 84)$. To find t when $s = 20$, replace s by 20 and solve the equation for t:

$$-16t^2 + 48t + 84 = 20$$

$-16t^2 + 48t + 64 = 0$ Subtract 20 from each side.

$t^2 - 3t - 4 = 0$ Divide each side by -16.

$(t - 4)(t + 1) = 0$ Factor.

$t - 4 = 0 \quad \text{or} \quad t + 1 = 0$ Zero factor property

$t = 4 \quad \text{or} \quad t = -1$

The ordered pairs are $(-1, 20)$ and $(4, 20)$. ∎

CAUTION   When variables other than x and y are used, the independent variable is the first coordinate of an ordered pair, and the dependent variable is the second coordinate. In Example 1(b), t is the independent variable and first coordinate because s depends on t by the formula $s = -16t^2 + 48t + 84$.

Graphing Quadratic Functions

Any real number may be used for x in $f(x) = ax^2 + bx + c$. So the domain (the set of x-coordinates) for any quadratic function is the set of all real numbers, $(-\infty, \infty)$. The range (the set of y-coordinates) can be determined from the graph. All quadratic functions have graphs that are similar in shape. The graph of any quadratic function is called a **parabola.**

E X A M P L E   2

Graphing the simplest quadratic function

Graph the function $f(x) = x^2$, and state the domain and range.

Solution

Make a table of values for x and y:

x	-2	-1	0	1	2
$y = x^2$	4	1	0	1	4

See Fig. 8.2 on the next page for the graph. The domain is the set of all real numbers, $(-\infty, \infty)$, because we can use any real number for x. From the graph we see that the smallest y-coordinate of the function is 0. So the range is the set of real numbers that are greater than or equal to 0, $[0, \infty)$.

Calculator Close-Up

This close-up view of $y = x^2$ shows how rounded the curve is at the bottom. When drawing a parabola by hand, be sure to draw it smoothly.

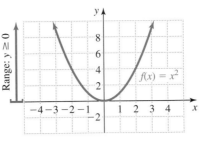

FIGURE 8.2

The parabola in Fig. 8.2 is said to **open upward.** In the next example we see a parabola that **opens downward.** If $a > 0$ in the equation $y = ax^2 + bx + c$, then the parabola opens upward. If $a < 0$, then the parabola opens downward.

EXAMPLE 3

A quadratic function

Graph the function $g(x) = 4 - x^2$, and state the domain and range.

Solution

We plot enough points to get the correct shape of the graph:

x	-2	-1	0	1	2
$y = 4 - x^2$	0	3	4	3	0

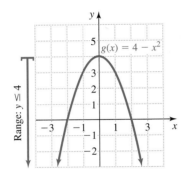

FIGURE 8.3

See Fig. 8.3 for the graph. The domain is the set of all real numbers, $(-\infty, \infty)$. From the graph we see that the largest y-coordinate is 4. So the range is $(-\infty, 4]$.

The Vertex and Intercepts

The lowest point on a parabola that opens upward or the highest point on a parabola that opens downward is called the **vertex.** The y-coordinate of the vertex is the **minimum value** of the function if the parabola opens upward, and it is the **maximum value** of the function if the parabola opens downward. For $f(x) = x^2$ the vertex is $(0, 0)$, and 0 is the minimum value of the function. For $g(x) = 4 - x^2$ the vertex is $(0, 4)$, and 4 is the maximum value of the function.

If $y = ax^2 + bx + c$ has x-intercepts, they can be found by solving $ax^2 + bx + c = 0$ by the quadratic formula. The vertex is midway between the x-intercepts as shown in Fig. 8.4. Note that in the quadratic formula

$$x = \frac{-b \pm \sqrt{b^2 - 4ac}}{2a},$$

$\sqrt{b^2 - 4ac}$ is added and subtracted from the numerator of $\frac{-b}{2a}$. So $\left(\frac{-b}{2a}, 0\right)$ is the point midway between the x-intercepts and the vertex has the same x-coordinate. Even if the parabola has no x-intercepts, the x-coordinate of the vertex is still $\frac{-b}{2a}$.

Vertex of a Parabola

The x-coordinate of the vertex of $y = ax^2 + bx + c$ is $\frac{-b}{2a}$, provided that $a \neq 0$.

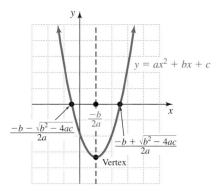

FIGURE 8.4

When you graph a parabola, you should always locate the vertex because it is the point at which the graph "turns around." With the vertex and several nearby points you can see the correct shape of the parabola.

E X A M P L E   4   **Using the vertex in graphing a quadratic function**
Graph $f(x) = -x^2 - x + 2$, and state the domain and range.

Solution
First find the x-coordinate of the vertex:

$$x = \frac{-b}{2a} = \frac{-(-1)}{2(-1)} = \frac{1}{-2} = -\frac{1}{2}$$

Now find $f\left(-\frac{1}{2}\right)$:

$$f\left(-\frac{1}{2}\right) = -\left(-\frac{1}{2}\right)^2 - \left(-\frac{1}{2}\right) + 2 = -\frac{1}{4} + \frac{1}{2} + 2 = \frac{9}{4}$$

The vertex is $\left(-\frac{1}{2}, \frac{9}{4}\right)$. Now find a few points on either side of the vertex:

x	-2	-1	$-\dfrac{1}{2}$	0	1
$f(x) = -x^2 - x + 2$	0	2	$\dfrac{9}{4}$	2	0

Sketch a parabola through these points as in Fig. 8.5. The domain is $(-\infty, \infty)$. Because the graph goes no higher than $\frac{9}{4}$, the range is $\left(-\infty, \frac{9}{4}\right]$.

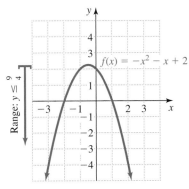

FIGURE 8.5

The *y*-intercept of a parabola is the point that has 0 as the first coordinate. The *x*-intercepts are the points that have 0 as their second coordinates.

E X A M P L E   5   **Using the intercepts in graphing a quadratic function**

Find the vertex and intercepts, and sketch the graph of each function.

a) $f(x) = x^2 - 2x - 8$ **b)** $s = -16t^2 + 64t$

Solution

a) Use $x = \frac{-b}{2a}$ to get $x = 1$ as the *x*-coordinate of the vertex. If $x = 1$, then

$$f(1) = 1^2 - 2 \cdot 1 - 8$$
$$= -9.$$

So the vertex is $(1, -9)$. If $x = 0$, then

$$f(0) = 0^2 - 2 \cdot 0 - 8$$
$$= -8.$$

The *y*-intercept is $(0, -8)$. To find the *x*-intercepts, replace $f(x)$ by 0:

$$x^2 - 2x - 8 = 0$$
$$(x - 4)(x + 2) = 0$$
$$x - 4 = 0 \quad \text{or} \quad x + 2 = 0$$
$$x = 4 \quad \text{or} \quad x = -2$$

The *x*-intercepts are $(-2, 0)$ and $(4, 0)$. The graph is shown in Fig. 8.6.

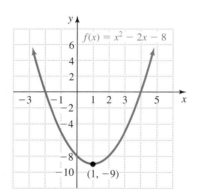

FIGURE 8.6

b) Because s is expressed as a function of t, the first coordinate is t. Use $t = \frac{-b}{2a}$ to get

$$t = \frac{-64}{2(-16)} = 2.$$

If $t = 2$, then

$$s = -16 \cdot 2^2 + 64 \cdot 2$$
$$= 64.$$

So the vertex is $(2, 64)$. If $t = 0$, then

$$s = -16 \cdot 0^2 + 64 \cdot 0$$
$$= 0.$$

So the *s*-intercept is (0, 0). To find the *t*-intercepts, replace *s* by 0:

$$-16t^2 + 64t = 0$$
$$-16t(t - 4) = 0$$
$$-16t = 0 \quad \text{or} \quad t - 4 = 0$$
$$t = 0 \quad \text{or} \quad t = 4$$

The *t*-intercepts are (0, 0) and (4, 0). The graph is shown in Fig. 8.7.

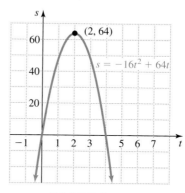

FIGURE 8.7

Calculator Close-Up

You can find the vertex of a parabola with a calculator by using either the maximum or minimum feature. First graph the parabola as shown.

Because this parabola opens upward, the *y*-coordinate of the vertex is the minimum

y-coordinate on the graph. Press CALC and choose minimum.

The calculator will ask for a left bound, a right bound, and a guess. For the left bound choose a point to the left of the vertex by

moving the cursor to the point and pressing ENTER. For the right bound choose a point to the right of the vertex. For the guess choose a point close to the vertex.

Applications

In applications we are often interested in finding the maximum or minimum value of a variable. If the graph of a quadratic function opens downward, then the maximum value of the second coordinate is the second coordinate of the vertex. If the parabola opens upward, then the minimum value of the second coordinate is the second coordinate of the vertex.

E X A M P L E   6

Finding the maximum height

If a projectile is launched with an initial velocity of v_0 feet per second from an initial height of s_0 feet, then its height $s(t)$ in feet is determined by the quadratic function $s(t) = -16t^2 + v_0 t + s_0$, where *t* is the time in seconds. If a ball is tossed upward with velocity 64 feet per second from a height of 5 feet, then what is the maximum height reached by the ball?

Solution

The height $s(t)$ of the ball for any time t is given by $s(t) = -16t^2 + 64t + 5$. Because the maximum height occurs at the vertex of the parabola, we use $t = \dfrac{-b}{2a}$ to find the vertex:

$$t = \frac{-64}{2(-16)} = 2$$

Now use $t = 2$ to find the second coordinate of the vertex:

$$s(2) = -16(2)^2 + 64(2) + 5 = 69$$

The maximum height reached by the ball is 69 feet. See Fig. 8.8. ■

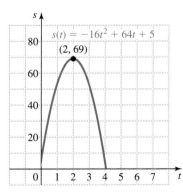

FIGURE 8.8

WARM-UPS

True or false? Explain your answer.

1. The ordered pair $(-2, -1)$ satisfies $f(x) = x^2 - 5$.
2. The y-intercept for $g(x) = x^2 - 3x + 9$ is $(9, 0)$.
3. The x-intercepts for $y = x^2 - 5$ are $(\sqrt{5}, 0)$ and $(-\sqrt{5}, 0)$.
4. The graph of $f(x) = x^2 - 12$ opens upward.
5. The graph of $y = 4 + x^2$ opens downward.
6. The vertex of $y = x^2 + 2x$ is $(-1, -1)$.
7. The parabola $y = x^2 + 1$ has no x-intercepts.
8. The y-intercept for $g(x) = ax^2 + bx + c$ is $(0, c)$.
9. If $w = -2v^2 + 9$, then the maximum value of w is 9.
10. If $y = 3x^2 - 7x + 9$, then the maximum value of y occurs when $x = \dfrac{7}{6}$.

8.3 EXERCISES

Reading and Writing   *After reading this section, write out the answers to these questions. Use complete sentences.*

1. What is a quadratic function?

2. What is a parabola?

3. When does a parabola open upward and when does a parabola open downward?

4. What is the domain of any quadratic function?

5. What is the vertex of a parabola?

6. How can you find the vertex of a parabola?

Complete each ordered pair so that it satisfies the given equation. See Example 1.

7. $f(x) = x^2 - x - 12$ $(3, \quad), (\quad, 0)$

8. $f(x) = -\dfrac{1}{2}x^2 - x + 1$ $(0, \quad), (\quad, -3)$

9. $s = -16t^2 + 32t$ $(4, \quad), (\quad, 0)$

10. $a = b^2 + 4b + 5$ $(-2, \quad), (\quad, 2)$

Graph each quadratic function, and state its domain and range. See Examples 2 and 3.

11. $f(x) = x^2 + 2$

12. $g(x) = x^2 - 4$

13. $y = \dfrac{1}{2}x^2 - 4$

14. $y = \dfrac{1}{3}x^2 - 6$

15. $f(x) = -2x^2 + 5$

16. $g(x) = -x^2 - 1$

17. $y = -\dfrac{1}{3}x^2 + 5$

18. $y = -\dfrac{1}{2}x^2 + 3$

19. $h(x) = (x - 2)^2$

20. $h(x) = (x + 3)^2$

Find the vertex and intercepts for each quadratic function. Sketch the graph, and state the domain and range. See Examples 4 and 5.

21. $f(x) = x^2 - x - 2$

22. $f(x) = x^2 + 2x - 3$

23. $g(x) = x^2 + 2x - 8$

24. $g(x) = x^2 + x - 6$

25. $y = -x^2 - 4x - 3$

26. $y = -x^2 - 5x - 4$

27. $h(x) = -x^2 + 3x + 4$

28. $h(x) = -x^2 - 2x + 8$

29. $a = b^2 - 6b - 16$

30. $v = -u^2 - 8u + 9$

Find the maximum or minimum value of y for each function.

31. $y = x^2 - 8$ **32.** $y = 33 - x^2$

33. $y = -3x^2 + 14$ **34.** $y = 6 + 5x^2$

35. $y = x^2 + 2x + 3$ **36.** $y = x^2 - 2x + 5$

37. $y = -2x^2 - 4x$ **38.** $y = -3x^2 + 24x$

Solve each problem. See Example 6.

39. *Maximum height.* If a baseball is projected upward from ground level with an initial velocity of 64 feet per second, then its height is a function of time, given by $s(t) = -16t^2 + 64t$. Graph this function for $0 \leq t \leq 4$. What is the maximum height reached by the ball?

40. Maximum height. If a soccer ball is kicked straight up with an initial velocity of 32 feet per second, then its height above the earth is a function of time given by $s(t) = -16t^2 + 32t$. Graph this function for $0 \leq t \leq 2$. What is the maximum height reached by this ball?

41. Minimum cost. It costs Acme Manufacturing C dollars per hour to operate its golf ball division. An analyst has determined that C is related to the number of golf balls produced per hour, x, by the equation $C = 0.009x^2 - 1.8x + 100$. What number of balls per hour should Acme produce to minimize the cost per hour of manufacturing these golf balls?

42. Maximum profit. A chain store manager has been told by the main office that daily profit, P, is related to the number of clerks working that day, x, according to the equation $P = -25x^2 + 300x$. What number of clerks will maximize the profit, and what is the maximum possible profit?

43. Maximum area. Jason plans to fence a rectangular area with 100 meters of fencing. He has written the formula $A = w(50 - w)$ to express the area in terms of the width w. What is the maximum possible area that he can enclose with his fencing?

FIGURE FOR EXERCISE 43

44. Minimizing cost. A company uses the function $C(x) = 0.02x^2 - 3.4x + 150$ to model the unit cost in dollars for producing x stabilizer bars. For what number of bars

is the unit cost at its minimum? What is the unit cost at that level of production?

45. Air pollution. The amount of nitrogen dioxide A in parts per million (ppm) that was present in the air in the city of Homer on a certain day in June is modeled by the function

$$A(t) = -2t^2 + 32t + 12,$$

where t is the number of hours after 6:00 A.M. Use this function to find the time at which the nitrogen dioxide level was at its maximum.

46. Stabilization ratio. The stabilization ratio (births/deaths) for South and Central America can be modeled by the function

$$y = -0.0012x^2 + 0.074x + 2.69$$

where y is the number of births divided by the number of deaths in the year $1950 + x$ (World Resources Institute, www.wri.org).

a) Use the graph to estimate the year in which the stabilization ratio was at its maximum.

b) Use the function to find the year in which the stabilization ratio was at its maximum.

c) What was the maximum stabilization ratio from part (b)?

d) What is the significance of a stabilization ratio of 1?

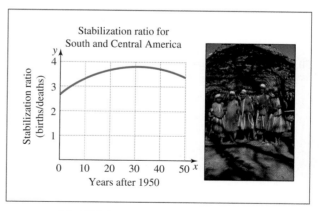

FIGURE FOR EXERCISE 46

47. Suspension bridge. The cable of the suspension bridge shown in the figure on the next page hangs in the shape of a parabola with equation $y = 0.0375x^2$, where x and y are in meters. What is the height of each tower above the roadway? What is the length z for the cable bracing the tower?

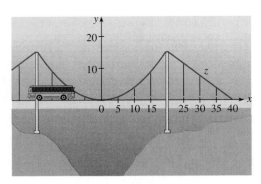

FIGURE FOR EXERCISE 47

51. The equation $x = y^2$ is equivalent to $y = \pm\sqrt{x}$. Graph both $y = \sqrt{x}$ and $y = -\sqrt{x}$ on a graphing calculator. How does the graph of $x = y^2$ compare to the graph of $y = x^2$?

52. Graph each of the following equations by solving for y.
   a) $x = y^2 - 1$

   b) $x = -y^2$

   c) $x^2 + y^2 = 4$

GETTING MORE INVOLVED

48. *Exploration.*
   a) Write the function $y = 3(x - 2)^2 + 6$ in the form $y = ax^2 + bx + c$, and find the vertex of the parabola using the formula $x = \frac{-b}{2a}$.
   b) Repeat part (a) with the functions $y = -4(x - 5)^2 - 9$ and $y = 3(x + 2)^2 - 6$.
   c) What is the vertex for a parabola that is written in the form $y = a(x - h)^2 + k$? Explain your answer.

GRAPHING CALCULATOR EXERCISES

49. Graph $y = x^2$, $y = \frac{1}{2}x^2$, and $y = 2x^2$ on the same coordinate system. What can you say about the graph of $y = kx^2$?

50. Graph $y = x^2$, $y = (x - 3)^2$, and $y = (x + 3)^2$ on the same coordinate system. How does the graph of $y = (x - k)^2$ compare to the graph of $y = x^2$?

53. Determine the approximate vertex, domain, range, and x-intercepts for each quadratic function.
   a) $y = 3.2x^2 - 5.4x + 1.6$
   b) $y = -1.09x^2 + 13x + 7.5$

In This Section

- Using the Discriminant in Factoring
- Writing a Quadratic with Given Solutions
- Equations Quadratic in Form
- Applications

8.4   MORE ON QUADRATIC EQUATIONS

In this section we use the ideas and methods of the previous sections to explore additional topics involving quadratic equations.

Using the Discriminant in Factoring

Consider $ax^2 + bx + c$, where a, b, and c are integers with a greatest common factor of 1. If $b^2 - 4ac$ is a perfect square, then $\sqrt{b^2 - 4ac}$ is a whole number, and the solutions to $ax^2 + bx + c = 0$ are rational numbers. If the solutions to a quadratic equation are rational numbers, then they could be found by the factoring method. So if $b^2 - 4ac$ is a perfect square, then $ax^2 + bx + c$ factors. It is also true that if $b^2 - 4ac$ is not a perfect square, then $ax^2 + bx + c$ is prime.

E X A M P L E   1

Using the discriminant
Use the discriminant to determine whether each polynomial can be factored.
a) $6x^2 + x - 15$ b) $5x^2 - 3x + 2$

Solution

a) Use $a = 6$, $b = 1$, and $c = -15$ to find $b^2 - 4ac$:

$$b^2 - 4ac = 1^2 - 4(6)(-15) = 361$$

Because $\sqrt{361} = 19$, $6x^2 + x - 15$ can be factored. Using the ac method, we get

$$6x^2 + x - 15 = (2x - 3)(3x + 5).$$

b) Use $a = 5$, $b = -3$, and $c = 2$ to find $b^2 - 4ac$:

$$b^2 - 4ac = (-3)^2 - 4(5)(2) = -31$$

Because the discriminant is not a perfect square, $5x^2 - 3x + 2$ is prime. ∎

Writing a Quadratic with Given Solutions

Not every quadratic equation can be solved by factoring, but the factoring method can be used (in reverse) to write a quadratic equation with any given solutions. For example, if the solutions to a quadratic equation are 5 and -3, we can reverse the steps in the factoring method as follows:

$$x = 5 \quad \text{or} \quad x = -3$$
$$x - 5 = 0 \quad \text{or} \quad x + 3 = 0$$
$$(x - 5)(x + 3) = 0 \quad \text{Zero factor property}$$
$$x^2 - 2x - 15 = 0 \quad \text{Multiply the factors.}$$

This method will produce the equation even if the solutions are irrational or imaginary.

E X A M P L E   2

Writing a quadratic given the solutions
Write a quadratic equation that has each given pair of solutions.
a) $4, -6$ b) $-\sqrt{2}, \sqrt{2}$ c) $-3i, 3i$

Solution

a) Reverse the factoring method using solutions 4 and -6:

$$x = 4 \quad \text{or} \quad x = -6$$
$$x - 4 = 0 \quad \text{or} \quad x + 6 = 0$$
$$(x - 4)(x + 6) = 0 \quad \text{Zero factor property}$$
$$x^2 + 2x - 24 = 0 \quad \text{Multiply the factors.}$$

Calculator Close-Up

The graph of $y = x^2 + 2x - 24$ supports the conclusion in Example 2(a) because the graph crosses the x-axis at $(4, 0)$ and $(-6, 0)$.

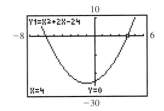

b) Reverse the factoring method using solutions $-\sqrt{2}$ and $\sqrt{2}$:

$$x = -\sqrt{2} \quad \text{or} \quad x = \sqrt{2}$$
$$x + \sqrt{2} = 0 \quad \text{or} \quad x - \sqrt{2} = 0$$
$$(x + \sqrt{2})(x - \sqrt{2}) = 0 \quad \text{Zero factor property}$$
$$x^2 - 2 = 0 \quad \text{Multiply the factors.}$$

c) Reverse the factoring method using solutions $-3i$ and $3i$:

$$x = -3i \quad \text{or} \quad x = 3i$$
$$x + 3i = 0 \quad \text{or} \quad x - 3i = 0$$
$$(x + 3i)(x - 3i) = 0 \quad \text{Zero factor property}$$
$$x^2 - 9i^2 = 0 \quad \text{Multiply the factors.}$$
$$x^2 + 9 = 0 \quad \text{Note: } i^2 = -1$$

Equations Quadratic in Form

In a quadratic equation we have a variable and its square (x and x^2). An equation that contains an expression and the square of that expression is **quadratic in form** if substituting a single variable for that expression results in a quadratic equation. Equations that are quadratic in form can be solved by using methods for quadratic equations.

E X A M P L E   3

An equation quadratic in form

Solve $(x + 15)^2 - 3(x + 15) - 18 = 0$

Solution

Note that $x + 15$ and $(x + 15)^2$ both appear in the equation. Let $a = x + 15$ and substitute a for $x + 15$ in the equation:

$$(x + 15)^2 - 3(x + 15) - 18 = 0$$
$$a^2 - 3a - 18 = 0$$
$$(a - 6)(a + 3) = 0 \quad \text{Factor.}$$
$$a - 6 = 0 \quad \text{or} \quad a + 3 = 0$$
$$a = 6 \quad \text{or} \quad a = -3$$
$$x + 15 = 6 \quad \text{or} \quad x + 15 = -3 \quad \text{Replace } a \text{ by } x + 15.$$
$$x = -9 \quad \text{or} \quad x = -18$$

Check in the original equation. The solution set is $\{-18, -9\}$.

In Example 4 we have a fourth-degree equation that is quadratic in form. Note that the fourth-degree equation has four solutions.

E X A M P L E   4

A fourth-degree equation

Solve $x^4 - 6x^2 + 8 = 0$.

Solution

Note that x^4 is the square of x^2. If we let $w = x^2$, then $w^2 = x^4$. Substitute these expressions into the original equation.

$$x^4 - 6x^2 + 8 = 0$$
$$w^2 - 6w + 8 = 0 \qquad \text{Replace } x^4 \text{ by } w^2 \text{ and } x^2 \text{ by } w.$$
$$(w - 2)(w - 4) = 0 \qquad \text{Factor.}$$

$$w - 2 = 0 \qquad \text{or} \qquad w - 4 = 0$$
$$w = 2 \qquad \text{or} \qquad w = 4$$
$$x^2 = 2 \qquad \text{or} \qquad x^2 = 4 \qquad \text{Substitute } x^2 \text{ for } w.$$
$$x = \pm\sqrt{2} \qquad \text{or} \qquad x = \pm 2 \qquad \text{Even-root property}$$

Check. The solution set is $\{-2, -\sqrt{2}, \sqrt{2}, 2\}$. ■

CAUTION If you replace x^2 by w, do not quit when you find the values of w. If the variable in the original equation is x, then you must solve for x.

EXAMPLE 5

A quadratic within a quadratic

Solve $(x^2 + 2x)^2 - 11(x^2 + 2x) + 24 = 0$.

Solution

Note that $x^2 + 2x$ and $(x^2 + 2x)^2$ appear in the equation. Let $a = x^2 + 2x$ and substitute.

$$a^2 - 11a + 24 = 0$$
$$(a - 8)(a - 3) = 0 \qquad \text{Factor.}$$

$$a - 8 = 0 \quad \text{or} \qquad\qquad a - 3 = 0$$
$$a = 8 \quad \text{or} \qquad\qquad a = 3$$
$$x^2 + 2x = 8 \quad \text{or} \qquad x^2 + 2x = 3 \qquad \text{Replace } a \text{ by } x^2 + 2x.$$
$$x^2 + 2x - 8 = 0 \quad \text{or} \qquad x^2 + 2x - 3 = 0$$
$$(x - 2)(x + 4) = 0 \quad \text{or} \quad (x + 3)(x - 1) = 0$$
$$x - 2 = 0 \quad \text{or} \quad x + 4 = 0 \qquad \text{or} \quad x + 3 = 0 \qquad \text{or} \quad x - 1 = 0$$
$$x = 2 \quad \text{or} \qquad x = -4 \qquad \text{or} \qquad x = -3 \qquad \text{or} \qquad x = 1$$

Check. The solution set is $\{-4, -3, 1, 2\}$. ■

Example 6 involves a fractional exponent. To identify this type of equation as quadratic in form, recall how to square an expression with a fractional exponent. For example, $(x^{1/2})^2 = x$, $(x^{1/4})^2 = x^{1/2}$, and $(x^{1/3})^2 = x^{2/3}$.

EXAMPLE 6

A fractional exponent

Solve $x - 9x^{1/2} + 14 = 0$.

Solution

Note that the square of $x^{1/2}$ is x. Let $w = x^{1/2}$; then $w^2 = (x^{1/2})^2 = x$. Now substitute w and w^2 into the original equation:

$$w^2 - 9w + 14 = 0$$

$$(w - 7)(w - 2) = 0$$

$$w - 7 = 0 \quad \text{or} \quad w - 2 = 0$$

$$w = 7 \quad \text{or} \quad w = 2$$

$$x^{1/2} = 7 \quad \text{or} \quad x^{1/2} = 2 \quad \text{\small Replace } w \text{ by } x^{1/2}.$$

$$x = 49 \quad \text{or} \quad x = 4 \quad \text{\small Square each side.}$$

Because we squared each side, we must check for extraneous roots. First evaluate $x - 9x^{1/2} + 14$ for $x = 49$:

$$49 - 9 \cdot 49^{1/2} + 14 = 49 - 9 \cdot 7 + 14 = 0$$

Now evaluate $x - 9x^{1/2} + 14$ for $x = 4$:

$$4 - 9 \cdot 4^{1/2} + 14 = 4 - 9 \cdot 2 + 14 = 0$$

Because each solution checks, the solution set is $\{4, 49\}$. ◼

> **CAUTION**   An equation of quadratic form must have a term that is the square of another. Equations such as $x^4 - 5x^3 + 6 = 0$ or $x^{1/2} - 3x^{1/3} - 18 = 0$ are not quadratic in form and cannot be solved by substitution.

Applications

Applied problems often result in quadratic equations that cannot be factored. For such equations we use the quadratic formula to find exact solutions and a calculator to find decimal approximations for the exact solutions.

EXAMPLE 7   Changing area

Marvin's flower bed is rectangular in shape with a length of 10 feet and a width of 5 feet (ft). He wants to increase the length and width by the same amount to obtain a flower bed with an area of 75 square feet (ft²). What should the amount of increase be?

Solution

Let x be the amount of increase. The length and width of the new flower bed are $x + 10$ ft and $x + 5$ ft, as shown in Fig. 8.9. Because the area is to be 75 ft², we have

$$(x + 10)(x + 5) = 75.$$

Write this equation in the form $ax^2 + bx + c = 0$:

$$x^2 + 15x + 50 = 75$$

$$x^2 + 15x - 25 = 0 \quad \text{\small Get 0 on the right.}$$

$$x = \frac{-15 \pm \sqrt{225 - 4(1)(-25)}}{2(1)}$$

$$= \frac{-15 \pm \sqrt{325}}{2} = \frac{-15 \pm 5\sqrt{13}}{2}$$

Because the value of x must be positive, the exact increase is

$$\frac{-15 + 5\sqrt{13}}{2} \text{ feet.}$$

FIGURE 8.9

Using a calculator, we can find that x is approximately 1.51 ft. If $x = 1.51$ ft, then the new length is 11.51 ft, and the new width is 6.51 ft. The area of a rectangle with these dimensions is 74.93 ft^2. Of course, the approximate dimensions do not give exactly 75 ft^2. ∎

E X A M P L E   8

Mowing the lawn

It takes Carla 1 hour longer to mow the lawn than it takes Sharon to mow the lawn. If they can mow the lawn in 5 hours working together, then how long would it take each girl by herself?

Solution

If Sharon can mow the lawn by herself in x hours, then she works at the rate of $\frac{1}{x}$ of the lawn per hour. If Carla can mow the lawn by herself in $x + 1$ hours, then she works at the rate of $\frac{1}{x+1}$ of the lawn per hour. We can use a table to list all of the important quantities.

	Rate	Time	Work
Sharon	$\dfrac{1}{x} \dfrac{\text{lawn}}{\text{hr}}$	5 hr	$\dfrac{5}{x}$ lawn
Carla	$\dfrac{1}{x+1} \dfrac{\text{lawn}}{\text{hr}}$	5 hr	$\dfrac{5}{x+1}$ lawn

Because they complete the lawn in 5 hours, the portion of the lawn done by Sharon and the portion done by Carla have a sum of 1:

$$\frac{5}{x} + \frac{5}{x+1} = 1$$

$$x(x+1)\frac{5}{x} + x(x+1)\frac{5}{x+1} = x(x+1)1 \quad \text{Multiply by the LCD.}$$

$$5x + 5 + 5x = x^2 + x$$

$$10x + 5 = x^2 + x$$

$$-x^2 + 9x + 5 = 0$$

$$x^2 - 9x - 5 = 0$$

$$x = \frac{9 \pm \sqrt{(-9)^2 - 4(1)(-5)}}{2(1)}$$

$$= \frac{9 \pm \sqrt{101}}{2}$$

Helpful Hint

Note that the equation concerns the portion of the job done by each girl. We could have written an equation about the rates at which the two girls work. Because they can finish the lawn together in 5 hours, they are mowing together at the rate of $\frac{1}{5}$ lawn per hour. So

$$\frac{1}{x} + \frac{1}{x+1} = \frac{1}{5}.$$

Using a calculator, we find that $\frac{9 - \sqrt{101}}{2}$ is negative. So Sharon's time alone is

$$\frac{9 + \sqrt{101}}{2} \text{ hours.}$$

To find Carla's time alone, we add one hour to Sharon's time. So Carla's time alone is

$$\frac{9 + \sqrt{101}}{2} + 1 = \frac{9 + \sqrt{101}}{2} + \frac{2}{2} = \frac{11 + \sqrt{101}}{2} \text{ hours.}$$

Sharon's time alone is approximately 9.525 hours, and Carla's time alone is approximately 10.525 hours. ∎

True or false? Explain your answer.

1. To solve $x^4 - 5x^2 + 6 = 0$ by substitution, we can let $w = x^2$.
2. We can solve $x^5 - 3x^3 - 10 = 0$ by substitution if we let $w = x^3$.
3. We always use the quadratic formula on equations of quadratic form.
4. If $w = x^{1/6}$, then $w^2 = x^{1/3}$.
5. To solve $x - 7\sqrt{x} + 10 = 0$ by substitution, we let $\sqrt{w} = x$.
6. If $y = 2^{1/2}$, then $y^2 = 2^{1/4}$.
7. If John paints a 100-foot fence in x hours, then his rate is $\frac{100}{x}$ of the fence per hour.
8. If Elvia drives 300 miles in x hours, then her rate is $\frac{300}{x}$ miles per hour (mph).
9. If Ann's boat goes 10 mph in still water, then against a 5-mph current, it will go 2 mph.
10. If squares with sides of length x inches are cut from the corners of an 11-inch by 14-inch rectangular piece of sheet metal and the sides are folded up to form a box, then the dimensions of the bottom will be $11 - x$ by $14 - x$.

8.4   EXERCISES

Reading and Writing *After reading this section, write out the answers to these questions. Use complete sentences.*

1. How can you use the discriminant to determine if a quadratic polynomial can be factored?

2. What is the relationship between solutions to a quadratic equation and factors of a quadratic polynomial?

3. How do we write a quadratic equation with given solutions?

4. What is an equation quadratic in form?

Use the discriminant to determine whether each quadratic polynomial can be factored, then factor the ones that are not prime. See Example 1.

5. $2x^2 - x + 4$

6. $2x^2 + 3x - 5$

7. $2x^2 + 6x - 5$

8. $3x^2 + 5x - 1$

9. $6x^2 + 19x - 36$

10. $8x^2 + 6x - 27$

11. $4x^2 - 5x - 12$

12. $4x^2 - 27x + 45$

13. $8x^2 - 18x - 45$

14. $6x^2 + 9x - 16$

Write a quadratic equation that has each given pair of solutions. See Example 2.

15. $3, -7$

16. $-8, 2$

17. $4, 1$

18. $3, 2$

19. $\sqrt{5}, -\sqrt{5}$

20. $-\sqrt{7}, \sqrt{7}$

21. $4i, -4i$

22. $-3i, 3i$

23. $i\sqrt{2}, -i\sqrt{2}$

24. $3i\sqrt{2}, -3i\sqrt{2}$

25. $\frac{1}{2}, \frac{1}{3}$

26. $-\frac{1}{5}, -\frac{1}{2}$

Find all real solutions to each equation. See Example 3.

27. $(2a - 1)^2 + 2(2a - 1) - 8 = 0$

28. $(3a + 2)^2 - 3(3a + 2) = 10$

29. $(w - 1)^2 + 5(w - 1) + 5 = 0$

30. $(2x - 1)^2 - 4(2x - 1) + 2 = 0$

Find all real solutions to each equation. See Example 4.

31. $x^4 - 14x^2 + 45 = 0$ **32.** $x^4 + 2x^2 = 15$

33. $x^6 + 7x^3 = 8$ **34.** $a^6 + 6a^3 = 16$

Find all real solutions to each equation. See Example 5.

35. $(x^2 + 2x)^2 - 7(x^2 + 2x) + 12 = 0$
36. $(x^2 + 3x)^2 + (x^2 + 3x) - 20 = 0$
37. $(y^2 + y)^2 - 8(y^2 + y) + 12 = 0$
38. $(w^2 - 2w)^2 + 24 = 11(w^2 - 2w)$

Find all real solutions to each equation. See Example 6.
39. $x^{1/2} - 5x^{1/4} + 6 = 0$ **40.** $2x - 5\sqrt{x} + 2 = 0$

41. $2x - 5x^{1/2} - 3 = 0$ **42.** $x^{1/4} + 2 = x^{1/2}$

Find all real solutions to each equation.
43. $x^{-2} + x^{-1} - 6 = 0$ **44.** $x^{-2} - 2x^{-1} = 8$

45. $x^{1/6} - x^{1/3} + 2 = 0$ **46.** $x^{2/3} - x^{1/3} - 20 = 0$

47. $\left(\dfrac{1}{y-1}\right)^2 + \left(\dfrac{1}{y-1}\right) = 6$

48. $\left(\dfrac{1}{w+1}\right)^2 - 2\left(\dfrac{1}{w+1}\right) - 24 = 0$

49. $2x^2 - 3 - 6\sqrt{2x^2 - 3} + 8 = 0$

50. $x^2 + x + \sqrt{x^2 + x} - 2 = 0$

51. $x^{-2} - 2x^{-1} - 1 = 0$ **52.** $x^{-2} - 6x^{-1} + 6 = 0$

Find the exact solution to each problem. If the exact solution is an irrational number, then also find an approximate decimal solution. See Examples 7 and 8.

53. *Country singers.* Harry and Gary are traveling to Nashville to make their fortunes. Harry leaves on the train at 8:00 A.M. and Gary travels by car, starting at 9:00 A.M. To complete the 300-mile trip and arrive at the same time as Harry, Gary travels 10 miles per hour (mph) faster than the train. At what time will they both arrive in Nashville?

54. *Gone fishing.* Debbie traveled by boat 5 miles upstream to fish in her favorite spot. Because of the 4-mph current, it took her 20 minutes longer to get there than to return. How fast will her boat go in still water?

55. *Cross-country cycling.* Erin was traveling across the desert on her bicycle. Before lunch she traveled 60 miles (mi); after lunch she traveled 46 mi. She put in one hour more after lunch than before lunch, but her speed was 4 mph slower than before. What was her speed before lunch and after lunch?

FIGURE FOR EXERCISE 55

56. *Extreme hardship.* Kim starts to walk 3 mi to school at 7:30 A.M. with a temperature of 0°F. Her brother Bryan starts at 7:45 A.M. on his bicycle, traveling 10 mph faster than Kim. If they get to school at the same time, then how fast is each one traveling?

57. *American pie.* John takes 3 hours longer than Andrew to peel 500 pounds (lb) of apples. If together they can peel 500 lb of apples in 8 hours, then how long would it take each one working alone?

58. *On the half shell.* It takes Brent one hour longer than Calvin to shuck a sack of oysters. If together they shuck a sack of oysters in 45 minutes, then how long would it take each one working alone?

59. *The growing garden.* Eric's garden is 20 ft by 30 ft. He wants to increase the length and width by the same amount to have a 1000-ft^2 garden. What should be the new dimensions of the garden?

60. *Open-top box.* Thomas is going to make an open-top box by cutting equal squares from the four corners of an 11 inch by 14 inch sheet of cardboard and folding up the sides. If the area of the base is to be 80 square inches, then what size square should be cut from each corner?

FIGURE FOR EXERCISE 60

61. *Pumping the pool.* It takes pump A 2 hours less time than pump B to empty a certain swimming pool. Pump A is started at 8:00 A.M., and pump B is started at 11:00 A.M. If the pool is still half full at 5:00 P.M., then how long would it take pump A working alone?

62. *Time off for lunch.* It usually takes Eva 3 hours longer to do the monthly payroll than it takes Cicely. They start working on it together at 9:00 A.M. and at 5:00 P.M. they have 90% of it done. If Eva took a 2-hour lunch break while Cicely had none, then how much longer will it take for them to finish the payroll working together?

63. *Golden Rectangle.* One principle used by the ancient Greeks to get shapes that are pleasing to the eye in art and architecture was the Golden Rectangle. If a square is removed from one end of a Golden Rectangle, as shown in the figure, the sides of the remaining rectangle are

proportional to the original rectangle. So the length and width of the original rectangle satisfy

$$\frac{L}{W} = \frac{W}{L - W}.$$

If the length of a Golden Rectangle is 10 meters, then what is its width?

FIGURE FOR EXERCISE 63

GETTING MORE INVOLVED

64. *Exploration.*
   a) Given that $P(x) = x^4 + 6x^2 - 27$, find $P(3i)$, $P(-3i)$, $P(\sqrt{3})$, and $P(-\sqrt{3})$.
   b) What can you conclude about the values $3i$, $-3i$, $\sqrt{3}$, and $-\sqrt{3}$ and their relationship to each other?

65. *Cooperative learning.* Work with a group to write a quadratic equation that has each given pair of solutions.
   a) $3 + \sqrt{5}, 3 - \sqrt{5}$ **b)** $4 - 2i, 4 + 2i$
   c) $\dfrac{1 + i\sqrt{3}}{2}, \dfrac{1 - i\sqrt{3}}{2}$

GRAPHING CALCULATOR EXERCISES

Solve each equation by locating the x-intercepts on the graph of a corresponding function. Round approximate answers to two decimal places.

66. $(5x - 7)^2 - (5x - 7) - 6 = 0$

67. $x^4 - 116x^2 + 1600 = 0$

68. $(x^2 + 3x)^2 - 7(x^2 + 3x) + 9 = 0$

69. $x^2 - 3x^{1/2} - 12 = 0$

8.5 QUADRATIC AND RATIONAL INEQUALITIES

In this section we solve inequalities involving quadratic polynomials. We use a new technique based on the rules for multiplying real numbers.

Solving Quadratic Inequalities with a Sign Graph

An inequality involving a quadratic polynomial is called a **quadratic** inequality.

> **Quadratic Inequality**
>
> A quadratic inequality is an inequality of the form
>
> $$ax^2 + bx + c > 0,$$
>
> where a, b, and c are real numbers with $a \neq 0$. The inequality symbols $<$, $\leq$, and $\geq$ may also be used.

If we can factor a quadratic inequality, then the inequality can be solved with a **sign graph**, which shows where each factor is positive, negative, or zero.

E X A M P L E   1

Solving a quadratic inequality

Use a sign graph to solve the inequality $x^2 + 3x - 10 > 0$.

Solution

Because the left-hand side can be factored, we can write the inequality as

$$(x + 5)(x - 2) > 0.$$

This inequality says that the product of $x + 5$ and $x - 2$ is positive. If both factors are negative or both are positive, the product is positive. To analyze the signs of each factor, we make a sign graph as follows. First consider the possible values of the factor $x + 5$:

Value	Where	On the number line
$x + 5 = 0$	if $x = -5$	Put a 0 above -5.
$x + 5 > 0$	if $x > -5$	Put $+$ signs to the right of -5.
$x + 5 < 0$	if $x < -5$	Put $-$ signs to the left of -5.

The sign graph shown in Fig. 8.10 for the factor $x + 5$ is made from the information in the preceding table.

FIGURE 8.10

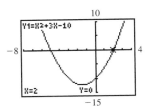
Now consider the possible values of the factor $x - 2$:

Value	Where	On the number line
$x - 2 = 0$	if $x = 2$	Put a 0 above 2.
$x - 2 > 0$	if $x > 2$	Put + signs to the right of 2.
$x - 2 < 0$	if $x < 2$	Put − signs to the left of 2.

We put the information for the factor $x - 2$ on the sign graph for the factor $x + 5$ as shown in Fig. 8.11. We can see from Fig. 8.11 that the product is positive if $x < -5$ and the product is positive if $x > 2$. The solution set for the quadratic inequality is shown in Fig. 8.12. Note that -5 and 2 are not included in the graph because for those values of x the product is zero. The solution set is $(-\infty, -5) \cup (2, \infty)$.

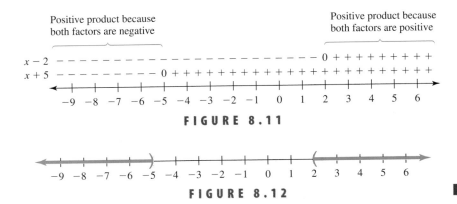

FIGURE 8.11

FIGURE 8.12

In Example 2 we will make the procedure from Example 1 a bit more efficient.

EXAMPLE 2

Solving a quadratic inequality

Solve $2x^2 + 5x \leq 3$ and graph the solution set.

Solution

Rewrite the inequality with 0 on one side:

$$2x^2 + 5x - 3 \leq 0$$
$$(2x - 1)(x + 3) \leq 0 \quad \text{Factor.}$$

Examine the signs of each factor:

$$2x - 1 = 0 \quad \text{if} \quad x = \frac{1}{2}$$

$$2x - 1 > 0 \quad \text{if} \quad x > \frac{1}{2}$$

$$2x - 1 < 0 \quad \text{if} \quad x < \frac{1}{2}$$

$$x + 3 = 0 \quad \text{if} \quad x = -3$$
$$x + 3 > 0 \quad \text{if} \quad x > -3$$
$$x + 3 < 0 \quad \text{if} \quad x < -3$$

Calculator Close-Up

Use Y= to set $y_1 = 2x - 1$ and $y_2 = x + 3$. The table of values for y_1 and y_2 supports the sign graph in Fig. 8.13.

Note that the graph of $y = 2x^2 + 5x - 3$ is below the x-axis when x is between -3 and $\frac{1}{2}$.

Make a sign graph as shown in Fig. 8.13. The product of the factors is negative between -3 and $\frac{1}{2}$, when one factor is negative and the other is positive. The product is 0 at -3 and at $\frac{1}{2}$. So the solution set is the interval $\left[-3, \frac{1}{2}\right]$. The graph of the solution set is shown in Fig. 8.14.

FIGURE 8.13

FIGURE 8.14

We summarize the strategy used for solving a quadratic inequality as follows.

> ### Strategy for Solving a Quadratic Inequality with a Sign Graph
>
> 1. Write the inequality with 0 on the right.
> 2. Factor the quadratic polynomial on the left.
> 3. Make a sign graph showing where each factor is positive, negative, or zero.
> 4. Use the rules for multiplying signed numbers to determine which intervals satisfy the original inequality.
> 5. Write the solution set using interval notation.

Solving Rational Inequalities with a Sign Graph

The inequalities

$$\frac{x + 2}{x - 3} \le 2, \qquad \frac{2x - 3}{x + 5} \le 0 \qquad \text{and} \qquad \frac{2}{x + 4} \ge \frac{1}{x + 1}$$

are called **rational inequalities.** When we solve *equations* that involve rational expressions, we usually multiply each side by the LCD. However, if we multiply each side of any inequality by a negative number, we must reverse the inequality, and when we multiply by a positive number, we do not reverse the inequality. For this reason we generally *do not multiply inequalities by expressions involving variables.* The values of the expressions might be positive or negative. Examples 3 and 4 show how to use a sign graph to solve rational inequalities that have variables in the denominator.

E X A M P L E   3

Solving a rational inequality

Solve $\frac{x + 2}{x - 3} \leq 2$ and graph the solution set.

Helpful Hint

Solution

We *do not* multiply each side by $x - 3$. Instead, subtract 2 from each side to get 0 on the right:

$$\frac{x + 2}{x - 3} - 2 \leq 0$$

$$\frac{x + 2}{x - 3} - \frac{2(x - 3)}{x - 3} \leq 0 \quad \text{Get a common denominator.}$$

$$\frac{x + 2}{x - 3} - \frac{2x - 6}{x - 3} \leq 0 \quad \text{Simplify.}$$

$$\frac{x + 2 - 2x + 6}{x - 3} \leq 0 \quad \text{Subtract the rational expressions.}$$

$$\frac{-x + 8}{x - 3} \leq 0 \quad \begin{array}{l}\text{The quotient of } -x + 8 \text{ and } x - 3 \text{ is less} \\ \text{than or equal to 0.}\end{array}$$

Calculator Close-Up

Graph $y = \frac{-x + 8}{x - 3}$ to support the conclusion that $y \leq 0$ when $x < 3$ or $x \geq 8$.

Examine the signs of the numerator and denominator:

$$x - 3 = 0 \quad \text{if} \quad x = 3 \qquad -x + 8 = 0 \quad \text{if} \quad x = 8$$
$$x - 3 > 0 \quad \text{if} \quad x > 3 \qquad -x + 8 > 0 \quad \text{if} \quad x < 8$$
$$x - 3 < 0 \quad \text{if} \quad x < 3 \qquad -x + 8 < 0 \quad \text{if} \quad x > 8$$

Make a sign graph as shown in Fig. 8.15. Using the rule for dividing signed numbers and the sign graph, we can identify where the quotient is negative or zero. The solution set is $(-\infty, 3) \cup [8, \infty)$. Note that 3 is not in the solution set because the quotient is undefined if $x = 3$. The graph of the solution set is shown in Fig. 8.16.

FIGURE 8.15

FIGURE 8.16

C A U T I O N   Remember to reverse the inequality sign when multiplying or dividing by a negative number. For example, $x - 3 > 0$ is equivalent to $x > 3$. But $-x + 8 > 0$ is equivalent to $-x > -8$, or $x < 8$.

E X A M P L E   4

Solving a rational inequality

Solve $\frac{2}{x + 4} \geq \frac{1}{x + 1}$ and graph the solution set.

Solution

We do not multiply by the LCD as we do in solving equations. Instead, subtract $\dfrac{1}{x+1}$ from each side:

$$\frac{2}{x+4} - \frac{1}{x+1} \geq 0$$

$$\frac{2(x+1)}{(x+4)(x+1)} - \frac{1(x+4)}{(x+1)(x+4)} \geq 0 \qquad \text{Get a common denominator.}$$

$$\frac{2x+2-x-4}{(x+1)(x+4)} \geq 0 \qquad \text{Simplify.}$$

$$\frac{x-2}{(x+1)(x+4)} \geq 0$$

Make a sign graph as shown in Fig. 8.17.

FIGURE 8.17

The computation of

$$\frac{x-2}{(x+1)(x+4)}$$

involves multiplication and division. The result of this computation is positive if all of the three binomials are positive or if only one is positive and the other two are negative. The sign graph shows that this rational expression will have a positive value when x is between -4 and -1 and again when x is larger than 2. The solution set is $(-4, -1) \cup [2, \infty)$. Note that -1 and -4 are not in the solution set because they make the denominator zero. The graph of the solution set is shown in Fig. 8.18.

FIGURE 8.18   ■

Solving rational inequalities with a sign graph is summarized below.

> ### Strategy for Solving a Rational Inequality with a Sign Graph
>
> 1. Rewrite the inequality with 0 on the right-hand side.
> 2. Use only addition and subtraction to get an equivalent inequality.
> 3. Factor the numerator and denominator if possible.
> 4. Make a sign graph showing where each factor is positive, negative, or zero.
> 5. Use the rules for multiplying and dividing signed numbers to determine the intervals that satisfy the original inequality.
> 6. Write the solution set using interval notation.

Another method for solving quadratic and rational inequalities will be shown in Example 5. This method, called the **test point method,** can be used instead of the sign graph to solve the inequalities of Examples 1, 2, 3, and 4.

Quadratic Inequalities That Cannot Be Factored

Example 5 shows how to solve a quadratic inequality that involves a prime polynomial.

E X A M P L E   5   **Solving a quadratic inequality using the quadratic formula**

Solve $x^2 - 4x - 6 > 0$ and graph the solution set.

Solution

The quadratic polynomial is prime, but we can solve $x^2 - 4x - 6 = 0$ by the quadratic formula:

$$x = \frac{4 \pm \sqrt{16 - 4(1)(-6)}}{2(1)} = \frac{4 \pm \sqrt{40}}{2} = \frac{4 \pm 2\sqrt{10}}{2} = 2 \pm \sqrt{10}$$

As in the previous examples, the solutions to the equation divide the number line into the intervals $(-\infty, 2 - \sqrt{10})$, $(2 - \sqrt{10}, 2 + \sqrt{10})$, and $(2 + \sqrt{10}, \infty)$ on which the quadratic polynomial has either a positive or negative value. To determine which, we select an arbitrary **test point** in each interval. Because $2 + \sqrt{10} \approx 5.2$ and $2 - \sqrt{10} \approx -1.2$, we choose a test point that is less than -1.2, one between -1.2 and 5.2, and one that is greater than 5.2. We have selected -2, 0, and 7 for test points, as shown in Fig. 8.19. Now evaluate $x^2 - 4x - 6$ at each test point.

F I G U R E   8 . 1 9

Test point	Value of $x^2 - 4x - 6$ at the test point	Sign of $x^2 - 4x - 6$ in interval of test point
-2	6	Positive
0	-6	Negative
7	15	Positive

Because $x^2 - 4x - 6$ is positive at the test points -2 and 7, it is positive at every point in the intervals containing those test points. So the solution set to the inequality $x^2 - 4x - 6 > 0$ is

$$(-\infty, 2 - \sqrt{10}) \cup (2 + \sqrt{10}, \infty),$$

and its graph is shown in Fig. 8.20.

F I G U R E   8 . 2 0

The test point method used in Example 5 can be used also on inequalities that do factor. We summarize the strategy for solving inequalities using test points in the following box.

Strategy for Solving Quadratic Inequalities Using Test Points

1. Rewrite the inequality with 0 on the right.
2. Solve the quadratic equation that results from replacing the inequality symbol with the equals symbol.
3. Locate the solutions to the quadratic equation on a number line.
4. Select a test point in each interval determined by the solutions to the quadratic equation.
5. Test each point in the original quadratic inequality to determine which intervals satisfy the inequality.
6. Write the solution set using interval notation.

Applications

Example 6 shows how a quadratic inequality can be used to solve a problem.

E X A M P L E   6

Making a profit

Charlene's daily profit P (in dollars) for selling x magazine subscriptions is determined by the formula

$$P = -x^2 + 80x - 1500.$$

For what values of x is her profit positive?

Solution

We can find the values of x for which $P > 0$ by solving a quadratic inequality:

$$-x^2 + 80x - 1500 > 0$$
$$x^2 - 80x + 1500 < 0 \quad \text{Multiply each side by } -1.$$
$$(x - 30)(x - 50) < 0 \quad \text{Factor.}$$

Make a sign graph as shown in Fig. 8.21. The product of the two factors is negative for x between 30 and 50. Because the last inequality is equivalent to the first, the profit is positive when the number of magazine subscriptions sold is greater than 30 and less than 50.

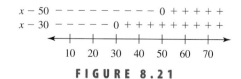

F I G U R E   8 . 2 1

True or false? Explain.

1. The solution set to $x^2 > 4$ is $(2, \infty)$.
2. The inequality $\frac{x}{x-3} > 2$ is equivalent to $x > 2x - 6$.
3. The inequality $(x - 1)(x + 2) < 0$ is equivalent to $x - 1 < 0$ or $x + 2 < 0$.
4. We cannot solve quadratic inequalities that do not factor.
5. One technique for solving quadratic inequalities is based on the rules for multiplying signed numbers.
6. Multiplying each side of an inequality by a variable should be avoided.
7. In solving quadratic or rational inequalities, we always get 0 on one side.
8. The inequality $\frac{x}{2} > 3$ is equivalent to $x > 6$.
9. The inequality $\frac{x-3}{x+2} < 1$ is equivalent to $\frac{x-3}{x+2} - 1 < 0$.
10. The solution set to $\frac{x+2}{x-4} \geq 0$ is $(-\infty, -2] \cup [4, \infty)$.

8.5   EXERCISES

Reading and Writing   *After reading this section, write out the answers to these questions. Use complete sentences.*

1. What is a quadratic inequality?

2. What is a sign graph?

3. What is a rational inequality?

4. Why don't we usually multiply each side of an inequality by an expression involving a variable?

Solve each inequality. Graph the solution set and state the solution set using interval notation. See Examples 1 and 2.

5. $x^2 + x - 6 < 0$

6. $x^2 - 3x - 4 \geq 0$

7. $y^2 - 4 > 0$

8. $z^2 - 16 < 0$

9. $2u^2 + 5u \geq 12$

10. $2v^2 + 7v < 4$

11. $4x^2 - 8x \geq 0$

12. $x^2 + x > 0$

13. $5x - 10x^2 < 0$

14. $3x - x^2 > 0$

15. $x^2 + 6x + 9 \geq 0$

16. $x^2 + 25 < 10x$

Solve each rational inequality. State and graph the solution set. See Examples 3 and 4.

17. $\dfrac{x}{x-3} > 0$

18. $\dfrac{a}{a+2} > 0$

19. $\dfrac{x+2}{x} \leq 0$

20. $\dfrac{w-6}{w} \leq 0$

21. $\dfrac{t-3}{t+6} > 0$

22. $\dfrac{x-2}{2x+5} < 0$

23. $\dfrac{x}{x+2} > -1$

24. $\dfrac{x+3}{x} \leq -2$

25. $\dfrac{2}{x-5} > \dfrac{1}{x+4}$

26. $\dfrac{3}{x+2} > \dfrac{2}{x-1}$

27. $\dfrac{m}{m-5} + \dfrac{3}{m-1} > 0$

28. $\dfrac{p}{p-16} + \dfrac{2}{p-6} \leq 0$

29. $\dfrac{x}{x-3} \leq \dfrac{-8}{x-6}$

30. $\dfrac{x}{x+20} > \dfrac{2}{x+8}$

Solve each inequality. State and graph the solution set. See Example 5.

31. $x^2 - 2x - 4 > 0$

32. $x^2 - 2x - 5 \leq 0$

33. $2x^2 - 6x + 3 \geq 0$

34. $2x^2 - 8x + 3 < 0$

35. $y^2 - 3y - 9 \leq 0$

36. $z^2 - 5z - 7 < 0$

In Exercises 37–60, solve each inequality. State the solution set using interval notation.

37. $x^2 \leq 9$

38. $x^2 \geq 36$

39. $16 - x^2 > 0$

40. $9 - x^2 < 0$

41. $x^2 - 4x \geq 0$

42. $4x^2 - 9 > 0$

43. $3(2w^2 - 5) < w$

44. $6(y^2 - 2) + y < 0$

45. $z^2 \geq 4(z + 3)$

46. $t^2 < 3(2t - 3)$

47. $(q + 4)^2 > 10q + 31$

48. $(2p + 4)(p - 1) < (p + 2)^2$

49. $\frac{1}{2}x^2 \geq 4 - x$

50. $\frac{1}{2}x^2 \leq x + 12$

51. $\frac{x - 4}{x + 3} \leq 0$

52. $\frac{2x - 1}{x + 5} \geq 0$

53. $(x - 2)(x + 1)(x - 5) \geq 0$

54. $(x - 1)(x + 2)(2x - 5) < 0$

55. $x^3 + 3x^2 - x - 3 < 0$

56. $x^3 + 5x^2 - 4x - 20 \geq 0$

57. $0.23x^2 + 6.5x + 4.3 < 0$

58. $0.65x^2 + 3.2x + 5.1 > 0$

59. $\frac{x}{x - 2} > \frac{-1}{x + 3}$

60. $\frac{x}{3 - x} > \frac{2}{x + 5}$

Solve each problem by using a quadratic inequality. See Example 6.

61. *Positive profit.* The monthly profit P (in dollars) that Big Jim makes on the sale of x mobile homes is determined by the formula $P = x^2 + 5x - 50$. For what values of x is his profit positive?

62. *Profitable fruitcakes.* Sharon's revenue R (in dollars) on the sale of x fruitcakes is determined by the formula $R = 50x - x^2$. Her cost C (in dollars) for producing x fruitcakes is given by the formula $C = 2x + 40$. For what values of x is Sharon's profit positive? (Profit = revenue − cost.)

If an object is given an initial velocity straight upward of v_0 feet per second from a height of s_0 feet, then its altitude S after t seconds is given by the formula

$$S = -16t^2 + v_0t + s_0.$$

63. *Flying high.* An arrow is shot straight upward with a velocity of 96 feet per second (ft/sec) from an altitude of 6 feet. For how many seconds is this arrow more than 86 feet high?

 64. *Putting the shot.* In 1978 Udo Beyer (East Germany) set a world record in the shot-put of 72 ft 8 in. If Beyer had projected the shot straight upward with a velocity of 30 ft/sec from a height of 5 ft, then for what values of t would the shot be under 15 ft high?

If a projectile is fired at a 45° angle from a height of s_0 feet with initial velocity v_0 ft/sec, then its altitude S in feet after t seconds is given by

$$S = -16t^2 + \frac{v_0}{\sqrt{2}}t + s_0.$$

65. *Siege and garrison artillery.* An 8-inch mortar used in the Civil War fired a 44.5-lb projectile from ground level a distance of 3600 ft when aimed at a 45° angle (Harold R. Peterson, *Notes on Ordinance of the American Civil War*). The accompanying graph shows the altitude of the projectile when it is fired with a velocity of $240\sqrt{2}$ ft/sec.

a) Use the graph to estimate the maximum altitude reached by the projectile.

b) Use the graph to estimate approximately how long the altitude of the projectile was greater than 864 ft.

c) Use the formula to determine the length of time for which the projectile had an altitude of more than 864 ft.

FIGURE FOR EXERCISE 65

 66. *Seacoast artillery.* The 13-inch mortar used in the Civil War fired a 220-lb projectile a distance of 12,975 ft when aimed at a 45° angle. If the 13-inch mortar was fired from a hill 100 ft above sea level with an initial velocity of 644 ft/sec, then for how long was the projectile more than 800 ft above sea level?

FIGURE FOR EXERCISE 66

GETTING MORE INVOLVED

67. *Cooperative learning.* Work in a small group to solve each inequality for x, given that h and k are real numbers with $h < k$.

a) $(x - h)(x - k) < 0$

b) $(x - h)(x - k) > 0$

c) $(x + h)(x + k) < 0$

d) $(x + h)(x + k) \geq 0$

e) $\dfrac{x - h}{x - k} \geq 0$

f) $\dfrac{x + h}{x + k} \leq 0$

68. *Cooperative learning.* Work in a small group to solve $ax^2 + bx + c > 0$ for x in each case.

a) $b^2 - 4ac = 0$ and $a > 0$

b) $b^2 - 4ac = 0$ and $a < 0$

c) $b^2 - 4ac < 0$ and $a > 0$

d) $b^2 - 4ac < 0$ and $a < 0$

e) $b^2 - 4ac > 0$ and $a > 0$

f) $b^2 - 4ac > 0$ and $a < 0$

GRAPHING CALCULATOR EXERCISES

Match the given inequalities with their solution sets (a through d) by examining a table or a graph.

69. $x^2 - 2x - 8 < 0$ **a.** $(-2, 2) \cup (8, \infty)$

70. $x^2 - 3x > 54$ **b.** $(2, 4)$

71. $\dfrac{x}{x - 2} > 2$ **c.** $(-2, 4)$

72. $\dfrac{3}{x - 2} < \dfrac{5}{x + 2}$ **d.** $(-\infty, -6) \cup (9, \infty)$

COLLABORATIVE ACTIVITIES

Completing the Square

Al-Khwarizmi, an Arab mathematician who lived in Baghdad in the mid-800s, wrote the first book on algebra that is more analytic than geometric. It looks like our algebra books today. The word "algebra" comes from his book called *The Book of Algebra and Almucabola*. His book describes methods of solving quadratic equations that are based on a geometric understanding of what the equations represent. In this activity you will explore how to derive the quadratic formula geometrically and learn why the method is called "completing the square."

Consider the equation $2x^2 + 4x = 8$. To solve it geometrically, we first divide by the leading coefficient, 2, to get

$$x^2 + 2x = 4.$$

Grouping: 3 students per group

Topic: A geometric solution to a quadratic

Now this equation can be viewed geometrically as an x by x square and an x by 2 rectangle having a total area of 4:

To complete the square, divide the x by 2 rectangle into four x by $\frac{1}{2}$ rectangles and add them to the sides of the x by x square:

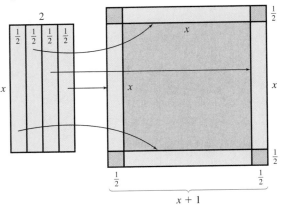

The square is complete except for the four $\frac{1}{2}$ by $\frac{1}{2}$ squares in the corners, each of which has area $\frac{1}{4}$. Filling those in will add

1 square unit of area to the 4 we had already for a total of 5. Since the sides of the completed square are $x + 1$, we have

$$(x + 1)^2 = 5.$$

Solve for x to get $x + 1 = \pm\sqrt{5}$ or $x = -1 \pm \sqrt{5}$.

Complete the following in your groups:

1. Verify and write down the steps for the geometric method of completing the square.

2. Use the geometric method of completing the square to solve each equation for x:
   a) $3x^2 + 12x = 18$
   b) $2x^2 + 6x = 5$
   c) $3x^2 + 4x = 9$

3. Solve $ax^2 + bx = c$ by the geometric method. Explain why the formula found in this general case is not quite the quadratic formula.

W R A P - U P

CHAPTER 8

SUMMARY

Quadratic Equations

Examples

| Quadratic equation | An equation of the form $ax^2 + bx + c = 0$, where a, b, and c are real numbers, with $a \neq 0$ | $x^2 = 11$
 $(x - 5)^2 = 99$
 $x^2 + 3x - 20 = 0$ |

Methods for solving quadratic equations	**Factoring:** Factor the quadratic polynomial, then set each factor equal to 0.	$x^2 + x - 6 = 0$ $(x + 3)(x - 2) = 0$ $x + 3 = 0$ or $x - 2 = 0$
	The even-root property: If $x^2 = k$ $(k > 0)$, then $x = \pm\sqrt{k}$. If $x^2 = 0$, then $x = 0$. There are no real solutions to $x^2 = k$ for $k < 0$.	$(x - 5)^2 = 10$ $x - 5 = \pm\sqrt{10}$
	Completing the square: Take one-half of middle term, square it, then add it to each side.	$x^2 + 6x = -4$ $x^2 + 6x + 9 = -4 + 9$ $(x + 3)^2 = 5$
	Quadratic formula: Solves $ax^2 + bx + c = 0$ with $a \neq 0$: $$x = \frac{-b \pm \sqrt{b^2 - 4ac}}{2a}$$	$2x^2 + 3x - 5 = 0$ $$x = \frac{-3 \pm \sqrt{3^2 - 4(2)(-5)}}{2(2)}$$

Number of solutions	Determined by the discriminant $b^2 - 4ac$: $b^2 - 4ac > 0$ 2 real solutions $b^2 - 4ac = 0$ 1 real solution $b^2 - 4ac < 0$ no real solutions, 2 imaginary solutions	$x^2 + 6x - 12 = 0$ $6^2 - 4(1)(-12) > 0$ $x^2 + 10x + 25 = 0$ $10^2 - 4(1)(25) = 0$ $x^2 + 2x + 20 = 0$ $2^2 - 4(1)(20) < 0$
Factoring	The quadratic polynomial $ax^2 + bx + c$ (with integral coefficients) can be factored if and only if $b^2 - 4ac$ is a perfect square.	$2x^2 - 11x + 12$ $b^2 - 4ac = 25$ $(2x - 3)(x - 4)$
Writing equations	To write an equation with given solutions, reverse the steps in solving an equation by factoring.	$x = 2$ or $x = -3$ $(x - 2)(x + 3) = 0$ $x^2 + x - 6 = 0$
Equations quadratic in form	Use substitution to convert to a quadratic.	$x^4 + 3x^2 - 10 = 0$ Let $a = x^2$ $a^2 + 3a - 10 = 0$

Quadratic Functions

Examples

Quadratic function	A function of the form $f(x) = ax^2 + bx + c$, where a, b, and c are real numbers and $a \neq 0$	$f(x) = 3x^2 - 8x + 9$ $p = -3q^2 - 8q + 1$
Graphing a quadratic function	The graph is a parabola opening upward if $a > 0$ and downward if $a < 0$. The first coordinate of the vertex is $\frac{-b}{2a}$. The second coordinate of the vertex is either the minimum value of the function if $a > 0$ or the maximum value of the function if $a < 0$.	$y = x^2 - 2x + 5$ Opens upward Vertex: $(1, 4)$ Minimum value of y is 4.

Quadratic and Rational Inequalities

Examples

Quadratic inequality	An inequality involving a quadratic polynomial	$2x^2 - 7x + 6 \geq 0$ $x^2 - 4x - 5 < 0$
Rational inequality	An inequality involving a rational expression	$\dfrac{1}{x - 1} < \dfrac{3}{x - 2}$
Solving quadratic and rational inequalities	Get 0 on one side and express the other side as a product and/or quotient of linear factors. Make a sign graph showing the signs of the factors. Use test points if the quadratic polynomial is prime.	$(x - 5)(x + 1) < 0$ $x + 1$ $- -$ $0 + + + + + + + + +$ $x - 5$ $- - - - - - - - -$ $0 + +$ $-3\ -2\ -1\ \ 0\ \ 1\ \ 2\ \ 3\ \ 4\ \ 5\ \ 6\ \ 7$

ENRICHING YOUR MATHEMATICAL WORD POWER

For each mathematical term, choose the correct meaning.

1. **quadratic equation**
   a. $ax + b = c$ with $a \neq 0$
   b. $ax^2 + bx + c = 0$ with $a \neq 0$
   c. $ax + b = 0$ with $a \neq 0$
   d. $a/x^2 + b/x = c$ with $x \neq 0$

2. **perfect square trinomial**
   a. a trinomial of the form $a^2 + 2ab + b^2$
   b. a trinomial of the form $a^2 + b^2$
   c. a trinomial of the form $a^2 + ab + b^2$
   d. a trinomial of the form $a^2 - 2ab - b^2$

3. **completing the square**
   a. drawing a perfect square
   b. evaluating $(a + b)^2$
   c. drawing the fourth side when given three sides of a square
   d. finding the third term of a perfect square trinomial

4. **quadratic formula**
   a. $x = \dfrac{-b \pm \sqrt{b^2 - 4ac}}{2}$
   b. $x = -b \pm \dfrac{\sqrt{b^2 - 4ac}}{2a}$
   c. $x = \dfrac{-b \pm \sqrt{b^2 - 4ac}}{2a}$
   d. $x = \dfrac{b \pm \sqrt{b^2 - 4ac}}{2a}$

5. **discriminant**
   a. the vertex of a parabola
   b. the radicand in the quadratic formula
   c. the leading coefficient in $ax^2 + bx + c$
   d. to treat unfairly

6. **quadratic function**
   a. $y = ax + b$ with $a \neq 0$
   b. a parabola
   c. $y = ax^2 + bx + c$ with $a \neq 0$
   d. the quadratic formula

7. **quadratic in form**
   a. $ax^2 + bx + c = 0$
   b. a parabola
   c. an equation that is quadratic after a substitution
   d. having four equal sides

8. **quadratic inequality**
   a. $ax^2 + bx + c > 0$ with $a \neq 0$ or with $\geq$, $<$, or $\leq$
   b. $ax + b > 0$ with $a \neq 0$ or with $\geq$, $<$, or $\leq$
   c. completing the square
   d. the Pythagorean theorem

9. **sign graph**
   a. a graph showing the sign of x
   b. a sign on which a graph is drawn
   c. a number line showing the signs of factors
   d. to graph in sign language

10. **rational inequality**
    a. an inequality involving a rational expression(s)
    b. a quadratic inequality
    c. an inequality with rational exponents
    d. an inequality that compares two fractions

11. **test point**
    a. the end of a chapter
    b. to check if a point is in the right location
    c. a number that is used to check if an inequality is satisfied
    d. a positive integer

REVIEW EXERCISES

8.1 *Solve by factoring.*

1. $x^2 - 2x - 15 = 0$

2. $x^2 - 2x - 24 = 0$

3. $2x^2 + x = 15$

4. $2x^2 + 7x = 4$

5. $w^2 - 25 = 0$

6. $a^2 - 121 = 0$

7. $4x^2 - 12x + 9 = 0$

8. $x^2 - 12x + 36 = 0$

Solve by using the even-root property.

9. $x^2 = 12$

10. $x^2 = 20$

11. $(x - 1)^2 = 9$

12. $(x + 4)^2 = 4$

13. $(x - 2)^2 = \dfrac{3}{4}$

14. $(x - 3)^2 = \dfrac{1}{4}$

15. $4x^2 = 9$

16. $2x^2 = 3$

43. $3x^2 + 2x + 2 = 0$

44. $x^2 + 2 = 2x$

Solve by completing the square.

17. $x^2 - 6x + 8 = 0$

18. $x^2 + 4x + 3 = 0$

45. $\frac{1}{2}x^2 + 3x + 8 = 0$

19. $x^2 - 5x + 6 = 0$

20. $x^2 - x - 6 = 0$

21. $2x^2 - 7x + 3 = 0$

22. $2x^2 - x = 6$

46. $\frac{1}{2}x^2 - 5x + 13 = 0$

23. $x^2 + 4x + 1 = 0$

24. $x^2 + 2x - 2 = 0$

8.3 *Find the vertex and intercepts for each quadratic function, and sketch its graph.*

8.2 *Solve by the quadratic formula.*

47. $f(x) = x^2 - 6x$

25. $x^2 - 3x - 10 = 0$

26. $x^2 - 5x - 6 = 0$

27. $6x^2 - 7x = 3$

28. $6x^2 = x + 2$

29. $x^2 + 4x + 2 = 0$

30. $x^2 + 6x = 2$

31. $3x^2 + 1 = 5x$

48. $f(x) = x^2 + 4x$

32. $2x^2 + 3x - 1 = 0$

Find the value of the discriminant and the number of real solutions to each equation.

33. $25x^2 - 20x + 4 = 0$

34. $16x^2 + 1 = 8x$

49. $g(x) = x^2 - 4x - 12$

35. $x^2 - 3x + 7 = 0$

36. $3x^2 - x + 8 = 0$

37. $2x^2 + 1 = 5x$

38. $-3x^2 + 6x - 2 = 0$

Find the complex solutions to the quadratic equations.

39. $2x^2 - 4x + 3 = 0$

40. $2x^2 - 6x + 5 = 0$

50. $g(x) = x^2 + 2x - 24$

41. $2x^2 + 3 = 3x$

42. $x^2 + x + 1 = 0$

51. $h(x) = -2x^2 + 8x$

52. $h(x) = -3x^2 + 6x$

53. $y = -x^2 + 2x + 3$

54. $y = -x^2 - 3x - 2$

Find the domain and range of each quadratic function.

55. $f(x) = x^2 + 4x + 1$

56. $f(x) = x^2 - 6x + 2$

57. $y = -2x^2 - x + 4$

58. $y = -3x^2 + 2x + 7$

8.4 *Use the discriminant to determine whether each quadratic polynomial can be factored, then factor the ones that are not prime.*

59. $8x^2 - 10x - 3$ **60.** $18x^2 + 9x - 2$

61. $4x^2 - 5x + 2$ **62.** $6x^2 - 7x - 4$

63. $8y^2 + 10y - 25$ **64.** $25z^2 - 15z - 18$

Write a quadratic equation that has each given pair of solutions.

65. $-3, -6$ **66.** $4, -9$

67. $-5\sqrt{2}, 5\sqrt{2}$ **68.** $-2i\sqrt{3}, 2i\sqrt{3}$

Find all real solutions to each equation.

69. $x^6 + 7x^3 - 8 = 0$

70. $8x^6 + 63x^3 - 8 = 0$

71. $x^4 - 13x^2 + 36 = 0$

72. $x^4 + 7x^2 + 12 = 0$

73. $(x^2 + 3x)^2 - 28(x^2 + 3x) + 180 = 0$

74. $(x^2 + 1)^2 - 8(x^2 + 1) + 15 = 0$

75. $x^2 - 6x + 6\sqrt{x^2 - 6x} - 40 = 0$

76. $x^2 - 3x - 3\sqrt{x^2 - 3x} + 2 = 0$

77. $t^{-2} + 5t^{-1} - 36 = 0$

78. $a^{-2} + a^{-1} - 6 = 0$

79. $w - 13\sqrt{w} + 36 = 0$

80. $4a - 5\sqrt{a} + 1 = 0$

8.5 *Solve each inequality. State the solution set using interval notation and graph it.*

81. $a^2 + a > 6$

82. $x^2 - 5x + 6 > 0$

83. $x^2 - x - 20 \leq 0$

84. $a^2 + 2a \leq 15$

85. $w^2 - w < 0$

86. $x - x^2 \leq 0$

87. $\dfrac{x-4}{x+2} \geq 0$

88. $\dfrac{x-3}{x+5} < 0$

89. $\dfrac{x-2}{x+3} < 1$

90. $\dfrac{x-3}{x+4} > 2$

91. $\dfrac{3}{x+2} > \dfrac{1}{x+1}$

92. $\dfrac{1}{x+1} < \dfrac{1}{x-1}$

MISCELLANEOUS

In Exercises 93–104, find all real or imaginary solutions to each equation.

93. $144x^2 - 120x + 25 = 0$

94. $49x^2 + 9 = 42x$

95. $(2x + 3)^2 + 7 = 12$

96. $6x = -\dfrac{19x + 25}{x + 1}$

97. $1 + \dfrac{20}{9x^2} = \dfrac{8}{3x}$

98. $\dfrac{x-1}{x+2} = \dfrac{2x-3}{x+4}$

99. $\sqrt{3x^2 + 7x - 30} = x$

100. $\dfrac{x^4}{3} = x^2 + 6$

101. $2(2x + 1)^2 + 5(2x + 1) = 3$

102. $(w^2 - 1)^2 + 2(w^2 - 1) = 15$

103. $x^{1/2} - 15x^{1/4} + 50 = 0$

104. $x^{-2} - 9x^{-1} + 18 = 0$

Find exact and approximate solutions to each problem.

105. *Missing numbers.* Find two positive real numbers that differ by 4 and have a product of 4.

106. *One on one.* Find two positive real numbers that differ by 1 and have a product of 1.

107. *Big screen TV.* On a 19-inch diagonal measure television picture screen, the height is 4 inches less than the width. Find the height and width.

19 in.

$x - 4$ in.

x in.

FIGURE FOR EXERCISE 107

108. *Boxing match.* A boxing ring is in the shape of a square, 20 ft on each side. How far apart are the fighters when they are in opposite corners of the ring?

109. *Students for a Clean Environment.* A group of environmentalists plans to print a message on an 8 inch by 10 inch

STOP THE POLLUTION!

10 in.

8 in.

FIGURE FOR EXERCISE 109

paper. If the typed message requires 24 square inches of paper and the group wants an equal border on all sides, then how wide should the border be?

110. *Winston works faster.* Winston can mow his dad's lawn in 1 hour less than it takes his brother Willie. If they take 2 hours to mow it when working together, then how long would it take Winston working alone?

111. *Ping Pong.* The table used for table tennis is 4 ft longer than it is wide and has an area of 45 ft^2. What are the dimensions of the table?

FIGURE FOR EXERCISE 111

112. *Swimming pool design.* An architect has designed a motel pool within a rectangular area that is fenced on three sides as shown in the figure. If she uses 60 yards of fencing to enclose an area of 352 square yards, then what are the dimensions marked L and W in the figure? Assume L is greater than W.

FIGURE FOR EXERCISE 112

113. *Minimizing cost.* The unit cost in dollars for manufacturing n starters is given by $C(n) = 0.004n^2 - 3.2n + 660$. What is the unit cost when 390 starters are manufactured? For what number of starters is the unit cost at a minimum?

114. *Maximizing profit.* The total profit (in dollars) for sales of x rowing machines is given by $P(x) = -0.2x^2 + 300x - 200$. What is the profit if 500 are sold? For what value of x will the profit be at a maximum?

115. *Decathlon champion.* For 1989 and 1990 Dave Johnson had the highest decathlon score in the world. When Johnson reached a speed of 32 ft/sec on the pole vault runway, his height above the ground t seconds after leaving the ground was given by $h = -16t^2 + 32t$. (The elasticity of the pole converts the horizontal speed into vertical speed.) Find the value of t for which his height was 12 ft.

116. *Time of flight.* Use the information from Exercise 115 to determine how long Johnson was in the air. For how long was he more than 14 ft in the air?

CHAPTER 8 TEST

Calculate the value of $b^2 - 4ac$, and state how many real solutions each equation has.

1. $2x^2 - 3x + 2 = 0$

2. $-3x^2 + 5x - 1 = 0$

3. $4x^2 - 4x + 1 = 0$

Solve by using the quadratic formula.

4. $2x^2 + 5x - 3 = 0$

5. $x^2 + 6x + 6 = 0$

Solve by completing the square.

6. $x^2 + 10x + 25 = 0$

7. $2x^2 + x - 6 = 0$

Solve by any method.

8. $x(x + 1) = 12$

9. $a^4 - 5a^2 + 4 = 0$

10. $x - 2 - 8\sqrt{x - 2} + 15 = 0$

Find the complex solutions to the quadratic equations.

11. $x^2 + 36 = 0$

12. $x^2 + 6x + 10 = 0$

13. $3x^2 - x + 1 = 0$

Graph each quadratic function. State the domain and range.

14. $f(x) = 16 - x^2$

15. $g(x) = x^2 - 3x$

Write a quadratic equation that has each given pair of solutions.

16. $-4, 6$

17. $-5i, 5i$

Solve each inequality. State and graph the solution set.

18. $w^2 + 3w < 18$

19. $\dfrac{2}{x - 2} < \dfrac{3}{x + 1}$

Find the exact solution to each problem.

20. The length of a rectangle is 2 ft longer than the width. If the area is 16 ft^2, then what are the length and width?

21. A new computer can process a company's monthly payroll in 1 hour less time than the old computer. To really save time, the manager used both computers and finished the payroll in 3 hours. How long would it take the new computer to do the payroll by itself?

Solve each problem.

22. Find the x-intercepts for the parabola $y = x^2 - 6x + 5$.

23. The height in feet for a ball thrown upward at 48 feet per second is given by $s(t) = -16t^2 + 48t$, where t is the time in seconds after the ball is tossed. What is the maximum height that the ball will reach?

Solve each equation.

1. $2x - 15 = 0$

2. $2x^2 - 15 = 0$

3. $2x^2 + x - 15 = 0$

4. $2x^2 + 4x - 15 = 0$

5. $|4x + 11| = 3$

6. $|4x^2 + 11x| = 3$

7. $\sqrt{x} = x - 6$

8. $(2x - 5)^{2/3} = 4$

Solve each inequality. State the solution set using interval notation.

9. $1 - 2x < 5 - x$

10. $(1 - 2x)(5 - x) \le 0$

11. $\dfrac{1 - 2x}{5 - x} \le 0$

12. $|5 - x| < 3$

13. $3x - 1 < 5$ and $-3 \le x$

14. $x - 3 < 1$ or $2x \ge 8$

Solve each equation for y.

15. $2x - 3y = 9$

16. $\dfrac{y - 3}{x + 2} = -\dfrac{1}{2}$

17. $3y^2 + cy + d = 0$

18. $my^2 - ny = w$

19. $\dfrac{1}{3}x - \dfrac{2}{5}y = \dfrac{5}{6}$

20. $y - 3 = -\dfrac{2}{3}(x - 4)$

Let $m = \dfrac{y_2 - y_1}{x_2 - x_1}$. Find the value of m for each of the following choices of x_1, x_2, y_1, and y_2.

21. $x_1 = 2,\ x_2 = 5,\ y_1 = 3,\ y_2 = 7$

22. $x_1 = -3,\ x_2 = 4,\ y_1 = 5,\ y_2 = -6$

23. $x_1 = 0.3,\ x_2 = 0.5,\ y_1 = 0.8,\ y_2 = 0.4$

24. $x_1 = \dfrac{1}{2},\ x_2 = \dfrac{1}{3},\ y_1 = \dfrac{3}{5},\ y_2 = -\dfrac{4}{3}$

Solve each problem.

25. **Ticket prices.** If the price of a concert ticket goes up, then the number sold will go down, as shown in the figure. If you use the formula $n = 48{,}000 - 400p$ to predict the number sold depending on the price p, then how many will be sold at $20 per ticket? How many will be sold at $25 per ticket? Use the bar graph to estimate the price if 35,000 tickets were sold.

FIGURE FOR EXERCISE 25

26. **Increasing revenue.** Even though the number of tickets sold for a concert decreases with increasing price, the revenue generated does not necessarily decrease. Use the formula $R = p(48{,}000 - 400p)$ to determine the revenue when the price is $20 and when the price is $25. What price would produce a revenue of $1.28 million? Use the graph to find the price that determines the maximum revenue.

FIGURE FOR EXERCISE 26

CHAPTER 9

Additional Function Topics

orking in a world of numbers, designers of racing boats blend art with science to design attractive boats that are also fast and safe. If the sail area is increased, the boat will go faster but will be less stable in open seas. If the displacement is increased, the boat will be more stable but slower. Increasing length increases speed but reduces stability. To make yacht racing both competitive and safe, racing boats must satisfy complex systems of rules, many of which involve mathematical formulas.

After the 1988 mismatch between Dennis Conner's catamaran and New Zealander Michael Fay's 133-foot monohull, an international group of yacht designers rewrote the America's Cup rules to ensure the fairness of the race. In addition to hundreds of pages of other rules, every yacht must satisfy the basic inequality

$$\frac{L + 1.25\sqrt{S} - 9.8\sqrt[3]{D}}{0.679} \leq 24.000,$$

which balances the length L, the sail area S, and the displacement D.

In the 1979 Fastnet Race 15 sailors lost their lives. After *Exide Challenger*'s carbon-fiber keel snapped off, Tony Bullimore spent 4 days inside the overturned hull before being rescued by the Australian navy. Yacht racing is a dangerous sport. To determine the general performance and safety of a yacht, designers calculate the displacement-length ratio, the sail area-displacement ratio, the ballast-displacement ratio, and the capsize screening value. In Exercises 73 and 74 of Section 9.3 we will see how composition of functions is used to define the displacement-length ratio and the sail area-displacement ratio.

9.1 GRAPHS OF FUNCTIONS AND RELATIONS

Functions were introduced in Section 3.5. In this section we will study the graphs of several types of functions. We graphed linear functions in Chapter 3 and quadratic functions in Chapter 8, but for completeness we will review them here.

Linear and Constant Functions

Linear functions get their name from the fact that their graphs are straight lines.

> **Linear Function**
>
> A **linear function** is a function of the form
>
> $$f(x) = mx + b,$$
>
> where m and b are real numbers with $m \neq 0$.

The graph of the linear function $f(x) = mx + b$ is exactly the same as the graph of the linear equation $y = mx + b$. If $m = 0$, then we get $f(x) = b$, which is called a **constant function.** If $m = 1$ and $b = 0$, then we get the function $f(x) = x$, which is called the **identity function.** When we graph a function given in function notation, we usually label the vertical axis as $f(x)$ rather than y.

E X A M P L E   1

Graphing a constant function

Graph $f(x) = 3$ and state the domain and range.

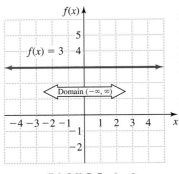

FIGURE 9.1

Solution

The graph of $f(x) = 3$ is the same as the graph of $y = 3$, which is the horizontal line in Fig. 9.1. Since any real number can be used for x in $f(x) = 3$ and since the line in Fig. 9.1 extends without bounds to the left and right, the domain is the set of all real numbers, $(-\infty, \infty)$. Since the only y-coordinate for $f(x) = 3$ is 3, the range is $\{3\}$. ∎

The domain and range of a function can be determined from the formula or the graph. However, the graph is usually very helpful for understanding domain and range.

E X A M P L E   2

Graphing a linear function

Graph the function $f(x) = 3x - 4$ and state the domain and range.

Solution

The y-intercept is $(0, -4)$ and the slope of the line is 3. We can use the y-intercept and the slope to draw the graph in Fig. 9.2. Since any real number can be used for x in $f(x) = 3x - 4$, and since the line in Fig. 9.2 extends without bounds to the left and right, the domain is the set of all real numbers, $(-\infty, \infty)$. Since the graph extends without bounds upward and downward, the range is the set of all real numbers, $(-\infty, \infty)$.

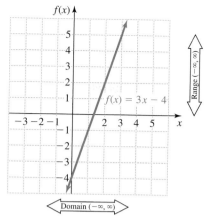

FIGURE 9.2

Absolute Value Functions

The equation $y = |x|$ defines a function because every value of x determines a unique value of y. We call this function the absolute value function.

> ### Absolute Value Function
>
> The **absolute value function** is the function defined by
> $$f(x) = |x|.$$

To graph the absolute value function, we simply plot enough ordered pairs of the function to see what the graph looks like.

E X A M P L E   3

The absolute value function

Graph $f(x) = |x|$ and state the domain and range.

Solution

To graph this function, we find points that satisfy the equation $f(x) = |x|$.

x	-2	-1	0	1	2
$f(x) = |x|$	2	1	0	1	2

Helpful Hint

The most important feature of an absolute value function is its V-shape. If we had plotted only points in the first quadrant, we would not have seen the V-shape. So for an absolute value function we always plot enough points to see the V-shape.

Plotting these points, we see that they lie along the V-shaped graph shown in Fig. 9.3. Since any real number can be used for x in $f(x) = |x|$ and since the graph extends without bounds to the left and right, the domain is $(-\infty, \infty)$. Because the graph does not go below the x-axis and because $|x|$ is never negative, the range is the set of nonnegative real numbers, $[0, \infty)$.

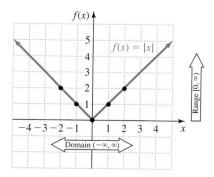

FIGURE 9.3

Many functions involving absolute value have graphs that are V-shaped, as in Fig. 9.3. To graph functions involving absolute value, we must choose points that determine the correct shape and location of the V-shaped graph.

E X A M P L E   4

Other functions involving absolute value

Graph each function and state the domain and range.

a) $f(x) = |x| - 2$ **b)** $g(x) = |2x - 6|$

Solution

a) Choose values for x and find $f(x)$.

x	-2	-1	0	1	2
$f(x) = |x| - 2$	0	-1	-2	-1	0

Plot these points and draw a V-shaped graph through them as shown in Fig. 9.4. The domain is $(-\infty, \infty)$, and the range is $[-2, \infty)$.

FIGURE 9.4

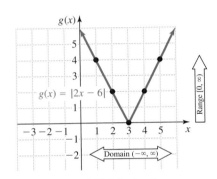

FIGURE 9.5

b) Make a table of values for x and $g(x)$.

x	1	2	3	4	5
$g(x) = |2x - 6|$	4	2	0	2	4

Draw the graph as shown in Fig. 9.5. The domain is $(-\infty, \infty)$, and the range is $[0, \infty)$.

Quadratic Functions

In Chapter 8 we learned that the graph of any quadratic function is a parabola, which opens upward or downward. The vertex of a parabola is the lowest point on a parabola that opens upward or the highest point on a parabola that opens downward. Parabolas will be discussed again when we study conic sections later in this text.

> **Quadratic Function**
>
> A **quadratic function** is a function of the form
> $$f(x) = ax^2 + bx + c,$$
> where a, b, and c are real numbers, with $a \neq 0$.

EXAMPLE 5

A quadratic function

Graph the function $g(x) = 4 - x^2$ and state the domain and range.

Calculator Close-Up

You can find the vertex of a parabola with a calculator. For example, graph

$$y = -x^2 - x + 2.$$

Then use the maximum feature, which is found in the CALC menu. For the left bound pick a point to the left of the vertex; for the right bound pick a point to the right of the vertex; and for the guess pick a point near the vertex.

Solution

We plot enough points to get the correct shape of the graph.

x	-2	-1	0	1	2
$g(x) = 4 - x^2$	0	3	4	3	0

See Fig. 9.6 for the graph. The domain is $(-\infty, \infty)$. From the graph we see that the largest y-coordinate is 4. So the range is $(-\infty, 4]$.

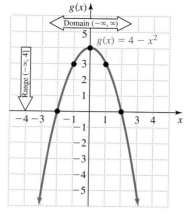

FIGURE 9.6

Square-Root Functions

Functions involving square roots typically have graphs that look like half a parabola.

Square-Root Function

The **square-root function** is the function defined by

$$f(x) = \sqrt{x}.$$

EXAMPLE 6

Square-root functions

Graph each equation and state the domain and range.

a) $y = \sqrt{x}$ **b)** $y = \sqrt{x + 3}$

Solution

a) The graph of the equation $y = \sqrt{x}$ and the graph of the function $f(x) = \sqrt{x}$ are the same. Because $\sqrt{x}$ is a real number only if $x \geq 0$, the domain of this function is the set of nonnegative real numbers. The following ordered pairs are on the graph:

x	0	1	4	9
$y = \sqrt{x}$	0	1	2	3

The graph goes through these ordered pairs as shown in Fig. 9.7. Note that x is chosen from the nonnegative numbers. The domain is $[0, \infty)$ and the range is $[0, \infty)$.

b) Note that $\sqrt{x + 3}$ is a real number only if $x + 3 \geq 0$, or $x \geq -3$. So we make a table of ordered pairs in which $x \geq -3$:

x	-3	-2	1	6
$y = \sqrt{x + 3}$	0	1	2	3

The graph goes through these ordered pairs as shown in Fig. 9.8. The domain is $[-3, \infty)$ and the range is $[0, \infty)$.

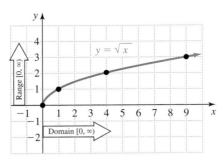

FIGURE 9.7   **FIGURE 9.8**

Graphing Relations

A function is a set of ordered pairs in which no two have the same first coordinate and different second coordinates. A relation is any set of ordered pairs. The domain of a relation is the set of x-coordinates of the ordered pairs and the range of a relation is the set of y-coordinates of the ordered pairs. In Example 7 we graph the relation $x = y^2$. Note that this relation is not a function because ordered pairs such as $(4, 2)$ and $(4, -2)$ satisfy $x = y^2$.

E X A M P L E 7

Graphing relations that are not functions

Graph each relation and state the domain and range.

a) $x = y^2$ **b)** $x = |y - 3|$

Solution

a) Because the equation $x = y^2$ expresses x in terms of y, it is easier to choose the y-coordinate first and then find the x-coordinate:

$x = y^2$	4	1	0	1	4
y	-2	-1	0	1	2

Figure 9.9 shows the graph. The domain is $[0, \infty)$ and the range is $(-\infty, \infty)$.

b) Again we select values for y first and find the corresponding x-coordinates:

$x = |y - 3|$	2	1	0	1	2
y	1	2	3	4	5

Plot these points as shown in Fig. 9.10. The domain is $[0, \infty)$ and the range is $(-\infty, \infty)$.

FIGURE 9.9

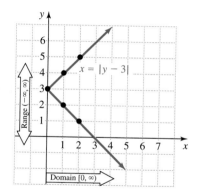

FIGURE 9.10

WARM-UPS

True or false? Explain your answer.

1. The graph of a function is a picture of all ordered pairs of the function.

2. The graph of every linear function is a straight line.
3. The absolute value function has a V-shaped graph.
4. The domain of $f(x) = 3$ is $(-\infty, \infty)$.
5. The graph of a quadratic function is a parabola.
6. The range of any quadratic function is $(-\infty, \infty)$.
7. The y-axis and the $f(x)$-axis are the same.
8. The domain of $x = y^2$ is $[0, \infty)$.
9. The domain of $f(x) = \sqrt{x - 1}$ is $(1, \infty)$.
10. The domain of any quadratic function is $(-\infty, \infty)$.

9.1 EXERCISES

Reading and Writing   *After reading this section, write out the answers to these questions. Use complete sentences.*

1. What is a linear function?

2. What is a constant function?

3. What is the graph of a constant function?

4. What shape is the graph of an absolute value function?

5. What is the graph of quadratic function called?

6. What is the identity function?

Graph each function and state its domain and range. See Examples 1 and 2.

7. $h(x) = -2$ 8. $f(x) = 4$

9. $f(x) = 2x - 1$

10. $g(x) = x + 2$

19. $h(x) = |x + 1|$

20. $f(x) = |x - 2|$

21. $g(x) = |3x|$

22. $h(x) = |-2x|$

11. $g(x) = \frac{1}{2}x + 2$

12. $h(x) = \frac{2}{3}x - 4$

23. $f(x) = |2x - 1|$

24. $y = |2x - 3|$

13. $y = -\frac{2}{3}x + 3$

14. $y = -\frac{3}{4}x + 4$

25. $f(x) = |x - 2| + 1$

26. $y = |x - 1| + 2$

15. $y = -0.3x + 6.5$

16. $y = 0.25x - 0.5$

Graph each quadratic function and state its domain and range. See Example 5.

27. $g(x) = x^2 + 2$

28. $f(x) = x^2 - 4$

Graph each absolute value function and state its domain and range. See Examples 3 and 4.

17. $f(x) = |x| + 1$

18. $g(x) = |x| - 3$

29. $f(x) = 2x^2$

30. $h(x) = -3x^2$

39. $y = \sqrt{x} + 2$

40. $y = 2\sqrt{x} + 1$

31. $y = 6 - x^2$

32. $y = -2x^2 + 3$

Graph each relation and state its domain and range. See Example 7.

41. $x = |y|$

42. $x = -|y|$

Graph each square-root function and state its domain and range. See Example 6.

33. $g(x) = 2\sqrt{x}$

34. $g(x) = \sqrt{x} - 1$

43. $x = -y^2$

44. $x = 1 - y^2$

45. $x = 5$

46. $x = -3$

35. $f(x) = \sqrt{x - 1}$

36. $f(x) = \sqrt{x + 1}$

47. $x + 9 = y^2$

48. $x + 3 = |y|$

37. $h(x) = -\sqrt{x}$

38. $h(x) = -\sqrt{x - 1}$

49. $x = \sqrt{y}$

50. $x = -\sqrt{y}$

59. $y = \sqrt{x} - 3$

60. $y = 2|x|$

51. $x = (y - 1)^2$

52. $x = (y + 2)^2$

61. $y = 3x - 5$

62. $g(x) = (x + 2)^2$

Graph each function and state the domain and range.

53. $f(x) = 1 - |x|$

54. $h(x) = \sqrt{x - 3}$

63. $y = -x^2 + 4x - 4$

64. $y = -2|x - 1| + 4$

55. $y = (x - 3)^2 - 1$

56. $y = x^2 - 2x - 3$

GRAPHING CALCULATOR EXERCISES

65. Graph the function $f(x) = \sqrt{x^2}$ and explain what this graph illustrates.

66. Graph the function $f(x) = \frac{1}{x}$ and state the domain and range.

57. $y = |x + 3| + 1$

58. $f(x) = -2x + 4$

67. Graph $y = x^2$, $y = \frac{1}{2}x^2$, and $y = 2x^2$ on the same coordinate system. What can you say about the graph of $y = kx^2$?

68. Graph $y = x^2$, $y = x^2 + 2$, and $y = x^2 - 3$ on the same screen. What can you say about the position of $y = x^2 + k$ relative to $y = x^2$.

69. Graph $y = x^2$, $y = (x + 5)^2$, and $y = (x - 2)^2$ on the same screen. What can you say about the position of $y = (x - k)^2$ relative to $y = x^2$.

70. You can graph the relation $x = y^2$ by graphing the two functions $y = \sqrt{x}$ and $y = -\sqrt{x}$. Try it and explain why this works.

71. Graph $y = (x - 3)^2$, $y = |x - 3|$, and $y = \sqrt{x - 3}$ on the same coordinate system. How does the graph of $y = f(x - k)$ compare to the graph of $y = f(x)$?

In This Section

- Reflecting
- Translating
- Stretching and Shrinking
- Multiple Transformations

Calculator Close-Up

With a graphing calculator, you can quickly see the result of modifying the formula for a function. If you have a graphing calculator, use it to graph the functions in the examples. Experimenting with it will help you to understand the ideas in this section.

9.2 TRANSFORMATIONS OF GRAPHS

We can discover what the graph of almost any function looks like if we plot enough points. However, it is helpful to know something about a graph so that we do not have to plot very many points. In this section we will learn how one graph can be transformed into another by modifying the formula that defines the function.

Reflecting

Consider the graphs of $f(x) = x^2$ and $g(x) = -x^2$ shown in Fig. 9.11. Notice that the graph of g is a mirror image of the graph of f. For any value of x we compute the y-coordinate of an ordered pair of f by squaring x. For an ordered pair of g we square first and then find the opposite because of the order of operations. This gives a correspondence between the ordered pairs of f and the ordered pairs of g. For every ordered pair on the graph of f there is a corresponding ordered pair directly below it on the graph of g, and these ordered pairs are the same distance from the x-axis. We say that the graph of g is obtained by reflecting the graph of f in the x-axis or that g is a reflection of the graph of f.

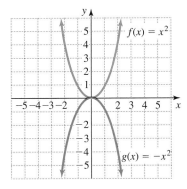

FIGURE 9.11

Reflection

The graph of $y = -f(x)$ is a **reflection** in the x-axis of the graph of $y = f(x)$.

E X A M P L E 1

Reflection

Sketch the graphs of each pair of functions on the same coordinate system.

a) $f(x) = \sqrt{x}$, $g(x) = -\sqrt{x}$

b) $f(x) = |x|$, $g(x) = -|x|$

Solution

In each case the graph of g is a reflection of the graph of f. Recall that we graphed the square root function and the absolute value function in the last section. Figures 9.12 and 9.13 show the graphs for these functions.

FIGURE 9.12

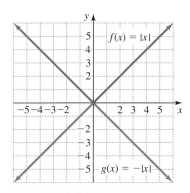

FIGURE 9.13

Translating

Consider the graphs of the functions $f(x) = \sqrt{x}$, $g(x) = \sqrt{x} + 2$, and $h(x) = \sqrt{x} - 6$ shown in Fig. 9.14. In the expression $\sqrt{x} + 2$, adding 2 is the last operation to perform. So every point on the graph of g is exactly two units above a corresponding point on the graph of f, and g has the same shape as the graph of f. Every point on the graph of h is exactly six units below a corresponding point on the graph of f. The graph of g is an upward translation of the graph of f, and the graph of h is a downward translation of the graph of f.

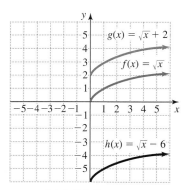

FIGURE 9.14

Translating Upward or Downward

If $k > 0$, then the graph of $y = f(x) + k$ is an **upward translation** of the graph of $y = f(x)$ and the graph of $y = f(x) - k$ is a **downward translation** of the graph of $y = f(x)$.

Consider the graphs of $f(x) = \sqrt{x}$, $g(x) = \sqrt{x} - 2$, and $h(x) = \sqrt{x} + 6$ shown in Fig. 9.15. In the expression $\sqrt{x} - 2$ subtracting 2 is the first operation to

Calculator Close-Up

Note that for a translation of six units to the left, $x + 6$ must be written in parentheses on a graphing calculator.

perform. So every point on the graph of g is exactly two units to the right of a corresponding point on the graph of f. (We must start with a larger value of x to get the same y-coordinate because we first subtract 2.) Every point on the graph of h is exactly six units to the left of a corresponding point on the graph of f.

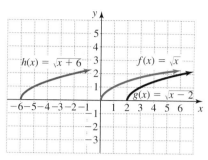

FIGURE 9.15

Translating to the Right or Left

If $h > 0$, then the graph of $y = f(x - h)$ is a **translation to the right** of the graph of $y = f(x)$, and the graph of $y = f(x + h)$ is a **translation to the left** of the graph of $y = f(x)$.

EXAMPLE 2

Translation

Sketch the graph of each function.

a) $f(x) = |x| - 6$ **b)** $f(x) = (x - 2)^2$ **c)** $f(x) = |x + 3|$

Solution

a) The graph of $f(x) = |x| - 6$ is a translation six units downward of the familiar graph of $f(x) = |x|$. Calculate a few ordered pairs to get an accurate graph. The pairs $(0, -6)$, $(1, -5)$, and $(-1, -5)$ are on the graph shown in Fig. 9.16.

b) The graph of $f(x) = (x - 2)^2$ is a translation two units to the right of the familiar graph of $f(x) = x^2$. Calculate a few ordered pairs to get an accurate graph. The pairs $(2, 0)$, $(0, 4)$, and $(4, 4)$ are on the graph shown in Fig. 9.17.

c) The graph of $f(x) = |x + 3|$ is a translation three units to the left of the familiar graph of $f(x) = |x|$. The pairs $(0, 3)$, $(-3, 0)$, and $(-6, 3)$ are on the graph shown in Fig. 9.18.

FIGURE 9.16

FIGURE 9.17

FIGURE 9.18

Stretching and Shrinking

Consider the graphs of $f(x) = x^2$, $g(x) = 2x^2$, and $h(x) = \frac{1}{2}x^2$ shown in Fig. 9.19. Every point on $g(x) = 2x^2$ corresponds to a point directly below on the graph of $f(x) = x^2$. The y-coordinate on g is exactly twice as large as the corresponding y-coordinate on f. This situation occurs because in the expression $2x^2$, multiplying by 2 is the last operation performed. Every point on h corresponds to a point directly above on f, where the y-coordinate on h is half as large as the y-coordinate on f. The factor 2 has stretched the graph of f to form the graph of g, and the factor $\frac{1}{2}$ has shrunk the graph of f to form the graph of h.

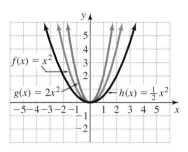

FIGURE 9.19

> **Stretching and Shrinking**
>
> If $a > 1$, then the graph of $y = af(x)$ is obtained by **stretching** the graph of $y = f(x)$. If $0 < a < 1$, then the graph of $y = af(x)$ is obtained by **shrinking** the graph of $y = f(x)$.

Note that the last operation to be performed in stretching or shrinking is multiplication by a. Whereas the function $g(x) = 2\sqrt{x}$ is obtained by stretching $f(x) = \sqrt{x}$ by a factor of 2, $h(x) = \sqrt{2x}$ is not.

E X A M P L E   3

Stretching and shrinking

Graph the functions $f(x) = \sqrt{x}$, $g(x) = 2\sqrt{x}$, and $h(x) = \frac{1}{2}\sqrt{x}$ on the same coordinate system.

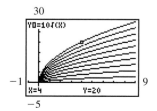

Solution

The graph of g is obtained by stretching the graph of f, and the graph of h is obtained by shrinking the graph of f. The graph of f includes the points $(0, 0)$, $(1, 1)$, and $(4, 2)$. The graph of g includes the points $(0, 0)$, $(1, 2)$, and $(4, 4)$. The graph of h includes the points $(0, 0)$, $(1, 0.5)$, and $(4, 1)$. The graphs are shown in Fig. 9.20.

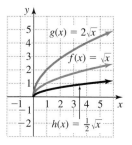

FIGURE 9.20

Multiple Transformations

When graphing a function containing more than one transformation perform the transformations in the following order:

1. Left or right translation
2. Stretching or shrinking
3. Reflection in the x-axis
4. Upward or downward translation

For example, the graph of $y = -2|x + 3| + 5$ is obtained by translating $y = |x|$ to the left 3 units, then stretching by a factor of 2, reflecting in the x-axis, and finally translating 5 units upward.

E X A M P L E   4

A multiple transformation of $y = \sqrt{x}$

Graph the function $y = -2\sqrt{x - 3}$.

Calculator Close-Up

You can check Example 4 by graphing $y = -2\sqrt{x - 3}$ with a graphing calculator.

Solution

Start with the graph of $y = \sqrt{x}$ through $(0, 0)$, $(1, 1)$, and $(4, 2)$, as shown in Fig. 9.21. Translate it three units to the right to get the graph of $y = \sqrt{x - 3}$. Stretch this graph by a factor of two to get the graph of $y = 2\sqrt{x - 3}$ shown in Fig. 9.21. Now reflect in the x-axis to get the graph of $y = -2\sqrt{x - 3}$. To get an accurate graph calculate a few points on the final graph as follows:

x	3	4	7
$y = -2\sqrt{x - 3}$	0	-2	-4

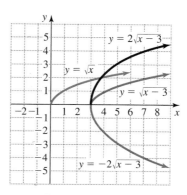

FIGURE 9.21

The graph of $y = x^2$ is a parabola opening upward with vertex $(0, 0)$. The graph of a function of the form $y = a(x - h)^2 + k$ is a transformation of $y = x^2$ and is also a parabola. It opens upward if $a > 0$ and downward if $a < 0$. Its vertex is (h, k). In Example 5 we graph a transformation of $y = x^2$.

E X A M P L E   5

A multiple transformation of the parabola $y = x^2$

Graph the function $y = -2(x + 3)^2 + 4$.

Solution

Think of the parabola $y = x^2$ through $(-1, 1)$, $(0, 0)$, and $(1, 1)$. To get the graph of $y = -2(x + 3)^2 + 4$, translate it three units to the left, stretch by a factor of two, reflect in the x-axis, and finally translate upward four units. The graph is a stretched parabola opening downward from the vertex $(-3, 4)$ as shown in Fig. 9.22. To get an accurate graph calculate a few points around the vertex as follows:

x	-5	-4	-3	-2	-1
$y = -2(x + 3)^2 + 4$	-4	2	4	2	-4

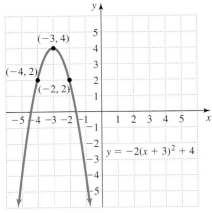

FIGURE 9.22

Understanding transformations helps us to see the location of the graph of a function. To get an accurate graph we must still calculate ordered pairs that satisfy the equation. However, if we know where to expect the graph it is easier to choose appropriate ordered pairs.

EXAMPLE 6

A multiple transformation of the absolute value function $y = |x|$

Graph the function $y = \frac{1}{2}|x - 4| - 1$.

Solution

Think of the V-shaped graph of $y = |x|$ through $(-1, 1)$, $(0, 0)$, and $(1, 1)$. To get the graph of $y = \frac{1}{2}|x - 4| - 1$, translate $y = |x|$ to the right four units, shrink by a factor of $\frac{1}{2}$, and finally translate downward one unit. The graph is shown in Fig. 9.23. To get an accurate graph calculate a few points around the lowest point on the V-shaped graph as follows:

x	2	4	6
$y = \frac{1}{2}|x - 4| - 1$	0	-1	0

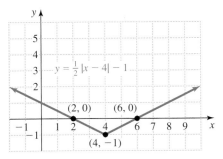

FIGURE 9.23

WARM-UPS

True or false? Explain your answer.

1. The graph of $f(x) = (-x)^2$ is a reflection in the x-axis of the graph of $g(x) = x^2$.

2. The graph of $f(x) = -2$ is a reflection in the x-axis of the graph of $f(x) = 2$.

3. The graph of $f(x) = x + 3$ lies three units to the left of the graph of $f(x) = x$.

4. The graph of $y = |x - 3|$ lies three units to the left of the graph of $y = |x|$.

5. The graph of $y = |x| - 3$ lies three units below the graph of $y = |x|$.

6. The graph of $y = -2x^2$ can be obtained by stretching and reflecting the graph of $y = x^2$.

7. The graph of $f(x) = (x - 2)^2$ is symmetric about the y-axis.

8. For each point on the graph of $y = \sqrt{x/9}$ there is a corresponding point on $y = \sqrt{x}$ that has a y-coordinate three times as large.

9. The graph of $y = \sqrt{x - 3} + 5$ has the same shape as the graph of $y = \sqrt{x}$.

10. The graph of $y = -(x + 2)^2 - 7$ can be obtained by moving $y = x^2$ two units to the left and down seven units and then reflecting in the x-axis.

9.2 EXERCISES

Reading and Writing *After reading this section, write out the answers to these questions. Use complete sentences.*

1. What is a reflection in the x-axis of a graph?

2. What is an upward translation of a graph?

3. What is a downward translation of a graph?

4. What is a translation to the right of a graph?

5. What is a translation to the left of a graph?

6. What is stretching and shrinking of a graph?

Sketch the graphs of each pair of functions on the same coordinate system. See Example 1.

7. $f(x) = \sqrt{2x}$,
$g(x) = -\sqrt{2x}$

8. $y = x, y = -x$

9. $f(x) = x^2 + 1,$
    $g(x) = -(x^2 + 1)$

10. $f(x) = |x| + 1,$
    $g(x) = -|x| - 1$

17. $y = x + 3$

18. $y = x - 1$

19. $f(x) = (x - 3)^2$

20. $f(x) = (x + 1)^2$

11. $y = \sqrt{x - 2},$
    $y = -\sqrt{x - 2}$

12. $y = |x - 1|,$
    $y = -|x - 1|$

21. $y = \sqrt{x} + 1$

22. $y = \sqrt{x} - 3$

13. $f(x) = x - 3,$
    $g(x) = 3 - x$

14. $f(x) = x^2 - 2,$
    $g(x) = 2 - x^2$

23. $f(x) = |x + 2|$

24. $f(x) = |x - 4|$

Use the ideas of translation to graph each function. See Example 2.

15. $f(x) = x^2 - 4$

16. $f(x) = x^2 + 2$

25. $y = |x| + 2$

26. $y = |x| - 4$

27. $f(x) = \sqrt{x} - 1$

28. $f(x) = \sqrt{x} + 6$

Sketch the graph of each function. See Examples 4–6.

37. $y = \sqrt{x - 2} + 1$

38. $y = -\sqrt{x + 3}$

Use the ideas of stretching and shrinking to graph each function. See Example 3.

39. $y = -|x + 3|$

40. $y = |x - 2| + 1$

29. $f(x) = 3x^2$

30. $f(x) = \frac{1}{3}x^2$

31. $y = \frac{1}{5}x$

32. $y = 5x$

41. $f(x) = (x + 3)^2 - 5$

42. $f(x) = -2x^2$

43. $y = -\sqrt{x + 1} - 2$

44. $y = -3\sqrt{x + 4} + 6$

33. $f(x) = 3\sqrt{x}$

34. $f(x) = \frac{1}{3}\sqrt{x}$

35. $y = \frac{1}{4}|x|$

36. $y = 4|x|$

45. $y = -2|x - 3| + 4$

46. $y = 3|x - 1| + 2$

47. $y = -2x + 3$ **48.** $y = 3x - 1$

a)

b)

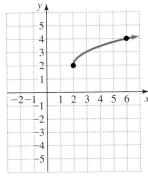

49. $y = 2(x + 3)^2 + 1$ **50.** $y = 2(x + 1)^2 - 2$

c)

d)

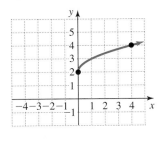

51. $y = -2(x - 4)^2 + 2$ **52.** $y = -2(x - 1)^2 + 3$

e)

f)

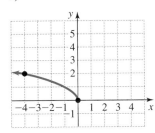

53. $y = -3(x - 1)^2 + 6$ **54.** $y = 3(x + 2)^2 - 6$

g)

h)

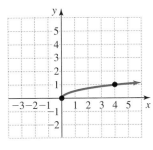

Match each function with its graph a–h.

55. $y = 2 + \sqrt{x}$ **56.** $y = \sqrt{2 + x}$

57. $y = 2\sqrt{x}$ **58.** $y = \sqrt{\dfrac{x}{2}}$

59. $y = \dfrac{1}{2}\sqrt{x}$ **60.** $y = 2 + \sqrt{x - 2}$

61. $y = -2\sqrt{x}$ **62.** $y = \sqrt{-x}$

GETTING MORE INVOLVED

63. If the graph of $y = x^2$ is translated eight units upward, then what is the equation of the curve at that location?

64. If the graph of $y = x^2$ is translated six units to the right, then what is the equation of the curve at that location?

65. If the graph of $y = \sqrt{x}$ is translated five units to the left, then what is the equation of the curve at that location?

66. If the graph of $y = \sqrt{x}$ is translated four units downward, then what is the equation of the curve at that location?

67. If the graph of $y = |x|$ is translated three units to the left and then five units upward, then what is the equation of the curve at that location?

68. If the graph of $y = |x|$ is translated four units downward and then nine units to the right, then what is the equation of the curve at that location?

 GRAPHING CALCULATOR EXERCISES

69. Graph $f(x) = |x|$ and $g(x) = |x - 20| + 30$ on the same screen of your calculator. What transformations will transform the graph of f into the graph of g?

70. Graph $f(x) = (x + 3)^2$, $g(x) = x^2 + 3^2$, and $h(x) = x^2 + 6x + 9$ on the same screen of your calculator.

a) Which two of these functions has the same graph? Why are they the same?

b) Is it true that $(x + 3)^2 = x^2 + 9$ for all real numbers x?

c) Describe each graph in terms of a transformation of the graph of $y = x^2$.

In This Section

- Basic Operations with Functions
- Composition

 9.3   COMBINING FUNCTIONS

In this section you will learn how to combine functions to obtain new functions.

Basic Operations with Functions

An entrepreneur plans to rent a stand at a farmers market for $25 per day to sell strawberries. If she buys x flats of berries for $5 per flat and sells them for $9 per flat, then her daily cost in dollars can be written as a function of x:

$$C(x) = 5x + 25$$

Assuming she sells as many flats as she buys, her revenue in dollars is also a function of x:

$$R(x) = 9x$$

Because profit is revenue minus cost, we can find a function for the profit by subtracting the functions for cost and revenue:

$$\begin{aligned} P(x) &= R(x) - C(x) \\ &= 9x - (5x + 25) \\ &= 4x - 25 \end{aligned}$$

The function $P(x) = 4x - 25$ expresses the daily profit as a function of x. Since $P(6) = -1$ and $P(7) = 3$, the profit is negative if 6 or fewer flats are sold and positive if 7 or more flats are sold.

In the example of the entrepreneur we subtracted two functions to find a new function. In other cases we may use addition, multiplication, or division to combine two functions. For any two given functions we can define the sum, difference, product, and quotient functions as follows.

Sum, Difference, Product, and Quotient Functions

Given two functions f and g, the functions $f + g$, $f - g$, $f \cdot g$, and $\frac{f}{g}$ are defined as follows:

Sum function:	$(f + g)(x) = f(x) + g(x)$
Difference function:	$(f - g)(x) = f(x) - g(x)$
Product function:	$(f \cdot g)(x) = f(x) \cdot g(x)$
Quotient function:	$\left(\dfrac{f}{g}\right)(x) = \dfrac{f(x)}{g(x)}$ provided that $g(x) \neq 0$

The domain of the function $f + g$, $f - g$, $f \cdot g$, or $\frac{f}{g}$ is the intersection of the domain of f and the domain of g. For the function $\frac{f}{g}$ we also rule out any values of x for which $g(x) = 0$.

E X A M P L E   1

Operations with functions

Let $f(x) = 4x - 12$ and $g(x) = x - 3$. Find the following.

a) $(f + g)(x)$ **b)** $(f - g)(x)$

c) $(f \cdot g)(x)$ **d)** $\left(\dfrac{f}{g}\right)(x)$

Helpful Hint

Note that we use $f + g, f - g, f \cdot g$, and f/g to name these functions only because there is no application in mind here. We generally use a single letter to name functions after they are combined as we did when using P for the profit function rather than $R - C$.

Solution

a) $(f + g)(x) = f(x) + g(x)$
$$= 4x - 12 + x - 3$$
$$= 5x - 15$$

b) $(f - g)(x) = f(x) - g(x)$
$$= 4x - 12 - (x - 3)$$
$$= 3x - 9$$

c) $(f \cdot g)(x) = f(x) \cdot g(x)$
$$= (4x - 12)(x - 3)$$
$$= 4x^2 - 24x + 36$$

d) $\left(\dfrac{f}{g}\right)(x) = \dfrac{f(x)}{g(x)} = \dfrac{4x - 12}{x - 3} = \dfrac{4(x - 3)}{x - 3} = 4$ for $x \neq 3$. ■

E X A M P L E   2

Evaluating a sum function

Let $f(x) = 4x - 12$ and $g(x) = x - 3$. Find $(f + g)(2)$.

Solution

In Example 1(a) we found a general formula for the function $f + g$, namely, $(f + g)(x) = 5x - 15$. If we replace x by 2, we get

$$(f + g)(2) = 5(2) - 15$$
$$= -5.$$

We can also find $(f + g)(2)$ by evaluating each function separately and then adding the results. Because $f(2) = -4$ and $g(2) = -1$, we get

$$(f + g)(2) = f(2) + g(2)$$
$$= -4 + (-1)$$
$$= -5.$$ ∎

Helpful Hint

The difference between the first four operations with functions and composition is like the difference between parallel and series in electrical connections. Components connected in parallel operate simultaneously and separately. If components are connected in series, then electricity must pass through the first component to get to the second component.

Composition

A salesperson's monthly salary is a function of the number of cars he sells: $1000 plus $50 for each car sold. If we let S be his salary and n be the number of cars sold, then S in dollars is a function of n:

$$S = 1000 + 50n$$

Each month the dealer contributes $100 plus 5% of his salary to a profit-sharing plan. If P represents the amount put into profit sharing, then P (in dollars) is a function of S:

$$P = 100 + 0.05S$$

Now P is a function of S, and S is a function of n. Is P a function of n? The value of n certainly determines the value of P. In fact, we can write a formula for P in terms of n by substituting one formula into the other:

$$P = 100 + 0.05S$$
$$= 100 + 0.05(1000 + 50n) \quad \text{Substitute } S = 1000 + 50n.$$
$$= 100 + 50 + 2.5n \quad\quad\quad \text{Distributive property}$$
$$= 150 + 2.5n$$

Now P is written as a function of n, bypassing S. We call this idea **composition of functions.**

E X A M P L E   3

The composition of two functions

Given that $y = x^2 - 2x + 3$ and $z = 2y - 5$, write z as a function of x.

Solution

Replace y in $z = 2y - 5$ by $x^2 - 2x + 3$:

$$z = 2y - 5$$
$$= 2(x^2 - 2x + 3) - 5 \quad \text{Replace } y \text{ by } x^2 - 2x + 3.$$
$$= 2x^2 - 4x + 1$$

The equation $z = 2x^2 - 4x + 1$ expresses z as a function of x. ∎

The composition of two functions using function notation is defined as follows.

Composition of Functions

The **composition** of f and g is denoted $f \circ g$ and is defined by the equation

$$(f \circ g)(x) = f(g(x)),$$

provided that $g(x)$ is in the domain of f.

The notation $f \circ g$ is read as "the composition of f and g" or "f compose g." The diagram in Fig. 9.24 shows a function g pairing numbers in its domain with numbers in its range. If the range of g is contained in or equal to the domain of f, then f pairs the second coordinates of g with numbers in the range of f. The composition function $f \circ g$ is a rule for pairing numbers in the domain of g directly with numbers in the range of f, bypassing the middle set. The domain of the function $f \circ g$ is the domain of g (or a subset of it) and the range of $f \circ g$ is the range of f (or a subset of it).

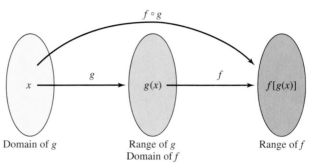

FIGURE 9.24

CAUTION   The order in which functions are written is important in composition. For the function $f \circ g$ the function f is applied to $g(x)$. For the function $g \circ f$ the function g is applied to $f(x)$. The function closest to the variable x is applied first.

EXAMPLE 4

Evaluating compositions

Let $f(x) = 3x - 2$ and $g(x) = x^2 + 2x$. Evaluate each of the following expressions.

a) $g(f(3))$ **b)** $f(g(-4))$ **c)** $(g \circ f)(2)$ **d)** $(f \circ g)(2)$

Calculator Close-Up

Set $y_1 = 3x - 2$ and $y_2 = x^2 + 2x$. You can find the composition for Examples 4(a) and 4(b) by evaluating $y_2(y_1(2))$ and $y_1(y_2(2))$. Note that the order in which you evaluate the functions is critical.

Solution

a) Because $f(3) = 3(3) - 2 = 7$, we have

$$g(f(3)) = g(7) = 7^2 + 2 \cdot 7 = 63.$$

So $g(f(3)) = 63$.

b) Because $g(-4) = (-4)^2 + 2(-4) = 8$, we have

$$f(g(-4)) = f(8) = 3(8) - 2 = 22.$$

So $f(g(-4)) = 22$.

c) Because $(g \circ f)(2) = g(f(2))$ we first find $f(2)$:

$$f(2) = 3(2) - 2 = 4$$

Because $f(2) = 4$, we have

$$(g \circ f)(2) = g(f(2)) = g(4) = 4^2 + 2(4) = 24.$$

So $(g \circ f)(2) = 24$.

d) Because $(f \circ g)(2) = f(g(2))$, we first find $g(2)$:

$$g(2) = 2^2 + 2(2) = 8.$$

Because $g(2) = 8$, we have

$$(f \circ g)(2) = f(g(2)) = f(8) = 3(8) - 2 = 22.$$

So $(f \circ g)(2) = 22.$ ∎

In Example 4 we found specific values of compositions of two functions. In Example 5 we find a general formula for the two functions from Example 4.

E X A M P L E   5

Finding formulas for compositions

Let $f(x) = 3x - 2$ and $g(x) = x^2 + 2x$. Find the following.

a) $(g \circ f)(x)$

b) $(f \circ g)(x)$

Solution

a) Since $f(x) = 3x - 2$ we replace $f(x)$ with $3x - 2$:

$$\begin{aligned}
(g \circ f)(x) &= g(f(x)) \\
&= g(3x - 2) \\
&= (3x - 2)^2 + 2(3x - 2) \\
&= 9x^2 - 12x + 4 + 6x - 4 \\
&= 9x^2 - 6x
\end{aligned}$$

So $(g \circ f)(x) = 9x^2 - 6x.$

b) Since $g(x) = x^2 + 2x$ we replace $g(x)$ with $x^2 + 2x$:

$$\begin{aligned}
(f \circ g)(x) &= f(g(x)) \\
&= f(x^2 + 2x) \\
&= 3(x^2 + 2x) - 2 \\
&= 3x^2 + 6x - 2
\end{aligned}$$

So $(f \circ g)(x) = 3x^2 + 6x - 2.$ ∎

Helpful Hint

A composition of functions can be viewed as two function machines where the output of the first is the input of the second.

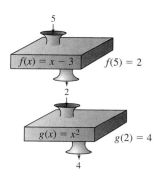

Notice that in Example 4(c) and (d), $(g \circ f)(2) \neq (f \circ g)(2)$. In Example 5(a) and (b) we see that $(g \circ f)(x)$ and $(f \circ g)(x)$ have different formulas defining them. In general, $f \circ g \neq g \circ f$. However, in Section 9.4 we will see some functions for which the composition in either order results in the same function.

It is often useful to view a complicated function as a composition of simpler functions. For example, the function $Q(x) = (x - 3)^2$ consists of two operations, subtracting 3 and squaring. So Q can be described as a composition of the functions $f(x) = x - 3$ and $g(x) = x^2$. To check this, we find $(g \circ f)(x)$:

$$\begin{aligned}
(g \circ f)(x) &= g(f(x)) \\
&= g(x - 3) \\
&= (x - 3)^2
\end{aligned}$$

We can express the fact that Q is the same as the composition function $g \circ f$ by writing $Q = g \circ f$ or $Q(x) = (g \circ f)(x)$.

E X A M P L E   6

Expressing a function as a composition of simpler functions

Let $f(x) = x - 2$, $g(x) = 3x$, and $h(x) = \sqrt{x}$. Write each of the following functions as a composition, using f, g, and h.

a) $F(x) = \sqrt{x - 2}$

b) $H(x) = x - 4$

c) $K(x) = 3x - 6$

Study Tip

Solution

a) The function F consists of first subtracting 2 from x and then taking the square root of that result. So $F = h \circ f$. Check this result by finding $(h \circ f)(x)$:

$$(h \circ f)(x) = h(f(x)) = h(x - 2) = \sqrt{x - 2}$$

b) Subtracting 4 from x can be accomplished by subtracting 2 from x and then subtracting 2 from that result. So $H = f \circ f$. Check by finding $(f \circ f)(x)$:

$$(f \circ f)(x) = f(f(x)) = f(x - 2) = x - 2 - 2 = x - 4$$

c) Notice that $K(x) = 3(x - 2)$. The function K consists of subtracting 2 from x and then multiplying the result by 3. So $K = g \circ f$. Check by finding $(g \circ f)(x)$:

$$(g \circ f)(x) = g(f(x)) = g(x - 2) = 3(x - 2) = 3x - 6 \qquad \blacksquare$$

> **C A U T I O N**   In Example 6(a) we have $F = h \circ f$ because in F we subtract 2 before taking the square root. If we had the function $G(x) = \sqrt{x} - 2$, we would take the square root before subtracting 2. So $G = f \circ h$. Notice how important the order of operations is here.

In Example 7 we see functions for which the composition is the identity function. Each function undoes what the other function does. We will study functions of this type further in Section 9.4.

E X A M P L E   7

Composition of functions

Show that $(f \circ g)(x) = x$ for each pair of functions.

a) $f(x) = 2x - 1$ and $g(x) = \dfrac{x + 1}{2}$

b) $f(x) = x^3 + 5$ and $g(x) = (x - 5)^{1/3}$

Solution

a) $(f \circ g)(x) = f(g(x)) = f\left(\dfrac{x + 1}{2}\right)$

$$= 2\left(\dfrac{x + 1}{2}\right) - 1$$

$$= x + 1 - 1$$

$$= x$$

b) $(f \circ g)(x) = f(g(x)) = f((x - 5)^{1/3})$

$$= ((x - 5)^{1/3})^3 + 5$$

$$= x - 5 + 5$$

$$= x \qquad \blacksquare$$

WARM-UPS

True or false? Explain your answer.

1. If $f(x) = x - 2$ and $g(x) = x + 3$, then $(f - g)(x) = -5$.
2. If $f(x) = x + 4$ and $g(x) = 3x$, then $\left(\dfrac{f}{g}\right)(2) = 1$.
3. The functions $f \circ g$ and $g \circ f$ are always the same.
4. If $f(x) = x^2$ and $g(x) = x + 2$, then $(f \circ g)(x) = x^2 + 2$.
5. The functions $f \circ g$ and $f \cdot g$ are always the same.
6. If $f(x) = \sqrt{x}$ and $g(x) = x - 9$, then $g(f(x)) = f(g(x))$ for every x.
7. If $f(x) = 3x$ and $g(x) = \frac{x}{3}$, then $(f \circ g)(x) = x$.
8. If $a = 3b^2 - 7b$, and $c = a^2 + 3a$, then c is a function of b.
9. The function $F(x) = \sqrt{x - 5}$ is a composition of two functions.
10. If $F(x) = (x - 1)^2$, $h(x) = x - 1$, and $g(x) = x^2$, then $F = g \circ h$.

9.3   EXERCISES

Reading and Writing   *After reading this section, write out the answers to these questions. Use complete sentences.*

1. What are the basic operations with functions?

2. How do we perform the basic operations with functions?

3. What is the composition of two functions?

4. How is the order of operations related to composition of functions?

Let $f(x) = 4x - 3$, and $g(x) = x^2 - 2x$. Find the following. See Examples 1 and 2.

5. $(f + g)(x)$ 6. $(f - g)(x)$

7. $(f \cdot g)(x)$ 8. $\left(\dfrac{f}{g}\right)(x)$

9. $(f + g)(3)$ 10. $(f + g)(2)$
11. $(f - g)(-3)$ 12. $(f - g)(-2)$
13. $(f \cdot g)(-1)$ 14. $(f \cdot g)(-2)$
15. $\left(\dfrac{f}{g}\right)(4)$ 16. $\left(\dfrac{f}{g}\right)(-2)$

For Exercises 17–24, use the two functions to write y as a function of x. See Example 3.

17. $y = 3a - 2$, $a = 2x - 6$
18. $y = 2c + 3$, $c = -3x + 4$
19. $y = 2d + 1$, $d = \dfrac{x + 1}{2}$
20. $y = -3d + 2$, $d = \dfrac{2 - x}{3}$
21. $y = m^2 - 1$, $m = x + 1$
22. $y = n^2 - 3n + 1$, $n = x + 2$
23. $y = \dfrac{a - 3}{a + 2}$, $a = \dfrac{2x + 3}{1 - x}$
24. $y = \dfrac{w + 2}{w - 5}$, $w = \dfrac{5x + 2}{x - 1}$

Let $f(x) = 2x - 3$, $g(x) = x^2 + 3x$, and $h(x) = \dfrac{x + 3}{2}$. Find the following. See Examples 4 and 5.

25. $(g \circ f)(1)$ 26. $(f \circ g)(-2)$
27. $(f \circ g)(1)$ 28. $(g \circ f)(-2)$
29. $(f \circ f)(4)$ 30. $(h \circ h)(3)$
31. $(h \circ f)(5)$ 32. $(f \circ h)(0)$
33. $(f \circ h)(5)$ 34. $(h \circ f)(0)$

35. $(g \circ h)(-1)$ 36. $(h \circ g)(-1)$

37. $(f \circ g)(2.36)$ 38. $(h \circ f)(23.761)$

39. $(g \circ f)(x)$ 40. $(g \circ h)(x)$

41. $(f \circ g)(x)$ **42.** $(h \circ g)(x)$

43. $(h \circ f)(x)$ **44.** $(f \circ h)(x)$

45. $(f \circ f)(x)$ **46.** $(g \circ g)(x)$

47. $(h \circ h)(x)$ **48.** $(f \circ f \circ f)(x)$

Let $f(x) = \sqrt{x}$, $g(x) = x^2$, and $h(x) = x - 3$. Write each of the following functions as a composition using f, g, or h. See Example 6.

49. $F(x) = \sqrt{x - 3}$ **50.** $N(x) = \sqrt{x} - 3$

51. $G(x) = x^2 - 6x + 9$ **52.** $P(x) = x$ for $x \geq 0$

53. $H(x) = x^2 - 3$ **54.** $M(x) = x^{1/4}$

55. $J(x) = x - 6$ **56.** $R(x) = \sqrt{x^2 - 3}$

57. $K(x) = x^4$ **58.** $Q(x) = \sqrt{x^2 - 6x + 9}$

Show that $(f \circ g)(x) = x$ and $(g \circ f)(x) = x$ for each given pair of functions. See Example 7.

59. $f(x) = 3x + 5$, $g(x) = \dfrac{x - 5}{3}$

60. $f(x) = 3x - 7$, $g(x) = \dfrac{x + 7}{3}$

61. $f(x) = x^3 - 9$, $g(x) = \sqrt[3]{x + 9}$
62. $f(x) = x^3 + 1$, $g(x) = \sqrt[3]{x - 1}$

63. $f(x) = \dfrac{x - 1}{x + 1}$, $g(x) = \dfrac{x + 1}{1 - x}$

64. $f(x) = \dfrac{x + 1}{x - 3}$, $g(x) = \dfrac{3x + 1}{x - 1}$

65. $f(x) = \dfrac{1}{x}$, $g(x) = \dfrac{1}{x}$

66. $f(x) = 2x^3$, $g(x) = \left(\dfrac{x}{2}\right)^{1/3}$

Solve each problem.

67. *Area.* A square gate in a wood fence has a diagonal brace with a length of 10 feet.
   a) Find the area of the square gate.
   b) Write a formula for the area of a square as a function of the length of its diagonal.

68. *Perimeter.* Write a formula for the perimeter of a square as a function of its area.

69. *Profit function.* A plastic bag manufacturer has determined that the company can sell as many bags as it can produce each month. If it produces x thousand bags in a month, the revenue is $R(x) = x^2 - 10x + 30$ dollars, and the cost is $C(x) = 2x^2 - 30x + 200$ dollars. Use the fact that profit is revenue minus cost to write the profit as a function of x.

70. *Area of a sign.* A sign is in the shape of a square with a semicircle of radius x adjoining one side and a semicircle of diameter x removed from the opposite side. If the sides of the square are length $2x$, then write the area of the sign as a function of x.

FIGURE FOR EXERCISE 70

71. *Junk food expenditures.* Suppose the average family spends 25% of its income on food, $F = 0.25I$, and 10% of each food dollar on junk food, $J = 0.10F$. Write J as a function of I.

72. *Area of an inscribed circle.* A pipe of radius r must pass through a square hole of area M as shown in the figure. Write the cross-sectional area of the pipe A as a function of M.

FIGURE FOR EXERCISE 72

73. *Displacement-length ratio.* To find the displacement-length ratio D for a sailboat, first find x, where $x = (L/100)^3$ and L is the length at the water line in feet (www.sailing.com). Next find D, where $D = (d/2240)/x$ and d is the displacement in pounds.

   a) For the Pacific Seacraft 40, $L = 30$ ft 3 in. and $d = 24,665$ pounds. Find D.

FIGURE FOR EXERCISE 73

b) For a boat with a displacement of 25,000 pounds, write D as a function of L.

c) The graph for the function in part (b) is shown in the accompanying figure. For a fixed displacement, does the displacement-length ratio increase or decrease as the length increases?

74. *Sail area-displacement ratio.* To find the sail area-displacement ratio S, first find y, where $y = (d/64)^{2/3}$ and d is the displacement in pounds. Next find S, where $S = A/y$ and A is the sail area in square feet.

a) For the Pacific Seacraft 40, $A = 846$ square feet (ft^2) and $d = 24{,}665$ pounds. Find S.

b) For a boat with a sail area of 900 ft^2, write S as a function of d.

c) For a fixed sail area, does S increase or decrease as the displacement increases?

GETTING MORE INVOLVED

75. *Discussion.* Let $f(x) = \sqrt{x} - 4$ and $g(x) = \sqrt{x}$. Find the domains of f, g, and $g \circ f$.

76. *Discussion.* Let $f(x) = \sqrt{x - 4}$ and $g(x) = \sqrt{x - 8}$. Find the domains of f, g, and $f + g$.

GRAPHING CALCULATOR EXERCISES

77. Graph $y_1 = x$, $y_2 = \sqrt{x}$, and $y_3 = x + \sqrt{x}$ in the same screen. Find the domain and range of $y_3 = x + \sqrt{x}$ by examining its graph. (On some graphing calculators you can enter y_3 as $y_3 = y_1 + y_2$.)

78. Graph $y_1 = |x|$, $y_2 = |x - 3|$, and $y_3 = |x| + |x - 3|$. Find the domain and range of $y_3 = |x| + |x - 3|$ by examining its graph.

In This Section

- Inverse of a Function
- Identifying Inverse Functions
- Switch-and-Solve Strategy
- Even Roots or Even Powers
- Graphs of f and f^{-1}

9.4 INVERSE FUNCTIONS

In Section 9.3 we introduced the idea of a pair of functions such that $(f \circ g)(x) = x$ and $(g \circ f)(x) = x$. Each function reverses what the other function does. In this section we explore that idea further.

Inverse of a Function

You can buy a 6-, 7-, or 8-foot conference table in the K-LOG Catalog for $299, $329, or $349, respectively. The set

$$f = \{(6, 299), (7, 329), (8, 349)\}$$

gives the price as a function of the length. We use the letter f as a name for this set or function, just as we use the letter f as a name for a function in the function notation. In the function f, lengths in the domain $\{6, 7, 8\}$ are paired with prices in the range $\{299, 329, 349\}$. The **inverse** of the function f, denoted f^{-1}, is a function whose ordered pairs are obtained from f by interchanging the x- and y-coordinates:

$$f^{-1} = \{(299, 6), (329, 7), (349, 8)\}$$

We read f^{-1} as "f inverse." The domain of f^{-1} is $\{299, 329, 349\}$, and the range of f^{-1} is $\{6, 7, 8\}$. The inverse function reverses what the function does: it pairs prices in the range of f with lengths in the domain of f. For example, to find the cost of a 7-foot table, we use the function f to get $f(7) = 329$. To find the length of a table, that costs \$349, we use the function f^{-1} to get $f^{-1}(349) = 8$. Of course, we could find the length of a \$349 table by looking at the function f, but f^{-1} is a function whose input is price and whose output is length. In general, *the domain of f^{-1} is the range of f, and the range of f^{-1} is the domain of f*. See Fig. 9.25.

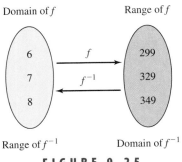

FIGURE 9.25

CAUTION   The -1 in f^{-1} is not read as an exponent. It does not mean $\frac{1}{f}$.

The cost per ribbon for Apple Imagewriter ribbons is a function of the number of boxes purchased:

$$g = \{(1, 4.85), (2, 4.60), (3, 4.60), (4, 4.35)\}$$

If we interchange the first and second coordinates in the ordered pairs of this function, we get

$$\{(4.85, 1), (4.60, 2), (4.60, 3), (4.35, 4)\}.$$

This set of ordered pairs is not a function because it contains ordered pairs with the same first coordinates and different second coordinates. So g does not have an inverse function. A function is **invertible** if you obtain a function when the coordinates of all ordered pairs are reversed. So f is invertible and g is not invertible. The function g is not invertible because the definition of function allows more than one number of the domain to be paired with the same number in the range. Of course, when this pairing is reversed, the definition of function is violated.

Helpful Hint

Consider the universal product codes (UPC) and the prices for all of the items in your favorite grocery store. The price of an item is a function of the UPC because every UPC determines a price. This function is not invertible because you cannot determine the UPC from a given price.

One-to-One Function

If a function is such that no two ordered pairs have different x-coordinates and the same y-coordinate, then the function is called a **one-to-one** function.

In a one-to-one function each member of the domain corresponds to just one member of the range, and each member of the range corresponds to just one member of the domain. *Functions that are one-to-one are invertible functions.*

Inverse Function

The inverse of a one-to-one function f is the function f^{-1}, which is obtained from f by interchanging the coordinates in each ordered pair of f.

E X A M P L E   1

Identifying invertible functions

Determine whether each function is invertible. If it is invertible, then find the inverse function.

a) $f = \{(2, 4), (-2, 4), (3, 9)\}$

b) $g = \left\{\left(2, \dfrac{1}{2}\right), \left(5, \dfrac{1}{5}\right), \left(7, \dfrac{1}{7}\right)\right\}$

c) $h = \{(3, 5), (7, 9)\}$

Solution

a) Since $(2, 4)$ and $(-2, 4)$ have the same y-coordinate, this function is not one-to-one, and it is not invertible.

b) This function is one-to-one, and so it is invertible.

$$g^{-1} = \left\{\left(\dfrac{1}{2}, 2\right), \left(\dfrac{1}{5}, 5\right), \left(\dfrac{1}{7}, 7\right)\right\}$$

c) This function is invertible, and $h^{-1} = \{(5, 3), (9, 7)\}$.   ∎

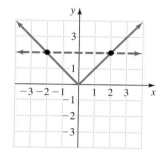

FIGURE 9.26

You learned to use the vertical-line test in Section 3.5 to determine whether a graph is the graph of a function. The **horizontal-line test** is a similar visual test for determining whether a function is invertible. If a horizontal line crosses a graph two (or more) times, as in Fig. 9.26, then there are two points on the graph, say (x_1, y) and (x_2, y), that have different x-coordinates and the same y-coordinate. So the function is not one-to-one, and the function is not invertible.

Horizontal-Line Test

A function is invertible if and only if no horizontal line crosses its graph more than once.

E X A M P L E   2

Using the horizontal-line test

Determine whether each function is invertible by examining its graph.

a)

b)

Helpful Hint

Tests such as the vertical-line test and the horizontal-line test are certainly not accurate in all cases. We discuss these tests to get a visual idea of what graphs of functions and invertible functions look like.

Solution

a) This function is not invertible because a horizontal line can be drawn so that it crosses the graph at $(2, 4)$ and $(-2, 4)$.

b) This function is invertible because every horizontal line that crosses the graph crosses it only once.   ∎

Identifying Inverse Functions

Consider the one-to-one function $f(x) = 3x$. The inverse function must reverse the ordered pairs of the function. Because division by 3 undoes multiplication by 3, we could guess that $g(x) = \frac{x}{3}$ is the inverse function. To verify our guess, we can use the following rule for determining whether two given functions are inverses of each other.

Identifying Inverse Functions

Functions f and g are inverses of each other if and only if

$$(g \circ f)(x) = x \text{ for every number } x \text{ in the domain of } f \text{ and}$$
$$(f \circ g)(x) = x \text{ for every number } x \text{ in the domain of } g.$$

In the next example we verify that $f(x) = 3x$ and $g(x) = \frac{x}{3}$ are inverses.

E X A M P L E   3   **Identifying inverse functions**
Determine whether the functions f and g are inverses of each other.

a) $f(x) = 3x$ and $g(x) = \dfrac{x}{3}$

b) $f(x) = 2x - 1$ and $g(x) = \dfrac{1}{2}x + 1$

c) $f(x) = x^2$ and $g(x) = \sqrt{x}$

Study Tip

Personal issues can have a tremendous effect on your progress in any course. So do not hesitate to deal with personal problems. If you need help, get it. Most schools have counseling centers that can help you to overcome personal issues that are affecting your studies.

Solution

a) Find $g \circ f$ and $f \circ g$:

$$(g \circ f)(x) = g(f(x)) = g(3x) = \frac{3x}{3} = x$$
$$(f \circ g)(x) = f(g(x)) = f\left(\frac{x}{3}\right) = 3 \cdot \frac{x}{3} = x$$

Because each of these equations is true for any real number x, f and g are inverses of each other. We write $g = f^{-1}$ or $f^{-1}(x) = \frac{x}{3}$.

b) Find the composition of g and f:

$$(g \circ f)(x) = g(f(x))$$
$$= g(2x - 1) = \frac{1}{2}(2x - 1) + 1 = x + \frac{1}{2}$$

So f and g are not inverses of each other.

c) If x is any real number, we can write

$$(g \circ f)(x) = g(f(x))$$
$$= g(x^2) = \sqrt{x^2} = |x|.$$

The domain of f is $(-\infty, \infty)$, and $|x| \neq x$ if x is negative. So g and f are not inverses of each other. Note that $f(x) = x^2$ is not a one-to-one function, since both $(3, 9)$ and $(-3, 9)$ are ordered pairs of this function. Thus $f(x) = x^2$ does not have an inverse. ■

Switch-and-Solve Strategy

If an invertible function is defined by a list of ordered pairs, as in Example 1, then the inverse function is found by simply interchanging the coordinates in the ordered pairs. If an invertible function is defined by a formula, then the inverse function must reverse or undo what the function does. Because the inverse function interchanges the roles of x and y, we interchange x and y in the formula and then solve the new formula for y to undo what the original function did. This **switch-and-solve** strategy is illustrated in Examples 4 and 5.

E X A M P L E   4

The switch-and-solve strategy

Find the inverse of $h(x) = 2x + 1$.

Solution

First write the function as $y = 2x + 1$, then interchange x and y:

$$y = 2x + 1$$
$$x = 2y + 1 \quad \text{Interchange } x \text{ and } y.$$
$$x - 1 = 2y \quad \text{Solve for } y.$$
$$\frac{x - 1}{2} = y$$
$$h^{-1}(x) = \frac{x - 1}{2} \quad \text{Replace } y \text{ by } h^{-1}(x).$$

We can verify that h and h^{-1} are inverses by using composition:

$$(h^{-1} \circ h)(x) = h^{-1}(h(x)) = h^{-1}(2x + 1) = \frac{2x + 1 - 1}{2} = \frac{2x}{2} = x$$
$$(h \circ h^{-1})(x) = h(h^{-1}(x)) = h\left(\frac{x - 1}{2}\right) = 2 \cdot \frac{x - 1}{2} + 1 = x - 1 + 1 = x \quad \blacksquare$$

E X A M P L E   5

The switch-and-solve strategy

If $f(x) = \dfrac{x + 1}{x - 3}$, find $f^{-1}(x)$.

Solution

Replace $f(x)$ by y, interchange x and y, then solve for y:

$$y = \frac{x + 1}{x - 3} \quad \text{Use } y \text{ in place of } f(x).$$
$$x = \frac{y + 1}{y - 3} \quad \text{Switch } x \text{ and } y.$$
$$x(y - 3) = y + 1 \quad \text{Multiply each side by } y - 3.$$
$$xy - 3x = y + 1 \quad \text{Distributive property}$$
$$xy - y = 3x + 1$$
$$y(x - 1) = 3x + 1 \quad \text{Factor out } y.$$
$$y = \frac{3x + 1}{x - 1} \quad \text{Divide each side by } x - 1.$$
$$f^{-1}(x) = \frac{3x + 1}{x - 1} \quad \text{Replace } y \text{ by } f^{-1}(x).$$

You should check that $(f \circ f^{-1})(x) = x$ and $(f^{-1} \circ f)(x) = x$. $\blacksquare$

The strategy for finding the inverse of a function $f(x)$ is summarized as follows.

Switch-and-Solve Strategy for Finding f^{-1}

1. Replace $f(x)$ by y.
2. Interchange x and y.
3. Solve the equation for y.
4. Replace y by $f^{-1}(x)$.

Helpful Hint

You should know from memory the inverses of simple functions that involve one or two operations. For example, the inverse of $f(x) = x + 99$ is $f^{-1}(x) = x - 99$. The inverse of $f(x) = x/33 + 22$ is $f^{-1}(x) = 33(x - 22)$.

If we use the switch-and-solve strategy to find the inverse of $f(x) = x^3$, then we get $f^{-1}(x) = x^{1/3}$. For $h(x) = 6x$ we have $h^{-1}(x) = \frac{x}{6}$. The inverse of $k(x) = x - 9$ is $k^{-1}(x) = x + 9$. For each of these functions there is an appropriate operation of arithmetic that undoes what the function does.

If a function involves two operations, the inverse function undoes those operations in the opposite order from which the function does them. For example, the function $g(x) = 3x - 5$ multiplies x by 3 and then subtracts 5 from that result. To undo these operations, we add 5 and then divide the result by 3. So

$$g^{-1}(x) = \frac{x + 5}{3}.$$

Note that $g^{-1}(x) \neq \frac{x}{3} + 5$.

Even Roots or Even Powers

We need to use special care in finding inverses for functions that involve even roots or even powers. We saw in Example 3(c) that $f(x) = x^2$ is not the inverse of $g(x) = \sqrt{x}$. However, because $g(x) = \sqrt{x}$ is a one-to-one function, it has an inverse. The domain of g is $[0, \infty)$, and the range is $[0, \infty)$. So the inverse of g must have domain $[0, \infty)$ and range $[0, \infty)$. See Fig. 9.27. The only reason that $f(x) = x^2$ is not the inverse of g is that it has the wrong domain. So to write the inverse function, we must use the appropriate domain:

$$g^{-1}(x) = x^2 \qquad \text{for} \quad x \geq 0$$

Note that by restricting the domain of g^{-1} to $[0, \infty)$, g^{-1} is one-to-one. With this restriction it is true that $(g \circ g^{-1})(x) = x$ and $(g^{-1} \circ g)(x) = x$ for every nonnegative number x.

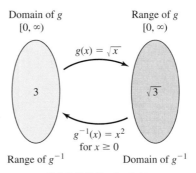

FIGURE 9.27

MATH AT WORK

When a serious automobile accident occurs in Massachusetts, Stephen Benanti, the Commanding Officer of the Accident Reconstruction Section of the State Police, may be called to examine the physical evidence at the scene. Physical evidence can consist of debris, scrapes, and gouges on the road; damage to fixed objects such as utility poles, trees, or guardrails; and the final resting position of and damage to the vehicles.

STATE POLICE OFFICER

One critical type of evidence that is sometimes found are skid marks on the road. Sergeant Benanti can use the lengths of the skid marks to calculate the speeds of accident vehicles. Using a sophisticated laser measuring device, Benanti can store data that later can be downloaded into a computer to reconstruct the accident scene. He must also conduct tests on the road surface to calculate the drag factor, which is the resistance between the tire and the road surface. A smooth, icy surface yields a much lower drag factor than a dry asphalt surface. The minimum speed formula that state troopers use to determine vehicles' speeds is a function of the drag factor and the skid distance: $S = \sqrt{30DF}$, where S = speed, D = distance skidded, and F = drag factor.

In Exercise 73 of this section you will use this minimum speed formula with a given length of skid marks to determine the speed of a vehicle.

EXAMPLE 6   **Inverse of a function with an even exponent**

Find the inverse of the function $f(x) = (x - 3)^2$ for $x \geq 3$.

Solution

Because of the restriction $x \geq 3$, f is a one-to-one function with domain $[3, \infty)$ and range $[0, \infty)$. The domain of the inverse function is $[0, \infty)$, and its range is $[3, \infty)$. Use the switch-and-solve strategy to find the formula for the inverse:

$$y = (x - 3)^2$$
$$x = (y - 3)^2$$
$$y - 3 = \pm\sqrt{x}$$
$$y = 3 \pm \sqrt{x}$$

Because the inverse function must have range $[3, \infty)$, we use the formula $f^{-1}(x) = 3 + \sqrt{x}$. Because the domain of f^{-1} is assumed to be $[0, \infty)$, no restriction is required on x. ∎

Graphs of f and f^{-1}

Consider $f(x) = x^2$ for $x \geq 0$ and $f^{-1}(x) = \sqrt{x}$. Their graphs are shown in Fig. 9.28. Notice the symmetry. If we folded the paper along the line $y = x$, the two graphs would coincide.

FIGURE 9.28

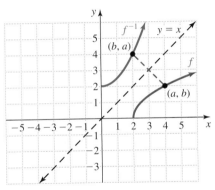

FIGURE 9.29

If a point (a, b) is on the graph of the function f, then (b, a) must be on the graph of $f^{-1}(x)$. See Fig. 9.29. The points (a, b) and (b, a) lie on opposite sides of the diagonal line $y = x$ and are the same distance from it. For this reason the graphs of f and f^{-1} are symmetric with respect to the line $y = x$.

E X A M P L E   7   **Inverses and their graphs**

Find the inverse of the function $f(x) = \sqrt{x - 1}$ and graph f and f^{-1} on the same pair of axes.

Solution

To find f^{-1}, first switch x and y in the formula $y = \sqrt{x - 1}$:

$$x = \sqrt{y - 1}$$
$$x^2 = y - 1 \quad \text{Square both sides.}$$
$$x^2 + 1 = y$$

Because the range of f is the set of nonnegative real numbers $[0, \infty)$, we must restrict the domain of f^{-1} to be $[0, \infty)$. Thus $f^{-1}(x) = x^2 + 1$ for $x \geq 0$. The two graphs are shown in Fig. 9.30.

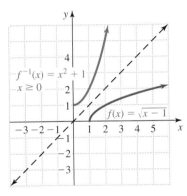

FIGURE 9.30

WARM-UPS

True or false? Explain your answer.

1. The inverse of $\{(1, 3), (2, 5)\}$ is $\{(3, 1), (2, 5)\}$.
2. The function $f(x) = 3$ is a one-to-one function.
3. If $g(x) = 2x$, then $g^{-1}(x) = \frac{1}{2x}$.
4. Only one-to-one functions are invertible.
5. The domain of g is the same as the range of g^{-1}.
6. The function $f(x) = x^4$ is invertible.
7. If $f(x) = -x$, then $f^{-1}(x) = -x$.
8. If h is invertible and $h(7) = -95$, then $h^{-1}(-95) = 7$.
9. If $k(x) = 3x - 6$, then $k^{-1}(x) = \frac{1}{3}x + 2$.
10. If $f(x) = 3x - 4$, then $f^{-1}(x) = x + 4$.

9.4   EXERCISES

Reading and Writing   *After reading this section, write out the answers to these questions. Use complete sentences.*

1. What is the inverse of a function?

2. What is the domain of f^{-1}?

3. What is the range of f^{-1}?

4. What does the -1 in f^{-1} mean?

5. What is a one-to-one function?

6. What is the horizontal-line test?

7. What is the switch-and-solve strategy?

8. How are the graphs of f and f^{-1} related?

Determine whether each function is invertible. If it is invertible, then find the inverse. See Example 1.

9. $\{(-3, 3), (-2, 2), (0, 0), (2, 2)\}$
10. $\{(1, 1), (2, 8), (3, 27)\}$
11. $\{(16, 4), (9, 3), (0, 0)\}$
12. $\{(-1, 1), (-3, 81), (3, 81)\}$
13. $\{(0, 5), (5, 0), (6, 0)\}$
14. $\{(3, -3), (-2, 2), (1, -1)\}$
15. $\{(0, 0), (2, 2), (9, 9)\}$
16. $\{(9, 1), (2, 1), (7, 1), (0, 1)\}$

Determine whether each function is invertible by examining the graph of the function. See Example 2.

17.

18.

19.

20.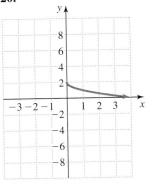

Determine whether each pair of functions f and g are inverses of each other. See Example 3.

21. $f(x) = 2x$ and $g(x) = 0.5x$

22. $f(x) = 3x$ and $g(x) = 0.33x$

23. $f(x) = 2x - 10$ and $g(x) = \dfrac{1}{2}x + 5$

24. $f(x) = 3x + 7$ and $g(x) = \dfrac{x - 7}{3}$

25. $f(x) = -x$ and $g(x) = -x$

26. $f(x) = \dfrac{1}{x}$ and $g(x) = \dfrac{1}{x}$

27. $f(x) = x^4$ and $g(x) = x^{1/4}$

28. $f(x) = |2x|$ and $g(x) = \left|\dfrac{x}{2}\right|$

Determine f^{-1} for each function by using the switch-and-solve strategy. Check that $(f \circ f^{-1})(x) = x$ and $(f^{-1} \circ f)(x) = x$. See Examples 4 and 5.

29. $f(x) = 5x$

30. $h(x) = -3x$

31. $g(x) = x - 9$

32. $j(x) = x + 7$

33. $k(x) = 5x - 9$

34. $r(x) = 2x - 8$

35. $m(x) = \dfrac{2}{x}$

36. $s(x) = \dfrac{-1}{x}$

37. $f(x) = \sqrt[3]{x - 4}$

38. $f(x) = \sqrt[3]{x + 2}$

39. $f(x) = \dfrac{3}{x - 4}$

40. $f(x) = \dfrac{2}{x + 1}$

41. $f(x) = \sqrt[3]{3x + 7}$

42. $f(x) = \sqrt[3]{7 - 5x}$

43. $f(x) = \dfrac{x + 1}{x - 2}$

44. $f(x) = \dfrac{1 - x}{x + 3}$

45. $f(x) = \dfrac{x + 1}{3x - 4}$

46. $g(x) = \dfrac{3x + 5}{2x - 3}$

Find the inverse of each function. See Example 6.

47. $p(x) = \sqrt[6]{x}$

48. $v(x) = \sqrt[6]{x}$

49. $f(x) = (x - 2)^2$ for $x \geq 2$

50. $g(x) = (x + 5)^2$ for $x \geq -5$

51. $f(x) = x^2 + 3$ for $x \geq 0$

52. $f(x) = x^2 - 5$ for $x \geq 0$

53. $f(x) = \sqrt{x + 2}$

54. $f(x) = \sqrt{x - 4}$

In Exercises 55–64, find the inverse of each function and graph f and f^{-1} on the same pair of axes. See Example 7.

55. $f(x) = 2x + 3$

56. $f(x) = -3x + 2$

57. $f(x) = x^2 - 1$ for $x \geq 0$

58. $f(x) = x^2 + 3$ for $x \geq 0$

63. $f(x) = \sqrt{x - 2}$

59. $f(x) = 5x$

64. $f(x) = \sqrt{x + 3}$

60. $f(x) = \dfrac{x}{4}$

For each pair of functions, find $(f^{-1} \circ f)(x)$

65. $f(x) = x^3 - 1$ and $f^{-1}(x) = \sqrt[3]{x + 1}$

66. $f(x) = 2x^3 + 1$ and $f^{-1}(x) = \sqrt[3]{\dfrac{x - 1}{2}}$

61. $f(x) = x^3$

67. $f(x) = \dfrac{1}{2}x - 3$ and $f^{-1}(x) = 2x + 6$

68. $f(x) = 3x - 9$ and $f^{-1}(x) = \dfrac{1}{3}x + 3$

69. $f(x) = \dfrac{1}{x} + 2$ and $f^{-1}(x) = \dfrac{1}{x - 2}$

62. $f(x) = 2x^3$

70. $f(x) = 4 - \dfrac{1}{x}$ and $f^{-1}(x) = \dfrac{1}{4 - x}$

71. $f(x) = \dfrac{x + 1}{x - 2}$ and $f^{-1}(x) = \dfrac{2x + 1}{x - 1}$

72. $f(x) = \dfrac{3x - 2}{x + 2}$ and $f^{-1}(x) = \dfrac{2x + 2}{3 - x}$

Solve each problem.

73. Accident reconstruction. The distance that it takes a car to stop is a function of the speed and the drag factor. The drag factor is a measure of the resistance between the tire and the road surface. The formula $S = \sqrt{30LD}$ is used to determine the minimum speed S [in miles per hour (mph)] for a car that has left skid marks of length L feet (ft) on a surface with drag factor D.

a) Find the minimum speed for a car that has left skid marks of length 50 ft where the drag factor is 0.75.

b) Does the drag factor increase or decrease for a road surface when it gets wet?

c) Write L as a function of S for a road surface with drag factor 1 and graph the function.

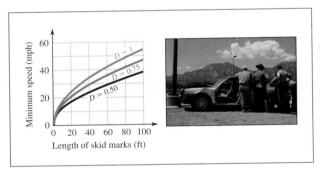

FIGURE FOR EXERCISE 73

74. Area of a circle. Let x be the radius of a circle and $h(x)$ be the area of the circle. Write a formula for $h(x)$ in terms of x. What does x represent in the notation $h^{-1}(x)$? Write a formula for $h^{-1}(x)$.

75. Vehicle cost. At Bill Hood Ford in Hammond a sales tax of 9% of the selling price x and a $125 title and license fee are added to the selling price to get the total cost of a vehicle. Find the function $T(x)$ that the dealer uses to get the total cost as a function of the selling price x. Citizens National Bank will not include sales tax or fees in a loan. Find the function $T^{-1}(x)$ that the bank can use to get the selling price as a function of the total cost x.

76. Carpeting cost. At the Windrush Trace apartment complex all living rooms are square, but the length of x feet may vary. The cost of carpeting a living room is $18 per square yard plus a $50 installation fee. Find the function $C(x)$ that gives the total cost of carpeting a living room of length x. The manager has an invoice for the total cost of a living room carpeting job but does not know in which apartment it was done. Find the function $C^{-1}(x)$ that gives the length of a living room as a function of the total cost of the carpeting job x.

GETTING MORE INVOLVED

77. Discussion. Let $f(x) = x^n$ for n a positive integer. For which values of n is f an invertible function? Explain.

78. Discussion. Suppose f is a function with range $(-\infty, \infty)$ and g is a function with domain $(0, \infty)$. Is it possible that g and f are inverse functions? Explain.

GRAPHING CALCULATOR EXERCISES

79. Most graphing calculators can form compositions of functions. Let $f(x) = x^2$ and $g(x) = \sqrt{x}$. To graph the composition $g \circ f$, let $y_1 = x^2$ and $y_2 = \sqrt{y_1}$. The graph of y_2 is the graph of $g \circ f$. Use the graph of y_2 to determine whether f and g are inverse functions.

80. Let $y_1 = x^3 - 4$, $y_2 = \sqrt[3]{x + 4}$, and $y_3 = \sqrt[3]{y_1 + 4}$. The function y_3 is the composition of the first two functions. Graph all three functions on the same screen. What do the graphs indicate about the relationship between y_1 and y_2?

In This Section

- Direct Variation
- Finding the Proportionality Constant
- Inverse Variation
- Joint Variation
- More Variation

9.5   VARIATION

If $y = 3x$, then as x varies so does y. Certain functions are customarily expressed in terms of variation. In this section you will learn to write formulas for those functions from verbal descriptions of the functions.

Direct Variation

In a community with an 8% sales tax rate, the amount of tax, t (in dollars), is a function of the amount of the purchase, a (in dollars). This function is expressed by the formula

$$t = 0.08a.$$

If the amount increases, then the tax increases. If a decreases, then t decreases. In this situation we say that *t varies directly with a, or t is directly proportional to a.* The constant tax rate, 0.08, is called the **variation constant** or **proportionality constant.** Notice that t is just a simple linear function of a. We are merely introducing some new terms to express an old idea.

Direct Variation

The statement **y varies directly as x,** or **y is directly proportional to x,** means that

$$y = kx$$

for some constant, k. The constant, k, is a fixed nonzero real number.

Finding the Proportionality Constant

If y varies directly as x and we know corresponding values for x and y, then we can find the proportionality constant.

E X A M P L E   1

Finding the proportionality constant

Joyce is traveling by car, and the distance she travels, d, varies directly with the amount of time, t, that she drives. In 3 hours she drove 120 miles. Find the proportionality constant and write d as a function of t.

Calculator Close-Up

The graph of $d = 40t$ is a straight line through the origin.

Solution

Because d varies directly as t, we must have a constant k such that

$$d = kt.$$

Because $d = 120$ when $t = 3$, we can write

$$120 = k \cdot 3,$$

or

$$40 = k.$$

So the proportionality constant is 40 mph, and $d = 40t$. ∎

E X A M P L E   2

Direct variation

In a downtown office building the monthly rent for an office is directly proportional to the size of the office. If a 420-square-foot office rents for $1260 per month, then what is the rent for a 900-square-foot office?

Solution

Because the rent, R, varies directly with the area of the office, A, we have

$$R = kA.$$

Because a 420-square-foot office rents for $1260, we can substitute to find k:

$$1260 = k \cdot 420$$
$$3 = k$$

Now that we know the value of k, we can write

$$R = 3A.$$

To get the rent for a 900-square-foot office, insert 900 into this formula:

$$R = 3 \cdot 900$$
$$= 2700$$

So a 900-square-foot office rents for $2700 per month. ∎

Inverse Variation

In making a 500-mile trip by car, the time it takes is a function of the speed of the car. The greater the speed, the less time it will take. If you decrease the speed, the time increases. We say that the time is *inversely proportional* to the speed. Using the formula $D = RT$ or $T = \dfrac{D}{R}$, we can write

$$T = \frac{500}{R}.$$

In general, we make the following definition.

Inverse Variation

The statement **y varies inversely as x**, or **y is inversely proportional to x,** means that

$$y = \frac{k}{x}$$

for some nonzero constant, k.

CAUTION   Be sure to understand the difference between direct and inverse variation. If y varies directly as x (with $k > 0$), then as x increases, y increases. If y varies inversely as x (with $k > 0$), then as x increases, y decreases.

E X A M P L E   3   **Inverse variation**

Suppose a is inversely proportional to b, and when $b = 5$, $a = \frac{1}{2}$. Find a when $b = 12$.

Solution

Because a is inversely proportional to b, we have

$$a = \frac{k}{b}$$

for some constant, k. Because $a = \frac{1}{2}$ when $b = 5$, we can find k by substituting these values into the formula:

$$\frac{1}{2} = \frac{k}{5}$$

$$\frac{5}{2} = k \qquad \text{Multiply each side by 5.}$$

Now to find a when $b = 12$, we use the formula with k replaced by $\frac{5}{2}$:

$$a = \frac{\frac{5}{2}}{b}$$

$$a = \frac{\frac{5}{2}}{12} = \frac{5}{2} \cdot \frac{1}{12} = \frac{5}{24}$$ ∎

Joint Variation

On a deposit of \$5000 in a savings account, the interest earned, I, depends on the rate, r, and the time, t. Assuming the interest is simple interest, we can use the formula $I = Prt$ to write

$$I = 5000rt.$$

The variable I is a function of two independent variables, r and t. In this case we say that I *varies jointly* as r and t.

Joint Variation

The statement **y varies jointly as x and z, or y is jointly proportional to x and z,** means that

$$y = kxz$$

for some nonzero constant, k.

E X A M P L E   4   **Joint variation**

Suppose y varies jointly with x and z, and $y = 12$ when $x = 5$ and $z = 2$. Find y when $x = 10$ and $z = -3$.

Solution

Because y varies jointly with x and z, we can write

$$y = kxz$$

for some constant, k. Now substitute $y = 12$, $x = 5$, and $z = 2$, and solve for k:

$$12 = k \cdot 5 \cdot 2$$
$$12 = 10k$$
$$\frac{6}{5} = k$$

Now that we know the value of k, we can rewrite the equation as

$$y = \frac{6}{5}xz.$$

To find y when $x = 10$ and $z = -3$, substitute into the equation:

$$y = \frac{6}{5}(10)(-3)$$
$$y = -36$$ ∎

E X A M P L E   5   **An application of joint variation**

The labor cost for installing ceramic floor tile varies jointly with the length and width of the room in which it is installed. If the labor cost for a 9 foot by 12 foot room is $324, then what is the labor cost for a 6 foot by 8 foot room?

Solution

Since the labor cost C varies jointly with the length L and width W we have $C = kLW$ for some constant k. Use $C = 324$, $L = 12$, and $W = 9$ in this formula to find k:

$$324 = k \cdot 12 \cdot 9$$
$$324 = 108k$$
$$k = \frac{324}{108} = 3$$

So the labor cost is $3 per square foot and the formula is $C = 3LW$. Now find C when $L = 8$ and $W = 6$:

$$C = 3LW$$
$$= 3 \cdot 8 \cdot 6 = 144$$

So the labor cost for a 6 foot by 8 foot room is $144.   ∎

More Variation

We frequently combine the ideas of direct, inverse, and joint variation with powers and roots. A combination of direct and inverse variation is referred to as **combined variation.** Study the examples that follow.

Helpful Hint

The language of variation is popular in science. Instead of saying $V = kT/P$, a chemist would say that the volume of a gas varies directly with the temperature and inversely with the pressure.

More Variation Examples

Statement	Formula
y varies directly as the square root of x.	$y = k\sqrt{x}$
y is directly proportional to the cube of x.	$y = kx^3$
y is inversely proportional to x^2.	$y = \dfrac{k}{x^2}$
y varies inversely as the square root of x.	$y = \dfrac{k}{\sqrt{x}}$
y varies jointly as x and the square of z.	$y = kxz^2$
y varies directly with x and inversely with the square root of z (combined variation).	$y = \dfrac{kx}{\sqrt{z}}$

C A U T I O N   The variation terms never signify addition or subtraction. We always use multiplication unless we see the word "inversely." In that case we divide.

E X A M P L E   6   **Newton's law of gravity**

According to Newton's law of gravity, the gravitational attraction F between two objects with masses m_1 and m_2 is directly proportional to the product of their masses and inversely proportional to the square of the distance r between their centers. Write a formula for Newton's law of gravity.

Solution

Letting k be the constant of proportionality, we have

$$F = \frac{km_1m_2}{r^2}.$$

■

E X A M P L E 7

House framing

The time t that it takes to frame a house varies directly with the size of the house s in square feet and inversely with the number of framers n working on the job. If three framers can complete a 2500-square-foot house in 6 days, then how long will it take six framers to complete a 4500-square-foot house?

Solution

Because t varies directly with s and inversely with n, we have

$$t = \frac{ks}{n}.$$

Substitute $t = 6$, $s = 2500$, and $n = 3$ into this equation to find k:

$$6 = \frac{k \cdot 2500}{3}$$

$$18 = 2500k$$

$$0.0072 = k$$

Now use $k = 0.0072$, $s = 4500$, and $n = 6$ to find t:

$$t = \frac{0.0072 \cdot 4500}{6}$$

$$t = 5.4$$

So six framers can frame a 4500-square-foot house in 5.4 days.

■

WARM-UPS

True or false? Explain your answer.

1. If a varies directly as b, then $a = kb$.
2. If a is inversely proportional to b, then $a = bk$.
3. If a is jointly proportional to b and c, then $a = bc$.
4. If a is directly proportional to the square root of c, then $a = k\sqrt{c}$.
5. If b is directly proportional to a, then $b = ka^2$.
6. If a varies directly as b and inversely as c, then $a = \frac{kb}{c}$.
7. If a is jointly proportional to c and the square of b, then $a = \frac{kc}{b^2}$.
8. If a varies directly as c and inversely as the square root of b, then $a = \frac{kc}{b}$.
9. If b varies directly as a and inversely as the square of c, then $b = ka\sqrt{c}$.

10. If b varies inversely with the square of c, then $b = \frac{k}{c^2}$.

9.5   EXERCISES

Reading and Writing   *After reading this section, write out the answers to these questions. Use complete sentences.*

1. What does it mean that y varies directly as x?

2. What is the constant of proportionality in a direct variation?

3. What does it mean that y is inversely proportional to x?

4. What is the difference between direct and inverse variation?

5. What does it mean that y is jointly proportional to x and z?

6. What is the difference between varies directly and directly proportional?

Write a formula that expresses the relationship described by each statement. Use k as a constant of variation. See Examples 1–7.

7. a varies directly as m.

8. w varies directly with P.

9. d varies inversely with e.

10. y varies inversely as x.

11. I varies jointly as r and t.

12. q varies jointly as w and v.

13. m is directly proportional to the square of p.

14. g is directly proportional to the cube of r.

15. B is directly proportional to the cube root of w.

16. F is directly proportional to the square of m.

17. t is inversely proportional to the square of x.

18. y is inversely proportional to the square root of z.

19. v varies directly as m and inversely as n.

20. b varies directly as the square of n and inversely as the square root of v.

Find the proportionality constant and write a formula that expresses the indicated variation. See Example 1.

21. y varies directly as x, and $y = 6$ when $x = 4$.

22. m varies directly as w, and $m = \frac{1}{3}$ when $w = \frac{1}{4}$.

23. A varies inversely as B, and $A = 10$ when $B = 3$.

24. c varies inversely as d, and $c = 0.31$ when $d = 2$.

25. m varies inversely as the square root of p, and $m = 12$ when $p = 9$.

26. s varies inversely as the square root of v, and $s = 6$ when $v = \frac{3}{2}$.

27. A varies jointly as t and u, and $A = 6$ when $t = 5$ and $u = 3$.

28. N varies jointly as the square of p and the cube of q, and $N = 72$ when $p = 3$ and $q = 2$.

29. y varies directly as x and inversely as z, and $y = 2.37$ when $x = \pi$ and $z = \sqrt{2}$.

30. a varies directly as the square root of m and inversely as the square of n, and $a = 5.47$ when $m = 3$ and $n = 1.625$.

Solve each variation problem. See Examples 2–7.

31. If y varies directly as x, and $y = 7$ when $x = 5$, find y when $x = -3$.

32. If n varies directly as p, and $n = 0.6$ when $p = 0.2$, find n when $p = \sqrt{2}$.

33. If w varies inversely as z, and $w = 6$ when $z = 2$, find w when $z = -8$.

34. If p varies inversely as q, and $p = 5$ when $q = \sqrt{3}$, find p when $q = 5$.

35. If A varies jointly as F and T, and $A = 6$ when $F = 3\sqrt{2}$ and $T = 4$, find A when $F = 2\sqrt{2}$ and $T = \frac{1}{2}$.

36. If j varies jointly as the square of r and the cube of v, and $j = -3$ when $r = 2\sqrt{3}$ and $v = \frac{1}{2}$, find j when $r = 3\sqrt{5}$ and $v = 2$.

37. If D varies directly with t and inversely with the square of s, and $D = 12.35$ when $t = 2.8$ and $s = 2.48$, find D when $t = 5.63$ and $s = 6.81$.

38. If M varies jointly with x and the square of v, and $M = 39.5$ when $x = \sqrt{10}$ and $v = 3.87$, find M when $x = \sqrt{30}$ and $v = 7.21$.

Determine whether each equation represents direct, inverse, joint, or combined variation.

39. $y = \dfrac{78}{x}$

40. $y = \dfrac{\pi}{x}$

41. $y = \dfrac{1}{2}x$

42. $y = \dfrac{x}{4}$

43. $y = \dfrac{3x}{w}$

44. $y = \dfrac{4t^2}{\sqrt{x}}$

45. $y = \dfrac{1}{3}xz$

46. $y = 99qv$

In Exercises 47–61, solve each problem.

47. *Lawn maintenance.* At Larry's Lawn Service the cost of lawn maintenance varies directly with the size of the lawn. If the monthly maintenance on a 4000-square-foot lawn is $280, then what is the maintenance fee for a 6000-square-foot lawn?

48. *Weight of the iguana.* The weight of an iguana is directly proportional to its length. If a 4-foot iguana weighs 30 pounds, then how much should a 5-foot iguana weigh?

49. *Gas laws.* The volume of a gas in a cylinder at a fixed temperature is inversely proportional to the weight on the piston. If the gas has a volume of 6 cubic centimeters (cm³) for a weight of 30 kilograms (kg), then what would the volume be for a weight of 20 kg?

50. *Selling software.* A software vendor sells a software package at a price that is inversely proportional to the number of packages sold per month. When they are selling 900 packages per month, the price is $80 each. If they sell 1000 packages per month, then what should the new price be?

51. *Costly culvert.* The price of an aluminum culvert is jointly proportional to its radius and length. If a 12-foot culvert with a 6-inch radius costs $324, then what is the price of a 10-foot culvert with an 8-inch radius?

52. *Pricing plastic.* The cost of a piece of PVC water pipe varies jointly as its diameter and length. If a 20-foot pipe with a diameter of 1 inch costs $6.80, then what will be the cost of a 10-foot pipe with a $\frac{3}{4}$-inch diameter?

53. *Reinforcing rods.* The price of a steel rod varies jointly as the length and the square of the diameter. If an 18-foot rod with a 2-inch diameter costs $12.60, then what is the cost of a 12-foot rod with a 3-inch diameter?

54. *Pea soup.* The weight of a cylindrical can of pea soup varies jointly with the height and the square of the radius. If a 4-inch-high can with a 1.5-inch radius weighs 16 ounces, then what is the weight of a 5-inch-high can with a radius of 3 inches?

55. *Falling objects.* The distance an object falls in a vacuum varies directly with the square of the time it is falling. In the first 0.1 second after an object is dropped, it falls 0.16 feet.

a) Find the formula that expresses the distance d an object falls as a function of the time it is falling t.

b) How far does an object fall in the first 0.5 second after it is dropped?

c) How long does it take for a watermelon to reach the ground when dropped from a height of 100 feet?

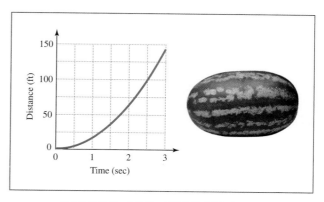

FIGURE FOR EXERCISE 55

56. *Making Frisbees.* The cost of material used in making a Frisbee varies directly with the square of the diameter. If it costs the manufacturer $0.45 for the material in a Frisbee with a 9-inch diameter, then what is the cost for the material in a 12-inch-diameter Frisbee?

57. *Using leverage.* The basic law of leverage is that the force required to lift an object is inversely proportional to the length of the lever. If a force of 2000 pounds applied 2 feet from the pivot point would lift a car, then what force would be required at 10 feet to lift the car?

58. Resistance. The resistance of a wire varies directly with the length and inversely as the square of the diameter. If a wire of length 20 feet and diameter 0.1 inch has a resistance of 2 ohms, then what is the resistance of a 30-foot wire with a diameter of 0.2 inch?

59. Computer programming. The time t required to complete a programming job varies directly with the complexity of the job and inversely with the number n of programmers working on the job. The complexity c is an arbitrarily assigned number between 1 and 10, with 10 being the most complex. It takes 8 days for a team of three programmers to complete a job with complexity 6. How long will it take five programmers to complete a job with complexity 9?

60. Shock absorbers. The volume of gas in a gas shock absorber varies directly with the temperature and inversely with the pressure. The volume is 10 cubic centimeters (cm^3) when the temperature is 20°C and the pressure is 40 kg. What is the volume when the temperature is 30°C and the pressure is 25 kg?

61. Bicycle gear ratio. A bicycle's gear ratio G varies jointly with the number of teeth on the chain ring N (by the pedals) and the diameter of the wheel d, and inversely with the number of teeth on the cog c (on the rear wheel). A bicycle with 27-inch-diameter wheels, 26 teeth on the cog, and 52 teeth on the chain ring has a gear ratio of 54.

a) Find a formula that expresses the gear ratio as a function of N, d, and c.

b) What is the gear ratio for a bicycle with 26-inch-diameter wheels, 42 teeth on the chain ring, and 13 teeth on the cog?

c) A five-speed bicycle with 27-inch-diameter wheels and 44 teeth on the chain ring has gear ratios of 52, 59, 70, 79, and 91. Find the number of teeth on the cog for each gear ratio.

d) For a fixed wheel size and chain ring, does the gear ratio increase or decrease as the number of teeth on the cog increases?

FIGURE FOR EXERCISE 61

GRAPHING CALCULATOR EXERCISES

62. To see the difference between direct and inverse variation, graph $y_1 = 2x$ and $y_2 = \frac{2}{x}$ using $0 \le x \le 5$ and $0 \le y \le 10$. Which of these functions is increasing and which is decreasing?

63. Graph $y_1 = 2\sqrt{x}$ and $y_2 = \frac{2}{\sqrt{x}}$ by using $0 \le x \le 5$ and $0 \le y \le 10$. At what point in the first quadrant do the curves cross? Which function is increasing and which is decreasing? Which represents direct variation and which represents inverse variation?

COLLABORATIVE ACTIVITIES

Life's a Function of What?

Suppose that alertness is a function of the number of cups of coffee consumed. Let x (the independent variable) represent the number of cups of coffee consumed in a morning and y (the dependent variable) represent alertness (as a percent). Suppose an average coffee drinker drinks between 0 and 5 cups in a morning. Let's say that a person is 20% alert for 0 cups and 100% alert for 5 cups. Then the domain is the interval [0, 5] and the range is [0, 1].

If our function is linear, we need only two points to draw its graph. Plot the pairs (0, 0.2) and (5, 1), and draw a line through them.

Grouping: Three students per group

Topic: Functions, dependence, domain, and range

Find the slope of the line through (5, 1) and (0, 0.2):

$$m = \frac{1 - 0.2}{5 - 0} = \frac{0.8}{5} = 0.16$$

Using slope-intercept form the equation is $y = 0.16x + 0.2$. So the linear function that gives alertness in terms of cups of coffee is $f(x) = 0.16x + 0.2$.

In your groups do the following:

1. Decide on something in your life that could be modeled by a function of one variable.

2. Determine the domain and range of your function using interval notation.

3. Find two points that would make sense in your function. Graph a line through these points.
4. Find a linear equation for your graph. Write it in function notation.
5. Trade with a group near you and add, subtract, multiply, divide, and compose your functions. Discuss in your groups if these operations make sense for your functions. What would need to be true for composition to make sense? Write down the things your group discovers about operations on functions.
6. Assuming that your function is nonlinear, plot at least four points that you think would be in your function. Use the different regression programs on a graphing calculator to find the function that fits your data points the best.

WRAP-UP   CHAPTER 9

SUMMARY

Types of Functions

		Examples
Linear function	$y = mx + b$ or $f(x) = mx + b$ for $m \neq 0$ Domain $(-\infty, \infty)$, range $(-\infty, \infty)$ If $m = 0$, $y = b$ is a constant function. Domain $(-\infty, \infty)$, range $\{b\}$	$f(x) = 2x - 3$
Absolute value function	$y = |x|$ or $f(x) = |x|$ Domain $(-\infty, \infty)$, range $[0, \infty)$	$f(x) = |x + 5|$
Quadratic function	$f(x) = ax^2 + bx + c$ for $a \neq 0$	$f(x) = x^2 - 4x + 3$
Square-root function	$f(x) = \sqrt{x}$ Domain $[0, \infty)$, range $[0, \infty)$	$f(x) = \sqrt{x - 4}$

Transformations of Graphs

Reflecting	The graph of $y = -f(x)$ is a reflection in the x-axis of the graph of $y = f(x)$.	The graph of $y = -x^2$ is a reflection of the graph of $y = x^2$.
Translating	If $k > 0$, the graph of $y = f(x) + k$ is k units above $y = f(x)$ and $y = f(x) - k$ is k units below $y = f(x)$. If $h > 0$, the graph of $y = f(x - h)$ is h units to the right of $y = f(x)$ and $y = f(x + h)$ is h units to the left of $y = f(x)$.	The graph of $y = x^2 + 3$ is three units above $y = x^2$, and $y = x^2 - 3$ is three units below $y = x^2$. The graph of $y = (x - 3)^2$ is three units to the right of $y = x^2$, and $y = (x + 3)^2$ is three units to the left.

Stretching and shrinking	The graph of $y = af(x)$ is obtained by stretching (if $a > 1$) or shrinking (if $0 < a < 1$) the graph of $y = f(x)$.	The graph of $y = 5x^2$ is obtained by stretching $y = x^2$, and $y = 0.1x^2$ is obtained by shrinking $y = x^2$.

Combining Functions

Examples

Sum	$(f + g)(x) = f(x) + g(x)$	For $f(x) = x^2$ and $g(x) = x + 1$ $(f + g)(x) = x^2 + x + 1$
Difference	$(f - g)(x) = f(x) - g(x)$	$(f - g)(x) = x^2 - x - 1$
Product	$(f \cdot g)(x) = f(x) \cdot g(x)$	$(f \cdot g)(x) = x^3 + x^2$
Quotient	$\left(\dfrac{f}{g}\right)(x) = \dfrac{f(x)}{g(x)}$	$\left(\dfrac{f}{g}\right)(x) = \dfrac{x^2}{x + 1}$
Composition of functions	$(g \circ f)(x) = g(f(x))$ $(f \circ g)(x) = f(g(x))$	$(g \circ f)(x) = g(x^2) = x^2 + 1$ $(f \circ g)(x) = f(x + 1)$ $\qquad = x^2 + 2x + 1$

Inverse Functions

Examples

One-to-one function	A function in which no two ordered pairs have different x-coordinates and the same y-coordinate.	$f = \{(2, 20), (3, 30)\}$
Inverse function	The inverse of a one-to-one function f is the function f^{-1}, which is obtained from f by interchanging the coordinates in each ordered pair of f. The domain of f^{-1} is the range of f, and the range of f^{-1} is the domain of f.	$f^{-1} = \{(20, 2), (30, 3)\}$
Horizontal-line test	If there is a horizontal line that crosses the graph of a function more than once, then the function is not invertible.	
Function notation for inverse	Two functions f and g are inverses of each other if and only if both of the following conditions are met. 1. $(g \circ f)(x) = x$ for every number x in the domain of f. 2. $(f \circ g)(x) = x$ for every number x in the domain of g.	$f(x) = x^3 + 1$ $f^{-1}(x) = \sqrt[3]{x - 1}$
Switch-and-solve strategy for finding f^{-1}	1. Replace $f(x)$ by y. 2. Interchange x and y. 3. Solve for y. 4. Replace y by $f^{-1}(x)$.	$y = x^3 + 1$ $x = y^3 + 1$ $x - 1 = y^3$ $y = \sqrt[3]{x - 1}$ $f^{-1}(x) = \sqrt[3]{x - 1}$
Graphs of f and f^{-1}	Graphs of inverse functions are symmetric with respect to the line $y = x$.	

The Language of Variation

		Examples
Direct	y varies directly as x, $y = kx$	$z = 5m$
Inverse	y varies inversely as x, $y = \dfrac{k}{x}$	$a = \dfrac{1}{c}$
Joint	y varies jointly as x and z, $y = kxz$	$V = 6LW$
Combined	y varies directly as x and inversely as z, $y = \dfrac{kx}{z}$	$S = \dfrac{3A}{B}$

ENRICHING YOUR MATHEMATICAL WORD POWER

For each mathematical term, choose the correct meaning.

1. **composition of f and g**
   a. the function $f \circ g$ where $(f \circ g)(x) = f(g(x))$
   b. the function $f \circ g$ where $(f \circ g)(x) = g(f(x))$
   c. the function $f \cdot g$ where $(f \cdot g)(x) = f(x) \cdot g(x)$
   d. a diagram showing f and g

2. **sum of f and g**
   a. the function $f \cdot g$ where $(f \cdot g)(x) = f(x) \cdot g(x)$
   b. the function $f + g$ where $(f + g)(x) = f(x) + g(x)$
   c. the function $f \circ g$ where $(f \circ g)(x) = g(f(x))$
   d. the function obtained by adding the domains of f and g

3. **inverse of the function f**
   a. a function with the same ordered pairs as f
   b. the opposite of the function f
   c. the function $1/f$
   d. a function in which the ordered pairs of f are reversed

4. **one-to-one function**
   a. a constant function
   b. a function that pairs 1 with 1
   c. a function in which no two ordered pairs have the same first coordinate and different second coordinates
   d. a function in which no two ordered pairs have the same second coordinate and different first coordinates

5. **vertical-line test**
   a. a visual method for determining whether a graph is a graph of a function
   b. a visual method for determining whether a function is one-to-one
   c. using a vertical line to check a graph
   d. a test on vertical lines

6. **horizontal-line test**
   a. a test that horizontal lines must pass
   b. a visual method for determining whether a function is one-to-one

   c. a graph that does not cross the x-axis
   d. a visual method for determining whether a graph is a graph of a function

7. **proportionality constant**
   a. a direct variation
   b. a constant proportion
   c. a ratio that is constant
   d. the constant k in $y = kx$

8. **y varies directly as x**
   a. $y = kx^2$ where k is a constant
   b. $y = mx + b$ where m and b are nonzero constants
   c. $y = kx$ where k is a nonzero constant
   d. $y = k/x$ where k is a nonzero constant

9. **y varies inversely as x**
   a. $y = x/k$ where k is a nonzero constant
   b. $y = -x$
   c. $y = kx$ where k is a nonzero constant
   d. $y = k/x$ where k is a nonzero constant

10. **reflection in the x-axis**
    a. the graph of $y = f(-x)$
    b. the graph of $y = -f(x)$
    c. the graph of $y = -f(-x)$
    d. the line of symmetry

11. **upward translation**
    a. the graph of $y = f(x) + c$ for $c > 0$
    b. the graph of $y = f(x + c)$ for $c < 0$
    c. the graph of $y = f(x - c)$ for $c > 0$
    d. the graph of $y = f(x) + c$ for $c < 0$

12. **translation to the left**
    a. the graph of $y = f(x) - c$ for $c > 0$
    b. the graph of $y = f(x) + c$ for $c > 0$
    c. the graph of $y = f(x - c)$ for $c > 0$
    d. the graph of $y = f(x + c)$ for $c > 0$

9.1 *Graph each function and state the domain and range.*

1. $f(x) = 3x - 4$

2. $y = 0.3x$

3. $h(x) = |x| - 2$

4. $y = |x - 2|$

5. $y = x^2 - 2x + 1$

6. $g(x) = x^2 - 2x - 15$

7. $k(x) = \sqrt{x} + 2$

8. $y = \sqrt{x - 2}$

9. $y = 30 - x^2$

10. $y = 4 - x^2$

Graph each relation and state its domain and range.

11. $x = 2$

12. $x = y^2 - 1$

13. $x = |y| + 1$

14. $x = \sqrt{y - 1}$

9.2 *Sketch the graph of each function.*

15. $y = \sqrt{x}$

16. $y = -\sqrt{x}$

17. $y = -2\sqrt{x}$

18. $y = 2\sqrt{x}$

19. $y = \sqrt{x - 2}$

20. $y = \sqrt{x + 2}$

21. $y = \frac{1}{2}\sqrt{x}$

22. $y = \sqrt{x - 1} + 2$

23. $y = -\sqrt{x + 1} + 3$

24. $y = 3\sqrt{x + 4} - 5$

47. $g(x) = 13x - 6$

48. $h(x) = \sqrt[3]{x - 6}$

49. $j(x) = \dfrac{x + 1}{x - 1}$

50. $k(x) = |x| + 7$

51. $m(x) = (x - 1)^2$

52. $n(x) = \dfrac{3}{x}$

Find the inverse of each function, and graph f and f^{-1} on the same pair of axes.

53. $f(x) = 3x - 1$

54. $f(x) = 2 - x^2$ for $x \geq 0$

9.3 *Let* $f(x) = 3x + 5$, $g(x) = x^2 - 2x$, *and* $h(x) = \dfrac{x - 5}{3}$.
Find the following.

25. $f(-3)$

26. $h(-4)$

27. $(h \circ f)(\sqrt{2})$

28. $(f \circ h)(\pi)$

29. $(g \circ f)(2)$

30. $(g \circ f)(x)$

31. $(f + g)(3)$

32. $(f - g)(x)$

33. $(f \cdot g)(x)$

34. $\left(\dfrac{f}{g}\right)(1)$

35. $(f \circ f)(0)$

36. $(f \circ f)(x)$

55. $f(x) = \dfrac{x^3}{2}$

56. $f(x) = -\dfrac{1}{4}x$

Let $f(x) = |x|$, $g(x) = x + 2$, and $h(x) = x^2$. Write each of the following functions as a composition of functions, using f, g, or h.

37. $F(x) = |x + 2|$

38. $G(x) = |x| + 2$

39. $H(x) = x^2 + 2$

40. $K(x) = x^2 + 4x + 4$

41. $I(x) = x + 4$

42. $J(x) = x^4 + 2$

9.4 *Determine whether each function is invertible. If it is invertible, find the inverse.*

43. $\{(-2, 4), (2, 4)\}$

44. $\{(1, 1), (3, 3)\}$

45. $f(x) = 8x$

46. $i(x) = -\dfrac{x}{3}$

9.5 *Solve each variation problem.*

57. If y varies directly as m and $y = -3$ when $m = \frac{1}{4}$, find y when $m = -2$.

58. If a varies inversely as b and $a = 6$ when $b = -3$, find a when $b = 4$.

59. If c varies directly as m and inversely as n, and $c = 20$ when $m = 10$ and $n = 4$, find c when $m = 6$ and $n = -3$.

60. If V varies jointly as h and the square of r, and $V = 32$ when $h = 6$ and $r = 3$, find V when $h = 3$ and $r = 4$.

MISCELLANEOUS

61. *Falling object.* If a ball is dropped from a tall building, then the distance traveled by the ball in t seconds varies directly as the square of the time t. If the ball travels 144 feet (ft) in 3 seconds, then how far does it travel in 4 seconds?

62. *Studying or partying.* Evelyn's grade on a math test varies directly with the number of hours spent studying and inversely with the number of hours spent partying during the 24 hours preceding the test. If she scored a 90 on a test after she studied 10 hours and partied 2 hours, then what should she score after studying 4 hours and partying 6 hours?

63. *Inscribed square.* Given that B is the area of a square inscribed in a circle of radius r and area A, write B as a function of A.

64. *Area of a window.* A window is in the shape of a square of side s, with a semicircle of diameter s above it. Write a function that expresses the total area of the window as a function of s.

65. *Composition of functions.* Given that $a = 3k + 2$ and $k = 5w - 6$, write a as a function of w.

66. *Volume of a cylinder.* The volume of a cylinder with a fixed height of 10 centimeters (cm) is given by $V = 10\pi r^2$,

FIGURE FOR EXERCISE 64

where r is the radius of the circular base. Write the volume as a function of the area of the base, A.

67. *Square formulas.* Write the area of a square A as a function of the length of a side of the square s. Write the length of a side of a square as a function of the area.

68. *Circle formulas.* Write the area of a circle A as a function of the radius of the circle r. Write the radius of a circle as a function of the area of the circle. Write the area as a function of the diameter d.

CHAPTER 9 TEST

Sketch the graph of each function or relation.

1. $f(x) = -\dfrac{2}{3}x + 1$

2. $y = |x| - 4$

3. $g(x) = x^2 + 2x - 8$

4. $x = y^2$

5. $y = -|x - 2|$

6. $y = \sqrt{x + 5} - 2$

Let $f(x) = -2x + 5$ *and* $g(x) = x^2 + 4$. *Find the following.*

7. $f(-3)$

8. $(g \circ f)(-3)$

9. $f^{-1}(11)$

10. $f^{-1}(x)$

11. $(g + f)(x)$

12. $(f \cdot g)(1)$

13. $(f^{-1} \circ f)(1776)$

14. $(f/g)(2)$

15. $(f \circ g)(x)$

16. $(g \circ f)(x)$

Let $f(x) = x - 7$ *and* $g(x) = x^2$. *Write each of the following functions as a composition of functions using f and g.*

17. $H(x) = x^2 - 7$

18. $W(x) = x^2 - 14x + 49$

Determine whether each function is invertible. If it is invertible, find the inverse.

19. $\{(2, 3), (4, 3)\}$

20. $f(x) = \sqrt[3]{x} + 9$

Solve each problem.

21. Find the domain and range of the function $f(x) = |x|$.

22. Find the inverse of $f(x) = \frac{2x + 1}{x - 1}$.

23. The volume of a sphere varies directly as the cube of the radius. If a sphere with radius 3 feet (ft) has a volume of 36π cubic feet (ft^3), then what is the volume of a sphere with a radius of 2 ft?

24. Suppose y varies directly as x and inversely as the square root of z. If $y = 12$ when $x = 7$ and $z = 9$, then what is the proportionality constant?

25. The cost of a Persian rug varies jointly as the length and width of the rug. If the cost is $2256 for a 6 foot by 8 foot rug, then what is the cost of a 9 foot by 12 foot rug?

Simplify each expression.

1. $125^{-2/3}$

2. $\left(\dfrac{8}{27}\right)^{-1/3}$

3. $\sqrt{18} - \sqrt{8}$

4. $x^5 \cdot x^3$

5. $16^{1/4}$

6. $\dfrac{x^{12}}{x^3}$

Find the real solution set to each equation.

7. $x^2 = 9$

8. $x^2 = 8$

9. $x^2 = x$

10. $x^2 - 4x - 6 = 0$

11. $x^{1/4} = 3$

12. $x^{1/6} = -2$

13. $|x| = 8$

14. $|5x - 4| = 21$

15. $x^3 = 8$

16. $(3x - 2)^3 = 27$

17. $\sqrt{2x - 3} = 9$

18. $\sqrt{x - 2} = x - 8$

Sketch the graph of each set.

19. $\{(x, y) \mid y = 5\}$

20. $\{(x, y) \mid y = 2x - 5\}$

21. $\{(x, y) \mid x = 5\}$

22. $\{(x, y) \mid 3y = x\}$

23. $\{(x, y) \mid y = 5x^2\}$

24. $\{(x, y) \mid y = -2x^2\}$

Find the missing coordinates in each ordered pair so that the ordered pair satisfies the given equation.

25. $(2, \ ), (3, \ ), (\ , 2), (\ , 16), \quad 2^x = y$

26. $\left(\dfrac{1}{2}, \ \right), (-1, \ ), (\ , 16), (\ , 1), \quad 4^x = y$

Find the domain of each expression.

27. $\sqrt{x}$

28. $\sqrt{6 - 2x}$

29. $\dfrac{5x - 3}{x^2 + 1}$

30. $\dfrac{x - 3}{x^2 - 10x + 9}$

Solve each problem.

31. *Capital cost and operating cost.* To decide when to replace company cars, an accountant looks at two cost components: capital cost and operating cost. The capital cost C (the difference between the original cost and the salvage value) for a certain car is $3000 plus $0.12 for each mile that the car is driven.

  a) Write the capital cost C as a linear function of x, the number of miles that the car is driven.

FIGURE FOR EXERCISE 31(a)

b) The operating cost P is \$0.15 per mile initially and increases linearly to \$0.25 per mile when the car reaches 100,000 miles. Write P as a function of x, the number of miles that the car is driven.

FIGURE FOR EXERCISE 31(b)

32. ***Total cost.*** The accountant in the previous exercise uses the function $T = \dfrac{C}{x} + P$ to find the total cost per mile.

a) Find T for $x = 20{,}000$, $30{,}000$, and $90{,}000$.

b) Sketch a graph of the total cost function.

c) The accountant has decided to replace the car when T reaches \$0.38 for the second time. At what mileage will the car be replaced?

d) For what values of x is T less than or equal to \$0.38?

Polynomial and Rational Functions

New products are coming to market daily. Television ads are constantly touting the features and benefits of new exercise devices, diets, can openers, bag sealers, vacuum cleaners, cars, trucks, drugs, makeup, toothpaste, and so on. By some estimates 90% of new products are failures. But how can products fail to make money? The answer to that question lies in the tremendous cost of research, development, manufacturing, distribution, and advertising.

It now takes an average of 14.8 years and $350 million to get a new drug to market. However, the payoff can be quick and tremendous. At around $9 per pill sales of a new miracle drug can top $1 billion in the first year.

Mercedes-Benz introduced a new sport utility vehicle in 1998 that took 5 years to design. Mercedes-Benz spent $700 million on design, $300 million to build the Alabama plant for manufacturing the SUV, $400 million to design the engine, and $450 million to construct a plant for making the engine—not to mention the cost of manufacturing each car. Mercedes-Benz expects to sell 40,000 of these vehicles the first year at around $35,000 each. Making a profit will take a while.

For any product, profits are made when the average cost of the product is below the price at which the company sells the product. In Exercises 55 and 56 of Section 10.5 we will see how rational functions can be used to model average cost.

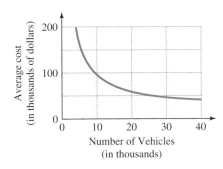

10.1 THE FACTOR THEOREM

We have worked with polynomials on many occassions in this text. In this section we study functions defined by polynomials and learn to solve some higher-degree polynomial equations.

The Factor Theorem

If a polynomial is used to define a function, then the function is called a **polynomial function.** For example, the functions

$$m(x) = 2, \quad n(x) = 3x - 6, \quad h(x) = 5x^2 - 2x + 6, \quad \text{and} \quad j(x) = x^3$$

are polynomial functions. The degree of a polynomial function is the degree of the polynomial used to define it. The polynomials m, n, h, and j have degrees 0, 1, 2, and 3, respectively. If $f(c) = 0$, then c is called a **root** or **zero** of the function f.

Consider the polynomial function $P(x) = x^2 + 2x - 15$. We can find the zeros of the function by solving the equation $P(x) = 0$:

$$x^2 + 2x - 15 = 0$$
$$(x + 5)(x - 3) = 0$$
$$x + 5 = 0 \quad \text{or} \quad x - 3 = 0$$
$$x = -5 \quad \text{or} \quad x = 3$$

Helpful Hint

Note that the zeros of the polynomial function are factors of the constant term 15.

Because $x + 5$ is a factor of $x^2 + 2x - 15$, -5 is a solution to the equation $x^2 + 2x - 15 = 0$ and a zero of the function $P(x) = x^2 + 2x - 15$. We can check that -5 is a zero of $P(x) = x^2 + 2x - 15$ as follows:

$$P(-5) = (-5)^2 + 2(-5) - 15$$
$$= 25 - 10 - 15$$
$$= 0$$

Because $x - 3$ is a factor of the polynomial, 3 is also a solution to the equation $x^2 + 2x - 15 = 0$ and a zero of the polynomial function. Check that $P(3) = 0$:

$$P(3) = 3^2 + 2 \cdot 3 - 15$$
$$= 9 + 6 - 15$$
$$= 0$$

Every linear factor of the polynomial corresponds to a zero of the polynomial function, and every zero of the polynomial function corresponds to a linear factor. Now suppose $P(x)$ represents an arbitrary polynomial. If $x - c$ is a factor of the polynomial $P(x)$, then c is a solution to the equation $P(x) = 0$, and so $P(c) = 0$. If we divide $P(x)$ by $x - c$ and the remainder is 0, we must have

$$P(x) = (x - c)(\text{quotient}). \quad \text{Dividend equals the divisor times the quotient.}$$

If the remainder is 0, then $x - c$ is a factor of $P(x)$.
The **factor theorem** summarizes these ideas.

The Factor Theorem

The following statements are equivalent for any polynomial $P(x)$.

1. The remainder is zero when $P(x)$ is divided by $x - c$.
2. $x - c$ is a factor of $P(x)$.
3. c is a solution to $P(x) = 0$.
4. c is a zero of the function $P(x)$, or $P(c) = 0$.

To say that statements are equivalent means that the truth of any one of them implies that the others are true.

According to the factor theorem, if we want to determine whether a given number c is a zero of a polynomial function, we can divide the polynomial by $x - c$. The remainder is zero if and only if c is a zero of the polynomial function. The quickest way to divide by $x - c$ is to use synthetic division from Section 6.5.

E X A M P L E   1

Calculator Close-Up

You can perform the multiply-and-add steps for synthetic division with a graphing calculator as shown here.

```
Ans*2+-3        1
               -1
Ans*2+5
                3
Ans*2+-2
                4
```

Using the factor theorem

Use synthetic division to determine whether 2 is a zero of $P(x) = x^3 - 3x^2 + 5x - 2$.

Solution

By the factor theorem, 2 is a zero of the function if and only if the remainder is zero when $P(x)$ is divided by $x - 2$. We can use synthetic division to determine the remainder. If we divide by $x - 2$, we use 2 on the left in synthetic division along with the coefficients $1, -3, 5, -2$ from the polynomial:

$$
\begin{array}{r|rrrr}
2 & 1 & -3 & 5 & -2 \\
  &   & 2 & -2 & 6 \\
\hline
  & 1 & -1 & 3 & 4
\end{array}
$$

Because the remainder is 4, 2 is not a zero of the function. ■

E X A M P L E   2

Using the factor theorem

Use synthetic division to determine whether -4 is a solution to the equation $2x^4 - 28x^2 + 14x - 8 = 0$.

Solution

By the factor theorem, -4 is a solution to the equation if and only if the remainder is zero when $P(x)$ is divided by $x + 4$. When dividing by $x + 4$, we use -4 in the synthetic division:

$$
\begin{array}{r|rrrrr}
-4 & 2 & 0 & -28 & 14 & -8 \\
   &   & -8 & 32 & -16 & 8 \\
\hline
   & 2 & -8 & 4 & -2 & 0
\end{array}
$$

Because the remainder is zero, -4 is a solution to $2x^4 - 28x^2 + 14x - 8 = 0$. ■

In Example 3 we use the factor theorem to determine whether a given binomial is a factor of a polynomial.

E X A M P L E   3

Using the factor theorem

Use synthetic division to determine whether $x + 4$ is a factor of $x^3 + 3x^2 + 16$.

Solution

According to the factor theorem, $x + 4$ is a factor of $x^3 + 3x^2 + 16$ if and only if the remainder is zero when the polynomial is divided by $x + 4$. Use synthetic division to determine the remainder:

$$
\begin{array}{r|rrrr}
-4 & 1 & 3 & 0 & 16 \\
   &   & -4 & 4 & -16 \\
\hline
   & 1 & -1 & 4 & 0
\end{array}
$$

Because the remainder is zero, $x + 4$ is a factor, and the polynomial can be written as

$$x^3 + 3x^2 + 16 = (x + 4)(x^2 - x + 4).$$

Because $x^2 - x + 4$ is a prime polynomial, the factoring is complete.   ■

Solving Polynomial Equations

The techniques used to solve polynomial equations of degree 3 or higher are not as straightforward as those used to solve linear equations and quadratic equations. The next example shows how the factor theorem can be used to solve a third-degree polynomial equation.

E X A M P L E   4   Solving a third-degree equation

Suppose the equation $x^3 - 4x^2 - 17x + 60 = 0$ is known to have a solution that is an integer between -3 and 3 inclusive. Find the solution set.

Helpful Hint

How did we know where to find a solution to the equation in Example 4? One way to get a good idea of where the solutions are is to graph

$$y = x^3 - 4x^2 - 17x + 60.$$

Every *x*-intercept on this graph corresponds to a solution to the equation.

Solution

Because one of the numbers -3, -2, -1, 0, 1, 2, and 3 is a solution to the equation, we can use synthetic division with these numbers until we discover which one is a solution. We arbitrarily select 1 to try first:

$$
\begin{array}{r|rrrr}
1 & 1 & -4 & -17 & 60 \\
  &   & 1 & -3 & -20 \\
\hline
  & 1 & -3 & -20 & 40
\end{array}
$$

Because the remainder is 40, 1 is not a solution to the equation. Next try 2:

$$
\begin{array}{r|rrrr}
2 & 1 & -4 & -17 & 60 \\
  &   & 2 & -4 & -42 \\
\hline
  & 1 & -2 & -21 & 18
\end{array}
$$

Because the remainder is not zero, 2 is not a solution to the equation. Next try 3:

$$
\begin{array}{r|rrrr}
3 & 1 & -4 & -17 & 60 \\
  &   & 3 & -3 & -60 \\
\hline
  & 1 & -1 & -20 & 0
\end{array}
$$

The remainder is zero, so 3 is a solution to the equation, and $x - 3$ is a factor of the polynomial. (If 3 had not produced a remainder of zero, then we would have tried -3, -2, -1, and 0.) The other factor is the quotient, $x^2 - x - 20$.

$$x^3 - 4x^2 - 17x + 60 = 0$$
$$(x - 3)(x^2 - x - 20) = 0 \quad \text{Use the results of synthetic division to factor.}$$
$$(x - 3)(x - 5)(x + 4) = 0 \quad \text{Factor completely.}$$
$$x - 3 = 0 \quad \text{or} \quad x - 5 = 0 \quad \text{or} \quad x + 4 = 0$$
$$x = 3 \quad \text{or} \quad x = 5 \quad \text{or} \quad x = -4$$

Check each of these solutions in the original equation. The solution set is $\{3, 5, -4\}$.   ■

WARM-UPS

True or false? Explain your answers.

1. To divide $x^3 - 4x^2 - 3$ by $x - 5$, use 5 in the synthetic division.

2. To divide $5x^4 - x^3 + x - 2$ by $x + 7$, use -7 in the synthetic division.

3. The number 2 is a zero of $P(x) = 3x^3 - 5x^2 - 2x + 2$.

4. If $x^3 - 8$ is divided by $x - 2$, then $R = 0$.

5. If $R = 0$ when $x^4 - 1$ is divided by $x - a$, then $x - a$ is a factor of $x^4 - 1$.

6. If -2 satisfies $x^4 + 8x = 0$, then $x + 2$ is a factor of $x^4 + 8x$.

7. The binomial $x - 1$ is a factor of $x^{35} - 3x^{24} + 2x^{18}$.

8. The binomial $x + 1$ is a factor of $x^3 - 3x^2 + x + 5$.

9. If $x^3 - 5x + 4$ is divided by $x - 1$, then $R = 0$.

10. If $R = 0$ when $P(x) = x^3 - 5x - 2$ is divided by $x + 2$, then $P(-2) = 0$.

10.1 EXERCISES

Reading and Writing   *After reading this section, write out the answers to these questions. Use complete sentences.*

1. What is a zero of a function?

2. What is a root of a function?

3. What does it mean that statements are equivalent?

4. What is the quickest way to divide a polynomial by $x - c$?

5. If the remainder is zero when you divide $P(x)$ by $x - c$, then what can you say about $P(c)$?

6. What are two ways to determine whether c is a zero of a polynomial?

Determine whether each given value of x is a zero of the given function. See Example 1.

7. $x = 1$, $P(x) = x^3 - x^2 + x - 1$

8. $x = -2$, $P(x) = -2x^3 - 5x^2 + 3x + 10$

9. $x = -3$, $P(x) = -x^4 - 3x^3 - 2x^2 + 18$

10. $x = 4$, $P(x) = x^4 - x^2 - 8x - 16$

11. $x = 2$, $P(x) = 2x^3 - 4x^2 - 5x + 9$

12. $x = -3$, $P(x) = x^3 + 5x^2 + 2x + 1$

Use synthetic division to determine whether each given value of x is a solution to the given equation. See Example 2.

13. $x = -3$, $x^3 + 5x^2 + 2x - 12 = 0$

14. $x = -5$, $x^2 - 3x - 40 = 0$

15. $x = -2$, $x^4 + 3x^3 - 5x^2 - 10x + 5 = 0$

16. $x = -3$, $-x^3 - 4x^2 + x + 12 = 0$

17. $x = 4$, $-2x^4 + 30x^2 + 5x + 12 = 0$

18. $x = 6$, $x^4 + x^3 - 40x^2 - 72 = 0$

19. $x = 3$, $0.8x^2 - 0.3x - 6.3 = 0$

20. $x = 5$, $6.2x^2 - 28.2x - 41.7 = 0$

Use synthetic division to determine whether the first polynomial is a factor of the second. If it is, then factor the polynomial completely. See Example 3.

21. $x - 3$, $x^3 - 6x - 9$

22. $x + 2$, $x^3 - 6x - 4$

23. $x + 5$, $x^3 + 9x^2 + 23x + 15$

24. $x - 3$, $x^4 - 9x^2 + x - 7$

25. $x - 2$, $x^3 - 8x^2 + 4x - 6$

26. $x + 5$, $x^3 + 125$

27. $x + 1$, $x^4 + x^3 - 8x - 8$

28. $x - 2$, $x^3 - 6x^2 + 12x - 8$

29. $x - 0.5$, $2x^3 - 3x^2 - 11x + 6$

30. $x - \dfrac{1}{3}$, $3x^3 - 10x^2 - 27x + 10$

Solve each equation, given that at least one of the solutions to each equation is an integer between -5 and 5. See Example 4.

31. $x^3 - 13x + 12 = 0$
32. $x^3 + 2x^2 - 5x - 6 = 0$

33. $2x^3 - 9x^2 + 7x + 6 = 0$

34. $6x^3 + 13x^2 - 4 = 0$

35. $2x^3 - 3x^2 - 50x - 24 = 0$

36. $x^3 - 7x^2 + 2x + 40 = 0$
37. $x^3 + 5x^2 + 3x - 9 = 0$
38. $x^3 + 6x^2 + 12x + 8 = 0$
39. $x^4 - 4x^3 + 3x^2 + 4x - 4 = 0$
40. $x^4 + x^3 - 7x^2 - x + 6 = 0$

GETTING MORE INVOLVED

 41. *Exploration.* We can find the zeros of a polynomial function by solving a polynomial equation. We can also work backward to find a polynomial function that has given zeros.

   a) Write a first-degree polynomial function whose zero is -2.

b) Write a second-degree polynomial function whose zeros are 5 and -5.

c) Write a third-degree polynomial function whose zeros are 1, -3, and 4.

d) Is there a polynomial function with any given number of zeros? What is its degree?

 ### GRAPHING CALCULATOR EXERCISES

42. The x-coordinate of each x-intercept on the graph of a polynomial function is a zero of the polynomial function. Find the zeros of each function from its graph. Use synthetic division to check that the zeros found on your calculator really are zeros of the function.
   a) $P(x) = x^3 - 2x^2 - 5x + 6$

   b) $P(x) = 12x^3 - 20x^2 + x + 3$

43. With a graphing calculator an equation can be solved without the kind of hint that was given for Exercises 31–40. Solve each of the following equations by examining the graph of a corresponding function. Use synthetic division to check.
   a) $x^3 - 4x^2 - 7x + 10 = 0$

   b) $8x^3 - 20x^2 - 18x + 45 = 0$

In This Section

 10.2

ZEROS OF A POLYNOMIAL FUNCTION

- The Remainder Theorem
- The Fundamental Theorem of Algebra
- The Rational Root Theorem

In this section we continue our study of zeros of polynomial functions, which we began in Section 10.1. An essential theorem in this regard is the remainder theorem, which was introduced in Section 6.5. For completeness we review and restate the remainder theorem here.

The Remainder Theorem

The factor theorem in Section 10.1 indicates what happens when a polynomial is divided by $x - c$ and the remainder is zero. The remainder theorem gives us more information about the remainder.

> **The Remainder Theorem**
>
> If R is the remainder when a polynomial $P(x)$ is divided by $x - c$, then $R = P(c)$.

E X A M P L E   1

Helpful Hint

If we only wanted the value of the function, we probably would not use synthetic division. We use synthetic division because it gives us the value of the polynomial, $f(c)$, and the quotient of division by $x - c$.

Calculator Close-Up

With a calculator you can evaluate a function by using Y= to define $y_1 = x^3 - 3x^2 + 5x - 12$.

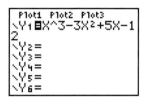

Then you can use the function variables to evaluate the function.

E X A M P L E   2

Calculator Close-Up

You can use a calculator to perform the arithmetic in synthetic division as shown here.

```
Ans*2
              -6
           -12
Ans*2+15
            -9
Ans*2+3
           -15
```

Evaluating a polynomial function

Let $f(x) = x^3$ and $g(x) = x^3 - 3x^2 + 5x - 12$. Use synthetic division to find the following function values.

a) $f(-2)$ b) $g(4)$

Solution

a) Use synthetic division to divide x^3 by $x + 2$ as follows:

$$
\begin{array}{r|rrrr}
-2 & 1 & 0 & 0 & 0 \\
   &   & -2 & 4 & -8 \\
\hline
   & 1 & -2 & 4 & -8
\end{array}
$$

The synthetic division shows that the quotient is $x^2 - 2x + 4$ and the remainder is -8. So $f(-2) = -8$. The answer is correct because $f(-2) = (-2)^3 = -8$.

b) Use synthetic division to divide $x^3 - 3x^2 + 5x - 12$ by $x - 4$ as follows:

$$
\begin{array}{r|rrrr}
4 & 1 & -3 & 5 & -12 \\
  &   & 4 & 4 & 36 \\
\hline
  & 1 & 1 & 9 & 24
\end{array}
$$

The synthetic division shows that the quotient is $x^2 + x + 9$ and the remainder is 24. So $g(4) = 24$. We can check this answer by evaluating the polynomial $x^3 - 3x^2 + 5x - 12$ for $x = 4$. We get $4^3 - 3(4^2) + 5(4) - 12 = 24$. ■

Note that we now have two different ways to find the value of a polynomial $P(x)$ when $x = c$. We can find the remainder when the polynomial is divided by $x - c$, or we can evaluate the polynomial by using c in place of x. In Example 1(a) it is easier to find $(-2)^3$ than to do synthetic division to get $f(-2) = -8$. In Example 1(b) synthetic division is easier because there are fewer arithmetic operations in the synthetic division than in evaluating the polynomial. For polynomials of higher degree there may be an even bigger difference between the number of operations in evaluating the polynomial and finding the remainder of synthetic division.

In Example 2 we use synthetic division and the remainder theorem to determine whether a given number is a zero to a polynomial function.

Zeros of polynomial functions

Determine whether each given number is a zero of the polynomial function following the number.

a) $2, f(x) = -6x^3 + 15x + 3$ b) $-2, g(x) = x^4 - 3x^3 + 5x^2 - 6x - 72$

Solution

a) Use synthetic division to find $f(2)$ as follows:

$$
\begin{array}{r|rrrr}
2 & -6 & 0 & 15 & 3 \\
  &   & -12 & -24 & -18 \\
\hline
  & -6 & -12 & -9 & -15
\end{array}
$$

So $f(2) = -15$, and 2 is not a zero of the polynomial function.

b) Use synthetic division to find $g(-2)$ as follows:

$$
\begin{array}{r|rrrrr}
-2 & 1 & -3 & 5 & -6 & -72 \\
   &   & -2 & 10 & -30 & 72 \\
\hline
   & 1 & -5 & 15 & -36 & 0
\end{array}
$$

So $g(-2) = 0$, and -2 is a zero of the polynomial function. ■

CAUTION   To evaluate a polynomial for $x = -2$, use -2 in synthetic division just as we use -2 in place of x in the polynomial. If -2 is a zero of the polynomial, then $x - (-2)$ or $x + 2$ is a factor of the polynomial. Note that if $x + 2 = 0$, then $x = -2$.

The Fundamental Theorem of Algebra

It is easy to determine whether a number is a zero of a polynomial function. But does every polynomial function have a zero? The answer comes from a theorem that is extremely important in algebra, the fundamental theorem of algebra.

> ### The Fundamental Theorem of Algebra
>
> If $P(x)$ is a polynomial function of positive degree, then $P(x)$ has at least one zero in the set of complex numbers.

Note that a polynomial function of zero degree might not have any zeros. For example, $P(x) = 7$ has no zeros. We already know how to find the zeros of many polynomial functions.

EXAMPLE 3

Finding all zeros of a polynomial function

Find all real and imaginary zeros of each polynomial function.

a) $f(x) = 3x - 5$

b) $g(x) = x^3 - 3x^2 + 4x - 12$

Solution

a) To find the zeros of the function, we solve the equation $3x - 5 = 0$:

$$3x - 5 = 0$$
$$3x = 5$$
$$x = \frac{5}{3}$$

The only zero of the function $f(x) = 3x - 5$ is $\frac{5}{3}$.

b) To find the zeros of the function, we solve $x^3 - 3x^2 + 4x - 12 = 0$:

$$x^3 - 3x^2 + 4x - 12 = 0$$
$$x^2(x - 3) + 4(x - 3) = 0$$
$$(x^2 + 4)(x - 3) = 0$$

$$x^2 + 4 = 0 \qquad \text{or} \qquad x - 3 = 0$$
$$x^2 = -4 \qquad \text{or} \qquad x = 3$$
$$x = \pm 2i \qquad \text{or} \qquad x = 3$$

The zeros of g are $-2i$, $2i$, and 3. ∎

Calculator Close-Up

The zeros of a function correspond to the x-intercepts on the graph of the function. With a graphing calculator you can check numerically and graphically that $\frac{5}{3}$ is a zero of $f(x) = 3x - 5$.

The Rational Root Theorem

We can find the zeros of any first-degree polynomial function because we can solve any linear equation. We can find the zeros of any second-degree polynomial function because we can solve any quadratic equation. Keep in mind that the zeros of a

Calculator Close-Up

The zeros of a function correspond to the *x*-intercepts on the graph of the function. Because this function has only one real zero, its graph has only one *x*-intercept.

function $P(x)$ are exactly the same as the solutions to the equation $P(x) = 0$. In Example 2(b) we found the zeros of a third-degree polynomial function, but it is generally not so easy to factor a third- or higher-degree polynomial. The rational root theorem describes the rational zeros of a polynomial function.

The Rational Root Theorem

If $P(x) = a_n x^n + a_{n-1} x^{n-1} + a_{n-2} x^{n-2} + \cdots + a_1 x + a_0$ is a polynomial function with integral coefficients ($a_n \neq 0$ and $a_0 \neq 0$) and p/q (in its lowest terms) is a rational zero of $P(x)$, then p is a factor of the constant term a_0, and q is a factor of the leading coefficient a_n.

To understand the rational root theorem, consider the quadratic function $P(x) = 6x^2 - x - 12$. We find the zeros of the function as follows:

$$6x^2 - x - 12 = 0$$
$$(2x - 3)(3x + 4) = 0$$
$$2x - 3 = 0 \quad \text{or} \quad 3x + 4 = 0$$
$$2x = 3 \quad \text{or} \quad 3x = -4$$
$$x = \frac{3}{2} \quad \text{or} \quad x = -\frac{4}{3}$$

The solutions to the equation are $\frac{3}{2}$ and $-\frac{4}{3}$. For the zero $\frac{3}{2}$, notice that 3 is a factor of 12 and 2 is a factor of 6. For the zero $-\frac{4}{3}$, notice that 4 is a factor 12 and 3 is a factor of 6. Of course, these observations are not surprising since we used these facts to factor the quadratic polynomial in the first place. Note that there are a lot of other factors of 12 and 6 for which the ratio is not a zero of this function because a quadratic function has at most two distinct zeros. The rational root theorem does not identify exactly which numbers are zeros of a function, it only gives the possibilities for the rational zeros.

E X A M P L E   4

Finding possible rational zeros

Find all possible rational zeros for each polynomial function.

a) $f(x) = 2x^3 - 3x^2 - 11x + 6$

b) $g(x) = 3x^3 - 8x^2 - 8x + 8$

Helpful Hint

Remember that the rational numbers listed here are only possibilities for the rational roots. There might not be any rational roots.

Solution

a) If the rational number p/q is a zero of $f(x)$, then p must be a factor of 6 and q must be a factor of 2. The factors of 6 are 1, 2, 3, and 6. The factors of 2 are 1 and 2. For simplicity we have listed only the positive factors. If we take each factor of 6 and divide by 1, we get $\frac{1}{1}, \frac{2}{1}, \frac{3}{1}$, and $\frac{6}{1}$. If we take each factor of 6 and divide by 2, we get $\frac{1}{2}, \frac{2}{2}, \frac{3}{2}$, and $\frac{6}{2}$. Simplify the ratios, eliminate duplications, and put in the negative factors to get

$$\pm 1, \quad \pm 2, \quad \pm 3, \quad \pm 6, \quad \pm\frac{1}{2}, \quad \text{and} \quad \pm\frac{3}{2}$$

as the possible rational zeros to the function $f(x)$.

b) If the rational number p/q is a zero of $g(x)$, then p must be a factor of 8 and q must be a factor of 3. The factors of 8 are 1, 2, 4, and 8. The factors of 3 are 1 and 3. If we take all possible ratios of a factor of 8 over a factor of 3, we get

$$\pm 1, \quad \pm 2, \quad \pm 4, \quad \pm 8, \quad \pm\frac{1}{3}, \quad \pm\frac{2}{3}, \quad \pm\frac{4}{3}, \quad \text{and} \quad \pm\frac{8}{3}$$

as the possible rational zeros of the function $g(x)$.   ■

A polynomial function might or might not have any rational zeros, but with the rational root theorem we have a place to start in the problem of finding all of the zeros of a polynomial function. Synthetic division is used to determine whether a possible rational zero is actually a zero of the function.

E X A M P L E   5   **Finding all zeros of a polynomial function**

Find all of the real and imaginary zeros for each polynomial function of Example 4.

a) $f(x) = 2x^3 - 3x^2 - 11x + 6$

b) $g(x) = 3x^3 - 8x^2 - 8x + 8$

Solution

a) The possible rational zeros are listed in Example 4(a) for the function $f(x)$. Now use synthetic division to check each possible zero to see whether it is actually a zero. Try $\frac{1}{2}$ first. (If $\frac{1}{2}$ does not produce a remainder of 0, then we would try another number from the list of possible rational zeros.)

$$\begin{array}{r|rrrr} \frac{1}{2} & 2 & -3 & -11 & 6 \\ & & 1 & -1 & -6 \\ \hline & 2 & -2 & -12 & 0 \end{array}$$

Since the remainder is 0, the remainder theorem indicates that $\frac{1}{2}$ is a zero of the function and a root of the equation $2x^3 - 3x^2 - 11x + 6 = 0$. By the factor theorem, $x - \frac{1}{2}$ is a factor of the polynomial, and the other factor is the quotient:

$$2x^3 - 3x^2 - 11x + 6 = 0$$
$$\left(x - \frac{1}{2}\right)(2x^2 - 2x - 12) = 0$$
$$(2x - 1)(x^2 - x - 6) = 0$$
$$(2x - 1)(x - 3)(x + 2) = 0$$

$$2x - 1 = 0 \quad \text{or} \quad x - 3 = 0 \quad \text{or} \quad x + 2 = 0$$

$$x = \frac{1}{2} \quad \text{or} \quad x = 3 \quad \text{or} \quad x = -2$$

The zeros of the function f are $\frac{1}{2}$, 3, and -2.

b) We listed the possible rational roots in Example 4(b) for the function $g(x)$. We will first check $\frac{2}{3}$ to see whether it produces a remainder of 0:

$$\begin{array}{r|rrrr} \frac{2}{3} & 3 & -8 & -8 & 8 \\ & & 2 & -4 & -8 \\ \hline & 3 & -6 & -12 & 0 \end{array}$$

Calculator Close-Up

Note how the graph of the function supports the solutions obtained algebraically. When the function is evaluated at $1 + \sqrt{5}$, or approximately 3.236068, the calculator does not get exactly 0 because it cannot perform this computation exactly. However, the answer 2×10^{-12} is very close to 0.

Since the remainder is 0, by the remainder theorem $\frac{2}{3}$ is a zero of the function and a root of the equation $3x^3 - 8x^2 - 8x + 8 = 0$. By the factor theorem we know that $x - \frac{2}{3}$ is a factor of the polynomial and the quotient is the other factor:

$$3x^3 - 8x^2 - 8x + 8 = 0$$

$$\left(x - \frac{2}{3}\right)(3x^2 - 6x - 12) = 0$$

$$(3x - 2)(x^2 - 2x - 4) = 0$$

$$3x - 2 = 0 \quad \text{or} \quad x^2 - 2x - 4 = 0$$

$$x = \frac{2}{3} \quad \text{or} \quad x = \frac{2 \pm \sqrt{20}}{2}$$

$$x = \frac{2}{3} \quad \text{or} \quad x = 1 \pm \sqrt{5}$$

There is one rational root and two irrational roots to the equation. So the zeros of the function $g(x)$ are $\frac{2}{3}$, $1 + \sqrt{5}$, and $1 - \sqrt{5}$. ∎

Note that in Example 5(a) all of the zeros were rational. We could have found all three by continuing to check the possible rational roots using synthetic division. In Example 5(b) we would be wasting time if we continued to check the possible rational roots because there is only one. When we get to the point in the equation at which one of the factors of the polynomial is a quadratic polynomial, it is best either to factor the quadratic polynomial or to use the quadratic formula to find the remaining solutions to the equation.

WARM-UPS

True or false? Explain your answer.

1. The function $f(x) = x^{-1}$ is a polynomial function.

2. To find the value of $f(x) = x^3 - 4x^2 + 3x - 7$ when $x = 3$, we use -3 in the synthetic division.

3. If we divide $P(x) = x^3 - 6x^2 + 3x - 7$ by $x - 5$, then $P(5)$ is equal to the remainder.

4. If we divide $x^4 - 1$ by $x - 2$, then the remainder is 15.

5. The polynomial function $P(x) = 5$ has at least one zero.

6. If $P(x) = x^3 - 7x + 3$ and c is a number such that $P(c) = 0$, then $c^3 - 7c + 3 = 0$.

7. If $P(x) = x^3 - 3x^2 + 5x - 14$, then $P(3) = 0$.

8. If $P(x) = 5x^3 - 5x^2 + 7x - 9$, then $\frac{1}{3}$ is not a zero of the polynomial.

9. The polynomial $x - 1$ is a factor of $x^4 - x^3 + x^2 - x + 1$.

10. The polynomial $x + 3$ is a factor of $3x^5 - 5x^4 - 6x^3 + 8x^2 + 9x - 2$.

10.2 EXERCISES

Reading and Writing *After reading this section, write out the answers to these questions. Use complete sentences.*

1. What is a polynomial function?

2. What is a root of a function?

3. What is a zero of a function?

4. What is the remainder theorem?

5. What is the rational root theorem?

6. What is the fundamental theorem of algebra?

Let $f(x) = x^4 - 1$, $g(x) = x^3 - 3x^2 + 5$, and $h(x) = 4x^4 - 3x^2 + 3x - 1$. Find the following function values by using two different methods. See Example 1.

7. $f(1)$ **8.** $f(-3)$

9. $f(-2)$ **10.** $f(5)$

11. $g(1)$ **12.** $g(-1)$

13. $g(-2)$ **14.** $g(2)$

15. $h\left(\dfrac{1}{2}\right)$ **16.** $h\left(-\dfrac{1}{2}\right)$

17. $h\left(\dfrac{3}{2}\right)$ **18.** $h\left(-\dfrac{3}{2}\right)$

Determine whether each given number is a zero of the polynomial function following the number. See Example 2.

19. $3, f(x) = 3x^3 - 6x^2 - 4x - 15$

20. $-2, f(x) = 3x^3 - 6x^2 - 4x - 15$

21. $-2, P(x) = x^3 + 2x^2 + 3x + 2$

22. $-1, P(x) = x^3 + 2x^2 + 3x + 2$

23. $-1, g(x) = x^4 + 3x^3 + 5x^2 + 5x + 2$

24. $3, g(x) = x^4 + 3x^3 + 5x^2 + 5x + 2$

25. $\dfrac{1}{2}, h(x) = x^3 + 3x^2 - 4x + 1$

26. $-\dfrac{1}{2}, h(x) = x^3 + 3x^2 - 4x + 1$

Find all real and imaginary zeros of each polynomial function. See Example 3.

27. $f(x) = 5x - 9$

28. $h(x) = 3x + 12$

29. $k(x) = x^2 - 5x + 6$

30. $m(x) = x^2 - x - 12$

31. $P(t) = t^2 + 9$

32. $W(t) = t^2 - 2t + 6$

33. $H(x) = x^3 - 3x^2 + 4x - 12$

34. $A(x) = x^3 + x^2 + x + 1$

35. $K(s) = 2s^3 - 5s^2 - 3s$

36. $J(s) = 2s^3 + s^2 - 3s$

37. $L(x) = -x^3 - x^2 + 7x + 7$

38. $Q(x) = -3x^3 + 3x^2 + 2x - 2$

39. $M(x) = x^3 - 1$

40. $N(x) = x^3 - 8$

Find all possible rational zeros for each polynomial function. See Example 4.

41. $P(x) = 2x^3 - 5x^2 + x + 2$

42. $P(x) = x^3 - 2x^2 - 5x + 6$

43. $P(x) = x^3 + 9x^2 + 26x + 24$

44. $P(x) = 3x^3 + 4x^2 - 5x - 2$

45. $P(x) = x^3 + 5x^2 - 6$

46. $P(x) = 3x^3 + 16x^2 - 8$

Find all of the real and imaginary zeros for each polynomial function. See Example 5.

47. $P(x) = 2x^3 - 5x^2 + x + 2$

48. $P(x) = x^3 - 2x^2 - 5x + 6$

49. $P(x) = x^3 + 9x^2 + 26x + 24$

50. $P(x) = 3x^3 + 4x^2 - 5x - 2$

51. $P(x) = x^3 + 5x^2 - 6$

52. $P(x) = 3x^3 + 16x^2 - 8$

53. $P(x) = x^3 + 2x^2 - 16$
54. $P(x) = x^3 + 6x^2 + 13x + 10$

55. $P(x) = 24x^3 - 26x^2 + 9x - 1$

56. $P(x) = 12x^3 - 20x^2 + x + 3$

Solve each problem.

57. The total profit in dollars on the sale of x Electronic Tummy Trimmers is given by the polynomial function $P(x) = x^3 - 40x^2 + 400x$. Find the profit when 10 are sold. How many must be sold to get a profit of 0 dollars?

58. The velocity in feet per second (ft/sec) of a rocket t seconds (sec) after launching is given by the polynomial function $v(t) = t^3 - 20t^2 + 110t$. What is the velocity of the rocket 10 sec after launching? For what value of t does the rocket have 0 velocity?

FIGURE FOR EXERCISE 58

 GRAPHING CALCULATOR EXERCISES

Find all real zeros to each polynomial function by graphing the function and locating the x-intercepts.

59. $f(x) = x^3 - 0.2x^2 - 0.05x + 0.006$
60. $f(x) = x^3 - 13x^2 + 32x - 20$
61. $f(x) = x^3 - 60x^2 + 1100x - 6000$
62. $f(x) = x^3 - 3x^2 - 2200x + 50{,}000$

In This Section

- The Number of Roots to a Polynomial Equation
- The Conjugate Pairs Theorem
- Descartes' Rule of Signs
- Bounds on the Roots

10.3   THE THEORY OF EQUATIONS

The zeros of a polynomial function $P(x)$ are the same as the roots of the polynomial equation $P(x) = 0$. Remember that one of our main goals in algebra is to keep expanding our knowledge of solving equations. In this section we will learn several facts that are useful in solving polynomial equations.

The Number of Roots to a Polynomial Equation

In solving a polynomial equation by factoring, we find that a factor may occur more than once.

> **Multiplicity**
>
> If the factor $x - c$ occurs n times in the complete factorization of the polynomial $P(x)$, then we say that c is a root of the equation $P(x) = 0$ with **multiplicity** n.

For example, the equation $x^2 - 10x + 25 = 0$ is equivalent to $(x - 5)(x - 5) = 0$. The only root to this equation is 5. Since the factor $x - 5$ occurs twice, we say that 5 is a root with multiplicity 2. Counting multiplicity, every quadratic equation has two roots.

Consider a polynomial equation $P(x) = 0$ of positive degree n. By the fundamental theorem of algebra there is at least one complex root c_1 to this equation. By the factor theorem $P(x) = 0$ is equivalent to $(x - c_1)Q_1(x) = 0$, where $Q_1(x)$ is a polynomial with degree $n - 1$ (the quotient when $P(x)$ is divided by $x - c_1$). By the fundamental theorem of algebra there is at least one complex root c_2 to $Q_1(x) = 0$. By the factor theorem $P(x) = 0$ can be written as $(x - c_1)(x - c_2)Q_2(x) = 0$, where $Q_2(x)$ is a polynomial with degree $n - 2$. Continuing this reasoning n times, we get a quotient polynomial that has 0 degree, n factors for $P(x)$, and n complex roots, not necessarily all different. We have just proved the following theorem.

n-Root Theorem

If $P(x) = 0$ is a polynomial equation with real or complex coefficients and positive degree n, then counting multiplicities, $P(x) = 0$ has n complex roots.

Note that the n-root theorem also means that a polynomial function of positive degree n has n zeros, counting multiplicities.

E X A M P L E   1   **Finding all roots to a polynomial equation**
State the degree of each polynomial equation. Find all of the real and imaginary roots to each equation, stating multiplicity when it is greater than 1.
a) $6x^5 + 24x^3 = 0$
b) $(x - 3)^2(x + 4)^5 = 0$

Calculator Close-Up

You can check Example 1 by examining the graphs shown here.

The roots to the equations correspond to the x-intercepts.

Solution
a) The equation is a fifth-degree equation. We can solve it by factoring:

$$6x^3(x^2 + 4) = 0$$

$$6x^3 = 0 \quad \text{or} \quad x^2 + 4 = 0$$

$$x^3 = 0 \quad \text{or} \quad x^2 = -4$$

$$x = 0 \quad \text{or} \quad x = \pm 2i$$

The roots are $\pm 2i$ and 0. Since 0 is a root with multiplicity 3, counting multiplicities there are five roots.

b) If we would multiply the factors in this polynomial equation, then the highest power of x would be 7. So the degree of the equation is 7. There are only two distinct roots to the equation, 3 and -4. We say that 3 is a root with multiplicity 2 and -4 is a root with multiplicity 5. So counting multiplicities, there are seven roots to the equation. ∎

The Conjugate Pairs Theorem

The solutions to the quadratic equation $x^2 - 2x + 5 = 0$ are the complex numbers $1 - 2i$ and $1 + 2i$. These numbers are conjugates of one another. The quadratic formula guarantees that complex solutions of quadratic equations with real coefficients occur in conjugate pairs. This situation also occurs for polynomial equations of higher degree.

Conjugate Pairs Theorem

If $P(x) = 0$ is a polynomial equation with real coefficients and the complex number $a + bi$ ($b \neq 0$) is a root, then the complex number $a - bi$ is also a root.

EXAMPLE 2

Calculator Close-Up

You can check Example 2 by examining the graph shown here. The graph should cross the x-axis only once because the function has only one real root.

Finding an equation with given roots

Find a polynomial equation with real coefficients that has 2 and $1 - i$ as roots.

Solution

Since the polynomial is to have real coefficients, the imaginary roots occur in conjugate pairs. So a polynomial with these two roots actually must have at least three roots: 2, $1 - i$, and $1 + i$. Since each root of the equation comes from a factor of the polynomial, we can write the following equation:

$$(x - 2)(x - [1 - i])(x - [1 + i]) = 0$$
$$(x - 2)(x^2 - 2x + 2) = 0 \quad {\scriptstyle (1 - i)(1 + i) = 1 - i^2 = 2}$$
$$x^3 - 4x^2 + 6x - 4 = 0$$

This equation has the required solutions and the smallest degree. Any multiple of this equation would also have the required solutions but would not be as simple. ∎

Descartes' Rule of Signs

None of the theorems in this chapter tells us how to find all of the n roots to a polynomial equation of degree n. The theorems and rules presented here add to our knowledge of polynomial equations and help us to solve more equations. Descartes' rule of signs is a method for looking at a polynomial equation and estimating the number of positive, negative, and imaginary solutions.

When a polynomial is written in descending order, a variation of sign occurs when the signs of consecutive terms change. For example, if $P(x) = 3x^5 - 7x^4 - 8x^3 - x^2 + 3x - 9$, there are sign changes in going from the first to the second terms, from the fourth to the fifth terms, and from the fifth to the sixth terms. So there are three variations in sign for $P(x)$. Descartes' rule requires that we also count the variations in sign for $P(-x)$ after it is simplified:

$$P(-x) = 3(-x)^5 - 7(-x)^4 - 8(-x)^3 - (-x)^2 + 3(-x) - 9$$
$$= -3x^5 - 7x^4 + 8x^3 - x^2 - 3x - 9$$

In the polynomial $P(-x)$ the signs of the terms change from the second to the third terms, and then the signs change again from the third to the fourth terms. So there are two variations in sign for $P(-x)$.

Descartes' Rule of Signs

If $P(x) = 0$ is a polynomial equation with real coefficients, then the number of positive roots of the equation is either equal to the number of variations of sign of $P(x)$ or less than that by an even number. The number of negative roots of the equation is either equal to the number of variations in sign of $P(-x)$ or less than that by an even number.

EXAMPLE 3

Discussing the possibilities for the roots

Discuss the possibilities for the roots to $2x^3 - 5x^2 - 6x + 4 = 0$.

Calculator Close-Up

The following graph shows us that there are actually two positive roots, one negative root, and no imaginary roots to the equation in Example 3.

Solution

The number of variations of sign in $P(x) = 2x^3 - 5x^2 - 6x + 4$ is 2. According to Descartes' rule, the number of positive roots is either 2 or 0. Since $P(-x) = 2(-x)^3 - 5(-x)^2 - 6(-x) + 4 = -2x^3 - 5x^2 + 6x + 4$, there is only one variation of sign in $P(-x)$. So there is exactly one negative root. If only one negative root exists, then the other two roots must be positive or imaginary. The number of imaginary roots is determined by the number of positive and negative roots because the total number of roots must be three. The following table summarizes these two possibilities.

Number of Positive Roots	Number of Negative Roots	Number of Imaginary Roots
2	1	0
0	1	2

EXAMPLE 4

Discussing the possibilities for the roots

Discuss the possibilities for the roots to $3x^4 - 5x^3 - x^2 - 8x + 4 = 0$.

Calculator Close-Up

From the graph it appears that there are actually two positive roots, no negative roots, and two imaginary roots to the equation in Example 4.

Solution

The number of variations of sign in $P(x) = 3x^4 - 5x^3 - x^2 - 8x + 4$ is two. According to Descartes' rule, there are either two or no positive roots to the equation. Since $P(-x) = 3(-x)^4 - 5(-x)^3 - (-x)^2 - 8(-x) + 4 = 3x^4 + 5x^3 - x^2 + 8x + 4$, there are two variations of sign in $P(-x)$. So the number of negative roots is either two or zero. Each line of the following table gives a possible distribution of the type of roots to the equation.

Number of Positive Roots	Number of Negative Roots	Number of Imaginary Roots
2	2	0
2	0	2
0	2	2
0	0	4

Descartes' rule of signs adds to our knowledge of the roots of an equation. It is especially helpful when the number of variations of sign is zero or one. If there are no variations in sign for $P(x)$, then there are no positive roots. If there is one variation of sign in $P(x)$, then we know that one positive root exists.

Bounds on the Roots

The next theorem on roots has to do with determining the size of the roots.

Theorem on Bounds

Suppose $P(x)$ is a polynomial with real coefficients and a positive leading coefficient, and synthetic division with c is performed.

- If $c > 0$ and all terms in the bottom row are nonnegative, then no number greater than c can be a root of $P(x) = 0$.

- If $c < 0$ and the terms in the bottom row alternate in sign, then no number less than c can be a root of $P(x) = 0$.

If there are no roots greater than c, then c is called an **upper bound** for the roots. If there are no roots less than c, then c is called a **lower bound** for the roots. If 0 appears in the bottom row of the synthetic division, we may consider it as positive or negative term in determining whether the signs alternate.

EXAMPLE 5

Integral bounds for the roots

Use the theorem on bounds to establish the best integral bounds for the roots of $2x^3 - 5x^2 - 6x + 4 = 0$.

Solution

Try synthetic division with the integers 1, 2, 3, and so on. The first integer for which all terms on the bottom row are nonnegative is the best upper bound for the roots:

$$
\begin{array}{r|rrrr}
1 & 2 & -5 & -6 & 4 \\
  &   & 2 & -3 & -9 \\
\hline
  & 2 & -3 & -9 & -5
\end{array}
\qquad
\begin{array}{r|rrrr}
2 & 2 & -5 & -6 & 4 \\
  &   & 4 & -2 & -16 \\
\hline
  & 2 & -1 & -8 & -12
\end{array}
$$

$$
\begin{array}{r|rrrr}
3 & 2 & -5 & -6 & 4 \\
  &   & 6 & 3 & -9 \\
\hline
  & 2 & 1 & -3 & -5
\end{array}
\qquad
\begin{array}{r|rrrr}
4 & 2 & -5 & -6 & 4 \\
  &   & 8 & 12 & 24 \\
\hline
  & 2 & 3 & 6 & 28
\end{array}
$$

By the theorem on bounds no number greater than 4 can be a root to the equation. Now try synthetic division with the integers -1, -2, -3, and so on. The first negative integer for which the terms on the bottom row alternate in sign is the best lower bound for the roots:

$$
\begin{array}{r|rrrr}
-1 & 2 & -5 & -6 & 4 \\
   &   & -2 & 7 & -1 \\
\hline
   & 2 & -7 & 1 & 3
\end{array}
\qquad
\begin{array}{r|rrrr}
-2 & 2 & -5 & -6 & 4 \\
   &   & -2 & 14 & -16 \\
\hline
   & 2 & -7 & 8 & -12
\end{array}
$$

By the theorem on bounds no number less than -2 can be a root to the equation. So all of the real roots to this equation are between -2 and 4.   ■

In Example 6 we will use all of the information available to find all of the solutions to a polynomial equation.

EXAMPLE 6

Finding all solutions to a polynomial equation

Find all of the solutions to $2x^3 - 5x^2 - 6x + 4 = 0$.

Solution

In Example 3 we saw that this equation has either two positive roots and one negative root or one negative root and two imaginary roots. In Example 5 we saw that all of the real roots to this equation are between -2 and 4. From the rational root theorem we have ± 1, ± 2, ± 4, and $\pm\frac{1}{2}$ as the possible rational roots. Since there must be one negative root and it must be greater than -2, the only possible

Calculator Close-Up

Because all x-intercepts are between -2 and 4, the graph supports the conclusion that all of the roots to the equation are between -2 and 4.

numbers from the list are -1 and $-\frac{1}{2}$. So start by checking $-\frac{1}{2}$ and -1 with synthetic division:

$$
\begin{array}{r|rrrr}
-\frac{1}{2} & 2 & -5 & -6 & 4 \\
 & & -1 & 3 & \frac{3}{2} \\
\hline
 & 2 & -6 & -3 & \frac{11}{2}
\end{array}
\qquad
\begin{array}{r|rrrr}
-1 & 2 & -5 & -6 & 4 \\
 & & -2 & 7 & -1 \\
\hline
 & 2 & -7 & 1 & 3
\end{array}
$$

Since neither -1 nor $-\frac{1}{2}$ is a root, the negative root must be irrational. Since there might be two positive roots smaller than 4, we check $\frac{1}{2}$, 1, and 2:

$$
\begin{array}{r|rrrr}
\frac{1}{2} & 2 & -5 & -6 & 4 \\
 & & 1 & -2 & -4 \\
\hline
 & 2 & -4 & -8 & 0
\end{array}
$$

Since $\frac{1}{2}$ is a root of the equation, $x - \frac{1}{2}$ is a factor of the polynomial:

$$
\left(x - \frac{1}{2}\right)(2x^2 - 4x - 8) = 0
$$

$$
(2x - 1)(x^2 - 2x - 4) = 0
$$

$$
2x - 1 = 0 \quad \text{or} \quad x^2 - 2x - 4 = 0
$$

$$
x = \frac{1}{2} \quad \text{or} \quad x = \frac{2 \pm \sqrt{4 - 4(1)(-4)}}{2} = 1 \pm \sqrt{5}
$$

There are two positive roots, $\frac{1}{2}$ and $1 + \sqrt{5}$. The negative root is $1 - \sqrt{5}$. Note that the roots guaranteed by Descartes' rule of signs are real numbers but not necessarily rational numbers. ∎

WARM-UPS

True or false? Explain your answer.

1. The number 3 is a root of $x^2 - 9 = 0$ with multiplicity 2.

2. Counting multiplicities, the equation $x^8 = 1$ has eight solutions in the set of complex numbers.

3. The number $\frac{2}{3}$ is a root of multiplicity 4 for the equation
   $(3x - 2)^4(x^2 + 2x + 1) = 0$.

4. The number 2 is a root of multiplicity 3 for the equation
   $(x - 2)^3(x^2 + x - 6) = 0$.

5. If $2 - 3i$ is a solution to a polynomial equation with real coefficients, then $-2 + 3i$ is also a solution to the equation.

6. If $P(x) = 0$ is a polynomial equation with real coefficients and $5 - 4i$ and $3 + 6i$ are solutions to $P(x) = 0$, then the degree of $P(x)$ is at least 4.

7. Both $-1 - i\sqrt{2}$ and $1 - i\sqrt{2}$ are solutions to $7x^3 - 5x^2 + 6x - 8 = 0$.

8. If $P(x) = x^3 - 6x^2 + 3x - 2$, then $P(-x) = -x^3 + 6x^2 - 3x + 2$.

9. The equation $x^3 + 5x^2 + 6x + 1 = 0$ has no positive solutions.

10. The equation $x^3 - 5 = 0$ has two imaginary solutions.

10.3 EXERCISES

Reading and Writing *After reading this section, write out the answers to these questions. Use complete sentences.*

1. What is multiplicity?

2. What is the *n*-root theorem?

3. What is the conjugate pairs theorem?

4. What is Descartes' rule of signs?

5. What is an upper bound for the roots of a polynomial?

6. What is a lower bound for the roots?

State the degree of each polynomial equation. Find all of the real and imaginary roots to each equation. State the multiplicity of a root when it is greater than 1. See Example 1.

7. $x^5 - 4x^3 = 0$

8. $x^6 + 9x^4 = 0$

9. $x^4 + 2x^3 + x^2 = 0$

10. $x^5 - 4x^4 + 4x^3 = 0$

11. $x^4 - 6x^2 + 9 = 0$

12. $x^4 - 8x^2 + 16 = 0$

13. $(x - 1)^2(x + 2)^2 = 0$

14. $(2x + 1)^2(3x - 5)^4 = 0$

15. $x^4 - 2x^2 + 1 = 0$

16. $4x^4 - 4x^2 + 1 = 0$

Find a polynomial equation with real coefficients that has the given roots. See Example 2.

17. $3, 2 - i$

18. $-4, 3 + i$

19. $-2, i$

20. $4, -i$

21. $0, i\sqrt{2}$

22. $-3, i\sqrt{3}$

23. $i, 1 - i$

24. $2i, -i$

25. $1, 2$

26. $\dfrac{1}{2}, -1$

27. $-1, 2, 3$

28. $-2, 3, 2$

Discuss the possibilities for the roots to each equation. Do not solve the equation. See Examples 3 and 4.

29. $x^3 + 3x^2 + 5x + 7 = 0$

30. $2x^3 - 3x^2 + 5x - 6 = 0$

31. $-2x^3 - x^2 + 3x + 2 = 0$

32. $x^3 + x^2 - 5x - 1 = 0$

33. $x^4 - x^3 + x^2 - x + 1 = 0$

34. $x^4 - 1 = 0$

35. $x^4 + x^2 + 1 = 0$

36. $x^6 + 3x^4 + 2x^2 + 6 = 0$

37. $x^3 + x - 1 = 0$

38. $-x^4 + 3x^3 + 5x + 5 = 0$

39. $x^5 + x^3 + 3x = 0$

40. $x^3 - 5x^2 + 6x = 0$

Establish the best integral bounds for the roots of each equation according to the theorem on bounds. See Example 5.

41. $x^4 - 5x^2 + 7 = 0$

42. $2x^3 - x^2 - 7x + 7 = 0$

43. $2x^3 - 5x^2 + 9x - 18 = 0$

44. $x^2 - 7x - 16 = 0$

45. $x^2 + x - 13 = 0$

46. $x^3 - 15x + 25 = 0$

47. $2x^3 - 13x^2 + 25x - 14 = 0$

48. $x^3 - 6x^2 + 11x - 6 = 0$

Use the rational root theorem, Descartes' rule of signs, and the theorem on bounds as aids in finding all solutions to each equation. See Example 6.

49. $x^3 + x + 10 = 0$

50. $x^3 - 7x^2 + 17x - 15 = 0$

51. $2x^3 - 5x^2 - 6x + 4 = 0$

52. $3x^3 - 17x^2 + 12x + 6 = 0$

53. $4x^3 - 6x^2 - 2x + 1 = 0$

54. $x^3 + 5x^2 - 20x - 42 = 0$

55. $x^4 - 5x^3 + 5x^2 + 5x - 6 = 0$

56. $x^4 - 2x^3 + 5x^2 - 8x + 4 = 0$

57. $x^4 - 7x^3 + 17x^2 - 17x + 6 = 0$

58. $x^4 + 7x^3 + 17x^2 + 17x + 6 = 0$

59. $x^6 - x^5 + 2x^4 - 2x^3 - 15x^2 + 15x = 0$

60. $2x^6 + 4x^5 + x^4 + 2x^3 - x^2 - 2x = 0$

Solve each problem.

61. Willard is designing a cylindrical tank with cone-shaped ends. The length of the cylinder is to be 20 feet (ft) larger than the radius of the cylinder, and the height of the cone is 2 ft. If the volume of the tank is 984π cubic feet (ft³), then what is the radius of the cylinder?

FIGURE FOR EXERCISE 61

62. Dr. Hu is designing a chemical storage tank in the shape of a cylinder with hemispherical ends. If the length of the cylinder is to be 20 ft larger than its radius and the volume is to be $3,321\pi$ ft³, then what is the radius?

FIGURE FOR EXERCISE 62

63. A box of frozen specimens measures 4 inches by 5 inches by 3 inches. It is wrapped in an insulating material of uniform thickness for shipment. The volume of the box including the insulating material is 120 cubic inches (in.³). How thick is the insulation?

64. An independent marketing research agency has determined that the best box for breakfast cereal has a height that is 6 inches (in.) larger than its thickness and a width that is 5 in. larger than its thickness. If such a box is to have a volume of 112 in.³, then what should the thickness be?

GRAPHING CALCULATOR EXERCISES

Find all real roots to each polynomial equation by graphing the corresponding function and locating the x-intercepts.

65. $x^4 - 12x^2 + 10 = 0$

66. $x^5 + x^4 - 7x^3 - 7x^2 + 12x + 12 = 0$

67. $x^6 - 9x^4 + 20x^2 - 12 = 0$

68. $4x^5 + 16x^4 - 5x^3 - 20x^2 + x + 8 = 0$

In This Section

- Symmetry
- Behavior at the *x*-Intercepts
- Sketching Some Graphs

10.4

GRAPHS OF POLYNOMIAL FUNCTIONS

The graph of a polynomial function of degree 0 or 1 is a straight line and the graph of a second-degree polynomial function is a parabola. In this section we will concentrate on graphs of polynomial functions of degree larger than 2.

Symmetry

Consider the graph of the quadratic function $f(x) = x^2$ shown in Fig. 10.1. Notice that both $(2, 4)$ and $(-2, 4)$ are on the graph. In fact, $f(x) = f(-x)$ for any value of x. We get the same y-coordinate whether we evaluate the function at a number or its opposite. This fact causes the graph to be symmetric about the y-axis. If we folded the paper along the y-axis, the two halves of the graph would coincide.

FIGURE 10.1

FIGURE 10.2

Symmetric about the y-Axis

If $f(x)$ is a function such that $f(x) = f(-x)$ for any value of x in its domain, then the graph of the function is said to be **symmetric about the y-axis**.

Consider the graph of $f(x) = x^3$ shown in Fig. 10.2. It is not symmetric about the y-axis like the graph of $f(x) = x^2$, but it has a different kind of symmetry. On the graph of $f(x) = x^3$ we find the points $(2, 8)$ and $(-2, -8)$. In this case $f(x)$ and $f(-x)$ are not equal, but $f(-x) = -f(x)$. Notice that the points $(2, 8)$ and $(-2, -8)$ are the same distance from the origin and lie on a line through the origin.

Symmetric about the Origin

If $f(x)$ is a function such that $f(-x) = -f(x)$ for any value of x in its domain, then the graph of the function is said to be **symmetric about the origin**.

E X A M P L E   1

Determining the symmetry of a graph

Discuss the symmetry of the graph of each polynomial function.

a) $f(x) = 5x^3 - x$

b) $f(x) = 2x^4 - 3x^2$

c) $f(x) = x^2 - 3x + 6$

Solution

a) Since $f(-x) = 5(-x)^3 - (-x) = -5x^3 + x$, we have $f(-x)$ equal to the opposite of $f(x)$. So the graph is symmetric about the origin.

b) Since $f(-x) = 2(-x)^4 - 3(-x)^2 = 2x^4 - 3x^2$, we have $f(x) = f(-x)$. So the graph is symmetric about the y-axis.

c) In this case $f(-x) = (-x)^2 - 3(-x) + 6 = x^2 + 3x + 6$. So $f(-x) \neq f(x)$ and $f(-x) \neq -f(x)$. This graph has neither type of symmetry. ■

Calculator Close-Up

We can use graphs to check the conclusions about symmetry that were arrived at algebraically in Example 1. The graph of $f(x) = 5x^3 - x$ appears to be symmetric about the origin.

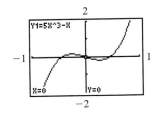

The graph of $f(x) = 2x^4 - 3x^2$ appears to be symmetric about the y-axis.

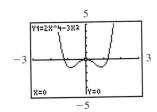

The graph of $f(x) = x^2 - 3x + 6$ does not appear to have either type of symmetry.

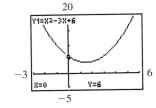

Behavior at the x-Intercepts

Each of the graphs of $f(x) = x^2$ and $f(x) = x^3$ has one x-intercept $(0, 0)$. If we use a positive or negative number very close to 0 for x in $f(x) = x^2$, the y-coordinate is positive because the power on x is even. That is why the graph just touches the x-axis at $(0, 0)$ but does not cross the x-axis there. If we use a positive number very close to 0 for x in $f(x) = x^3$, we get a positive y-coordinate. If we use a negative number very close to 0 for x in $f(x) = x^3$, we get a negative y-coordinate because the power on x is odd. That is why the graph crosses the x-axis at $(0, 0)$. In general, the graph crosses the x-axis at an x-intercept if the factor that produces that intercept has an odd power and the graph does not cross if the factor has an even power.

E X A M P L E   2

Behavior at the x-intercepts

Find the x-intercepts and discuss the behavior of the graph of each polynomial function at its x-intercepts.

a) $f(x) = (x - 1)^2(x - 3)$ **b)** $f(x) = x^3 + 2x^2 - 3x$

Solution

a) The x-intercepts are found by solving $(x - 1)^2(x - 3) = 0$. The x-intercepts are $(1, 0)$ and $(3, 0)$. The graph does not cross the x-axis at $(1, 0)$ but does cross the x-axis at $(3, 0)$.

b) The x-intercepts are found by solving $x^3 + 2x^2 - 3x = 0$. By factoring, we get $x(x + 3)(x - 1) = 0$. The x-intercepts are $(0, 0)$, $(-3, 0)$, and $(1, 0)$. Since each factor occurs an odd number of times, the graph crosses the x-axis at each of the x-intercepts. ∎

Calculator Close-Up

The graphs of the functions in Example 2 support the conclusions about the behavior at the x-intercepts.

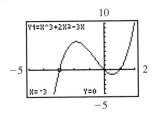

Sketching Some Graphs

We can use our knowledge of symmetry and the behavior at the x-intercepts to sketch some graphs of polynomial functions. To find the x-intercepts, we might have to use the ideas of Section 10.2 to find the roots of a polynomial equation.

E X A M P L E   3

Graphing a polynomial function

Sketch the graph of each polynomial function.

a) $f(x) = x^3 - 5x^2 + 7x - 3$

b) $f(x) = x^4 - 2x^2 + 1$

Calculator Close-Up

This calculator graph supports the conclusions made in Example 3(a).

Solution

a) Since $f(-x) = -x^3 - 5x^2 - 7x - 3$, the graph has neither type of symmetry. By Descartes' rule of signs there are no negative roots to the equation $x^3 - 5x^2 + 7x - 3 = 0$, and the number of positive roots is either 3 or 1. So the only possible rational roots are 1 and 3:

$$
\begin{array}{r|rrr}
1 & 1 & -5 & 7 & -3 \\
  &   & 1 & -4 & 3 \\
\hline
  & 1 & -4 & 3 & 0
\end{array}
$$

From the synthetic division we get $f(x) = (x - 1)(x^2 - 4x + 3)$, and if we factor again, we get $f(x) = (x - 1)^2(x - 3)$. The x-intercepts are $(1, 0)$ and $(3, 0)$. The discussion of Example 2(a) applies to this function. The points $(0, -3)$, $(2, -1)$, and $(4, 9)$ are also on the graph. The graph is shown in Fig. 10.3.

b) Since $f(-x) = (-x)^4 - 2(-x)^2 + 1 = x^4 - 2x^2 + 1$, we have $f(x) = f(-x)$. So the graph is symmetric about the y-axis. We can factor the polynomial as follows:

$$
\begin{aligned}
f(x) &= x^4 - 2x^2 + 1 \\
&= (x^2 - 1)(x^2 - 1) \\
&= (x - 1)(x + 1)(x - 1)(x + 1) \\
&= (x - 1)^2(x + 1)^2
\end{aligned}
$$

Calculator Close-Up

This calculator graph supports the conclusions made in Example 3(b).

The x-intercepts are $(1, 0)$ and $(-1, 0)$. Since each factor for these intercepts has an even power, the graph does not cross the x-axis at the intercepts. The points $(0, 1)$, $(2, 9)$, and $(-2, 9)$ are also on the graph shown in Fig. 10.4.

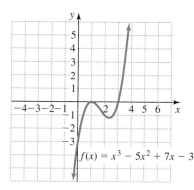

$f(x) = x^3 - 5x^2 + 7x - 3$

F I G U R E   10.3

$f(x) = x^4 - 2x^2 + 1$

F I G U R E   10.4

WARM-UPS

True or false? Explain your answer.

1. The graph of $f(x) = x^3 - x$ is symmetric about the y-axis.
2. The graph of $y = 2x - 1$ is symmetric about the origin.
3. If the graph of a polynomial function $y = P(x)$ is symmetric about the y-axis and $P(3) = 16$, then $P(-3) = -16$.
4. For the function $f(x) = 3x$ we have $f(x) = f(-x)$ for any value of x.
5. If $f(x) = 3x^4 - 5x^3 + 2x^2 - 6x + 7$, then
   $f(-x) = 3x^4 + 5x^3 + 2x^2 + 6x + 7$.
6. There is only one x-intercept for the graph of $f(x) = x^2 - 4x + 4$.
7. The points $(0, 2)$ and $(0, -3)$ are the x-intercepts for the graph of the function $P(x) = (x - 2)^2(x + 3)$.
8. The y-intercept for the graph of $P(x) = 3x^3 - 7x^2 + 8x - 9$ is $(0, 9)$.

9. The graph of $f(x) = (x - 1)^2(x + 4)^2$ does not cross the x-axis at either of its x-intercepts.
10. The graph of $f(x) = x^3 - 8$ has three x-intercepts.

10.4 EXERCISES

Reading and Writing *After reading this section, write out the answers to these questions. Use complete sentences.*

1. What does symmetric about the y-axis mean?

2. What does symmetric about the origin mean?

3. What is an x-intercept?

4. How can you determine whether the graph of a polynomial function crosses the x-axis at an x-intercept?

Discuss the symmetry of the graph of each polynomial function. See Example 1.

5. $f(x) = x^4$
6. $f(x) = x^4 - x$
7. $f(x) = x^3 - 5x + 1$
8. $f(x) = 5x^3 + 7x$
9. $f(x) = 6x^6 - 3x^2 - x$
10. $f(x) = x^6 - x^4 + x^2 - 8$
11. $f(x) = (x - 3)^2$

12. $f(x) = 3(x + 2)^2$
13. $f(x) = (x^2 - 5)^3$
14. $f(x) = (x^2 + 1)^2$
15. $f(x) = x$
16. $f(x) = -3x$

Find the x-intercepts and discuss the behavior of the graph of each polynomial function at its x-intercepts. See Example 2.

17. $f(x) = (x - 5)^2$
18. $f(x) = 3x - 2$

19. $f(x) = x^2 - 3x - 4$
20. $f(x) = 9x^2 - 12x + 4$
21. $f(x) = x^4$
22. $f(x) = x^4 - 1$
23. $f(x) = (x - 3)^2(x + 5)$

24. $f(x) = (2x + 1)^3$
25. $f(x) = x^3 - x^2$

26. $f(x) = x^3 - x^2 - x + 1$

27. $f(x) = 2x^3 + 3x^2 - 1$

28. $f(x) = x^3 + 3x^2 - 4$

Match each polynomial function with its graph a–h.

29. $f(x) = -2x + 3$　　**30.** $f(x) = -2x^2 + 3$　　**31.** $f(x) = -2x^3 + 3$　　**32.** $f(x) = -2x^2 + 4x + 3$

33. $f(x) = -x^4 + 3$　　**34.** $f(x) = x^3 - 3x^2$　　**35.** $f(x) = x^3 + 3x^2 - x - 3$　　**36.** $f(x) = \dfrac{1}{2}x^4 - 3$

(a)

(b)

(c)

(d)

(e)

(f)

(g)

(h)

Sketch the graph of each polynomial function. See Example 3.

37. $f(x) = 2x - 6$　　**38.** $f(x) = -3x + 3$　　**39.** $f(x) = -x^2$　　**40.** $f(x) = x^2 - 3$

41. $f(x) = x^3 - 2x^2$　　**42.** $f(x) = x^3 - 4x$　　**43.** $f(x) = (x - 1)^2(x + 1)^2$

44. $f(x) = (x + 2)^2(x - 1)$

45. $f(x) = x^3 - 5x^2 + 7x - 3$

46. $f(x) = x^3 + 2x^2 - 3x$

47. $f(x) = x^4 - 4x^3 + 4x^2$

48. $f(x) = -x^4 + 6x^3 - 9x^2$

GRAPHING CALCULATOR EXERCISES

Sketch the graph of each polynomial function. First graph the function on a calculator and use the calculator graph as a guide.

49. $f(x) = x - 20$

50. $f(x) = (x - 20)^2$

51. $f(x) = (x - 20)^2(x + 30)$

52. $f(x) = (x - 20)^2(x + 30)^2$

53. $f(x) = (x - 20)^2(x + 30)^2x$

54. $f(x) = (x - 20)^2(x + 30)^2x^2$

10.5 GRAPHS OF RATIONAL FUNCTIONS

We first studied rational expressions in Chapter 6. In this section we will study functions that are defined by rational expressions.

Domain

A rational expression was defined in Chapter 6 as a ratio of two polynomials. If a ratio of two polynomials is used to define a function, then the function is called a rational function.

> **Rational Function**
>
> If $P(x)$ and $Q(x)$ are polynomials with no common factor and $f(x) = \frac{P(x)}{Q(x)}$ for $Q(x) \neq 0$, then $f(x)$ is called a **rational function.**

The domain of a rational function is the set of all real numbers except those that cause the denominator to have a value of 0.

EXAMPLE 1

Calculator Close-Up

If the viewing window is too large, a rational function will appear to touch its asymptotes.

Because the asymptotes are an important feature of a rational function, we should draw it so that it approaches but does not touch its asymptotes.

Domain of a rational function

Find the domain of each rational function.

a) $f(x) = \dfrac{x - 3}{x - 1}$

b) $g(x) = \dfrac{2x - 3}{x^2 - 4}$

Solution

a) Since $x - 1 = 0$ only for $x = 1$, the domain of f is the set of all real numbers except 1, $(-\infty, 1) \cup (1, \infty)$.

b) Since $x^2 - 4 = 0$ for $x = \pm 2$, the domain of g is the set of all real numbers excluding 2 and -2, $(-\infty, -2) \cup (-2, 2) \cup (2, \infty)$. ■

Horizontal and Vertical Asymptotes

Consider the simplest rational function $f(x) = 1/x$. Its domain does not include 0, but 0 is an important number for the graph of this function. The behavior of the graph of f when x is very close to 0 is what interests us. For this function the y-coordinate is the reciprocal of the x-coordinate. When the x-coordinate is close to 0, the y-coordinate is far from 0. Consider the following tables of ordered pairs that satisfy $f(x) = 1/x$:

$x > 0$			$x < 0$	
x	**y**		**x**	**y**
0.1	10		−0.1	−10
0.01	100		−0.01	−100
0.001	1000		−0.001	−1000
0.0001	10,000		−0.0001	−10,000

As x gets closer and closer to 0 from above 0, the value of y gets larger and larger. We say that y goes to positive infinity. As x gets closer and closer to 0 from below 0, the values of y are negative but $|y|$ gets larger and larger. We say that y goes to negative infinity. The graph of f gets closer and closer to the vertical line $x = 0$, and so $x = 0$ is called a **vertical asymptote.** On the other hand, as $|x|$ gets larger and larger, y gets closer and closer to 0. The graph approaches the x-axis as x goes to infinity, and so the x-axis is a **horizontal asymptote** for the graph of f. See Fig. 10.5 for the graph of $f(x) = 1/x$.

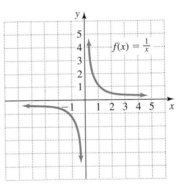

FIGURE 10.5

In general, a rational function has a vertical asymptote for every number excluded from the domain of the function. The horizontal asymptotes are determined by the behavior of the function when $|x|$ is large.

E X A M P L E 2 **Horizontal and vertical asymptotes**
Find the horizontal and vertical asymptotes for each rational function.

a) $f(x) = \dfrac{3}{x^2 - 1}$ **b)** $g(x) = \dfrac{x}{x^2 - 4}$ **c)** $h(x) = \dfrac{2x + 1}{x + 3}$

Solution

a) The denominator $x^2 - 1$ has a value of 0 if $x = \pm 1$. So the lines $x = 1$ and $x = -1$ are vertical asymptotes. If $|x|$ is very large, the value of $\dfrac{3}{x^2 - 1}$ is approximately 0. So the x-axis is a horizontal asymptote.

b) The denominator $x^2 - 4$ has a value of 0 if $x = \pm 2$. So the lines $x = 2$ and $x = -2$ are vertical asymptotes. If $|x|$ is very large, the value of $\dfrac{x}{x^2 - 4}$ is approximately 0. So the x-axis is a horizontal asymptote.

Calculator Close-Up

The graph for Example 2(b) should consist of three separate pieces, but in connected mode the calculator connects the separate pieces. Even though the calculator does not draw a very good graph of this function, it does support the conclusion that the horizontal asymptote is the x-axis and the vertical asymptotes are $x = -1$ and $x = 1$.

c) The denominator $x + 3$ has a value of 0 if $x = -3$. So the line $x = -3$ is a vertical asymptote. If $|x|$ is very large, the value of $h(x)$ is not approximately 0. To understand the value of $h(x)$, we change the form of the rational expression by using long division:

$$
\begin{array}{r}
2 \\
x + 3 \overline{)\, 2x + 1} \\
\underline{2x + 6} \\
-5
\end{array}
$$

Writing the rational expression as quotient $+ \frac{\text{remainder}}{\text{divisor}}$, we get $h(x) = \frac{2x + 1}{x + 3} = 2 + \frac{-5}{x + 3}$. If $|x|$ is very large, $\frac{-5}{x + 3}$ is approximately 0, and so the y-coordinate is approximately 2. The line $y = 2$ is a horizontal asymptote. ∎

Example 2 illustrates two important facts about horizontal asymptotes. If the degree of the numerator is less than the degree of the denominator, then the x-axis is the horizontal asymptote. For example, $y = \frac{x - 4}{x^2 - 7}$ has the x-axis as a horizontal asymptote. If the degree of the numerator is equal to the degree of the denominator, then the ratio of the leading coefficients determines the horizontal asymptote. For example, $y = \frac{2x - 7}{3x - 5}$ has $y = \frac{2}{3}$ as its horizontal asymptote. The remaining case is when the degree of the numerator is greater than the degree of the denominator. This case is discussed next.

Oblique Asymptotes

Each rational function of Example 2 had one horizontal asymptote and a vertical asymptote for each number that caused the denominator to be 0. The horizontal asymptote $y = 0$ occurs because as $|x|$ gets larger and larger, the y-coordinate gets closer and closer to 0. Some rational functions have a nonhorizontal line for an asymptote. An asymptote that is neither horizontal nor vertical is called an **oblique asymptote** or **slant asymptote.**

E X A M P L E 3

Finding an oblique asymptote

Determine all of the asymptotes for

$$
g(x) = \frac{2x^2 + 3x - 5}{x + 2}.
$$

Study Tip

The last couple of weeks of the semester is not the time to slack off. This is the time to double your efforts. Make a schedule and plan every hour of your time. Don't schedule anything that isn't necessary. Get an early start on studying for your final exams.

Solution

If $x + 2 = 0$, then $x = -2$. So the line $x = -2$ is a vertical asymptote. Use long division to rewrite the function as quotient $+ \frac{\text{remainder}}{\text{divisor}}$:

$$
g(x) = \frac{2x^2 + 3x - 5}{x + 2} = 2x - 1 + \frac{-3}{x + 2}
$$

If $|x|$ is large, the value of $\frac{-3}{x + 2}$ is approximately 0. So when $|x|$ is large, the value of $g(x)$ is approximately $2x - 1$. The line $y = 2x - 1$ is an oblique asymptote for the graph of g. ∎

We can summarize this discussion of asymptotes with the following strategy for finding asymptotes for a rational function.

> ### Strategy for Finding Asymptotes for a Rational Function
>
> Suppose $f(x) = \frac{P(x)}{Q(x)}$ is a rational function with the degree of $Q(x)$ at least 1.
>
> 1. Solve the equation $Q(x) = 0$. The graph of f has a vertical asymptote corresponding to each solution to the equation.
> 2. If the degree of $P(x)$ is less than the degree of $Q(x)$, then the x-axis is a horizontal asymptote.
> 3. If the degree of $P(x)$ is equal to the degree of $Q(x)$, then find the ratio of the leading coefficients. The horizontal line through that ratio is the horizontal asymptote.
> 4. If the degree of $P(x)$ is one larger than the degree of $Q(x)$, then use division to rewrite the function as
>
> $$\text{quotient} + \frac{\text{remainder}}{\text{divisor}}.$$
>
> The equation formed by setting y equal to the quotient gives us an oblique asymptote.

MATH AT WORK

MATHEMATICS MACHINES

Machines that do computations have been around for thousands of years. The abacus, the slide rule, and the calculator have simplified computations. However, recent calculators have gone way beyond numerical computations. Graphing calculators now draw two- and three-dimensional graphs and even do symbolic computations. Modern calculators are great, but to use one effectively you must still learn the underlying principles of mathematics.

Consider the fairly simple process of drawing a graph of a function. The graph of a function is a picture of all ordered pairs of the function. When we graph a function, we typically plot a few ordered pairs and then use our knowledge about the function to draw a graph that shows all of the important features of the function. A typical graphing calculator plots 96 ordered pairs of a function on a screen that is not much bigger than a postage stamp. The calculator does not generalize and does not make conclusions. We are still responsible for looking at what the calculator shows and making conclusions. For example, if we graphed $y = 1/(x - 100)$ with the window set for $-10 \le x \le 10$, we would not see the vertical asymptote $x = 100$. Would we believe the calculator and conclude that the graph has no vertical asymptote? If we graph $y = 1/x$ with the window set for $-500 \le x \le 500$ and $-500 \le y \le 500$, the graph will be too close to its horizontal and vertical asymptotes for us to see it. Would we conclude that there is no graph for $y = 1/x$?

If you have a graphing calculator, use it to help you graph the functions in this chapter and to reinforce your understanding of the properties of functions that we are learning. Do not attempt to use it as a substitute for learning.

Sketching the Graphs

We now use asymptotes and symmetry to help us sketch the graphs of some rational functions.

E X A M P L E 4

Graphing a rational function

Sketch the graph of each rational function.

a) $f(x) = \dfrac{3}{x^2 - 1}$

b) $g(x) = \dfrac{x}{x^2 - 4}$

Calculator Close-Up

This calculator graph supports the graph drawn in Fig. 10.7. Remember that the calculator graph can be misleading. The vertical lines drawn by the calculator are not part of the graph of the function.

Solution

a) From Example 2(a) we know that the lines $x = 1$ and $x = -1$ are vertical asymptotes and the x-axis is a horizontal asymptote. Draw the vertical asymptotes on the graph with dashed lines. Since all of the powers of x are even, $f(x) = f(-x)$, and the graph is symmetric about the y-axis. The ordered pairs $(0, -3)$, $(0.9, -15.789)$, $(1.1, 14.286)$, $(2, 1)$, and $\left(3, \dfrac{3}{8}\right)$ are also on the graph. Use the symmetry to sketch the graph shown in Fig. 10.6.

b) Draw the vertical asymptotes $x = 2$ and $x = -2$ from Example 2(b) as dashed lines. The x-axis is a horizontal asymptote. Because $f(-x) = -f(x)$, the graph is symmetric about the origin. The ordered pairs $(0, 0)$, $\left(1, -\dfrac{1}{3}\right)$, $(1.9, -4.872)$, $(2.1, 5.122)$, $\left(3, \dfrac{3}{5}\right)$, and $\left(4, \dfrac{1}{3}\right)$ are on the graph. Use the symmetry to get the graph shown in Fig. 10.7.

FIGURE 10.6

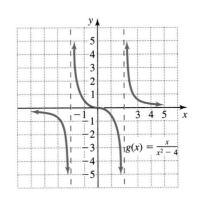

FIGURE 10.7

E X A M P L E 5

Graphing a rational function

Sketch the graph of each rational function.

a) $h(x) = \dfrac{2x + 1}{x + 3}$

b) $g(x) = \dfrac{2x^2 + 3x - 5}{x + 2}$

Solution

a) Draw the vertical asymptote $x = -3$ and the horizontal asymptote $y = 2$ from Example 2(c) as dashed lines. The points $(-2, -3)$, $\left(0, \frac{1}{3}\right)$, $\left(-\frac{1}{2}, 0\right)$, $(7, 1.5)$, $(-4, 7)$, and $(-13, 2.5)$ are on the graph shown in Fig. 10.8.

b) Draw the vertical asymptote $x = -2$ and the oblique asymptote $y = 2x - 1$ from Example 3 as dashed lines. The points $(-1, -6)$, $\left(0, -\frac{5}{2}\right)$, $(1, 0)$, $(4, 6.5)$, and $(-2.5, 0)$ are on the graph shown in Fig. 10.9.

FIGURE 10.8

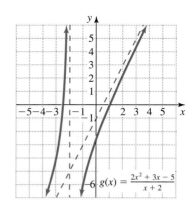

FIGURE 10.9

WARM-UPS

True or false? Explain your answer.

1. The domain of $f(x) = \dfrac{1}{x - 9}$ is $x = 9$.

2. The domain of $f(x) = \dfrac{x - 1}{x + 2}$ is $(-\infty, -2) \cup (-2, 1) \cup (1, \infty)$.

3. The domain of $f(x) = \dfrac{1}{x^2 + 1}$ is $(-\infty, -1) \cup (-1, 1) \cup (1, \infty)$.

4. The line $x = 2$ is the only vertical asymptote for the graph of $f(x) = \dfrac{1}{x^2 - 4}$.

5. The x-axis is a horizontal asymptote for the graph of $f(x) = \dfrac{x^2 - 3x + 5}{x^3 - 9x}$.

6. The x-axis is a horizontal asymptote for the graph of $f(x) = \dfrac{3x - 5}{x - 2}$.

7. The line $y = 2x - 5$ is an asymptote for the graph of $f(x) = 2x - 5 + \dfrac{1}{x}$.

8. The line $y = 2x - 5$ is an asymptote for the graph of $f(x) = 2x - 5 + x^2$.

9. The graph of $f(x) = \dfrac{x^2}{x^2 - 9}$ is symmetric about the y-axis.

10. The graph of $f(x) = \dfrac{3x}{x^2 - 25}$ is symmetric about the origin.

10.5 EXERCISES

Reading and Writing *After reading this section, write out the answers to these questions. Use complete sentences.*

1. What is a rational function?

2. What is the domain of a rational function?

3. What is a vertical asymptote?

4. What is a horizontal asymptote?

5. What is an oblique asymptote?

6. What is a slant asymptote?

Find the domain of each rational function. See Example 1.

7. $f(x) = \dfrac{2}{x - 1}$

8. $f(x) = \dfrac{-2}{x + 3}$

9. $f(x) = \dfrac{x^2 - 1}{x}$

10. $f(x) = \dfrac{-2x + 3}{x^2}$

11. $f(x) = \dfrac{5}{x^2 - 16}$

12. $f(x) = \dfrac{x + 12}{x^2 - x - 6}$

Determine all asymptotes for the graph of each rational function. See Examples 2 and 3.

13. $f(x) = \dfrac{7}{x + 4}$

14. $f(x) = \dfrac{-8}{x - 9}$

15. $f(x) = \dfrac{1}{x^2 - 16}$

16. $f(x) = \dfrac{-2}{x^2 - 5x + 6}$

17. $f(x) = \dfrac{5x}{x - 7}$

18. $f(x) = \dfrac{3x + 8}{x - 2}$

19. $f(x) = \dfrac{2x^2}{x - 3}$

20. $f(x) = \dfrac{3x^2 + 2}{x + 1}$

Match each rational function with its graph a–h.

21. $f(x) = -\dfrac{2}{x}$

22. $f(x) = -\dfrac{1}{x - 2}$

23. $f(x) = \dfrac{x}{x - 2}$

24. $f(x) = \dfrac{x - 2}{x}$

25. $f(x) = \dfrac{1}{x^2 - 2x}$

26. $f(x) = \dfrac{x^2}{x^2 - 4}$

27. $f(x) = -\dfrac{x + 4}{2}$

28. $f(x) = \dfrac{x^2 + 2x + 1}{x}$

(a)

(b)

(c)

(d)

(e)

(f)

(g)

(h)

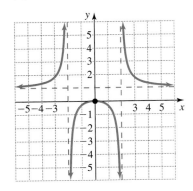

Determine all asymptotes and sketch the graph of each function. See Examples 4 and 5.

29. $f(x) = \dfrac{2}{x + 4}$

30. $f(x) = \dfrac{-3}{x - 1}$

31. $f(x) = \dfrac{x}{x^2 - 9}$

32. $f(x) = \dfrac{-2}{x^2 + x - 2}$

33. $f(x) = \dfrac{2x - 1}{x + 3}$

38. $f(x) = \dfrac{-x^2 + 5x - 5}{x - 3}$

34. $f(x) = \dfrac{5 - 2x}{x - 2}$

Find all asymptotes, x-intercepts, and y-intercepts for the graph of each rational function and sketch the graph of the function.

39. $f(x) = \dfrac{1}{x^2}$

35. $f(x) = \dfrac{x^2 - 3x + 1}{x}$

40. $f(x) = \dfrac{2}{x^2 - 4x + 4}$

36. $f(x) = \dfrac{x^3 + 1}{x^2}$

41. $f(x) = \dfrac{2x - 3}{x^2 + x - 6}$

37. $f(x) = \dfrac{3x^2 - 2x}{x - 1}$

42. $f(x) = \dfrac{x}{x^2 + 4x + 4}$

43. $f(x) = \dfrac{x + 1}{x^2}$

44. $f(x) = \dfrac{x - 1}{x^2}$

45. $f(x) = \dfrac{2x - 1}{x^3 - 9x}$

46. $f(x) = \dfrac{2x^2 + 1}{x^3 - x}$

47. $f(x) = \dfrac{x}{x^2 - 1}$

48. $f(x) = \dfrac{x}{x^2 + x - 2}$

49. $f(x) = \dfrac{2}{x^2 + 1}$

50. $f(x) = \dfrac{x}{x^2 + 1}$

51. $f(x) = \dfrac{x^2}{x + 1}$

52. $f(x) = \dfrac{x^2}{x-1}$

Solve each problem.

53. *Oscillating modulators.* The number of oscillating modulators produced by a factory in t hours is given by the polynomial function $n(t) = t^2 + 6t$ for $t \geq 1$. The cost in dollars of operating the factory for t hours is given by the function $c(t) = 36t + 500$ for $t \geq 1$. The average cost per modulator is given by the rational function $f(t) = \dfrac{36t + 500}{t^2 + 6t}$ for $t \geq 1$. Graph the function f. What is the average cost per modulator at time $t = 20$ and time $t = 30$? What can you conclude about the average cost per modulator after a long period of time?

54. *Nonoscillating modulators.* The number of nonoscillating modulators produced by a factory in t hours is given by the polynomial function $n(t) = 16t$ for $t \geq 1$. The cost in dollars of operating the factory for t hours is given by the function $c(t) = 64t + 500$ for $t \geq 1$. The average cost per modulator is given by the rational function $f(t) = \dfrac{64t + 500}{16t}$ for $t \geq 1$. Graph the function f. What is the average cost per modulator at time $t = 10$ and $t = 20$? What can you conclude about the average cost per modulator after a long period of time?

55. *Average cost of an SUV.* Mercedes-Benz spent $700 million to design its new 1998 SUV (Motor Trend, www.motortrend.com). If it costs $25,000 to manufacture each SUV, then the average cost per vehicle in dollars when x vehicles are manufactured is given by the rational function

$$A(x) = \dfrac{25{,}000x + 700{,}000{,}000}{x}.$$

a) What is the horizontal asymptote for the graph of this function?

b) What is the average cost per vehicle when 50,000 vehicles are made?

c) For what number of vehicles is the average cost $30,000?

d) Graph this function for x ranging from 0 to 100,000.

56. *Average cost of a pill.* Assuming Pfizer spent a typical $350 million to develop its latest miracle drug and $0.10 each to make the pills, then the average cost per pill in

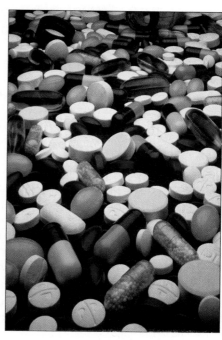

FIGURE FOR EXERCISE 56

dollars when x pills are made is given by the rational function

$$A(x) = \frac{0.10x + 350,000,000}{x}.$$

a) What is the horizontal asymptote for the graph of this function?

b) What is the average cost per pill when 100 million pills are made?

c) For what number of pills is the average cost per pill $2?

d) Graph this function for x ranging from 0 to 100 million.

 GRAPHING CALCULATOR EXERCISES

Sketch the graph of each pair of functions in the same coordinate system. What do you observe in each case?

57. $f(x) = x^2$, $g(x) = x^2 + 1/x$

58. $f(x) = x^2$, $g(x) = x^2 + 1/x^2$

59. $f(x) = |x|$, $g(x) = |x| + 1/x$

60. $f(x) = |x|$, $g(x) = |x| + 1/x^2$

61. $f(x) = \sqrt{x}$, $g(x) = \sqrt{x} + 1/x$

62. $f(x) = x^3$, $g(x) = x^3 + 1/x^2$

COLLABORATIVE ACTIVITIES

Betting on Rockets

Gretchen and Rafael are launching model rockets in the park. They have a bet to see whose rocket can go the highest. Both have taken this math course and have some clues on how to use algebra to find out whose went the highest. Below is the formula that they will use to determine whose rocket has gone the highest:

$$h = -16t^2 + v_0t,$$

where h is the distance (feet) of the rocket above the ground, t is the time passed (seconds) since the rocket was launched, and v_0 is the speed of the rocket when launched (initial velocity).

They have decided to do three trials and to see whose is the highest two out of the three times.

From the following list, have each member of your group choose a different trial.

- **First Trial:** On the first launch Gretchen's rocket has a time in the air of 14 seconds, and Rafael's rocket has a time of 10 seconds.

Grouping: 3 students per group

Topic: Applications of maximum and minimum of a parabola

- **Second Trial:** On the second launch Gretchen's rocket was in the air 11.5 seconds, and Rafael's rocket was in the air 12 seconds.

- **Third Trial:** On the third launch Gretchen's rocket was in the air 11.25 seconds, and Rafael's rocket was in the air 11.3 seconds.

Individually, complete the following for the trial you selected.

1. Find the initial velocity for each rocket using the formula $h = -16t^2 + v_0t$.

2. Graph the two quadratic functions. What is the h-value for each vertex? Whose rocket went the highest?

Together in your groups, compare your results and decide who wins the bet.

WRAP-UP

CHAPTER 10

SUMMARY

Polynomial Functions		Examples
Polynomial function	A function defined by a polynomial	$P(x) = x^2 - x - 12$
Root or zero of a function	A number c such that $f(c) = 0$	Since $P(4) = 4^2 - 4 - 12 = 0$, 4 is a root or zero of the function P.
Factor theorem	The following are equivalent for $P(x)$ a polynomial in x. 1. The remainder is zero when $P(x)$ is divided by $x - c$. 2. $x - c$ is a factor of $P(x)$. 3. c is a solution to $P(x) = 0$. 4. c is a zero of the function $P(x)$, or $P(c) = 0$.	$P(x) = x^2 - x - 2$ $P(x) = (x - 2)(x + 1)$ $P(-1) = 0, P(2) = 0$ -1 and 2 both satisfy $x^2 - x - 2 = 0$
Remainder theorem	If R is the remainder when a polynomial $P(x)$ is divided by $x - c$, then $R = P(c)$.	$P(x) = x^2 - x - 12, P(2) = \mathbf{-10}$ $\dfrac{x^2 - x - 12}{x - 2} = x + 1 + \dfrac{\mathbf{-10}}{x - 2}$
Fundamental theorem of algebra	If $P(x)$ is a polynomial function of positive degree, then $P(x)$ has at least one complex zero.	$H(x) = x^7 - \pi x^6 + 99x^5 + x - \sqrt{2}$ has at least one complex zero.
Rational root theorem	If $P(x)$ is a polynomial with integral coefficients, then any rational zero is a factor of the constant term divided by a factor of the leading coefficient.	The possible rational zeros for $P(x) = 2x^2 - 3x + 1$ are ± 1 and $\pm\dfrac{1}{2}$.
Multiplicity	If $x - c$ occurs n times in the complete factorization of $P(x)$, then c is a root of $P(x) = 0$ with multiplicity n.	If $P(x) = (x - 2)^2$, then 2 is a root of $(x - 2)^2 = 0$ with multiplicity 2.
n-root theorem	If $P(x) = 0$ is a polynomial equation with real or complex coefficients and positive degree n, then counting multiplicity $P(x) = 0$ has n complex roots.	$x^3 - 5x = 0$ has three roots. $x^4 - 1 = 0$ has four roots.
Conjugate pairs theorem	If $P(x) = 0$ is a polynomial equation with real coefficients and $a + bi$ ($b \neq 0$) is a root, then $a - bi$ is also a root.	The roots to $x^2 - 6x + 13 = 0$ are $3 + 2i$ and $3 - 2i$.

Descartes' rule of signs	If $P(x) = 0$ is a polynomial equation with real coefficients, then the number of positive roots of the equation is either equal to the number of variations of sign of $P(x)$ or less than that by an even number. The number of negative roots of the equation is either equal to the number of variations in sign of $P(-x)$ or less than that by an even number.	The number of positive roots to $x^3 - x^2 + x - 5 = 0$ is either 3 or 1. Since $P(-x) = -x^3 - x^2 - x - 5$, there are no negative roots.
Theorem on bounds	Suppose $P(x)$ is a polynomial with real coefficients and a positive leading coefficient, and synthetic division with c is performed. If $c > 0$ and all terms in the bottom row are nonnegative, then no number larger than c can be a root of $P(x) = 0$. If $c < 0$ and the terms in the bottom row alternate in sign, then no number less than c can be a root of $P(x) = 0$.	$P(x) = 2x^2 + 7x - 4$ $\begin{array}{r\|rrr} 1 & 2 & 7 & -4 \\ & & 2 & 9 \\ \hline & 2 & 9 & 5 \end{array}$ $\begin{array}{r\|rrr} -5 & 2 & 7 & -4 \\ & & -10 & 15 \\ \hline & 2 & -3 & 11 \end{array}$ Any real root of $P(x) = 0$ is between -5 and 1.

Symmetry

Examples

Symmetric about the y-axis	If $f(x)$ is a function such that $f(x) = f(-x)$ for any value of x in its domain, then the graph of f is symmetric about the y-axis.	If $f(x) = x^4 - x^2$, then $f(-x) = (-x)^4 - (-x)^2 = x^4 - x^2$, and $f(x) = f(-x)$.
Symmetric about the origin	If $f(x)$ is a function such that $f(-x) = -f(x)$ for any value of x in its domain, then the graph of f is symmetric about the origin.	If $f(x) = x^3 + x$, then $f(-x) = (-x)^3 + (-x) = -x^3 - x$, and $f(-x) = -f(x)$.

Rational Functions

Examples

Rational function	If $P(x)$ and $Q(x)$ are polynomials with no common factor and $f(x) = \dfrac{P(x)}{Q(x)}$ for $Q(x) \neq 0$, then $f(x)$ is a rational function.	$f(x) = \dfrac{x^2 - 1}{3x - 2}, f(x) = \dfrac{1}{x - 3}$
Finding asymptotes for a rational function $f(x) = \dfrac{P(x)}{Q(x)}$	1. The graph of f has a vertical asymptote for each solution to the equation $Q(x) = 0$. 2. If the degree of $P(x)$ is less than the degree of $Q(x)$, then the x-axis is a horizontal asymptote.	$f(x) = \dfrac{1}{x - 2}$ Vertical: $x = 2$ Horizontal: x-axis

3. If the degree of $P(x)$ is equal to the degree of $Q(x)$, then the horizontal asymptote is determined by the ratio of the leading coefficients.

$$f(x) = \frac{x}{x-2}$$
Vertical: $x = 2$
Horizontal: $y = 1$

4. If the degree of $P(x)$ is one larger than the degree of $Q(x)$, then use long division to find the quotient of $P(x)$ and $Q(x)$.

$$f(x) = \frac{2x^2 + 3x - 5}{x + 2} = 2x - 1 + \frac{-3}{x + 2}$$
Vertical: $x = -2$
Oblique: $y = 2x - 1$

ENRICHING YOUR MATHEMATICAL WORD POWER

For each mathematical term, choose the correct meaning.

1. polynomial function
   a.   a function with many numbers
   b.   a function with many names
   c.   a function defined by a polynomial
   d.   a function that is symmetric to a polynomial

2. root
   a.   an exponent
   b.   a number c such that $f(c) = 0$
   c.   a number c such that $f(c) = 1$
   d.   an asymptote

3. zero
   a.   a root
   b.   a number c such that $f(0) = c$
   c.   the empty set
   d.   a conjugate

4. multiplicity
   a.   the product of a and b
   b.   the degree of complexity
   c.   the product of a and $1/a$, provided $a \neq 0$
   d.   the number of times a linear factor occurs in a polynomial

5. upper bound for the roots
   a.   a number M such that no root is bigger than M
   b.   a limit on the roots
   c.   a root larger than 0
   d.   a boundary line

6. lower bound for the roots
   a.   a number m such that no root is smaller than m
   b.   the number 0

   c.   no root is negative
   d.   the average root

7. symmetric about the y-axis
   a.   the origin
   b.   a mirror image
   c.   a function f such that $f(-x) = -f(x)$
   d.   a function f such that $f(-x) = f(x)$

8. symmetric about the origin
   a.   circular function
   b.   a function f such that $f(0) = 0$
   c.   a function f such that $f(-x) = f(x)$
   d.   a function f such that $f(-x) = -f(x)$

9. rational function
   a.   a ratio of two polynomial functions
   b.   a function that has only rational roots
   c.   a polynomial function with rational coefficients
   d.   a commonsense function

10. asymptote
   a.   the graph of a rational function
   b.   a line that is approached by a curve
   c.   the graph of an asymmetrical function
   d.   a line of symmetry

11. oblique asymptote
   a.   an asymptote that is neither horizontal nor vertical
   b.   an asymptote of an odd function
   c.   a really large asymptote
   d.   a dashed line

REVIEW EXERCISES

10.1 *Given that either 2 or −2 is a solution to each of the following equations, solve each equation.*

1. $x^3 - 4x^2 - 11x + 30 = 0$
2. $x^3 - 2x^2 - 6x + 12 = 0$
3. $x^3 - 5x^2 - 2x + 24 = 0$
4. $x^3 + 7x^2 + 4x - 12 = 0$

Determine whether the first polynomial is a factor of the second. If it is, then factor the polynomial completely.

5. $x - 3,\quad x^3 + 4x^2 - 11x - 30$
6. $x + 4,\quad x^3 + x^2 - 10x + 8$
7. $x + 2,\quad x^3 - 5x - 6$
8. $x - 1,\quad 2x^3 - 5x^2 + 2x - 9$

10.2 *For each polynomial find $P(-2)$ and $P\left(\frac{1}{2}\right)$ in two different ways.*

9. $P(x) = 4x^3 - 2x^2 + 3x + 1$

10. $P(x) = 2x^3 - 3x^2 + 5x - 2$

Use the rational root theorem to list all possible rational roots for each polynomial function.

11. $f(x) = 3x^3 - 5x^2 + 7x - 4$

12. $f(x) = 2x^4 - 5x^2 + 3x - 5$

13. $f(x) = 4x^4 - 5x^2 - 3x + 3$

14. $f(x) = 6x^3 + x^2 - 25x - 9$

Find all real and imaginary zeros for each polynomial function.

15. $f(x) = 2x - 3$

16. $f(x) = 5$

17. $f(x) = x^2 - 100$

18. $f(x) = 2x^2 - 1$

19. $f(x) = x^3 - 64$

20. $f(x) = x^3 - 27$

21. $f(x) = x^4 - 64$

22. $f(x) = 4x^4 - 1$

23. $f(x) = 12x^3 - 4x^2 - 3x + 1$

24. $f(x) = 18x^3 + 9x^2 - 2x - 1$

10.3 *Find a polynomial equation with real coefficients that has the given roots.*

25. $\frac{1}{2}, 2$

26. $\frac{1}{3}, -4$

27. $5 - 2i$

28. $3 + 2i$

29. $3, 1 + 3i$

30. $-5, 2 - 4i$

Use Descartes' rule of signs to discuss the possibilities for the roots to each equation. Do not solve the equation.

31. $x^6 + x^4 + x^2 = 0$

32. $2x^3 - 3x^2 - 5x - 9 = 0$

33. $x^3 - 5x^2 + 3x - 9 = 0$

34. $x^5 + x^3 + 5x = 0$

Establish the best integral bounds for the roots of each equation according to the theorem on bounds.

35. $x^2 - 2x - 4 = 0$

36. $x^2 - 2x - 6 = 0$

37. $x^3 - 3x^2 - 5x - 6 = 0$

38. $2x^3 - 4x^2 - 12x - 7 = 0$

Find all real and imaginary solutions to each equation, stating multiplicity when it is greater than 1.

39. $2x^3 - 19x^2 + 49x - 20 = 0$

40. $3x^3 + 2x^2 - 37x + 12 = 0$

41. $8x^3 - 12x^2 - 26x + 15 = 0$

42. $12x^3 - 16x^2 - 5x + 3 = 0$

43. $4x^3 - 24x^2 + 25x - 25 = 0$

44. $2x^3 + 4x^2 - 5x + 3 = 0$

45. $4x^4 - 28x^3 + 59x^2 - 30x - 9 = 0$

46. $2x^4 - 6x^3 + 5x^2 - 1 = 0$

47. $x^3 - 3x^2 + 3x - 1 = 0$

48. $x^4 - 4x^3 + 6x^2 - 4x + 1 = 0$

10.4 *Discuss the symmetry of the graph of each function.*

49. $f(x) = 3x^4 - 2x^2$

50. $f(x) = x^7 - 3x^5 + x^3$

51. $f(x) = -x^3 + 3x$

52. $f(x) = -2x^4 + 6x^2 + 3$

58. $f(x) = x^3 - 6x^2 + 8x$

Find the x-intercepts and y-intercept for the graph of each function, and sketch the graph.

53. $f(x) = x^3 - 3x + 2$

54. $f(x) = -x^3 - 3x^2 + 4$

55. $f(x) = -x^4 + 2x^2 - 1$

56. $f(x) = x^4 - 2x^2$

57. $f(x) = \dfrac{1}{2}x^3 - 2x$

10.5 *Find the domain of each rational function.*

59. $f(x) = \dfrac{x^2 - 1}{2x + 3}$

60. $f(x) = \dfrac{3x + 2}{x^2 - x - 12}$

61. $f(x) = \dfrac{1}{x^2 + 9}$

62. $f(x) = \dfrac{x - 4}{x^2 - 9}$

Find all asymptotes for each rational function and sketch the graph of the function.

63. $f(x) = \dfrac{2}{x - 3}$

64. $f(x) = \dfrac{-1}{x + 1}$

65. $f(x) = \dfrac{x}{x^2 - 4}$

66. $f(x) = \dfrac{x^2}{x^2 - 4}$

67. $f(x) = \dfrac{2x - 1}{x - 1}$

68. $f(x) = \dfrac{-x - 1}{x}$

75. $f(x) = \dfrac{1}{x^2 - 3}$

76. $f(x) = \dfrac{x}{(x - 1)(x + 2)}$

77. $f(x) = x(x - 1)(x + 2)$

69. $f(x) = \dfrac{x^2 - 2x + 1}{x - 2}$

70. $f(x) = \dfrac{-x^2 + x + 2}{x - 1}$

78. $f(x) = x^3 - 4x^2 + 4x$

MISCELLANEOUS

Sketch the graph of each function.

71. $f(x) = 3$

72. $f(x) = 2x - 3$

Solve each problem.

79. Tanya is designing a trophy for a golf tournament. The trophy consists of a solid bronze sphere mounted on a solid bronze square base. The diameter of the sphere will equal

73. $f(x) = x^2 - 3$

74. $f(x) = 3 - x^2$

FIGURE FOR EXERCISE 79

the length of the side of the square, and the thickness of the base will be π inches (in.). If she wants to use 72π cubic inches (in.³) of bronze for the trophy, then what is the radius of the sphere?

80. Joshua is designing a metal silo for storing grain. The silo consists of a cylindrical base with a cone-shaped roof. He wants the radius of the base to be equal to its height and the height of the cone to be 5 feet (ft). If the silo is to have a volume of 864π ft³, then what is the radius of the base?

FIGURE FOR EXERCISE 80

CHAPTER 10 TEST

Find the following values for $f(x) = 3x^4 + 5x^3 - 10x^2 + 3x - 2$ using two different methods.

1. $f(2)$

2. $f(-3)$

Find all possible rational zeros for each polynomial function.

3. $f(x) = x^4 + x^3 - 7x^2 + 5x - 6$

4. $f(x) = 2x^3 - 5x^2 + 9x - 3$

Find all of the real and imaginary zeros for each polynomial function.

5. $f(x) = x^3 - 13x + 12$

6. $f(x) = 2x^3 - 9x^2 + 14x - 5$

Write a polynomial equation with real coefficients that has the given roots.

7. $-1, 1, 2$

8. $2, 3 - i$

Solve each problem.

9. Is $x + 1$ a factor of $2x^4 - 5x^3 + 3x^2 + 6x - 4$? Explain.

10. Factor $x^3 - 12x^2 + 47x - 60$ completely.

Use Descartes' rule of signs to discuss the possibilities for the roots to each equation. Do not solve the equation.

11. $2x^3 - 6x^2 + 5x - 9 = 0$

12. $x^5 + 5x^3 + x = 0$

Establish the best integral bounds for the roots of each equation according to the theorem on bounds.

13. $4x^2 - 4x - 15 = 0$

14. $2x^3 - 3x^2 - 7x + 4 = 0$

Determine whether the graph of each function is symmetric about the y-axis or the origin.

15. $f(x) = x^3 - 16x$

16. $f(x) = x^4 - 25x^2 + 1$

Graph each function.

17. $f(x) = (x + 2)(x - 2)^2$

18. $f(x) = \dfrac{1}{x^2 - 4x + 4}$

19. $f(x) = \dfrac{2x - 3}{x - 2}$

20. $f(x) = x^3 - x^2 - 4x + 4$

Find all real and imaginary solutions to each equation.

1. $2x - 3 = x - 5$

2. $(2x - 3)(x - 5) = 0$

3. $\dfrac{2x - 3}{x - 5} = 0$

4. $2x^2 - 3 = 0$

5. $\dfrac{3}{2x - 3} = \dfrac{2}{x - 5}$

6. $2x^4 + 7x^2 - 15 = 0$

7. $\dfrac{1}{x} + \dfrac{3}{x - 5} = -\dfrac{1}{2}$

8. $30x^3 - 29x^2 - 22x - 3 = 0$

Sketch the graph of each function.

9. $y = 2x$

10. $y = 2 - x$

11. $y = x - 2$

12. $y = \dfrac{1}{x - 2}$

13. $y = x^2 - 2$

14. $y = (x - 2)^2$

15. $y = \dfrac{1}{(x - 2)^2}$

16. $y = x^3 - 2$

17. $y = x^3 - x$

18. $y = x^4 - x^2$

19. $y = \sqrt{x + 5} - 2$

20. $y = -|x - 2|$

11

Exponential and Logarithmic Functions

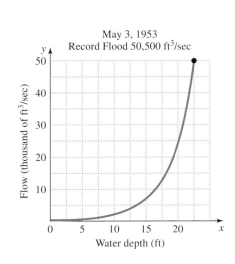

May 3, 1953
Record Flood 50,500 ft³/sec

Flow (thousand of ft³/sec)

Water depth (ft)

Water is one of the essentials of life, yet it is something that most of us take for granted. Among other things, the U.S. Geological Survey (U.S.G.S.) studies freshwater. For over 50 years the Water Resources Division of the U.S.G.S. has been gathering basic data about the flow of both freshwater and saltwater from streams and groundwater surfaces. This division collects, compiles, analyzes, verifies, organizes, and publishes data gathered from groundwater data collection networks in each of the 50 states, Puerto Rico, and the Trust Territories. Records of stream flow, groundwater levels, and water quality provide hydrological information needed by local, state, and federal agencies as well as the private sector.

There are many instances of the importance of the data collected by the U.S.G.S. For example, before 1987 the Tangipahoa River in Louisiana was used extensively for swimming and boating. In 1987 data gathered by the U.S.G.S. showed that fecal coliform levels in the river exceeded safe levels. Consequently, Louisiana banned recreational use of the river. Other studies by the Water Resources Division include the results of pollutants on salt marsh environments and the effect that salting highways in winter has on our drinking water supply.

In Exercises 85 and 86 of Section 11.2 you will see how data from the U.S.G.S. is used in a logarithmic function to measure water quality.

11.1 EXPONENTIAL FUNCTIONS AND THEIR APPLICATIONS

We have studied functions such as

$$f(x) = x^2, \qquad g(x) = x^3, \qquad \text{and} \qquad h(x) = x^{1/2}.$$

For these functions the variable is the base. In this section we discuss functions that have a variable as an exponent. These functions are called *exponential functions*.

Definition

Some examples of exponential functions are

$$f(x) = 2^x, \qquad f(x) = \left(\frac{1}{2}\right)^x, \qquad \text{and} \qquad f(x) = 3^x.$$

> **Exponential Function**
>
> An **exponential function** is a function of the form
>
> $$f(x) = a^x,$$
>
> where $a > 0$ and $a \neq 1$.

We rule out the base 1 in the definition because $f(x) = 1^x$ is the same as the constant function $f(x) = 1$. Zero is not used as a base because $0^x = 0$ for any positive x and nonpositive powers of 0 are undefined. Negative numbers are not used as bases because an expression such as $(-4)^x$ is not a real number if $x = \frac{1}{2}$.

EXAMPLE 1 **Evaluating exponential functions**

Let $f(x) = 2^x$, $g(x) = \left(\frac{1}{4}\right)^{1-x}$, and $h(x) = -3^x$. Find the following.

a) $f\left(\frac{3}{2}\right)$ **b)** $f(-3)$ **c)** $g(3)$ **d)** $h(2)$

Solution

a) $f\left(\frac{3}{2}\right) = 2^{3/2} = \sqrt{2^3} = \sqrt{8} = 2\sqrt{2}$

b) $f(-3) = 2^{-3} = \dfrac{1}{2^3} = \dfrac{1}{8}$

c) $g(3) = \left(\frac{1}{4}\right)^{1-3} = \left(\frac{1}{4}\right)^{-2} = 4^2 = 16$

d) $h(2) = -3^2 = -9$ Note that $-3^2 \neq (-3)^2$. ∎

For many applications of exponential functions we use base 10 or another base called e. The number e is an irrational number that is approximately 2.718. We will see how e is used in compound interest in Example 10 of this section. Base 10 will be used in the next section. Base 10 is called the **common base,** and base e is called the **natural base.**

E X A M P L E   2

Base 10 and base *e*

Let $f(x) = 10^x$ and $g(x) = e^x$. Find the following and round approximate answers to four decimal places.

a) $f(3)$ **b)** $f(1.51)$ **c)** $g(0)$ **d)** $g(2)$

Calculator Close-Up

Most graphing calculators have keys for the functions 10^x and e^x.

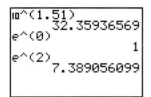

Solution

a) $f(3) = 10^3 = 1000$

b) $f(1.51) = 10^{1.51} \approx 32.3594$ Use the 10^x key on a calculator.

c) $g(0) = e^0 = 1$

d) $g(2) = e^2 \approx 7.3891$ Use the e^x key on a calculator.   ■

Domain

In the definition of an exponential function no restrictions were placed on the exponent x because the domain of an exponential function is the set of all real numbers. So both rational and irrational numbers can be used as the exponent. We have been using rational numbers for exponents since Chapter 7, but we have not yet seen an irrational number as an exponent. Even though we do not formally define irrational exponents in this text, an irrational number such as π can be used as an exponent, and you can evaluate an expression such as 2^π by using a calculator. Try it:

$$2^\pi \approx 8.824977827$$

Graphing Exponential Functions

Even though the domain of an exponential function is the set of all real numbers, we can graph an exponential function by evaluating it for just a few integers.

E X A M P L E   3

Exponential functions with base greater than 1

Sketch the graph of each function.

a) $f(x) = 2^x$ **b)** $g(x) = 3^x$

Calculator Close-Up

The graph of $f(x) = 2^x$ on a calculator appears to touch the x-axis. When drawing this graph by hand, make sure that it does not touch the x-axis.

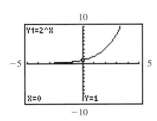

Solution

a) We first make a table of ordered pairs that satisfy $f(x) = 2^x$:

x	-2	-1	0	1	2	3
$f(x) = 2^x$	$\frac{1}{4}$	$\frac{1}{2}$	1	2	4	8

As x increases, 2^x increases and 2^x is always positive. Because the domain of the function is $(-\infty, \infty)$, we draw the graph in Fig. 11.1 as a smooth curve through these points. From the graph we can see that the range is $(0, \infty)$.

FIGURE 11.1

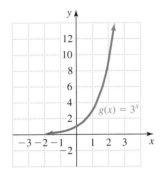

FIGURE 11.2

b) Make a table of ordered pairs that satisfy $g(x) = 3^x$:

x	-2	-1	0	1	2	3
$g(x) = 3^x$	$\frac{1}{9}$	$\frac{1}{3}$	1	3	9	27

As x increases, 3^x increases and 3^x is always positive. The graph is shown in Fig. 11.2. From the graph we see that the range is $(0, \infty)$.   ■

Because $e \approx 2.718$, the graph of $f(x) = e^x$ lies between the graphs of $f(x) = 2^x$ and $g(x) = 3^x$, as shown in Fig. 11.3. Note that all three functions have the same domain and range and the same y-intercept. In general, the function $f(x) = a^x$ for $a > 1$ has the following characteristics:

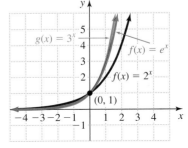

FIGURE 11.3

1. The y-intercept of the curve is $(0, 1)$.
2. The domain is $(-\infty, \infty)$, and the range is $(0, \infty)$.
3. The curve approaches the negative x-axis but does not touch it.
4. The y-values are increasing as we go from left to right along the curve.

E X A M P L E   4

Exponential functions with base between 0 and 1

Graph each function.

a) $f(x) = \left(\frac{1}{2}\right)^x$

b) $f(x) = 4^{-x}$

Solution

a) First make a table of ordered pairs that satisfy $f(x) = \left(\frac{1}{2}\right)^x$:

x	-2	-1	0	1	2	3
$f(x) = \left(\frac{1}{2}\right)^x$	4	2	1	$\frac{1}{2}$	$\frac{1}{4}$	$\frac{1}{8}$

As x increases, $\left(\frac{1}{2}\right)^x$ decreases, getting closer and closer to 0. Draw a smooth curve through these points as shown in Fig. 11.4.

FIGURE 11.4

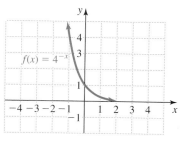

FIGURE 11.5

b) Because $4^{-x} = \left(\frac{1}{4}\right)^{x}$, we make a table for $f(x) = \left(\frac{1}{4}\right)^{x}$:

x	-2	-1	0	1	2	3
$f(x) = \left(\frac{1}{4}\right)^{x}$	16	4	1	$\frac{1}{4}$	$\frac{1}{16}$	$\frac{1}{64}$

As x increases, $\left(\frac{1}{4}\right)^{x}$, or 4^{-x}, decreases, getting closer and closer to 0. Draw a smooth curve through these points as shown in Fig. 11.5. ∎

Notice the similarities and differences between the exponential function with $a > 1$ and with $0 < a < 1$. The function $f(x) = a^{x}$ for $0 < a < 1$ has the following characteristics:

1. The y-intercept of the curve is $(0, 1)$.
2. The domain is $(-\infty, \infty)$, and the range is $(0, \infty)$.
3. The curve approaches the positive x-axis but does not touch it.
4. The y-values are decreasing as we go from left to right along the curve.

CAUTION   An exponential function can be written in more than one form. For example, $f(x) = \left(\frac{1}{2}\right)^{x}$ is the same as $f(x) = \frac{1}{2^{x}}$, or $f(x) = 2^{-x}$.

Although exponential functions have the form $f(x) = a^{x}$, other functions that have similar forms are also called exponential functions. Notice how changing the form $f(x) = a^{x}$ in Examples 5 and 6 changes the shape and location of the graph.

E X A M P L E 5

Changing the shape and location
Sketch the graph of $f(x) = 3^{2x-1}$.

Solution

Make a table of ordered pairs:

x	-1	0	$\frac{1}{2}$	1	2
$f(x) = 3^{2x-1}$	$\frac{1}{27}$	$\frac{1}{3}$	1	3	27

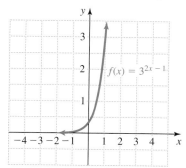

FIGURE 11.6

The graph through these points is shown in Fig. 11.6. ∎

E X A M P L E 6

Changing the shape and location
Sketch the graph of $y = -2^{-x}$.

Solution

Because $-2^{-x} = -(2^{-x})$, all y-coordinates are negative. Make a table of ordered pairs:

x	-2	-1	0	1	2
$f(x) = -2^{-x}$	-4	-2	-1	$-\frac{1}{2}$	$-\frac{1}{4}$

FIGURE 11.7

The graph through these points is shown in Fig. 11.7. ∎

Exponential Equations

In Chapter 9 we used the horizontal-line test to determine whether a function is one-to-one. Because no horizontal line can cross the graph of an exponential function more than once, exponential functions are one-to-one functions. For an exponential function one-to-one means that *if two exponential expressions with the same base are equal, then the exponents are equal.*

One-to-One Property of Exponential Functions

For $a > 0$ and $a \neq 1$,

$$\text{if} \quad a^m = a^n, \quad \text{then} \quad m = n.$$

In the next example we use the one-to-one property to solve equations involving exponential functions.

E X A M P L E   7

Using the one-to-one property

Solve each equation.

a) $2^{2x-1} = 8$ **b)** $9^{|x|} = 3$ **c)** $\dfrac{1}{8} = 4^x$

Solution

a) Because 8 is 2^3, we can write each side as a power of the same base, 2:

$$2^{2x-1} = 8 \qquad \text{Original equation}$$
$$2^{2x-1} = 2^3 \qquad \text{Write each side as a power of the same base.}$$
$$2x - 1 = 3 \qquad \text{One-to-one property}$$
$$2x = 4$$
$$x = 2$$

Check: $2^{2 \cdot 2 - 1} = 2^3 = 8$. The solution set is $\{2\}$.

b) Because $9 = 3^2$, we can write each side as a power of 3:

$$9^{|x|} = 3 \qquad \text{Original equation}$$
$$(3^2)^{|x|} = 3^1$$
$$3^{2|x|} = 3^1 \qquad \text{Power of a power rule}$$
$$2|x| = 1 \qquad \text{One-to-one property}$$
$$|x| = \frac{1}{2}$$
$$x = \pm\frac{1}{2}$$

Check $x = \pm\frac{1}{2}$ in the original equation. The solution set is $\left\{ -\frac{1}{2}, \frac{1}{2} \right\}$.

c) Because $\frac{1}{8} = 2^{-3}$ and $4 = 2^2$, we can write each side as a power of 2:

$$\frac{1}{8} = 4^x \qquad \text{Original equation}$$
$$2^{-3} = (2^2)^x \qquad \text{Write each side as a power of 2.}$$
$$2^{-3} = 2^{2x} \qquad \text{Power of a power rule}$$
$$2x = -3 \qquad \text{One-to-one property}$$
$$x = -\frac{3}{2}$$

Check $x = -\frac{3}{2}$ in the original equation. The solution set is $\left\{ -\frac{3}{2} \right\}$.   ■

The one-to-one property is also used to find the first coordinate when given the second coordinate of an exponential function.

E X A M P L E   8

Finding the x-coordinate in an exponential function

Let $f(x) = 2^x$ and $g(x) = \left(\frac{1}{2}\right)^{1-x}$. Find x if:

a) $f(x) = 32$

b) $g(x) = 8$

Solution

a) Because $f(x) = 2^x$ and $f(x) = 32$, we can find x by solving $2^x = 32$:

$$2^x = 32$$

$$2^x = 2^5 \qquad \text{Write both sides as a power of the same base.}$$

$$x = 5 \qquad \text{One-to-one property}$$

b) Because $g(x) = \left(\frac{1}{2}\right)^{1-x}$ and $g(x) = 8$, we can find x by solving $\left(\frac{1}{2}\right)^{1-x} = 8$:

$$\left(\frac{1}{2}\right)^{1-x} = 8$$

$$(2^{-1})^{1-x} = 2^3 \qquad \text{Because } \tfrac{1}{2} = 2^{-1} \text{ and } 8 = 2^3$$

$$2^{x-1} = 2^3 \qquad \text{Power of a power rule}$$

$$x - 1 = 3 \qquad \text{One-to-one property}$$

$$x = 4$$

∎

Applications

Exponential functions are used to describe phenomena such as population growth, radioactive decay, and compound interest. Here we discuss compound interest. If an investment is earning **compound interest,** then interest is periodically paid into the account and the interest that is paid also earns interest. If a bank pays 6% compounded quarterly on an account, then the interest is computed four times per year (every 3 months) at 1.5% (one-quarter of 6%). Suppose an account has $5000 in it at the beginning of a quarter. We can apply the simple interest formula $A = P + Prt$, with $r = 6\%$ and $t = \frac{1}{4}$, to find how much is in the account at the end of the first quarter.

$$A = P + Prt$$

$$= P(1 + rt) \qquad \text{Factor.}$$

$$= 5000\left(1 + 0.06 \cdot \frac{1}{4}\right) \qquad \text{Substitute.}$$

$$= 5000(1.015)$$

$$= \$5075$$

To repeat this computation for another quarter, we multiply $5075 by 1.015. If A represents the amount in the account at the end of n quarters, we can write A as an exponential function of n:

$$A = \$5000(1.015)^n$$

In general, the amount A is given by the following formula.

Compound Interest Formula

If P represents the principal, i the interest rate per period, n the number of periods, and A the amount at the end of n periods, then

$$A = P(1 + i)^n.$$

E X A M P L E   9

Compound interest formula

If \$350 is deposited in an account paying 12% compounded monthly, then how much is in the account at the end of 6 years and 6 months?

Solution

Interest is paid 12 times per year, so the account earns $\frac{1}{12}$ of 12%, or 1% each month, for 78 months. So $i = 0.01$, $n = 78$, and $P = \$350$:

$$A = P(1 + i)^n$$
$$A = \$350(1.01)^{78}$$
$$\approx \$760.56$$ ∎

If we shorten the length of the time period (yearly, quarterly, monthly, daily, hourly, etc.), the number of periods n increases while the interest rate for the period decreases. As n increases, the amount A also increases but will not exceed a certain amount. That certain amount is the amount obtained from *continuous compounding* of the interest. It is shown in more advanced courses that the following formula gives the amount when interest is compounded continuously.

Continuous-Compounding Formula

If P is the principal or beginning balance, r is the annual percentage rate compounded continuously, t is the time in years, and A is the amount or ending balance, then

$$A = Pe^{rt}.$$

C A U T I O N   The value of t in the continuous-compounding formula must be in years. For example, if the time is 1 year and 3 months, then $t = 1.25$ years. If the time is 3 years and 145 days, then

$$t = 3 + \frac{145}{365}$$

$$\approx 3.3973 \text{ years.}$$

EXAMPLE 10

Continuous-compounding formula

If $350 is deposited in an account paying 12% compounded continuously, then how much is in the account after 6 years and 6 months?

Calculator Close-Up

Graph $y = 350e^{0.12x}$ to see the growth of the $350 deposit in Example 10 over time. After 30 years it is worth $12,809.38.

15,000

Y1=350e^(.12X)

X=30   Y=12809.382

0   30

Solution

Use $r = 12\%$, $t = 6.5$ years, and $P = \$350$ in the formula for compounding interest continuously:

$$A = Pe^{rt}$$
$$= 350e^{(0.12)(6.5)}$$
$$= 350e^{0.78}$$
$$\approx \$763.52 \quad \text{Use the } e^x \text{ key on a scientific calculator.}$$

Note that compounding continuously amounts to a few dollars more than compounding monthly did in Example 9.

MATH AT WORK

Neal Driscoll, a geophysicist at the Lamont-Doherty Earth Observatory of Columbia University, explores both the ocean and the continents to understand the processes that shape the earth. What he finds fascinating is the interaction between the ocean and the land—not just at the shoreline, but underneath the sea as well.

To get a preliminary picture of the ocean floor, Dr. Driscoll has worked with the U.S.G.S., studying the effects of storms on beaches and underwater landscapes. The results of these studies can be used as a baseline to provide help to coastal planners who are building waterfront homes. Other information obtained can be used to direct transporters of dredged material to

GEOPHYSICIST

places where the material is least likely to affect plant, fish, and human life. The most recent study found many different types of ocean floor, ranging from sand and mud to large tracts of algae.

Imaging the seafloor is a difficult problem. It can be a costly venture, and there are numerous logistical problems. Recently developed technology, such as towable undersea cameras and satellite position systems, has made the task easier. Dr. Driscoll and his team use this new technology and sound reflection to gather data about how the sediment on the ocean floor changes in response to storm events. This research is funded by the Office of Naval Research (ONR).

In Exercise 28 of the Making Connections exercises you will see how a geophysicist uses sound to measure the depth of the ocean.

WARM-UPS

True or false? Explain your answer.

1. If $f(x) = 4^x$, then $f\left(-\frac{1}{2}\right) = -2$.

2. If $f(x) = \left(\frac{1}{3}\right)^x$, then $f(-1) = 3$.

3. The function $f(x) = x^4$ is an exponential function.

4. The functions $f(x) = \left(\frac{1}{2}\right)^x$ and $g(x) = 2^{-x}$ have the same graph.

5. The function $f(x) = 2^x$ is invertible.

6. The graph of $y = \left(\frac{1}{3}\right)^x$ has an x-intercept.

7. The y-intercept for $f(x) = e^x$ is $(0, 1)$.

8. The expression $2^{\sqrt{2}}$ is undefined.

9. The functions $f(x) = 2^{-x}$ and $g(x) = \frac{1}{2^x}$ have the same graph.

10. If \$500 earns 6% compounded monthly, then at the end of 3 years the investment is worth $500(1.005)^3$ dollars.

11.1   EXERCISES

Reading and Writing   *After reading this section, write out the answers to these questions. Use complete sentences.*

1. What is an exponential function?

2. What is the domain of every exponential function?

3. What are the two most popular bases?

4. What is the one-to-one property of exponential functions?

5. What is the compound interest formula?

6. What does compounded continuously mean?

Let $f(x) = 4^x$, $g(x) = \left(\frac{1}{3}\right)^{x+1}$, *and* $h(x) = -2^x$. *Find the following. See Example 1.*

7. $f(2)$

8. $f(-1)$

9. $f\left(\frac{1}{2}\right)$

10. $f\left(-\frac{3}{2}\right)$

11. $g(-2)$

12. $g(1)$

13. $g(0)$

14. $g(-3)$

15. $h(0)$

16. $h(3)$

17. $h(-2)$

18. $h(-4)$

Let $h(x) = 10^x$ *and* $j(x) = e^x$. *Find the following. Use a calculator as necessary and round approximate answers to three decimal places. See Example 2.*

19. $h(0)$

20. $h(-1)$

21. $h(2)$

22. $h(3.4)$

23. $j(1)$

24. $j(3.5)$

25. $j(-2)$

26. $j(0)$

Sketch the graph of each function. See Examples 3 and 4.

27. $f(x) = 4^x$

28. $g(x) = 5^x$

29. $h(x) = \left(\frac{1}{3}\right)^x$

30. $i(x) = \left(\frac{1}{5}\right)^x$

31. $y = 10^x$

32. $y = (0.1)^x$

 43. $P = 5000(1.05)^t$

44. $d = 800 \cdot 10^{-4t}$

Sketch the graph of each function. See Examples 5 and 6.

33. $y = 10^{x+2}$

34. $y = 3^{2x+1}$

35. $f(x) = -2^x$

36. $k(x) = -2^{x-2}$

37. $g(x) = 2^{-x}$

38. $A(x) = 10^{1-x}$

39. $f(x) = -e^x$

40. $g(x) = e^{-x}$

41. $H(x) = 10^{|x|}$

42. $s(x) = 2^{(x^2)}$

Solve each equation. See Example 7.

45. $2^x = 64$

46. $3^x = 9$

47. $10^x = 0.001$

48. $10^{2x} = 0.1$

49. $2^x = \dfrac{1}{4}$

50. $3^x = \dfrac{1}{9}$

51. $\left(\dfrac{2}{3}\right)^{x-1} = \dfrac{9}{4}$

52. $\left(\dfrac{1}{4}\right)^{3x} = 16$

53. $5^{-x} = 25$

54. $10^{-x} = 0.01$

55. $-2^{1-x} = -8$

56. $-3^{2-x} = -81$

57. $10^{|x|} = 1000$

58. $3^{|2x-5|} = 81$

Let $f(x) = 2^x$, $g(x) = \left(\dfrac{1}{3}\right)^x$, and $h(x) = 4^{2x-1}$. Find x in each case. See Example 8.

59. $f(x) = 4$

60. $f(x) = \dfrac{1}{4}$

61. $f(x) = 4^{2/3}$

62. $f(x) = 1$

63. $g(x) = 9$

64. $g(x) = \dfrac{1}{9}$

65. $g(x) = 1$

66. $g(x) = \sqrt{3}$

67. $h(x) = 16$

68. $h(x) = \dfrac{1}{2}$

69. $h(x) = 1$

70. $h(x) = \sqrt{2}$

 Solve each problem. See Example 9.

71. *Compounding quarterly.* If $6000 is deposited in an account paying 5% compounded quarterly, then what amount will be in the account after 10 years?

72. *Compounding quarterly.* If $400 is deposited in an account paying 10% compounded quarterly, then what amount will be in the account after 7 years?

73. *Outstanding performance.* The top growth fund at Fidelity Investments from 1992 to 2002 was the Low-Priced Stock Fund (www.fidelity.com), which returned an average of 18.21% annually for those 10 years.

    a) How much was an investment of $10,000 in this fund in 1992 worth in 2002 at 18.21% compounded annually?

FIGURE FOR EXERCISE 73

b) Use the accompanying graph to estimate the year in which the $10,000 investment would be worth $200,000 if it continued to grow at 18.21% annually.

74. *Second place.* The second best growth fund at Fidelity Investments from 1992 to 2002 was the Contrafund Fund, which returned an average of 13.47% annually for those 10 years. How much was an investment of $10,000 in this fund in 1992 worth in 2002?

75. *Depreciating knowledge.* The value of a certain textbook seems to decrease according to the formula $V = 45 \cdot 2^{-0.9t}$, where V is the value in dollars and t is the age of the book in years. What is the book worth when it is new? What is it worth when it is 2 years old?

76. *Mosquito abatement.* In a Minnesota swamp in the springtime the number of mosquitoes per acre appears to grow according to the formula $N = 10^{0.1t + 2}$, where t is the number of days since the last frost. What is the size of the mosquito population at times $t = 10$, $t = 20$, and $t = 30$?

   In Exercises 77–82, solve each problem. See Example 10.

77. *Compounding continuously.* If $500 is deposited in an account paying 7% compounded continuously, then how much will be in the account after 3 years?

78. *Compounding continuously.* If $7000 is deposited in an account paying 8% compounded continuously, then what will it amount to after 4 years?

79. *One year's interest.* How much interest will be earned the first year on $80,000 on deposit in an account paying 7.5% compounded continuously?

80. *Partial year.* If $7500 is deposited in an account paying 6.75% compounded continuously, then how much will be in the account after 5 years and 215 days?

81. *Radioactive decay.* The number of grams of a certain radioactive substance present at time t is given by the

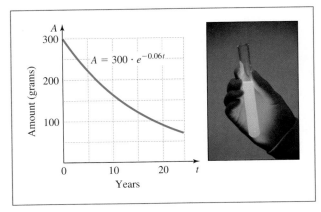

FIGURE FOR EXERCISE 81

formula $A = 300 \cdot e^{-0.06t}$, where t is the number of years. Find the amount present at time $t = 0$. Find the amount present after 20 years. Use the accompanying graph to estimate the number of years that it takes for one-half of the substance to decay. Will the substance ever decay completely?

82. *Population growth.* The population of a certain country appears to be growing according to the formula $P = 20 \cdot e^{0.1t}$, where P is the population in millions and t is the number of years since 1990. What was the population in 1990? What will the population be in the year 2010?

GETTING MORE INVOLVED

 83. *Exploration.* An approximate value for e can be found by adding the terms in the following infinite sum:

$$1 + \frac{1}{1} + \frac{1}{2 \cdot 1} + \frac{1}{3 \cdot 2 \cdot 1} + \frac{1}{4 \cdot 3 \cdot 2 \cdot 1} + \cdots$$

Use a calculator to find the sum of the first four terms. Find the difference between the sum of the first four terms and e. (For e, use all of the digits that your calculator gives for e^1.) What is the difference between e and the sum of the first eight terms?

GRAPHING CALCULATOR EXERCISES

84. Graph $y_1 = 2^x$, $y_2 = e^x$, and $y_3 = 3^x$ on the same coordinate system. Which point do all three graphs have in common?

85. Graph $y_1 = 3^x$, $y_2 = 3^{x-1}$, and $y_3 = 3^{x-2}$ on the same coordinate system. What can you say about the graph of $y = 3^{x-k}$ for any real number k?

In This Section

11.2 LOGARITHMIC FUNCTIONS AND THEIR APPLICATIONS

In Section 11.1 you learned that exponential functions are one-to-one functions. Because they are one-to-one functions, they have inverse functions. In this section we study the inverses of the exponential functions.

Definition

We define $\log_a(x)$ as *the exponent that is used on the base a to obtain x.* Read $\log_a(x)$ as "the base a logarithm of x." The expression $\log_a(x)$ is called a **logarithm.** Because $2^3 = 8$, the exponent is 3 and $\log_2(8) = 3$. Because $5^2 = 25$, the exponent is 2 and $\log_5(25) = 2$. Because $2^{-5} = \frac{1}{32}$, the exponent is -5 and $\log_2\left(\frac{1}{32}\right) = -5$. So the logarithmic equation $y = \log_a(x)$ is equivalent to the exponential equation $a^y = x$.

$\log_a(x)$

For any $a > 0$ and $a \neq 1$,

$$y = \log_a(x) \qquad \text{if and only if} \qquad a^y = x.$$

E X A M P L E   1

Using the definition of logarithm

Write each logarithmic equation as an exponential equation and each exponential equation as a logarithmic equation.

a) $\log_5(125) = 3$ **b)** $6 = \log_{1/4}(x)$ **c)** $\left(\frac{1}{2}\right)^m = 8$ **d)** $7 = 3^z$

Solution

a) "The base-5 logarithm of 125 equals 3" means that 3 is the exponent on 5 that produces 125. So $5^3 = 125$.

b) The equation $6 = \log_{1/4}(x)$ is equivalent to $\left(\frac{1}{4}\right)^6 = x$ by the definition of logarithm.

c) The equation $\left(\frac{1}{2}\right)^m = 8$ is equivalent to $\log_{1/2}(8) = m$.

d) The equation $7 = 3^z$ is equivalent to $\log_3(7) = z$.   ■

The inverse of the base-a exponential function $f(x) = a^x$ is the **base-a logarithmic function** $f^{-1}(x) = \log_a(x)$. For example, $f(x) = 2^x$ and $f^{-1}(x) = \log_2(x)$ are inverse functions as shown in Fig. 11.8. Each function undoes the other.

$$f(5) = 2^5 = 32 \quad \text{and} \quad g(32) = \log_2(32) = 5.$$

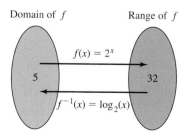

FIGURE 11.8

To evaluate logarithmic functions remember that a logarithm is an exponent: $\log_a(x)$ is the exponent that is used on the base a to obtain x.

EXAMPLE 2

Finding logarithms

Evaluate each logarithm.

a) $\log_5(25)$ **b)** $\log_2\left(\dfrac{1}{8}\right)$ **c)** $\log_{1/2}(4)$

d) $\log_{10}(0.001)$ **e)** $\log_9(3)$

Helpful Hint

When we write $C(x) = 12x$, we may think of C as a variable and write $C = 12x$, or we may think of C as the name of a function, the cost function. In $y = \log_a(x)$ we are thinking of $\log_a$ only as the name of the function that pairs an x-value with a y-value.

Solution

a) The number $\log_5(25)$ is the exponent that is used on the base 5 to obtain 25. Because $25 = 5^2$, we have $\log_5(25) = 2$.

b) The number $\log_2\left(\frac{1}{8}\right)$ is the power of 2 that gives us $\frac{1}{8}$. Because $\frac{1}{8} = 2^{-3}$, we have $\log_2\left(\frac{1}{8}\right) = -3$.

c) The number $\log_{1/2}(4)$ is the power of $\frac{1}{2}$ that produces 4. Because $4 = \left(\frac{1}{2}\right)^{-2}$, we have $\log_{1/2}(4) = -2$.

d) Because $0.001 = 10^{-3}$, we have $\log_{10}(0.001) = -3$.

e) Because $9^{1/2} = 3$, we have $\log_9(3) = \frac{1}{2}$.   ■

There are two bases for logarithms that are used more frequently than the others: They are 10 and e. The base-10 logarithm is called the **common logarithm** and is usually written as $\log(x)$. The base-e logarithm is called the **natural logarithm** and is usually written as $\ln(x)$. Most scientific calculators have function keys for $\log(x)$ and $\ln(x)$. The simplest way to obtain a common or natural logarithm is to use a scientific calculator. However, a table of common logarithms can be found in Appendix C of this text.

In the next example we find natural and common logarithms of certain numbers without a calculator or a table.

EXAMPLE 3

Finding common and natural logarithms

Evaluate each logarithm.

a) $\log(1000)$

b) $\ln(e)$

c) $\log\left(\dfrac{1}{10}\right)$

Calculator Close-Up

A graphing calculator has keys for the common logarithm (LOG) and the natural logarithm (LN).

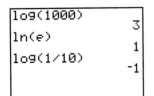

```
log(1000)
              3
ln(e)
              1
log(1/10)
             -1
```

Solution

a) Because $10^3 = 1000$, we have $\log(1000) = 3$.

b) Because $e^1 = e$, we have $\ln(e) = 1$.

c) Because $10^{-1} = \frac{1}{10}$, we have $\log\left(\frac{1}{10}\right) = -1$.   ■

Domain and Range

The domain of the exponential function $y = 2^x$ is $(-\infty, \infty)$, and its range is $(0, \infty)$. Because the logarithmic function $y = \log_2(x)$ is the inverse of $y = 2^x$, the domain of $y = \log_2(x)$ is $(0, \infty)$, and its range is $(-\infty, \infty)$.

CAUTION   Because the domain of $y = \log_a(x)$ is $(0, \infty)$ for any $a > 0$ and $a \neq 1$, expressions such as $\log_2(-4)$, $\log_{1/3}(0)$, and $\ln(-1)$ are undefined.

Graphing Logarithmic Functions

In Chapter 9 we saw that the graphs of a function and its inverse function are symmetric about the line $y = x$. Because the logarithm functions are inverses of exponential functions, their graphs are also symmetric about $y = x$.

E X A M P L E   4

A logarithmic function with base greater than 1

Sketch the graph of $g(x) = \log_2(x)$ and compare it to the graph of $y = 2^x$.

Solution

Make a table of ordered pairs for $g(x) = \log_2(x)$ using positive numbers for x:

x	$\frac{1}{4}$	$\frac{1}{2}$	1	2	4	8
$g(x) = \log_2(x)$	-2	-1	0	1	2	3

Draw a curve through these points as shown in Fig. 11.9. The graph of the inverse function $y = 2^x$ is also shown in Fig. 11.9 for comparison. Note the symmetry of the two curves about the line $y = x$.

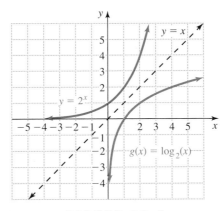

FIGURE 11.9

All logarithmic functions with the base greater than 1 have graphs that are similar to the one in Fig. 11.9. In general, the graph of $f(x) = \log_a(x)$ for $a > 1$ has the following characteristics (see Fig. 11.10):

1. The x-intercept of the curve is $(1, 0)$.
2. The domain is $(0, \infty)$, and the range is $(-\infty, \infty)$.
3. The curve approaches the negative y-axis but does not touch it.
4. The y-values are increasing as we go from left to right along the curve.

E X A M P L E   5

A logarithmic function with base less than 1

Sketch the graph of $f(x) = \log_{1/2}(x)$ and compare it to the graph of $y = \left(\frac{1}{2}\right)^x$.

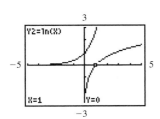

Calculator Close-Up

The graphs of $y = \ln(x)$ and $y = e^x$ are symmetric with respect to the line $y = x$. Logarithmic functions with bases other than e and 10 will be graphed on a calculator in Section 11.4.

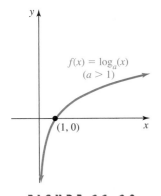

$f(x) = \log_a(x)$
$(a > 1)$

$(1, 0)$

FIGURE 11.10

FIGURE 11.11

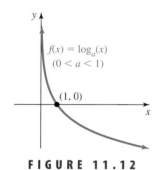

FIGURE 11.12

Solution

Make a table of ordered pairs for $f(x) = \log_{1/2}(x)$ using positive numbers for x:

x	$\frac{1}{4}$	$\frac{1}{2}$	1	2	4	8
$f(x) = \log_{1/2}(x)$	2	1	0	-1	-2	-3

The curve through these points is shown in Fig. 11.11. The graph of the inverse function $y = \left(\frac{1}{2}\right)^x$ is also shown in Fig. 11.11 for comparison. Note the symmetry with respect to the line $y = x$. ∎

All logarithmic functions with the base between 0 and 1 have graphs that are similar to the one in Fig. 11.11. In general, the graph of $f(x) = \log_a(x)$ for $0 < a < 1$ has the following characteristics (see Fig. 11.12):

1. The x-intercept of the curve is $(1, 0)$.
2. The domain is $(0, \infty)$, and the range is $(-\infty, \infty)$.
3. The curve approaches the positive y-axis but does not touch it.
4. The y-values are decreasing as we go from left to right along the curve.

Figures 11.9 and 11.11 illustrate the fact that $y = \log_a(x)$ and $y = a^x$ are inverse functions for any base a. For any given exponential or logarithmic function the inverse function can be easily obtained from the definition of logarithm.

E X A M P L E 6

Inverses of logarithmic and exponential functions
Find the inverse of each function.
a) $f(x) = 10^x$ **b)** $g(x) = \log_3(x)$

Solution

a) To find any inverse function we switch the roles of x and y. So $y = 10^x$ becomes $x = 10^y$. Now $x = 10^y$ is equivalent to $y = \log_{10}(x)$. So the inverse of $f(x) = 10^x$ is $y = \log(x)$ or $f^{-1}(x) = \log(x)$.

b) In $g(x) = \log_3(x)$ or $y = \log_3(x)$ we switch x and y to get $x = \log_3(y)$. Now $x = \log_3(y)$ is equivalent to $y = 3^x$. So the inverse of $g(x) = \log_3(x)$ is $y = 3^x$ or $g^{-1}(x) = 3^x$. ∎

Logarithmic Equations

In Section 11.1 we learned that the exponential functions are one-to-one functions. Because logarithmic functions are inverses of exponential functions, they are one-to-one functions also. For a base-a logarithmic function *one-to-one means that if the base-a logarithms of two numbers are equal, then the numbers are equal.*

One-to-One Property of Logarithms

For $a > 0$ and $a \neq 1$,

$$\text{if} \quad \log_a(m) = \log_a(n), \quad \text{then} \quad m = n.$$

The one-to-one property of logarithms and the definition of logarithms are the two basic tools that we use to solve equations involving logarithms. We use these tools in Example 7.

E X A M P L E   7

Logarithmic equations

Solve each equation.

a) $\log_3(x) = -2$ b) $\log_x(8) = -3$ c) $\log(x^2) = \log(4)$

Study Tip

Establish a regular routine of eating, sleeping, and exercise. The ability to concentrate depends on adequate sleep, decent nutrition, and the physical well-being that comes with exercise.

Solution

a) Use the definition of logarithms to rewrite the logarithmic equation as an equivalent exponential equation:

$$\log_3(x) = -2$$
$$3^{-2} = x \quad \text{Definition of logarithm}$$
$$\frac{1}{9} = x$$

Because $3^{-2} = \frac{1}{9}$ or $\log_3\left(\frac{1}{9}\right) = -2$, the solution set is $\left\{\frac{1}{9}\right\}$.

b) Use the definition of logarithms to rewrite the logarithmic equation as an equivalent exponential equation:

$$\log_x(8) = -3$$
$$x^{-3} = 8 \qquad \text{Definition of logarithm}$$
$$(x^{-3})^{-1} = 8^{-1} \qquad \text{Raise each side to the } -1 \text{ power.}$$
$$x^3 = \frac{1}{8}$$
$$x = \sqrt[3]{\frac{1}{8}} = \frac{1}{2} \quad \text{Odd-root property}$$

Because $\left(\frac{1}{2}\right)^{-3} = 2^3 = 8$ or $\log_{1/2}(8) = -3$ the solution set is $\left\{\frac{1}{2}\right\}$.

c) To write an equation equivalent to $\log(x^2) = \log(4)$, we use the one-to-one property of logarithms:

$$\log(x^2) = \log(4)$$
$$x^2 = 4 \qquad \text{One-to-one property of logarithms}$$
$$x = \pm 2 \quad \text{Even-root property}$$

If $x = \pm 2$, then $x^2 = 4$ and $\log(4) = \log(4)$. The solution set is $\{-2, 2\}$.   ■

C A U T I O N   If we have equality of two logarithms with the same base, we use the one-to-one property to eliminate the logarithms. If we have an equation with only one logarithm, such as $\log_a(x) = y$, we use the definition of logarithm to write $a^y = x$ and to eliminate the logarithm.

Applications

The definition of logarithm indicates that $y = \log_a(x)$ if and only if $a^y = x$. If the base is e, then the definition indicates that

$$y = \ln(x) \quad \text{if and only if} \quad e^y = x.$$

In Example 8, we will use the definition of logarithm to solve a problem involving the continuous-compounding formula

$$A = Pe^{rt},$$

where A is the amount after t years of an investment of P dollars at annual percentage rate r compounded continuously.

E X A M P L E   8   **Finding the time with continuous compounding**

How long does it take for $80 to grow to $240 at 12% annual percentage rate compounded continuously?

Solution

Use $r = 0.12$, $P = \$80$, and $A = \$240$ in the formula $A = Pe^{rt}$ to get $240 = 80e^{0.12t}$. Now use the definition of logarithm to solve for t:

$$240 = 80e^{0.12t}$$

$$3 = e^{0.12t} \quad \text{Divide each side by 80.}$$

$$0.12t = \ln(3) \quad \begin{array}{l}\text{Definition of logarithm:}\\ y = e^x \text{ means } x = \ln(y)\end{array}$$

$$t = \frac{\ln(3)}{0.12} \quad \text{Divide each side by 0.12.}$$

$$t \approx 9.155$$

The time is approximately 9.155 years. Multiply 365 by 0.155 to get approximately 57 days. So the time is 9 years and 57 days to the nearest day. ∎

Note that we can also use the technique of Example 8 to solve a continuous-compounding problem in which the rate is the only unknown quantity.

WARM-UPS

True or false? Explain your answer.

1. The equation $a^3 = 2$ is equivalent to $\log_a(2) = 3$.
2. If (a, b) satisfies $y = 8^x$, then (a, b) satisfies $y = \log_8(x)$.
3. If $f(x) = a^x$ for $a > 0$ and $a \neq 1$, then $f^{-1}(x) = \log_a(x)$.
4. If $f(x) = \ln(x)$, then $f^{-1}(x) = e^x$.
5. The domain of $f(x) = \log_6(x)$ is $(-\infty, \infty)$.
6. $\log_{25}(5) = 2$
7. $\log(-10) = 1$
8. $\log(0) = 0$
9. $5^{\log_5(125)} = 125$
10. $\log_{1/2}(32) = -5$

11.2   EXERCISES

Reading and Writing *After reading this section, write out the answers to these questions. Use complete sentences.*

1. What is the inverse function for the function $f(x) = 2^x$?

2. What is $\log_a(x)$?

3. What is the difference between the common logarithm and the natural logarithm?

4. What is the domain of $f(x) = \log_a(x)$?

5. What is the one-to-one property of logarithmic functions?

6. What is the relationship between the graphs of $f(x) = a^x$ and $f^{-1}(x) = \log_a(x)$ for $a > 0$ and $a \neq 1$?

Write each exponential equation as a logarithmic equation and each logarithmic equation as an exponential equation. See Example 1.

7. $\log_2(8) = 3$

8. $\log_{10}(10) = 1$

9. $10^2 = 100$

10. $5^3 = 125$

11. $y = \log_5(x)$

12. $m = \log_b(N)$

13. $2^a = b$

14. $a^3 = c$

15. $\log_3(x) = 10$

16. $\log_c(t) = 4$

17. $e^3 = x$

18. $m = e^x$

Evaluate each logarithm. See Examples 2 and 3.

19. $\log_2(4)$

20. $\log_2(1)$

21. $\log_2(16)$

22. $\log_4(16)$

23. $\log_2(64)$

24. $\log_8(64)$

25. $\log_4(64)$

26. $\log_{64}(64)$

27. $\log_2\left(\dfrac{1}{4}\right)$

28. $\log_2\left(\dfrac{1}{8}\right)$

29. $\log(100)$

30. $\log(1)$

31. $\log(0.01)$

32. $\log(10,000)$

33. $\log_{1/3}\left(\dfrac{1}{3}\right)$

34. $\log_{1/3}\left(\dfrac{1}{9}\right)$

35. $\log_{1/3}(27)$

36. $\log_{1/3}(1)$

37. $\log_{25}(5)$

38. $\log_{16}(4)$

39. $\ln(e^2)$

40. $\ln\left(\dfrac{1}{e}\right)$

 Use a calculator to evaluate each logarithm. Round answers to four decimal places.

41. $\log(5)$

42. $\log(0.03)$

43. $\ln(6.238)$

44. $\ln(0.23)$

Sketch the graph of each function. See Examples 4 and 5.

45. $f(x) = \log_3(x)$

46. $g(x) = \log_{10}(x)$

47. $y = \log_4(x)$

48. $y = \log_5(x)$

49. $h(x) = \log_{1/4}(x)$

50. $y = \log_{1/3}(x)$

51. $y = \log_{1/5}(x)$

52. $y = \log_{1/6}(x)$

Find the inverse of each function. See Example 6.

53. $f(x) = 6^x$

54. $f(x) = 4^x$

55. $f(x) = \ln(x)$

56. $f(x) = \log(x)$

57. $f(x) = \log_{1/2}(x)$

58. $f(x) = \log_{1/4}(x)$

Solve each equation. See Example 7.

59. $x = \left(\dfrac{1}{2}\right)^{-2}$

60. $x = 16^{-1/2}$

61. $5 = 25^x$

62. $0.1 = 10^x$

63. $\log(x) = -3$

64. $\log(x) = 5$

65. $\log_x(36) = 2$

66. $\log_x(100) = 2$

67. $\log_x(5) = -1$

68. $\log_x(16) = -2$

69. $\log(x^2) = \log(9)$

70. $\ln(2x - 3) = \ln(x + 1)$

Use a calculator to solve each equation. Round answers to four decimal places.

71. $3 = 10^x$

72. $10^x = 0.03$

73. $10^x = \dfrac{1}{2}$

74. $75 = 10^x$

75. $e^x = 7.2$

76. $e^{3x} = 0.4$

Solve each problem. See Example 8. Use a calculator as necessary.

77. Double your money. How long does it take $5000 to grow to $10,000 at 12% compounded continuously?

78. Half the rate. How long does it take $5000 to grow to $10,000 at 6% compounded continuously?

79. Earning interest. How long does it take to earn $1000 in interest on a deposit of $6000 at 8% compounded continuously?

80. Lottery winnings. How long does it take to earn $1000 interest on a deposit of one million dollars at 9% compounded continuously?

81. Investing. An investment of $10,000 in Bonavista Petroleum in 1997 grew to $20,733 in 2002.
  a) Assuming that the investment grew continuously, what was the annual growth rate?
  b) If Bonavista Petroleum continued to grow continuously at the rate from part (a), then what would the investment be worth in 2010?

82. Investing. An investment of $10,000 in Baytex Energy in 1997 was worth $19,568 in 2002.
  a) Assuming that the investment grew continuously, what was the annual rate?
  b) If Baytex Energy continued to grow continuously at the rate from part (a), then what would the investment be worth in 2012?

In chemistry the pH *of a solution is defined by*

$$pH = -\log_{10}[H+],$$

where H+ is the hydrogen ion concentration of the solution in moles per liter. Distilled water has a pH *of approximately 7. A solution with a* pH *under 7 is called an acid, and one with a* pH *over 7 is called a base.*

83. Tomato juice. Tomato juice has a hydrogen ion concentration of $10^{-4.1}$ mole per liter (mol/L). Find the pH of tomato juice.

84. Stomach acid. The gastric juices in your stomach have a hydrogen ion concentration of 10^{-1} mol/L. Find the pH of your gastric juices.

85. Neuse River pH. The pH of a water sample is one of the many measurements of water quality done by the U.S. Geological Survey. The hydrogen ion concentration of the water in the Neuse River at New Bern, North Carolina, was 1.58×10^{-7} mol/L on April 8, 2002 (Water Resources for North Carolina, wwwnc.usgs.gov). What was the pH of the water at that time?

86. Roanoke River pH. On April 8, 2002, the hydrogen ion concentration of the water in the Roanoke River at Janesville, North Carolina, was 1.995×10^{-7} mol/L (Water Resources for North Carolina, wwwnc.usgs.gov). What was the pH of the water at that time?

FIGURE FOR EXERCISE 86

Solve each problem.

87. Sound level. The level of sound in decibels (db) is given by the formula

$$L = 10 \cdot \log(I \times 10^{12}),$$

where I is the intensity of the sound in watts per square meter. If the intensity of the sound at a rock concert is 0.001 watt per square meter at a distance of 75 meters from the stage, then what is the level of the sound at this point in the audience?

88. Logistic growth. If a rancher has one cow with a contagious disease in a herd of 1000, then the time in days t for n of the cows to become infected is modeled by

$$t = -5 \cdot \ln\left(\frac{1000 - n}{999n}\right).$$

Find the number of days that it takes for the disease to spread to 100, 200, 998, and 999 cows. This model, called a *logistic growth model,* describes how a disease can spread very rapidly at first and then very slowly as nearly all of the population has become infected.

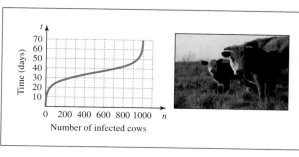

FIGURE FOR EXERCISE 88

GETTING MORE INVOLVED

89. *Discussion.* Use the switch-and-solve method from Chapter 9 to find the inverse of the function $f(x) = 5 + \log_2(x - 3)$. State the domain and range of the inverse function.

90. *Discussion.* Find the inverse of the function $f(x) = 2 + e^{x+4}$. State the domain and range of the inverse function.

GRAPHING CALCULATOR EXERCISES

91. *Composition of inverses.* Graph the functions $y = \ln(e^x)$ and $y = e^{\ln(x)}$. Explain the similarities and differences between the graphs.

92. *The population bomb.* The population of the earth is growing continuously with an annual rate of about 1.6%. If the present population is 6 billion, then the function $y = 6e^{0.016x}$ gives the population in billions x years from now. Graph this function for $0 \le x \le 200$. What will the population be in 100 years and in 200 years?

In This Section

- Product Rule for Logarithms
- Quotient Rule for Logarithms
- Power Rule for Logarithms
- Inverse Properties
- Using the Properties

11.3   PROPERTIES OF LOGARITHMS

The properties of logarithms are very similar to the properties of exponents because *logarithms are exponents.* In this section we use the properties of exponents to write some properties of logarithms. The properties will be used in solving logarithmic equations in Section 11.4.

Product Rule for Logarithms

If $M = a^x$ and $N = a^y$, we can use the product rule for exponents to write

$$MN = a^x \cdot a^y = a^{x+y}.$$

The equation $MN = a^{x+y}$ is equivalent to

$$\log_a(MN) = x + y.$$

Because $M = a^x$ and $N = a^y$ are equivalent to $x = \log_a(M)$ and $y = \log_a(N)$, we can replace x and y in $\log_a(MN) = x + y$ to get

$$\log_a(MN) = \log_a(M) + \log_a(N).$$

So *the logarithm of a product is the sum of the logarithms,* provided that all of the logarithms are defined. This rule is called the **product rule for logarithms.**

> ### **Product Rule for Logarithms**
>
> $$\log_a(MN) = \log_a(M) + \log_a(N)$$

Calculator Close-Up

You can illustrate the product rule for logarithms with a graphing calculator.

```
log(7)+log(8)
        1.748188027
log(56)
        1.748188027
```

E X A M P L E   1

Using the product rule for logarithms

Write each expression as a single logarithm.

a) $\log_2(7) + \log_2(5)$

b) $\ln(\sqrt{2}) + \ln(\sqrt{3})$

Solution

a) $\log_2(7) + \log_2(5) = \log_2(35)$ Product rule for logarithms

b) $\ln(\sqrt{2}) + \ln(\sqrt{3}) = \ln(\sqrt{6})$ Product rule for logarithms

Quotient Rule for Logarithms

If $M = a^x$ and $N = a^y$, we can use the quotient rule for exponents to write

$$\frac{M}{N} = \frac{a^x}{a^y} = a^{x-y}.$$

By the definition of logarithm, $\frac{M}{N} = a^{x-y}$ is equivalent to

$$\log_a\left(\frac{M}{N}\right) = x - y.$$

Because $x = \log_a(M)$ and $y = \log_a(N)$, we have

$$\log_a\left(\frac{M}{N}\right) = \log_a(M) - \log_a(N).$$

So *the logarithm of a quotient is equal to the difference of the logarithms,* provided that all logarithms are defined. This rule is called the **quotient rule for logarithms.**

> **Quotient Rule for Logarithms**
>
> $$\log_a\left(\frac{M}{N}\right) = \log_a(M) - \log_a(N)$$

E X A M P L E   2   **Using the quotient rule for logarithms**
Write each expression as a single logarithm.

a) $\log_2(3) - \log_2(7)$ **b)** $\ln(w^8) - \ln(w^2)$

Solution

a) $\log_2(3) - \log_2(7) = \log_2\left(\dfrac{3}{7}\right)$ Quotient rule for logarithms

b) $\ln(w^8) - \ln(w^2) = \ln\left(\dfrac{w^8}{w^2}\right)$ Quotient rule for logarithms

$\qquad\qquad\qquad\quad = \ln(w^6)$ Quotient rule for exponents

Power Rule for Logarithms

If $M = a^x$, we can use the power rule for exponents to write

$$M^N = (a^x)^N = a^{Nx}.$$

By the definition of logarithms, $M^N = a^{Nx}$ is equivalent to

$$\log_a(M^N) = Nx.$$

Because $x = \log_a(M)$, we have

$$\log_a(M^N) = N \cdot \log_a(M).$$

So *the logarithm of a power of a number is the power times the logarithm of the number,* provided that all logarithms are defined. This rule is called the **power rule for logarithms.**

Power Rule for Logarithms

$$\log_a(M^N) = N \cdot \log_a(M)$$

E X A M P L E   3

Using the power rule for logarithms

Rewrite each logarithm in terms of log(2).

a) $\log(2^{10})$ b) $\log(\sqrt{2})$ c) $\log\left(\frac{1}{2}\right)$

Solution

a) $\log(2^{10}) = 10 \cdot \log(2)$ Power rule for logarithms

b) $\log(\sqrt{2}) = \log(2^{1/2})$ Write $\sqrt{2}$ as a power of 2.

$\quad\quad\quad\; = \frac{1}{2}\log(2)$ Power rule for logarithms

c) $\log\left(\frac{1}{2}\right) = \log(2^{-1})$ Write $\frac{1}{2}$ as a power of 2.

$\quad\quad\quad\; = -1 \cdot \log(2)$ Power rule for logarithms

$\quad\quad\quad\; = -\log(2)$ ∎

Inverse Properties

An exponential function and logarithmic function with the same base are inverses of each other. For example, the logarithm of 32 base 2 is 5 and the fifth power of 2 is 32. In symbols, we have

$$2^{\log_2(32)} = 2^5 = 32.$$

If we raise 3 to the fourth power, we get 81; and if we find the base-3 logarithm of 81, we get 4. In symbols, we have

$$\log_3(3^4) = \log_3(81) = 4.$$

We can state the inverse relationship between exponential and logarithm functions in general with the following inverse properties.

Inverse Properties

1. $\log_a(a^M) = M$ **2.** $a^{\log_a(M)} = M$

E X A M P L E   4

Using the inverse properties

Simplify each expression.

a) $\ln(e^5)$ b) $2^{\log_2(8)}$

Solution

a) Using the first inverse property, we get $\ln(e^5) = 5$.

b) Using the second inverse property, we get $2^{\log_2(8)} = 8$. ∎

Note that there is more than one way to simplify the expressions in Example 4. Using the power rule for logarithms and the fact that $\ln(e) = 1$, we have $\ln(e^5) = 5 \cdot \ln(e) = 5$. Using $\log_2(8) = 3$, we have $2^{\log_2(8)} = 2^3 = 8$.

Using the Properties

We have already seen many properties of logarithms. There are three properties that we have not yet formally stated. Because $a^1 = a$ and $a^0 = 1$, we have $\log_a(a) = 1$ and $\log_a(1) = 0$ for any positive number a. If we apply the quotient rule to $\log_a(1/N)$, we get

$$\log_a\left(\frac{1}{N}\right) = \log_a(1) - \log_a(N) = 0 - \log_a(N) = -\log_a(N).$$

So $\log_a\left(\frac{1}{N}\right) = -\log_a(N)$. These three new properties along with all of the other properties of logarithms are summarized as follows.

Properties of Logarithms

If M, N, and a are positive numbers, $a \neq 1$, then

1. $\log_a(a) = 1$ **2.** $\log_a(1) = 0$

3. $\log_a(a^M) = M$ Inverse properties   **4.** $a^{\log_a(M)} = M$

5. $\log_a(MN) = \log_a(M) + \log_a(N)$ Product rule

6. $\log_a\left(\frac{M}{N}\right) = \log_a(M) - \log_a(N)$ Quotient rule

7. $\log_a\left(\frac{1}{N}\right) = -\log_a(N)$ **8.** $\log_a(M^N) = N \cdot \log_a(M)$ Power rule

---

We have already seen several ways in which to use the properties of logarithms. In Examples 5, 6, and 7 we see more uses of the properties. First we use the rules of logarithms to write the logarithm of a complicated expression in terms of logarithms of simpler expressions.

E X A M P L E 5   **Using the properties of logarithms**

Rewrite each expression in terms of $\log(2)$ and/or $\log(3)$.

a) $\log(6)$ **b)** $\log(16)$ **c)** $\log\left(\frac{9}{2}\right)$ **d)** $\log\left(\frac{1}{3}\right)$

Solution

a) $\log(6) = \log(2 \cdot 3)$

$= \log(2) + \log(3)$ Product rule

b) $\log(16) = \log(2^4)$

$= 4 \cdot \log(2)$ Power rule

c) $\log\left(\frac{9}{2}\right) = \log(9) - \log(2)$ Quotient rule

$= \log(3^2) - \log(2)$

$= 2 \cdot \log(3) - \log(2)$ Power rule

d) $\log\left(\frac{1}{3}\right) = -\log(3)$ Property 7

CAUTION Do not confuse $\frac{\log(9)}{\log(2)}$ with $\log\left(\frac{9}{2}\right)$. We can use the quotient rule to write $\log\left(\frac{9}{2}\right) = \log(9) - \log(2)$, but $\frac{\log(9)}{\log(2)} \neq \log(9) - \log(2)$. The expression $\frac{\log(9)}{\log(2)}$ means $\log(9) \div \log(2)$. Use your calculator to verify these two statements.

The properties of logarithms can be used to combine several logarithms into a single logarithm (as in Examples 1 and 2) or to write a logarithm of a complicated expression in terms of logarithms of simpler expressions.

E X A M P L E   6 **Using the properties of logarithms**

Rewrite each expression as a sum or difference of multiples of logarithms.

a) $\log\left(\frac{xz}{y}\right)$

b) $\log_3\left(\frac{(x-3)^{2/3}}{\sqrt{x}}\right)$

Solution

a) $\log\left(\frac{xz}{y}\right) = \log(xz) - \log(y)$ Quotient rule

$= \log(x) + \log(z) - \log(y)$ Product rule

b) $\log_3\left(\frac{(x-3)^{2/3}}{\sqrt{x}}\right) = \log_3\left((x-3)^{2/3}\right) - \log_3\left(x^{1/2}\right)$ Quotient rule

$= \frac{2}{3}\log_3(x-3) - \frac{1}{2}\log_3(x)$ Power rule

In Example 7 we use the properties of logarithms to convert expressions involving several logarithms into a single logarithm. The skills we are learning here will be used to solve logarithmic equations in Section 11.4.

E X A M P L E   7 **Combining logarithms**

Rewrite each expression as a single logarithm.

a) $\frac{1}{2}\log(x) - 2 \cdot \log(x+1)$

b) $3 \cdot \log(y) + \frac{1}{2}\log(z) - \log(x)$

Solution

a) $\frac{1}{2}\log(x) - 2 \cdot \log(x+1) = \log(x^{1/2}) - \log((x+1)^2)$ Power rule

$= \log\left(\frac{\sqrt{x}}{(x+1)^2}\right)$ Quotient rule

b) $3 \cdot \log(y) + \frac{1}{2}\log(z) - \log(x) = \log(y^3) + \log(\sqrt{z}) - \log(x)$ Power rule

$= \log(y^3 \cdot \sqrt{z}) - \log(x)$ Product rule

$= \log\left(\frac{y^3 \cdot \sqrt{z}}{x}\right)$ Quotient rule

True or false? Explain your answer.

1. $\log_2\left(\dfrac{x^2}{8}\right) = \log_2(x^2) - 3$

2. $\dfrac{\log(100)}{\log(10)} = \log(100) - \log(10)$

3. $\ln(\sqrt{2}) = \dfrac{\ln(2)}{2}$

4. $3^{\log_3(17)} = 17$

5. $\log_2\left(\dfrac{1}{8}\right) = \dfrac{1}{\log_2(8)}$

6. $\ln(8) = 3 \cdot \ln(2)$

7. $\ln(1) = e$

8. $\dfrac{\log(100)}{10} = \log(10)$

9. $\dfrac{\log_2(8)}{\log_2(2)} = \log_2(4)$

10. $\ln(2) + \ln(3) - \ln(7) = \ln\left(\dfrac{6}{7}\right)$

11.3   EXERCISES

Reading and Writing *After reading this section, write out the answers to these questions. Use complete sentences.*

1. What is the product rule for logarithms?

2. What is the quotient rule for logarithms?

3. What is the power rule for logarithms?

4. Why is it true that $\log_a(a^M) = M$?

5. Why is it true that $a^{\log_a(M)} = M$?

6. Why is it true that $\log_a(1) = 0$ for $a > 0$ and $a \neq 1$?

Assume all variables involved in logarithms represent numbers for which the logarithms are defined.

Write each expression as a single logarithm and simplify. See Example 1.

7. $\log(3) + \log(7)$

8. $\ln(5) + \ln(4)$

9. $\log_3(\sqrt{5}) + \log_3(\sqrt{x})$

10. $\ln(\sqrt{x}) + \ln(\sqrt{y})$

11. $\log(x^2) + \log(x^3)$

12. $\ln(a^3) + \ln(a^5)$

13. $\ln(2) + \ln(3) + \ln(5)$

14. $\log_2(x) + \log_2(y) + \log_2(z)$

15. $\log(x) + \log(x + 3)$

16. $\ln(x - 1) + \ln(x + 1)$

17. $\log_2(x - 3) + \log_2(x + 2)$

18. $\log_3(x - 5) + \log_3(x - 4)$

Write each expression as a single logarithm. See Example 2.

19. $\log(8) - \log(2)$

20. $\ln(3) - \ln(6)$

21. $\log_2(x^6) - \log_2(x^2)$

22. $\ln(w^9) - \ln(w^3)$

23. $\log(\sqrt{10}) - \log(\sqrt{2})$

24. $\log_3(\sqrt{6}) - \log_3(\sqrt{3})$

25. $\ln(4h - 8) - \ln(4)$

26. $\log(3x - 6) - \log(3)$

27. $\log_2(w^2 - 4) - \log_2(w + 2)$

28. $\log_3(k^2 - 9) - \log_3(k - 3)$

29. $\ln(x^2 + x - 6) - \ln(x + 3)$

30. $\ln(t^2 - t - 12) - \ln(t - 4)$

Write each expression in terms of $\log(3)$*. See Example 3.*

31. $\log(27)$

32. $\log\left(\dfrac{1}{9}\right)$

33. $\log(\sqrt{3})$

34. $\log(\sqrt[4]{3})$

35. $\log(3^x)$

36. $\log(3^{-99})$

Simplify each expression. See Example 4.

37. $\log_2(2^{10})$

38. $\ln(e^9)$

39. $5^{\log_5(19)}$

40. $10^{\log(2.3)}$

41. $\log(10^8)$

42. $\log_4(4^5)$

43. $e^{\ln(4.3)}$

44. $3^{\log_3(5.5)}$

Rewrite each expression in terms of $\log(3)$ *and/or* $\log(5)$*. See Example 5.*

45. $\log(15)$

46. $\log(9)$

47. $\log\left(\dfrac{5}{3}\right)$

48. $\log\left(\dfrac{3}{5}\right)$

49. $\log(25)$

50. $\log\left(\dfrac{1}{27}\right)$

51. $\log(75)$

52. $\log(0.6)$

53. $\log\left(\dfrac{1}{3}\right)$

54. $\log(45)$

55. $\log(0.2)$

56. $\log\left(\dfrac{9}{25}\right)$

Rewrite each expression as a sum or a difference of multiples of logarithms. See Example 6.

57. $\log(xyz)$

58. $\log(3y)$

59. $\log_2(8x)$

60. $\log_2(16y)$

61. $\ln\left(\dfrac{x}{y}\right)$

62. $\ln\left(\dfrac{z}{3}\right)$

63. $\log(10x^2)$

64. $\log(100\sqrt{x})$

65. $\log_5\left(\dfrac{(x-3)^2}{\sqrt{w}}\right)$

66. $\log_3\left(\dfrac{(y+6)^3}{y-5}\right)$

67. $\ln\left(\dfrac{yz\sqrt{x}}{w}\right)$

68. $\ln\left(\dfrac{(x-1)\sqrt{w}}{x^3}\right)$

Rewrite each expression as a single logarithm. See Example 7.

69. $\log(x) + \log(x - 1)$

70. $\log_2(x - 2) + \log_2(5)$

71. $\ln(3x - 6) - \ln(x - 2)$

72. $\log_3(x^2 - 1) - \log_3(x - 1)$

73. $\ln(x) - \ln(w) + \ln(z)$

74. $\ln(x) - \ln(3) - \ln(7)$

75. $3 \cdot \ln(y) + 2 \cdot \ln(x) - \ln(w)$

76. $5 \cdot \ln(r) + 3 \cdot \ln(t) - 4 \cdot \ln(s)$

77. $\dfrac{1}{2}\log(x - 3) - \dfrac{2}{3}\log(x + 1)$

78. $\dfrac{1}{2}\log(y - 4) + \dfrac{1}{2}\log(y + 4)$

79. $\dfrac{2}{3}\log_2(x - 1) - \dfrac{1}{4}\log_2(x + 2)$

80. $\dfrac{1}{2}\log_3(y + 3) + 6 \cdot \log_3(y)$

Determine whether each equation is true or false.

81. $\log(56) = \log(7) \cdot \log(8)$

82. $\log\left(\dfrac{5}{9}\right) = \dfrac{\log(5)}{\log(9)}$

83. $\log_2(4^2) = (\log_2(4))^2$

84. $\ln(4^2) = (\ln(4))^2$

85. $\ln(25) = 2 \cdot \ln(5)$

86. $\ln(3e) = 1 + \ln(3)$

87. $\dfrac{\log_2(64)}{\log_2(8)} = \log_2(8)$

88. $\dfrac{\log_2(16)}{\log_2(4)} = \log_2(4)$

89. $\log\left(\dfrac{1}{3}\right) = -\log(3)$

90. $\log_2(8 \cdot 2^{59}) = 62$

91. $\log_2(16^5) = 20$

92. $\log_2\left(\dfrac{5}{2}\right) = \log_2(5) - 1$

93. $\log(10^3) = 3$

94. $\log_3(3^7) = 7$

95. $\log(100 + 3) = 2 + \log(3)$ **96.** $\dfrac{\log_7(32)}{\log_7(8)} = \dfrac{5}{3}$

Solve each problem.

97. *Richter scale.* The Richter scale rating of an earthquake is given by the formula $r = \log(I) - \log(I_0)$, where I is the *intensity* of the earthquake and I_0 is the intensity of a small "benchmark" earthquake. Use the appropriate property of logarithms to rewrite this formula using a single logarithm. Find r if $I = 100 \cdot I_0$.

98. *Diversity index.* The U.S.G.S. measures the quality of a water sample by using the diversity index d, given by

$$d = -[p_1 \cdot \log_2(p_1) + p_2 \cdot \log_2(p_2) + \cdots + p_n \cdot \log_2(p_n)],$$

where n is the number of different taxons (biological classifications) represented in the sample and p_1 through p_n are the percentages of organisms in each of the n taxons. The value of d ranges from 0 when all organisms in the water sample are the same to some positive number when all organisms in the sample are different. If two-thirds of the organisms in a water sample are in one taxon and one-third of the organisms are in a second taxon, then $n = 2$ and

$$d = -\left[\frac{2}{3}\log_2\left(\frac{2}{3}\right) + \frac{1}{3}\log_2\left(\frac{1}{3}\right)\right].$$

Use the properties of logarithms to write the expression on the right-hand side as $\log_2\left(\frac{3\sqrt[3]{2}}{2}\right)$. (In Section 11.4 you will learn how to evaluate a base-2 logarithm using a calculator.)

GETTING MORE INVOLVED

99. *Discussion.* Which of the following equations is an identity? Explain.
   a) $\ln(3x) = \ln(3) \cdot \ln(x)$
   b) $\ln(3x) = \ln(3) + \ln(x)$
   c) $\ln(3x) = 3 \cdot \ln(x)$
   d) $\ln(3x) = \ln(x^3)$

100. *Discussion.* Which of the following expressions is not equal to $\log(5^{2/3})$? Explain.
   a) $\dfrac{2}{3}\log(5)$
   b) $\dfrac{\log(5) + \log(5)}{3}$
   c) $\left(\log(5)\right)^{2/3}$
   d) $\dfrac{1}{3}\log(25)$

GRAPHING CALCULATOR EXERCISES

101. Graph the functions $y_1 = \ln(\sqrt{x})$ and $y_2 = 0.5 \cdot \ln(x)$ on the same screen. Explain your results.

102. Graph the functions $y_1 = \log(x)$, $y_2 = \log(10x)$, $y_3 = \log(100x)$, and $y_4 = \log(1000x)$ using the viewing window $-2 \le x \le 5$ and $-2 \le y \le 5$. Why do these curves appear as they do?

103. Graph the function $y = \log(e^x)$. Explain why the graph is a straight line. What is its slope?

In This Section

- Logarithmic Equations
- Exponential Equations
- Changing the Base
- Strategy for Solving Equations
- Applications

11.4 SOLVING EQUATIONS AND APPLICATIONS

We solved some equations involving exponents and logarithms in Sections 11.1 and 11.2. In this section we use the properties of exponents and logarithms to solve more complex equations.

Logarithmic Equations

The main tool that we have for solving logarithmic equations is the definition of logarithms: $y = \log_a(x)$ if and only if $a^y = x$. We can use the definition to rewrite any equation that has only one logarithm as an equivalent exponential equation.

E X A M P L E   1   **A logarithmic equation with only one logarithm**

Solve $\log(x + 3) = 2$.

Solution

Write the equivalent exponential equation:

$$\log(x + 3) = 2 \qquad \text{Original equation}$$
$$10^2 = x + 3 \qquad \text{Definition of logarithm}$$
$$100 = x + 3$$
$$97 = x$$

Check: $\log(97 + 3) = \log(100) = 2$. The solution set is $\{97\}$. ■

In Example 2 we use the product rule for logarithms to write a sum of two logarithms as a single logarithm.

E X A M P L E   2   **Using the product rule to solve an equation**

Solve $\log_2(x + 3) + \log_2(x - 3) = 4$.

Solution

Rewrite the sum of the logarithms as the logarithm of a product:

$$\log_2(x + 3) + \log_2(x - 3) = 4 \qquad \text{Original equation}$$
$$\log_2[(x + 3)(x - 3)] = 4 \qquad \text{Product rule}$$
$$\log_2[x^2 - 9] = 4 \qquad \text{Multiply the binomials.}$$
$$x^2 - 9 = 2^4 \qquad \text{Definition of logarithm}$$
$$x^2 - 9 = 16$$
$$x^2 = 25$$
$$x = \pm 5 \qquad \text{Even-root property}$$

To check, first let $x = -5$ in the original equation:

$$\log_2(-5 + 3) + \log_2(-5 - 3) = 4$$
$$\log_2(-2) + \log_2(-8) = 4 \qquad \text{Incorrect}$$

Because the domain of any logarithm function is the set of positive real numbers, these logarithms are undefined. Now check $x = 5$ in the original equation:

$$\log_2(5 + 3) + \log_2(5 - 3) = 4$$
$$\log_2(8) + \log_2(2) = 4$$
$$3 + 1 = 4 \qquad \text{Correct}$$

The solution set is $\{5\}$. ■

C A U T I O N   Always check that your solutions to a logarithmic equation do not produce undefined logarithms in the original equation.

E X A M P L E 3

Calculator Close-Up

Graph

$$y_1 = \log(x) + \log(x - 1)$$

and

$$y_2 = \log(8x - 12) - \log(2)$$

to see the two solutions to the equation in Example 3.

Using the one-to-one property of logarithms

Solve $\log(x) + \log(x - 1) = \log(8x - 12) - \log(2)$.

Solution

Apply the product rule to the left-hand side and the quotient rule to the right-hand side to get a single logarithm on each side:

$$\log(x) + \log(x - 1) = \log(8x - 12) - \log(2).$$

$$\log[x(x - 1)] = \log\left(\frac{8x - 12}{2}\right) \qquad \text{Product rule; quotient rule}$$

$$\log(x^2 - x) = \log(4x - 6) \qquad \text{Simplify.}$$

$$x^2 - x = 4x - 6 \qquad \text{One-to-one property of logarithms}$$

$$x^2 - 5x + 6 = 0$$

$$(x - 2)(x - 3) = 0$$

$$x - 2 = 0 \qquad \text{or} \qquad x - 3 = 0$$

$$x = 2 \qquad \text{or} \qquad x = 3$$

Neither $x = 2$ nor $x = 3$ produces undefined terms in the original equation. Use a calculator to check that they both satisfy the original equation. The solution set is $\{2, 3\}$. ◼

CAUTION   The product rule, quotient rule, and power rule do not eliminate logarithms from equations. To do so, we use the definition to change $y = \log_a(x)$ into $a^y = x$ or the one-to-one property to change $\log_a(m) = \log_a(n)$ into $m = n$.

Exponential Equations

If an equation has a single exponential expression, we can write the equivalent logarithmic equation.

E X A M P L E 4

A single exponential expression

Find the exact solution to $2^x = 10$.

Solution

The equivalent logarithmic equation is

$$x = \log_2(10).$$

The solution set is $\{\log_2(10)\}$. The number $\log_2(10)$ is the exact solution to the equation. Later in this section you will learn how to use the base-change formula to find an approximate value for an expression of this type. ◼

In Section 11.1 we solved some exponential equations by writing each side as a power of the same base and then applying the one-to-one property of exponential functions. We review that method in Example 5.

EXAMPLE 5

Powers of the same base

Solve $2^{(x^2)} = 4^{3x-4}$.

Solution

We can write each side as a power of the same base:

$$2^{(x^2)} = (2^2)^{3x-4} \qquad \text{Because } 4 = 2^2$$
$$2^{(x^2)} = 2^{6x-8} \qquad \text{Power of a power rule}$$
$$x^2 = 6x - 8 \qquad \text{One-to-one property of exponential functions}$$
$$x^2 - 6x + 8 = 0$$
$$(x - 4)(x - 2) = 0$$
$$x - 4 = 0 \quad \text{or} \quad x - 2 = 0$$
$$x = 4 \quad \text{or} \quad x = 2$$

Check $x = 2$ and $x = 4$ in the original equation. The solution set is $\{2, 4\}$. ∎

For some exponential equations we cannot write each side as a power of the same base as we did in Example 5. In this case we take a logarithm of each side and simplify, using the rules for logarithms.

EXAMPLE 6

Exponential equation with two different bases

Find the exact and approximate solution to $2^{x-1} = 3^x$.

Solution

We first take the base-10 logarithm of each side:

$$2^{x-1} = 3^x \qquad \text{Original equation}$$
$$\log(2^{x-1}) = \log(3^x) \qquad \text{Take log of each side.}$$
$$(x - 1)\log(2) = x \cdot \log(3) \qquad \text{Power rule}$$
$$x \cdot \log(2) - \log(2) = x \cdot \log(3) \qquad \text{Distributive property}$$
$$x \cdot \log(2) - x \cdot \log(3) = \log(2) \qquad \text{Get all } x\text{-terms on one side.}$$
$$x[\log(2) - \log(3)] = \log(2) \qquad \text{Factor out } x.$$
$$x = \frac{\log(2)}{\log(2) - \log(3)} \qquad \text{Exact solution}$$
$$x \approx -1.7095 \qquad \text{Approximate solution}$$

You can use a calculator to check -1.7095 in the original equation. As the first step of the solution, we could have taken the logarithm of each side using any base. We chose base 10 so that we could use a calculator to find an approximate solution from the exact solution. ∎

Changing the Base

Scientific calculators have an x^y key for computing any power of any base, in addition to the function keys for computing 10^x and e^x. For logarithms we have the keys ln and log, but there are no function keys for logarithms using other bases. To solve this problem, we develop a formula for expressing a base-a logarithm in terms of base-b logarithms.

If $y = \log_a(M)$, then $a^y = M$. Now we solve $a^y = M$ for y, using base-b logarithms:

$$a^y = M$$
$$\log_b(a^y) = \log_b(M) \quad \text{Take the base-}b\text{ logarithm of each side.}$$
$$y \cdot \log_b(a) = \log_b(M) \quad \text{Power rule}$$
$$y = \frac{\log_b(M)}{\log_b(a)} \quad \text{Divide each side by } \log_b(a).$$

Because $y = \log_a(M)$, we can write $\log_a(M)$ in terms of base-b logarithms.

Base-Change Formula

If a and b are positive numbers not equal to 1 and M is positive, then

$$\log_a(M) = \frac{\log_b(M)}{\log_b(a)}.$$

In words, we take the logarithm with the new base and divide by the logarithm of the old base. The most important use of the base-change formula is to find base-a logarithms using a calculator. If the new base is 10 or e, then

$$\log_a(M) = \frac{\log(M)}{\log(a)} = \frac{\ln(M)}{\ln(a)}.$$

E X A M P L E 7 **Using the base-change formula**

Find $\log_7(99)$ to four decimal places.

Solution

Use the base-change formula with $a = 7$ and $b = 10$:

$$\log_7(99) = \frac{\log(99)}{\log(7)} \approx 2.3614$$

Check by finding $7^{2.3614}$ with your calculator. Note that we also have

$$\log_7(99) = \frac{\ln(99)}{\ln(7)} \approx 2.3614.$$ ∎

Strategy for Solving Equations

There is no formula that will solve every equation in this section. However, we have a strategy for solving exponential and logarithmic equations. The following list summarizes the ideas that we need for solving these equations.

> **Solving Exponential and Logarithmic Equations**
>
> 1. If the equation has a single logarithm or a single exponential expression, rewrite the equation using the definition $y = \log_a(x)$ if and only if $a^y = x$.
> 2. Use the properties of logarithms to combine logarithms as much as possible.
> 3. Use the one-to-one properties:
>   a) If $\log_a(m) = \log_a(n)$, then $m = n$.
>   b) If $a^m = a^n$, then $m = n$.
> 4. To get an approximate solution of an exponential equation, take the common or natural logarithm of each side of the equation.

Applications

In compound interest problems, logarithms are used to find the time it takes for money to grow to a specified amount.

EXAMPLE 8

Finding the time

If $500 is deposited into an account paying 8% compounded quarterly, then in how many quarters will the account have $1000 in it?

Solution

We use the compound interest formula $A = P(1 + i)^n$ with a principal of $500, an amount of $1000, and an interest rate of 2% each quarter:

$$A = P(1 + i)^n$$
$$1000 = 500(1.02)^n \quad \text{Substitute.}$$
$$2 = (1.02)^n \quad \text{Divide each side by 500.}$$
$$n = \log_{1.02}(2) \quad \text{Definition of logarithm}$$
$$= \frac{\ln(2)}{\ln(1.02)} \quad \text{Base-change formula}$$
$$\approx 35.0028 \quad \text{Use a calculator.}$$

It takes approximately 35 quarters, or 8 years and 9 months, for the initial investment to be worth $1000. Note that we could also solve $2 = (1.02)^n$ by taking the common or natural logarithm of each side. Try it. ∎

In Example 9 we find the rate in a radioactive decay problem.

Helpful Hint

When we get $2 = (1.02)^n$, we can use the definition of log as in Example 8 or take the natural log of each side:

$$\ln(2) = \ln(1.02^n)$$
$$\ln(2) = n \cdot \ln(1.02)$$
$$n = \frac{\ln(2)}{\ln(1.02)}$$

In either way we arrive at the same solution.

EXAMPLE 9

Finding the rate in radioactive decay

The number of grams of a radioactive substance that is present in an old bone after t years is given by

$$A = 8e^{rt},$$

where r is the decay rate. How many grams of the radioactive substance were present when the bone was in a living organism at time $t = 0$? If it took 6300 years for the radioactive substance to decay from 8 grams to 4 grams, then what is the decay rate?

Solution

If $t = 0$, then $A = 8e^{r \cdot 0} = 8e^0 = 8 \cdot 1 = 8$. So the bone contained 8 grams of the substance when it was in a living organism. Now use $A = 4$ and $t = 6300$ in the formula $A = 8e^{rt}$ and solve for r:

$$4 = 8e^{6300r}$$
$$0.5 = e^{6300r} \quad \text{Divide each side by 8.}$$
$$6300r = \ln(0.5) \quad \text{Definition of logarithm}$$
$$r = \frac{\ln(0.5)}{6300} \quad \text{Divide each side by 6300.}$$
$$r \approx -1.1 \times 10^{-4} \text{ or } -0.00011$$

Note that the rate is negative because the substance is decaying. ∎

WARM-UPS

True or false? Explain your answer.

1. If $\log(x - 2) + \log(x + 2) = 7$, then $\log(x^2 - 4) = 7$.
2. If $\log(3x + 7) = \log(5x - 8)$, then $3x + 7 = 5x - 8$.
3. If $e^{x-6} = e^{x^2-5x}$, then $x - 6 = x^2 - 5x$.
4. If $2^{3x-1} = 3^{5x-4}$, then $3x - 1 = 5x - 4$.
5. If $\log_2(x^2 - 3x + 5) = 3$, then $x^2 - 3x + 5 = 8$.
6. If $2^{2x-1} = 3$, then $2x - 1 = \log_2(3)$.
7. If $5^x = 23$, then $x \cdot \ln(5) = \ln(23)$.
8. $\log_3(5) = \dfrac{\ln(3)}{\ln(5)}$
9. $\dfrac{\ln(2)}{\ln(6)} = \dfrac{\log(2)}{\log(6)}$
10. $\log(5) = \ln(5)$

11.4   EXERCISES

Reading and Writing *After reading this section, write out the answers to these questions. Use complete sentences.*

1. What exponential equation is equivalent to $\log_a(x) = y$?

2. How can you find a logarithm with a base other than 10 or e using a calculator?

Solve each equation. See Examples 1 and 2.

3. $\log_2(x + 1) = 3$
4. $\log_3(x^2) = 4$
5. $3 \log_2(x + 1) - 2 = 13$

6. $4 \log_3(2x) - 1 = 7$

7. $12 + 2 \ln(x) = 14$
8. $23 = 3 \ln(x - 1) + 14$
9. $\log(x) + \log(5) = 1$

10. $\ln(x) + \ln(3) = 0$

11. $\log_2(x - 1) + \log_2(x + 1) = 3$
12. $\log_3(x - 4) + \log_3(x + 4) = 2$
13. $\log_2(x - 1) - \log_2(x + 2) = 2$
14. $\log_4(8x) - \log_4(x - 1) = 2$
15. $\log_2(x - 4) + \log_2(x + 2) = 4$
16. $\log_6(x + 6) + \log_6(x - 3) = 2$

Solve each equation. See Example 3.

17. $\ln(x) + \ln(x + 5) = \ln(x + 1) + \ln(x + 3)$
18. $\log(x) + \log(x + 5) = 2 \cdot \log(x + 2)$
19. $\log(x + 3) + \log(x + 4) = \log(x^3 + 13x^2) - \log(x)$

20. $\log(x^2 - 1) - \log(x - 1) = \log(6)$
21. $2 \cdot \log(x) = \log(20 - x)$

22. $2 \cdot \log(x) + \log(3) = \log(2 - 5x)$

Solve each equation. See Examples 4 and 5.

23. $3^x = 7$
24. $2^{x-1} = 5$

25. $e^{2x} = 7$
26. $e^{x+3} = 2$

27. $2^{3x+4} = 4^{x-1}$
28. $9^{2x-1} = 27^{1/2}$

29. $\left(\dfrac{1}{3}\right)^x = 3^{1+x}$
30. $4^{3x} = \left(\dfrac{1}{2}\right)^{1-x}$

 Find the exact solution and approximate solution to each equation. See Example 6.

31. $2^x = 3^{x+5}$

32. $e^x = 10^x$

33. $5^{x+2} = 10^{x-4}$

34. $3^{2x} = 6^{x+1}$

35. $8^x = 9^{x-1}$

36. $5^{x+1} = 8^{x-1}$

Use the base-change formula to find each logarithm to four decimal places. See Example 7.

37. $\log_2(3)$ **38.** $\log_3(5)$

39. $\log_3\left(\dfrac{1}{2}\right)$ **40.** $\log_5(2.56)$

41. $\log_{1/2}(4.6)$ **42.** $\log_{1/3}(3.5)$
43. $\log_{0.1}(0.03)$ **44.** $\log_{0.2}(1.06)$

For each equation, find the exact solution and an approximate solution when appropriate. Round approximate answers to three decimal places.

45. $x \cdot \ln(2) = \ln(7)$

46. $x \cdot \log(3) = \log(5)$

47. $3x - x \cdot \ln(2) = 1$

48. $2x + x \cdot \log(5) = \log(7)$

49. $3^x = 5$

50. $2^x = \dfrac{1}{3}$

51. $2^{x-1} = 9$

52. $10^{x-2} = 6$
53. $3^x = 20$
54. $2^x = 128$

55. $\log_3(x) + \log_3(5) = 1$

56. $\log(x) - \log(3) = \log(6)$

57. $8^x = 2^{x+1}$

58. $2^x = 5^{x+1}$

In Exercises 59–74, solve each problem. See Examples 8 and 9.

59. Finding the time. How many months does it take for $1000 to grow to $1500 in an account paying 12% compounded monthly?

60. Finding the time. How many years does it take for $25 to grow to $100 in an account paying 8% compounded annually?

61. Finding days. How many days does it take for a deposit of $100 to grow to $105 at 3% annual percentage rate compounded daily? Round to the nearest day.

62. Finding quarters. How many quarters does it take for a deposit of $500 to grow to $600 at 2% annual percentage rate compounded quarterly? Round to the nearest quarter.

63. Radioactive decay. The number of grams of a radioactive substance that is present in an old piece of cloth after t years is given by
$$A = 10e^{-0.0001t}.$$
How many grams of the radioactive substance did the cloth contain when it was made at time $t = 0$? If the cloth now contains only 4 grams of the substance then when was the cloth made?

64. Finding the decay rate. The number of grams of a radioactive substance that is present in an old log after t years is given by
$$A = 5e^{rt},$$
where r is the decay rate. How many grams of the radioactive substance were present when the log was alive at time $t = 0$? If it took 5000 years for the substance to decay from 5 grams to 2 grams, then what is the decay rate?

65. Going with the flow. The flow y [in cubic feet per second (ft³/sec)] of the Tangipahoa River at Robert, Louisiana, is modeled by the exponential function $y = 114.308e^{0.265x}$, where x is the depth in feet. Find the flow when the depth is 15.8 feet.

FIGURE FOR EXERCISES 65 AND 66

66. Record flood. Use the formula of the previous exercise to find the depth of the Tangipahoa River at Robert, Louisiana, on May 3, 1953 when the flow reached an all-time record of 50,500 ft³/sec (U.S.G.S., waterdata.usgs.gov).

67. Above the poverty level. In a certain country the number of people above the poverty level is currently 28 million and growing 5% annually. Assuming the population is growing continuously, the population P (in millions), t years from now, is determined by the formula $P = 28e^{0.05t}$. In how many years will there be 40 million people above the poverty level?

68. *Below the poverty level.* In the same country as in Exercise 67, the number of people below the poverty level is currently 20 million and growing 7% annually. This population (in millions), t years from now, is determined by the formula $P = 20e^{0.07t}$. In how many years will there be 40 million people below the poverty level?

69. *Fifty-fifty.* For this exercise, use the information given in Exercises 67 and 68. In how many years will the number of people above the poverty level equal the number of people below the poverty level?

70. *Golden years.* In a certain country there are currently 100 million workers and 40 million retired people. The population of workers is decreasing according to the formula $W = 100e^{-0.01t}$, where t is in years and W is in millions. The population of retired people is increasing according to the formula $R = 40e^{0.09t}$, where t is in years and R is in millions. In how many years will the number of workers equal the number of retired people?

71. *Ions for breakfast.* Orange juice has a pH of 3.7. What is the hydrogen ion concentration of orange juice? (See Exercises 83–86 of Section 11.2.)

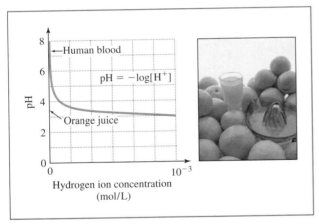

FIGURE FOR EXERCISES 71 AND 72

72. *Ions in your veins.* Normal human blood has a pH of 7.4. What is the hydrogen ion concentration of normal human blood?

73. *Diversity index.* In Exercise 98 of Section 11.3 we expressed the diversity index d for a certain water sample as

$$d = \log_2\left(\frac{3\sqrt[3]{2}}{2}\right).$$

Use the base-change formula and a calculator to calculate the value of d. Round the answer to four decimal places.

74. *Quality water.* In a certain water sample, 5% of the organisms are in one taxon, 10% are in a second taxon, 20% are in a third taxon, 15% are in a fourth taxon, 23% are in a fifth taxon, and the rest are in a sixth taxon. Use the formula given in Exercise 98 of Section 11.3 with $n = 6$ to find the diversity index of the water sample.

GETTING MORE INVOLVED

75. *Exploration.* Logarithms were designed to solve equations that have variables in the exponents, but logarithms can be used to solve certain polynomial equations. Consider the following example:

$$x^5 = 88$$

$$5 \cdot \ln(x) = \ln(88)$$

$$\ln(x) = \frac{\ln(88)}{5} \approx 0.895467$$

$$x = e^{0.895467} \approx 2.4485$$

Solve $x^3 = 12$ by taking the natural logarithm of each side. Round the approximate solution to four decimal places. Solve $x^3 = 12$ without using logarithms and compare with your previous answer.

76. *Discussion.* Determine whether each logarithm is positive or negative without using a calculator. Explain your answers.

  a) $\log_2(0.45)$

  b) $\ln(1.01)$

  c) $\log_{1/2}(4.3)$

  d) $\log_{1/3}(0.44)$

GRAPHING CALCULATOR EXERCISES

77. Graph $y_1 = 2^x$ and $y_2 = 3^{x-1}$ on the same coordinate system. Use the intersect feature of your calculator to find the point of intersection of the two curves. Round to two decimal places.

78. Bob invested $1000 at 6% compounded continuously. At the same time Paula invested $1200 at 5% compounded monthly. Write two functions that give the amounts of Bob's and Paula's investments after x years. Graph these functions on a graphing calculator. Use the intersect feature of your graphing calculator to find the approximate value of x for which the investments are equal in value.

79. Graph the functions $y_1 = \log_2(x)$ and $y_2 = 3^{x-4}$ on the same coordinate system and use the intersect feature to find the points of intersection of the curves. Round to two decimal places. (*Hint:* To graph $y = \log_2(x)$, use the base-change formula to write the function as $y = \ln(x)/\ln(2)$.)

COLLABORATIVE ACTIVITIES

In How Much Space Could We Live?

The formula for population growth is $P(t) = P_0 e^{kt}$, where $P(t)$ is the population after t years, P_0 is the initial population, k is the growth rate per year, and t is the number of years. In the following exercises you will find out how long it would take to cover the habitable part of the earth if the human population grows exponentially.

1. The population of the earth in 2000 was 6.06×10^9 people. If the population was 2.75×10^9 in 1964, then what is the current growth rate to the nearest tenth of a percent?

2. The earth has a total surface area of 5.1×10^{14} square meters. Seventy percent of this surface area is rock, ice, sand, and ocean. Another 8% is tundra, lakes and streams, continental shelves, algal beds and reefs, and estuaries. Assuming that the remaining area is suitable for growing food and living space find that area.

Grouping: 2 students per group

Topic: Exponential and logarithmic functions

3. If 100 square meters of the earth's surface is needed for each person to grow food and live, in how many years after 2000 will all of the available surface of the earth be used?

4. Does 100 square meters per person for living space and growing food seem reasonable? Remember that tall apartment buildings use less surface area than single family dwellings.

5. Think about the land use issues for different types of foods. Would it take more surface area to grow animals for food? Would food grow better on some parts of the earth's surface than on others? Would there be any space left for wild animals or natural plant life? Would there be any space left for shopping malls, movie theaters, concert halls, factories, office buildings, or parking lots?

WRAP-UP   CHAPTER 11

SUMMARY

Exponential and Logarithmic Functions

		Examples
Exponential function	A function of the form $f(x) = a^x$ for $a > 0$ and $a \neq 1$	$f(x) = 3^x$
Logarithm function	A function of the form $f(x) = \log_a(x)$ for $a > 0$ and $a \neq 1$	$f(x) = \log_2(x)$
	$y = \log_a(x)$ if and only if $a^y = x$.	$\log_3(8) = x \leftrightarrow 3^x = 8$
Common logarithm	Base-10: $f(x) = \log(x)$	$\log(100) = 2$ because $100 = 10^2$.
Natural logarithm	Base-e: $f(x) = \ln(x)$ $e \approx 2.718$	$\ln(e) = 1$ because $e^1 = e$.
Inverse functions	$f(x) = a^x$ and $g(x) = \log_a(x)$ are inverse functions.	If $f(x) = e^x$, then $f^{-1}(x) = \ln(x)$.

Properties

Examples

M, N, and a are positive numbers with $a \neq 1$.

$$\log_a(a) = 1 \qquad \log_a(1) = 0$$

$$\log_5(5) = 1, \log_5(1) = 0$$

Inverse properties	$\log_a(a^M) = M \qquad a^{\log_a(M)} = M$	$\log(10^7) = 7,\ e^{\ln(3.4)} = 3.4$
Product rule	$\log_a(MN) = \log_a(M) + \log_a(N)$	$\ln(3x) = \ln(3) + \ln(x)$
Quotient rule	$\log_a\left(\dfrac{M}{N}\right) = \log_a(M) - \log_a(N)$	$\ln\left(\dfrac{2}{3}\right) = \ln(2) - \ln(3)$
	$\log_a\left(\dfrac{1}{N}\right) = -\log_a(N)$	$\ln\left(\dfrac{1}{3}\right) = -\ln(3)$
Power rule	$\log_a(M^N) = N \cdot \log_a(M)$	$\log(x^3) = 3 \cdot \log(x)$
Base-change formula	$\log_a(M) = \dfrac{\log_b(M)}{\log_b(a)}$	$\log_3(5) = \dfrac{\ln(5)}{\ln(3)}$

Equations Involving Logarithms and Exponents

Examples

Strategy

1. If there is a single logarithm or a single exponential expression, rewrite the equation using the definition of logarithms:
   $y = \log_a(x)$ if and only if $a^y = x$.

   $2^x = 3$ and $x = \log_2(3)$ are equivalent.

2. Use the properties of logarithms to combine logarithms as much as possible.

   $\log(x) + \log(x - 3) = 1$
   $\log(x^2 - 3x) = 1$

3. Use the one-to-one properties:
   a) If $\log_a(m) = \log_a(n)$, then $m = n$.

   $\ln(x) = \ln(5 - x)$,
   $x = 5 - x$

   b) If $a^m = a^n$, then $m = n$.

   $2^{3x} = 2^{5x-7}$, $3x = 5x - 7$

4. To get an approximate solution, take the common or natural logarithm of each side of an exponential equation.

   $2^x = 3$, $\ln(2^x) = \ln(3)$
   $x \cdot \ln(2) = \ln(3)$
   $x = \dfrac{\ln(3)}{\ln(2)}$

ENRICHING YOUR MATHEMATICAL WORD POWER

For each mathematical term, choose the correct meaning.

1. **exponential function**
   a. $f(x) = a^x$ where $a > 0$ and $a \neq 1$
   b. $f(x) = ax^2$ where $a \neq 0$
   c. $f(x) = ax + b$ where $a \neq 0$
   d. $f(x) = x^n$ where n is an integer

2. **common base**
   a. base 2
   b. base e
   c. base π
   d. base 10

3. **natural base**
   a. base 2
   b. base e
   c. base π
   d. base 10

4. **domain**
   a. the range
   b. the set of second coordinates of a relation
   c. the independent variable
   d. the set of first coordinates of a relation

5. **compound interest**
   a. simple interest
   b. $A = Prt$
   c. an irrational interest rate
   d. interest is periodically paid into the account and the interest earns interest

6. **continuous compounding**
   a. compound interest
   b. using $A = Pe^{rt}$ to compute the amount
   c. frequent compounding
   d. using $A = P(1 + i)^n$ to compute the amount

7. **base-*a* logarithm of *x***
   a. the exponent that is used on the base *a* to obtain *x*
   b. the exponent that is used on *x* to obtain *a*
   c. the power of 10 that produces *x*
   d. the power of *e* that produces *a*

8. **base-*a* logarithm function**
   a. $f(x) = a^x$ where $a > 0$ and $a \neq 1$
   b. $f(x) = \log_a(x)$ where $a > 0$ and $a \neq 1$
   c. $f(x) = \log_x(a)$ where $a > 0$ and $a \neq 1$
   d. $f(x) = \log(x)$ where $x > 0$

9. **common logarithm**
   a. $\log_2(x)$
   b. $\log(x)$
   c. $\ln(x)$
   d. $\log_3(x)$

10. **natural logarithm**
    a. $\log_2(x)$
    b. $\log(x)$
    c. $\ln(x)$
    d. $\log_3(x)$

REVIEW EXERCISES

11.1 *Use* $f(x) = 5^x$, $g(x) = 10^{x-1}$, *and* $h(x) = \left(\frac{1}{4}\right)^x$ *for Exercises 1–28. Find the following.*

1. $f(-2)$

2. $f(0)$

3. $f(3)$

4. $f(4)$

5. $g(1)$

6. $g(-1)$

7. $g(0)$

8. $g(3)$

9. $h(-1)$

10. $h(2)$

11. $h\left(\frac{1}{2}\right)$

12. $h\left(-\frac{1}{2}\right)$

Find x in each case.

13. $f(x) = 25$

14. $f(x) = -\frac{1}{125}$

15. $g(x) = 1000$

16. $g(x) = 0.001$

17. $h(x) = 32$

18. $h(x) = 8$

19. $h(x) = \frac{1}{16}$

20. $h(x) = 1$

 Find the following.

21. $f(1.34)$

22. $f(-3.6)$

23. $g(3.25)$

24. $g(4.87)$

25. $h(2.82)$

26. $h(\pi)$

27. $h(\sqrt{2})$

28. $h\left(\frac{1}{3}\right)$

Sketch the graph of each function.

29. $f(x) = 5^x$

30. $g(x) = e^x$

31. $y = \left(\frac{1}{5}\right)^x$

32. $y = e^{-x}$

33. $f(x) = 3^{-x}$

34. $f(x) = -3^{x-1}$

35. $y = 1 + 2^x$

58. $f(x) = \log_8(x)$

36. $y = 1 - 2^x$

59. $f(x) = e^x$

11.2 *Write each exponential equation as a logarithmic equation and each logarithmic equation as an exponential equation.*

37. $10^m = n$ **38.** $b = a^5$

39. $h = \log_k(t)$ **40.** $\log_v(5) = u$

Let $f(x) = \log_2(x)$, $g(x) = \log(x)$, *and* $h(x) = \log_{1/2}(x)$. *Find the following.*

60. $f(x) = \log_3(x)$

41. $f\left(\dfrac{1}{8}\right)$ **42.** $f(64)$

43. $g(0.1)$ **44.** $g(1)$

45. $g(100)$ **46.** $h\left(\dfrac{1}{8}\right)$

47. $h(1)$ **48.** $h(4)$

49. x, if $f(x) = 8$ **50.** x, if $g(x) = 3$

51. $f(77)$ **52.** $g(88.4)$

11.3 *Rewrite each expression as a sum or a difference of multiples of logarithms.*

53. $h(33.9)$ **54.** $h(0.05)$

61. $\log(x^2 y)$

62. $\log_3(x^2 + 2x)$

55. x, if $f(x) = 2.475$ **56.** x, if $g(x) = 1.426$

63. $\ln(16)$

64. $\log\left(\dfrac{y}{\sqrt{x}}\right)$

For each function f, find f^{-1} *and sketch the graphs of f and* f^{-1} *on the same set of axes.*

65. $\log_5\left(\dfrac{1}{x}\right)$

57. $f(x) = 10^x$

66. $\ln\left(\dfrac{xy}{z}\right)$

Rewrite each expression as a single logarithm.

67. $\dfrac{1}{2}\log(x + 2) - 2 \cdot \log(x - 1)$

68. $3 \cdot \ln(x) + 2 \cdot \ln(y) - \dfrac{1}{3}\ln(z)$

11.4 *Find the exact solution to each equation.*

69. $\log_2(x) = 8$

70. $\log_3(x) = 0.5$

71. $\log_2(8) = x$

72. $3^x = 8$

73. $x^3 = 8$

74. $3^2 = x$

75. $\log_x(27) = 3$

76. $\log_x(9) = -\dfrac{1}{3}$

77. $x \cdot \ln(3) - x = \ln(7)$

78. $x \cdot \log(8) = x \cdot \log(4) + \log(9)$

79. $3^x = 5^{x-1}$

80. $5^{(2x^2)} = 5^{3-5x}$

81. $4^{2x} = 2^{x+1}$

82. $\log(12) = \log(x) + \log(7 - x)$

83. $\ln(x + 2) - \ln(x - 10) = \ln(2)$

84. $2 \cdot \ln(x + 3) = 3 \cdot \ln(4)$

85. $\log(x) - \log(x - 2) = 2$

86. $\log_2(x) = \log_2(x + 16) - 1$

 Use a calculator to find an approximate solution to each of the following. Round your answers to four decimal places.

87. $6^x = 12$

88. $5^x = 8^{3x+2}$

89. $3^{x+1} = 5$

90. $\log_3(x) = 2.634$

MISCELLANEOUS

 Solve each problem.

91. *Compounding annually.* What does $10,000 invested at 11.5% compounded annually amount to after 15 years?

92. *Doubling time.* How many years does it take for an investment to double at 6.5% compounded annually?

93. *Decaying substance.* The amount, A, of a certain radioactive substance remaining after t years, is given by the formula $A = A_0 e^{-0.0003t}$, where A_0 is the initial amount. If we have 218 grams of this substance today, then how much of it will be left 1000 years from now?

94. *Wildlife management.* The number of white-tailed deer in the Hiawatha National Forest is believed to be growing according to the function

$$P = 517 + 10 \cdot \ln(8t + 1),$$

where t is the time in years from the year 2000.

a) What is the size of the population in 2000?

b) In what year will the population reach 600?

c) Does the population as shown on the accompanying graph appear to be growing faster during the period 2000 to 2005 or during the period 2005 to 2010?

d) What is the average rate of change of the population for each period in part (c)?

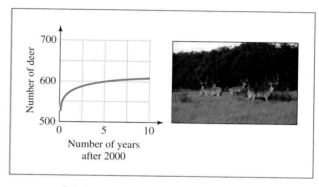

FIGURE FOR EXERCISE 94

95. *Comparing investments.* Melissa deposited $1000 into an account paying 5% annually; on the same day Frank deposited $900 into an account paying 7% compounded continuously. Find the number of years that it will take for the amounts in the accounts to be equal.

96. *Imports and exports.* The value of imports for a small Central American country is believed to be growing according to the function

$$I = 15 \cdot \log(16t + 33),$$

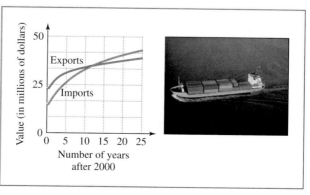

FIGURE FOR EXERCISE 96

and the value of exports appears to be growing according to the function

$$E = 30 \cdot \log(t + 3),$$

where I and E are in millions of dollars and t is the number of years after 2000.

a) What are the values of imports and exports in 2000?

b) Use the accompanying graph to estimate the year in which imports will equal exports.

c) Algebraically find the year in which imports will equal exports.

97. *Finding river flow.* The U.S.G.S. measures the water height h (in feet above sea level) for the Tangipahoa River at Robert, Louisiana, and then finds the flow y [in cubic feet per second (ft^3/sec)], using the formula

$$y = 114.308e^{0.265(h-6.87)}.$$

Find the flow when the river at Robert is 20.6 ft above sea level.

98. *Finding the height.* Rewrite the formula in Exercise 97 to express h as a function of y. Use the new formula to find the water height above sea level when the flow is 10,000 ft^3/sec.

CHAPTER 11 TEST

Let $f(x) = 5^x$ and $g(x) = \log_5(x)$. Find the following.

1. $f(2)$

2. $f(-1)$

3. $f(0)$

4. $g(125)$

5. $g(1)$

6. $g\left(\dfrac{1}{5}\right)$

Sketch the graph of each function.

7. $y = 2^x$

8. $f(x) = \log_2(x)$

9. $y = \left(\dfrac{1}{3}\right)^x$

10. $g(x) = \log_{1/3}(x)$

Suppose $\log_a(M) = 6$ and $\log_a(N) = 4$. Find the following.

11. $\log_a(MN)$

12. $\log_a\left(\dfrac{M^2}{N}\right)$

13. $\dfrac{\log_a(M)}{\log_a(N)}$

14. $\log_a(a^3 M^2)$

15. $\log_a\left(\dfrac{1}{N}\right)$

Find the exact solution to each equation.

16. $3^x = 12$

17. $\log_3(x) = \dfrac{1}{2}$

18. $5^x = 8^{x-1}$

19. $\log(x) + \log(x + 15) = 2$

20. $2 \cdot \ln(x) = \ln(3) + \ln(6 - x)$

 Use a scientific calculator to find an approximate solution to each of the following. Round your answers to four decimal places.

21. Solve $20^x = 5$.

22. Solve $\log_3(x) = 2.75$.

23. The number of bacteria present in a culture at time t is given by the formula $N = 10e^{0.4t}$, where t is in hours. How many bacteria are present initially? How many are present after 24 hours?

24. How many hours does it take for the bacteria population of Problem 23 to double?

Find the exact solution to each equation.

1. $(x - 3)^2 = 8$

2. $\log_2(x - 3) = 8$

3. $2^{x-3} = 8$

4. $2x - 3 = 8$

5. $|x - 3| = 8$

6. $\sqrt{x - 3} = 8$

7. $\log_2(x - 3) + \log_2(x) = \log_2(18)$

8. $2 \cdot \log_2(x - 3) = \log_2(5 - x)$

9. $\dfrac{1}{2}x - \dfrac{2}{3} = \dfrac{3}{4}x + \dfrac{1}{5}$

10. $3x^2 - 6x + 2 = 0$

Find the inverse of each function.

11. $f(x) = \dfrac{1}{3}x$

12. $g(x) = \log_3(x)$

13. $f(x) = 2x - 4$

14. $h(x) = \sqrt{x}$

15. $j(x) = \dfrac{1}{x}$

16. $k(x) = 5^x$

17. $m(x) = e^{x-1}$

18. $n(x) = \ln(x)$

Sketch the graph of each equation.

19. $y = 2x$

20. $y = 2^x$

21. $y = x^2$

22. $y = \log_2(x)$

23. $y = \dfrac{1}{2}x - 4$

24. $y = |2 - x|$

25. $y = 2 - x^2$

26. $y = e^2$

Solve each problem.

27. *Civilian labor force.* The number of workers in the civilian labor force can be modeled by the linear function

$$n(t) = 1.51t + 125.5$$

or by the exponential function

$$n(t) = 125.6e^{0.011t},$$

where t is the number of years since 1990 and $n(t)$ is in millions of workers (Bureau of Labor Statistics, www.bls.gov).

a) Graph both functions on the same coordinate system for $0 \leq t \leq 30$.

b) What does each model predict for the value of n in 2010?

c) What does each model predict for the value of n in the present year? Which model's prediction is closest to the actual size of the present civilian labor force?

28. *Measuring ocean depths.* In this exercise you will see how a geophysicist uses sound reflection to measure the depth of the ocean. Let v be the speed of sound through the water and d_1 be the depth of the ocean below the ship, as shown in the accompanying figure.

a) The time it takes for sound to travel from the ship at point S straight down to the ocean floor at point B_1 and back to point S is 0.270 second. Write d_1 as a function of v.

b) It takes 0.432 second for sound to travel from point S to point B_2 and then to a receiver at R, which is towed 500 meters behind the ship. Assuming $d_2 = d_3$, write d_2 as a function of v.

c) Use the Pythagorean theorem to find v. Then find the ocean depth d_1.

FIGURE FOR EXERCISE 28

Nonlinear Systems and the Conic Sections

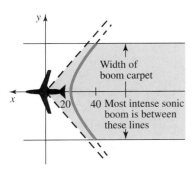

Width of boom carpet

20   40 Most intense sonic boom is between these lines

A t a cruising speed of 1540 miles per hour, the Concorde can fly from London to New York in about 3 hours. So why isn't the same aircraft used for a fast flight from New York to Los Angeles? Concerns about cost efficiency and pollution are two reasons. However, most people agree that the biggest problem is noise. Traveling at Mach 2, the supersonic jet is flying faster than the speed of sound. At this speed the Concorde creates a cone-shaped wave in the air, on which there is a momentary change in air pressure. This change in air pressure causes a thunderlike sonic boom. When the jet is traveling parallel to the ground, the cone-shaped wave intersects the ground along one branch of a hyperbola. People on the ground hear the boom as the hyperbola passes them.

Sonic booms not only are noisy, but they have also been known to cause physical destruction such as broken windows and cracked plaster. For this reason supersonic jets are restricted from flying over land areas in the United States and much of the world. Some engineers believe that changing the silhouette of the plane can lessen the sonic boom, but most agree that it is impossible to eliminate the noise altogether.

In this chapter we discuss curves, including the hyperbola, that occur when a geometric plane intersects a cone. In Exercise 60 of Section 12.4 you will see how the altitude of the aircraft is related to the width of the area where the sonic boom is heard.

12.1 NONLINEAR SYSTEMS OF EQUATIONS

We studied systems of linear equations in Chapter 4. In this section we turn our attention to nonlinear systems of equations.

Solving by Elimination

Equations such as

$$y = x^2, \qquad y = \sqrt{x}, \qquad y = |x|, \qquad y = 2^x, \qquad \text{and} \qquad y = \log_2(x)$$

are **nonlinear equations** because their graphs are not straight lines. We say that a system of equations is nonlinear if at least one equation in the system is nonlinear. We solve a nonlinear system just like a linear system, by elimination of variables. However, because the graphs of nonlinear equations may intersect at more than one point, there may be more than one ordered pair in the solution set to the system.

EXAMPLE 1

A parabola and a line

Solve the system of equations and draw the graph of each equation on the same coordinate system:

$$y = x^2 - 1$$
$$x + y = 1$$

Solution

We can eliminate y by substituting $y = x^2 - 1$ into $x + y = 1$:

$$x + y = 1$$
$$x + (x^2 - 1) = 1 \quad \text{Substitute } x^2 - 1 \text{ for } y.$$
$$x^2 + x - 2 = 0$$
$$(x - 1)(x + 2) = 0$$
$$x - 1 = 0 \quad \text{or} \quad x + 2 = 0$$
$$x = 1 \quad \text{or} \quad x = -2$$

Replace x by 1 and -2 in $y = x^2 - 1$ to find the corresponding values of y:

$$y = (1)^2 - 1 \qquad y = (-2)^2 - 1$$
$$y = 0 \qquad\qquad y = 3$$

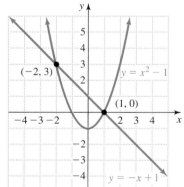

Check that each of the points $(1, 0)$ and $(-2, 3)$ satisfies both of the original equations. The solution set is $\{(1, 0), (-2, 3)\}$. If we solve $x + y = 1$ for y, we get $y = -x + 1$. The line $y = -x + 1$ has y-intercept $(0, 1)$ and slope -1. The graph of $y = x^2 - 1$ is a parabola with vertex $(0, -1)$. Of course, $(1, 0)$ and $(-2, 3)$ are on both graphs. The two graphs are shown in Fig. 12.1. ∎

FIGURE 12.1

Graphing is not an accurate method for solving any system of equations. However, the graphs of the equations in a nonlinear system help us to understand how many solutions we should have for the system. It is not necessary to graph a system to solve it. Even when the graphs are too difficult to sketch, we can solve the system.

EXAMPLE 2

Solving a system algebraically with substitution

Solve the system:

$$x^2 + y^2 + 2y = 3$$
$$x^2 - y = 5$$

Solution

If we substitute $y = x^2 - 5$ into the first equation to eliminate y, we will get a fourth-degree equation to solve. Instead, we can eliminate the variable x by writing $x^2 - y = 5$ as $x^2 = y + 5$. Now replace x^2 by $y + 5$ in the first equation:

$$x^2 + y^2 + 2y = 3$$
$$(y + 5) + y^2 + 2y = 3$$
$$y^2 + 3y + 5 = 3$$
$$y^2 + 3y + 2 = 0$$
$$(y + 2)(y + 1) = 0 \quad \text{Solve by factoring.}$$

$$y + 2 = 0 \quad \text{or} \quad y + 1 = 0$$
$$y = -2 \quad \text{or} \quad y = -1$$

Let $y = -2$ in the equation $x^2 = y + 5$ to find the corresponding x:

$$x^2 = -2 + 5$$
$$x^2 = 3$$
$$x = \pm\sqrt{3}$$

Now let $y = -1$ in the equation $x^2 = y + 5$ to find the corresponding x:

$$x^2 = -1 + 5$$
$$x^2 = 4$$
$$x = \pm 2$$

Check these values in the original equations. The solution set is

$$\{(\sqrt{3}, -2), (-\sqrt{3}, -2), (2, -1), (-2, -1)\}.$$

The graphs of these two equations intersect at four points. ■

E X A M P L E   3

Solving a system with the addition method

Solve each system:

a) $x^2 - y^2 = 5$
$\quad\ x^2 + y^2 = 7$

b) $\dfrac{2}{x} + \dfrac{1}{y} = \dfrac{1}{5}$

$\quad\ \dfrac{1}{x} - \dfrac{3}{y} = \dfrac{1}{3}$

Study Tip

When you take notes leave space. Go back later and fill in more details, make corrections, or work another problem of the same type.

Solution

a) We can eliminate y by adding the equations:

$$x^2 - y^2 = 5$$
$$\underline{x^2 + y^2 = 7}$$
$$2x^2 \qquad = 12$$
$$x^2 = 6$$
$$x = \pm\sqrt{6}$$

Since $x^2 = 6$, the second equation yields $6 + y^2 = 7$, $y^2 = 1$, and $y = \pm 1$. If $x^2 = 6$ and $y^2 = 1$, then both of the original equations are satisfied. The solution set is

$$\{(\sqrt{6}, 1)(\sqrt{6}, -1), (-\sqrt{6}, 1), (-\sqrt{6}, -1)\}$$

b) Usually with equations involving rational expressions we first multiply by the least common denominator (LCD), but this would make the given system more complicated. So we will just use the addition method to eliminate y:

$$\frac{6}{x} + \frac{3}{y} = \frac{3}{5} \qquad \text{Eq. (1) multiplied by 3}$$

$$\frac{1}{x} - \frac{3}{y} = \frac{1}{3} \qquad \text{Eq. (2)}$$

$$\overline{\frac{7}{x} \qquad = \frac{14}{15}} \qquad \frac{3}{5} + \frac{1}{3} = \frac{14}{15}$$

$$14x = 7 \cdot 15$$

$$x = \frac{7 \cdot 15}{14} = \frac{15}{2}$$

To find y, substitute $x = \frac{15}{2}$ into Eq. (1):

$$\frac{2}{\frac{15}{2}} + \frac{1}{y} = \frac{1}{5}$$

$$\frac{4}{15} + \frac{1}{y} = \frac{1}{5} \qquad \frac{2}{\frac{15}{2}} = 2 \cdot \frac{2}{15} = \frac{4}{15}$$

$$15y \cdot \frac{4}{15} + 15y \cdot \frac{1}{y} = 15y \cdot \frac{1}{5} \qquad \text{Multiply each side by the LCD, } 15y.$$

$$4y + 15 = 3y$$

$$y = -15$$

Check that $x = \frac{15}{2}$ and $y = -15$ satisfy both original equations. The solution set is $\left\{ \left(\frac{15}{2}, -15 \right) \right\}$. ■

A system of nonlinear equations might involve exponential or logarithmic functions. To solve such systems, you will need to recall some facts about exponents and logarithms.

E X A M P L E   4   A system involving logarithms

Solve the system

$$y = \log_2(x + 28)$$
$$y = 3 + \log_2(x)$$

Solution

Eliminate y by substituting $\log_2(x + 28)$ for y in the second equation:

$$\log_2(x + 28) = 3 + \log_2(x) \qquad \text{Eliminate } y.$$

$$\log_2(x + 28) - \log_2(x) = 3 \qquad \text{Subtract } \log_2(x) \text{ from each side.}$$

$$\log_2\left(\frac{x + 28}{x} \right) = 3 \qquad \text{Quotient rule for logarithms}$$

$$\frac{x + 28}{x} = 8 \qquad \text{Definition of logarithm}$$

$$x + 28 = 8x \qquad \text{Multiply each side by } x.$$

$$28 = 7x \qquad \text{Subtract } x \text{ from each side.}$$

$$4 = x \qquad \text{Divide each side by 7.}$$

If $x = 4$, then $y = \log_2(4 + 28) = \log_2(32) = 5$. Check $(4, 5)$ in both equations. The solution to the system is $\{(4, 5)\}$. ∎

Applications

Example 5 shows a geometric problem that can be solved with a system of nonlinear equations.

EXAMPLE 5

Nonlinear equations in applications

A 15-foot ladder is leaning against a wall so that the distance from the bottom of the ladder to the wall is one-half of the distance from the top of the ladder to the ground. Find the distance from the top of the ladder to the ground.

Calculator Close-Up

To see the solutions, graph
$$y_1 = \sqrt{15^2 - x^2},$$
$$y_2 = -\sqrt{15^2 - x^2},$$
and $y_3 = 2x$.

The line intersects the circle twice.

Solution

Let x be the number of feet from the bottom of the ladder to the wall and y be the number of feet from the top of the ladder to the ground (see Fig. 12.2). We can write two equations involving x and y:

$$x^2 + y^2 = 15^2 \quad \text{Pythagorean theorem}$$
$$y = 2x$$

Solve by substitution:

$$x^2 + (2x)^2 = 225 \quad \text{Replace } y \text{ by } 2x.$$
$$x^2 + 4x^2 = 225$$
$$5x^2 = 225$$
$$x^2 = 45$$
$$x = \pm\sqrt{45} = \pm 3\sqrt{5}$$

Because x represents distance, x must be positive. So $x = 3\sqrt{5}$. Because $y = 2x$, we get $y = 6\sqrt{5}$. The distance from the top of the ladder to the ground is $6\sqrt{5}$ feet.

FIGURE 12.2 ∎

Example 6 shows how a nonlinear system can be used to solve a problem involving work.

EXAMPLE 6

Nonlinear equations in applications

A large fish tank at the Gulf Aquarium can usually be filled in 10 minutes using pumps A and B. However, pump B can pump water in or out at the same rate. If pump B is inadvertently run in reverse, then the tank will be filled in 30 minutes. How long would it take each pump to fill the tank by itself?

Solution

Let a represent the number of minutes that it takes pump A to fill the tank alone and b represent the number of minutes it takes pump B to fill the tank alone. The rate at which pump A fills the tank is $\frac{1}{a}$ of the tank per minute, and the rate at which pump B fills the tank is $\frac{1}{b}$ of the tank per minute. Because the work completed is the product of the rate and time, we can make the following table when the pumps work together to fill the tank:

	Rate	Time	Work
Pump A	$\frac{1}{a}\frac{\text{tank}}{\text{min}}$	10 min	$\frac{10}{a}$ tank
Pump B	$\frac{1}{b}\frac{\text{tank}}{\text{min}}$	10 min	$\frac{10}{b}$ tank

Note that each pump fills a fraction of the tank and those fractions have a sum of 1:

$$(1) \qquad \frac{10}{a} + \frac{10}{b} = 1$$

In the 30 minutes in which pump B is working in reverse, A puts in $\frac{30}{a}$ of the tank whereas B takes out $\frac{30}{b}$ of the tank. Since the tank still gets filled, we can write the following equation:

$$(2) \qquad \frac{30}{a} - \frac{30}{b} = 1$$

Multiply Eq. (1) by 3 and add the result to Eq. (2) to eliminate b:

$$\frac{30}{a} + \frac{30}{b} = 3 \quad \text{Eq. (1) multiplied by 3}$$
$$\frac{30}{a} - \frac{30}{b} = 1 \quad \text{Eq. (2)}$$
$$\frac{60}{a} = 4$$
$$4a = 60$$
$$a = 15$$

Use $a = 15$ in Eq. (1) to find b:

$$\frac{10}{15} + \frac{10}{b} = 1$$
$$\frac{10}{b} = \frac{1}{3} \quad \text{Subtract } \tfrac{10}{15} \text{ from each side.}$$
$$b = 30$$

So pump A fills the tank in 15 minutes working alone, and pump B fills the tank in 30 minutes working alone.

WARM-UPS

True or false? Explain your answer.

1. The graph of $y = x^2$ is a parabola.
2. The graph of $y = |x|$ is a straight line.
3. The point $(3, -4)$ satisfies both $x^2 + y^2 = 25$ and $y = \sqrt{5x + 1}$.
4. The graphs of $y = \sqrt{x}$ and $y = -x - 2$ do not intersect.
5. Substitution is the only method for eliminating a variable when solving a nonlinear system.
6. If Bob paints a fence in x hours, then he paints $\frac{1}{x}$ of the fence per hour.
7. In a triangle whose angles are 30°, 60°, and 90°, the length of the side opposite the 30° angle is one-half the length of the hypotenuse.
8. The formula $V = LWH$ gives the volume of a rectangular box in which the sides have lengths L, W, and H.
9. The surface area of a rectangular box is $2LW + 2WH + 2LH$.
10. The area of a right triangle is one-half the product of the lengths of its legs.

12.1 EXERCISES

Reading and Writing *After reading this section, write out the answers to these questions. Use complete sentences.*

1. Why are some equations called nonlinear?

2. Why do we graph the equations in a nonlinear system?

3. Why don't we solve systems by graphing?

4. What techniques do we use to solve nonlinear systems?

Solve each system and graph both equations on the same set of axes. See Example 1.

5. $y = x^2$
   $x + y = 6$

6. $y = x^2 - 1$
   $x + y = 11$

7. $y = |x|$
   $2y - x = 6$

8. $y = |x|$
   $3y = x + 6$

9. $y = \sqrt{2x}$
   $x - y = 4$

10. $y = \sqrt{x}$
   $x - y = 6$

11. $4x - 9y = 9$
    $xy = 1$

12. $2x + 2y = 3$
    $xy = -1$

25. $\dfrac{1}{x} - \dfrac{1}{y} = 5$

$\dfrac{2}{x} + \dfrac{1}{y} = -3$

26. $\dfrac{2}{x} - \dfrac{3}{y} = \dfrac{1}{2}$

$\dfrac{3}{x} + \dfrac{1}{y} = \dfrac{1}{2}$

27. $\dfrac{2}{x} - \dfrac{1}{y} = \dfrac{5}{12}$

$\dfrac{1}{x} - \dfrac{3}{y} = -\dfrac{5}{12}$

28. $\dfrac{3}{x} - \dfrac{2}{y} = 5$

$\dfrac{4}{x} + \dfrac{3}{y} = 18$

13. $y = -x^2 + 1$
    $y = x^2$

14. $y = x^2$
    $y = \sqrt{x}$

29. $x^2 y = 20$
    $xy + 2 = 6x$

30. $y^2 x = 3$
    $xy + 1 = 6x$

31. $x^2 + xy - y^2 = -11$
    $x + y = 7$

32. $x^2 + xy + y^2 = 3$
    $y = 2x - 5$

33. $3y - 2 = x^4$
    $y = x^2$

34. $y - 3 = 2x^4$
    $y = 7x^2$

Solve each system. See Examples 2 and 3.

15. $x^2 + y^2 = 25$
    $y = x^2 - 5$

16. $x^2 + y^2 = 25$
    $y = x + 1$

17. $xy - 3x = 8$
    $y = x + 1$

18. $xy + 2x = 9$
    $x - y = 2$

19. $xy - x = 8$
    $xy + 3x = -4$

20. $2xy - 3x = -1$
    $xy + 5x = -7$

21. $x^2 + y^2 = 8$
    $x^2 - y^2 = 2$

22. $y^2 - 2x^2 = 1$
    $y^2 + 2x^2 = 5$

23. $x^2 + 2y^2 = 8$
    $2x^2 - y^2 = 1$

24. $2x^2 + 3y^2 = 8$
    $3x^2 + 2y^2 = 7$

Solve the following systems involving logarithmic and exponential functions. See Example 4.

35. $y = \log_2(x - 1)$
    $y = 3 - \log_2(x + 1)$

36. $y = \log_3(x - 4)$
    $y = 2 - \log_3(x + 4)$

37. $y = \log_2(x - 1)$
    $y = 2 + \log_2(x + 2)$

38. $y = \log_4(8x)$
    $y = 2 + \log_4(x - 1)$

39. $y = 2^{3x+4}$
    $y = 4^{x-1}$

40. $y = 4^{3x}$
    $y = \left(\dfrac{1}{2}\right)^{1-x}$

Solve each problem by using a system of two equations in two unknowns. See Examples 5 and 6.

41. *Known hypotenuse.* Find the lengths of the legs of a right triangle whose hypotenuse is $\sqrt{15}$ feet and whose area is 3 square feet.

42. *Known diagonal.* A small television is advertised to have a picture with a diagonal measure of 5 inches and a viewing area of 12 square inches (in.²). What are the length and width of the screen?

FIGURE FOR EXERCISE 42

43. *House of seven gables.* Vincent has plans to build a house with seven gables. The plans call for an attic vent in the shape of an isosceles triangle in each gable. Because of the slope of the roof, the ratio of the height to the base of each triangle must be 1 to 4. If the vents are to provide a total ventilating area of 3500 in.², then what should be the height and base of each triangle?

FIGURE FOR EXERCISE 43

44. *Known perimeter.* Find the lengths of the sides of a triangle whose perimeter is 6 feet (ft) and whose angles are 30°, 60°, and 90° (see Appendix A).

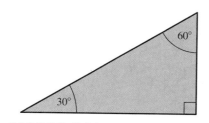

FIGURE FOR EXERCISE 44

45. *Filling a tank.* Pump A can either fill a tank or empty it in the same amount of time. If pump A and pump B are working together, the tank can be filled in 6 hours. When pump A was inadvertently left in the drain position while pump B was trying to fill the tank, it took 12 hours to fill the tank. How long would it take either pump working alone to fill the tank?

46. *Cleaning a house.* Roxanne either cleans the house or messes it up at the same rate. When Roxanne is cleaning with her mother, they can clean up a completely messed up house in 6 hours. If Roxanne is not cooperating, it takes her mother 9 hours to clean the house, with Roxanne continually messing it up. How long would it take her mother to clean the entire house if Roxanne were sent to her grandmother's house?

47. *Cleaning fish.* Jan and Beth work in a seafood market that processes 200 pounds of catfish every morning. On Monday, Jan started cleaning catfish at 8:00 A.M. and finished cleaning 100 pounds just as Beth arrived. Beth then took over and finished the job at 8:50 A.M. On Tuesday they both started at 8 A.M. and worked together to finish the job at 8:24 A.M. On Wednesday, Beth was sick. If Jan is the faster worker, then how long did it take Jan to complete all of the catfish by herself?

FIGURE FOR EXERCISE 47

48. *Building a patio.* Richard has already formed a rectangular area for a flagstone patio, but his wife Susan is unsure of the size of the patio they want. If the width is increased by 2 ft, then the area is increased by 30 square feet (ft²). If the width is increased by 1 ft and the length by 3 ft, then the area is increased by 54 ft². What are the dimensions of the rectangle that Richard has already formed?

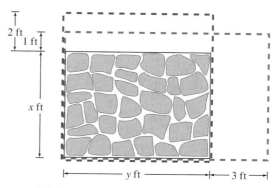

FIGURE FOR EXERCISE 48

49. *Fencing a rectangle.* If 34 ft of fencing are used to enclose a rectangular area of 72 ft², then what are the dimensions of the area?

50. *Real numbers.* Find two numbers that have a sum of 8 and a product of 10.

51. *Imaginary numbers.* Find two complex numbers whose sum is 8 and whose product is 20.

52. *Imaginary numbers.* Find two complex numbers whose sum is −6 and whose product is 10.

53. *Making a sign.* Rico's Sign Shop has a contract to make a sign in the shape of a square with an isosceles triangle on top of it, as shown in the figure. The contract calls for a total height of 10 ft with an area of 72 ft². How long should Rico make the side of the square and what should be the height of the triangle?

54. *Designing a box.* Angelina is designing a rectangular box of 120 cubic inches that is to contain new Eaties breakfast cereal. The box must be 2 inches thick so that it is easy to hold. It must have 184 square inches of surface area to provide enough space for all of the special offers and coupons. What should be the dimensions of the box?

FIGURE FOR EXERCISE 53

 GRAPHING CALCULATOR EXERCISES

55. Solve each system by graphing each pair of equations on a graphing calculator and using the intersect feature to estimate the point of intersection. Find the coordinates of each intersection to the nearest hundredth.

a) $y = e^x - 4$
     $y = \ln(x + 3)$

b) $3^{y-1} = x$
     $y = x^2$

c) $x^2 + y^2 = 4$
     $y = x^3$

In This Section

- The Distance Formula
- The Geometric Definition of Parabola
- Developing the Equation
- Parabolas in the Form $y = a(x - h)^2 + k$
- Finding the Vertex, Focus, and Directrix
- Axis of Symmetry
- Changing Forms
- Parabolas Opening to the Right or Left

12.2   THE PARABOLA

The **conic sections** are the four curves that are obtained by intersecting a cone and a plane as in Fig. 12.3. The figure explains why the parabola, ellipse, circle, and hyperbola are called conic sections, but it does not help us find equations for the curves. To develop equations for these curves we will redefine them more precisely using distance between points. So we will first review the distance formula that we used in Section 3.1.

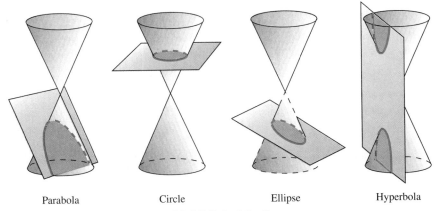

Parabola   Circle   Ellipse   Hyperbola

FIGURE 12.3

The Distance Formula

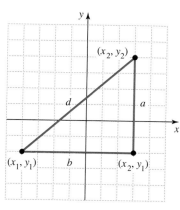

FIGURE 12.4

Consider the points (x_1, y_1) and (x_2, y_2) as shown in Fig. 12.4. The distance between these points is the length of the hypotenuse of a right triangle as shown in the figure. The length of side a is $y_2 - y_1$ and the length of side b is $x_2 - x_1$. Using the Pythagorean theorem, we can write

$$d^2 = (x_2 - x_1)^2 + (y_2 - y_1)^2.$$

If we apply the even-root property and omit the negative square root (because the distance is positive), we can express this formula as follows.

Distance Formula

The distance d between (x_1, y_1) and (x_2, y_2) is given by the formula

$$d = \sqrt{(x_2 - x_1)^2 + (y_2 - y_1)^2}.$$

E X A M P L E   1

Using the distance formula

Find the length of the line segment with endpoints $(-8, -10)$ and $(6, -4)$.

Solution

Let $(x_1, y_1) = (-8, -10)$ and $(x_2, y_2) = (6, -4)$. Now substitute the appropriate values into the distance formula:

$$\begin{aligned}
d &= \sqrt{[6 - (-8)]^2 + [-4 - (-10)]^2} \\
&= \sqrt{(14)^2 + (6)^2} \\
&= \sqrt{196 + 36} \\
&= \sqrt{232} \\
&= \sqrt{4 \cdot 58} \\
&= 2\sqrt{58} \quad \text{Simplified form}
\end{aligned}$$

The exact length of the segment is $2\sqrt{58}$. ■

The Geometric Definition of Parabola

In Section 8.3 we called the graph of $y = ax^2 + bx + c$ a parabola. This equation is the **standard equation** of a parabola. In this section you will see that the following geometric definition describes the same curve as the equation.

Parabola

Given a line (the **directrix**) and a point not on the line (the **focus**), the set of all points in the plane that are equidistant from the point and the line is called a **parabola.**

In Section 8.3 we defined the vertex as the highest point on a parabola that opens downward or the lowest point on a parabola that opens upward. We learned that $x = -b/(2a)$ gives the x-coordinate of the vertex. We can also describe the vertex of a parabola as the midpoint of the line segment that joins the focus and directrix, perpendicular to the directrix. See Fig. 12.5.

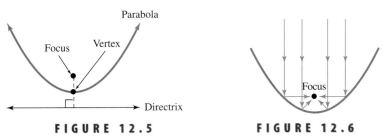

FIGURE 12.5   FIGURE 12.6

The focus of a parabola is important in applications. When parallel rays of light travel into a parabolic reflector, they are reflected toward the focus as in Fig. 12.6. This property is used in telescopes to see the light from distant stars. If the light source is at the focus, as in a searchlight, the light is reflected off the parabola and projected outward in a narrow beam. This reflecting property is also used in camera lenses, satellite dishes, and eavesdropping devices.

Developing the Equation

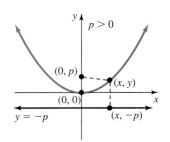

FIGURE 12.7

To develop an equation for a parabola, given the focus and directrix, choose the point $(0, p)$, where $p > 0$ as the focus and the line $y = -p$ as the directrix, as shown in Fig. 12.7. The vertex of this parabola is $(0, 0)$. For an arbitrary point (x, y) on the parabola the distance to the directrix is the distance from (x, y) to $(x, -p)$. The distance to the focus is the distance between (x, y) and $(0, p)$. We use the fact that these distances are equal to write the equation of the parabola:

$$\sqrt{(x - 0)^2 + (y - p)^2} = \sqrt{(x - x)^2 + (y - (-p))^2}$$

To simplify the equation, first remove the parentheses inside the radicals:

$$\sqrt{x^2 + y^2 - 2py + p^2} = \sqrt{y^2 + 2py + p^2}$$
$$x^2 + y^2 - 2py + p^2 = y^2 + 2py + p^2 \qquad \text{Square each side.}$$
$$x^2 = 4py \qquad \text{Subtract } y^2 \text{ and } p^2 \text{ from each side.}$$
$$y = \frac{1}{4p}x^2$$

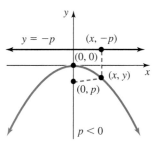

FIGURE 12.8

So the parabola with focus $(0, p)$ and directrix $y = -p$ for $p > 0$ has equation $y = \frac{1}{4p}x^2$. This equation has the form $y = ax^2 + bx + c$, where $a = \frac{1}{4p}$, $b = 0$, and $c = 0$.

If the focus is $(0, p)$ with $p < 0$ and the directrix is $y = -p$, then the parabola opens downward as shown in Fig. 12.8. Deriving the equation using the distance formula again yields $y = \frac{1}{4p}x^2$.

Parabolas in the Form $y = a(x - h)^2 + k$

The simplest parabola, $y = x^2$, has vertex $(0, 0)$. The transformation $y = a(x - h)^2 + k$ is also a parabola and its vertex is (h, k). The focus and directrix of the transformation are found as follows:

> ### Parabolas in the Form $y = a(x - h)^2 + k$
>
> The graph of the equation $y = a(x - h)^2 + k$ $(a \neq 0)$ is a parabola with vertex (h, k), focus $(h, k + p)$, and directrix $y = k - p$, where $a = \frac{1}{4p}$. If $a > 0$, the parabola opens upward; if $a < 0$, the parabola opens downward.

$a > 0$

$a = \dfrac{1}{4p}$

$a < 0$

$(h, k + p)$

(h, k) $y = a(x - h)^2 + k$

Directrix: $y = k - p$

Directrix: $y = k - p$

(h, k)

$y = a(x - h)^2 + k$

$(h, k + p)$

FIGURE 12.9

Figure 12.9 shows the location of the focus and directrix for parabolas with vertex (h, k) and opening either upward or downward. Note that the location of the focus and directrix determine the value of a and the shape and opening of the parabola.

CAUTION   For a parabola that opens upward, $p > 0$, and the focus $(h, k + p)$ is above the vertex (h, k). For a parabola that opens downward, $p < 0$, and the focus $(h, k + p)$ is below the vertex (h, k). In either case the distance from the vertex to the focus and the vertex to the directrix is $|p|$.

Finding the Vertex, Focus, and Directrix

In Example 2 we find the vertex, focus, and directrix from an equation of a parabola. In Example 3 we find the equation given the focus and directrix.

E X A M P L E   2

Finding the vertex, focus, and directrix, given an equation
Find the vertex, focus, and directrix for the parabola $y = x^2$.

FIGURE 12.10

Solution
Compare $y = x^2$ to the general formula $y = a(x - h)^2 + k$. We see that $h = 0$, $k = 0$, and $a = 1$. So the vertex is $(0, 0)$. Because $a = 1$, we can use $a = \dfrac{1}{4p}$ to get

$$1 = \frac{1}{4p},$$

or $p = \frac{1}{4}$. Use $(h, k + p)$ to get the focus $\left(0, \frac{1}{4}\right)$. Use the equation $y = k - p$ to get $y = -\frac{1}{4}$ as the equation of the directrix. See Fig. 12.10.   ■

E X A M P L E   3

Finding an equation, given a focus and directrix
Find the equation of the parabola with focus $(-1, 4)$ and directrix $y = 3$.

Solution
Because the vertex is halfway between the focus and directrix, the vertex is $\left(-1, \frac{7}{2}\right)$. See Fig. 12.11 on the next page. The distance from the vertex to the focus is $\frac{1}{2}$. Because the focus is above the vertex, p is positive. So $p = \frac{1}{2}$, and $a = \dfrac{1}{4p} = \dfrac{1}{2}$. The equation is

$$y = \frac{1}{2}(x - (-1))^2 + \frac{7}{2}.$$

FIGURE 12.11

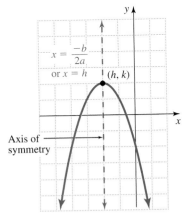

FIGURE 12.12

Convert to $y = ax^2 + bx + c$ form as follows:

$$y = \frac{1}{2}(x + 1)^2 + \frac{7}{2}$$

$$y = \frac{1}{2}(x^2 + 2x + 1) + \frac{7}{2}$$

$$y = \frac{1}{2}x^2 + x + 4$$

∎

Axis of Symmetry

The graph of $y = x^2$ shown in Fig. 12.10 is **symmetric about the y-axis** because the two halves of the parabola would coincide if the paper were folded on the y-axis. In general, the vertical line through the vertex is the **axis of symmetry** for the parabola. See Fig. 12.12. In the form $y = ax^2 + bx + c$ the x-coordinate of the vertex is $-b/(2a)$ and the equation of the axis of symmetry is $x = -b/(2a)$. In the form $y = a(x - h)^2 + k$ the vertex is (h, k) and the equation for the axis of symmetry is $x = h$.

Changing Forms

Since there are two forms for the equation of a parabola, it is sometimes useful to change from one form to the other. To change from $y = a(x - h)^2 + k$ to the form $y = ax^2 + bx + c$, we square the binomial and combine like terms, as in Example 3. To change from $y = ax^2 + bx + c$ to the form $y = a(x - h)^2 + k$, we complete the square, as in Example 4.

E X A M P L E   4   **Converting $y = ax^2 + bx + c$ to $y = a(x - h)^2 + k$**
Write $y = 2x^2 - 4x + 5$ in the form $y = a(x - h)^2 + k$ and identify the vertex, focus, directrix, and axis of symmetry of the parabola.

Solution
Use completing the square to rewrite the equation:

$$y = 2(x^2 - 2x) + 5$$
$$y = 2(x^2 - 2x + 1 - 1) + 5 \quad \text{Complete the square.}$$
$$y = 2(x^2 - 2x + 1) - 2 + 5 \quad \text{Move } 2(-1) \text{ outside the parentheses.}$$
$$y = 2(x - 1)^2 + 3$$

The vertex is $(1, 3)$. Because $a = \frac{1}{4p}$, we have

$$\frac{1}{4p} = 2,$$

and $p = \frac{1}{8}$. Because the parabola opens upward, the focus is $\frac{1}{8}$ unit above the vertex at $\left(1, 3\frac{1}{8}\right)$, or $\left(1, \frac{25}{8}\right)$, and the directrix is the horizontal line $\frac{1}{8}$ unit below the vertex, $y = 2\frac{7}{8}$ or $y = \frac{23}{8}$. The axis of symmetry is $x = 1$. ∎

Calculator Close-Up

The graphs of

$$y_1 = 2x^2 - 4x + 5$$

and

$$y_2 = 2(x - 1)^2 + 3$$

appear to be identical. This supports the conclusion that the equations are equivalent.

CAUTION   Be careful when you complete a square within parentheses as in Example 4. For another example, consider the equivalent equations

$$y = -3(x^2 + 4x),$$
$$y = -3(x^2 + 4x + 4 - 4),$$

and

$$y = -3(x + 2)^2 + 12.$$

EXAMPLE 5

Finding the features of a parabola from standard form

Find the vertex, focus, directrix, and axis of symmetry of the parabola $y = -3x^2 + 9x - 5$, and determine whether the parabola opens upward or downward.

Solution

The x-coordinate of the vertex is

$$x = \frac{-b}{2a} = \frac{-9}{2(-3)} = \frac{-9}{-6} = \frac{3}{2}.$$

To find the y-coordinate of the vertex, let $x = \frac{3}{2}$ in $y = -3x^2 + 9x - 5$:

$$y = -3\left(\frac{3}{2}\right)^2 + 9\left(\frac{3}{2}\right) - 5 = -\frac{27}{4} + \frac{27}{2} - 5 = \frac{7}{4}$$

The vertex is $\left(\frac{3}{2}, \frac{7}{4}\right)$. Because $a = -3$, the parabola opens downward. To find the focus, use $-3 = \frac{1}{4p}$ to get $p = -\frac{1}{12}$. The focus is $\frac{1}{12}$ of a unit below the vertex at $\left(\frac{3}{2}, \frac{7}{4} - \frac{1}{12}\right)$ or $\left(\frac{3}{2}, \frac{5}{3}\right)$. The directrix is the horizontal line $\frac{1}{12}$ of a unit above the vertex, $y = \frac{7}{4} + \frac{1}{12}$ or $y = \frac{11}{6}$. The equation of the axis of symmetry is $x = \frac{3}{2}$. ∎

Parabolas Opening to the Right or Left

If we interchange x and y in the equation $y = a(x - h)^2 + k$ we get the equation $x = a(y - k)^2 + h$, which is a parabola opening to the right or left.

Parabolas in the Form $x = a(y - k)^2 + h$

The graph of $x = a(y - k)^2 + h$ $(a \neq 0)$ is a parabola with vertex (h, k), focus $(h + p, k)$, and directrix $x = h - p$, where $a = \frac{1}{4p}$. If $a > 0$, the parabola opens to the right; if $a < 0$, the parabola opens to the left.

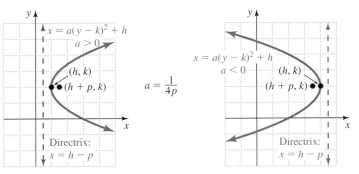

FIGURE 12.13

Figure 12.13 shows the location of the focus and directrix for parabolas with vertex (h, k) and opening either right or left. The location of the focus and directrix determine the value of a and the shape and opening of the parabola. Note that a and p have the same sign because $a = \frac{1}{4p}$.

The equation $x = ay^2 + by + c$ could be converted to the form $x = a(y - k)^2 + h$ from which the vertex, focus, and directrix could be determined. Without converting we can determine that the graph of $x = ay^2 + by + c$ opens to the right for $a > 0$ and to the left for $a < 0$. The y-coordinate of the vertex is $\frac{-b}{2a}$. The x-coordinate of the vertex can be determined by substituting $\frac{-b}{2a}$ for y in $x = ay^2 + by + c$.

E X A M P L E   6

Graphing a parabola opening to the right

Find the vertex, focus, and directrix for the parabola $x = \frac{1}{2}(y - 2)^2 + 1$ and sketch the graph.

Solution

In the form $x = a(y - k)^2 + h$ the vertex is (h, k). So the vertex for $x = \frac{1}{2}(y - 2)^2 + 1$ is $(1, 2)$. Since $a = \frac{1}{4p}$ and $a = \frac{1}{2}$, we have $p = \frac{1}{2}$ and the focus is $\left(\frac{3}{2}, 2\right)$. The directrix is the vertical line $x = \frac{1}{2}$. Find a few points that satisfy $x = \frac{1}{2}(y - 2)^2 + 1$ as follows:

$x = \frac{1}{2}(y - 2)^2 + 1$	3	$\frac{3}{2}$	1	$\frac{3}{2}$	3
y	0	1	2	3	4

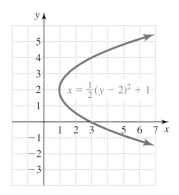

FIGURE 12.14

Sketch the graph through these points, as shown in Fig. 12.14.

The equation $x = ay^2 + by + c$ could be converted to the form $x = a(y - k)^2 + h$ from which the vertex, focus, and directrix could be determined. Without converting we can determine that the graph of $x = ay^2 + by + c$ opens to the right for $a > 0$ and to the left for $a < 0$. The y-coordinate of the vertex is $\frac{-b}{2a}$. The x-coordinate of the vertex can be determined by substituting $\frac{-b}{2a}$ for y in $x = ay^2 + by + c$.

WARM-UPS

True or false? Explain your answer.

1. There is a parabola with focus $(2, 3)$, directrix $y = 1$, and vertex $(0, 0)$.

2. The focus for the parabola $y = \frac{1}{4}x^2 + 1$ is $(0, 2)$.

3. The graph of $y - 3 = 5(x - 4)^2$ is a parabola with vertex $(4, 3)$.

4. The graph of $y = 6x + 3x + 2$ is a parabola.

5. The graph of $y = 2x - x^2 + 9$ is a parabola opening upward.

6. For $y = x^2$ the vertex and y-intercept are the same point.

7. A parabola with vertex $(2, 3)$ and focus $(2, 4)$ has no x-intercepts.

8. The parabola with focus $(0, 2)$ and directrix $y = 1$ opens upward.

9. The axis of symmetry for $y = a(x - 2)^2 + k$ is $x = 2$.

10. If $a = \frac{1}{(4p)}$ and $a = 1$, then $p = \frac{1}{4}$.

12.2   EXERCISES

Reading and Writing   *After reading this section, write out the answers to these questions. Use complete sentences.*

1. What is the definition of a parabola given in this section?

2. What is the location of the vertex?

3. What are the two forms of the equation of a parabola?

4. What is the distance from the focus to the vertex in any parabola of the form $y = ax^2 + bx + c$?

5. How do we convert an equation of the form $y = ax^2 + bx + c$ into the form $y = a(x - h)^2 + k$?

6. How do we convert an equation of the form $y = a(x - h)^2 + k$ into the form $y = ax^2 + bx + c$?

Find the distance between each given pair of points. See Example 1.

7. $(6, 5), (4, 2)$

8. $(7, 3), (5, 1)$

9. $(3, 5), (1, -3)$

10. $(6, 2), (3, -5)$

11. $(4, -2), (-3, -6)$

12. $(-2, 3), (1, -4)$

Find the vertex, focus, and directrix for each parabola. See Example 2.

13. $y = 2x^2$

14. $y = \frac{1}{2}x^2$

15. $y = -\frac{1}{4}x^2$

16. $y = -\frac{1}{12}x^2$

17. $y = \frac{1}{2}(x - 3)^2 + 2$

18. $y = \frac{1}{4}(x + 2)^2 - 5$

19. $y = -(x + 1)^2 + 6$

20. $y = -3(x - 4)^2 + 1$

Find the equation of the parabola with the given focus and directrix. See Example 3.

21. Focus $(0, 2)$, directrix $y = -2$

22. Focus $(0, -3)$, directrix $y = 3$

23. Focus $\left(0, -\frac{1}{2}\right)$, directrix $y = \frac{1}{2}$

24. Focus $\left(0, \frac{1}{8}\right)$, directrix $y = -\frac{1}{8}$

25. Focus $(3, 2)$, directrix $y = 1$

26. Focus $(-4, 5)$, directrix $y = 4$

27. Focus $(1, -2)$, directrix $y = 2$

28. Focus $(2, -3)$, directrix $y = 1$

29. Focus $(-3, 1.25)$, directrix $y = 0.75$

30. Focus $\left(5, \dfrac{17}{8}\right)$, directrix $y = \dfrac{15}{8}$

Write each equation in the form $y = a(x - h)^2 + k$. Identify the vertex, focus, directrix, and axis of symmetry of each parabola. See Example 4.

31. $y = x^2 - 6x + 1$

32. $y = x^2 + 4x - 7$

33. $y = 2x^2 + 12x + 5$

34. $y = 3x^2 + 6x - 7$

35. $y = -2x^2 + 16x + 1$

36. $y = -3x^2 - 6x + 7$

37. $y = 5x^2 + 40x$

38. $y = -2x^2 + 10x$

Find the vertex, focus, directrix, and axis of symmetry of each parabola (without completing the square), and determine whether the parabola opens upward or downward. See Example 5.

39. $y = x^2 - 4x + 1$

40. $y = x^2 - 6x - 7$

41. $y = -x^2 + 2x - 3$

42. $y = -x^2 + 4x + 9$

43. $y = 3x^2 - 6x + 1$

44. $y = 2x^2 + 4x - 3$

45. $y = -x^2 - 3x + 2$

46. $y = -x^2 + 3x - 1$

47. $y = 3x^2 + 5$

48. $y = -2x^2 - 6$

Find the vertex, focus, and directrix for each parabola. See Example 6.

49. $x = (y - 2)^2 + 3$

50. $x = (y + 3)^2 - 1$

51. $x = \dfrac{1}{4}(y - 1)^2 - 2$

52. $x = \dfrac{1}{4}(y + 1)^2 + 2$

53. $x = -\dfrac{1}{2}(y - 2)^2 + 4$

54. $x = -\dfrac{1}{2}(y + 1)^2 - 1$

Sketch the graph of each parabola.

55. $y = (x - 2)^2 + 3$ **56.** $y = (x + 3)^2 - 1$

57. $y = -2(x - 1)^2 + 3$ **58.** $y = -\dfrac{1}{2}(x + 1)^2 + 5$

the vertex at the origin and the focus at $(0, 15)$. Find the equation of the parabola.

64. *Arecibo Observatory.* The largest radio telescope in the world uses a 1000-ft parabolic dish, suspended in a valley in Arecibo, Puerto Rico. The antenna hangs above the vertex of the dish on cables stretching from two towers. The accompanying figure shows a cross section of the parabolic dish and the towers. Assuming the vertex is at $(0, 0)$, find the equation for the parabola. Find the distance from the vertex to the antenna located at the focus.

59. $x = (y - 2)^2 + 3$ **60.** $x = (y + 3)^2 - 1$

61. $x = -2(y - 1)^2 + 3$ **62.** $x = -\dfrac{1}{2}(y + 1)^2 + 5$

FIGURE FOR EXERCISE 64

Graph both equations of each system on the same coordinate axes. Use elimination of variables to find all points of intersection.

65. $y = -x^2 + 3$
$\quad\ y = x^2 + 1$

Solve each problem.

63. *World's largest telescope.* The largest reflecting telescope in the world is the 6-meter (m) reflector on Mount Pastukhov in Russia. The accompanying figure shows a cross section of a parabolic mirror 6 m in diameter with

FIGURE FOR EXERCISE 63

66. $y = x^2 - 3$
$\quad\ y = -x^2 + 5$

67. $y = x^2 - 2$
$y = 2x - 3$

68. $y = x^2 + x - 6$
$y = 7x - 15$

69. $y = x^2 + 3x - 4$
$y = -x^2 - 2x + 8$

70. $y = x^2 + 2x - 8$
$y = -x^2 - x + 12$

71. $y = x^2 + 3x - 4$
$y = 2x + 2$

72. $y = x^2 + 5x + 6$
$y = x + 11$

Solve each problem.

73. Find all points of intersection of the parabola $y = x^2 - 2x - 3$ and the x-axis.

74. Find all points of intersection of the parabola $y = 80x^2 - 33x + 255$ and the y-axis.

75. Find all points of intersection of the parabola $y = 0.01x^2$ and the line $y = 4$.

76. Find all points of intersection of the parabola $y = 0.02x^2$ and the line $y = x$.

77. Find all points of intersection of the parabolas $y = x^2$ and $x = y^2$.

78. Find all points of intersection of the parabolas $y = x^2$ and $y = (x - 3)^2$.

GETTING MORE INVOLVED

79. *Exploration.* Consider the parabola with focus $(p, 0)$ and directrix $x = -p$ for $p > 0$. Let (x, y) be an arbitrary point on the parabola. Write an equation expressing the fact that the distance from (x, y) to the focus is equal to the distance from (x, y) to the directrix. Rewrite the equation in the form $x = ay^2$, where $a = \frac{1}{4p}$.

 80. *Exploration.* In general, the graph of $x = a(y - k)^2 + h$ for $a \neq 0$ is a parabola opening left or right with vertex at (h, k).

a) For which values of a does the parabola open to the right, and for which values of a does it open to the left?

b) What is the equation of its axis of symmetry?

c) Sketch the graphs $x = 2(y - 3)^2 + 1$ and $x = -(y + 1)^2 + 2$.

GRAPHING CALCULATOR EXERCISES

81. Graph $y = x^2$ using the viewing window with $-1 \leq x \leq 1$ and $0 \leq y \leq 1$. Next graph $y = 2x^2 - 1$ using the viewing window $-2 \leq x \leq 2$ and $-1 \leq y \leq 7$. Explain what you see.

82. Graph $y = x^2$ and $y = 6x - 9$ in the viewing window $-5 \leq x \leq 5$ and $-5 \leq y \leq 20$. Does the line appear to be tangent to the parabola? Solve the system $y = x^2$ and $y = 6x - 9$ to find all points of intersection for the parabola and the line.

In This Section

- Developing the Equation
- Equations Not in Standard Form
- Systems of Equations

12.3 THE CIRCLE

In this section we continue the study of the conic sections with a discussion of the circle.

Developing the Equation

A circle is obtained by cutting a cone, as was shown in Fig. 12.3. We can also define a circle using points and distance, as we did for the parabola.

> **Circle**
>
> A **circle** is the set of all points in a plane that lie a fixed distance from a given point in the plane. The fixed distance is called the **radius,** and the given point is called the **center.**

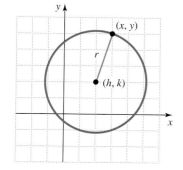

FIGURE 12.15

We can use the distance formula of Section 12.2 to write an equation for the circle with center (h, k) and radius r, shown in Fig. 12.15. If (x, y) is a point on the circle, its distance from the center is r. So

$$\sqrt{(x - h)^2 + (y - k)^2} = r.$$

We square both sides of this equation to get the **standard form** for the equation of a circle.

> **Standard Equation for a Circle**
>
> The graph of the equation
>
> $$(x - h)^2 + (y - k)^2 = r^2$$
>
> with $r > 0$, is a circle with center (h, k) and radius r.

Note that a circle centered at the origin with radius r $(r > 0)$ has the standard equation

$$x^2 + y^2 = r^2.$$

E X A M P L E   1

Finding the equation, given the center and radius

Write the standard equation for the circle with the given center and radius.

a) Center $(0, 0)$, radius 2

b) Center $(-1, 2)$, radius 4

Solution

a) The center at $(0, 0)$ means that $h = 0$ and $k = 0$ in the standard equation. So the equation is $(x - 0)^2 + (y - 0)^2 = 2^2$, or $x^2 + y^2 = 4$. The circle with radius 2 centered at the origin is shown in Fig. 12.16.

b) The center at $(-1, 2)$ means that $h = -1$ and $k = 2$. So

$$[x - (-1)]^2 + [y - 2]^2 = 4^2.$$

Simplify this equation to get

$$(x + 1)^2 + (y - 2)^2 = 16.$$

The circle with center $(-1, 2)$ and radius 4 is shown in Fig. 12.17.

FIGURE 12.16

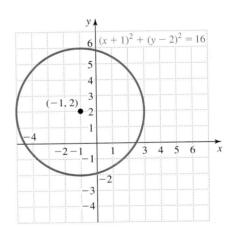

FIGURE 12.17

CAUTION The equations $(x - 1)^2 + (y + 3)^2 = -9$ and $(x - 1)^2 + (y + 3)^2 = 0$ might look like equations of circles, but they are not. The first equation is not satisfied by any ordered pair of real numbers because the left-hand side is nonnegative for any x and y. The second equation is satisfied only by the point $(1, -3)$.

E X A M P L E   2

Finding the center and radius, given the equation

Determine the center and radius of the circle $x^2 + (y + 5)^2 = 2$.

Solution

We can write this equation as

$$(x - 0)^2 + [y - (-5)]^2 = (\sqrt{2})^2.$$

In this form we see that the center is $(0, -5)$ and the radius is $\sqrt{2}$.

E X A M P L E   3

Graphing a circle

Find the center and radius of $(x - 1)^2 + (y + 2)^2 = 9$, and sketch the graph.

Solution

The graph of this equation is a circle with center at $(1, -2)$ and radius 3. See Fig. 12.18 for the graph.   ∎

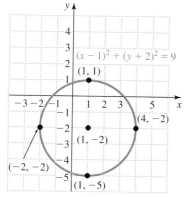

FIGURE 12.18

Calculator Close-Up

To graph the circle in Example 3, graph

$$y_1 = -2 + \sqrt{9 - (x - 1)^2}$$

and

$$y_2 = -2 - \sqrt{9 - (x - 1)^2}.$$

To get the circle to look round, you must use the same unit length on each axis. Most calculators have a *square* feature that automatically adjusts the window to use the same unit length on each axis.

Equations Not in Standard Form

It is not easy to recognize that $x^2 - 6x + y^2 + 10y = -30$ is the equation of a circle, but it is. In Example 4 we convert this equation into the standard form for a circle by completing the squares for the variables x and y.

E X A M P L E   4

Converting to standard form

Find the center and radius of the circle given by the equation

$$x^2 - 6x + y^2 + 10y = -30.$$

Helpful Hint

What do circles and lines have in common? They are the two simplest graphs to draw. We have compasses to make our circles look good and rulers to make our lines look good.

Solution

To complete the square for $x^2 - 6x$, we add 9, and for $y^2 + 10y$, we add 25. To get an equivalent equation, we must add on both sides:

$$x^2 - 6x + \quad y^2 + 10y = -30$$
$$x^2 - 6x + 9 + y^2 + 10y + 25 = -30 + 9 + 25 \quad \text{Add 9 and 25 to both sides.}$$
$$(x - 3)^2 + (y + 5)^2 = 4 \quad \text{Factor the trinomials on the left-hand side.}$$

From the standard form we see that the center is $(3, -5)$ and the radius is 2.   ∎

Systems of Equations

We first solved systems of nonlinear equations in two variables in Section 12.1. We found the points of intersection of two graphs without drawing the graphs. Here we will solve systems involving circles, parabolas, and lines. In the next example we find the points of intersection of a line and a circle.

E X A M P L E   5

Intersection of a line and a circle

Graph both equations of the system

$$(x - 3)^2 + (y + 1)^2 = 9$$
$$y = x - 1$$

on the same coordinate axes, and solve the system by elimination of variables.

Solution

The graph of the first equation is a circle with center at $(3, -1)$ and radius 3. The graph of the second equation is a straight line with slope 1 and y-intercept $(0, -1)$. Both graphs are shown in Fig. 12.19. To solve the system by elimination, we substitute $y = x - 1$ into the equation of the circle:

$$(x - 3)^2 + (x - 1 + 1)^2 = 9$$
$$(x - 3)^2 + x^2 = 9$$
$$x^2 - 6x + 9 + x^2 = 9$$
$$2x^2 - 6x = 0$$
$$x^2 - 3x = 0$$
$$x(x - 3) = 0$$

$x = 0$　or　$x = 3$

$y = -1$　　　$y = 2$　Because $y = x - 1$

Check $(0, -1)$ and $(3, 2)$ in the original system and with the graphs in Fig. 12.19. The solution set is $\{(0, -1), (3, 2)\}$. ■

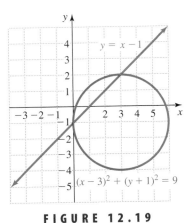

FIGURE 12.19

(graph labels: $y = x - 1$; $(x - 3)^2 + (y + 1)^2 = 9$)

M A T H   A T   W O R K

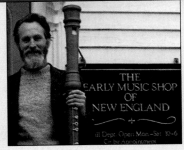

THE
EARLY MUSIC SHOP
OF
NEW ENGLAND

EARLY MUSICAL INSTRUMENT MAKER

Friedrich von Huene, a flautist and recorder player, has been crafting woodwind instruments in his family business for over 30 years. Because it is best to play music of earlier centuries on the instruments of their time, von Huene is using many originals as models for his flutes, recorders, and oboes of different sizes.

Because museum instruments have many different pitch standards, their dimensions frequently have to be changed to accommodate pitch standards that musicians use today. For a lower pitch the length of the instrument as well as the inside diameter must be increased. For a higher pitch the length has to be shortened and the diameter decreased. However, the factor for changing the length will be different from the factor for changing the diameter. A row of organ pipes demonstrates that the larger and longer pipes are proportionately more slender than the shorter high-pitched pipes. A pipe an octave higher in pitch is about half as long as the pipe an octave lower, but its diameter will be about 0.6 as large as the diameter of the lower pipe.

When making a very large recorder, von Huene carefully chooses the length, the position of the tone holes, and the bore to get the proper volume of air inside the instrument. In Exercises 57 and 58 of this section you will make the kinds of calculations von Huene makes when he crafts a modern reproduction of a Renaissance flute.

WARM-UPS

True or false? Explain your answer.

1. The radius of a circle can be any nonzero real number.
2. The coordinates of the center must satisfy the equation of the circle.
3. The circle $x^2 + y^2 = 4$ has its center at the origin.
4. The graph of $x^2 + y^2 = 9$ is a circle centered at $(0, 0)$ with radius 9.

5. The graph of $(x - 2)^2 + (y - 3)^2 + 4 = 0$ is a circle of radius 2.
6. The graph of $(x - 3) + (y + 5) = 9$ is a circle of radius 3.
7. There is only one circle centered at $(-3, -1)$ passing through the origin.

8. The center of the circle $(x - 3)^2 + (y - 4)^2 = 10$ is $(-3, -4)$.
9. The center of the circle $x^2 + y^2 + 6y - 4 = 0$ is on the y-axis.
10. The radius of the circle $x^2 - 3x + y^2 = 4$ is 2.

12.3 EXERCISES

Reading and Writing After reading this section, write out the answers to these questions. Use complete sentences.

1. What is the definition of a circle?

2. What is the standard equation of a circle?

Write the standard equation for each circle with the given center and radius. See Example 1.

3. Center $(0, 3)$, radius 5
4. Center $(2, 0)$, radius 3
5. Center $(1, -2)$, radius 9
6. Center $(-3, 5)$, radius 4
7. Center $(0, 0)$, radius $\sqrt{3}$
8. Center $(0, 0)$, radius $\sqrt{2}$
9. Center $(-6, -3)$, radius $\frac{1}{2}$
10. Center $(-3, -5)$, radius $\frac{1}{4}$
11. Center $\left(\frac{1}{2}, \frac{1}{3}\right)$, radius 0.1
12. Center $\left(-\frac{1}{2}, 3\right)$, radius 0.2

Find the center and radius for each circle. See Example 2.
13. $(x - 3)^2 + (y - 5)^2 = 2$
14. $(x + 3)^2 + (y - 7)^2 = 6$

15. $x^2 + \left(y - \frac{1}{2}\right)^2 = \frac{1}{2}$
16. $5x^2 + 5y^2 = 5$
17. $4x^2 + 4y^2 = 9$
18. $9x^2 + 9y^2 = 49$
19. $3 - y^2 = (x - 2)^2$
20. $9 - x^2 = (y + 1)^2$

Sketch the graph of each equation. See Example 3.
21. $x^2 + y^2 = 9$
22. $x^2 + y^2 = 16$

23. $x^2 + (y - 3)^2 = 9$
24. $(x - 4)^2 + y^2 = 16$

25. $(x + 1)^2 + (y - 1)^2 = 2$ **26.** $(x - 2)^2 + (y + 2)^2 = 8$

38. $x^2 - 3x + y^2 = 0$

39. $x^2 - 3x + y^2 - y = 1$

40. $x^2 - 5x + y^2 + 3y = 2$

27. $(x - 4)^2 + (y + 3)^2 = 16$ **28.** $(x - 3)^2 + (y - 7)^2 = 25$

41. $x^2 - \dfrac{2}{3}x + y^2 + \dfrac{3}{2}y = 0$

42. $x^2 + \dfrac{1}{3}x + y^2 - \dfrac{2}{3}y = \dfrac{1}{9}$

29. $\left(x - \dfrac{1}{2}\right)^2 + \left(y + \dfrac{1}{2}\right)^2 = \dfrac{1}{4}$ **30.** $\left(x + \dfrac{1}{3}\right)^2 + y^2 = \dfrac{1}{9}$

Graph both equations of each system on the same coordinate axes. Solve the system by elimination of variables to find all points of intersection of the graphs. See Example 5.

43. $x^2 + y^2 = 10$ **44.** $x^2 + y^2 = 4$
    $y = 3x$ $y = x - 2$

Rewrite each equation in the standard form for the equation of a circle, and identify its center and radius. See Example 4.

31. $x^2 + 4x + y^2 + 6y = 0$

32. $x^2 - 10x + y^2 + 8y = 0$

33. $x^2 - 2x + y^2 - 4y - 3 = 0$

45. $x^2 + y^2 = 9$ **46.** $x^2 + y^2 = 4$
    $y = x^2 - 3$ $y = x^2 - 2$

34. $x^2 - 6x + y^2 - 2y + 9 = 0$

35. $x^2 + y^2 = 8y + 10x - 32$

36. $x^2 + y^2 = 8x - 10y$

37. $x^2 - x + y^2 + y = 0$

47. $(x - 2)^2 + (y + 3)^2 = 4$ **48.** $(x + 1)^2 + (y - 4)^2 = 17$
     $y = x - 3$ $y = x + 2$

The units for x
and y are millimeters.

$x^2 + y^2 = 193.21$

$x^2 + y^2 = 83.72$
(Bore hole)

FIGURE FOR EXERCISES 57 AND 58

In Exercises 49–58, solve each problem.

49. Determine all points of intersection of the circle $(x - 1)^2 + (y - 2)^2 = 4$ with the y-axis.

50. Determine the points of intersection of the circle $x^2 + (y - 3)^2 = 25$ with the x-axis.

51. Find the radius of the circle that has center $(2, -5)$ and passes through the origin.

52. Find the radius of the circle that has center $(-2, 3)$ and passes through $(3, -1)$.

53. Determine the equation of the circle that is centered at $(2, 3)$ and passes through $(-2, -1)$.

54. Determine the equation of the circle that is centered at $(3, 4)$ and passes through the origin.

55. Find all points of intersection of the circles $x^2 + y^2 = 9$ and $(x - 5)^2 + y^2 = 9$.

56. A donkey is tied at the point $(2, -3)$ on a rope of length 12. Turnips are growing at the point $(6, 7)$. Can the donkey reach them?

57. *Volume of a flute.* The volume of air in a flute is a critical factor in determining its pitch. A cross section of a Renaissance flute in C is shown in the accompanying figure. If the length of the flute is 2874 millimeters, then what is the volume of air in the flute (to the nearest cubic millimeter (mm^3))? (*Hint:* Use the formula for the volume of a cylinder.)

58. *Flute reproduction.* To make the smaller C# flute, Friedrich von Huene multiplies the length and cross-sectional area of the flute of Exercise 57 by 0.943. Find the equation for the bore hole (centered at the origin) and the volume of air in the C# flute.

Graph each equation.

59. $x^2 + y^2 = 0$ **60.** $x^2 - y^2 = 0$

61. $y = \sqrt{1 - x^2}$ **62.** $y = -\sqrt{1 - x^2}$

GETTING MORE INVOLVED

63. *Cooperative learning.* The equation of a circle is a special case of the general equation $Ax^2 + Bx + Cy^2 + Dy = E$, where A, B, C, D, and E are real numbers. Working in small groups, find restrictions that must be placed on A, B, C, D, and E so that the graph of this equation is a circle. What does the graph of $x^2 + y^2 = -9$ look like?

64. *Discussion.* Suppose lighthouse A is located at the origin and lighthouse B is located at coordinates $(0, 6)$. The captain of a ship has determined that the ship's distance from lighthouse A is 2 and its distance from lighthouse B is 5. What are the possible coordinates for the location of the ship?

GRAPHING CALCULATOR EXERCISES

Graph each relation on a graphing calculator by solving for y and graphing two functions.

65. $x^2 + y^2 = 4$
66. $(x - 1)^2 + (y + 2)^2 = 1$

67. $x = y^2$
68. $x = (y + 2)^2 - 1$

69. $x = y^2 + 2y + 1$
70. $x = 4y^2 + 4y + 1$

In This Section

- The Ellipse
- The Hyperbola

12.4 THE ELLIPSE AND HYPERBOLA

In this section we study the remaining two conic sections: the ellipse and the hyperbola.

The Ellipse

An ellipse can be obtained by intersecting a plane and a cone, as was shown in Fig. 12.3. We can also give a definition of an ellipse in terms of points and distance.

> **Ellipse**
>
> An **ellipse** is the set of all points in a plane such that the sum of their distances from two fixed points is a constant. Each fixed point is called a **focus** (plural: foci).

FIGURE 12.20

An easy way to draw an ellipse is illustrated in Fig. 12.20. A string is attached at two fixed points, and a pencil is used to take up the slack. As the pencil is moved around the paper, the sum of the distances of the pencil point from the two fixed points remains constant. Of course, the length of the string is that constant. You may wish to try this.

Like the parabola, the ellipse also has interesting reflecting properties. All light or sound waves emitted from one focus are reflected off the ellipse to concentrate at the other focus (see Fig. 12.21). This property is used in light fixtures where a concentration of light at a point is desired or in a whispering gallery such as Statuary Hall in the U.S. Capitol Building.

The orbits of the planets around the sun and satellites around the earth are elliptical. For the orbit of the earth around the sun, the sun is at one focus. For the elliptical path of an earth satellite, the earth is at one focus and a point in space is the other focus.

FIGURE 12.21

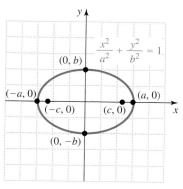

FIGURE 12.22

Figure 12.22 shows an ellipse with foci $(c, 0)$ and $(-c, 0)$. The origin is the center of this ellipse. In general, the **center** of an ellipse is a point midway between the foci. The ellipse in Fig. 12.22 has x-intercepts at $(a, 0)$ and $(-a, 0)$ and y-intercepts at $(0, b)$ and $(0, -b)$. The distance formula can be used to write the following equation for this ellipse. (See Exercise 55.)

Equation of an Ellipse Centered at the Origin

An ellipse centered at $(0, 0)$ with foci at $(\pm c, 0)$ and constant sum $2a$ has equation

$$\frac{x^2}{a^2} + \frac{y^2}{b^2} = 1,$$

where a, b, and c are positive real numbers with $c^2 = a^2 - b^2$.

To draw a "nice-looking" ellipse, we would locate the foci and use string as shown in Fig. 12.20. We can get a rough sketch of an ellipse centered at the origin by using the x- and y-intercepts only.

EXAMPLE 1   **Graphing an ellipse**

Find the x- and y-intercepts for the ellipse and sketch its graph.

$$\frac{x^2}{9} + \frac{y^2}{4} = 1$$

Solution

To find the y-intercepts, let $x = 0$ in the equation:

$$\frac{0}{9} + \frac{y^2}{4} = 1$$

$$\frac{y^2}{4} = 1$$

$$y^2 = 4$$

$$y = \pm 2$$

To find the x-intercepts, let $y = 0$. We get $x = \pm 3$. The four intercepts are $(0, 2)$, $(0, -2)$, $(3, 0)$, and $(-3, 0)$. Plot the intercepts and draw an ellipse through them as in Fig. 12.23.

Calculator Close-Up

To graph the ellipse in Example 1, graph

$$y_1 = \sqrt{4 - 4x^2/9}$$

and

$$y_2 = -\sqrt{4 - 4x^2/9}.$$

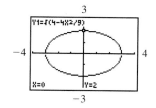

Helpful Hint

When sketching ellipses or circles by hand, use your hand like a compass and rotate your paper as you draw the curve.

FIGURE 12.23

Ellipses, like circles, may be centered at any point in the plane. To get the equation of an ellipse centered at (h, k), we replace x by $x - h$ and y by $y - k$ in the equation of the ellipse centered at the origin.

Equation of an Ellipse Centered at (h, k)

An ellipse centered at (h, k) has equation

$$\frac{(x - h)^2}{a^2} + \frac{(y - k)^2}{b^2} = 1,$$

where a and b are positive real numbers.

E X A M P L E   2   **An ellipse with center (h, k)**

Sketch the graph of the ellipse:

$$\frac{(x - 1)^2}{9} + \frac{(y + 2)^2}{4} = 1$$

Solution

The graph of this ellipse is exactly the same size and shape as the ellipse

$$\frac{x^2}{9} + \frac{y^2}{4} = 1,$$

which was graphed in Example 1. However, the center for

$$\frac{(x - 1)^2}{9} + \frac{(y + 2)^2}{4} = 1$$

is $(1, -2)$. The denominator 9 is used to determine that the ellipse passes through points that are three units to the right and three units to the left of the center: $(4, -2)$ and $(-2, -2)$. See Fig. 12.24. The denominator 4 is used to determine that the ellipse passes through points that are two units above and two units below the center: $(1, 0)$ and $(1, -4)$. We draw an ellipse using these four points, just as we did for an ellipse centered at the origin.

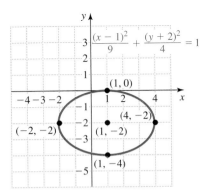

FIGURE   12.24

The Hyperbola

A hyperbola is the curve that occurs at the intersection of a cone and a plane, as was shown in Fig. 12.3 in Section 12.2. A hyperbola can also be defined in terms of points and distance.

Hyperbola

A **hyperbola** is the set of all points in the plane such that the difference of their distances from two fixed points (foci) is constant.

Like the parabola and the ellipse, the hyperbola also has reflecting properties. If a light ray is aimed at one focus, it is reflected off the hyperbola and goes to the other focus, as shown in Fig. 12.25. Hyperbolic mirrors are used in conjunction with parabolic mirrors in telescopes.

The definitions of a hyperbola and an ellipse are similar, and so are their equations. However, their graphs are very different. Figure 12.26 shows a hyperbola in which the distance from a point on the hyperbola to the closer focus is N and the distance to the farther focus is M. The value $M - N$ is the same for every point on the hyperbola.

FIGURE 12.25

FIGURE 12.26

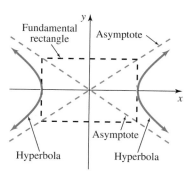

FIGURE 12.27

A hyperbola has two parts called **branches.** These branches look like parabolas, but they are not parabolas. The branches of the hyperbola shown in Fig. 12.27 get closer and closer to the dashed lines, called **asymptotes,** but they never intersect them. The asymptotes are used as guidelines in sketching a hyperbola. The asymptotes are found by extending the diagonals of the **fundamental rectangle,** shown in Fig. 12.27. The key to drawing a hyperbola is getting the fundamental rectangle and extending its diagonals to get the asymptotes. You will learn how to find the fundamental rectangle from the equation of a hyperbola. The hyperbola in Fig. 12.27 opens to the left and right.

If we start with foci at $(\pm c, 0)$ and a positive number a, then we can use the definition of a hyperbola to derive the following equation of a hyperbola in which the constant difference between the distances to the foci is $2a$.

Equation of a Hyperbola Centered at (0, 0) Opening Left and Right

A hyperbola centered at $(0, 0)$ with foci $(c, 0)$ and $(-c, 0)$ and constant difference $2a$ has equation

$$\frac{x^2}{a^2} - \frac{y^2}{b^2} = 1,$$

where a, b, and c are positive real numbers such that $c^2 = a^2 + b^2$.

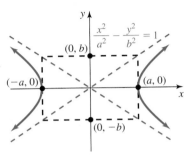

FIGURE 12.28

The graph of a general equation for a hyperbola is shown in Fig. 12.28. Notice that the fundamental rectangle extends to the x-intercepts along the x-axis and extends b units above and below the origin along the y-axis. Use the following procedure for graphing a hyperbola centered at the origin and opening to the left and to the right.

Graphing a Hyperbola Centered at the Origin, Opening Left and Right

To graph the hyperbola $\frac{x^2}{a^2} - \frac{y^2}{b^2} = 1$:

1. Locate the x-intercepts at $(a, 0)$ and $(-a, 0)$.
2. Draw the fundamental rectangle through $(\pm a, 0)$ and $(0, \pm b)$.
3. Draw the extended diagonals of the rectangle to use as asymptotes.
4. Draw the hyperbola to the left and right approaching the asymptotes.

E X A M P L E   3

A hyperbola opening left and right

Sketch the graph of $\frac{x^2}{36} - \frac{y^2}{9} = 1$, and find the equations of its asymptotes.

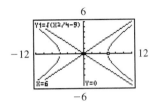
Solution

The x-intercepts are $(6, 0)$ and $(-6, 0)$. Draw the fundamental rectangle through these x-intercepts and the points $(0, 3)$ and $(0, -3)$. Extend the diagonals of the fundamental rectangle to get the asymptotes. Now draw a hyperbola passing through the x-intercepts and approaching the asymptotes as shown in Fig. 12.29.

From the graph in Fig. 12.29 we see that the slopes of the asymptotes are $\frac{1}{2}$ and $-\frac{1}{2}$.

Because the y-intercept for both asymptotes is the origin, their equations are $y = \frac{1}{2}x$ and $y = -\frac{1}{2}x.$

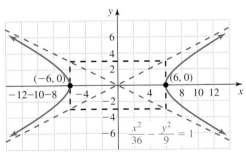

FIGURE 12.29

If the variables x and y are interchanged in the equation of the hyperbola, then the hyperbola opens up and down.

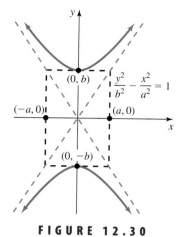

$$\frac{y^2}{b^2} - \frac{x^2}{a^2} = 1$$

FIGURE 12.30

> ### Equation of a Hyperbola Centered at (0, 0) Opening Up and Down
>
> A hyperbola centered at $(0, 0)$ with foci $(0, c)$ and $(0, -c)$ and constant difference $2a$ has equation
>
> $$\frac{y^2}{b^2} - \frac{x^2}{a^2} = 1,$$
>
> where a, b, and c are positive real numbers such that $c^2 = a^2 + b^2$.

The graph of the general equation for a hyperbola opening up and down is shown in Fig. 12.30. Notice that the fundamental rectangle extends to the y-intercepts along the y-axis and extends a units to the left and right of the origin along the x-axis. The procedure for graphing a hyperbola opening up and down follows.

> ### Graphing a Hyperbola Centered at the Origin, Opening Up and Down
>
> To graph the hyperbola $\frac{y^2}{b^2} - \frac{x^2}{a^2} = 1$:
>
> **1.** Locate the y-intercepts at $(0, b)$ and $(0, -b)$.
> **2.** Draw the fundamental rectangle through $(0, \pm b)$ and $(\pm a, 0)$.
> **3.** Draw the extended diagonals of the rectangle to use as asymptotes.
> **4.** Draw the hyperbola opening up and down approaching the asymptotes.

E X A M P L E   4   **A hyperbola opening up and down**
Graph the hyperbola $\frac{y^2}{9} - \frac{x^2}{4} = 1$ and find the equations of its asymptotes.

Helpful Hint

We could include here general formulas for the equations of the asymptotes, but that is not necessary. It is easier first to draw the asymptotes as suggested and then to figure out their equations by looking at the graph.

Solution
If $y = 0$, we get

$$-\frac{x^2}{4} = 1$$
$$x^2 = -4.$$

Because this equation has no real solution, the graph has no x-intercepts. Let $x = 0$ to find the y-intercepts:

$$\frac{y^2}{9} = 1$$
$$y^2 = 9$$
$$y = \pm 3$$

The y-intercepts are $(0, 3)$ and $(0, -3)$, and the hyperbola opens up and down. From $a^2 = 4$ we get $a = 2$. So the fundamental rectangle extends to the intercepts $(0, 3)$ and $(0, -3)$ on the y-axis and to the points $(2, 0)$ and $(-2, 0)$ along the x-axis. We extend the diagonals of the rectangle and draw the graph of the hyperbola as shown

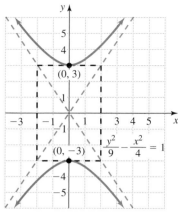

FIGURE 12.31

in Fig. 12.31. From the graph in Fig. 12.31 we see that the asymptotes have slopes $\frac{3}{2}$ and $-\frac{3}{2}$. Because the y-intercept for both asymptotes is the origin, their equations are $y = \frac{3}{2}x$ and $y = -\frac{3}{2}x$. ■

Like circles and ellipses, hyperbolas may be centered at any point in the plane. To get the equation of a hyperbola centered at (h, k), we replace x by $x - h$ and y by $y - k$ in the equation of the hyperbola centered at the origin.

Equation of a Hyperbola Centered at (h, k)

A hyperbola centered at (h, k) has one of the following equations depending on which way it opens.

Opening left and right: Opening up and down:

$$\frac{(x - h)^2}{a^2} - \frac{(y - k)^2}{b^2} = 1 \qquad \frac{(y - k)^2}{b^2} - \frac{(x - h)^2}{a^2} = 1$$

EXAMPLE 5   **Graphing a hyperbola centered at (h, k)**

Graph the hyperbola $\frac{(x - 3)^2}{16} - \frac{(y + 1)^2}{4} = 1$.

Solution

This hyperbola is centered at $(3, -1)$ and opens left and right. It is a transformation of the graph of $\frac{x^2}{16} - \frac{y^2}{4} = 1$. The fundamental rectangle for $\frac{x^2}{16} - \frac{y^2}{4} = 1$ is centered at the origin and goes through $(\pm 4, 0)$ and $(0, \pm 2)$. So draw a fundamental rectangle centered at $(3, -1)$ that extends four units to the right and left and two units up and down as shown in Fig. 12.32. Draw the asymptotes through the vertices of the fundamental rectangle and the hyperbola opening to the left and right.

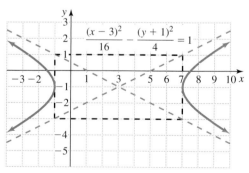

FIGURE 12.32   ■

EXAMPLE 6   **A hyperbola not in standard form**

Sketch the graph of the hyperbola $4x^2 - y^2 = 4$.

Solution

First write the equation in standard form. Divide each side by 4 to get

$$x^2 - \frac{y^2}{4} = 1.$$

There are no y-intercepts. If $y = 0$, then $x = \pm 1$. The hyperbola opens left and right with x-intercepts at $(1, 0)$ and $(-1, 0)$. The fundamental rectangle extends to the intercepts along the x-axis and to the points $(0, 2)$ and $(0, -2)$ along the y-axis. We extend the diagonals of the rectangle for the asymptotes and draw the graph as shown in Fig. 12.33.

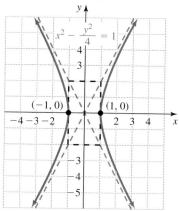

FIGURE 12.33

WARM-UPS

True or false? Explain your answer.

1. The x-intercepts of the ellipse $\frac{x^2}{36} + \frac{y^2}{25} = 1$ are $(5, 0)$ and $(-5, 0)$.
2. The graph of $\frac{x^2}{9} + \frac{y}{4} = 1$ is an ellipse.
3. If the foci of an ellipse coincide, then the ellipse is a circle.
4. The graph of $2x^2 + y^2 = 2$ is an ellipse centered at the origin.
5. The y-intercepts of $x^2 + \frac{y^2}{3} = 1$ are $(0, \sqrt{3})$ and $(0, -\sqrt{3})$.
6. The graph of $\frac{x^2}{9} + \frac{y}{4} = 1$ is a hyperbola.
7. The graph of $\frac{x^2}{25} - \frac{y^2}{16} = 1$ has y-intercepts at $(0, 4)$ and $(0, -4)$.
8. The hyperbola $\frac{y^2}{9} - x^2 = 1$ opens up and down.
9. The graph of $4x^2 - y^2 = 4$ is a hyperbola.
10. The asymptotes of a hyperbola are the extended diagonals of a rectangle.

12.4   EXERCISES

Reading and Writing   *After reading this section, write out the answers to these questions. Use complete sentences.*

1. What is the definition of an ellipse?

2. How can you draw an ellipse with a pencil and string?

3. Where is the center of an ellipse?

4. What is the equation of an ellipse centered at the origin?

5. What is the equation of an ellipse centered at (h, k)?

6. What is the definition of a hyperbola?

7. How do you find the asymptotes of a hyperbola?

8. What is the equation of a hyperbola centered at the origin and opening left and right?

Sketch the graph of each ellipse. See Example 1.

9. $\dfrac{x^2}{9} + \dfrac{y^2}{4} = 1$

10. $\dfrac{x^2}{9} + \dfrac{y^2}{16} = 1$

11. $\dfrac{x^2}{9} + y^2 = 1$

12. $x^2 + \dfrac{y^2}{4} = 1$

13. $\dfrac{x^2}{36} + \dfrac{y^2}{25} = 1$

14. $\dfrac{x^2}{25} + \dfrac{y^2}{49} = 1$

15. $\dfrac{x^2}{24} + \dfrac{y^2}{5} = 1$

16. $\dfrac{x^2}{6} + \dfrac{y^2}{17} = 1$

17. $9x^2 + 16y^2 = 144$

18. $9x^2 + 25y^2 = 225$

19. $25x^2 + y^2 = 25$

20. $x^2 + 16y^2 = 16$

21. $4x^2 + 9y^2 = 1$

22. $25x^2 + 16y^2 = 1$

Sketch the graph of each ellipse. See Example 2.

23. $\dfrac{(x-3)^2}{4} + \dfrac{(y-1)^2}{9} = 1$

24. $\dfrac{(x+5)^2}{49} + \dfrac{(y-2)^2}{25} = 1$

25. $\dfrac{(x+1)^2}{16} + \dfrac{(y-2)^2}{25} = 1$

26. $\dfrac{(x-3)^2}{36} + \dfrac{(y+4)^2}{64} = 1$

27. $(x - 2)^2 + \dfrac{(y + 1)^2}{36} = 1$ **28.** $\dfrac{(x + 3)^2}{9} + (y + 1)^2 = 1$ **35.** $x^2 - \dfrac{y^2}{25} = 1$ **36.** $\dfrac{x^2}{9} - y^2 = 1$

Sketch the graph of each hyperbola and write the equations of its asymptotes. See Examples 3–6.

29. $\dfrac{x^2}{4} - \dfrac{y^2}{9} = 1$ **30.** $\dfrac{x^2}{16} - \dfrac{y^2}{9} = 1$ **37.** $9x^2 - 16y^2 = 144$

31. $\dfrac{y^2}{4} - \dfrac{x^2}{25} = 1$ **32.** $\dfrac{y^2}{9} - \dfrac{x^2}{16} = 1$ **38.** $9x^2 - 25y^2 = 225$

33. $\dfrac{x^2}{25} - y^2 = 1$ **34.** $x^2 - \dfrac{y^2}{9} = 1$ **39.** $x^2 - y^2 = 1$

40. $y^2 - x^2 = 1$

45. $\dfrac{(y-2)^2}{9} - \dfrac{(x-4)^2}{4} = 1$

Sketch the graph of each hyperbola.

41. $\dfrac{(x-2)^2}{4} - (y+1)^2 = 1$

46. $\dfrac{(y+3)^2}{16} - \dfrac{(x+1)^2}{9} = 1$

42. $(x+3)^2 - \dfrac{(y-1)^2}{4} = 1$

Graph both equations of each system on the same coordinate axes. Use elimination of variables to find all points of intersection.

47. $\dfrac{x^2}{4} + \dfrac{y^2}{9} = 1$

$\qquad x^2 - \dfrac{y^2}{9} = 1$

43. $\dfrac{(x+1)^2}{16} - \dfrac{(y-1)^2}{9} = 1$

48. $x^2 - \dfrac{y^2}{4} = 1$

$\qquad \dfrac{x^2}{9} + \dfrac{y^2}{4} = 1$

44. $\dfrac{(x-2)^2}{9} - \dfrac{(y+2)^2}{16} = 1$

49. $\dfrac{x^2}{4} + \dfrac{y^2}{16} = 1$

$x^2 + y^2 = 1$

50. $x^2 + \dfrac{y^2}{9} = 1$

$x^2 + y^2 = 4$

51. $x^2 + y^2 = 4$

$x^2 - y^2 = 1$

52. $x^2 + y^2 = 16$

$x^2 - y^2 = 4$

53. $x^2 + 9y^2 = 9$

$x^2 + y^2 = 4$

54. $x^2 + y^2 = 25$

$x^2 + 25y^2 = 25$

55. $x^2 + 9y^2 = 9$

$y = x^2 - 1$

56. $4x^2 + y^2 = 4$

$y = 2x^2 - 2$

57. $9x^2 - 4y^2 = 36$

$2y = x - 2$

58. $25y^2 - 9x^2 = 225$

$y = 3x + 3$

Solve each problem.

59. Marine navigation. The loran (long-range navigation) system is used by boaters to determine their location at sea. The loran unit on a boat measures the difference in time that it takes for radio signals from pairs of fixed points to reach the boat. The unit then finds the equations of two hyperbolas that pass through the location of the boat. Suppose a boat is located in the first quadrant at the intersection of $x^2 - 3y^2 = 1$ and $4y^2 - x^2 = 1$.

a) Use the accompanying graph to approximate the location of the boat.

b) Algebraically find the exact location of the boat.

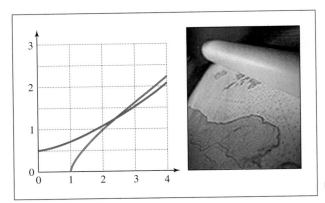

FIGURE FOR EXERCISE 59

60. Sonic boom. An aircraft traveling at supersonic speed creates a cone-shaped wave that intersects the ground along a hyperbola, as shown in the accompanying figure. A thunderlike sound is heard at any point on the hyperbola. This sonic boom travels along the ground, following the aircraft. The area where the sonic boom is most noticeable is called the *boom carpet*. The width of the boom carpet is roughly five times the altitude of the aircraft. Suppose the equation of the hyperbola in the figure is

$$\frac{x^2}{400} - \frac{y^2}{100} = 1,$$

where the units are miles and the width of the boom carpet is measured 40 miles behind the aircraft. Find the altitude of the aircraft.

GETTING MORE INVOLVED

61. Cooperative learning. Let (x, y) be an arbitrary point on an ellipse with foci $(c, 0)$ and $(-c, 0)$ for $c > 0$. The following equation expresses the fact that the distance from (x, y) to $(c, 0)$ plus the distance from (x, y) to $(-c, 0)$ is the constant value $2a$ (for $a > 0$):

$$\sqrt{(x - c)^2 + (y - 0)^2} + \sqrt{(x - (-c))^2 + (y - 0)^2} = 2a$$

Working in groups, simplify this equation. First get the radicals on opposite sides of the equation, then square both sides twice to eliminate the square roots. Finally, let $b^2 = a^2 - c^2$ to get the equation

$$\frac{x^2}{a^2} + \frac{y^2}{b^2} = 1.$$

62. Cooperative learning. Let (x, y) be an arbitrary point on a hyperbola with foci $(c, 0)$ and $(-c, 0)$ for $c > 0$. The following equation expresses the fact that the distance from (x, y) to $(c, 0)$ minus the distance from (x, y) to $(-c, 0)$ is the constant value $2a$ (for $a > 0$):

$$\sqrt{(x - c)^2 + (y - 0)^2} - \sqrt{(x - (-c))^2 + (y - 0)^2} = 2a$$

Working in groups, simplify the equation. You will need to square both sides twice to eliminate the square roots. Finally, let $b^2 = c^2 - a^2$ to get the equation

$$\frac{x^2}{a^2} - \frac{y^2}{b^2} = 1.$$

GRAPHING CALCULATOR EXERCISES

63. Graph $y_1 = \sqrt{x^2 - 1}$, $y_2 = -\sqrt{x^2 - 1}$, $y_3 = x$, and $y_4 = -x$ to get the graph of the hyperbola $x^2 - y^2 = 1$ along with its asymptotes. Use the viewing window $-3 \leq x \leq 3$ and $-3 \leq y \leq 3$. Notice how the branches of the hyperbola approach the asymptotes.

64. Graph the same four functions in Exercise 63, but use $-30 \leq x \leq 30$ and $-30 \leq y \leq 30$ as the viewing window. What happened to the hyperbola?

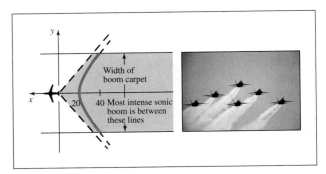

FIGURE FOR EXERCISE 60

12.5 SECOND-DEGREE INEQUALITIES

In this section we graph second-degree inequalities and systems of inequalities involving second-degree inequalities.

Graphing a Second-Degree Inequality

A second-degree inequality is an inequality involving squares of at least one of the variables. Changing the equal sign to an inequality symbol for any of the equations of the conic sections gives us a second-degree inequality. Second-degree inequalities are graphed in the same manner as linear inequalities.

E X A M P L E   1

A second-degree inequality

Graph the inequality $y < x^2 + 2x - 3$.

Solution

We first graph $y = x^2 + 2x - 3$. This parabola has x-intercepts at $(1, 0)$ and $(-3, 0)$, y-intercept at $(0, -3)$, and vertex at $(-1, -4)$. The graph of the parabola is drawn with a dashed line, as shown in Fig. 12.34. The graph of the parabola divides the plane into two regions. Every point on one side of the parabola satisfies the inequality $y < x^2 + 2x - 3$, and every point on the other side satisfies the inequality $y > x^2 + 2x - 3$. To determine which side is which, we test a point that is not on the parabola, say $(0, 0)$. Because

$$0 < 0^2 + 2 \cdot 0 - 3$$

is false, the region not containing the origin is shaded, as in Fig. 12.34.

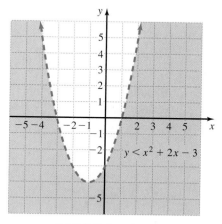

$y < x^2 + 2x - 3$

FIGURE 12.34

E X A M P L E   2

A second-degree inequality

Graph the inequality $x^2 + y^2 < 9$.

Solution

The graph of $x^2 + y^2 = 9$ is a circle of radius 3 centered at the origin. The circle divides the plane into two regions. Every point in one region satisfies $x^2 + y^2 < 9$, and every point in the other region satisfies $x^2 + y^2 > 9$. To identify the regions, we pick a point and test it. Select $(0, 0)$. The inequality

$$0^2 + 0^2 < 9$$

is true. Because $(0, 0)$ is inside the circle, all points inside the circle satisfy the inequality $x^2 + y^2 < 9$, as shown in Fig. 12.35. The points outside the circle satisfy the inequality $x^2 + y^2 > 9$.

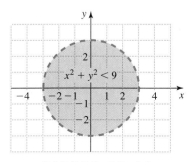

FIGURE 12.35

E X A M P L E   3   **A second-degree inequality**

Graph the inequality $\dfrac{x^2}{4} - \dfrac{y^2}{9} > 1$.

Solution

First graph the hyperbola $\dfrac{x^2}{4} - \dfrac{y^2}{9} = 1$. Because the hyperbola shown in Fig. 12.36 divides the plane into three regions, we select a test point in each region and check to see whether it satisfies the inequality. Testing the points $(-3, 0)$, $(0, 0)$, and $(3, 0)$ gives us the inequalities

$$\frac{(-3)^2}{4} - \frac{0^2}{9} > 1, \qquad \frac{0^2}{4} - \frac{0^2}{9} > 1, \qquad \text{and} \qquad \frac{3^2}{4} - \frac{0^2}{9} > 1.$$

Because only the first and third inequalities are correct, we shade only the regions containing $(3, 0)$ and $(-3, 0)$, as shown in Fig. 12.36.

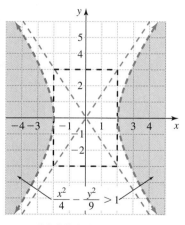

FIGURE 12.36

Systems of Inequalities

A point is in the solution set to a system of inequalities if it satisfies all inequalities of the system. We graph a system of inequalities by first determining the graph of each inequality and then finding the intersection of the graphs.

E X A M P L E   4 **Systems of second-degree inequalities**
Graph the system of inequalities:

$$\frac{y^2}{4} - \frac{x^2}{9} > 1$$

$$\frac{x^2}{9} + \frac{y^2}{16} < 1$$

Solution

Figure 12.37(a) shows the graph of the first inequality. Figure 12.37(b) shows the graphs of both inequalities on the same coordinate system. Points that are shaded for both inequalities in Fig. 12.37(b) satisfy the system. Figure 12.37(c) shows the graph of the system.

(a)

(b)

(c)

FIGURE 12.37

WARM-UPS

True or false? Explain your answer.

1. The graph of $x^2 + y = 4$ is a circle of radius 2.
2. The graph of $x^2 + 9y^2 = 9$ is an ellipse.
3. The graph of $y^2 = x^2 + 1$ is a hyperbola.
4. The point $(0, 0)$ satisfies the inequality $2x^2 - y < 3$.
5. The graph of the inequality $y > x^2 - 3x + 2$ contains the origin.
6. The origin should be used as a test point for graphing $x^2 > y$.
7. The solution set to $x^2 + 3x + y^2 + 8y + 3 < 0$ includes the origin.
8. The graph of $x^2 + y^2 < 4$ is the region inside a circle of radius 2.
9. The point $(0, 4)$ satisfies $x^2 - y^2 < 1$ and $y > x^2 - 2x + 3$.
10. The point $(0, 0)$ satisfies $x^2 + y^2 < 1$ and $y < x^2 + 1$.

12.5   EXERCISES

Graph each inequality. See Examples 1–3.

1. $y > x^2$

2. $y \leq x^2 + 1$

3. $y < x^2 - x$

4. $y > x^2 + x$

5. $y > x^2 - x - 2$

6. $y < x^2 + x - 6$

7. $x^2 + y^2 \leq 9$

8. $x^2 + y^2 > 16$

9. $x^2 + 4y^2 > 4$

10. $4x^2 + y^2 \leq 4$

11. $4x^2 - 9y^2 < 36$

12. $25x^2 - 4y^2 > 100$

13. $(x - 2)^2 + (y - 3)^2 < 4$

14. $(x + 1)^2 + (y - 2)^2 > 1$

15. $x^2 + y^2 > 1$

16. $x^2 + y^2 < 25$

17. $4x^2 - y^2 > 4$

18. $x^2 - 9y^2 \leq 9$

19. $y^2 - x^2 \leq 1$

20. $x^2 - y^2 > 1$

27. $y > x^2 + x$
    $y < 5$

28. $y > x^2 + x - 6$
    $y < x + 3$

21. $x > y$

22. $x < 2y - 1$

29. $y \geq x + 2$
    $y \leq 2 - x$

30. $y \geq 2x - 3$
    $y \leq 3 - 2x$

Graph the solution set to each system of inequalities. See Example 4.

23. $x^2 + y^2 < 9$
    $y > x$

24. $x^2 + y^2 > 1$
    $x > y$

31. $4x^2 - y^2 < 4$
    $x^2 + 4y^2 > 4$

32. $x^2 - 4y^2 < 4$
    $x^2 + 4y^2 > 4$

25. $x^2 - y^2 > 1$
    $x^2 + y^2 < 4$

26. $y^2 - x^2 < 1$
    $x^2 + y^2 > 9$

33. $x - y < 0$
    $y + x^2 < 1$

34. $y + 1 > x^2$
    $x + y < 2$

35. $y < 5x - x^2$
$x^2 + y^2 < 9$

36. $y < x^2 + 5x$
$x^2 + y^2 < 16$

Solve the problem.

43. ***Buried treasure.*** An old pirate on his deathbed gave the following description of where he had buried some treasure on a deserted island: "Starting at the large palm tree, I walked to the north and then to the east, and there I buried the treasure. I walked at least 50 paces to get to that spot, but I was not more than 50 paces, as the crow flies, from the large palm tree. I am sure that I walked farther in the northerly direction than in the easterly direction." With the large palm tree at the origin and the positive y-axis pointing to the north, graph the possible locations of the treasure.

37. $y \geq 3$
$x \leq 1$

38. $x > -3$
$y < 2$

39. $4y^2 - 9x^2 < 36$
$x^2 + y^2 < 16$

40. $25y^2 - 16x^2 < 400$
$x^2 + y^2 > 4$

FIGURE FOR EXERCISE 43

 GRAPHING CALCULATOR EXERCISES

41. $y < x^2$
$x^2 + y^2 < 1$

42. $y > x^2$
$4x^2 + y^2 < 4$

44. Use graphs to find an ordered pair that is in the solution set to the system of inequalities:

$$y > x^2 - 2x + 1$$
$$y < -1.1(x - 4)^2 + 5$$

Verify that your answer satisfies both inequalities.

45. Use graphs to find the solution set to the system of inequalities:

$$y > 2x^2 - 3x + 1$$
$$y < -2x^2 - 8x - 1$$

COLLABORATIVE ACTIVITIES

Focus on Comets

Conic sections are used to model many different things in the natural world. Astronomers use mirrors in the shape of parabolas in telescopes. They have learned that planets can have elliptical as well as circular orbits around the sun and that comets may have orbits that resemble hyperbolas, parabolas, or ellipses. In this activity we will consider comets with these three types of orbits.

The orbit that a comet will take as it approaches the sun depends on its velocity (as well as other factors). If it has enough velocity to escape from the pull of the sun, it may take either a parabolic orbit or a hyperbolic orbit. If it doesn't have enough velocity, then it will take an elliptical orbit. Of course, a comet that has a parabolic or hyperbolic orbit will not come back again around our sun. Only comets with elliptical orbits do we see again.

For the problems below, round all your answers to two decimal places.

1. Halley's comet is in an elliptical orbit about the sun with the sun at one of the foci. In this problem we will make a scale model of the orbit of Halley's comet about the sun. We will choose our coordinate system so that the ellipse is centered at (0, 0). Halley's comet comes within 0.6 astronomical unit[1] from the sun at its closest point and 35 astronomical units at its farthest point. The position of the comet at these points

[1]An astronomical unit is the distance of the earth from the sun. The earth's orbit is almost circular and so is about the same distance from the sun at any point in its orbit.

Grouping: 2 students per group

Topic: Conic sections

will correspond to the horizontal vertices. Find the equation for the ellipse. Determine where the foci should be. On a piece of cardboard, put thumbtacks at the foci. Determine the length of string you will need to draw the ellipse using the scale 1 centimeter = 1 astronomical unit (AU). Draw the comet's orbit, indicating which focus is the sun.

2. If the velocity of a comet equals the escape velocity (it is going just fast enough to get away), then its orbit will be parabolic. The sun will be at the focus of the parabola. We will place the vertex at the point (0, 0); in this case the vertex will be where the comet is the closest to the sun. Suppose we have a comet that is 0.75 AU from the sun at its closest point. Find the equation for the parabola. Graph the parabola.

3. If the velocity of a comet is greater than the escape velocity (it can easily escape from the sun's gravitational pull), its path will resemble one-half of a hyperbola with the sun as one focus. Assuming we have a left- and a right-opening hyperbola, we can model the path of such a comet along one of its branches. We will center the hyperbola at (0, 0), and place the sun at the left focus and draw the path of the comet as it approaches from the left. Suppose that the comet will be 1.5 AUs from the sun at its closest point. Assume the sun is at the point (−3, 0). Draw a sketch of this scenario. What is the equation for the hyperbola? Graph the hyperbola.

Extension: Graph all three equations on a graphing calculator or computer.

WRAP-UP CHAPTER 12

SUMMARY

Nonlinear Systems

		Examples
Nonlinear systems in two variables	Use substitution or addition to eliminate variables. Nonlinear systems may have several points in the solution set.	$y = x^2$ $x^2 + y^2 = 4$ Substitution: $y + y^2 = 4$

The Distance Formula

		Examples
Distance formula	The distance between (x_1, y_1) and (x_2, y_2) is $\sqrt{(x_2 - x_1)^2 + (y_2 - y_1)^2}$.	Distance between $(1, -2)$ and $(3, -4)$ is $\sqrt{2^2 + (-2)^2}$ or $2\sqrt{2}$.

Examples

Parabola

$y = a(x - h)^2 + k$

Opens upward for $a > 0$, downward for $a < 0$
Vertex at (h, k)
To find focus and directrix, use $a = \frac{1}{4p}$.
Distance from vertex to focus or directrix is $|p|$.

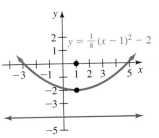

$x = a(y - k)^2 + h$

Opens right for $a > 0$, left for $a < 0$
Vertex at (h, k)
To find focus and directrix use $a = \frac{1}{4p}$.
Distance from vertex to focus or directrix is $|p|$.

$y = ax^2 + bx + c$

Opens upward for $a > 0$, downward for $a < 0$
The x-coordinate of the vertex is $\frac{-b}{2a}$.
Find the y-coordinate of the vertex by evaluating
$y = ax^2 + bx + c$ for $x = \frac{-b}{2a}$.

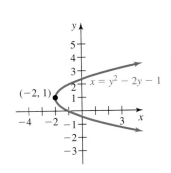

$x = ay^2 + by + c$

Opens right for $a > 0$, left for $a < 0$
The y-coordinate of the vertex is $\frac{-b}{2a}$.
Find the x-coordinate of the vertex by evaluating
$x = ay^2 + by + c$ for $y = \frac{-b}{2a}$.

Examples

Circle

$(x - h)^2 + (y - k)^2 = r^2$

Center (h, k)
Radius r (for $r > 0$)

Centered at origin
$x^2 + y^2 = r^2$

Center $(0, 0)$
Radius r (for $r > 0$)

Ellipse

Examples

Centered at origin

$$\frac{x^2}{a^2} + \frac{y^2}{b^2} = 1$$

Center: $(0, 0)$
x-intercepts: $(a, 0)$ and $(-a, 0)$
y-intercepts: $(0, b)$ and $(0, -b)$
Foci: $(\pm c, 0)$ if $a^2 > b^2$ and $c^2 = a^2 - b^2$
$\qquad (0, \pm c)$ if $b^2 > a^2$ and $c^2 = b^2 - a^2$

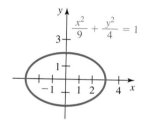

Arbitrary center

$$\frac{(x - h)^2}{a^2} + \frac{(y - k)^2}{b^2} = 1$$

Center: (h, k)

Hyperbola

Examples

Opening left and right

Centered at origin: $\dfrac{x^2}{a^2} - \dfrac{y^2}{b^2} = 1$
$\quad$ Center: $(0, 0)$

$\quad x$-intercepts: $(a, 0)$ and $(-a, 0)$

$\quad y$-intercepts: none

Centered at (h, k): $\dfrac{(x - h)^2}{a^2} - \dfrac{(y - k)^2}{b^2} = 1$

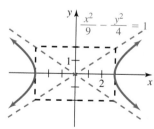

Opening up and down

Centered at origin: $\dfrac{y^2}{b^2} - \dfrac{x^2}{a^2} = 1$
$\quad$ Center: $(0, 0)$

$\quad x$-intercepts: none

$\quad y$-intercepts: $(0, b)$ and $(0, -b)$

Centered at (h, k): $\dfrac{(y - k)^2}{b^2} - \dfrac{(x - h)^2}{a^2} = 1$

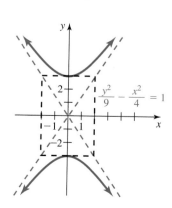

Second-Degree Inequalities

Examples

Solution set for
a single inequality

Graph the boundary curve obtained by replacing
the inequality symbol by the equal sign.
Use test points to determine which regions satisfy
the inequality.

$x^2 + y^2 < 16$

Solution set for a system
of inequalities

Graph the boundary curves. Then select a test
point in each region. Shade only the regions for
which the test point satisfies all inequalities of
the system.

$x^2 + y^2 < 16$
$y > x^2 - 1$

$x^2 + y^2 < 16$ and
$y > x^2 - 1$

ENRICHING YOUR MATHEMATICAL WORD POWER

For each mathematical term, choose the correct meaning.

1. nonlinear equation
   a. an equation that is not lined up
   b. an equation whose graph is a straight line
   c. an equation whose graph is not a straight line
   d. an exponential equation

2. parabola
   a. the points in a plane that are equidistant from a point and a line
   b. the points in a plane that are a fixed distance from a fixed point
   c. the points in a plane that are equidistant from two fixed points
   d. the points in a plane the sum of whose distances from two fixed points is a constant

3. directrix
   a. the line $y = x$
   b. the line of symmetry of a parabola
   c. the x-axis
   d. the fixed line in the definition of parabola

4. vertex of a parabola
   a. the midpoint of the line segment joining the focus and directrix perpendicular to the directrix
   b. the focus
   c. the x-intercept
   d. the endpoint

5. conic sections
   a. the two halves of a cone
   b. the vertex and focus
   c. the curves obtained at the intersection of a cone and a plane
   d. the asymptotes

6. axis of symmetry
   a. the x-axis
   b. the y-axis
   c. the directrix
   d. the line of symmetry of a parabola

7. circle
   a. the points in a plane that are equidistant from a point and a line

b.   the points in a plane that are a fixed distance from a fixed point
c.   the points in a plane that are equidistant from two fixed points
d.   the points in a plane the sum of whose distances from two fixed points is a constant

8. ellipse
a.   the points in a plane that are equidistant from a point and a line
b.   the points in a plane that are a fixed distance from a fixed point
c.   the points in a plane that are equidistant from two fixed points
d.   the points in a plane such that the sum of their distances from two fixed points is constant

9. hyperbola
a.   the points in a plane that are equidistant from a point and a line
b.   the points in a plane that are a fixed distance from a fixed point
c.   the points in a plane such that the difference of their distances from two fixed points is constant
d.   the points in a plane such that the sum of their distances from two fixed points is a constant

10. asymptotes
a.   lines approached by a hyperbola
b.   lines approached by parabolas
c.   tangent lines to a circle
d.   lines that pass through the vertices of an ellipse

REVIEW EXERCISES

12.1 *Graph both equations on the same set of axes, then determine the points of intersection of the graphs by solving the system.*

1. $y = x^2$
$y = -2x + 15$

2. $y = \sqrt{x}$
$y = \frac{1}{3}x$

3. $y = 3x$
$y = \frac{1}{x}$

4. $y = |x|$
$y = -3x + 5$

Solve each system.

5. $x^2 + y^2 = 4$
$y = \frac{1}{3}x^2$

6. $12y^2 - 4x^2 = 9$
$x = y^2$

7. $x^2 + y^2 = 34$
$y = x + 2$

8. $y = 2x + 1$
$xy - y = 5$

9. $y = \log(x - 3)$
$y = 1 - \log(x)$

10. $y = \left(\frac{1}{2}\right)^x$
$y = 2^{x-1}$

11. $x^4 = 2(12 - y)$
$y = x^2$

12. $x^2 + 2y^2 = 7$
$x^2 - 2y^2 = -5$

12.2 *Find the distance between each pair of points.*

13. $(1, 1), (3, 3)$

14. $(1, 2), (4, 5)$

15. $(-4, 6), (2, -8)$

16. $(-3, -5), (5, -7)$

Determine the vertex, axis of symmetry, focus, and directrix for each parabola.

17. $y = x^2 + 3x - 18$

18. $y = x - x^2$

19. $y = x^2 + 3x + 2$

20. $y = -x^2 - 3x + 4$

21. $y = -\frac{1}{2}(x - 2)^2 + 3$

22. $y = \frac{1}{4}(x + 1)^2 - 2$

Write each equation in the form $y = a(x - h)^2 + k$, and identify the vertex of the parabola.

23. $y = 2x^2 - 8x + 1$

24. $y = -2x^2 - 6x - 1$

25. $y = -\frac{1}{2}x^2 - x + \frac{1}{2}$

26. $y = \frac{1}{4}x^2 + x - 9$

12.3 *Determine the center and radius of each circle, and sketch its graph.*

27. $x^2 + y^2 = 100$

28. $x^2 + y^2 = 20$

29. $(x - 2)^2 + (y + 3)^2 = 81$

30. $x^2 + 2x + y^2 = 8$

31. $9y^2 + 9x^2 = 4$

32. $x^2 + 4x + y^2 - 6y - 3 = 0$

Write the standard equation for each circle with the given center and radius.

33. Center $(0, 3)$, radius 6

34. Center $(0, 0)$, radius $\sqrt{6}$

35. Center $(2, -7)$, radius 5

36. Center $\left(\frac{1}{2}, -3\right)$, radius $\frac{1}{2}$

12.4 *Sketch the graph of each ellipse.*

37. $\dfrac{x^2}{36} + \dfrac{y^2}{49} = 1$ **38.** $\dfrac{x^2}{25} + y^2 = 1$

44. $6y^2 - 16x^2 = 96$

12.5 *Graph each inequality.*

39. $25x^2 + 4y^2 = 100$ **40.** $6x^2 + 4y^2 = 24$

45. $4x - 2y > 3$

Sketch the graph of each hyperbola.

46. $y < x^2 - 3x$

41. $\dfrac{x^2}{49} - \dfrac{y^2}{36} = 1$

47. $y^2 < x^2 - 1$

42. $\dfrac{y^2}{25} - \dfrac{x^2}{49} = 1$

43. $4x^2 - 25y^2 = 100$

48. $y^2 < 1 - x^2$

49. $4x^2 + 9y^2 > 36$

50. $x^2 + y > 2x - 1$

63. $\dfrac{x^2}{3} - \dfrac{y^2}{5} = 1$

64. $x^2 + \dfrac{y^2}{3} = 1$

65. $4y^2 - x^2 = 8$

66. $9x^2 + y = 9$

Sketch the graph of each equation.

67. $x^2 = 4 - y^2$

68. $x^2 = 4y^2 + 4$

Graph the solution set to each system of inequalities.

51. $y < 3x - x^2$
$\quad x^2 + y^2 < 9$

52. $x^2 - y^2 < 1$
$\quad y < 1$

69. $x^2 = 4y + 4$

70. $x = 4y + 4$

53. $4x^2 + 9y^2 > 36$
$\quad x^2 + y^2 < 9$

54. $y^2 - x^2 > 4$
$\quad y^2 + 16x^2 < 16$

71. $x^2 = 4 - 4y^2$

72. $x^2 = 4y - y^2$

MISCELLANEOUS

Identify each equation as the equation of a straight line, parabola, circle, hyperbola, or ellipse. Try to do these without rewriting the equations.

55. $x^2 = y^2 + 1$

56. $x = y + 1$

57. $x^2 = 1 - y^2$

58. $x^2 = y + 1$

59. $x^2 + x = 1 - y^2$

60. $(x - 3)^2 + (y + 2)^2 = 7$

61. $x^2 + 4x = 6y - y^2$

62. $4x + 6y = 1$

73. $x^2 = 4 - (y - 4)^2$

74. $(x - 2)^2 + (y - 4)^2 = 4$

Write the equation of the circle with the given features.

75. Centered at the origin and passing through $(3, 4)$

76. Centered at $(2, -3)$ and passing through $(-1, 4)$

77. Centered at $(-1, 5)$ with radius 6

78. Centered at $(0, -3)$ and passing through the origin

Write the equation of the parabola with the given features.

79. Focus $(1, 4)$ and directrix $y = 2$

80. Focus $(-2, 1)$ and directrix $y = 5$

81. Vertex $(0, 0)$ and focus $\left(0, \frac{1}{4}\right)$

82. Vertex $(1, 2)$ and focus $\left(1, \frac{3}{2}\right)$

83. Vertex $(0, 0)$, passing through $(3, 2)$, and opening upward

84. Vertex $(1, 3)$, passing through $(0, 0)$, and opening downward

Solve each system of equations.

85. $x^2 + y^2 = 25$
$y = -x + 1$

86. $x^2 - y^2 = 1$
$x^2 + y^2 = 7$

87. $4x^2 + y^2 = 4$
$x^2 - y^2 = 21$

88. $y = x^2 + x$
$y = -x^2 + 3x + 12$

Solve each problem.

89. *Perimeter of a rectangle.* A rectangle has a perimeter of 16 feet and an area of 12 square feet. Find its length and width.

90. *Tale of two circles.* Find the radii of two circles such that the difference in areas of the two is 10π square inches and the difference in radii of the two is 2 inches.

Sketch the graph of each equation.

1. $x^2 + y^2 = 25$

2. $\dfrac{x^2}{16} - \dfrac{y^2}{25} = 1$

5. $y^2 - 4x^2 = 4$

6. $y = -x^2 - 2x + 3$

3. $y^2 + 4x^2 = 4$

4. $y = x^2 + 4x + 4$

Sketch the graph of each inequality.

7. $x^2 - y^2 < 9$

8. $x^2 + y^2 > 9$

9. $y > x^2 - 9$

Solve each system of equations.

12. $y = x^2 - 2x - 8$
$\quad y = 7 - 4x$

13. $x^2 + y^2 = 12$
$\quad y = x^2$

Graph the solution set to each system of inequalities.

Solve each problem.

14. Find the distance between $(-1, 4)$ and $(1, 6)$.

10. $x^2 + y^2 < 9$
$\quad x^2 - y^2 > 1$

15. Find the center and radius of the circle $x^2 + 2x + y^2 + 10y = 10$.

16. Find the vertex, focus, and directrix of the parabola $y = x^2 + x + 3$. State the axis of symmetry and whether the parabola opens up or down.

17. Write the equation $y = \frac{1}{2}x^2 - 3x - \frac{1}{2}$ in the form $y = a(x - h)^2 + k$.

11. $y < -x^2 + x$
$\quad y < x - 4$

18. Write the equation of a circle with center $(-1, 3)$ that passes through $(2, 5)$.

19. Find the length and width of a rectangular room that has an area of 108 square feet and a perimeter of 42 ft.

Sketch the graph of each equation.

1. $y = 9x - x^2$

2. $y = 9x$

3. $y = (x - 9)^2$

4. $y^2 = 9 - x^2$

5. $y = 9x^2$

6. $y = |9x|$

7. $4x^2 + 9y^2 = 36$

8. $4x^2 - 9y^2 = 36$

9. $y = 9 - x$

10. $y = 9^x$

Find the following products.

11. $(x + 2y)^2$

12. $(x + y)(x^2 + 2xy + y^2)$

13. $(a + b)^3$

14. $(a - 3b)^2$

15. $(2a + 1)(3a - 5)$

16. $(x - y)(x^2 + xy + y^2)$

Solve each system of equations.

17. $2x - 3y = -4$
$x + 2y = 5$

18. $x^2 + y^2 = 25$
$x + y = 7$

19. $2x - y + z = 7$
$x - 2y - z = 2$
$x + y + z = 2$

20. $y = x^2$
$y - 2x = 3$

Solve each formula for the specified variable.

21. $ax + b = 0$, for x

22. $wx^2 + dx + m = 0$, for x

23. $A = \dfrac{1}{2}h(B + b)$, for B

24. $\dfrac{1}{x} + \dfrac{1}{y} = \dfrac{1}{2}$, for x

25. $L = m + mxt$, for m

26. $y = 3a\sqrt{t}$, for t

Solve each problem.

27. Write the equation of the line in slope-intercept form that goes through the points $(2, -3)$ and $(-4, 1)$.

28. Write the equation of the line in slope-intercept form that contains the origin and is perpendicular to the line $2x - 4y = 5$.

29. Write the equation of the circle that has center $(2, 5)$ and passes through the point $(-1, -1)$.

30. Find the center and radius of the circle $x^2 + 3x + y^2 - 6y = 0$.

715

Perform the computations with complex numbers.

31. $2i(3 + 5i)$

32. i^6

33. $(2i - 3) + (6 - 7i)$

34. $(3 + i\sqrt{2})^2$

35. $(2 - 3i)(5 - 6i)$

36. $(3 - i) + (-6 + 4i)$

37. $(5 - 2i)(5 + 2i)$

38. $(2 - 3i) \div (2i)$

39. $(4 + 5i) \div (1 - i)$

40. $\dfrac{4 - \sqrt{-8}}{2}$

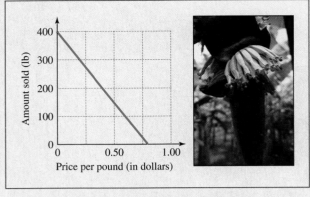

FIGURE FOR EXERCISE 41

Solve.

41. *Going bananas.* Salvadore has observed that when bananas are $0.30 per pound (lb), he sells 250 lb per day, and when bananas are $0.40 per lb, he sells only 200 lb per day.

    a) Assume the number of pounds sold, q, is a linear function of the price per pound, x, and find that function.

    b) Salvadore's daily revenue in dollars is the product of the number of pounds sold and the price per pound. Write the revenue as a function of x.

    c) Graph the revenue function.

    d) What price per pound maximizes his revenue?

    e) What is his maximum possible revenue?

CHAPTER 13

Sequences and Series

Everyone realizes the importance of investing for the future. Some people go to great pains to study the markets and to make wise investment decisions. Some stay away from investing because they do not want to take chances. However, the most important factor in investing is making regular investments (*Money*, www.money.com). According to *Money*, if you had invested $5000 in the stock market every year at the market high for that year (the worst time to invest) for the last 40 years, your investment would be worth $2.8 million today.

A sequence of periodic investments earning a fixed rate of interest can be thought of as a geometric sequence. In this chapter you will learn how to find the sum of a geometric sequence and to calculate the future value of a sequence of periodic investments. In Exercise 58 of Section 13.4 you will calculate the value of $5000 invested each year for 10 years in Fidelity's Magellan fund.

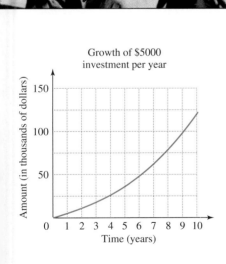

Growth of $5000 investment per year

Amount (in thousands of dollars)

Time (years)

13.1 SEQUENCES

The word "sequence" is a familiar word. We may speak of a sequence of events or say that something is out of sequence. In this section we give the mathematical definition of a sequence.

Definition

In mathematics we think of a sequence as a list of numbers. Each number in the sequence is called a **term** of the sequence. There is a first term, a second term, a third term, and so on. For example, the daily high temperature readings in Minot, North Dakota, for the first 10 days in January can be thought of as a finite sequence with 10 terms:

$$-9, -2, 8, -11, 0, 6, 14, 1, -5, -11$$

The set of all positive even integers,

$$2, 4, 6, 8, 10, 12, 14, \ldots,$$

can be thought of as an infinite sequence.

To give a precise definition of sequence, we use the terminology of functions. The list of numbers is the range of the function.

> **Sequence**
>
> A **finite sequence** is a function whose domain is the set of positive integers less than or equal to some fixed positive integer. An **infinite sequence** is a function whose domain is the set of all positive integers.

When the domain is apparent, we will refer to either a finite sequence or an infinite sequence simply as a sequence. For the independent variable of the function we will usually use n (for natural number) rather than x. For the dependent variable we write a_n (read "a sub n") rather than y. We call a_n the **nth term,** or the **general term** of the sequence. Rather than use the $f(x)$ notation for functions, we will define sequences with formulas. When n is used as a variable, we will assume it represents natural numbers only.

EXAMPLE 1

Listing terms of a finite sequence

List all of the terms of each finite sequence.

a) $a_n = n^2$ for $1 \leq n \leq 5$ **b)** $a_n = \dfrac{1}{n+2}$ for $1 \leq n \leq 4$

Solution

a) Using the natural numbers from 1 through 5 in $a_n = n^2$, we get

$$a_1 = 1^2 = 1,$$
$$a_2 = 2^2 = 4,$$
$$a_3 = 3^2 = 9,$$
$$a_4 = 4^2 = 16,$$

and

$$a_5 = 5^2 = 25.$$

The five terms of this sequence are 1, 4, 9, 16, and 25. We often refer to the listing of the terms of the sequence as the sequence.

Calculator Close-Up

We can define the sequence with the Y= key and make a list of the terms.

X	Y1
1	1
2	4
3	9
4	16
5	25
6	36
7	49

Y1 ◻ X²

b) Using the natural numbers from 1 through 4 in $a_n = \frac{1}{n+2}$, we get the terms

$$a_1 = \frac{1}{1+2} = \frac{1}{3},$$

$$a_2 = \frac{1}{2+2} = \frac{1}{4},$$

$$a_3 = \frac{1}{5},$$

and

$$a_4 = \frac{1}{6}.$$

The four terms of the sequence are $\frac{1}{3}, \frac{1}{4}, \frac{1}{5},$ and $\frac{1}{6}$. ■

E X A M P L E   2

Listing terms of an infinite sequence

List the first three terms of the infinite sequence whose nth term is

$$a_n = \frac{(-1)^n}{2^{n+1}}.$$

Calculator Close-Up

Some calculators have a sequence feature that allows you to specify the formula and which terms to evaluate. We can even get the terms as fractions.

Solution

Using the natural numbers 1, 2, and 3 in the formula for the nth term yields

$$a_1 = \frac{(-1)^1}{2^{1+1}} = -\frac{1}{4}, \qquad a_2 = \frac{(-1)^2}{2^{2+1}} = \frac{1}{8}, \qquad \text{and} \qquad a_3 = \frac{(-1)^3}{2^{3+1}} = -\frac{1}{16}.$$

We write the sequence as follows:

$$-\frac{1}{4}, \frac{1}{8}, -\frac{1}{16}, \ldots$$

■

Finding a Formula for the nth Term

We often know the terms of a sequence and want to write a formula that will produce those terms. To write a formula for the nth term of a sequence, examine the terms and look for a pattern. Each term is a function of the term number. The first term corresponds to $n = 1$, the second term corresponds to $n = 2$, and so on.

E X A M P L E   3

A familiar sequence

Write the general term for the infinite sequence

$$3, 5, 7, 9, 11, \ldots .$$

Solution

The even numbers are all multiples of 2 and can be represented as $2n$. Because each odd number is 1 more than an even number, a formula for the nth term might be

$$a_n = 2n + 1.$$

Helpful Hint

Finding a formula for a sequence could be extremely difficult. For example, there is no known formula that will produce the sequence of prime numbers:

2, 3, 5, 7, 11, 13, 17, 19, ...

To be sure, we write out a few terms using the formula:

$$a_1 = 2(1) + 1 = 3$$
$$a_2 = 2(2) + 1 = 5$$
$$a_3 = 2(3) + 1 = 7$$

So the general term is $a_n = 2n + 1$. ■

CAUTION   There can be more than one formula that produces the given terms of a sequence. For example, the sequence

$$1, 2, 4, \ldots$$

could have nth term $a_n = 2^{n-1}$ or $a_n = \frac{1}{2}n^2 - \frac{1}{2}n + 1$. The first three terms for both of these sequences are identical, but their fourth terms are different.

E X A M P L E   4

A sequence with alternating signs

Write the general term for the infinite sequence

$$1, -\frac{1}{4}, \frac{1}{9}, -\frac{1}{16}, \ldots\ldots$$

Solution

To obtain the alternating signs, we use powers of -1. Because any even power of -1 is positive and any odd power of -1 is negative, we use $(-1)^{n+1}$. The denominators are the squares of the positive integers. So the nth term of this infinite sequence is given by the formula

$$a_n = \frac{(-1)^{n+1}}{n^2}.$$

Check this sequence by using this formula to find the first four terms.   ■

In Example 5 we use a sequence to model a physical situation.

E X A M P L E   5

The bouncing ball

Suppose a ball always rebounds $\frac{2}{3}$ of the height from which it falls and the ball is dropped from a height of 6 feet. Write a sequence whose terms are the heights from which the ball falls. What is a formula for the nth term of this sequence?

Solution

On the first fall the ball travels 6 feet (ft), as shown in Fig. 13.1. On the second fall it travels $\frac{2}{3}$ of 6, or 4 ft. On the third fall it travels $\frac{2}{3}$ of 4, or $\frac{8}{3}$ ft, and so on. We write

F I G U R E   1 3 . 1

the sequence as follows:

$$6, 4, \frac{8}{3}, \frac{16}{9}, \frac{32}{27}, \ldots$$

The nth term can be written by using powers of $\frac{2}{3}$:

$$a_n = 6\left(\frac{2}{3}\right)^{n-1}$$

WARM-UPS

True or false? Explain your answer.

1. The nth term of the sequence 2, 4, 6, 8, 10, . . . is $a_n = 2n$.

2. The nth term of the sequence 1, 3, 5, 7, 9, . . . is $a_n = 2n - 1$.

3. A sequence is a function.

4. The domain of a finite sequence is the set of positive integers.

5. The nth term of $-1, 4, -9, 16, -25, \ldots$ is $a_n = (-1)^{n+1}n^2$.

6. For the infinite sequence $b_n = \frac{1}{n}$, the independent variable is $\frac{1}{n}$.

7. For the sequence $c_n = n^3$, the dependent variable is c_n.

8. The sixth term of the sequence $a_n = (-1)^{n+1}2^n$ is 64.

9. The symbol a_n is used for the dependent variable of a sequence.

10. The tenth term of the sequence 2, 4, 8, 16, 32, 64, 128, . . . is 1024.

Reading and Writing   *After reading this section, write out the answers to these questions. Use complete sentences.*

1. What is a sequence?

2. What is a term of a sequence?

3. What is a finite sequence?

4. What is an infinite sequence?

List all terms of each finite sequence. See Example 1.

5. $a_n = n^2$ for $1 \le n \le 8$

6. $a_n = -n^2$ for $1 \le n \le 4$

7. $b_n = \dfrac{(-1)^n}{n}$ for $1 \le n \le 10$

8. $b_n = \dfrac{(-1)^{n+1}}{n}$ for $1 \le n \le 6$

9. $c_n = (-2)^{n-1}$ for $1 \le n \le 5$

10. $c_n = (-3)^{n-2}$ for $1 \le n \le 5$

11. $a_n = 2^{-n}$ for $1 \le n \le 6$

12. $a_n = 2^{-n+2}$ for $1 \le n \le 5$

13. $b_n = 2n - 3$ for $1 \le n \le 7$

14. $b_n = 2n + 6$ for $1 \le n \le 7$

15. $c_n = n^{-1/2}$ for $1 \le n \le 5$

16. $c_n = n^{1/2}2^{-n}$ for $1 \le n \le 4$

Write the first four terms of the infinite sequence whose nth term is given. See Example 2.

17. $a_n = \dfrac{1}{n^2 + n}$

18. $b_n = \dfrac{1}{(n+1)(n+2)}$

19. $b_n = \dfrac{1}{2n - 5}$

20. $a_n = \dfrac{4}{2n + 5}$

21. $c_n = (-1)^n(n - 2)^2$

22. $c_n = (-1)^n(2n - 1)^2$

23. $a_n = \dfrac{(-1)^{2n}}{n^2}$

24. $a_n = (-1)^{2n+1}2^{n-1}$

Write a formula for the general term of each infinite sequence. See Examples 3 and 4.

25. 1, 3, 5, 7, 9, . . .

26. 5, 7, 9, 11, 13, . . .

27. 1, -1, 1, -1, . . .

28. -1, 1, -1, 1, . . .

29. 0, 2, 4, 6, 8, . . .

30. 4, 6, 8, 10, 12, . . .

31. 3, 6, 9, 12, . . .

32. 4, 8, 12, 16, . . .

33. 4, 7, 10, 13, . . .

34. 3, 7, 11, 15, . . .

35. -1, 2, -4, 8, -16, . . .

36. 1, -3, 9, -27, . . .

37. 0, 1, 4, 9, 16, . . .

38. 0, 1, 8, 27, 64, . . .

Solve each problem. See Example 5.

39. *Football penalties.* A football is on the 8-yard line, and five penalties in a row are given that move the ball half the distance to the (closest) goal. Write a sequence of five terms that specify the location of the ball after each penalty.

40. *Infestation.* Leona planted 9 acres of soybeans, but by the end of each week, insects had destroyed one-third of the acreage that was healthy at the beginning of the week. How many acres does she have left after 6 weeks?

41. *Constant rate of increase.* The MSRP for the 2002 Ford F-250 Lariat 4WD Super Duty Super Cab was $34,940 (Edmund's New Car Prices, www.edmunds.com). Suppose the price of this truck increases by 5% each year. Find the prices to the nearest dollar for the 2003 through 2008 models.

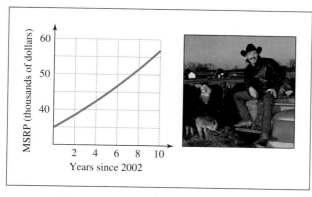

FIGURE FOR EXERCISE 41

42. *Constant increase.* The MSRP for a new 2002 Mercury Cougar was $20,395 (Edmund's New Car Prices, www.edmunds.com). Suppose the price of this car increases by $1000 each year. Find the prices of the 2003 through 2008 models.

43. *Economic impact.* To assess the economic impact of a factory on a community, economists consider the annual amount the factory spends in the community, then the portion of the money that is respent in the community, then the portion of the respent money that is respent in the community, and so on. Suppose a garment manufacturer spends $1 million annually in its community and 80% of all money received in the community is respent in the community. Find the first four terms of the economic impact sequence.

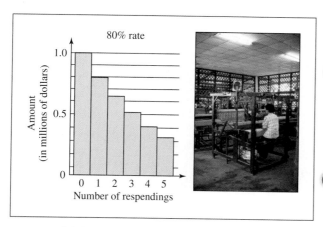

FIGURE FOR EXERCISE 43

44. *Less impact.* The rate at which money is respent in a community varies from community to community. Find the first four terms of the economic impact sequence for the manufacturer in Exercise 43, assuming only 50% of money received in the community is respent in the community.

45. *Fabric design.* A fabric designer must take into account the capability of textile machines to produce material with vertical repeats. A textile machine can be set up for a vertical repeat every $\frac{27}{n}$ inches (in.), where n is a natural number. Write the first five terms of the sequence $a_n = \frac{27}{n}$, which gives the possible vertical repeats for a textile machine.

46. *Musical tones.* The note middle C on a piano is tuned so that the string vibrates at 262 cycles per second, or 262 Hertz (Hz). The C note one octave higher is tuned to 524 Hz. The tuning for the 11 notes in between using the method called *equal temperament* is determined by the sequence $a_n = 262 \cdot 2^{n/12}$. Find the tuning for the 11 notes in between.

GETTING MORE INVOLVED

47. *Discussion.* Everyone has two (biological) parents, four grandparents, eight great-grandparents, 16 great-great-grandparents, and so on. If we put the word "great" in front of the word "grandparents" 35 times, then how many of this type of relative do you have? Is this more or less than the present population of the earth? Give reasons for your answers.

48. *Discussion.* If you deposit 1 cent into your piggy bank on September 1 and each day thereafter deposit twice as much as on the previous day, then how much will you be depositing on September 30? The total amount deposited for the month can be found without adding up all 30 deposits. Look at how the amount on deposit is increasing each day and see whether you can find the total for the month. Give reasons for your answers.

49. *Cooperative learning.* Working in groups, have someone in each group make up a formula for a_n, the nth term of a sequence, but do not show it to the other group members. Write the terms of the sequence on a piece of paper one at a time. After each term is given, ask whether anyone knows the next term. When the group can correctly give the next term, ask for a formula for the nth term.

50. *Exploration.* Find a real-life sequence in which all of the terms are the same. Find one in which each term after the first is one larger than the previous term. Find out what the sequence of fines is on your campus for your first, second, third, and fourth parking ticket.

51. *Exploration.* Consider the sequence whose nth term is $a_n = (0.999)^n$.

a) Calculate a_{100}, a_{1000}, and $a_{10,000}$.

b) What happens to a_n as n gets larger and larger?

13.2 SERIES

If you make a sequence of bank deposits, then you might be interested in the total value of the terms of the sequence. Of course, if the sequence has only a few terms, you can simply add them. In Sections 13.3 and 13.4 we will develop formulas that give the sum of the terms for certain finite and infinite sequences. In this section you will first learn a notation for expressing the sum of the terms of a sequence.

Summation Notation

To describe the sum of the terms of a sequence, we use **summation notation.** The Greek letter Σ (sigma) is used to indicate sums. For example, the sum of the first five terms of the sequence $a_n = n^2$ is written as

$$\sum_{n=1}^{5} n^2.$$

You can read this notation as "the sum of n^2 for n between 1 and 5, inclusive." To find the sum, we let n take the values 1 through 5 in the expression n^2:

$$\sum_{n=1}^{5} n^2 = 1^2 + 2^2 + 3^2 + 4^2 + 5^2$$
$$= 1 + 4 + 9 + 16 + 25$$
$$= 55$$

In this context the letter n is the **index of summation.** Other letters may also be used. For example, the expressions

$$\sum_{n=1}^{5} n^2, \quad \sum_{j=1}^{5} j^2, \quad \text{and} \quad \sum_{i=1}^{5} i^2$$

all have the same value. Note that i is used as a variable here and not as an imaginary number.

EXAMPLE 1

Evaluating a sum in summation notation

Find the value of the expression

$$\sum_{i=1}^{3} (-1)^i (2i + 1).$$

Solution

Replace i by 1, 2, and 3, and then add the results:

$$\sum_{i=1}^{3} (-1)^i (2i + 1) = (-1)^1 [2(1) + 1] + (-1)^2 [2(2) + 1] + (-1)^3 [2(3) + 1]$$
$$= -3 + 5 - 7$$
$$= -5 \qquad \blacksquare$$

Series

The sum of the terms of the sequence 1, 4, 9, 16, 25 is written as

$$1 + 4 + 9 + 16 + 25.$$

This expression is called a *series*. It indicates that we are to add the terms of the given sequence. The sum, 55, is the sum of the series.

> ### Series
>
> The indicated sum of the terms of a sequence is called a **series.**

Just as a sequence may be finite or infinite, a series may be finite or infinite. In this section we discuss finite series only. In Section 13.4 we will discuss one type of infinite series.

Summation notation is a convenient notation for writing a series.

E X A M P L E   2

Converting to summation notation

Write the series in summation notation:

$$2 + 4 + 6 + 8 + 10 + 12 + 14$$

Solution

The general term for the sequence of positive even integers is $2n$. If we let n take the values from 1 through 7, then $2n$ ranges from 2 through 14. So

$$2 + 4 + 6 + 8 + 10 + 12 + 14 = \sum_{n=1}^{7} 2n.$$ ■

E X A M P L E   3

Converting to summation notation

Write the series

$$\frac{1}{2} - \frac{1}{3} + \frac{1}{4} - \frac{1}{5} + \frac{1}{6} - \frac{1}{7} + \cdots + \frac{1}{50}$$

in summation notation.

Helpful Hint

A series is called an *indicated sum* because the addition is indicated but not actually being performed. The sum of a series is the real number obtained by actually performing the indicated addition.

Solution

For this series we let n be 2 through 50. The expression $(-1)^n$ produces alternating signs. The series is written as

$$\sum_{n=2}^{50} \frac{(-1)^n}{n}.$$ ■

Changing the Index

In Example 3 we saw the index go from 2 through 50, but this is arbitrary. A series can be written with the index starting at any given number.

E X A M P L E   4

Changing the index

Rewrite the series

$$\sum_{i=1}^{6} \frac{(-1)^i}{i^2}$$

with an index j, where j starts at 0.

Solution

Because i starts at 1 and j starts at 0, we have $i = j + 1$. Because i ranges from 1 through 6 and $i = j + 1$, j must range from 0 through 5. Now replace i by $j + 1$ in the summation notation:

$$\sum_{j=0}^{5} \frac{(-1)^{j+1}}{(j + 1)^2}$$

Check that these two series have exactly the same six terms. ■

True or false? Explain your answer.

1. A series is the indicated sum of the terms of a sequence.

2. The sum of a series can never be negative.

3. There are eight terms in the series $\sum\limits_{i=2}^{10} i^3$.

4. The series $\sum\limits_{i=1}^{9} (-1)^i i^2$ and $\sum\limits_{j=0}^{8} (-1)^j (j+1)^2$ have the same sum.

5. The ninth term of the series $\sum\limits_{i=1}^{100} \dfrac{(-1)^i}{(i+1)(i+2)}$ is $\dfrac{1}{110}$.

6. $\sum\limits_{i=1}^{2} (-1)^i 2^i = 2$

7. $\sum\limits_{i=1}^{5} 3i = 3\left(\sum\limits_{i=1}^{5} i\right)$

8. $\sum\limits_{i=1}^{5} 4 = 20$

9. $\sum\limits_{i=1}^{5} 2i + \sum\limits_{i=1}^{5} 7i = \sum\limits_{i=1}^{5} 9i$

10. $\sum\limits_{i=1}^{3} (2i+1) = \left(\sum\limits_{i=1}^{3} 2i\right) + 1$

13.2   EXERCISES

Reading and Writing *After reading this section, write out the answers to these questions. Use complete sentences.*

1. What is summation notation?

2. What is the index of summation?

3. What is a series?

4. What is a finite series?

Find the sum of each series. See Example 1.

5. $\sum\limits_{i=1}^{4} i^2$

6. $\sum\limits_{j=0}^{3} (j+1)^2$

7. $\sum\limits_{j=0}^{5} (2j-1)$

8. $\sum\limits_{i=1}^{6} (2i-3)$

9. $\sum\limits_{i=1}^{5} 2^{-i}$

10. $\sum\limits_{i=1}^{5} (-2)^{-i}$

11. $\sum\limits_{i=1}^{10} 5i^0$

12. $\sum\limits_{j=1}^{20} 3$

13. $\sum\limits_{i=1}^{3} (i-3)(i+1)$

14. $\sum\limits_{i=0}^{5} i(i-1)(i-2)(i-3)$

15. $\sum\limits_{j=1}^{10} (-1)^j$

16. $\sum\limits_{j=1}^{11} (-1)^j$

Write each series in summation notation. Use the index i, and let i begin at 1 in each summation. See Examples 2 and 3.

17. $1+2+3+4+5+6$

18. $2+4+6+8+10$

19. $-1+3-5+7-9+11$

20. $1-3+5-7+9$

21. $1+4+9+16+25+36$

22. $1+8+27+64+125$

23. $\dfrac{1}{3}+\dfrac{1}{4}+\dfrac{1}{5}+\dfrac{1}{6}$

24. $1-\dfrac{1}{2}+\dfrac{1}{3}-\dfrac{1}{4}+\dfrac{1}{5}-\dfrac{1}{6}$

25. $\ln(2) + \ln(3) + \ln(4)$

26. $e^1 + e^2 + e^3 + e^4$

27. $a_1 + a_2 + a_3 + a_4$

28. $a^2 + a^3 + a^4 + a^5$

29. $x_3 + x_4 + x_5 + \cdots + x_{50}$

30. $y_1 + y_2 + y_3 + \cdots + y_{30}$

31. $w_1 + w_2 + w_3 + \cdots + w_n$

32. $m_1 + m_2 + m_3 + \cdots + m_k$

Complete the rewriting of each series using the new index as indicated. See Example 4.

33. $\displaystyle\sum_{i=1}^{5} i^2 = \sum_{j=0}$

34. $\displaystyle\sum_{i=1}^{6} i^3 = \sum_{j=0}$

35. $\displaystyle\sum_{i=0}^{12} (2i - 1) = \sum_{j=1}$

36. $\displaystyle\sum_{i=1}^{3} (3i + 2) = \sum_{j=0}$

37. $\displaystyle\sum_{i=4}^{8} \frac{1}{i} = \sum_{j=1}$

38. $\displaystyle\sum_{i=5}^{10} 2^{-i} = \sum_{j=1}$

39. $\displaystyle\sum_{i=1}^{4} x^{2i+3} = \sum_{j=0}$

40. $\displaystyle\sum_{i=0}^{2} x^{3-2i} = \sum_{j=1}$

41. $\displaystyle\sum_{i=1}^{n} x^i = \sum_{j=0}$

42. $\displaystyle\sum_{i=0}^{n} x^{-i} = \sum_{j=1}$

Write out the terms of each series.

43. $\displaystyle\sum_{i=1}^{6} x^i$

44. $\displaystyle\sum_{i=1}^{5} (-1)^i x^{i-1}$

45. $\displaystyle\sum_{j=0}^{3} (-1)^j x_j$

46. $\displaystyle\sum_{j=1}^{5} \frac{1}{x_j}$

47. $\displaystyle\sum_{i=1}^{3} ix^i$

48. $\displaystyle\sum_{i=1}^{5} \frac{x}{i}$

A series can be used to model the situation in each of the following problems.

49. *Leap frog.* A frog with a vision problem is 1 yard away from a dead cricket. He spots the cricket and jumps halfway to the cricket. After the frog realizes that he has not reached the cricket, he again jumps halfway to the cricket. Write a series in summation notation to describe how far the frog has moved after nine such jumps.

50. *Compound interest.* Cleo deposited $1000 at the beginning of each year for 5 years into an account paying 10% interest compounded annually. Write a series using summation notation to describe how much she has in the account at the end of the fifth year. Note that the first $1000 will receive interest for 5 years, the second $1000 will receive interest for 4 years, and so on.

51. *Total economic impact.* In Exercise 43 of Section 13.1 we described a factory that spends $1 million annually in a community in which 80% of all money received in the community is respent in the community. Use summation notation to write the sum of the first four terms of the economic impact sequence for the factory.

52. *Total earnings.* Suppose you earn $1 on January 1, $2 on January 2, $3 on January 3, and so on. Use summation notation to write the sum of your earnings for the entire month of January.

GETTING MORE INVOLVED

53. *Discussion.* What is the difference between a sequence and a series?

54. *Discussion.* For what values of n is $\displaystyle\sum_{i=1}^{n} \frac{1}{i} > 4$?

Helpful Hint

Arithmetic used as an adjective (ar-ith-met'-ic) is pronounced differently from arithmetic used as a noun (a-rith'-me-tic). Arithmetic (the adjective) is accented similarly to geometric.

13.3 ARITHMETIC SEQUENCES AND SERIES

We defined sequences and series in Sections 13.1 and 13.2. In this section you will study a special type of sequence known as an arithmetic sequence. You will also study the series corresponding to this sequence.

Arithmetic Sequences

Consider the following sequence:

$$5, 9, 13, 17, 21, \ldots$$

This sequence is called an arithmetic sequence because of the pattern for the terms. Each term is 4 larger than the previous term.

> **Arithmetic Sequence**
>
> A sequence in which each term after the first is obtained by adding a fixed amount to the previous term is called an **arithmetic sequence.**

The fixed amount is called the **common difference** and is denoted by the letter d. If a_1 is the first term, then the second term is $a_1 + d$. The third term is $a_1 + 2d$, the fourth term is $a_1 + 3d$, and so on.

> **Formula for the nth Term of an Arithmetic Sequence**
>
> The nth term, a_n, of an arithmetic sequence with first term a_1 and common difference d is
>
> $$a_n = a_1 + (n - 1)d.$$

E X A M P L E   1

The nth term of an arithmetic sequence

Write a formula for the nth term of the arithmetic sequence

$$5, 9, 13, 17, 21, \ldots.$$

Solution

Each term of the sequence after the first is 4 more than the previous term. Because the common difference is 4 and the first term is 5, the nth term is given by

$$a_n = 5 + (n - 1)4.$$

We can simplify this expression to get

$$a_n = 4n + 1.$$

Check a few terms: $a_1 = 4(1) + 1 = 5$, $a_2 = 4(2) + 1 = 9$, and $a_3 = 4(3) + 1 = 13$. ∎

In the next example the common difference is negative.

E X A M P L E   2

An arithmetic sequence of decreasing terms

Write a formula for the nth term of the arithmetic sequence

$$4, 1, -2, -5, -8, \ldots.$$

Solution

Each term is 3 less than the previous term, so $d = -3$. Because $a_1 = 4$, we can write the nth term as

$$a_n = 4 + (n - 1)(-3),$$

or

$$a_n = -3n + 7.$$

Check a few terms: $a_1 = -3(1) + 7 = 4$, $a_2 = -3(2) + 7 = 1$, and $a_3 = -3(3) + 7 = -2$. ∎

In Example 3 we find some terms of an arithmetic sequence using a given formula for the nth term.

E X A M P L E   3   **Writing terms of an arithmetic sequence**

Write the first five terms of the sequence in which $a_n = 3 + (n - 1)6$.

Solution

Let n take the values from 1 through 5, and find a_n:

$$a_1 = 3 + (1 - 1)6 = 3$$
$$a_2 = 3 + (2 - 1)6 = 9$$
$$a_3 = 3 + (3 - 1)6 = 15$$
$$a_4 = 3 + (4 - 1)6 = 21$$
$$a_5 = 3 + (5 - 1)6 = 27$$

Notice that $a_n = 3 + (n - 1)6$ gives the general term for an arithmetic sequence with first term 3 and common difference 6. Because each term after the first is 6 more than the previous term, the first five terms that we found are correct. ∎

The formula $a_n = a_1 + (n - 1)d$ involves four variables: a_1, a_n, n, and d. If we know the values of any three of these variables, we can find the fourth.

E X A M P L E   4   **Finding a missing term of an arithmetic sequence**

Find the twelfth term of the arithmetic sequence whose first term is 2 and whose fifth term is 14.

Solution

Before finding the twelfth term, we use the given information to find the missing common difference. Let $n = 5$, $a_1 = 2$, and $a_5 = 14$ in the formula $a_n = a_1 + (n - 1)d$ to find d:

$$14 = 2 + (5 - 1)d$$
$$14 = 2 + 4d$$
$$12 = 4d$$
$$3 = d$$

Now use $a_1 = 2$, $d = 3$ and $n = 12$ in $a_n = a_1 + (n - 1)d$ to find a_{12}:

$$a_{12} = 2 + (12 - 1)3$$
$$a_{12} = 35$$ ∎

Arithmetic Series

The indicated sum of an arithmetic sequence is called an **arithmetic series.** For example, the series

$$2 + 4 + 6 + 8 + 10 + \cdots + 54$$

is an arithmetic series because there is a common difference of 2 between the terms.

We can find the actual sum of this arithmetic series without adding all of the terms. Write the series in increasing order, and below that write the series in decreasing order. We then add the corresponding terms:

$$
\begin{aligned}
S &= 2 + 4 + 6 + 8 + \cdots + 52 + 54 \\
S &= 54 + 52 + 50 + 48 + \cdots + 4 + 2 \\
\hline
2S &= 56 + 56 + 56 + 56 + \cdots + 56 + 56
\end{aligned}
$$

Now, how many times does 56 appear in the sum on the right? Because

$$2 + 4 + 6 + \cdots + 54 = 2 \cdot 1 + 2 \cdot 2 + 2 \cdot 3 + \cdots + 2 \cdot 27,$$

there are 27 terms in this sum. Because 56 appears 27 times on the right, we have $2S = 27 \cdot 56$, or

$$S = \frac{27 \cdot 56}{2} = 27 \cdot 28 = 756.$$

If $S_n = a_1 + a_2 + a_3 + \cdots + a_n$ is any arithmetic series, then we can find its sum using the same technique. Rewrite S_n as follows:

$$
\begin{aligned}
S_n &= a_1 + (a_1 + d) + (a_1 + 2d) + \cdots + a_n \\
S_n &= a_n + (a_n - d) + (a_n - 2d) + \cdots + a_1 \\
\hline
2S_n &= (a_1 + a_n) + (a_1 + a_n) + (a_1 + a_n) + \cdots + (a_1 + a_n) \quad \text{Add.}
\end{aligned}
$$

Because $(a_1 + a_n)$ appears n times on the right, we have $2S_n = n(a_1 + a_n)$. Divide each side by 2 to get the following formula.

Sum of an Arithmetic Series

The sum, S_n, of the first n terms of an arithmetic series with first term a_1 and nth term a_n, is given by

$$S_n = \frac{n}{2}(a_1 + a_n).$$

EXAMPLE 5 **The sum of an arithmetic series**

Find the sum of the positive integers from 1 to 100 inclusive.

Helpful Hint

Legend has it that Carl F. Gauss knew this formula when he was in grade school. Gauss's teacher told him to add up the numbers from 1 through 100 for busy work. He immediately answered 5050.

Solution

The described series, $1 + 2 + 3 + \cdots + 100$, has 100 terms. So we can use $n = 100$, $a_1 = 1$, and $a_n = 100$ in the formula for the sum of an arithmetic series:

$$S_n = \frac{n}{2}(a_1 + a_n)$$

$$S_{100} = \frac{100}{2}(1 + 100)$$

$$= 50(101)$$

$$= 5050$$

E X A M P L E   6   **The sum of an arithmetic series**

Find the sum of the series

$$12 + 16 + 20 + \cdots + 84.$$

Solution

This series is an arithmetic series with $a_n = 84$, $a_1 = 12$, and $d = 4$. To get the number of terms, n, we use $a_n = a_1 + (n - 1)d$:

$$84 = 12 + (n - 1)4$$
$$84 = 8 + 4n$$
$$76 = 4n$$
$$19 = n$$

Now find the sum of these 19 terms:

$$S_{19} = \frac{19}{2}(12 + 84) = 912$$

■

WARM-UPS

True or false? Explain your answer.

1. The arithmetic sequence $3, 1, -1, -3, -5, \ldots$ has common difference 2.

2. The sequence $2, 5, 9, 14, 20, 27, \ldots$ is an arithmetic sequence.

3. The sequence $2, 4, 2, 0, 2, 4, 2, 0, \ldots$ is an arithmetic sequence.

4. The nth term of an arithmetic sequence with first term a_1 and common difference d is given by the formula $a_n = a_1 + nd$.

5. If $a_1 = 5$ and $a_3 = 10$ in an arithmetic sequence, then $a_4 = 15$.

6. If $a_1 = 6$ and $a_3 = 2$ in an arithmetic sequence, then $a_2 = 10$.

7. An arithmetic series is the indicated sum of an arithmetic sequence.

8. The series $\sum_{i=1}^{5}(3 + 2i)$ is an arithmetic series.

9. The sum of the first n counting numbers is $\frac{n(n + 1)}{2}$.

10. The sum of the even integers from 8 through 28 inclusive is $5(8 + 28)$.

13.3   EXERCISES

Reading and Writing   *After reading this section, write out the answers to these questions. Use complete sentences.*

1. What is an arithmetic sequence?

2. What is the nth term of an arithmetic sequence?

3. What is an arithmetic series?

4. What is the formula for the sum of the first n terms of an arithmetic series?

Write a formula for the nth term of each arithmetic sequence. See Examples 1 and 2.

5. $0, 6, 12, 18, 24, \ldots$

6. $0, 5, 10, 15, 20, \ldots$

7. $7, 12, 17, 22, 27, \ldots$

8. $4, 15, 26, 37, 48, \ldots$

9. $-4, -2, 0, 2, 4, \ldots$

10. $-3, 0, 3, 6, 9, \ldots$

11. $5, 1, -3, -7, -11, \ldots$

12. $8, 5, 2, -1, -4, \ldots$

13. $-2, -9, -16, -23, \ldots$

14. $-5, -7, -9, -11, -13, \ldots$

15. $-3, -2.5, -2, -1.5, -1, \ldots$

16. $-2, -1.25, -0.5, 0.25, \ldots$

17. $-6, -6.5, -7, -7.5, -8, \ldots$

18. $1, 0.5, 0, -0.5, -1, \ldots$

In Exercises 19–32, write the first five terms of the arithmetic sequence whose nth term is given. See Example 3.

19. $a_n = 9 + (n - 1)4$

20. $a_n = 13 + (n - 1)6$

21. $a_n = 7 + (n - 1)(-2)$

22. $a_n = 6 + (n - 1)(-3)$

23. $a_n = -4 + (n - 1)3$

24. $a_n = -19 + (n - 1)12$

25. $a_n = -2 + (n - 1)(-3)$

26. $a_n = -1 + (n - 1)(-2)$

27. $a_n = -4n - 3$

28. $a_n = -3n + 1$

29. $a_n = 0.5n + 4$

30. $a_n = 0.3n + 1$

31. $a_n = 20n + 1000$

32. $a_n = -600n + 4000$

Find the indicated part of each arithmetic sequence. See Example 4.

33. Find the eighth term of the sequence that has a first term of 9 and a common difference of 6.

34. Find the twelfth term of the sequence that has a first term of -2 and a common difference of -3.

35. Find the common difference if the first term is 6 and the twentieth term is 82.

36. Find the common difference if the first term is -8 and the ninth term is -64.

37. If the common difference is -2 and the seventh term is 14, then what is the first term?

38. If the common difference is 5 and the twelfth term is -7, then what is the first term?

39. Find the sixth term of the sequence that has a fifth term of 13 and a first term of -3.

40. Find the eighth term of the sequence that has a sixth term of -42 and a first term of 3.

Find the sum of each given series. See Examples 5 and 6.

41. $1 + 2 + 3 + \cdots + 48$

42. $1 + 2 + 3 + \cdots + 12$

43. $8 + 10 + 12 + \cdots + 36$

44. $9 + 12 + 15 + \cdots + 72$

45. $-1 + (-7) + (-13) + \cdots + (-73)$

46. $-7 + (-12) + (-17) + \cdots + (-72)$

47. $-6 + (-1) + 4 + 9 + \cdots + 64$

48. $-9 + (-1) + 7 + \cdots + 103$

49. $20 + 12 + 4 + (-4) + \cdots + (-92)$

50. $19 + 1 + (-17) + \cdots + (-125)$

51. $\displaystyle\sum_{i=1}^{12} (3i - 7)$

52. $\displaystyle\sum_{i=1}^{7} (-4i + 6)$

53. $\displaystyle\sum_{i=1}^{11} (-5i + 2)$

54. $\displaystyle\sum_{i=1}^{19} (3i - 5)$

Solve each problem using the ideas of arithmetic sequences and series.

55. *Increasing salary.* If a lab technician has a salary of $22,000 her first year and is due to get a $500 raise each year, then what will her salary be in her seventh year?

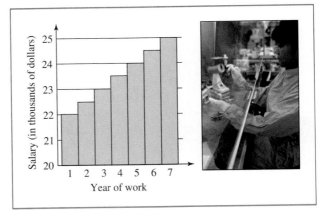

FIGURE FOR EXERCISE 55

56. *Seven years of salary.* What is the total salary for 7 years of work for the lab technician of Exercise 55?

57. *Light reading.* On the first day of October an English teacher suggests to his students that they read five pages

of a novel and every day thereafter increase their daily reading by two pages. If his students follow this suggestion, then how many pages will they read during October?

58. *Heavy penalties.* If an air-conditioning system is not completed by the agreed upon date, the contractor pays a penalty of $500 for the first day that it is overdue, $600 for the second day, $700 for the third day, and so on. If the system is completed 10 days late, then what is the total amount of the penalties that the contractor must pay?

GETTING MORE INVOLVED

59. *Discussion.* Which of the following sequences is not an arithmetic sequence? Explain your answer.

a) $\frac{1}{2}, 1, \frac{3}{2}, \ldots$ b) $\frac{1}{2}, \frac{1}{3}, \frac{1}{4}, \ldots$

c) $5, 0, -5, \ldots$ d) $2, 3, 4, \ldots$

60. *Discussion.* What is the smallest value of n for which

$$\sum_{i=1}^{n} \frac{i}{2} > 50?$$

13.4   GEOMETRIC SEQUENCES AND SERIES

In Section 13.3 you studied the arithmetic sequences and series. In this section you will study sequences in which each term is a *multiple* of the term preceding it. You will also learn how to find the sum of the corresponding series.

Geometric Sequences

In an arithmetic sequence such as $2, 4, 6, 8, 10, \ldots$ there is a common difference between consecutive terms. In a geometric sequence there is a common ratio between consecutive terms. The following table contains several geometric sequences and the common ratios between consecutive terms.

Geometric Sequence	Common Ratio
$3, 6, 12, 24, 48, \ldots$	2
$27, 9, 3, 1, \frac{1}{3}, \ldots$	$\frac{1}{3}$
$1, -10, 100, -1000, \ldots$	-10

Note that every term after the first term of each geometric sequence can be obtained by multiplying the previous term by the common ratio.

Geometric Sequence

A sequence in which each term after the first is obtained by multiplying the preceding term by a constant is called a **geometric sequence.**

The constant is denoted by the letter r and is called the **common ratio.** If a_1 is the first term, then the second term is $a_1 r$. The third term is $a_1 r^2$, the fourth term is $a_1 r^3$, and so on. We can write a formula for the nth term of a geometric sequence by following this pattern.

Formula for the *n*th Term of a Geometric Sequence

The *n*th term, a_n, of a geometric sequence with first term a_1 and common ratio *r* is

$$a_n = a_1 r^{n-1}.$$

The first term and the common ratio determine all of the terms of a geometric sequence.

E X A M P L E 1   **Finding the *n*th term**

Write a formula for the *n*th term of the geometric sequence

$$6, 2, \frac{2}{3}, \frac{2}{9}, \ldots$$

Solution

We can obtain the common ratio by dividing any term after the first by the term preceding it. So

$$r = 2 \div 6 = \frac{1}{3}.$$

Because each term after the first is $\frac{1}{3}$ of the term preceding it, the *n*th term is given by

$$a_n = 6\left(\frac{1}{3}\right)^{n-1}.$$

Check a few terms: $a_1 = 6\left(\frac{1}{3}\right)^{1-1} = 6$, $a_2 = 6\left(\frac{1}{3}\right)^{2-1} = 2$, and $a_3 = 6\left(\frac{1}{3}\right)^{3-1} = \frac{2}{3}$.   ■

E X A M P L E 2   **Finding the *n*th term**

Find a formula for the *n*th term of the geometric sequence

$$2, -1, \frac{1}{2}, -\frac{1}{4}, \ldots$$

Solution

We obtain the ratio by dividing a term by the term preceding it:

$$r = -1 \div 2 = -\frac{1}{2}$$

Each term after the first is obtained by multiplying the preceding term by $-\frac{1}{2}$. The formula for the *n*th term is

$$a_n = 2\left(-\frac{1}{2}\right)^{n-1}.$$

Check a few terms: $a_1 = 2\left(-\frac{1}{2}\right)^{1-1} = 2$, $a_2 = 2\left(-\frac{1}{2}\right)^{2-1} = -1$, and $a_3 = 2\left(-\frac{1}{2}\right)^{3-1} = \frac{1}{2}$.   ■

In Example 3 we use the formula for the *n*th term to write some terms of a geometric sequence.

E X A M P L E   3

Writing the terms

Write the first five terms of the geometric sequence whose nth term is

$$a_n = 3(-2)^{n-1}.$$

Solution

Let n take the values 1 through 5 in the formula for the nth term:

$$a_1 = 3(-2)^{1-1} = 3$$
$$a_2 = 3(-2)^{2-1} = -6$$
$$a_3 = 3(-2)^{3-1} = 12$$
$$a_4 = 3(-2)^{4-1} = -24$$
$$a_5 = 3(-2)^{5-1} = 48$$

Notice that $a_n = 3(-2)^{n-1}$ gives the general term for a geometric sequence with first term 3 and common ratio -2. Because every term after the first can be obtained by multiplying the previous term by -2, the terms 3, -6, 12, -24, and 48 are correct. ∎

The formula for the nth term involves four variables: a_n, a_1, r, and n. If we know the value of any three of them, we can find the value of the fourth.

E X A M P L E   4

Finding a missing term

Find the first term of a geometric sequence whose fourth term is 8 and whose common ratio is $\frac{1}{2}$.

Solution

Let $a_4 = 8$, $r = \frac{1}{2}$, and $n = 4$ in the formula $a_n = a_1 r^{n-1}$:

$$8 = a_1 \left(\frac{1}{2}\right)^{4-1}$$

$$8 = a_1 \cdot \frac{1}{8}$$

$$64 = a_1$$

So the first term is 64. ∎

Study Tip

Many schools have study skills centers that offer courses, work-shops, and individual help on how to study. A search for "study skills" on the World Wide Web will turn up more information than you could possibly read. If you are not having the success in school that you would like, do something about it. What you do now will affect you the rest of your life.

Finite Geometric Series

Consider the following series:

$$1 + 2 + 4 + 8 + 16 + \cdots + 512$$

The terms of this series are the terms of a finite geometric sequence. The indicated sum of a geometric sequence is called a **geometric series.**

We can find the actual sum of this finite geometric series by using a technique similar to the one used for the sum of an arithmetic series. Let

$$S = 1 + 2 + 4 + 8 + \cdots + 256 + 512.$$

Because the common ratio is 2, multiply each side by -2:

$$-2S = -2 - 4 - 8 - \cdots - 512 - 1024$$

Adding the last two equations eliminates all but two of the terms on the right:

$$
\begin{aligned}
S &= 1 + 2 + 4 + 8 + \cdots + 256 + 512 \\
-2S &= -2 - 4 - 8 - \cdots - 512 - 1024 \\
\hline
-S &= 1 - 1024 \quad \text{Add.} \\
-S &= -1023 \\
S &= 1023
\end{aligned}
$$

If $S_n = a_1 + a_1 r + a_1 r^2 + \cdots + a_1 r^{n-1}$ is any geometric series, we can find the sum in the same manner. Multiplying each side of this equation by $-r$ yields

$$-rS_n = -a_1 r - a_1 r^2 - a_1 r^3 - \cdots - a_1 r^n.$$

If we add S_n and $-rS_n$, all but two of the terms on the right are eliminated:

$$
\begin{aligned}
S_n &= a_1 + a_1 r + a_1 r^2 + \cdots + a_1 r^{n-1} \\
-rS_n &= - a_1 r - a_1 r^2 - a_1 r^3 - \cdots - a_1 r^n \\
\hline
S_n - rS_n &= a_1 \phantom{+a_1 r + a_1 r^2 + \cdots + a_1 r^{n-1}} - a_1 r^n \quad \text{Add.} \\
(1-r)S_n &= a_1(1 - r^n) \quad\quad \text{Factor out common factors.}
\end{aligned}
$$

Now divide each side of this equation by $1 - r$ to get the formula for S_n.

Sum of n Terms of a Geometric Series

If S_n represents the sum of the first n terms of a geometric series with first term a_1 and common ratio r $(r \neq 1)$, then

$$S_n = \frac{a_1(1 - r^n)}{1 - r}.$$

E X A M P L E   5   **The sum of a finite geometric series**

Find the sum of the series

$$\frac{1}{3} + \frac{1}{9} + \frac{1}{27} + \cdots + \frac{1}{729}.$$

Solution

The first term is $\frac{1}{3}$, and the common ratio is $\frac{1}{3}$. So the nth term can be written as

$$a_n = \frac{1}{3}\left(\frac{1}{3}\right)^{n-1}.$$

We can use this formula to find the number of terms in the series:

$$\frac{1}{729} = \frac{1}{3}\left(\frac{1}{3}\right)^{n-1}$$

$$\frac{1}{729} = \left(\frac{1}{3}\right)^{n}$$

Because $3^6 = 729$, we have $n = 6$. (Of course, you could use logarithms to solve for n.) Now use the formula for the sum of six terms of this geometric series:

$$S_6 = \frac{\frac{1}{3}\left[1 - \left(\frac{1}{3}\right)^6\right]}{1 - \frac{1}{3}} = \frac{\frac{1}{3}\left[1 - \frac{1}{729}\right]}{\frac{2}{3}}$$

$$= \frac{1}{3} \cdot \frac{728}{729} \cdot \frac{3}{2}$$

$$= \frac{364}{729}$$ ■

E X A M P L E   6

The sum of a finite geometric series

Find the sum of the series

$$\sum_{i=1}^{12} 3(-2)^{i-1}.$$

Solution

This series is geometric with first term 3, ratio -2, and $n = 12$. We use the formula for the sum of the first 12 terms of a geometric series:

$$S_{12} = \frac{3[1 - (-2)^{12}]}{1 - (-2)} = \frac{3[-4095]}{3} = -4095$$ ■

Calculator Close-Up

Experiment with your calculator to see what happens to r^n as n gets larger and larger.

```
.99^100
        .3660323413
.99^1000
     4.317124741E-5
.99^10000
     2.24877485E-44
```

Infinite Geometric Series

Consider how a very large value of n affects the formula for the sum of a finite geometric series,

$$S_n = \frac{a_1(1 - r^n)}{1 - r}.$$

If $|r| < 1$, then the value of r^n gets closer and closer to 0 as n gets larger and larger. For example, if $r = \frac{2}{3}$ and $n = 10, 20,$ and 100, then

$$\left(\frac{2}{3}\right)^{10} \approx 0.0173415, \quad \left(\frac{2}{3}\right)^{20} \approx 0.0003007, \quad \text{and} \quad \left(\frac{2}{3}\right)^{100} \approx 2.460 \times 10^{-18}.$$

Because r^n is approximately 0 for large values of n, $1 - r^n$ is approximately 1. If we replace $1 - r^n$ by 1 in the expression for S_n, we get

$$S_n \approx \frac{a_1}{1 - r}.$$

So as n gets larger and larger, the sum of the first n terms of the infinite geometric series

$$a_1 + a_1 r + a_1 r^2 + \cdots$$

gets closer and closer to $\frac{a_1}{1 - r}$, provided that $|r| < 1$. Therefore we say that $\frac{a_1}{1 - r}$ is the sum of *all* of the terms of the infinite geometric series.

Sum of an Infinite Geometric Series

If $a_1 + a_1 r + a_1 r^2 + \cdots$ is an infinite geometric series, with $|r| < 1$, then the sum S of all of the terms of this series is given by

$$S = \frac{a_1}{1 - r}.$$

E X A M P L E   7

Sum of an infinite geometric series

Find the sum

$$\frac{1}{2} + \frac{1}{4} + \frac{1}{8} + \frac{1}{16} + \cdots.$$

Helpful Hint

You can imagine this series in a football game. The Bears have the ball on the Lions' 1-yard line. The Lions continually get penalties that move the ball one-half of the distance to the goal. Theoretically, the ball will never reach the goal, but the total distance it moves will get closer and closer to 1 yard.

Solution

This series is an infinite geometric series with $a_1 = \frac{1}{2}$ and $r = \frac{1}{2}$. Because $r < 1$, we have

$$S = \frac{\frac{1}{2}}{1 - \frac{1}{2}} = 1.$$

For an infinite series the index of summation i takes the values 1, 2, 3, and so on, without end. To indicate that the values for i keep increasing without bound, we say that i *takes the values from* 1 *through* ∞ (infinity). Note that the symbol "∞" does not represent a number. Using the ∞ symbol, we can write the indicated sum of an infinite geometric series (with $|r| < 1$) by using summation notation as follows:

$$a_1 + a_1 r + a_1 r^2 + \cdots = \sum_{i=1}^{\infty} a_1 r^{i-1}$$

E X A M P L E   8

Sum of an infinite geometric series

Find the value of the sum

$$\sum_{i=1}^{\infty} 8 \left(\frac{3}{4} \right)^{i-1}.$$

Solution

This series is an infinite geometric series with first term 8 and ratio $\frac{3}{4}$. So

$$S = \frac{8}{1 - \frac{3}{4}} = 8 \cdot \frac{4}{1} = 32.$$

E X A M P L E   9

Follow the bouncing ball

Suppose a ball always rebounds $\frac{2}{3}$ of the height from which it falls and the ball is dropped from a height of 6 feet. Find the total distance that the ball travels.

Solution

The ball falls 6 feet (ft) and rebounds 4 ft, then falls 4 ft and rebounds $\frac{8}{3}$ ft. The following series gives the total distance that the ball falls:

$$F = 6 + 4 + \frac{8}{3} + \frac{16}{9} + \cdots$$

The distance that the ball rebounds is given by the following series:

$$R = 4 + \frac{8}{3} + \frac{16}{9} + \cdots$$

Each of these series is an infinite geometric series with ratio $\frac{2}{3}$. Use the formula for an infinite geometric series to find each sum:

$$F = \frac{6}{1 - \frac{2}{3}} = 6 \cdot \frac{3}{1} = 18 \text{ ft}, \qquad R = \frac{4}{1 - \frac{2}{3}} = 4 \cdot \frac{3}{1} = 12 \text{ ft}$$

The total distance traveled by the ball is the sum of F and R, 30 ft. ∎

Annuities

One of the most important applications of geometric series is in calculating the value of an annuity. An **annuity** is a sequence of periodic payments. The payments might be loan payments or investments.

E X A M P L E   1 0   **Value of an annuity**

A deposit of $1000 is made at the beginning of each year for 30 years and earns 6% interest compounded annually. What is the value of this annuity at the end of the thirtieth year?

Solution

The last deposit earns interest for only one year. So at the end of the thirtieth year it amounts to $1000(1.06). The next to last deposit earns interest for 2 years and amounts to $1000(1.06)^2$. The first deposit earns interest for 30 years and amounts to $1000(1.06)^{30}$. So the value of the annuity at the end of the thirtieth year is the sum of the finite geometric series

$$1000(1.06) + 1000(1.06)^2 + 1000(1.06)^3 + \cdots + 1000(1.06)^{30}.$$

Use the formula for the sum of 30 terms of a finite geometric series with $a_1 = 1000(1.06)$ and $r = 1.06$:

$$S_{30} = \frac{1000(1.06)(1 - (1.06)^{30})}{1 - 1.06} \approx \$83,801.68$$

So 30 annual deposits of $1000 each amount to $83,801.68. ∎

WARM-UPS

True or false? Explain your answer.

1. The sequence 2, 6, 24, 120, . . . is a geometric sequence.
2. For $a_n = 2^n$ there is a common difference between adjacent terms.
3. The common ratio for the geometric sequence $a_n = 3(0.5)^{n-1}$ is 0.5.
4. If $a_n = 3(2)^{-n+3}$, then $a_1 = 12$.
5. In the geometric sequence $a_n = 3(2)^{-n+3}$ we have $r = \frac{1}{2}$.
6. The terms of a geometric series are the terms of a geometric sequence.

(*continued*)

7. To evaluate $\displaystyle\sum_{i=1}^{10} 2^i$, we must list all of the terms.

8. $\displaystyle\sum_{i=1}^{5} 6\left(\frac{3}{4}\right)^{i-1} = \frac{9\left[1 - \left(\frac{3}{4}\right)^5\right]}{1 - \frac{3}{4}}$

9. $10 + 5 + \dfrac{5}{2} + \cdots = \dfrac{10}{1 - \dfrac{1}{2}}$

10. $2 + 4 + 8 + 16 + \cdots = \dfrac{2}{1 - 2}$

13.4   EXERCISES

Reading and Writing   *After reading this section, write out the answers to these questions. Use complete sentences.*

1. What is a geometric sequence?

2. What is the *n*th term of a geometric sequence?

3. What is a geometric series?

4. What is the formula for the sum of the first *n* terms of a geometric series?

5. What is the approximate value of r^n when *n* is large and $|r| < 1$?

6. What is the formula for the sum of an infinite geometric series?

Write a formula for the nth term of each geometric sequence. See Examples 1 and 2.

7. $\dfrac{1}{3}, 1, 3, 9, \ldots$

8. $\dfrac{1}{4}, 2, 16, \ldots$

9. $64, 8, 1, \ldots$

10. $100, 10, 1, \ldots$

11. $8, -4, 2, -1, \ldots$

12. $-9, 3, -1, \ldots$

13. $2, -4, 8, -16, \ldots$

14. $-\dfrac{1}{2}, 2, -8, 32, \ldots$

15. $-\dfrac{1}{3}, -\dfrac{1}{4}, -\dfrac{3}{16}, \ldots$

16. $-\dfrac{1}{4}, -\dfrac{1}{5}, -\dfrac{4}{25}, \ldots$

Write the first five terms of the geometric sequence with the given nth term. See Example 3.

17. $a_n = 2\left(\dfrac{1}{3}\right)^{n-1}$

18. $a_n = -5\left(\dfrac{1}{2}\right)^{n-1}$

19. $a_n = (-2)^{n-1}$

20. $a_n = \left(-\dfrac{1}{3}\right)^{n-1}$

21. $a_n = 2^{-n}$

22. $a_n = 3^{-n}$

23. $a_n = (0.78)^n$

24. $a_n = (-0.23)^n$

Find the required part of each geometric sequence. See Example 4.

25. Find the first term of the geometric sequence that has fourth term 40 and common ratio 2.

26. Find the first term of the geometric sequence that has fifth term 4 and common ratio $\frac{1}{2}$.

27. Find r for the geometric sequence that has $a_1 = 6$ and $a_4 = \frac{2}{9}$.

28. Find r for the geometric sequence that has $a_1 = 1$ and $a_4 = -27$.

29. Find a_4 for the geometric sequence that has $a_1 = -3$ and $r = \frac{1}{3}$.

30. Find a_5 for the geometric sequence that has $a_1 = -\frac{2}{3}$ and $r = -\frac{2}{3}$.

Find the sum of each geometric series. See Examples 5 and 6.

31. $\frac{1}{2} + \frac{1}{4} + \frac{1}{8} + \cdots + \frac{1}{512}$

32. $1 + \frac{1}{3} + \frac{1}{9} + \cdots + \frac{1}{81}$

33. $\frac{1}{2} - \frac{1}{4} + \frac{1}{8} - \frac{1}{16} + \frac{1}{32}$

34. $3 - 1 + \frac{1}{3} - \frac{1}{9} + \frac{1}{27} - \frac{1}{81}$

35. $30 + 20 + \frac{40}{3} + \cdots + \frac{1280}{729}$

36. $9 - 6 + 4 - \cdots - \frac{128}{243}$

37. $\sum_{i=1}^{10} 5(2)^{i-1}$

38. $\sum_{i=1}^{7} (10,000)(0.1)^{i-1}$

39. $\sum_{i=1}^{6} (0.1)^i$

40. $\sum_{i=1}^{5} (0.2)^i$

41. $\sum_{i=1}^{6} 100(0.3)^i$

42. $\sum_{i=1}^{7} 36(0.5)^i$

Find the sum of each infinite geometric series. See Examples 7 and 8.

43. $\frac{1}{8} + \frac{1}{16} + \frac{1}{32} + \cdots$

44. $\frac{1}{9} + \frac{1}{27} + \frac{1}{81} + \cdots$

45. $3 + 2 + \frac{4}{3} + \cdots$

46. $2 + 1 + \frac{1}{2} + \cdots$

47. $4 - 2 + 1 - \frac{1}{2} + \cdots$

48. $16 - 12 + 9 - \frac{27}{4} + \cdots$

49. $\sum_{i=1}^{\infty} (0.3)^i$

50. $\sum_{i=1}^{\infty} (0.2)^i$

51. $\sum_{i=1}^{\infty} 3(0.5)^{i-1}$

52. $\sum_{i=1}^{\infty} 7(0.4)^{i-1}$

53. $\sum_{i=1}^{\infty} 3(0.1)^i$

54. $\sum_{i=1}^{\infty} 6(0.1)^i$

55. $\sum_{i=1}^{\infty} 12(0.01)^i$

56. $\sum_{i=1}^{\infty} 72(0.01)^i$

Use the ideas of geometric series to solve each problem. See Examples 9 and 10.

57. *Retirement fund.* Suppose a deposit of $2000 is made at the beginning of each year for 45 years into an account paying 12% compounded annually. What is the amount of this annuity at the end of the forty-fifth year?

58. *World's largest mutual fund.* If you had invested $5000 at the beginning of each year for the past 10 years in the Fidelity's Magellan Fund you would have averaged 12.46% compounded annually (www.fidelity.com). Find the amount of this annuity at the end of the tenth year.

FIGURE FOR EXERCISE 58

59. *Big saver.* Suppose you deposit one cent into your piggy bank on the first day of December and, on each day of December after that, you deposit twice as much as on the previous day. How much will you have in the bank after the last deposit?

60. *Big family.* Consider yourself, your parents, your grandparents, your great-grandparents, your great-great-grandparents, and so on, back to your grandparents with the word "great" used in front 40 times. What is the total number of people you are considering?

61. *Total economic impact.* In Exercise 43 of Section 13.1 we described a factory that spends $1 million annually in a community in which 80% of the money received is respent in the community. Economists assume the money is respent again and again at the 80% rate. The total economic impact of the factory is the total of all of this spending. Find an approximation for the total by using the formula for the sum of an infinite geometric series with a rate of 80%.

62. *Less impact.* Repeat Exercise 61, assuming money is respent again and again at the 50% rate.

GETTING MORE INVOLVED

63. *Discussion.* Which of the following sequences is not a geometric sequence? Explain your answer.
   a) $1, 2, 4, \ldots$
   b) $0.1, 0.01, 0.001, \ldots$
   c) $-1, 2, -4, \ldots$
   d) $2, 4, 6, \ldots$

64. *Discussion.* The repeating decimal number $0.44444\ldots$ can be written as

$$\frac{4}{10} + \frac{4}{100} + \frac{4}{1000} + \cdots,$$

an infinite geometric series. Find the sum of this geometric series.

65. *Discussion.* Write the repeating decimal number $0.24242424\ldots$ as an infinite geometric series. Find the sum of the geometric series.

In This Section

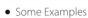

- Some Examples
- Obtaining the Coefficients
- The Binomial Theorem

 13.5 **BINOMIAL EXPANSIONS**

In Chapter 5 you learned how to square a binomial. In this section you will study higher powers of binomials.

Some Examples

We know that $(x + y)^2 = x^2 + 2xy + y^2$. To find $(x + y)^3$, we multiply $(x + y)^2$ by $x + y$:

$$(x + y)^3 = (x^2 + 2xy + y^2)(x + y)$$
$$= (x^2 + 2xy + y^2)x + (x^2 + 2xy + y^2)y$$
$$= x^3 + 2x^2y + xy^2 + x^2y + 2xy^2 + y^3$$
$$= x^3 + 3x^2y + 3xy^2 + y^3$$

The sum $x^3 + 3x^2y + 3xy^2 + y^3$ is called the **binomial expansion** of $(x + y)^3$. If we again multiply by $x + y$, we will get the binomial expansion of $(x + y)^4$. This method is rather tedious. However, if we examine these expansions, we can find a pattern and learn how to find binomial expansions without multiplying.

Consider the following binomial expansions:

$$(x + y)^0 = 1$$
$$(x + y)^1 = x + y$$
$$(x + y)^2 = x^2 + 2xy + y^2$$
$$(x + y)^3 = x^3 + 3x^2y + 3xy^2 + y^3$$
$$(x + y)^4 = x^4 + 4x^3y + 6x^2y^2 + 4xy^3 + y^4$$
$$(x + y)^5 = x^5 + 5x^4y + 10x^3y^2 + 10x^2y^3 + 5xy^4 + y^5$$

Observe that the exponents on the variable x are decreasing, whereas the exponents on the variable y are increasing, as we read from left to right. Also notice that the sum of the exponents in each term is the same for that entire line. For instance, in the fourth expansion the terms x^4, x^3y, x^2y^2, xy^3, and y^4 all have exponents with a sum of 4. If we continue the pattern, the expansion of $(x + y)^6$ will have seven terms containing x^6, x^5y, x^4y^2, x^3y^3, x^2y^4, xy^5, and y^6. Now we must find the pattern for the coefficients of these terms.

Obtaining the Coefficients

If we write out only the coefficients of the expansions that we already have, we can easily see a pattern. This triangular array of coefficients for the binomial expansions is called **Pascal's triangle.**

```
          1                    (x + y)^0 = 1
        1   1                  (x + y)^1 = 1x + 1y
      1   2   1                (x + y)^2 = 1x^2 + 2xy + 1y^2
    1   3   3   1              (x + y)^3 = 1x^3 + 3x^2y + 3xy^2 + 1y^3
  1   4   6   4   1            (x + y)^4 = 1x^4 + 4x^3y + 6x^2y^2 + 4xy^3 + 1y^4
1   5  10  10   5   1          Coefficients in (x + y)^5
```

Notice that each line starts and ends with a 1 and that each entry of a line is the sum of the two entries above it in the previous line. For instance, $4 = 3 + 1$, and $10 = 6 + 4$. Following this pattern, the sixth and seventh lines of coefficients are

```
   1    6   15    20    15    6    1
 1    7   21    35    35    21   7    1
```

Pascal's triangle gives us an easy way to get the coefficients for the binomial expansion with small powers, but it is impractical for larger powers. For larger powers we use a formula involving **factorial notation.**

$n!$ (n factorial)

If n is a positive integer, $n!$ (read "n factorial") is defined to be the product of all of the positive integers from 1 through n.

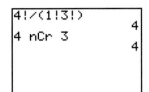
For example, $3! = 3 \cdot 2 \cdot 1 = 6$, and $5! = 5 \cdot 4 \cdot 3 \cdot 2 \cdot 1 = 120$. We also define $0!$ to be 1.

Before we state a general formula, consider how the coefficients for $(x + y)^4$ are found by using factorials:

$$\frac{4!}{4!\,0!} = \frac{4 \cdot 3 \cdot 2 \cdot 1}{4 \cdot 3 \cdot 2 \cdot 1 \cdot 1} = 1 \qquad \text{Coefficient of } x^4 \text{ (or } x^4 y^0\text{)}$$

$$\frac{4!}{3!\,1!} = \frac{4 \cdot 3 \cdot 2 \cdot 1}{3 \cdot 2 \cdot 1 \cdot 1} = 4 \qquad \text{Coefficient of } 4x^3 y$$

$$\frac{4!}{2!\,2!} = \frac{4 \cdot 3 \cdot 2 \cdot 1}{2 \cdot 1 \cdot 2 \cdot 1} = 6 \qquad \text{Coefficient of } 6x^2 y^2$$

$$\frac{4!}{1!\,3!} = \frac{4 \cdot 3 \cdot 2 \cdot 1}{1 \cdot 3 \cdot 2 \cdot 1} = 4 \qquad \text{Coefficient of } 4xy^3$$

$$\frac{4!}{0!\,4!} = \frac{4 \cdot 3 \cdot 2 \cdot 1}{1 \cdot 4 \cdot 3 \cdot 2 \cdot 1} = 1 \qquad \text{Coefficient of } y^4 \text{ (or } x^0 y^4\text{)}$$

Note that each expression has $4!$ in the numerator, with factorials in the denominator corresponding to the exponents on x and y.

The Binomial Theorem

We now summarize these ideas in the **binomial theorem.**

The Binomial Theorem

In the expansion of $(x + y)^n$ for a positive integer n, there are $n + 1$ terms, given by the following formula:

$$(x + y)^n = \frac{n!}{n!\,0!}x^n + \frac{n!}{(n - 1)!\,1!}x^{n-1}y + \frac{n!}{(n - 2)!\,2!}x^{n-2}y^2 + \cdots + \frac{n!}{0!\,n!}y^n$$

The notation $\binom{n}{r}$ is often used in place of $\frac{n!}{(n - r)!r!}$ in the binomial expansion. Using this notation, we write the expansion as

$$(x + y)^n = \binom{n}{0}x^n + \binom{n}{1}x^{n-1}y + \binom{n}{2}x^{n-2}y^2 + \cdots + \binom{n}{n}y^n.$$

Another notation for $\frac{n!}{(n - r)!r!}$ is $_nC_r$. Using this notation, we have

$$(x + y)^n = {_nC_0}\,x^n + {_nC_1}\,x^{n-1}y + {_nC_2}\,x^{n-2}y^2 + \cdots + {_nC_n}\,y^n.$$

E X A M P L E   1

Calculating the binomial coefficients

Evaluate each expression.

a) $\dfrac{7!}{4!\,3!}$

b) $\dfrac{10!}{8!\,2!}$

Solution

a) $\dfrac{7!}{4!\,3!} = \dfrac{7 \cdot 6 \cdot 5 \cdot 4 \cdot 3 \cdot 2 \cdot 1}{4 \cdot 3 \cdot 2 \cdot 1 \cdot 3 \cdot 2 \cdot 1} = \dfrac{7 \cdot 6 \cdot 5}{3 \cdot 2 \cdot 1} = 35$

b) $\dfrac{10!}{8!\,2!} = \dfrac{10 \cdot 9 \cdot 8 \cdot 7 \cdot 6 \cdot 5 \cdot 4 \cdot 3 \cdot 2 \cdot 1}{8 \cdot 7 \cdot 6 \cdot 5 \cdot 4 \cdot 3 \cdot 2 \cdot 1 \cdot 2 \cdot 1} = \dfrac{10 \cdot 9}{2 \cdot 1} = 45$ ■

E X A M P L E   2

Using the binomial theorem

Write out the first three terms of $(x + y)^9$.

Solution

$$(x + y)^9 = \frac{9!}{9!\,0!}x^9 + \frac{9!}{8!\,1!}x^8 y + \frac{9!}{7!\,2!}x^7 y^2 + \cdots = x^9 + 9x^8 y + 36x^7 y^2 + \cdots$$ ■

E X A M P L E   3

Using the binomial theorem

Write the binomial expansion for $(x^2 - 2a)^5$.

Solution

We expand a difference by writing it as a sum and using the binomial theorem:

$$(x^2 - 2a)^5 = (x^2 + (-2a))^5$$

$$= \frac{5!}{5!\,0!}(x^2)^5 + \frac{5!}{4!\,1!}(x^2)^4(-2a)^1 + \frac{5!}{3!\,2!}(x^2)^3(-2a)^2 + \frac{5!}{2!\,3!}(x^2)^2(-2a)^3$$

$$+ \frac{5!}{1!\,4!}(x^2)(-2a)^4 + \frac{5!}{0!\,5!}(-2a)^5$$

$$= x^{10} - 10x^8 a + 40x^6 a^2 - 80x^4 a^3 + 80x^2 a^4 - 32a^5$$ ■

E X A M P L E   4

Finding a specific term

Find the fourth term of the expansion of $(a + b)^{12}$.

Calculator Close-Up

Because $_nC_r = \dfrac{n!}{(n - r)!\,r!}$, we have

$_{12}C_9 = \dfrac{12!}{3!\,9!}$ and $_{12}C_3 = \dfrac{12!}{9!\,3!}.$

So there is more than one way to compute $12!/(9!3!)$:

```
12!/(9!3!)
              220
12 nCr 9
              220
12 nCr 3
              220
```

Solution

The variables in the first term are $a^{12}b^0$, those in the second term are $a^{11}b^1$, those in the third term are $a^{10}b^2$, and those in the fourth term are $a^9 b^3$. So

$$\frac{12!}{9!\,3!}a^9 b^3 = 220a^9 b^3.$$

The fourth term is $220a^9 b^3$.   ■

Using the ideas of Example 4, we can write a formula for any term of a binomial expansion.

Formula for the *k*th Term of $(x + y)^n$

For k ranging from 1 to $n + 1$, the kth term of the expansion of $(x + y)^n$ is given by the formula

$$\frac{n!}{(n - k + 1)!(k - 1)!}x^{n-k+1}y^{k-1}.$$

E X A M P L E   5

Finding a specific term

Find the sixth term of the expansion of $(a^2 - 2b)^7$.

Solution

Use the formula for the kth term with $k = 6$ and $n = 7$:

$$\frac{7!}{(7 - 6 + 1)!(6 - 1)!}(a^2)^2(-2b)^5 = 21a^4(-32b^5) = -672a^4b^5 \quad \blacksquare$$

We can think of the binomial expansion as a finite series. Using summation notation, we can write the binomial theorem as follows.

> **The Binomial Theorem (Using Summation Notation)**
>
> For any positive integer n,
>
> $$(x + y)^n = \sum_{i=0}^{n} \frac{n!}{(n - i)!\,i!}x^{n-i}y^i \qquad \text{or} \qquad (x + y)^n = \sum_{i=0}^{n} \binom{n}{i}x^{n-i}y^i.$$

E X A M P L E   6

Using summation notation

Write $(a + b)^5$ using summation notation.

Solution

Use $n = 5$ in the binomial theorem:

$$(a + b)^5 = \sum_{i=0}^{5} \frac{5!}{(5 - i)!\,i!}a^{5-i}b^i \quad \blacksquare$$

WARM-UPS

True or false? Explain your answer.

1. There are 12 terms in the expansion of $(a + b)^{12}$.
2. The seventh term of $(a + b)^{12}$ is a multiple of a^5b^7.
3. For all values of x, $(x + 2)^5 = x^5 + 32$.
4. In the expansion of $(x - 5)^8$ the signs of the terms alternate.
5. The eighth line of Pascal's triangle is

   1 8 28 56 70 56 28 8 1.

6. The sum of the coefficients in the expansion of $(a + b)^4$ is 2^4.
7. $(a + b)^3 = \sum_{i=0}^{3} \frac{3!}{(3 - i)!\,i!}a^{3-i}b^i$
8. The sum of the coefficients in the expansion of $(a + b)^n$ is 2^n.
9. $0! = 1!$
10. $\dfrac{7!}{5!2!} = 21$

13.5   EXERCISES

Reading and Writing   *After reading this section, write out the answers to these questions. Use complete sentences.*

1. What is a binomial expansion?

2. What is Pascal's triangle and how do you make it?

3. What does $n!$ mean?

4. What is the binomial theorem?

Evaluate each expression. See Example 1.

5. $\dfrac{5!}{2!\,3!}$

6. $\dfrac{6!}{5!\,1!}$

7. $\dfrac{8!}{5!\,3!}$

8. $\dfrac{9!}{2!\,7!}$

Use the binomial theorem to expand each binomial. See Examples 2 and 3.

9. $(r + t)^5$

10. $(r + t)^6$

11. $(m - n)^3$

12. $(m - n)^4$

13. $(x + 2a)^3$

14. $(a + 3b)^4$

15. $(x^2 - 2)^4$

16. $(x^2 - a^2)^5$

17. $(x - 1)^7$

18. $(x + 1)^6$

Write out the first four terms in the expansion of each binomial. See Examples 2 and 3.

19. $(a - 3b)^{12}$

20. $(x - 2y)^{10}$

21. $(x^2 + 5)^9$

22. $(x^2 + 1)^{20}$

23. $(x - 1)^{22}$

24. $(2x - 1)^8$

25. $\left(\dfrac{x}{2} + \dfrac{y}{3}\right)^{10}$

26. $\left(\dfrac{a}{2} + \dfrac{b}{5}\right)^8$

Find the indicated term of the binomial expansion. See Examples 4 and 5.

27. $(a + w)^{13}$, 6th term

28. $(m + n)^{12}$, 7th term

29. $(m - n)^{16}$, 8th term

30. $(a - b)^{14}$, 6th term

31. $(x + 2y)^8$, 4th term

32. $(3a + b)^7$, 4th term

33. $(2a^2 - b)^{20}$, 7th term

34. $(a^2 - w^2)^{12}$, 5th term

Write each expansion using summation notation. See Example 6.

35. $(a + m)^8$

36. $(z + w)^{13}$

37. $(a - 2x)^5$

38. $(w - 3m)^7$

GETTING MORE INVOLVED

39. **Discussion.** Find the trinomial expansion for $(a + b + c)^3$ by using $x = a$ and $y = b + c$ in the binomial theorem.

40. **Discussion.** What problem do you encounter when trying to find the fourth term in the binomial expansion for $(x + y)^{120}$? How can you overcome this problem? Find the fifth term in the binomial expansion for $(x - 2y)^{100}$.

COLLABORATIVE ACTIVITIES

A Sequence of Investments can be Series(ous)

Roberto, his brother Horatio, and his sister Genevieve each have a three-year-old child. Each would like to save money for his or her child's college expenses and decide to set aside $5 each week to the cause. Horatio plans to use his $5 to buy lottery tickets each week for the next 15 years, hoping to win and use the money for his child's college expenses. Genevieve plans to invest her $5 in a mutual fund and Roberto plans to invest in an education Individual Retirement Account (IRA).

1. Write the first 10 terms of the sequence in which the nth term is the total amount that Horatio has spent after n weeks. What type of sequence is this? How much money will Horatio spend on lottery tickets after 15 years? Assume that there are 52 weeks per year.

2. For every $5.00 Horatio spends each week on lottery tickets, his average winnings are $3.00 per week. He decides to buy a new certificate of deposit (CD) with his winnings at the end of each year. How much money will he put into a CD each year? At the end of the 15th year he has purchased 15 CDs.

Grouping: 2 to 4 students per group

Topic: Sequences and series

Assume his CDs pay 3.75% annual interest compounded annually. Write a sequence of 15 terms that gives the amounts of each of the 15 CDs at the end of the 15th year. What type of sequence is this? Find the sum of the 15 terms.

3. Roberto sets aside $5 per week and pays into his IRA at the end of each quarter. The education IRA pays 4.5% annual interest compounded quarterly. Assume that there are 13 weeks per quarter. Determine the amount Roberto will have at the end of the 15 years.

4. Genevieve sets aside $5 per week and pays into her mutual fund at the end of each year. If her mutual fund pays 7.375% annual interest compounded annually, then what amount will Genevieve have at the end of the 15 years?

5. Discuss in your groups the amount of risk in each of the investment strategies. Do Horatio's chances increase the longer he buys lottery tickets? What should he do if he "wins big"? Are Genevieve's and Roberto's investment strategies sure things?

WRAP-UP   CHAPTER 13

SUMMARY

Sequences and Series

		Examples
Sequence	Finite—A function whose domain is the set of positive integers less than or equal to a fixed positive integer	3, 5, 7, 9, 11 $a_n = 2n + 1$ $1 \le n \le 5$
	Infinite—A function whose domain is the set of positive integers	2, 4, 6, 8, . . . $a_n = 2n$
Series	The indicated sum of a sequence	$2 + 4 + 6 + \cdots + 50$
Summation notation	$\sum_{i=1}^{n} a_i = a_1 + a_2 + a_3 + \cdots + a_n$	$\sum_{i=1}^{25} 2i = 2 + 4 + \cdots + 50$

Arithmetic Sequences and Series

		Examples
Arithmetic sequence	Each term after the first is obtained by adding a fixed amount to the previous term.	6, 11, 16, 21, . . . Fixed amount, d, is 5.

*n*th term	The *n*th term of an arithmetic sequence is $a_n = a_1 + (n-1)d$.	If $a_1 = 6$ and $d = 5$, then $a_n = 6 + (n-1)5$.
Arithmetic series	The sum of an arithmetic sequence	$6 + 11 + 16 + 21$
Sum of first *n* terms	$S_n = \dfrac{n}{2}(a_1 + a_n)$	$S_4 = \dfrac{4}{2}(6 + 21) = 54$

Geometric Sequences and Series | | **Examples**

Geometric sequence	Each term after the first is obtained by multiplying the preceding term by a constant.	$2, 6, 18, 54, \ldots$ Constant, r, is 3.
*n*th term	The *n*th term of a geometric sequence is $$a_n = a_1 r^{n-1}.$$	$a_1 = 2, r = 3$ $a_n = 2 \cdot 3^{n-1}$
Geometric series (finite)	The indicated sum of a finite geometric sequence. $a_1 + a_1 r + a_1 r^2 + \cdots + a_1 r^{n-1}$	$2 + 6 + 18 + 54 + 162$
Sum of first *n* terms	$S_n = \dfrac{a_1(1 - r^n)}{1 - r}$	$a_1 = 2, r = 3, n = 5$ $S_5 = \dfrac{2(1 - 3^5)}{1 - 3} = 242$
Geometric series (infinite)	$a_1 + a_1 r + a_1 r^2 + a_1 r^3 + \cdots$	$8 + 4 + 2 + 1 + \dfrac{1}{2} + \cdots$
Sum of an infinite geometric series	$S = \dfrac{a_1}{1 - r}$, provided that $|r| < 1$	$a_1 = 8, r = \dfrac{1}{2}$ $S = \dfrac{8}{1 - \dfrac{1}{2}} = 16$
Factorial notation	The notation $n!$ represents the product of the positive integers from 1 through n.	$5! = 5 \cdot 4 \cdot 3 \cdot 2 \cdot 1 = 120$
Binomial theorem	$(x + y)^n = \dfrac{n!}{n!\,0!}x^n + \dfrac{n!}{(n-1)!\,1!}x^{n-1}y$ $+ \dfrac{n!}{(n-2)!\,2!}x^{n-2}y^2 + \cdots + \dfrac{n!}{0!\,n!}y^n$ Using summation notation: $(x + y)^n = \displaystyle\sum_{i=0}^{n} \dfrac{n!}{(n-i)!\,i!}x^{n-i}y^i = \sum_{i=0}^{n}\binom{n}{i}x^{n-i}y^i$	$(x + y)^3 = x^3 + 3x^2 y$ $+ 3xy^2 + y^3$
*k*th term of $(x + y)^n$	$\dfrac{n!}{(n-k+1)!(k-1)!}x^{n-k+1}y^{k-1}$	Third term of $(a + b)^{10}$ is $\dfrac{10!}{8!\,2!}a^8 b^2 = 45a^8 b^2$.

ENRICHING YOUR MATHEMATICAL WORD POWER

For each mathematical term, choose the correct meaning.

1. **sequence**
   a. a list of numbers
   b. a procedure for getting the answer
   c. events that happen in order
   d. a linear function

2. **finite sequence**
   a. a short sequence
   b. a sequence of whole numbers
   c. a function whose domain is the set of positive integers
   d. a function whose domain is the set of positive integers less than or equal to a fixed positive integer

3. **infinite sequence**
   a. a short sequence
   b. a sequence of whole numbers
   c. a function whose domain is the set of positive integers
   d. a function whose domain is the set of positive integers less than or equal to a fixed positive integer

4. **series**
   a. a special sequence
   b. the indicated sum of the terms of a sequence
   c. a sequence of positive numbers
   d. a show with many episodes

5. **arithmetic sequence**
   a. a sequence in which each term after the first is obtained by adding a fixed amount to the previous term
   b. a sequence of fractions
   c. a sequence found in arithmetic
   d. a finite sequence

6. **geometric sequence**
   a. a sequence of rectangles
   b. a sequence of geometric formulas
   c. a sequence in which each term after the first is obtained by multiplying the preceding term by a constant
   d. a sequence in which the terms are geometric

7. **geometric series**
   a. a series of geometric shapes
   b. the indicated sum of an arithmetic sequence
   c. a series of ratios
   d. the indicated sum of a geometric sequence

8. **binomial expansion**
   a. the trinomial obtained when a binomial is stretched
   b. the expression obtained from raising a binomial to a whole number power
   c. the coefficients of a binomial
   d. the various powers of a binomial

9. **Pascal's triangle**
   a. an equilateral triangle
   b. a triangle formed by the graphs of three linear equations
   c. the right triangle in the Pythagorean theorem
   d. a triangular array of coefficients for the binomial expansions

10. **$n!$**
   a. the product of the positive integers from 1 through n
   b. the binomial coefficients
   c. the n vertices of Pascal's triangle
   d. 3.141592654

REVIEW EXERCISES

13.1 *List all terms of each finite sequence.*

1. $a_n = n^3$ for $1 \le n \le 5$

2. $b_n = (n-1)^4$ for $1 \le n \le 4$

3. $c_n = (-1)^n(2n-3)$ for $1 \le n \le 6$

4. $d_n = (-1)^{n-1}(3-n)$ for $1 \le n \le 7$

Write the first three terms of the infinite sequence whose nth term is given.

5. $a_n = -\dfrac{1}{n}$

6. $b_n = \dfrac{(-1)^n}{n^2}$

7. $b_n = \dfrac{(-1)^{2n}}{2n+1}$

8. $a_n = \dfrac{-1}{2n-3}$

9. $c_n = \log_2(2^{n+3})$

10. $c_n = \ln(e^{2n})$

13.2 *Find the sum of each series.*

11. $\displaystyle\sum_{i=1}^{3} i^3$

12. $\displaystyle\sum_{i=0}^{4} 6$

13. $\displaystyle\sum_{n=1}^{5} n(n-1)$

14. $\displaystyle\sum_{j=0}^{3} (-2)^j$

Write each series in summation notation. Use the index i, and let i begin at 1.

15. $\dfrac{1}{4} + \dfrac{1}{6} + \dfrac{1}{8} + \cdots$

16. $\dfrac{1}{3} + \dfrac{1}{4} + \dfrac{1}{5} + \cdots$

17. $0 + 1 + 4 + 9 + 16 + \cdots$

18. $-1 + 2 - 3 + 4 - 5 + 6 - \cdots$

19. $x_1 - x_2 + x_3 - x_4 + \cdots$

20. $-x^2 + x^3 - x^4 + x^5 - \cdots$

13.3 *Write the first four terms of the arithmetic sequence with the given nth term.*

21. $a_n = 6 + (n - 1)5$

22. $a_n = -7 + (n - 1)4$

23. $a_n = -20 + (n - 1)(-2)$

24. $a_n = 10 + (n - 1)(-2.5)$

25. $a_n = 1000n + 2000$

26. $a_n = -500n + 5000$

Write a formula for the nth term of each arithmetic sequence.

27. $\dfrac{1}{3}, \dfrac{2}{3}, 1, \dfrac{4}{3}, \ldots$

28. $10, 6, 2, -2, \ldots$

29. $2, 4, 6, 8, \ldots$

30. $20, 10, 0, -10, \ldots$

Find the sum of each arithmetic series.

31. $1 + 2 + 3 + \cdots + 24$

32. $-5 + (-2) + 1 + 4 + \cdots + 34$

33. $\dfrac{1}{6} + \dfrac{1}{2} + \dfrac{5}{6} + \dfrac{7}{6} + \cdots + \dfrac{11}{2}$

34. $-3 - 6 - 9 - 12 - \cdots - 36$

35. $\displaystyle\sum_{i=1}^{7} (2i - 3)$

36. $\displaystyle\sum_{i=1}^{6} [12 + (i - 1)5]$

13.4 *Write the first four terms of the geometric sequence with the given nth term.*

37. $a_n = 3\left(\dfrac{1}{2}\right)^{n-1}$

38. $a_n = 6\left(-\dfrac{1}{3}\right)^{n}$

39. $a_n = 2^{1-n}$

40. $a_n = 5(10)^{n-1}$

41. $a_n = 23(10)^{-2n}$

42. $a_n = 4(10)^{-n}$

Write a formula for the nth term of each geometric sequence.

43. $\dfrac{1}{2}, 3, 18, \ldots$

44. $-6, 2, -\dfrac{2}{3}, \dfrac{2}{9}, \ldots$

45. $\dfrac{7}{10}, \dfrac{7}{100}, \dfrac{7}{1000}, \ldots$

46. $2, 2x, 2x^2, 2x^3, \ldots$

Find the sum of each geometric series.

47. $\dfrac{1}{3} + \dfrac{1}{9} + \dfrac{1}{27} + \dfrac{1}{81}$

48. $2 + 4 + 8 + 16 + \cdots + 512$

49. $\displaystyle\sum_{i=1}^{10} 3(10)^{-i}$

50. $\displaystyle\sum_{i=1}^{5} (0.1)^{i}$

51. $\dfrac{1}{4} + \dfrac{1}{12} + \dfrac{1}{36} + \dfrac{1}{108} + \cdots$

52. $12 + (-6) + 3 + \left(-\dfrac{3}{2}\right) + \cdots$

53. $\displaystyle\sum_{i=1}^{\infty} 18\left(\dfrac{2}{3}\right)^{i-1}$

54. $\displaystyle\sum_{i=1}^{\infty} 9(0.1)^{i}$

13.5 *Use the binomial theorem to expand each binomial.*

55. $(m + n)^5$

56. $(2m - y)^4$

57. $(a^2 - 3b)^3$

58. $\left(\dfrac{x}{2} + 2a\right)^5$

Find the indicated term of the binomial expansion.

59. $(x + y)^{12}$, 5th term

60. $(x - 2y)^9$, 5th term

61. $(2a - b)^{14}$, 3rd term

62. $(a + b)^{10}$, 4th term

Write each expression in summation notation.

63. $(a + w)^7$

64. $(m - 3y)^9$

MISCELLANEOUS

Identify each sequence as an arithmetic sequence, a geometric sequence, or neither.

65. $1, 3, 6, 10, 15, \ldots$

66. $9, 12, 16, \dfrac{64}{3}, \ldots$

67. 9, 12, 15, 18, . . .

68. 2, 4, 8, 16, . . .

69. 0, 2, 4, 6, 8, . . .

70. 0, 3, 9, 27, 81, . . .

Solve each problem.

71. Find the common ratio for the geometric sequence with first term 6 and fourth term $\frac{1}{30}$.

72. Find the common difference for an arithmetic sequence with first term 6 and fourth term 36.

73. Write out all of the terms of the series

$$\sum_{i=1}^{5} \frac{(-1)^i}{i!}.$$

74. Write out the first eight rows of Pascal's triangle.

75. Write out all of the terms of the series

$$\sum_{i=0}^{5} \frac{5!}{(5-i)!\,i!} a^{5-i} b^i.$$

76. Write out all of the terms of the series

$$\sum_{i=0}^{8} \frac{8!}{(8-i)!\,i!} x^{8-i} y^i.$$

77. How many terms are there in the expansion of $(a+b)^{25}$?

78. Calculate $\frac{12!}{8!4!}$.

79. If $3000 is deposited at the beginning of each year for 16 years into an account paying 10% compounded annually, then what is the value of the annuity at the end of the 16th year?

80. If $3000 is deposited at the beginning of each year for 8 years into an account paying 10% compounded annually, then what is the value of the annuity at the end of the eighth year? How does the value of the annuity in this exercise compare to that of Exercise 79?

81. If one deposit of $3000 is made into an account paying 10% compounded annually, then how much will be in the account at the end of 16 years? Note that a single deposit is not an annuity.

CHAPTER 13 TEST

List the first four terms of the sequence whose nth term is given.

1. $a_n = -10 + (n-1)6$

2. $a_n = 5(0.1)^{n-1}$

3. $a_n = \frac{(-1)^n}{n!}$

4. $a_n = \frac{2n-1}{n^2}$

Write a formula for the nth term of each sequence.

5. 7, 4, 1, −2, . . .

6. $-25, 5, -1, \frac{1}{5}, \ldots$

7. 2, −4, 6, −8, 10, −12, . . .

8. 1, 4, 9, 16, 25, . . .

Write out all of the terms of each series.

9. $\sum_{i=1}^{5} (2i+3)$

10. $\sum_{i=1}^{6} 5(2)^{i-1}$

11. $\sum_{i=0}^{4} \frac{4!}{(4-i)!\,i!} m^{4-i} q^i$

Find the sum of each series.

12. $\sum_{i=1}^{20} (6+3i)$

13. $\sum_{i=1}^{5} 10 \left(\frac{1}{2}\right)^{i-1}$

14. $\sum_{i=1}^{\infty} 0.35(0.93)^{i-1}$

15. $2 + 4 + 6 + \cdots + 200$

16. $\frac{1}{4} + \frac{1}{8} + \frac{1}{16} + \cdots$

17. $2 + 1 + \frac{1}{2} + \frac{1}{4} + \cdots + \frac{1}{128}$

Solve each problem.

18. Find the common ratio for the geometric sequence that has first term 3 and fifth term 48.

19. Find the common difference for the arithmetic sequence that has first term 1 and twelfth term 122.

20. Find the fifth term in the expansion of $(r-t)^{15}$.

21. Find the fourth term in the expansion of $(a^2 - 2b)^8$.

22. If $800 is deposited at the beginning of each year for 25 years into an account earning 10% compounded annually, then what is the value of this annuity at the end of the 25th year?

Let $f(x) = x^2 - 3$, $g(x) = 2x - 1$, $h(x) = 2^x$, and $m(x) = \log_2(x)$.
Find the following.

1. $f(3)$

2. $f(n)$

3. $f(x + h)$

4. $f(x) - g(x)$

5. $g(f(3))$

6. $(f \circ g)(2)$

7. $m(16)$

8. $(h \circ m)(32)$

9. $h(-1)$

10. $h^{-1}(8)$

11. $m^{-1}(0)$

12. $(m \circ h)(x)$

Solve each variation problem.

13. If y varies directly as x, and $y = -6$ when $x = 4$, find y
when $x = 9$.

14. If a varies inversely as b, and $a = 2$ when $b = -4$, find a
when $b = 3$.

15. If y varies directly as w and inversely as t, and $y = 16$ when
$w = 3$ and $t = -4$, find y when $w = 2$ and $t = 3$.

16. If y varies jointly as h and the square of r, and $y = 12$ when
$h = 2$ and $r = 3$, find y when $h = 6$ and $r = 2$.

Sketch the graph of each inequality or system of inequalities.

17. $x > 3$ and $x + y < 0$

18. $|x - y| \geq 2$

19. $y < -2x + 3$ and $y > 2^x$

20. $|y + 2x| < 1$

21. $x^2 + y^2 < 4$

22. $x^2 - y^2 < 1$

23. $y < \log_2(x)$

24. $x^2 + 2y < 4$

25. $\dfrac{x^2}{4} + \dfrac{y^2}{9} < 1$ and $y > x^2$

Perform the indicated operation and simplify. Write answers with positive exponents.

26. $\dfrac{a}{b} + \dfrac{b}{a}$

27. $1 - \dfrac{3}{y}$

28. $\dfrac{x-2}{x^2-9} - \dfrac{x-4}{x^2-2x-3}$

29. $\dfrac{x^2-16}{2x+8} \cdot \dfrac{4x^2+16x+64}{x^3-16}$

30. $\dfrac{(a^2b)^3}{(ab^2)^4} \cdot \dfrac{ab^3}{a^{-4}b^2}$

31. $\dfrac{x^2y}{(xy)^3} \div \dfrac{xy^2}{x^2y^4}$

Simplify.

32. $8^{2/3}$

33. $16^{-5/4}$

34. $-4^{1/2}$

35. $27^{-2/3}$

36. -2^{-3}

37. $2^{-3/5} \cdot 2^{-7/5}$

38. $5^{-2/3} \div 5^{1/3}$

39. $(9^{1/2} + 4^{1/2})^2$

Solve.

40. ***Predicting heights of preschoolers.*** A popular model in pediatrics for predicting the height of preschoolers is the JENNS model. According to this model, if $h(x)$ is the height [in centimeters (cm)] at age x (in years) for $0.25 \leq x \leq 6$, then

$$h(x) = 79.041 + 6.39x - e^{(3.261-0.993x)}.$$

a) Find the predicted height in inches for a child of age 4 years, 3 months.

b) If you have a graphing calculator, graph the function as shown in the accompanying figure.

c) Use your graphing calculator to find the age to the nearest tenth of a year for a child who has a height of 80 cm.

FIGURE FOR EXERCISE 40

Counting and Probability

otteries and gaming are as old as history records. Homer described
how Agamemnon had his soldiers cast lots to see who would face
Hector. In the Bible, Moses divided the lands among the tribes by
casting lots.

Today 36 of the 50 states have lotteries and they are prosperous.
Nationwide, state-run lotteries generate $26.6 billion in income
annually—sales minus commissions. Available proceeds—money left
over for the states after paying out prizes and paying for administration of
the games totals $10.1 billion.

But what are your chances of winning a lottery? In this chapter we
will study the basic ideas of counting and probability. We will find the
probability of winning a lottery when we do Exercises 43 and 44 in
Section 14.3.

14.1 COUNTING AND PERMUTATIONS

Although the main topic of this chapter is probability, we first study counting. We all know how to count, but here we will learn methods for counting the number of ways in which a sequence of events can occur.

The Fundamental Counting Principle

A new car is available in 3 different colors with 2 optional engines, V6 or V8. For example, you can get a red car with a V6 engine or a red car with a V8 engine. If the car comes in red, blue, or gray, then how many different cars are available? We can make a diagram showing all of the different possibilities. See Fig. 14.1. This diagram is called a **tree diagram.** Considering only color and engine type, we count 6 different cars that are available from the tree diagram. Of course, we can obtain 6 by multiplying 3 and 2. This example illustrates the fundamental counting principle.

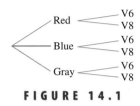

FIGURE 14.1

> #### Fundamental Counting Principle
>
> If event A has m different outcomes and event B has n different outcomes, then there are mn different ways for events A and B to occur.

The fundamental counting principle can also be used for more than two events.

EXAMPLE 1

Helpful Hint

When counting the number of different possibilities, it must be clear what "different" means. In one problem we might count a hamburger and fries differently from fries and a hamburger because we are interested in the order in which they occur. In another problem we will consider them as the same because they are the same meal.

The fundamental counting principle

At Windy's Hamburger Palace you can get a single, double, or triple burger. You also have a choice of whether to include pickles, mustard, ketchup, onions, tomatoes, lettuce, or cheese. How many different hamburgers are available at Windy's?

Solution

There are 3 outcomes to the event of choosing the amount of meat. For each of the condiments there are 2 outcomes: whether or not to include it. So the number of different hamburgers is $3 \cdot 2 \cdot 2 \cdot 2 \cdot 2 \cdot 2 \cdot 2 \cdot 2 = 384$. ∎

EXAMPLE 2

The fundamental counting principle

How many different license plates are possible if each plate consists of 2 letters followed by a 4-digit number? Assume repetitions in the letters or numbers are allowed and any of the 10 digits may be used in each place of the 4-digit number.

Solution

Since there are 26 choices for each of the 2 letters and 10 choices for each of the numbers, by the fundamental counting principle the number of license plates is $26 \cdot 26 \cdot 10 \cdot 10 \cdot 10 \cdot 10 = 6{,}760{,}000$. ∎

Permutations

The number of ways in which an event can occur often depends on what has already occurred. In Examples 1 and 2 each choice was independent of the previous choices. In Example 3 we will count permutations in which the number of choices depends on what has already been chosen. A **permutation** is any ordering or arrangement of distinct objects in a linear manner.

E X A M P L E   3

Permutations of *n* objects

How many different ways are there for 10 people to stand in line to buy basketball tickets?

Solution

For the event of choosing the first person in line we have 10 outcomes. For the event of choosing the second person to put in line only 9 people are left, so we have only 9 outcomes. For the third person we have 8 outcomes, and so on. So the number of permutations of 10 people is $10 \cdot 9 \cdot 8 \cdot 7 \cdot 6 \cdot 5 \cdot 4 \cdot 3 \cdot 2 \cdot 1 = 10! = 3,628,800$. ∎

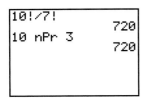
The number of arrangements of the 10 people in Example 3 is referred to as the number of permutations of 10 people taken 10 at a time, and we use the notation $P(10, 10)$ to represent this number. We have the following theorem.

> **Permutations of *n* Things *n* at a Time**
>
> The notation $P(n, n)$ represents the number of permutations of *n* things taken *n* at a time, and $P(n, n) = n!$.

Sometimes we are interested in permutations in which all of the objects are not used. For example, how many ways are there to fill the offices of president, vice-president, and treasurer in a club of 10 people, assuming no one holds more than one office? For the event of choosing the president there are 10 possible outcomes. Since no one can hold 2 offices, there are only 9 possibilities for vice-president, and only 8 possibilities for treasurer. So the number of ways to fill the offices is $10 \cdot 9 \cdot 8 = 720$. We say that the number of permutations of 10 people taken 3 at a time is 720. We use the notation $P(10, 3)$ to represent the number of permutations of 10 things taken 3 at a time. Notice that

$$P(10, 3) = \frac{10!}{7!} = \frac{\mathbf{10 \cdot 9 \cdot 8} \cdot 7 \cdot 6 \cdot 5 \cdot 4 \cdot 3 \cdot 2 \cdot 1}{7 \cdot 6 \cdot 5 \cdot 4 \cdot 3 \cdot 2 \cdot 1} = 10 \cdot 9 \cdot 8 = 720.$$

In general, we have the following theorem.

Study Tip

Be sure to ask your instructor what to expect on the final exam. Will it be written in the same format as the other tests? Will it be multiple choice? Are there any sample final exams available? Knowing what to expect will decrease your anxiety about the final exam.

> **Permutations of *n* Things *r* at a Time**
>
> The notation $P(n, r)$ represents the number of permutations of *n* things taken *r* at a time, and $P(n, r) = \frac{n!}{(n - r)!}$ for $0 \leq r \leq n$.

Even though we do not usually take *n* things 0 at a time, we allow 0 in the formula. For example,

$$P(8, 0) = \frac{8!}{8!} = 1 \qquad \text{and} \qquad P(0, 0) = \frac{0!}{0!} = \frac{1}{1} = 1.$$

EXAMPLE 4

Permutations of n things r at a time

Eight prize winners will be randomly selected from 25 people attending a sales meeting. There will be a first, second, third, fourth, fifth, sixth, seventh, and eighth prize, each prize being of lesser value than the one before it. In how many different ways can the prizes be awarded, assuming no one gets more than one prize?

Solution

The number of ways in which these prizes can be awarded is precisely the number of permutations of 25 things taken 8 at a time,

$$P(25, 8) = \frac{25!}{(25 - 8)!} = \frac{25!}{17!} = 25 \cdot 24 \cdot 23 \cdot 22 \cdot 21 \cdot 20 \cdot 19 \cdot 18$$
$$\approx 4.3609 \times 10^{10}.$$

■

WARM-UPS

True or false? Explain your answer.

1. If a manufacturer codes its products using a single letter followed by a single-digit number (0–9), then 36 different codes are available.

2. If a sorority name consists of 3 Greek letters chosen from the 24 letters in the Greek alphabet, with repetitions allowed, then $24 \cdot 23 \cdot 22$ different sorority names are possible.

3. If an outfit consists of a skirt, a blouse, and a hat and Mirna has 4 skirts, 5 blouses, and 4 hats, then she has 80 different outfits in her wardrobe.

4. The number of ways in which 4 people can line up for a group photo is 24.

5. $\frac{100!}{98!} = 9900$

6. $P(100, 98) = 9900$

7. The number of permutations of 5 things taken 2 at a time is 20.

8. $P(18, 0) = 1$

9. The number of different ways to mark the answers to a 10-question multiple-choice test in which each question has 5 choices is 10^5.

10. The number of different ways to mark the answers to this sequence of 10 Warm-up questions is 2^{10}.

14.1   EXERCISES

Reading and Writing   *After reading this section, write out the answers to these questions. Use complete sentences.*

1. What is a tree diagram?

2. What is the fundamental counting principle?

3. What is a permutation?

4. How many permutations are there for n things taken r at a time?

Solve each problem. See Examples 1 and 2.

5. A parcel delivery truck can take any one of 3 different roads from Clarksville to Leesville and any one of 4 different roads from Leesville to Jonesboro. How many different routes are available from Clarksville to Jonesboro?

6. A car can be ordered in any one of 8 different colors, with 3 different engine sizes, 2 different transmissions, 3 different body styles, 4 different interior designs, and 5 different stereos. How many different cars are available?

7. A poker hand consists of 5 cards drawn from a deck of 52. How many different poker hands are there consisting of an ace, king, queen, jack, and ten?

FIGURE FOR EXERCISE 7

8. A certain card game consists of 3 cards drawn from a poker deck of 52. How many different 3-card hands are there containing one heart, one diamond, and one club?

9. Wendy's Hamburgers once advertised that there were 256 different hamburgers available at Wendy's. This number was obtained by using the fundamental counting principle and considering whether to include each one of several different options on the burger. How many different optional items were used to get this number?

10. A pizza can be ordered with your choice of one of 4 different meats or no meat. You also have a choice of whether to include green peppers, onions, mushrooms,

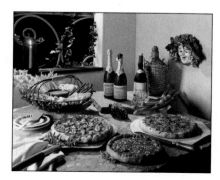

FIGURE FOR EXERCISE 10

anchovies, or black olives. How many different pizzas can be ordered?

Solve each problem. See Examples 3 and 4.

11. Randall has homework in mathematics, history, art, literature, and chemistry but cannot decide in which order to attack these subjects. How many different orders are possible?

12. Zita has packages to pick up at 8 different locations. How many different ways are there for her to pick up the packages?

13. Yesha has 12 schools to visit this week. In how many different ways can she pick a first, second, and third school to visit on Monday?

14. In how many ways can a history professor randomly assign exactly one A, and B, one C, one D, and six F's to a class of 10 students?

15. The program director for an independent television station has 34 one-hour shows available for Monday night prime time. How many different schedules are possible for the 7:00 to 10:00 P.M. time period?

16. A disc jockey must choose 8 songs from the top 40 to play in the next 30-minute segment of his show. How many different arrangements are possible for this segment?

Solve each counting problem.

17. How many different ways are there to mark the answers to a 20-question multiple-choice test in which each question has 4 possible answers?

18. A bookstore manager wants to make a window display that consists of a mathematics book, a history book, and an economics book in that order. He has 13 different mathematics books, 10 different history books, and 5 different economics books from which to choose. How many different displays are possible?

19. In how many ways can the 37 seats on a commuter flight be filled from the 39 people holding tickets?

20. If a couple has decided on 6 possible first names for their baby and 5 possible middle names, then how many ways are there for them to name their baby?

21. A developer builds houses with 3 different exterior styles. You have your choice of 3, 4, or 5 bedrooms, a fireplace, 2 or 3 baths, and 5 different kitchen designs. How many different houses are available?

22. How many different seven-digit phone numbers are available in Wentworth if the first 3 digits must be 286?

23. How many different seven-digit phone numbers are available in Creekside if the first digit cannot be a 0?

24. In how many different ways can a Mercedes, a Cadillac, and a Ford be awarded to 3 people chosen from the 9 finalists in a contest?

25. How many different ways are there to seat 7 students in a row?

FIGURE FOR EXERCISE 25

26. A supply boat must stop at 9 oil rigs in the Gulf of Mexico. How many different routes are possible?

27. How many different license plates can be formed by using 3 digits followed by a single letter followed by 3 more digits? How many if the single letter can occur anywhere except last?

28. How many different license plates can be formed by using any 3 letters followed by any 3 digits? How many if we allow either the 3 digits or the 3 letters to come first?

29. Make a list of all of the subsets of the set $\{a, b, c\}$. How many are there?

30. Use the fundamental counting principle to find the number of subsets of the set $\{a, b, c, d, e, f\}$.

31. How many ways are there to mark the answers to a test that consists of 10 true-false questions followed by 10 multiple-choice questions with 5 options each?

32. A fraternity votes on whether to accept each of 5 pledges. How many different outcomes are possible for the vote?

33. Make a list of all of the ways to arrange the letters in the word MILK. How many arrangements should be in your list?

34. Make a list of all of the permutations of the letters A, B, C, D, and E taken 3 at a time. How many permutations should be in your list?

Evaluate each expression.

35. $P(8, 3)$ **36.** $P(17, 4)$ **37.** $P(52, 0)$ **38.** $P(34, 1)$

39. $\dfrac{P(10, 4)}{4!}$ **40.** $\dfrac{P(8, 3)}{3!}$ **41.** $\dfrac{P(12, 3)}{3!}$ **42.** $\dfrac{P(15, 6)}{6!}$

43. $\dfrac{14!}{3!\,11!}$ **44.** $\dfrac{18!}{17!\,1!}$ **45.** $\dfrac{98!}{95!\,3!}$ **46.** $\dfrac{87!}{83!\,4!}$

In This Section

- Combinations of *n* Things *r* at a Time
- Permutations, Combinations, or Neither
- Labeling

14.2 COMBINATIONS

In Section 14.1 we learned the fundamental counting principle and applied it to finding the number of permutations of *n* objects taken *r* at a time. We will now learn how to count the number of combinations of *n* objects taken *r* at a time.

Combinations of *n* Things *r* at a Time

Consider the problem of awarding 2 identical scholarships to 2 students among 4 finalists: Ahmadi, Butler, Chen, and Davis. Since the scholarships are identical, we do not count Ahmadi and Butler as different from Butler and Ahmadi. We can easily list all possible choices of 2 students from the 4 possibilities A, B, C, and D:

$$\{A, B\} \quad \{A, C\} \quad \{A, D\} \quad \{B, C\} \quad \{B, D\} \quad \{C, D\}$$

It is convenient to use set notation to list these choices because in set notation we have $\{A, B\} = \{B, A\}$. Actually, we want the number of subsets or **combinations** of size 2 from a set of 4 elements. This number is referred to as the number of combinations of 4 things taken 2 at a time, and we use the notation $C(4, 2)$ to represent it. We have $C(4, 2) = 6$.

If we had a first and second prize to give to 2 of 4 finalists, then $P(4, 2) = 4 \cdot 3 = 12$ is the number of ways to award the prizes. If the prizes are identical, then we do not count AB as different from BA, or AC as different from CA, and so on. So we divide $P(4, 2)$ by $2!$, the number of permutations of the 2 prize winners, to get $C(4, 2)$.

In general, the number of subsets of size r taken from a set of size n can be found by dividing $P(n, r)$ by $r!$:

$$C(n, r) = \frac{P(n, r)}{r!}$$

Since $P(n, r) = \frac{n!}{(n - r)!}$, we can write this expression as follows:

$$C(n, r) = \frac{P(n, r)}{r!} = \frac{\dfrac{n!}{(n - r)!}}{r!} = \frac{n!}{(n - r)!\, r!}$$

The notation $\binom{n}{r}$ is also used for $C(n, r)$. We summarize these results in the following theorem.

Combinations of n Things r at a Time

The number of combinations of n things taken r at a time (or the number of subsets of size r from a set of n elements) is given by the formula

$$C(n, r) = \binom{n}{r} = \frac{n!}{(n - r)!\, r!} \qquad \text{for} \qquad 0 \le r \le n.$$

E X A M P L E   1

Combinations of n things r at a time

In how many ways can a committee of 4 people be chosen from a group of 12?

Solution

Choosing 4 people from a group of 12 is the same as choosing a subset of size 4 from a set of 12 elements. So the number of ways to choose the committee is the number of combinations of 12 things taken 4 at a time:

$$C(12, 4) = \frac{12!}{8!\,4!} = \frac{12 \cdot 11 \cdot 10 \cdot 9 \cdot 8 \cdot 7 \cdot 6 \cdot 5 \cdot 4 \cdot 3 \cdot 2 \cdot 1}{8 \cdot 7 \cdot 6 \cdot 5 \cdot 4 \cdot 3 \cdot 2 \cdot 1 \cdot 4 \cdot 3 \cdot 2 \cdot 1} = 495 \qquad ■$$

E X A M P L E   2

Finding a binomial coefficient

What is the coefficient of $a^4 b^2$ in the binomial expansion of $(a + b)^6$?

Solution

Write $(a + b)^6 = (a + b)(a + b)(a + b)(a + b)(a + b)(a + b)$. The terms of the product come from all of the different ways there are to select either a or b from each of the 6 factors and to multiply the selections. The number of ways to pick 4 factors for the selection of a is $C(6, 4) = \frac{6!}{2!\,4!} = 15$. From the remaining 2 we select b. So in the binomial expansion of $(a + b)^6$ we find the term $15a^4 b^2$.   ■

Note that as in Example 2, the coefficients of the terms in any binomial expansion are combinations. The coefficient of $a^r b^{n-r}$ in $(a + b)^n$ is $C(n, r)$.

Permutations, Combinations, or Neither

How do you know when to use the permutation formula and when to use the combination formula? The key to answering this question is understanding what each formula counts. In either case we are choosing from a group of distinct objects. Compare the following examples.

EXAMPLE 3   Permutations of *n* things *r* at a time

How many ways are there to choose a president, a vice-president, and a treasurer from a group of 9 people, assuming no one holds more than one office?

Solution

There are 9 choices for the president, 8 choices for the vice-president, and 7 choices for the treasurer. The number of ways to make these choices is $P(9, 3) = 9 \cdot 8 \cdot 7 = 504$. ∎

Note that in Example 3 we are not just counting the number of ways to select 3 people from 9. In the number $P(9, 3)$ every permutation of the 3 people selected is counted.

EXAMPLE 4   Combinations of *n* things *r* at a time

How many ways are there to choose 3 people to receive a $100 prize from a group of 9, assuming no one receives more than one prize?

Solution

Since each person chosen from the 9 is given the same treatment, the number of choices is the same as the number of subsets of size 3 from a set of 9 elements.

$$C(9, 3) = \frac{9!}{6!\,3!} = \frac{9 \cdot 8 \cdot 7}{3 \cdot 2 \cdot 1} = 84.$$ ∎

Note that in Example 4 we do not count different arrangements of the 3 people selected. Example 5 is neither a permutation nor a combination.

EXAMPLE 5   The fundamental counting principle

How many ways are there to answer a 9-question multiple-choice test in which each question has 3 possible answers?

Solution

There are 3 outcomes to the event of choosing the first answer, 3 outcomes to the event of choosing the second answer, and so on. By the fundamental counting principle there are $3^9 = 19{,}683$ ways to answer the 9 questions. ∎

Note that in choosing the answer to each question in Example 5 we may repeat answers, so we are not choosing from a set of distinct objects as in permutations and combinations. In Example 6 we use both the fundamental counting principle and the permutation formula.

EXAMPLE 6   The fundamental counting principle and permutations

Josephine has 4 different mathematics books, 3 different art books, and 5 different music books that she plans to display on a shelf. If she plans to keep each type of book together and put the types in the order mathematics–art–music, then how many different arrangements are possible?

Helpful Hint

Solution

First observe that the mathematics books can be arranged in $P(4, 4) = 4! = 24$ ways, the art books in $P(3, 3) = 3! = 6$ ways, and the music books in $P(5, 5) = 5! = 120$ ways. Now we use the fundamental counting principle to get $24 \cdot 6 \cdot 120 = 17{,}280$ as the number of ways to arrange the books on the shelf. ∎

Labeling

In a labeling problem we count the number of ways to put labels on distinct objects.

EXAMPLE 7

The fundamental counting principle and combinations

Twelve students have volunteered to help clean up a small oil spill. The project director needs 3 bird washers, 4 rock wipers, and 5 sand cleaners. In how many ways can these jobs (labels) be assigned to these 12 students?

Solution

Since the 3 bird washers all get the same label, the number of ways to select the 3 students is $C(12, 3)$. The number of ways to select 4 rock wipers from the remaining 9 students is $C(9, 4)$. The number of ways to select the 5 sand cleaners from the remaining 5 students is $C(5, 5)$. By the fundamental counting principle the number of ways to make all 3 selections is

$$C(12, 3) \cdot C(9, 4) \cdot C(5, 5) = \frac{12!}{9!\,3!} \cdot \frac{9!}{5!\,4!} \cdot \frac{5!}{0!\,5!} = \frac{12!}{3!\,4!\,5!} = 27{,}720. \quad ∎$$

Note that in Example 7 there were 12 distinct objects to be labeled with 3 labels of one type, 4 labels of another type, and 5 labels of a third type, and the number of ways to assign those labels was found to be $\frac{12!}{3!\,4!\,5!}$. Instead of using combinations and the fundamental counting principle as in Example 7, we can use the following theorem.

Labeling

In a **labeling problem** n distinct objects are each to be given a label with each object getting exactly one label. If there are r_1 labels of the first type, r_2 labels of the second type, . . . , and r_k labels of the kth type, where $r_1 + r_2 + \cdots + r_k = n$, then the number of ways to assign the labels to the objects is $\frac{n!}{r_1!\,r_2!\,\cdots\,r_k!}$.

EXAMPLE 8

A labeling problem

How many different arrangements are there for the 11 letters in the word MISSISSIPPI?

Solution

This problem is a labeling problem if we think of the 11 positions for the letters as 11 distinct objects to be labeled. There are 1 M-label, 4 S-labels, 4 I-labels, and 2 P-labels. So the number of ways to arrange the letters in MISSISSIPPI is $\frac{11!}{1!\,4!\,4!\,2!} = 34{,}650.$ ∎

E X A M P L E   9

Coefficients in a trinomial expansion

What is the coefficient of a^3b^2c in the expansion of $(a + b + c)^6$?

Solution

The terms of the product $(a + b + c)^6$ come from all of the different ways there are to select a, b, or c from each of the 6 distinct factors and to multiply the selections. The number of ways to pick 3 factors from which we select a, 2 factors from which we select b, and 1 factor from which we select c is $\frac{6!}{3!2!1!} = \frac{6 \cdot 5 \cdot 4 \cdot 3 \cdot 2 \cdot 1}{3 \cdot 2 \cdot 1 \cdot 2 \cdot 1 \cdot 1} = 60$. So in the expansion we have the term $60a^3b^2c$. ∎

The coefficients of the terms in an expansion such as that of Example 9 are called **multinomial coefficients.** Determining the coefficients is a labeling problem.

We may think of permutation and combination problems as being very different, but they are both labeling problems. For example, to find the number of subsets of size 3 from a set of size 5, we are assigning 3 I-labels and 2 O-labels (I for in and O for out) to the 5 distinct objects of the set. Note that $\frac{5!}{3!2!} = C(5, 3)$. To find the number of ways to give a **First**, **Second**, and **Third** prize to 3 of 10 people, we are assigning 1 **F**-label, 1 **S**-label, 1 **T**-label, and 7 **N**-labels (N for no prize) to the 10 distinct people. Note that $\frac{10!}{1!1!1!7!} = P(10, 3)$.

WARM-UPS

True or false? Explain your answer.

1. The number of ways to choose 2 questions to answer out of 3 questions on an essay test is $C(3, 2)$.
2. The number of ways to choose 1 question to omit out of 3 questions on an essay test is $C(3, 1)$.
3. $C(12, 4) = C(4, 12)$
4. $P(10, 6) < C(10, 6)$
5. There are $P(10, 3)$ ways to label randomly 3 of the top 10 restaurants in Philadelphia as "superior."
6. There are $\binom{20}{16}$ ways to select 4 of 20 students to stay after school.
7. $P(9, 4) = (4!) \cdot C(9, 4)$
8. $P(8, 3) = \binom{8}{5}$
9. $C(100, 1) = 100$
10. $\frac{8!}{1!1!1!5!} = P(8, 3)$

14.2   EXERCISES

Reading and Writing *After reading this section, write out the answers to these questions. Use complete sentences.*

1. What is a combination?

2. How many combinations are there for n things taken r at a time?

3. What is a labeling problem?

4. What are multinomial coefficients?

Solve each problem. See Examples 1 and 2.

5. How many 5-card poker hands are possible when you are dealt 5 cards from a deck of 52?

6. How many 13-card bridge hands are possible when you are dealt 13 cards from a deck of 52?

7. How many ways are there to select 3 candidates from the 5 finalists for an in-depth interview?

8. How many ways are there to select 12 welders to be laid off from 30 welders employed at the Ingalls Shipyard?

9. How many ways are there for a health inspector to select 5 restaurants to visit from a list of 20 restaurants?

10. The water inspector in drought-stricken Marin County randomly selects 10 homes for inspection from a list of 25 suspected violators of the rationing laws. How many ways are there to pick the 10 homes?

11. In the Florida Lottery you can win a lot of money for merely selecting 6 different numbers from the numbers 1 through 49. How many different ways are there to select the 6 numbers?

12. In the game Fantasy Five you can win by selecting 5 different numbers from the numbers 1 through 39. How many ways are there to select the 5 numbers?

13. What is the coefficient of $w^3 y^4$ in the expansion of $(w + y)^7$?

14. What is the coefficient of $a^5 z^9$ in the expansion of $(a + z)^{14}$?

Solve each problem. See Examples 3–5.

15. The Dean's Search Committee must choose 3 candidates from a list of 6 and rank them as first, second, and third. How many different outcomes are possible?

16. The Provost's Search Committee must choose 3 candidates from a list of 8 and submit the names to the president unranked. How many different outcomes are possible?

17. Charlotte must write on any 3 of the 8 essay questions on the final exam in History 201. How many ways are there for her to pick the questions?

18. How many ways are there for Murphy to mark the answers to 8 multiple-choice questions, each of which has 5 possible answers?

19. In how many different ways can Professor Reyes return his examination papers to a class of 12 students?

20. In how many different ways can Professor Lee return her examination papers to a class of 12 students if she always returns the best paper first and the worst paper last?

21. How many ways are there to select 5 seats from a 150-seat auditorium to be occupied by 5 plain-clothes officers?

22. For her final exam in Literature 302 Charlotte is allowed to omit any 5 of the 8 essay questions. How many ways are there for her to omit the 5 questions?

23. How many distinct chords (line segments with endpoints on the circle) are determined by 3 points lying on a circle? By 4 points? By 5 points? By n points?

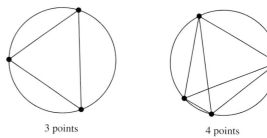

3 points   4 points

FIGURE FOR EXERCISE 23

24. How many distinct triangles are determined by 5 points lying on a circle, where the vertices of each triangle are chosen from the 5 points?

25. If the outcome of tossing a pair of dice is thought of as an ordered pair of numbers, then how many ordered pairs are there?

26. Francene is eligible to take 4 different mathematics classes, 5 different history classes, 6 different psychology classes, and 3 different literature classes. If her schedule is to consist of one class from each category, then how many different schedules are possible for her?

27. The outcome "heads" or "tails" is recorded on each toss of a coin. If we think of the outcome for 3 tosses as an ordered triple, then how many outcomes are there for 3 tosses of a coin?

28. A coin and a die are tossed. How many different outcomes are possible?

29. Explain why $C(n, r) = C(n, n - r)$.

30. Is $P(n, r) = P(n, n - r)$? Explain your answer.

Solve each problem. See Example 6.

31. Juanita is eligible to take 4 different mathematics classes and 5 different history classes. If her schedule is to consist of two classes from each category, then how many different schedules are possible for her?

32. A committee consisting of 2 men and 1 woman is to be formed from a department consisting of 8 men and 3 women. How many different committees are possible?

33. In a class of 20 students the teacher randomly assigns 4 A's, 5 B's, and 11 C's. In how many ways can these grades be assigned?

34. How many ways are there to seat 3 boys and 3 girls in a row with no 2 boys and no 2 girls sitting next to each other?

35. How many different orders are there for 4 marching bands and 4 floats to parade if a marching band must lead the parade and we cannot have 2 bands in a row or 2 floats in a row?

FIGURE FOR EXERCISE 35

36. In how many ways can 8 students be seated in a row if 2 of them must be seated next to one another?

Solve each problem. See Examples 7–9.

37. A teacher randomly assigns 6 A's, 3 B's, and 7 C's to a batch of 16 term papers. In how many different ways can she do this?

38. The 15 volunteers for the annual Bluegrass Festival are to be divided into 3 groups of 5 each and assigned to tickets, parking, and cleanup. In how many ways can these assignments be made?

39. Bob, Carol, Ted, and Alice are playing bridge. How many different ways are there to give each of them 13 cards

from the deck of 52? Is the answer larger or smaller than the number of seconds in a trillion years?

40. Bret, Bart, and Mad Dog are playing poker. How many different ways are there to give each of them 5 cards from a deck of 52?

41. How many different arrangements are there for the letters in the word TOYOTA? ALGEBRA? STATISTICS?

42. How many different orders are possible for 3 identical contemporary, 4 identical traditional, and 6 identical colonial homes to march in a parade of homes?

43. Twenty salespeople are getting new cars. How many ways are there to assign 6 identical Chevrolets, 5 identical Fords, 8 identical Buicks, and 1 Lincoln to them?

44. Twenty different Fords are being sent to 4 Ford dealers. In how many ways can Bill Poole Ford get 3 cars, Heritage Ford get 5 cars, Mid-City Ford get 5 cars, and Northside Ford get 7 cars?

45. Nine sofas are to be discounted at Sofa City with discounts as large as 75% off the manufacturers suggested retail price. (Sorry, none sold to dealers.) How many ways are there to mark 4 of the sofas 10% off, 4 of them 15% off, and 1 of them 75% off?

46. A combination for a safe is a sequence of 4 numbers with no repetitions selected from the integers 1 through 99. How many combinations are possible? Is combination the proper word to use here?

FIGURE FOR EXERCISE 46

47. What is the coefficient of $a^3b^2c^5$ in the expansion of $(a + b + c)^{10}$?

48. What is the coefficient of $wx^2y^3z^9$ in the expansion of $(w + x + y + z)^{15}$?

49. What is the coefficient of a^3b^5 in the expansion of $(a + b + c)^8$?

50. What is the coefficient of x^2z^5 in the expansion of $(x + y + z)^7$?

14.3 **PROBABILITY**

In Sections 14.1 and 14.2 we were concerned with counting the number of different outcomes to an experiment. We now use those counting techniques to find probabilities.

The Probability of an Event

In probability an **experiment** is a process such as tossing a coin, tossing a die, drawing a poker hand from a deck, or arranging people in a line. A **sample space** is the set of all possible outcomes to an experiment. An **event** is a subset of a sample space. For example, if we toss a coin, then the sample space consists of two equally likely outcomes, heads and tails. We write $S = \{H, T\}$. The subset $E = \{H\}$ is the event of getting heads when the coin is tossed. We use $n(S)$ to represent the number of equally likely outcomes in the sample space S and $n(E)$ to represent the number of outcomes in the event E. For the example of tossing a coin, $n(S) = 2$ and $n(E) = 1$.

> **The Probability of an Event**
>
> If S is a sample space of equally likely outcomes to an experiment and the event E is a subset of S, then the probability of E, $P(E)$, is defined to be
>
> $$P(E) = \frac{n(E)}{n(S)}.$$

When $S = \{H, T\}$ and $E = \{H\}$,

$$P(E) = \frac{n(E)}{n(S)} = \frac{1}{2}.$$

So the probability of getting heads on a single toss of a coin is $\frac{1}{2}$. If E is the event of getting 2 heads on a single toss of a coin, then $n(E) = 0$ and $P(E) = \frac{0}{2} = 0$. If E is the event of getting fewer than 2 heads on a single toss of a coin, then for either outcome H or T we have fewer than 2 heads. So $E = \{H, T\}$, $n(E) = 2$, and $P(E) = \frac{2}{2} = 1$. Note that the probability of an event is a number between 0 and 1 inclusive, 1 being the probability of an event that is certain to occur and 0 being the probability of an event that is impossible to occur.

EXAMPLE 1

Rolling a die

What is the probability of getting a number larger than 4 when a single die is rolled?

Solution

When we roll a die, we count the number of dots showing on the upper face of the die. So the sample space of equally likely outcomes is $S = \{1, 2, 3, 4, 5, 6\}$. Since only 5 and 6 are larger than 4, $E = \{5, 6\}$. According to the definition of probability,

$$P(E) = \frac{n(E)}{n(S)} = \frac{2}{6} = \frac{1}{3}.$$

■

LOTTERIES

The probability experiments discussed in this chapter are not just textbook examples that have no relationship to real life. For example, if a couple plans to have 6 children and the probability of having a girl on each try is $\frac{1}{2}$, then the couple can expect to have 3 girls. If you guess at the answer to each question of a 100-question, 5-choice multiple-choice test, then you have $\frac{1}{5}$ probability of getting each question correct, and you can expect to get 20 questions correct. Try it. The expected number of successes is the product of the probability of success and the number of tries.

Lotteries provide us an opportunity to observe massive probability experiments. In the Florida Lottery you can win by choosing 6 numbers from the numbers 1 through 49 and matching the 6 numbers chosen by the Florida Lottery. There are $C(49, 6)$ ways to choose 6 numbers from 49, so the probability of winning on any individual try is

$$\frac{1}{C(49, 6)} = \frac{1}{13{,}983{,}816}.$$

In the fall of 1990 the weekly drawing frequently had relatively few participants, and consequently there was no winner for many weeks. When the prize got up to $106.5 million, the lottery got national attention. People came from everywhere to participate. During the week prior to September 15, 1990, 109,163,978 tickets were sold. We expected $\frac{1}{13{,}983{,}816} \cdot 109{,}163{,}978 = 7.8$ winners. On September 15 the winning numbers were announced, and 6 winners shared the prize. Of course, probability cannot predict the future like a fortune-teller, but the power of probability to tell us what to expect is truly amazing.

E X A M P L E   2

Tossing coins

What is the probability of getting at least one head when a pair of coins is tossed?

Solution

Since there are 2 equally likely outcomes for the first coin and 2 equally likely outcomes for the second coin, by the fundamental counting principle there are 4 equally likely outcomes to the experiment of tossing a pair of coins. We can list the outcomes as ordered pairs: $S = \{(H, H), (H, T), (T, H), (T, T)\}$. Since 3 of these outcomes result in at least one head, $E = \{(H, H), (H, T), (T, H)\}$, and $n(E) = 3$. So

$$P(E) = \frac{n(E)}{n(S)} = \frac{3}{4}.$$

■

E X A M P L E   3

Rolling a pair of dice

What is the probability of getting a sum of 6 when a pair of dice is rolled?

Solution

Since there are 6 equally likely outcomes for each die, there are 36 equally likely outcomes to the experiment of rolling the pair. We can list the 36 outcomes as ordered pairs:

$$S = \{(1, 1), (1, 2), (1, 3), (1, 4), \mathbf{(1, 5)}, (1, 6),$$
$$(2, 1), (2, 2), (2, 3), \mathbf{(2, 4)}, (2, 5), (2, 6),$$
$$(3, 1), (3, 2), \mathbf{(3, 3)}, (3, 4), (3, 5), (3, 6),$$
$$(4, 1), \mathbf{(4, 2)}, (4, 3), (4, 4), (4, 5), (4, 6),$$
$$\mathbf{(5, 1)}, (5, 2), (5, 3), (5, 4), (5, 5), (5, 6),$$
$$(6, 1), (6, 2), (6, 3), (6, 4), (6, 5), (6, 6)\}$$

The sum of the numbers is 6, describes the event $E = \{(5, 1), (4, 2), (3, 3), (2, 4), (1, 5)\}$. So

$$P(E) = \frac{n(E)}{n(S)} = \frac{5}{36}.$$ ∎

The Addition Rule

In tossing a pair of dice, let A be the event that doubles occurs and B be the event that the sum is 4. We can list the following events and their probabilities:

$$A = \{(1, 1), (2, 2), (3, 3), (4, 4), (5, 5), (6, 6)\} \text{ and } P(A) = \frac{6}{36}$$
$$B = \{(3, 1), (2, 2), (1, 3)\} \text{ and } P(B) = \frac{3}{36}$$
$$A \cup B = \{(1, 1), (2, 2), (3, 3), (4, 4), (5, 5), (6, 6), (3, 1), (1, 3)\}$$
$$\text{and } P(A \cup B) = \frac{8}{36}$$
$$A \cap B = \{(2, 2)\} \text{ and } P(A \cap B) = \frac{1}{36}$$

Note that the probability of doubles or a sum of 4, $P(A \cup B)$, is $\frac{8}{36}$ and

$$\frac{8}{36} = \frac{6}{36} + \frac{3}{36} - \frac{1}{36}.$$

This equation makes sense because there is one outcome, (2, 2), that is in both the events A and B. This example illustrates the addition rule.

The Addition Rule

If A and B are any events in a sample space, then

$$P(A \cup B) = P(A) + P(B) - P(A \cap B).$$

If $P(A \cap B) = 0$, then A and B are called **mutually exclusive** events and

$$P(A \cup B) = P(A) + P(B).$$

Note that for mutually exclusive events it is impossible for both events to occur. The addition rule for mutually exclusive events is a special case of the general addition rule.

E X A M P L E 4

The addition rule

At Downtown College 60% of the students are commuters (C), 50% are female (F), and 30% are female commuters. If a student is selected at random, what is the probability that the student is either a female or a commuter?

Solution

By the addition rule the probability of selecting either a female or a commuter is $P(F \cup C) = P(F) + P(C) - P(F \cap C) = 0.50 + 0.60 - 0.30 = 0.80$. ∎

E X A M P L E 5

The addition rule with dice

In rolling a pair of dice, what is the probability that the sum is 12 or at least one die shows a 2?

Solution

Let A be the event that the sum is 12 and B be the event that at least one die shows a 2. Since A occurs on only one of the 36 equally likely outcomes (see Example 3), $P(A) = \frac{1}{36}$. Since B occurs on 11 of the equally likely outcomes, $P(B) = \frac{11}{36}$. Since A and B are mutually exclusive, we have

$$P(A \cup B) = P(A) + P(B)$$
$$= \frac{1}{36} + \frac{11}{36} = \frac{12}{36} = \frac{1}{3}.$$

∎

Complementary Events

If the probability of rain today is 60%, then the probability that it does not rain is 40%. Rain and not rain are called complementary events. There is no possibility that both occur, and one of them must occur. If A is an event, then $\overline{A}$ (read "A bar" or "A complement") represents the complement of the event A. Note that complementary events are mutually exclusive, but mutually exclusive events are not necessarily complementary.

> **Complementary Events**
>
> Two events A and $\overline{A}$ are called **complementary events** if $A \cap \overline{A} = \varnothing$ and $P(A) + P(\overline{A}) = 1$.

E X A M P L E 6

Complementary events

What is the probability of getting a number less than or equal to 4 when rolling a single die?

Solution

We saw in Example 1 that getting a number larger than 4 when rolling a single die has probability $\frac{1}{3}$. The complement to getting a number larger than 4 is getting a number less than or equal to 4. So the probability of getting a number less than or equal to 4 is $\frac{2}{3}$. ∎

E X A M P L E   7

Complementary events

If the probability that White Lightning will win the Kentucky Derby is 0.15, then what is the probability that White Lightning does not win the Kentucky Derby?

Solution

Let W be winning the Kentucky Derby and N be not winning the Kentucky Derby. Since W and N are complementary events, we have $P(W) + P(N) = 1$. So $P(N) = 1 - P(W) = 1 - 0.15 = 0.85$. ∎

Odds

If the probability is $\frac{2}{3}$ that the Giants win the Super Bowl and $\frac{1}{3}$ that they lose, then they are twice as likely to win as they are to lose. We say that the odds in favor of the Giants winning the Super Bowl are 2 to 1. Notice that odds are not probabilities. Odds are ratios of probabilities. We usually write odds as ratios of whole numbers.

> **Odds**
>
> If A is any event, then the **odds in favor of A** is the ratio $P(A)$ to $P(\overline{A})$ and the **odds against A** is the ratio of $P(\overline{A})$ to $P(A)$.

E X A M P L E   8

Determining odds

What are the odds in favor of getting a sum of 6 when rolling a pair of dice? What are the odds against a sum of 6?

Solution

In Example 3 we found the probability of a sum of 6 to be $\frac{5}{36}$. So the probability of the complement (the sum is not 6) is $\frac{31}{36}$. The odds in favor of getting a sum of 6 are $\frac{5}{36}$ to $\frac{31}{36}$. Multiply each fraction by 36 to get the odds 5 to 31. The odds against a sum of 6 are 31 to 5. ∎

E X A M P L E   9

Determining probability given the odds

If the odds in favor of Daddy's Darling winning the third race at Delta Downs are 4 to 1, then what is the probability that Daddy's Darling wins the third race?

Solution

Since 4 to 1 is the ratio of the probability of winning to not winning, the probability of winning is four times as large as the probability of not winning. Let $P(\overline{W}) = x$ and $P(W) = 4x$. Since $P(W) + P(\overline{W}) = 1$, we have $4x + x = 1$, or $5x = 1$, or $x = \frac{1}{5}$. So the probability of winning is $\frac{4}{5}$. ∎

We can write the idea found in Example 9 as a strategy for converting from odds to probabilities.

Strategy for Converting from Odds to Probability

If the odds in favor of event E are a to b, then

$$P(E) = \frac{a}{a + b} \quad \text{and} \quad P(\overline{E}) = \frac{b}{a + b}.$$

WARM-UPS

True or false? Explain your answer.

1. If S is a sample space of equally likely outcomes and E is a subset of S, then $P(E) = n(E)$.

2. If an experiment consists of tossing 3 coins, then the sample space consists of 6 equally likely outcomes.

3. The probability of getting at least one tail when a coin is tossed twice is 0.75.

4. The probability of getting at least one 4 when a pair of dice is tossed is $\frac{11}{36}$.

5. The probability of getting at least one head when 5 coins are tossed is $\frac{33}{32}$.

6. If 3 coins are tossed, then getting exactly 3 heads and getting exactly 3 tails are complementary events.

7. If the probability of getting exactly 3 tails in a toss of 3 coins is $\frac{1}{8}$, then the probability of getting at least one head is $\frac{7}{8}$.

8. If the probability of snow today is 80%, then the odds in favor of snow are 8 to 10.

9. If the odds in favor of an event E are 2 to 3, then $P(E) = \frac{2}{3}$.

10. The ratio of $\frac{1}{2}$ to $\frac{1}{3}$ is equivalent to the ratio of 2 to 3.

14.3 EXERCISES

Reading and Writing After reading this section, write out the answers to these questions. Use complete sentences.

1. What is an experiment?

2. What is a sample space?

3. What is an event?

4. What is the probability of an event?

5. What is the addition rule?

6. What are the odds in favor of an event?

Solve each probability problem. See Examples 1–3.

7. If a single die is tossed, then what is the probability of getting
   a) a number larger than 3?
   b) a number less than or equal to 5?
   c) a number other than 6?
   d) a number larger than 7?
   e) a number smaller than 9?

8. If a single coin is tossed once, then what is the probability of getting
   a) tails?
   b) fewer than two heads?
   c) exactly three heads?

9. If a pair of coins is tossed, then what is the probability of getting
   a) exactly two heads?
   b) at least one tail?
   c) exactly two tails?
   d) at most one tail?

10. If a single coin is tossed twice, then what is the probability of getting
   a) heads followed by tails?
   b) two heads in a row?
   c) a tail on the second toss?
   d) exactly one tail?

11. If a pair of dice is tossed, then what is the probability of getting
   a) a pair of 2's?
   b) at least one 2?
   c) a sum of 7?
   d) a sum greater than 1?
   e) a sum less than 2?

12. If a single die is tossed twice, then what is the probability of getting
   a) a 1 followed by a 2?
   b) a sum of 3?
   c) a 6 on the second toss?
   d) no more than two 5's?
   e) an even number followed by an odd number?

13. A ball is selected at random from a jar containing 3 red balls, 4 yellow balls, and 5 green balls. What is the probability that
   a) the ball is red?
   b) the ball is not yellow?
   c) the ball is either red or green?
   d) the ball is neither red nor green?

FIGURE FOR EXERCISE 13

14. A committee consists of 1 Democrat, 5 Republicans, and 6 independents. If one person is randomly selected from the committee to be the chairperson, then what is the probability that
   a) the person is a Democrat?
   b) the person is either a Democrat or a Republican?
   c) the person is not a Republican?

15. A jar contains 10 balls numbered 1 through 10. Two balls are randomly selected one at a time without replacement. What is the probability that
   a) 1 is selected first and 2 is selected second?
   b) the sum of the numbers selected is 3?
   c) the sum of the numbers selected is 6?

16. A small company consists of a president, a vice-president, and 14 salespeople. If 2 of the 16 people are randomly selected to win a Hawaiian vacation, then what is the probability that none of the salespeople is a winner?

17. If a 5-card poker hand is drawn from a deck of 52, then what is the probability that
   a) the hand contains the ace, king, queen, jack, and ten of spades?

   b) the hand contains one 2, one 3, one 4, one 5, and one 6?

18. If 5 people with different names and different weights randomly line up to buy concert tickets, then what is the

probability that

a) they line up in alphabetical order?

b) they line up in order of increasing weight?

Use the addition rule to solve each problem. See Examples 4 and 5.

19. Among the drivers insured by American Insurance, 65% are women, 38% of the drivers are in a high-risk category, and 24% of the drivers are high-risk women. If a driver is randomly selected from that company, what is the probability that the driver is either high-risk or a woman?

20. What is the probability of getting either a sum of 7 or at least one 4 in the toss of a pair of dice?

21. A couple plans to have 3 children. Assuming males and females are equally likely, what is the probability that they have either 3 boys or 3 girls.

22. What is the probability of getting a sum of 10 or a sum of 5 in the toss of a pair of dice?

23. What is the probability of getting either a heart or an ace when drawing a single card from a deck of 52 cards?

24. What is the probability of getting either a heart or a spade when drawing a single card from a deck of 52 cards?

Solve each problem. See Examples 6 and 7.

25. If the probability of surviving a head-on car accident at 55 mph is 0.005, then what is the probability of not surviving?

26. If the probability of a tax return not being audited by the IRS is 0.97, then what is the probability of a tax return being audited?

27. A pair of dice is tossed. What is the probability of

a) getting a pair of 4's?

b) not getting a pair of 4's?

c) getting at least one number that is not a 4?

28. Three coins are tossed. What is the probability of

a) getting three heads?

b) not getting three heads?

c) getting at least one tail?

Solve each problem. See Examples 8 and 9.

29. If the probability is 60% that the eye of Hurricane Edna comes ashore within 30 miles of Charleston, then what are the odds in favor of the eye of Edna coming ashore within 30 miles of Charleston?

30. If the probability that a Sidewinder missile hits its target is $\frac{8}{9}$, then what are the odds

a) in favor of the Sidewinder hitting its target?

b) against the Sidewinder hitting its target?

FIGURE FOR EXERCISE 29

31. If the probability that the stock market goes up tomorrow is $\frac{3}{5}$, then what are the odds

a) in favor of the stock market going up tomorrow?

b) against the stock market going up tomorrow?

32. If the probability of a coal miners' strike this year is $\frac{9}{10}$, then what are the odds

a) in favor of a strike?

b) against a strike?

33. If the odds are 3 to 1 in favor of the Black Hawks winning their next game, then

a) what are the odds against the Black Hawks winning their next game?

b) what is the probability that the Black Hawks win their next game?

34. If the odds are 5 to 1 against the Democratic presidential nominee winning the election, then

a) what are the odds in favor of the Democrat winning the election?

b) what is the probability that the Democrat wins the election?

35. What are the odds in favor of getting exactly 2 heads in 3 tosses of a coin?

36. What are the odds in favor of getting a 6 in a single toss of a die?

37. What are the odds in favor of getting a sum of 8 when tossing a pair of dice?

38. What are the odds in favor of getting at least one 6 when tossing a pair of dice?

FIGURE FOR EXERCISE 38

39. If one million lottery tickets are sold and only one of them is the winning ticket, then what are the odds in favor of winning if you hold a single ticket?

40. What are the odds in favor of winning a lottery where you must choose 6 numbers from the numbers 1 through 49?

41. If the odds in favor of getting 5 heads in 5 tosses of a coin are 1 to 31, then what is the probability of getting 5 heads in 5 tosses of a coin?

42. If the odds against Smith winning the election are 2 to 5, then what is the probability that Smith wins the election?

GETTING MORE INVOLVED

43. In the Louisiana Lottery a player chooses 6 numbers from the numbers 1 through 44. You win the big prize if the 6 chosen numbers match the 6 winning numbers chosen on Saturday night.

   a) What is the probability that you choose all 6 winning numbers?

   b) What is the probability that you do not get all 6 winning numbers?

   c) What are the odds in favor of winning the big prize with a single entry?

44. In the Louisiana Power Ball a player chooses 5 numbers from the numbers 1 through 49 and one number (the power ball) from 1 through 42.

   a) How many ways are there to choose the 5 numbers and, choose the power ball?

   b) What is the probability of winning the big prize in the Power Ball Lottery?

   c) What are the odds in favor of winning the big prize?

COLLABORATIVE ACTIVITIES

Extra Sensory Perception (ESP)

In this activity we will test each student in the class for ESP. Working in groups of three or four, start with a well-shuffled deck of ordinary playing cards. Place the stack of cards face down on a table. Have one student (the subject) try to guess whether the top card is a heart, diamond, spade, or club. After the student has guessed, remove the card and record whether the student was correct or incorrect. Do not let the subject know whether the guess was correct. Repeat the experiment for each of the 52 cards in the deck. The subject's score is the number of times he or she correctly guessed the suit of the card. Now choose a new subject and start over.

Answer the following questions in your group.

1. What is the probability that the subject will guess the correct suit of any card?

2. What score would you expect for each subject?

3. How many correct guesses would a subject have to make for you to think he or she was unusual?

Grouping: 3 or 4 students per group

Topic: Applications of probability

4. How many correct guesses would a subject have to make for you to be convinced he or she has ESP?

Using the results of all of the groups, make a bar graph with the possible scores (0 through 52) along the x-axis. The height of each bar should correspond to the number of subjects in the class who obtained the score.

5. Is there anyone in the class with an unusual score according to your answer to question 3?

6. Is there anyone in your class who has ESP according to your answer to question 4?

7. What percent of the class scored above 13 and what percent scored below 13? Would you say that the high scores have ESP and the low scores are unlucky?

8. Retest the student with the highest score and see what happens.

WRAP-UP

SUMMARY

Counting

Examples

Fundamental counting principle	If event A has m different outcomes and event B has n different outcomes, then there are mn different ways for events A and B to occur.	If a pie can be ordered with 2 different crusts and 5 fillings, then 10 pies are available.
Permutations of n things r at a time	The number of permutations of n things taken r at a time is $P(n, r) = \dfrac{n!}{(n - r)!}$ for $0 \leq r \leq n$. $P(n, n) = n!$ and $P(n, 0) = 1$.	The number of ways to choose Miss America and the First Runner Up from 5 finalists is $P(5, 2) = 5 \cdot 4$. The number of ways for 5 people to stand in line is $P(5, 5) = 5!$.
Combinations of n things r at a time	The number of combinations of n things taken r at a time is $C(n, r) = \dfrac{n!}{(n - r)!\, r!}$ for $0 \leq r \leq n$. $C(n, n) = 1$ and $C(n, 0) = 1$.	The number of ways to rate 2 of 5 people as excellent is $C(5, 2) = \dfrac{5!}{3!\,2!}$. $C(5, 5) = \dfrac{5!}{0!\,5!} = 1$, $C(5, 0) = \dfrac{5!}{5!\,0!} = 1$
Labeling	One label is given to each of n distinct objects. If there are r_1 labels of type 1, r_2 labels of type 2, . . . , and r_k labels of type k, then the number of ways to label is $\dfrac{n!}{r_1!\,r_2!\,\ldots\,r_k!}$.	If 5 students are randomly given 2 A's, 2 B's, and 1 C, then the number of ways to assign these grades is $\dfrac{5!}{2!\,2!\,1!}$.

Coefficients

Examples

Binomial coefficients	The coefficient of the term $a^r b^{n-r}$ in the expansion of $(a + b)^n$ is $C(n, r)$ for $0 \leq r \leq n$.	The coefficient of $a^3 b^2$ in $(a + b)^5$ is $C(5, 3) = \dfrac{5!}{3!\,2!} = 10$.
Multinomial coefficients	Determining the coefficients in a multinominal expansion is a labeling problem.	The coefficient of $a^2 b^2 c^3$ in $(a + b + c)^7$ is $\dfrac{7!}{2!\,2!\,3!} = 210$.

Probability

Examples

Probability of an event	If S is a sample space of equally likely outcomes to an experiment and E is a subset of S, then $P(E) = \dfrac{n(E)}{n(S)}$.	If a single die is tossed, then $S = \{1, 2, 3, 4, 5, 6\}$. If $A = \{4, 5, 6\}$, then $P(A) = \dfrac{3}{6}$.

Mutually exclusive events	Two events are called mutually exclusive when it is impossible for both to occur.	If a die is tossed once, then $\{1\}$ and $\{2\}$ are mutually exclusive.
Addition rule	If A and B are any events in a sample space, then $P(A \cup B) = P(A) + P(B) - P(A \cap B)$.	If $A = \{4, 5, 6\}$ and $B = \{3, 4\}$, then $P(A \cup B) = \dfrac{3}{6} + \dfrac{2}{6} - \dfrac{1}{6} = \dfrac{4}{6}$.
	If A and B are mutually exclusive events in a sample space, then $P(A \cup B) = P(A) + P(B)$.	If $C = \{1\}$ and $D = \{2\}$, then $P(C \cup D) = \dfrac{1}{6} + \dfrac{1}{6} = \dfrac{2}{6}$.
Complementary events	Two events A and $\overline{A}$ are complementary events if $A \cap \overline{A} = \varnothing$ and $P(A) + P(\overline{A}) = 1$.	If $C = \{1\}$, then $\overline{C} = \{2, 3, 4, 5, 6\}$ and $P(C) + P(\overline{C}) = \dfrac{1}{6} + \dfrac{5}{6} = 1$.

Odds

Examples

Odds	For an event A the odds in favor of A is the ratio of $P(A)$ to $P(\overline{A})$, and the odds against A is the ratio $P(\overline{A})$ to $P(A)$.	The odds in favor of getting 1 on a single toss of a die are 1 to 5, and the odds against getting 1 are 5 to 1.
Converting from odds to probability	If the odds in favor of E are a to b, then $P(E) = \dfrac{a}{a + b}$ and $P(\overline{E}) = \dfrac{b}{a + b}$.	Odds in favor of $E = \{1, 2, 3, 4\}$ in tossing a die are 2 to 1. So $P(E) = \dfrac{2}{2 + 1} = \dfrac{2}{3}$ and $P(\overline{E}) = \dfrac{1}{3}$.

ENRICHING YOUR MATHEMATICAL WORD POWER

For each mathematical term, choose the correct meaning.

1. **tree diagram**
   a. a prehistoric tree carving
   b. a family tree
   c. a diagram showing all possibilities
   d. a diagram of numbers and their square roots

2. **permutation**
   a. a linear rearrangement
   b. a distortion of the facts
   c. $P(n, r)$
   d. a factorial

3. **combination**
   a. a padlock
   b. a group or subset
   c. a factorial
   d. $C(n, r)$

4. **multinomial coefficients**
   a. multiple coefficients
   b. coefficients involving many numbers
   c. binomial coefficients
   d. the coefficients in the expansion of a power of a polynomial of more than 2 terms

5. **experiment**
   a. a chemistry problem
   b. a process with an uncertain outcome
   c. a guess
   d. trial and error

6. **sample space**
   a. the set of all possible outcomes to an experiment
   b. a space reserved for free samples
   c. to choose a space
   d. a typical outcome to an experiment

7. **event**
   a. an outcome to an experiment
   b. winning a lottery
   c. an experiment
   d. a subset of a sample space

8. **mutually exclusive events**
   a. events to which you would not go even if you were invited
   b. two events that cannot both occur
   c. two events that always occur together
   d. events that cannot happen

9. **complementary events**___
   a. events where everyone says nice things
   b. events that cannot both occur
   c. events that must occur
   d. two events that cannot both occur but one of them must occur

10. **odds in favor of an event**___
    a. the ratio of $P(A)$ to $P(\bar{A})$
    b. the probability of the event
    c. the probability that an event does not occur
    d. 2 to 1

REVIEW EXERCISES

14.1 *Solve each problem.*

1. How many different ways are there to mark the answers to a 15-question multiple-choice test in which each question has 3 possible answers?

2. Eight airplanes are scheduled to depart at 1 o'clock. In how many ways can they line up for departure?

3. John is trying to find all 3-letter words that can be formed without repetition using the letters in the word UNITED. He plans to write down all "possible" 3-letter words and then check each one with a dictionary to see whether it is actually a word in the English language. How many "possible" 3-letter words are there?

4. The sales manager for an insurance company must select a team of 2 agents to give a presentation. If the manager has 9 male agents and 7 female agents available, and the team must consist of one man and one woman, then how many different teams are possible?

5. A candidate for city council is going to place one newspaper advertisement, one radio advertisement, and one television advertisement. If there are 3 newspapers, 12 radio stations, and 4 television stations available, then in how many ways can the advertisements be placed?

6. A ship has 11 different flags available. A signal consists of 3 flags displayed on a vertical pole. How many different signals are possible?

FIGURE FOR EXERCISE 6

14.2 *Solve each problem.*

7. A travel agent offers a vacation in which you can visit any 4 cities, chosen from Paris, Rome, London, Istanbul, Monte Carlo, Vienna, Madrid, and Berlin. How many different vacations are possible, if the order in which the cities are visited is not important?

8. How many 5-element subsets are there from the set {a, b, c, d, e, f, g}?

9. A city council consists of 5 Democrats and 4 Republicans. In how many ways can 4 council members be selected by the mayor to go to a convention in San Diego if the mayor
   a) may choose any 4?
   b) must choose 4 Democrats?
   c) must choose 2 Democrats and 2 Republicans?

10. In a 5-card poker hand a full house is 3 cards of one kind and 2 cards of another. How many full houses are there consisting of three kings and two jacks?

11. What is the coefficient of x^7y^3 in the expansion of $(x + y)^{10}$?

12. What is the coefficient of a^4b^3 in the expansion of $(a + b)^7$?

13. What is the coefficient of $w^2x^3y^6$ in the expansion of $(w + x + y)^{11}$?

14. What is the coefficient of x^5y^7 in the expansion of $(w + x + y)^{12}$?

15. How many different arrangements are there for the letters in the word ARKANSAS? MARCH?

16. Eight Toyota pickups of different colors are on sale through Saturday only. How many ways are there for the dealer to mark 2 of them $7,000, 3 of them $8,000, and 3 of them $9,000?

17. A couple plans to have 6 children. How many different families are possible, considering the sex of each child and the order of birth?

18. The Galaxy Theater has 3 horror films to show on Saturday night. How many different triple features are possible?

14.3 *Solve each problem.*

19. If Miriam randomly marks the answers to a 12-question true-false test, then what is the probability that she gets all 12 correct? What is the probability that she gets all 12 wrong?

20. If a couple plans to have 6 children, then what is the probability that they will have 6 girls?

21. There are 6 red, 5 green, and 3 yellow jelly beans in a jar. If a jelly bean is selected at random, then what is the probability that

    a) the selected bean is green?

    b) the selected bean is either yellow or red?

    c) the selected bean is blue?

    d) the selected bean is not purple?

22. A pair of dice is tossed. What is the probability that

    a) at least one die shows an even number?

    b) the sum is an even number?

    c) the sum is 6?

    d) the sum is 6 and at least one die shows an even number?

    e) the sum is 6 or at least one die shows an even number?

23. Suppose a couple plans to have 3 children. What are the odds in favor of having 3 boys?

24. Suppose a pair of dice is tossed. What are the odds in favor of the sum being 6?

25. If 60% of the voters in Massachusetts are Democrats and a single voter is drawn at random, then what are the odds in favor of that voter being a Democrat?

26. Seventy percent of the students at Wellknown University have money as their primary goal in life. If a student is selected at random, then what are the odds against selecting one who has money as his or her primary goal in life?

27. At Wellknown University 60% of the students are enrolled in an English class, 70% are enrolled in a mathematics class, and 40% are enrolled in both. If a student is selected at random, then what is the probability that the student is enrolled in either mathematics or English?

28. If a pair of dice is tossed, then what is the probability that the sum is either 5 or 7?

MISCELLANEOUS

Evaluate each expression.

29. $8!$

30. $1!$

31. $\dfrac{5!}{3!}$

32. $\dfrac{7!}{(7-3)!}$

33. $\dfrac{9!}{3!\,3!\,3!}$

34. $\dfrac{10!}{0!\,2!\,3!\,5!}$

35. $C(8, 6)$

36. $\dbinom{12}{3}$

37. $P(8, 4)$

38. $P(4, 4)$

39. $C(8, 1)$

40. $C(12, 0)$

CHAPTER 14 TEST

Solve each problem.

1. The Turbo ZXS computer comes with your choice of any one of 4 color monitors, 6 sizes of hard disks, and 3 different keyboards. How many different configurations are possible for this model?

2. One gold, one silver, and one bronze medal will be awarded to 3 students who are randomly chosen from the 20 who are entered in the sack race at the Oak Ridge Elementary School picnic. In how many ways can the 3 prizes be awarded?

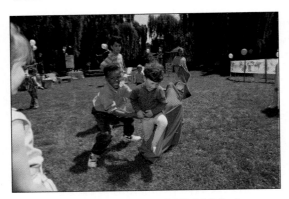

FIGURE FOR EXERCISE 2

3. A tour of New York City includes visits to any 3 attractions chosen from the Empire State Building, the United Nations, the Statue of Liberty, the Stock Exchange, and Central Park. How many different tours are possible, if the order in which the attractions are visited is not important?

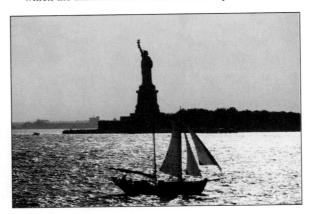

FIGURE FOR EXERCISE 3

4. From a class of 12 boys and 8 girls, the teacher must choose 2 boys and 2 girls for crossing guards. How many teams of 4 crossing guards are possible?

5. How many ways are there for Mother Nature to select 4 workers randomly out of the 12 available workers in the office to get the flu?

6. What is the coefficient of a^3b^8 in the expansion of $(a + b)^{11}$?

7. What is the coefficient of $w^4x^3y^2z^5$ in the expansion of $(w + x + y + z)^{14}$?

8. How many different arrangements are there for the 6 letters in the word ALASKA?

9. What is the probability that at least one head is showing when a pair of coins is tossed?

10. What is the probability that at least one head is showing or at least one tail is showing when a pair of coins is tossed?

11. One card is to be drawn from a deck of 52. What are the odds in favor of getting a spade?

12. The Fujimotos plan to have 3 children. What are the odds against having 3 boys?

13. At the start of the season professional odds makers in Las Vegas put the odds in favor of the Saints going to the Super Bowl at 1 to 20.

    a) What are the odds against the Saints going to the Super Bowl?

    b) What is the probability that the Saints go to the Super Bowl?

    c) What is the probability that the Saints do not go to the Super Bowl?

14. A pair of dice is tossed. Let A be the event that at least one die shows a 3 and B be the event that the sum is 7. Find the following probabilities.

    a) $P(A)$ b) $P(B)$

    c) $P(A \cap B)$ d) $P(A \cup B)$

Evaluate each expression.

15. $C(100, 2)$

16. $P(200, 3)$

17. $\dfrac{10!}{3!\,4!\,3!}$

Geometric Figures and Formulas

Triangle: A three-sided figure

Area: $A = \frac{1}{2}bh$, Perimeter: $P = a + b + c$

Sum of the measures of the angles is $180°$.

30-60-90 Right Triangle: The side opposite $30°$ is one-half the length of the hypotenuse.

Trapezoid: A four-sided figure with one pair of parallel sides

Area: $A = \frac{1}{2}h(b_1 + b_2)$

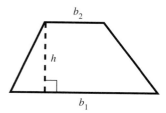

Right Triangle: A triangle with a $90°$ angle

Area $= \frac{1}{2}ab$, Perimeter: $P = a + b + c$

Pythagorean Theorem: A triangle is a right triangle if and only if $a^2 + b^2 = c^2$.

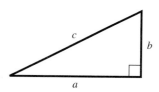

Parallelogram: A four-sided figure with opposite sides parallel

Area: $A = bh$

Rhombus: A four-sided figure with four equal sides

Perimeter: $P = 4a$

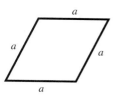

Rectangle: A four-sided figure with four right angles

Area: $A = LW$

Perimeter: $P = 2L + 2W$

Circle

Area: $A = \pi r^2$

Circumference: $C = 2\pi r$

Diameter: $d = 2r$

Right Circular Cone

Volume: $V = \frac{1}{3}\pi r^2 h$

Lateral Surface Area: $S = \pi r\sqrt{r^2 + h^2}$

Rectangular Solid

Volume: $V = LWH$

Surface Area: $A = 2LW + 2WH + 2LH$

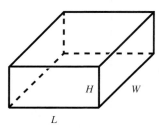

Square: A four-sided figure with four equal sides and four right angles

Area: $A = s^2$

Perimeter: $P = 4s$

Sphere

Volume: $V = \frac{4}{3}\pi r^3$

Surface Area: $S = 4\pi r^2$

Right Circular Cylinder

Volume: $V = \pi r^2 h$

Lateral Surface Area: $S = 2\pi rh$

Geometric Terms

An **angle** is a union of two rays with a common endpoint.

A **right angle** is an angle with a measure of 90°.

Two angles are **complementary** if the sum of their measures is 90°.

An **isosceles triangle** is a triangle that has two equal sides.

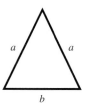

Similar triangles are triangles that have the same shape. Their corresponding angles are equal and corresponding sides are proportional:

$$\frac{a}{d} = \frac{b}{e} = \frac{c}{f}$$

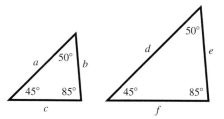

An **acute angle** is an angle with a measure between 0° and 90°.

An **obtuse angle** is an angle with a measure between 90° and 180°.

Two angles are **supplementary** if the sum of their measures is 180°.

An **equilateral triangle** is a triangle that has three equal sides.

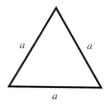

Geometry Review Exercises

(Answers are at the end of the answer section in this text.)

1. Find the perimeter of a triangle whose sides are 3 in., 4 in., and 5 in.

2. Find the area of a triangle whose base is 4 ft and height is 12 ft.

3. If two angles of a triangle are 30° and 90°, then what is the third angle?

4. If the area of a triangle is 36 ft^2 and the base is 12 ft, then what is the height?

5. If the side opposite 30° in a 30-60-90 right triangle is 10 cm, then what is the length of the hypotenuse?

6. Find the area of a trapezoid whose height is 12 cm and whose parallel sides are 4 cm and 20 cm.

7. Find the area of the right triangle that has sides of 6 ft, 8 ft, and 10 ft.

8. If a right triangle has sides of 5 ft, 12 ft, and 13 ft, then what is the length of the hypotenuse?

9. If the hypotenuse of a right triangle is 50 cm and the length of one leg is 40 cm, then what is the length of the other leg?

10. Is a triangle with sides of 5 ft, 10 ft, and 11 ft a right triangle?

11. What is the area of a triangle with sides of 7 yd, 24 yd, and 25 yd?

12. Find the perimeter of a parallelogram in which one side is 9 in. and another side is 6 in.

13. Find the area of a parallelogram which has a base of 8 ft and a height of 4 ft.

14. If one side of a rhombus is 5 km, then what is its perimeter?

15. Find the perimeter and area of a rectangle whose width is 18 in. and length is 2 ft.

16. If the width of a rectangle is 8 yd and its perimeter is 60 yd, then what is its length?

17. The radius of a circle is 4 ft. Find its area to the nearest tenth of a square foot.

18. The diameter of a circle is 12 ft. Find its circumference to the nearest tenth of a foot.

19. A right circular cone has radius 4 cm and height 9 cm. Find its volume to the nearest hundredth of a cubic centimeter.

20. A right circular cone has a radius 12 ft and a height of 20 ft. Find its lateral surface area to the nearest hundredth of a square foot.

21. A shoe box has a length of 12 in., a width of 6 in., and a height of 4 in. Find its volume and surface area.

22. The volume of a rectangular solid is 120 cm^3. If the area of its bottom is 30 cm^2, then what is its height?

23. What is the area and perimeter of a square in which one of the sides is 10 mi long?

24. Find the perimeter of a square whose area is 25 km^2.

25. Find the area of a square whose perimeter is 26 cm.

26. A sphere has a radius of 2 ft. Find its volume to the nearest thousandth of a cubic foot and its surface area to the nearest thousandth of a square foot.

27. A can of soup (right circular cylinder) has a radius of 2 in. and a height of 6 in. Find its volume to the nearest tenth of a cubic inch and total surface area to the nearest tenth of a square inch.

28. If one of two complementary angles is 34°, then what is the other angle?

29. If the perimeter of an isosceles triangle is 29 cm and one of the equal sides is 12 cm, then what is the length of the shortest side of the triangle?

30. A right triangle with sides of 6 in., 8 in., and 10 in., is similar to another right triangle that has a hypotenuse of 25 in. What are the lengths of the other two sides in the second triangle?

31. If one of two supplementary angles is 31°, then what is the other angle?

32. Find the perimeter of an equilateral triangle in which one of the sides is 4 km.

33. Find the length of a side of an equilateral triangle that has a perimeter of 30 yd.

APPENDIX B   TABLE OF SQUARES AND SQUARE ROOTS

n	n^2	$\sqrt{n}$	n	n^2	$\sqrt{n}$	n	n^2	$\sqrt{n}$
1	1	1.0000	41	1681	6.4031	81	6561	9.0000
2	4	1.4142	42	1764	6.4807	82	6724	9.0554
3	9	1.7321	43	1849	6.5574	83	6889	9.1104
4	16	2.0000	44	1936	6.6332	84	7056	9.1652
5	25	2.2361	45	2025	6.7082	85	7225	9.2195
6	36	2.4495	46	2116	6.7823	86	7396	9.2736
7	49	2.6458	47	2209	6.8557	87	7569	9.3274
8	64	2.8284	48	2304	6.9282	88	7744	9.3808
9	81	3.0000	49	2401	7.0000	89	7921	9.4340
10	100	3.1623	50	2500	7.0711	90	8100	9.4868
11	121	3.3166	51	2601	7.1414	91	8281	9.5394
12	144	3.4641	52	2704	7.2111	92	8464	9.5917
13	169	3.6056	53	2809	7.2801	93	8649	9.6437
14	196	3.7417	54	2916	7.3485	94	8836	9.6954
15	225	3.8730	55	3025	7.4162	95	9025	9.7468
16	256	4.0000	56	3136	7.4833	96	9216	9.7980
17	289	4.1231	57	3249	7.5498	97	9409	9.8489
18	324	4.2426	58	3364	7.6158	98	9604	9.8995
19	361	4.3589	59	3481	7.6811	99	9801	9.9499
20	400	4.4721	60	3600	7.7460	100	10000	10.0000
21	441	4.5826	61	3721	7.8102	101	10201	10.0499
22	484	4.6904	62	3844	7.8740	102	10404	10.0995
23	529	4.7958	63	3969	7.9373	103	10609	10.1489
24	576	4.8990	64	4096	8.0000	104	10816	10.1980
25	625	5.0000	65	4225	8.0623	105	11025	10.2470
26	676	5.0990	66	4356	8.1240	106	11236	10.2956
27	729	5.1962	67	4489	8.1854	107	11449	10.3441
28	784	5.2915	68	4624	8.2462	108	11664	10.3923
29	841	5.3852	69	4761	8.3066	109	11881	10.4403
30	900	5.4772	70	4900	8.3666	110	12100	10.4881
31	961	5.5678	71	5041	8.4261	111	12321	10.5357
32	1024	5.6569	72	5184	8.4853	112	12544	10.5830
33	1089	5.7446	73	5329	8.5440	113	12769	10.6301
34	1156	5.8310	74	5476	8.6023	114	12996	10.6771
35	1225	5.9161	75	5625	8.6603	115	13225	10.7238
36	1296	6.0000	76	5776	8.7178	116	13456	10.7703
37	1369	6.0828	77	5929	8.7750	117	13689	10.8167
38	1444	6.1644	78	6084	8.8318	118	13924	10.8628
39	1521	6.2450	79	6241	8.8882	119	14161	10.9087
40	1600	6.3246	80	6400	8.9443	120	14400	10.9545

APPENDIX C   COMMON LOGARITHMS

This table gives the common logarithms for numbers between 1 and 10. The common logarithms for other numbers can be found by using scientific notation and the properties of logarithms. For example, to find log(1230) we write

$$\log(1230) = \log(1.23 \times 10^3) = \log(1.23) + \log(10^3)$$
$$= 0.0899 + 3 = 3.0899$$

n	0	1	2	3	4	5	6	7	8	9
1.0	.0000	.0043	.0086	.0128	.0170	.0212	.0253	.0294	.0334	.0374
1.1	.0414	.0453	.0492	.0531	.0569	.0607	.0645	.0682	.0719	.0755
1.2	.0792	.0828	.0864	.0899	.0934	.0969	.1004	.1038	.1072	.1106
1.3	.1139	.1173	.1206	.1239	.1271	.1303	.1335	.1367	.1399	.1430
1.4	.1461	.1492	.1523	.1553	.1584	.1614	.1644	.1673	.1703	.1732
1.5	.1761	.1790	.1818	.1847	.1875	.1903	.1931	.1959	.1987	.2014
1.6	.2041	.2068	.2095	.2122	.2148	.2175	.2201	.2227	.2253	.2279
1.7	.2304	.2330	.2355	.2380	.2405	.2430	.2455	.2480	.2504	.2529
1.8	.2553	.2577	.2601	.2625	.2648	.2672	.2695	.2718	.2742	.2765
1.9	.2788	.2810	.2833	.2856	.2878	.2900	.2923	.2945	.2967	.2989
2.0	.3010	.3032	.3054	.3075	.3096	.3118	.3139	.3160	.3181	.3201
2.1	.3222	.3243	.3263	.3284	.3304	.3324	.3345	.3365	.3385	.3404
2.2	.3424	.3444	.3464	.3483	.3502	.3522	.3541	.3560	.3579	.3598
2.3	.3617	.3636	.3655	.3674	.3692	.3711	.3729	.3747	.3766	.3784
2.4	.3802	.3820	.3838	.3856	.3874	.3892	.3909	.3927	.3945	.3962
2.5	.3979	.3997	.4014	.4031	.4048	.4065	.4082	.4099	.4116	.4133
2.6	.4150	.4166	.4183	.4200	.4216	.4232	.4249	.4265	.4281	.4298
2.7	.4314	.4330	.4346	.4362	.4378	.4393	.4409	.4425	.4440	.4456
2.8	.4472	.4487	.4502	.4518	.4533	.4548	.4564	.4579	.4594	.4609
2.9	.4624	.4639	.4654	.4669	.4683	.4698	.4713	.4728	.4742	.4757
3.0	.4771	.4786	.4800	.4814	.4829	.4843	.4857	.4871	.4886	.4900
3.1	.4914	.4928	.4942	.4955	.4969	.4983	.4997	.5011	.5024	.5038
3.2	.5051	.5065	.5079	.5092	.5105	.5119	.5132	.5145	.5159	.5172
3.3	.5185	.5198	.5211	.5224	.5237	.5250	.5263	.5276	.5289	.5302
3.4	.5315	.5328	.5340	.5353	.5366	.5378	.5391	.5403	.5416	.5428
3.5	.5441	.5453	.5465	.5478	.5490	.5502	.5514	.5527	.5539	.5551
3.6	.5563	.5575	.5587	.5599	.5611	.5623	.5635	.5647	.5658	.5670
3.7	.5682	.5694	.5705	.5717	.5729	.5740	.5752	.5763	.5775	.5786
3.8	.5798	.5809	.5821	.5832	.5843	.5855	.5866	.5877	.5888	.5899
3.9	.5911	.5922	.5933	.5944	.5955	.5966	.5977	.5988	.5999	.6010
4.0	.6021	.6031	.6042	.6053	.6064	.6075	.6085	.6096	.6107	.6117
4.1	.6128	.6138	.6149	.6160	.6170	.6180	.6191	.6201	.6212	.6222
4.2	.6232	.6243	.6253	.6263	.6274	.6284	.6294	.6304	.6314	.6325
4.3	.6335	.6345	.6355	.6365	.6375	.6385	.6395	.6405	.6415	.6425
4.4	.6435	.6444	.6454	.6464	.6474	.6484	.6493	.6503	.6513	.6522
4.5	.6532	.6542	.6551	.6561	.6571	.6580	.6590	.6599	.6609	.6618
4.6	.6628	.6637	.6646	.6656	.6665	.6675	.6684	.6693	.6702	.6712
4.7	.6721	.6730	.6739	.6749	.6758	.6767	.6776	.6785	.6794	.6803
4.8	.6812	.6821	.6830	.6839	.6848	.6857	.6866	.6875	.6884	.6893
4.9	.6902	.6911	.6920	.6928	.6937	.6946	.6955	.6964	.6972	.6981
n	0	1	2	3	4	5	6	7	8	9

n	0	1	2	3	4	5	6	7	8	9
5.0	.6990	.6998	.7007	.7016	.7024	.7033	.7042	.7050	.7059	.7067
5.1	.7076	.7084	.7093	.7101	.7110	.7118	.7126	.7135	.7143	.7152
5.2	.7160	.7168	.7177	.7185	.7193	.7202	.7210	.7218	.7226	.7235
5.3	.7243	.7251	.7259	.7267	.7275	.7284	.7292	.7300	.7308	.7316
5.4	.7324	.7332	.7340	.7348	.7356	.7364	.7372	.7380	.7388	.7396
5.5	.7404	.7412	.7419	.7427	.7435	.7443	.7451	.7459	.7466	.7474
5.6	.7482	.7490	.7497	.7505	.7513	.7520	.7528	.7536	.7543	.7551
5.7	.7559	.7566	.7574	.7582	.7589	.7597	.7604	.7612	.7619	.7627
5.8	.7634	.7642	.7649	.7657	.7664	.7672	.7679	.7686	.7694	.7701
5.9	.7709	.7716	.7723	.7731	.7738	.7745	.7752	.7760	.7767	.7774
6.0	.7782	.7789	.7796	.7803	.7810	.7818	.7825	.7832	.7839	.7846
6.1	.7853	.7860	.7868	.7875	.7882	.7889	.7896	.7903	.7910	.7917
6.2	.7924	.7931	.7938	.7945	.7952	.7959	.7966	.7973	.7980	.7987
6.3	.7993	.8000	.8007	.8014	.8021	.8028	.8035	.8041	.8048	.8055
6.4	.8062	.8069	.8075	.8082	.8089	.8096	.8102	.8109	.8116	.8122
6.5	.8129	.8136	.8142	.8149	.8156	.8162	.8169	.8176	.8182	.8189
6.6	.8195	.8202	.8209	.8215	.8222	.8228	.8235	.8241	.8248	.8254
6.7	.8261	.8267	.8274	.8280	.8287	.8293	.8299	.8306	.8312	.8319
6.8	.8325	.8331	.8338	.8344	.8351	.8357	.8363	.8370	.8376	.8382
6.9	.8388	.8395	.8401	.8407	.8414	.8420	.8426	.8432	.8439	.8445
7.0	.8451	.8457	.8463	.8470	.8476	.8482	.8488	.8494	.8500	.8506
7.1	.8513	.8519	.8525	.8531	.8537	.8543	.8549	.8555	.8561	.8567
7.2	.8573	.8579	.8585	.8591	.8597	.8603	.8609	.8615	.8621	.8627
7.3	.8633	.8639	.8645	.8651	.8657	.8663	.8669	.8675	.8681	.8686
7.4	.8692	.8698	.8704	.8710	.8716	.8722	.8727	.8733	.8739	.8745
7.5	.8751	.8756	.8762	.8768	.8774	.8779	.8785	.8791	.8797	.8802
7.6	.8808	.8814	.8820	.8825	.8831	.8837	.8842	.8848	.8854	.8859
7.7	.8865	.8871	.8876	.8882	.8887	.8893	.8899	.8904	.8910	.8915
7.8	.8921	.8927	.8932	.8938	.8943	.8949	.8954	.8960	.8965	.8971
7.9	.8976	.8982	.8987	.8993	.8998	.9004	.9009	.9015	.9020	.9025
8.0	.9031	.9036	.9042	.9047	.9053	.9058	.9063	.9069	.9074	.9079
8.1	.9085	.9090	.9096	.9101	.9106	.9112	.9117	.9122	.9128	.9133
8.2	.9138	.9143	.9149	.9154	.9159	.9165	.9170	.9175	.9180	.9186
8.3	.9191	.9196	.9201	.9206	.9212	.9217	.9222	.9227	.9232	.9238
8.4	.9243	.9248	.9253	.9258	.9263	.9269	.9274	.9279	.9284	.9289
8.5	.9294	.9299	.9304	.9309	.9315	.9320	.9325	.9330	.9335	.9340
8.6	.9345	.9350	.9355	.9360	.9365	.9370	.9375	.9380	.9385	.9390
8.7	.9395	.9400	.9405	.9410	.9415	.9420	.9425	.9430	.9435	.9440
8.8	.9445	.9450	.9455	.9460	.9465	.9469	.9474	.9479	.9484	.9489
8.9	.9494	.9499	.9504	.9509	.9513	.9518	.9523	.9528	.9533	.9538
9.0	.9542	.9547	.9552	.9557	.9562	.9566	.9571	.9576	.9581	.9586
9.1	.9590	.9595	.9600	.9605	.9609	.9614	.9619	.9624	.9628	.9633
9.2	.9638	.9643	.9647	.9652	.9657	.9661	.9666	.9671	.9675	.9680
9.3	.9685	.9689	.9694	.9699	.9703	.9708	.9713	.9717	.9722	.9727
9.4	.9731	.9736	.9741	.9745	.9750	.9754	.9759	.9763	.9768	.9773
9.5	.9777	.9782	.9786	.9791	.9795	.9800	.9805	.9809	.9814	.9818
9.6	.9823	.9827	.9832	.9836	.9841	.9845	.9850	.9854	.9859	.9863
9.7	.9868	.9872	.9877	.9881	.9886	.9890	.9894	.9899	.9903	.9908
9.8	.9912	.9917	.9921	.9926	.9930	.9934	.9939	.9943	.9948	.9952
9.9	.9956	.9961	.9965	.9969	.9974	.9978	.9983	.9987	.9991	.9996
n	0	1	2	3	4	5	6	7	8	9

Chapter 1

Section 1.1 Warm-ups F F F F T T T F T T
1. A set is a collection of objects.
3. A Venn diagram is used to illustrate relationships between sets.
5. Every member of set A is also a member of set B.
7. F   **9.** T   **11.** T   **13.** F   **15.** F   **17.** F   **19.** $\varnothing$
21. $\{1, 3, 5\}$ **23.** $\{1, 2, 3, 4, 5, 6, 8\}$ **25.** A **27.** $\varnothing$
29. A **31.** $=$ **33.** $\cup$ **35.** $\cap$ **37.** $\notin$ **39.** $\in$
41. T   **43.** T   **45.** T   **47.** T   **49.** F   **51.** T
53. $\{2, 3, 4, 5, 6, 7, 8\}$ **55.** $\{3, 5\}$ **57.** $\{1, 2, 3, 4, 5, 6, 8\}$
59. $\{2, 3, 4, 5\}$ **61.** $\{2, 3, 4, 5, 7\}$ **63.** $\{2, 3, 4, 5\}$
65. $\{2, 3, 4, 5, 7\}$ **67.** $\subseteq$ **69.** $\in$ **71.** $\cap$
73. $\subseteq$ **75.** $\cap$ **77.** $\cup$ **79.** $\{2, 4, 6, \ldots, 18\}$
81. $\{13, 15, 17, \ldots\}$ **83.** $\{6, 8, 10, \ldots, 78\}$
85. $\{x \mid x$ is a natural number between 2 and $7\}$
87. $\{x \mid x$ is an odd natural number greater than $4\}$
89. $\{x \mid x$ is an even natural number between 5 and $83\}$
91. No
93. a) $3 \in \{1, 2, 3\}$ **b)** $\{3\} \subseteq \{1, 2, 3\}$ **c)** $\varnothing \neq \{\varnothing\}$

Section 1.2 Warm-ups F T F F T F T F T
1. The integers consist of the positive and negative counting numbers and zero.
3. The repeating or terminating decimal numbers are rational numbers.
5. The set of real numbers is the union of the rational and irrational numbers.
7. T   **9.** F   **11.** T   **13.** T
15. $\{0, 1, 2, 3, 4, 5\}$
17. $\{-4, -3, -2, -1, 0, 1, \ldots\}$
19. $\{1, 2, 3, 4\}$
21. $\{-2, -1, 0, 1, 2, 3, 4\}$
23. All   **25.** $\left\{0, \frac{8}{2}\right\}$ **27.** $\left\{-3, -\frac{5}{2}, -0.025, 0, 3\frac{1}{2}, \frac{8}{2}\right\}$
29. T   **31.** F   **33.** T   **35.** F   **37.** F   **39.** F   **41.** T
43. $\subseteq$ **45.** $\not\subseteq$ **47.** $\subseteq$ **49.** $\subseteq$ **51.** $\subseteq$ **53.** $\in$
55. $\in$ **57.** $\in$ **59.** $\notin$ **61.** $\subseteq$ **63.** $\subseteq$
65. $(1, \infty)$ **67.** $(-\infty, -1)$

69. $(3, 4)$ **71.** $[0, 2]$

73. $[1, 3)$

75. $[5, 7]$ **77.** $(-3, 0]$ **79.** $[60, \infty)$ **81.** $(-\infty, -5)$
83. $(1, 9)$ **85.** $(2, 3)$ **87.** $(-2, \infty)$ **89.** $(0, 2)$
91. $[2, 9]$ **93.** $[2, 6)$

Section 1.3 Warm-ups T T F T T F F F F T
1. The absolute value of a number is the number's distance from 0 on the number line.
3. Subtract their absolute values and use the sign of the number with the larger absolute value.
5. Multiply their absolute values, then affix a positive sign if the original numbers have the same sign and a negative sign if the original numbers have opposite signs.
7. 34   **9.** 0   **11.** 0   **13.** -9 **15.** 9   **17.** -3 **19.** 4
21. -7 **23.** -2 **25.** -10 **27.** -26 **29.** -2
31. -5 **33.** 0   **35.** $\frac{1}{10}$ **37.** $-\frac{1}{6}$ **39.** -14.98
41. -2.71 **43.** 2.803   **45.** -0.2649 **47.** -3
49. -11 **51.** 13   **53.** -6 **55.** -9 **57.** 23   **59.** 1
61. $-\frac{1}{2}$ **63.** 1.97   **65.** 7.3   **67.** -50.73 **69.** 1.27
71. -75 **73.** $\frac{1}{6}$ **75.** -0.09 **77.** 0.2   **79.** $\frac{1}{20}$ or 0.05
81. $-\frac{5}{6}$ **83.** $-\frac{10}{3}$ **85.** -2 **87.** -37.5 **89.** -0.08
91. 0.25   **93.** -12 **95.** $\frac{3}{5}$ **97.** -91.25 **99.** 17,000
101. -49 **103.** -7 **105.** 15   **107.** -342
109. $\frac{3}{4}$ **111.** -3 **113.** 20   **115.** 0   **117.** -180
119. $-\frac{1}{6}$ **121.** -55 **123.** -1 **125.** $-\frac{39}{2}$
127. 27.99   **129.** -29.3 **131.** -0.7 **133.** 2
135. \$44,400   **137.** $20°F$ **139.** 1014 ft

Section 1.4 Warm-ups F T T F F F T T F F
1. An arithmetic expression is the result of writing numbers in a meaningful combination with the ordinary operations of arithmetic.
3. Grouping symbols are used to indicate the order in which operations are to be performed.
5. The order of operations tells us the order in which to perform operations when we omit grouping symbols.

7. −22   **9.** −8   **11.** −14   **13.** 32   **15.** 1   **17.** $\frac{1}{9}$

19. 7   **21.** 10   **23.** 8   **25.** −8   **27.** 17   **29.** $\frac{1}{24}$

31. 58   **33.** −25   **35.** −200   **37.** 40   **39.** −25

41. −7.5   **43.** −22.4841   **45.** −1.9602   **47.** −276.48

49. −2   **51.** −1   **53.** −6   **55.** 0   **57.** −7   **59.** $-\frac{4}{3}$

61. −8   **63.** 5   **65.** $-\frac{5}{2}$ **67.** 4   **69.** $\frac{10}{9}$ **71.** $\frac{3}{4}$

73. −2.67   **75.** 41   **77.** 27   **79.** 1   **81.** 9   **83.** −1

85. 26   **87.** $-\frac{3}{2}$ **89.** −2   **91.** $\frac{5}{12}$ **93.** 17

95. −46   **97.** 3   **99.** −8

101. 26 beats per minute, age 43   **103.** 104 feet

105. a) $60,000   **b)** $60,776.47

107. $5500, $5441.96   **109.** $24,169

Section 1.5 Warm-ups T F F F F F T T F T

1. The commutative property of addition states that $a + b = b + a$ and the commutative property of multiplication states that $a \cdot b = b \cdot a$.

3. The commutative property of addition states that you get the same result when you add two numbers in either order. The associative property of addition has to do with which two numbers are added first when adding three numbers.

5. Zero is the additive identity because adding zero to a number does not change the number.

7. 1   **9.** −14   **11.** −24   **13.** −1.7   **15.** −19.8

17. $4x − 24$ **19.** $2(m + 5)$ **21.** $3a + at$

23. $−2w + 10$ **25.** $−6 + 2y$ **27.** $5(x − 1)$

29. $2x + y$ **31.** $6w + 9y$ **33.** $3(y − 5)$ **35.** $3(a + 3)$

37. $2x + 4$ **39.** $−x + 2$ **41.** 2   **43.** 1   **45.** $\frac{1}{6}$

47. 4   **49.** $-\frac{10}{7}$ **51.** $-\frac{5}{9}$ **53.** 0.6200

55. 0.7326   **57.** 1450 mph   **59.** 217 buttons per hour

61. Commutative property of addition

63. Distributive property

65. Associative property of multiplication

67. Multiplicative inverse property

69. Commutative property of multiplication

71. Multiplicative identity property

73. Distributive property

75. Additive inverse property

77. Multiplication property of zero

79. Distributive property

81. $w + 5$ **83.** $(5x)y$ **85.** $\frac{1}{2}(x − 1)$

87. $3(2x + 3)$ **89.** 1   **91.** 0   **93.** 4

Section 1.6 Warm-ups T F T T F T F F F T

1. A term is a single number or a product of a number and one or more variables.

3. The coefficient of a term is the number preceding the variables.

5. You can multiply and divide unlike terms.

7. 9000   **9.** 1   **11.** 527   **13.** 470   **15.** 38

17. 48,000   **19.** 0   **21.** 398   **23.** 1   **25.** 1700

27. 374   **29.** 0   **31.** $2n$ **33.** $7w$ **35.** $−11mw^2$

37. $−3x$ **39.** $−4 − 7z$ **41.** $9t^2$ **43.** $−4ab + 3a^2b$

45. $8mn$ **47.** $−2x^3y$ **49.** $−2kz^6$ **51.** $28t$ **53.** $10x^2$

55. h^2 **57.** $−28w$ **59.** $−x + x^2$ **61.** $25k^2$ **63.** y

65. $2y$ **67.** $3x^3$ **69.** $x^2y + 5x$ **71.** $−x + 2$

73. $\frac{1}{2}xt − 5$ **75.** $−3a + 1$ **77.** $10 − x$

79. $3m + 1$ **81.** $−12b + at$ **83.** $2t^2 − 3w$

85. $y^2 + z$ **87.** $9x + 8$ **89.** $2x − 2$ **91.** $−2a^2 + 2c$

93. $7t^2 − 9w$ **95.** $m − 12$ **97.** $−7k^3 − 17$

99. $0.96x − 2$ **101.** $0.06x − 1.5$ **103.** $−4k + 16$

105. $−4.5x + 17.83$ **107.** $−4xy − 22$ **109.** $−29w^2$

111. $−6a^2w^2$ **113.** $2x^2y + \frac{1}{3}$ **115.** $\frac{1}{4}m^2 − m$

117. $4t^3 + 3t^2 − 1$ **119.** $2xyz + xy − 3z$ **121.** $3s + 6$ ft

123. $\frac{13}{3}x$ m, $\frac{7}{6}x^2$ m^2

Chapter 1 Wrap-Up

Enriching Your Mathematical Word Power

1. a   **2.** c   **3.** a   **4.** d   **5.** a   **6.** c   **7.** a   **8.** d

9. b   **10.** a   **11.** b   **12.** a   **13.** b   **14.** c

Review Exercises

1. T   **3.** F   **5.** T   **7.** F   **9.** T   **11.** T   **13.** F

15. T   **17.** F   **19.** T   **21.** $\{0, 1, 31\}$

23. $\{−1, 0, 1, 31\}$ **25.** $\{−\sqrt{2}, \sqrt{3}, \pi\}$

27. $(0, \infty)$ **29.** $(5, 6)$

31. $[−1, 2)$

33. $(0, 5)$ **35.** $(3, 4)$ **37.** $[2, 8)$ **39.** 5   **41.** −12

43. −24   **45.** 2   **47.** $-\frac{1}{6}$ **49.** 10   **51.** 9.96

53. −4   **55.** 0   **57.** −4   **59.** 0   **61.** 39   **63.** 121

65. 23   **67.** 2   **69.** 23   **71.** −96   **73.** 5   **75.** −1

77. 0.76   **79.** 1   **81.** −3   **83.** 4   **85.** 1   **87.** −8

89. 1   **91.** −35   **93.** 2   **95.** 5   **97.** −1

99. Commutative property of addition

101. Distributive property

103. Associative property of multiplication

105. Multiplicative identity property

107. Multiplicative inverse property

109. Multiplication property of zero

111. Additive identity property

113. Additive inverse property

115. $3(x − a)$ **117.** $3w + 3$ **119.** $7(x + 1)$

121. $5x − 25$ **123.** $−6x + 15$ **125.** $p(1 − t)$

127. $7a + 2$ **129.** $−t − 2$ **131.** $−2a + 4$

133. $4x + 33$ **135.** $−0.8x − 0.48$ **137.** $−0.05x − 1.85$

139. $\frac{1}{4}x + 4$ **141.** $-3x^2 - 2x + 1$

143. 0, additive inverse, multiplication property of zero
145. 7680, distributive
147. 48, associative property of addition, additive inverse, additive identity
149. 0, distributive, additive inverse
151. 47, associative property of multiplication, multiplicative inverse
153. -24, commutative property of multiplication, associative property of multiplication
155. 0, additive inverse, multiplication property of zero
157. Seven shingles per minute
159. a) \$41,013   **b)** 2015

Chapter 1 Test

1. $\{2, 3, 4, 5, 6, 7, 8, 10\}$ **2.** $\{6, 7\}$ **3.** $\{4, 6, 8, 10\}$
4. $\{0, 8\}$ **5.** $\{-4, 0, 8\}$ **6.** $\left\{-4, -\frac{1}{2}, 0, 1.65, 8\right\}$
7. $\{-\sqrt{3}, \sqrt{5}, \pi\}$ **8.** ← + ● ● ● ● ● ● ● ● ● + →
$\qquad$ $-3\ -2\ -1\ \ 0\ \ 1\ \ 2\ \ 3\ \ 4\ \ 5$
9. ← (+ + + + + + +] →
$\qquad$ $-3\ -2\ -1\ \ 0\ \ 1\ \ 2\ \ 3\ \ 4\ \ 5$
10. $(-\infty, 4)$ **11.** $[4, 8)$ **12.** -9 **13.** 8
14. -11 **15.** -1.98 **16.** -2 **17.** -4
18. $\frac{1}{18}$ **19.** -12 **20.** 7   **21.** -3 **22.** 0
23. 4780   **24.** 240   **25.** 40   **26.** 7   **27.** 0
28. Distributive property
29. Commutative property of multiplication
30. Associative property of addition
31. Additive inverse property
32. Commutative property of multiplication
33. $11m - 3$ **34.** $0.95x + 2.9$
35. $\frac{3}{4}x - \frac{5}{4}$ **36.** $5x^2$ **37.** $3x^2 + 2x - 1$
38. $5(x - 8)$ **39.** $7(t - 1)$ **40.** 16 trees per hour
41. $4x - 8, x^2 - 4x$, 28 ft, 45 ft^2
42. 12.6 billion

Chapter 2

Section 2.1 Warm-ups F T F T T T T T T T

1. An equation is a sentence that expresses the equality of two algebraic expressions.
3. Equivalent equations are equations that have the same solution set.
5. If the equation involves fractions then multiply each side by the LCD.
7. A conditional equation is an equation that has at least one solution but is not an identity.
9. Yes   **11.** Yes   **13.** No   **15.** No   **17.** $\{-87\}$
19. $\{-24\}$ **21.** $\left\{\frac{3}{2}\right\}$ **23.** $\{-1\}$ **25.** $\{-3\}$ **27.** $\left\{\frac{5}{2}\right\}$
29. $\{18\}$ **31.** $\{18\}$ **33.** $\{0\}$ **35.** $\left\{-\frac{28}{3}\right\}$ **37.** $\left\{-\frac{28}{5}\right\}$

39. $\{2\}$ **41.** $\{12\}$ **43.** $\{-7\}$ **45.** $\{12\}$ **47.** $\{6\}$
49. $\{90\}$ **51.** $\{1000\}$ **53.** $\{800\}$ **55.** $\varnothing$, inconsistent
57. R, identity   **59.** $\{1\}$, conditional   **61.** R, identity
63. R, identity   **65.** $\varnothing$, inconsistent   **67.** R, identity
69. $\{-4\}$, conditional   **71.** $\{1\}$ **73.** $\left\{\frac{5}{18}\right\}$ **75.** $\left\{\frac{121}{48}\right\}$
77. $\left\{\frac{19}{13}\right\}$ **79.** $\left\{\frac{10}{29}\right\}$ **81.** $\{3\}$ **83.** $\{16\}$ **85.** $\left\{\frac{3}{4}\right\}$
87. $\{-15\}$ **89.** $\{6\}$ **91.** $\{6\}$ **93.** $\{-2\}$
95. $\{53,191.49\}$ **97.** $\{4.7\}$
99. a) 42.2 million   **b)** 2010   **c)** increasing

Section 2.2 Warm-ups F F F T F T F T T F

1. A formula is an equation involving two or more variables.
3. Solving for a variable means to rewrite the formula by isolating the indicated variable.
5. To find the value of a variable, solve for that variable, then replace all other variables with the given numbers.
7. $t = \frac{I}{Pr}$ **9.** $C = \frac{5}{9}(F - 32)$ **11.** $W = \frac{A}{L}$
13. $b_1 = 2A - b_2$ **15.** $L = \frac{P - 2W}{2}$ or $L = \frac{1}{2}P - W$
17. $h = \frac{V}{\pi r^2}$ **19.** $y = -\frac{2}{3}x + 3$ **21.** $y = x - 4$
23. $y = \frac{3}{2}x - 6$ **25.** $y = \frac{1}{2}x + \frac{1}{2}$ **27.** $t = \frac{A - P}{Pr}$
29. $a = \frac{1}{b + 1}$ **31.** $y = \frac{12}{1 - x}$ **33.** $x = \frac{6}{w^2 - y^2 - z^2}$
35. $R_1 = \frac{RR_2}{R_2 - R}$ **37.** 12.472   **39.** 34.932   **41.** 0.539
43. $\frac{1}{3}$ **45.** $\frac{13}{2}$ **47.** -1 **49.** 4   **51.** -4.4507
53. $\frac{5}{8}$ **55.** $-\frac{7}{2}$ **57.** -10 **59.** $-\frac{8}{3}$ **61.** 4
63. $A = \pi r^2$ **65.** $r = \frac{C}{2\pi}$ **67.** $W = \frac{P - 2L}{2}$ **69.** 15%
71. 5.75 yards   **73.** 7.2 feet   **75.** 5 feet   **77.** 15 feet
79. 14 inches   **81.** 168 feet   **83.** 1.5 meters
85. 3979 miles   **87.** 4.24 inches   **89.** 95,232 pounds
91. a) 2457   **b)** 420   **93.** 200 feet   **95.** \$1200

Section 2.3 Warm-ups F T F F T T F T F F

1. Three unknown consecutive integers are represented by x, $x + 1$, and $x + 2$.
3. The formula $P = 2L + 2W$ expresses the perimeter in terms of length and width.
5. The commission is a percentage of the selling price.
7. $x, x + 2$ **9.** $x, 10 - x$ **11.** $0.85x$ **13.** $3x$ miles
15. $4x + 10$ **17.** 27, 28, 29   **19.** 82, 84, 86   **21.** 63, 65
23. Width 46 meters, length 93 meters
25. 161 feet, 312 feet, 211 feet
27. Width 11.25 feet, length 27.5 feet
29. \$1500 at 6%, \$2500 at 10%   **31.** \$80,000
33. $\frac{40}{3}$ gallons   **35.** 1.36 ounces   **37.** 40 mph

39. 15 mph **41.** $86,957
43. $8450 **45.** 18 feet **47.** Packers 35, Chiefs 10
49. $8.67 per pound **51.** 30 pounds **53.** $\frac{40}{7}$ quarts
55. $10,720 million
57. Brian $14,400, Daniel $7,200, Raymond $3,800
59. 22, 23 **61.** 7.5 hours **63.** 20 meters by 20 meters
65. $500 at 8%, $2500 at 10%
67. 2 gallons of 5% solution, 3 gallons of 10% solution
69. Todd 46, Darla 32

Section 2.4 Warm-ups F F T F F F T T T T
1. An inequality is a sentence that expresses inequality between two algebraic expressions.
3. If a is less than b, then a lies to the left of b on the number line.
5. When you multiply or divide by a negative number, the inequality symbol is reversed.
7. F **9.** T **11.** T **13.** T **15.** Yes **17.** No
19. No
21. $(-\infty, -1]$ **23.** $(20, \infty)$

25. $[3, \infty)$ **27.** $(-\infty, 2.3)$

29. $>$ **31.** $>$ **33.** $\le$ **35.** $>$
37. $(-2, \infty)$ **39.** $[-4, \infty)$

41. $(5, \infty)$ **43.** $[-3, \infty)$

45. $(13, \infty)$ **47.** $[-1, \infty)$

49. $(-\infty, 4]$ **51.** $\left(\frac{2}{3}, \infty\right)$

53. $\left(\frac{13}{3}, \infty\right)$ **55.** $(-\infty, \infty)$

57. $\varnothing$ **59.** $(-\infty, \infty)$
61. $\varnothing$ **63.** $x = $ Tony's height, $x > 6$ feet
65. $s = $ Wilma's salary, $s < \$80,000$

67. $v = $ speed of the Concorde, $v \le 1450$ mph
69. $a = $ amount Julie can afford, $a \le \$400$
71. $b = $ Burt's height, $b \le 5$ feet
73. $t = $ Tina's hourly wage, $t \le \$8.20$
75. $x = $ price of car, $x < \$9100$
77. $x = $ price of truck, $x \ge \$9100.92$
79. a) Decreasing **b)** 2011
81. $x = $ final exam score, $x \ge 77$
83. $x = $ the price of A-Mart jeans, $x < \$16.67$
85. a) $[8, \infty)$ **b)** $(-\infty, -6)$ **c)** $(2, \infty)$
  d) $(-\infty, -12)$ **e)** $(2, \infty)$

Section 2.5 Warm-ups T T F T T T F T F T
1. A compound inequality consists of two inequalities joined with the words "and" or "or."
3. A compound inequality using "or" is true when either one or the other or both inequalities is true.
5. The inequality $a < b < c$ means that $a < b$ and $b < c$.
7. No **9.** Yes **11.** No **13.** No **15.** Yes **17.** Yes
19.   **21.**

23.   **25.** $\varnothing$

27.   **29.** $\varnothing$

31. $(-\infty, 1) \cup (10, \infty)$ **33.** $(9, \infty)$

35. $(-6, \infty)$ **37.** $(1, 4]$

39. $(-\infty, \infty)$ **41.** $\varnothing$

43. $(4, 7)$ **45.** $[-3, 2)$

47. $\left(-\frac{7}{3}, 3\right]$ **49.** $(-1, 5)$

51. $[2, 3]$ **53.** $(2, \infty)$ **55.** $(-\infty, 5)$

57. $[2, 4]$ **59.** $(-\infty, \infty)$ **61.** $\varnothing$ **63.** $[4, 5)$
65. $[1, 6]$ **67.** $x > 2$ **69.** $x < 3$
71. $x > 2$ or $x \le -1$ **73.** $-2 \le x < 3$ **75.** $x \ge -3$
77. $x = $ final exam score, $73 \le x \le 86.5$

79. x = price of truck, \$11,033 $\leq x \leq$ \$13,811
81. x = number of cigarettes on the run, $4 \leq x \leq 18$
83. a) 1,226,950 **b)** 2011 **c)** 2019 **d)** 2011
85. $-b < x < -a$ provided $a < b$
87. a) $(12, 32)$ **b)** $(-20, 10]$ **c)** $(0, 9)$ **d)** $[-3, -1]$

Section 2.6 Warm-ups T F F T F T F F T F
1. Absolute value of a number is the number's distance from 0 on the number line.
3. Since both 4 and -4 are four units from 0, $|x| = 4$ has two solutions.
5. Since the distance from 0 for every number on the number line is greater than or equal to 0, $|x| \geq 0$.
7. $\{-5, 5\}$ **9.** $\{2, 4\}$ **11.** $\{-3, 9\}$ **13.** $\left\{-\dfrac{8}{3}, \dfrac{16}{3}\right\}$
15. $\{12\}$ **17.** $\{-20, 80\}$ **19.** $\varnothing$ **21.** $\{0, 5\}$
23. $\{0.143, 1.298\}$ **25.** $\{-2, 2\}$ **27.** $\{-11, 5\}$
29. $\{0, 3\}$ **31.** $\left\{-6, \dfrac{4}{3}\right\}$ **33.** $\{1, 3\}$ **35.** $(-\infty, \infty)$
37. $|x| < 2$ **39.** $|x| > 3$ **41.** $|x| \leq 1$ **43.** $|x| \geq 2$
45. No **47.** Yes **49.** No **51.** Yes
53. $(-\infty, -6) \cup (6, \infty)$

55. $(-3, 3)$

57. $(-\infty, -1] \cup [5, \infty)$

59. $\left(-\dfrac{1}{2}, \dfrac{9}{2}\right)$

61. $[-2, 12]$

63. $\left(-\infty, -\dfrac{9}{2}\right] \cup \left[\dfrac{15}{2}, \infty\right)$

65. $(-\infty, 2) \cup (2, \infty)$

67. $(-\infty, \infty)$ **69.** $\varnothing$ **71.** $(-\infty, \infty)$
73. $(-\infty, -3) \cup (-1, \infty)$ **75.** $(-4, 4)$ **77.** $(-1, 1)$
79. $(0.255, 0.847)$ **81.** 1401 or 1429
83. Between 121 and 133 pounds
85. a) 1 sec **b)** 1 sec **c)** $0.5 < t < 1.5$
87. a) $(-\infty, \infty)$ **b)** $(-\infty, \infty)$ **c)** all reals except $n = 0$

Chapter 2 Wrap-Up

Enriching Your Mathematical Word Power
1. c **2.** b **3.** d **4.** c **5.** c **6.** d **7.** d **8.** a
9. d **10.** d **11.** d **12.** c **13.** d

Review Exercises
1. $\{8\}$ **3.** $\left\{-\dfrac{3}{2}\right\}$ **5.** R **7.** $\varnothing$ **9.** $\{0\}$ **11.** $\{20\}$
13. $\{5\}$ **15.** $\{5\}$ **17.** $x = \dfrac{-b}{a}$ **19.** $x = \dfrac{2}{c - a}$

21. $x = \dfrac{P}{mw}$ **23.** $x = \dfrac{2}{2w - 1}$ **25.** $y = \dfrac{3}{2}x + 3$
27. $y = -\dfrac{1}{3}x + 4$ **29.** $y = 2x - 20$
31. Length 8.5 inches, width 14 inches
33. Wife \$27,000, Roy \$35,000 **35.** \$9500
37. 11 nickels, 4 dimes **39.** 15 miles
41. $(-3, \infty)$ **43.** $(0, \infty)$

45. $(-\infty, -8]$ **47.** $\left(-\infty, \dfrac{11}{2}\right)$

49. $[48, \infty)$ **51.** $(-\infty, -4) \cup (1, \infty)$

53. $(0, 9)$ **55.** $(0, \infty)$

57. $(-\infty, 4)$

59. $\varnothing$ **61.** $(-\infty, \infty)$
63. $\left[-\dfrac{17}{2}, \dfrac{13}{2}\right]$

65. $[1, \infty)$ **67.** $(3, 6)$
69. $(-\infty, \infty)$ **71.** $[-2, -1]$
73. $\{-14, 14\}$

75. $\{3\}$

77. $\varnothing$ **79.** $\{-1, 2\}$

81. $(-\infty, -4] \cup [4, \infty)$

83. $(-\infty, -4) \cup (14, \infty)$

85. $\varnothing$ **87.** $(-\infty, \infty)$

89. $(-\infty, 1) \cup (3, \infty)$

91. x = rental price, \$3 $\leq x \leq$ \$5
93. $(40.2, 53.6)$ **95.** 81 or 91
97. \$50,000 accountant, \$60,000 employees
99. Washington County 1200, Cade County 2400
101. $x > 1$ **103.** $|x - 2| = 0$ **105.** $|x| = 3$

107. $x \leq -1$ **109.** $|x| \leq 2$ **111.** $x \leq 2$ or $x \geq 7$
113. $|x| > 3$ **115.** $5 < x < 7$ **117.** $|x| > 0$

Chapter 2 Test
1. $\{-4\}$ **2.** R **3.** $\{-6, 6\}$ **4.** $\{2, 5\}$ **5.** $y = \frac{2}{5}x - 4$

6. $y = \dfrac{5}{1 - 3x}$ **7.** $[4, 8]$

8. $(-\infty, -7) \cup (13, \infty)$

9. $(5, \infty)$

10. $\left(-8, -\dfrac{1}{2}\right)$

11. $[-5, 3)$

12. $(-\infty, 15)$

13. $\varnothing$ **14.** $(-\infty, \infty)$ **15.** $\varnothing$ **16.** $\{2.5\}$ **17.** $\varnothing$
18. R **19.** $\varnothing$ **20.** R **21.** $\{100\}$ **22.** 13 meters
23. 14 inches   **24.** $300   **25.** 30 liters
26. $|x - 28,000| > 3,000$, Brenda makes more than $31,000 or less than $25,000.

Making Connections Chapters 1–2
1. $11x$ **2.** $30x^2$ **3.** $3x + 1$ **4.** $4x - 3$ **5.** 899
6. 961   **7.** 841   **8.** 25   **9.** 13   **10.** -25 **11.** 5
12. -4 **13.** $-2x + 13$ **14.** 60   **15.** 72   **16.** -9
17. $-3x^3$ **18.** 1   **19.** $\{0\}$ **20.** R **21.** $\{0\}$ **22.** $\{1\}$
23. $\left\{-\dfrac{1}{3}\right\}$ **24.** $\{1\}$ **25.** R **26.** $\{1000\}$ **27.** $\left\{-\dfrac{17}{5}, 1\right\}$
28. a) 87,500   **b)** $C_r = 4,500 + 0.06x$, $C_b = 8,000 + 0.02x$
    c) 87,500   **d)** Buying is $1,300 cheaper.
    e) (75,000, 100,000)

Chapter 3

Section 3.1 Warm-ups F F F T T T T T F T
1. The origin is the point where the x-axis and y-axis intersect.
3. Intercepts are points where a graph crosses the axes.
5. The graph of an equation of the type $x = k$, where k is a fixed number is a vertical line.
7. I   **9.** III   **11.** y-axis   **13.** IV   **15.** II   **17.** x-axis
19. y-axis

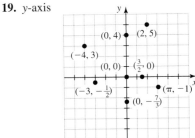

21. $\left(\dfrac{7}{2}, 3\right)$, 5   **23.** (2, 1), 10

25. $\left(-3, -\dfrac{3}{2}\right)$, 13   **27.** $\left(0, \dfrac{5}{2}\right)$, $\sqrt{13}$

29.

31.

33.

35.

37.

39.

41.

43.

45.

47.

49.

51.

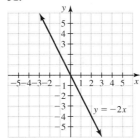

81. a) $25,325 **b)** $320
c)

53.

55.

83. a) $146 **b)**

85. a) $11.45.
b) The number of toppings on a $14.45 pizza is 11.
87. $n + 2b = 100$, 35 binders

57.

59.

89. a) Her weekly cost, revenue, and profit are $517.50, $1275, and $757.50.
b) 1100. She had a profit of $995 on selling 1100 roses.
c) 995. The difference between revenue and cost is $995, which is her profit.

61.

63.

91.

65.

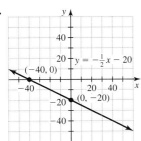

67. $(5, 0), (0, -3)$

93.

95.

69. $(0, 0)$ **71.** $\left(-\frac{1}{2}, 0\right)$ **73.** $\left(0, -\frac{2}{3}\right)$ **75.** $\left(\frac{1}{4}, 0\right)\left(0, \frac{1}{2}\right)$
77. $(2, 0), (3, -3)$ **79.** $(-4, -33), (22, 6)$

Section 3.2 Warm-ups T F F T F F F T F F

1. Slope measures the steepness of a line.
3. A horizontal line has zero slope because it has no rise.
5. If m_1 and m_2 are the slopes of perpendicular lines, then $m_1 = -\dfrac{1}{m_2}$.

7. $\dfrac{2}{3}$ 9. Undefined   11. 0   13. -1 15. $\dfrac{3}{2}$ 17. -1

19. $-\dfrac{5}{3}$ 21. $\dfrac{4}{7}$ 23. 5   25. $-\dfrac{5}{3}$ 27. $-\dfrac{3}{5}$ 29. $-\dfrac{2}{5}$

31. -3 33. 0   35. Undefined   37. 0.169   39. -1.273

41. $\dfrac{8}{3}$ 43. $\dfrac{3}{7}$

45. $-\dfrac{5}{4}$

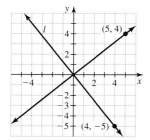

47. Yes   49. No   51. No
53. a) $625 per year   b) Approximately $29,000
    c) $28,635

55. $(3, 5), (0, -7)$ 57. $-\dfrac{5}{2}$ 59. -4.049

61. A horizontal line has zero slope and a vertical line has undefined slope.

63. $-2, \dfrac{1}{2}$, perpendicular

65. Increasing m makes the graph increase faster. The slopes of these lines are 1, 2, 3, and 4.

Section 3.3 Warm-ups T F F T T F T F F T

1. Point-slope form is $y - y_1 = m(x - x_1)$, where m is the slope and (x_1, y_1) is a point on the line.
3. We need the slope and a point on the line. (We might have to find the slope from two points or from knowing the line is parallel or perpendicular to another line.)
5. To find the slope from standard form solve the equation for y to get the form $y = mx + b$, where m is the slope.

7. $y = 2x - 7$ 9. $y = -\dfrac{1}{2}x + 2$ 11. $y = -x - 3$

13. $y = \dfrac{1}{3}x + \dfrac{4}{3}$ 15. $y = 4x - 8$ 17. $y = -\dfrac{3}{4}x$

19. $y = \dfrac{1}{2}x + 2$ 21. $y = -2$ 23. $x = 1$

25. $y = -x$ 27. $y = \dfrac{3}{2}x - 3$ 29. $y = -x + 2$

31. $x - 3y = 6$ 33. $x - 2y = -13$

35. $2x - 6y = 11$ 37. $5x + 6y = 890$

39. $y = -\dfrac{2}{5}x + \dfrac{1}{5}, -\dfrac{2}{5}, \left(0, \dfrac{1}{5}\right)$

41. $y = 3x - 2, 3, (0, -2)$ 43. $y = 2, 0, (0, 2)$

45. $y = 3x - 1, 3, (0, -1)$ 47. $y = \dfrac{3}{2}x + 11, \dfrac{3}{2}, (0, 11)$

49. $y = \dfrac{1}{3}x + \dfrac{7}{12}, \dfrac{1}{3}, \left(0, \dfrac{7}{12}\right)$

51. $y = 0.01x + 6057, 0.01, (0, 6057)$

53. $x - 2y = -10$ 55. $2x + y = 4$

57. $2x - y = -5$ 59. $x + 2y = 7$

61. $2x + y = 3$ 63. $3x - y = -9$

65. $y = 5$

67.   69.

71.   73.

75.   77.

79.

81.

11.

13.

83. Perpendicular   **85.** Parallel
87. Neither   **89.** Perpendicular

91. $t = \dfrac{7}{6}s + 60$, 95°F

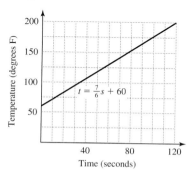

93. a) $y = 0.4x - 774$ **b)** 30 billion tons
95. a) $w = 310.77d - 1610.44$ **b)** 953 ft³/sec
   c) increasing
97. a) $(4, 0), (0, 6)$ **b)** $(a, 0), (0, b)$

   c) $\dfrac{x}{-5} + \dfrac{y}{3} = 1$

   d) Horizontal lines, vertical lines, and lines through $(0, 0)$
101. The lines intersect at $(50, 97)$.

Section 3.4 Warm-ups T F T F T T F T F T
1. A linear inequality is an inequality of the form $Ax + By \le C$ (or using $<$, $>$, or $\ge$), where A, B, and C are real numbers and A and B are not both zero.
3. If the inequality includes equality then the line should be solid.
5. The test point method is used to determine which side of the boundary line to shade.

7.

9.

15.

17.

19.

21.

23.

25.

27.

29.

31.

$\frac{1}{2}x + \frac{1}{3}y < 1$

33.

$y > x$ and $y > -2x + 3$

51.

$0 \leq y \leq x$ and $x \leq 1$

53.

$1 \leq x \leq 3$ and $2 \leq y \leq 5$

35.

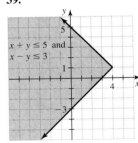

$y < x + 3$ or $y > -x + 2$

37.

$x - 4y < 0$ and $3x + 2y \geq 6$

55.

$|x + y| < 2$

57.

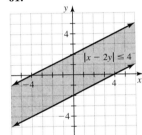

$|2x + y| \geq 1$

39.

$x + y \leq 5$ and $x - y \leq 3$

41.

$x - 2y \leq 4$ or $2x - 3y \leq 6$

59.

$|y - x| > 2$

61.

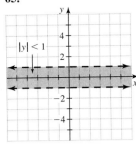

$|x - 2y| \leq 4$

43.

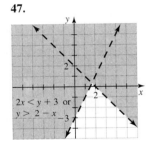

$y > 2$ and $x < 3$

45.

$y \geq x$ and $x \leq 2$

63.

$|x| > 2$

65.

$|y| < 1$

47.

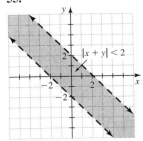

$2x < y + 3$ or $y > 2 - x$

49.

$x - 1 < y < x + 3$

67.

$|x| < 2$ and $|y| < 3$

69.

$|x - 3| < 1$ and $|y - 2| < 1$

71.

$x \geq 0, \ y \geq 0, \ 3x + 4y \leq 24$

73.

$x \geq 0, \ y \geq x, \ 3x + 4y \leq 24$

75.

$h \leq 187 - 0.85a,$
$h \geq 154 - 0.70a,$
$a \geq 20, \ a \leq 75$

77.

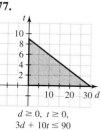

$d \geq 0, \ t \geq 0,$
$3d + 10t \leq 90$

Section 3.5 Warm-ups F T T F T F T F T T
1. It means that b is uniquely determined by a.
3. A relation is any set of ordered pairs.
5. The range of relation is the set of all second coordinates.
7. Yes   **9.** No   **11.** Yes   **13.** No   **15.** No   **17.** Yes
19. No   **21.** Yes   **23.** No   **25.** No   **27.** Yes
29. $(2, 1), (2, -1)$ **31.** $(8, 4), (8, -4)$ **33.** $(0, 1), (0, -1)$
35. $(16, 2), (16, -2)$ **37.** $(3, 1), (3, -1)$ **39.** Yes
41. No   **43.** Yes   **45.** No   **47.** Yes   **49.** No
51. No   **53.** Yes   **55.** No   **57.** $\{4, 7\}, \{1\}$
59. $\{2\}, \{3, 5, 7\}$ **61.** $(-\infty, \infty), (-\infty, \infty)$
63. $(-\infty, \infty), (-\infty, \infty)$ **65.** $[2, \infty), [0, \infty)$
67. $[0, \infty), [0, \infty)$ **69.** -2 **71.** 10 **73.** -12
75. 1 **77.** 2.236 **79.** 2 **81.** 0 **83.** -10
85.

87.

89.

91. a) 192 ft   **b)** 0 ft   **93.** $A = s^2$ or $A(s) = s^2$
95. $C(x) = 3.98x$, \$11.94
97. $C(n) = 14.95 + 0.50n$, \$17.95

Chapter 3 Wrap-Up

Enriching Your Mathematical Word Power
1. d   **2.** a   **3.** a   **4.** b   **5.** c   **6.** a   **7.** b   **8.** b
9. a   **10.** c   **11.** b   **12.** c   **13.** b   **14.** a
15. d   **16.** b

Review Exercises
1. III   **3.** x-axis   **5.** y-axis   **7.** IV   **9.** $(5, 2), 10$
11. $\left(\dfrac{5}{2}, -\dfrac{1}{2}\right), \sqrt{10}$ **13.** $(0, 2), \left(\dfrac{2}{3}, 0\right), (4, -10), \left(\dfrac{5}{3}, -3\right)$
15. 1 **17.** $\dfrac{3}{7}$ **19.** $\dfrac{3}{8}$ **21.** $\dfrac{7}{11}$ **23.** $-3, (0, 4)$
25. $\dfrac{2}{3}, \left(0, \dfrac{7}{3}\right)$ **27.** $2x - 3y = 12$ **29.** $x - 2y = -5$
31. $x - 2y = 7$ **33.** $3x + 4y = 18$ **35.** $y = 5$

37.

39.

41.

43.

45.

47.

49.

51.

69.

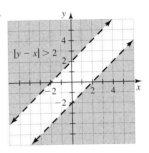

71. No   **73.** Yes   **75.** Yes   **77.** No
79. {3, 4, 5}, {1, 5, 9}   **81.** $(-\infty, \infty), (-\infty, \infty)$
83. $[-5, \infty), [0, \infty)$ **85.** -5 **87.** -6

89. $-\dfrac{21}{4}$ **91.** $3x - y = 6$ **93.** $x + 2y = 7$

95. $x = 2$ **97.** $y = 0$ **99.** $2x - y = -6$
101. $3x - y = -6$ **103.** $y = 5$
109. a) $h = 220 - a$ **b)** 180   **c)** Decreases
111. 62 days

53.

55.

57.

59.

Chapter 3 Test

1. $(0, 5), \left(\dfrac{5}{2}, 0\right), \left(\dfrac{13}{2}, -8\right)$ **2.** $-\dfrac{6}{5}$ **3.** $\left(-\dfrac{1}{2}, -\dfrac{1}{2}\right), \sqrt{26}$

4. $\dfrac{8}{5}, (0, 2)$ **6.** $V = -2,000a + 22,000$ **7.** $x + 2y = 6$

8. $4x + y = -7$ **9.** $5x + 3y = 19$ **10.** $x - 2y = -4$

11.

12.

61.

63.

13.

14.

65.

67.

15.

16.

27.

28.

17.

18. Yes   **19.** 11

29. a) $b = 500a - 24,000$, $b = 667a - 34,689$,
$b = 800a - 43,600$ **b)** \$8,000   **c)** 69
d) The slopes 500, 667, and 800 indicate the additional
amount per year received beyond the basic amount in
each category.

20. $[7, \infty)$, $[0, \infty)$ **21.** $S = 0.50n + 3$ **22.** 6 ft

Making Connections Chapters 1–3
1. 128   **2.** 64   **3.** 49   **4.** -29 **5.** -5 **6.** -5
7. $12t^2$ **8.** $7t$ **9.** $x + 2$ **10.** $7y$ **11.** $7x - 32$
12. $-21x^2 + 8x$ **13.** $\{27\}$ **14.** $\{200\}$ **15.** $\left\{\dfrac{7}{3}\right\}$
16. $\left\{\dfrac{4}{3}, \dfrac{10}{3}\right\}$ **17.** $\varnothing$ **18.** $\left\{0, \dfrac{14}{3}\right\}$

19.

20.

21.

22.

23.

24.

25.

26.

Chapter 4

Section 4.1 Warm-ups T F F T T T T T T
1. The intersection point of the graphs is the solution to an
independent system.
3. The graphing method can be very inaccurate.
5. If the equation you get after substituting turns out to be
incorrect, such as $0 = 9$, then the system has no solution.
7. $\{(1, 2)\}$ **9.** $\{(0, -1)\}$ **11.** $\{(2, -1)\}$ **13.** $\varnothing$
15. $\{(x, y)\} \mid x + 2y = 8\}$ **17.** $\{(-1, 2)\}$ **19.** $\varnothing$ **21.** c
23. b   **25.** $\{(8, 3)\}$, independent
27. $\{(-3, 2)\}$, independent   **29.** $\{(20, 10)\}$, independent
31. $\varnothing$, inconsistent   **33.** $\{(x, y) \mid y = 2x - 5\}$, dependent
35. $\{(5, -1)\}$, independent   **37.** $\{(7, 7)\}$, independent
39. $\{(15, 25)\}$, independent   **41.** $\left\{\left(\dfrac{11}{4}, \dfrac{9}{2}\right)\right\}$, independent
43. $\{(0, 0)\}$, independent   **45.** $\left\{\left(\dfrac{9}{2}, -\dfrac{1}{2}\right)\right\}$, independent
47. $\{(x, y) \mid 3y - 2x = -3\}$, dependent
49. $\varnothing$, inconsistent
51. $\{(0.8, 0.7)\}$, independent
53. Width 13 feet, length 28 feet
55. \$14,000 at 5%, \$16,000 at 10%
57. -12 and 14
59. 94 toasters, 6 vacation coupons
61. State tax \$3,553, federal tax \$28,934
63. \$20,000
65. a) \$500,000   **b)** \$300,000   **c)** 20,000   **d)** \$400,000
67. a
69. a) $(2.8, 2.6)$ **b)** $(1.0, -0.2)$

Section 4.2 Warm-ups T F T T F T T F T T
1. In this section we learned the addition method.
3. In some cases we multiply one or both of the equations on
each side to change the coefficients of the variable we are
trying to eliminate.
5. If an identity, such as $0 = 0$, results from addition of the
equations, then the equations are dependent.
7. $\{(8, -1)\}$ **9.** $\{(5, -7)\}$

11. $\left\{\left(\dfrac{3}{8}, -\dfrac{31}{8}\right)\right\}$ **13.** $\{(-1, 3)\}$ **15.** $\left\{\left(\dfrac{7}{9}, \dfrac{2}{3}\right)\right\}$

17. $\{(-1, -3)\}$ **19.** $\{(-2, -5)\}$ **21.** $\{(22, 26)\}$

23. $\varnothing$, inconsistent   **25.** $\{(x, y) \mid 5x - y = 1\}$, dependent

27. $\left\{\left(\dfrac{5}{2}, 0\right)\right\}$, independent   **29.** $\{(12, 6)\}$ **31.** $\{(-8, 6)\}$

33. $\{(16, 12)\}$ **35.** $\left\{\left(\dfrac{1}{2}, \dfrac{1}{3}\right)\right\}$ **37.** $\{(12, 7)\}$

39. $\{(400, 800)\}$ **41.** $\{(1.5, 1.25)\}$ **43.** $\left\{\left(\dfrac{3}{4}, \dfrac{2}{3}\right)\right\}$

45. $\{(5, 6)\}$ **47.** $\{(2, -17)\}$ **49.** $\{(0, 1)\}$

51. $\{(3, 4)\}$ **53.** $\left\{\left(\dfrac{1}{2}, \dfrac{1}{3}\right)\right\}$ **55.** $\varnothing$ **57.** $\{(x, y) \mid y = x\}$

59. $1.40   **61.** 1380 students   **63.** 31 dimes, 4 nickels

65. a) $(20, 30)$
  b) 20 pounds chocolate, 30 pounds peanut butter
67. 4 hours   **69.** 80%
71. Width 150 meters, length 200 meters

Section 4.3 Warm-ups F F T F F T T F F F
1. A linear equation in three variables is an equation of the form $Ax + By + Cz = D$, where A, B, and C cannot all be zero.
3. A solution to a system of linear equations in three variables is an ordered triple that satisfies all of the equations in the system.
5. The graph of a linear equation in three variables is a plane in a three-dimensional coordinate system.
7. $\{(1, 2, -1)\}$ **9.** $\{(1, 3, 2)\}$ **11.** $\{(1, -5, 3)\}$
13. $\{(-1, 2, -1)\}$ **15.** $\{(-1, -2, 4)\}$
17. $\{(1, 3, 5)\}$ **19.** $\{(3, 4, 5)\}$ **21.** $\varnothing$
23. $\{(x, y, z) \mid 3x - y + z = 5\}$ **25.** $\varnothing$
27. $\{(x, y, z) \mid 5x + 4y - 2z = 150\}$ **29.** $\{(0.1, 0.3, 2)\}$
31. Chevrolet $20,000, Ford $22,000, Toyota $24,000
33. First 10 hr, second 12 hr, third 14 hr
35. $1500 stocks, $4500 bonds, $6000 mutual fund
37. Anna 108 pounds, Bob 118 pounds, Chris 92 pounds
39. 3 nickels, 6 dimes, 4 quarters
41. $24,000 teaching, $18,000 painting, $6,000 royalties
43. Edwin 24, father 51, grandfather 84

Section 4.4 Warm-ups T T T F T F F F T F
1. A matrix is a rectangular array of numbers.
3. The order of a matrix is the number of rows and columns.
5. An augmented matrix is a matrix where the entries in the first column are the coefficients of x, the entries in the second column are the coefficients of y, and the entries in the third column are the constants from a system of two linear equations in two unknowns.
7. 2×2 **9.** 3×2 **11.** 3×1

13. $\begin{bmatrix} 2 & -3 & \mid & 9 \\ -3 & 1 & \mid & -1 \end{bmatrix}$ **15.** $\begin{bmatrix} 1 & -1 & 1 & \mid & 1 \\ 1 & 1 & -2 & \mid & 3 \\ 0 & 1 & -3 & \mid & 4 \end{bmatrix}$

17. $5x + y = -1$
$2x - 3y = 0$

19. $x = 6$
$-x + z = -3$
$x + y = 1$

21. $R_1 \leftrightarrow R_2$ **23.** $\dfrac{1}{5} R_2 \to R_2$ **25.** $\{(1, 2)\}$

27. $\{(4, 5)\}$ **29.** $\{(1, -1)\}$ **31.** $\{(7, 6)\}$ **33.** $\varnothing$
35. $\{(x, y) \mid x + 2y = 1\}$ **37.** $\{(1, 2, 3)\}$ **39.** $\{(1, 1, 1)\}$
41. $\{(1, 2, 0)\}$ **43.** $\{(1, 0, 1)\}$
45. $\{(x, y, z) \mid x - y + z = 1\}$ **47.** $\varnothing$

Section 4.5 Warm-ups T F F T T T T T T T
1. A determinant is a real number associated with a square matrix.
3. Cramer's rule works on systems that have exactly one solution.
5. A minor for an element is obtained by deleting the row and column of the element and finding the determinant of the 2×2 matrix that remains.
7. -1 **9.** -3 **11.** -14 **13.** 0.4 **15.** $\{(1, -3)\}$

17. $\{(1, 1)\}$ **19.** $\left\{\left(\dfrac{23}{13}, \dfrac{9}{13}\right)\right\}$ **21.** $\{(10, 15)\}$

23. $\left\{\left(\dfrac{27}{4}, \dfrac{13}{2}\right)\right\}$ **25.** 11   **27.** 4   **29.** 3   **31.** 1
33. -7 **35.** -1 **37.** 9   **39.** 5   **41.** 22   **43.** 6
45. 70   **47.** 25   **49.** $\{(1, 2, 3)\}$ **51.** $\{(-1, 1, 2)\}$

53. $\{(-3, 2, 1)\}$ **55.** $\left\{\left(\dfrac{3}{2}, \dfrac{1}{2}, 2\right)\right\}$ **57.** $\{(0, 1, -1)\}$

59. a) $(9, 11)$ **b)** 9 servings peas, 11 servings beets
61. Milk $2.40, magazine $2.25
63. 12 singles, 10 doubles   **65.** Gary 39, Harry 34

67. Square 10 feet, triangle $\dfrac{40}{3}$ feet

69. 10 gallons of 10% solution, 20 gallons of 25% solution
71. Mimi 36 pounds, Mitzi 32 pounds, Cassandra 107 pounds
73. $39°, 51°, 90°$ **75.** Use another method.
77. No. These are nonlinear equations.

Section 4.6 Warm-ups F F F F F T F T F T
1. A constraint is an inequality that restricts the values of the variables.
3. Constraints may be limitations on the amount of available supplies, money, or other resources.
5. The maximum or minimum of a linear function subject to linear constraints occurs at a vertex of the region determined by the constraints.

7.

9.

11.

13.

15.

17. a) 0, 320,000, 510,000, 450,000
   b) 30 TV ads and 60 radio ads
19. 6 doubles, 4 triples
21. 0 doubles, 8 triples
23. 1.75 cups Doggie Dinner, 5.5 cups Puppie Power
25. 10 cups Doggie Dinner, 0 cups Puppie Power
27. Laundromat $8,000, carwash $16,000

Chapter 4 Wrap-Up

Enriching Your Mathematical Word Power
1. c   **2.** a   **3.** a   **4.** d   **5.** b
6. c   **7.** a   **8.** c   **9.** d   **10.** b
11. a   **12.** d

Review Exercises
1. {(1, 1)}, independent   **3.** $\{(x, y) \mid x + 2y = 4\}$, dependent
5. $\varnothing$, inconsistent   **7.** {(−3, 2)}, independent
9. $\varnothing$, inconsistent   **11.** $\{(x, y) \mid 2x - y = 3\}$, dependent
13. {(30, 12)}, independent   **15.** $\left\{\left(\dfrac{1}{5}, \dfrac{2}{5}\right)\right\}$, independent
17. {(−1, 5)}, independent
19. $\{(x, y) \mid 3x - 2y = 12\}$, dependent
21. $\varnothing$, inconsistent   **23.** $\left\{\left(2, -\dfrac{1}{3}\right)\right\}$, independent
25. {(20, 60)}, independent   **27.** {(2, 4, 6)}
29. {(1, −3, 2)}   **31.** $\varnothing$ **33.** {(3, 4)}
35. {(2, −4)}   **37.** {(1, 1, 2)}   **39.** 2
41. −0.2   **43.** {(−1, −2)}
45. {(2, 1)}   **47.** 58   **49.** −30
51. {(1, 2, −3)}

53.
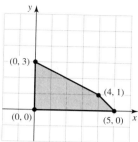

55. 30   **57.** 78   **59.** 36 minutes
61. 4 liters of A, 8 liters of B, 8 liters of C
63. Three servings of each

Chapter 4 Test
1. {(1, 3)}   **2.** $\left\{\left(\dfrac{5}{2}, -3\right)\right\}$ **3.** $\{(x, y) \mid y = x - 5\}$
4. {(−1, 3)}   **5.** $\varnothing$ **6.** Inconsistent   **7.** Dependent
8. Independent   **9.** {(1, −2, −3)}
10. {(2, 5)}   **11.** {(3, 1, 1)}   **12.** −18   **13.** −2
14. {(−1, 2)}   **15.** {(2, −2, 1)}
16. Singles $18, doubles $25
17. Jill 17 hours, Karen 14 hours, Betsy 62 hours   **18.** 44

Making Connections Chapters 1–4
1. −81   **2.** 7   **3.** 73   **4.** 5.94   **5.** $-t - 3$
6. $-0.9x + 0.9$ **7.** $3x^2 + 2x - 1$ **8.** y
9. $y = \dfrac{3}{5}x - \dfrac{7}{5}$ **10.** $y = \dfrac{C}{D}x - \dfrac{W}{D}$ **11.** $y = \dfrac{K}{W - C}$
12. $y = \dfrac{bw - 2A}{b}$ **13.** {(4, −1)}   **14.** {(500, 700)}
15. $\{(x, y) \mid x + 17 = 5y\}$ **16.** $\varnothing$ **17.** $y = \dfrac{5}{9}x + 55$
18. $y = -\dfrac{11}{6}x + \dfrac{2}{3}$ **19.** $y = 5x + 26$ **20.** $y = \dfrac{1}{2}x + 5$
21. $y = 5$ **22.** $x = -7$
23. a) Machine A
   b) Machine B $0.04 per copy, machine A $0.03 per copy
   c) The slopes 0.04 and 0.03 are the per copy cost for each machine.
   d) B: $y = 0.04x + 2000$, A: $y = 0.03x + 4000$
   e) 200,000

Chapter 5

Section 5.1 Warm-ups T F F F T F T T T F
1. An exponential expression is an expression of the form a^n.
3. The product rule states that $a^m a^n = a^{m+n}$.
5. To convert a number in scientific notation to standard notation, move the decimal point n places to the left if the exponent on 10 is $-n$ or move the decimal point n places to the right if the exponent on 10 is n, assuming that n is a positive integer.

7. $4, -4, 4, \dfrac{1}{4}, -\dfrac{1}{4}, \dfrac{1}{4}$ **9.** $8, -8, -8, \dfrac{1}{8}, -\dfrac{1}{8}, -\dfrac{1}{8}$

11. $\dfrac{1}{25}, -\dfrac{1}{25}, \dfrac{1}{25}, 25, -25, 25$ **13.** $7, -7, -7, \dfrac{1}{7}, -\dfrac{1}{7}, -\dfrac{1}{7}$

15. $\dfrac{1}{4}, \dfrac{1}{4}, -\dfrac{1}{4}, 4, 4, -4$ **17.** $\dfrac{8}{27}, -\dfrac{8}{27}, -\dfrac{8}{27}, \dfrac{27}{8}, -\dfrac{27}{8}, -\dfrac{27}{8}$

19. 2^{17} **21.** $-\dfrac{6}{x^6}$ **23.** $\dfrac{21}{b^{10}}$ **25.** $1, -1, 1, -1$

27. $1, 2, 1$ **29.** $3s, 3, 1$ **31.** 2 **33.** 32 **35.** $\dfrac{100}{3}$

37. $\dfrac{8y^2}{5x^2}$ **39.** $\dfrac{1}{48x^2}$ **41.** x^2 **43.** 3^8 **45.** $\dfrac{1}{3a^3}$

47. $\dfrac{-3}{w^8}$ **49.** $3^8 w^6$ **51.** $\dfrac{xy}{2}$ **53.** 9 **55.** -14

57. $\dfrac{1}{16}$ **59.** $\dfrac{3}{8}$ **61.** $\dfrac{4}{9}$ **63.** $-15a^4$ **65.** $8a^3$ **67.** a

69. $\dfrac{-2x^2 y^4}{3}$ **71.** $\dfrac{5}{3}$ **73.** 3 **75.** -2 **77.** -4

79. -3 **81.** $486{,}000{,}000$ **83.** 0.00000237

85. $4{,}000{,}000$ **87.** 0.000005 **89.** 3.2×10^5

91. 7.1×10^{-7} **93.** 7.03×10^{-5} **95.** 2.05×10^7

97. 6×10^3 **99.** 7.5×10^{-1} **101.** 3×10^{22}

103. -1.2×10^{13} **105.** 1.578×10^5

107. 9.187×10^{-5} **109.** 3.828×10^{30}

111. 4.910×10^{11} ft   **113.** 3.83×10^7 seconds

115. 2.6 lb/person/day

Section 5.2 Warm-ups F T T F F F T T T
1. The power of a power rule states that $(a^m)^n = a^{mn}$.
3. The power of a quotient rule states that $(a/b)^m = a^m/b^m$.
5. To compute the amount A when interest is compounded annually use $A = P(1 + i)^n$, where P is the principal, i is the annual interest rate, and n is the number of years.

7. 64 **9.** y^{10} **11.** $\dfrac{1}{x^8}$ **13.** m^{18} **15.** 1 **17.** $\dfrac{1}{x^2}$

19. $81y^2$ **21.** $25w^6$ **23.** $\dfrac{x^9}{y^6}$ **25.** $\dfrac{b^2}{9a^2}$ **27.** $\dfrac{6x^3}{y}$

29. $\dfrac{1}{8a^3 b^4}$ **31.** $\dfrac{w^3}{8}$ **33.** $-\dfrac{27a^3}{64}$ **35.** $\dfrac{x^2 y^2}{4}$ **37.** $\dfrac{y^2}{9x^6}$

39. $\dfrac{25}{4}$ **41.** 4 **43.** $-\dfrac{27}{8x^3}$ **45.** $\dfrac{27y^3}{8x^6}$ **47.** 5^{6t}

49. 2^{6w^2} **51.** 7^{m+3} **53.** 8^{5a+11} **55.** $6x^9$ **57.** $-8x^6$

59. $\dfrac{3z}{x^2 y}$ **61.** $-\dfrac{3}{2}$ **63.** $\dfrac{4x^6}{9}$ **65.** $-\dfrac{x^2}{2}$ **67.** $\dfrac{y^3}{8x^3}$

69. $\dfrac{b^{14}}{5a^7}$ **71.** $\dfrac{x^6}{16y^8}$ **73.** $3ac^8$ **75.** 2^{11} **77.** 2^{-4}

79. 2^{6n} **81.** 2^{4m^2} **83.** 25 **85.** 0.75 **87.** 850.559

89. 1.533 **91.** $\$56{,}197.12$ **93.** $\$2{,}958.64$

95. a) 75.1 yr   **b)** 81.4 yr   **99.** d

101. a) 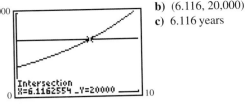   **b)** $(6.116, 20{,}000)$
c) 6.116 years

Section 5.3 Warm-ups F F F T F T F T T F
1. A term of a polynomial is a single number or the product of a number and one or more variables raised to whole number powers.
3. A constant is simply a number.
5. The degree of a polynomial in one variable is the highest power of the variable in the polynomial.

7. Yes   **9.** No   **11.** Yes   **13.** No
15. $4, -8$, binomial   **17.** $0, 0$, monomial
19. $7, 0$, monomial   **21.** $6, 1$, trinomial
23. 80 **25.** -29 **27.** 0 **29.** $3a + 2$ **31.** $5xy + 25$
33. $2x - 9$ **35.** $2x^3 - x^2 - 2x - 8$
37. $11x^2 - 2x - 9$ **39.** $x + 5$ **41.** $-6x^2 + 5x + 2$
43. $2x$ **45.** $-15x^6$ **47.** $-3x + 2$
49. $15x^4 y^4 - 20x^3 y^3$ **51.** $x^2 - 4$ **53.** $2x^3 - x^2 + x - 6$
55. $-10x^2 + 15x$ **57.** $x^2 + 10x + 25$
59. $2x^2 + 9x - 18$ **61.** $x^3 - y^3$ **63.** $2x - 5$
65. $4a^2 - 11a - 4$ **67.** $4w^2 - 8w - 7$ **69.** $x^3 - 8$
71. $xz - wz + 2xw - 2w^2$ **73.** $x^4 - x^2 + 4x - 4$
75. $14.4375x^2 - 29.592x - 9.72$
77. $15.369x^2 + 1.88x - 0.866$
79. $\dfrac{3}{4}x + \dfrac{3}{2}$ **81.** $-\dfrac{1}{2}x^2 + x$
83. $3x^2 - 21x + 1$ **85.** $-4x^2 - 62x - 168$
87. $x^4 - m^2 - 4m - 4$ **89.** $-6x^3 - 53x^2 - 8x$
91. $-4a^{2m} - 4a^m + 5$ **93.** $x^{2n} + 2x^n - 3$
95. $5z^{3w} - z^{1+w}$ **97.** $x^{6r} + y^3$ **99.** $\$75$
101. $\$49.35, \$15.61$
103. a) 6.2 years   **b)** no   **c)** 2037

Section 5.4 Warm-ups T T F T F T T T F F
1. The distributive property is used to multiply binomials.
3. FOIL quickly gives us the product of two binomials.
5. The square of a difference is the square of the first term minus twice the product of the two terms plus the square of the last term.
7. In general $(a + b)^2 = a^2 + 2ab + b^2$.
9. $x^2 + 2x - 8$ **11.** $2x^2 + 7x + 3$ **13.** $2a^2 - 7a - 15$
15. $4x^4 - 49$ **17.** $2x^6 + 7x^3 - 4$ **19.** $w^2 + 5wz - 6z^2$
21. $9k^2 + 6kt - 8t^2$ **23.** $xy - 3y + xw - 3w$
25. $m^2 + 6m + 9$ **27.** $a^2 - 8a + 16$
29. $4w^2 + 4w + 1$ **31.** $9t^2 - 30tu + 25u^2$
33. $x^2 + 2x + 1$ **35.** $a^2 - 6ay^3 + 9y^6$
37. $w^2 - 81$ **39.** $w^6 - y^2$ **41.** $49 - 4x^2$
43. $9x^4 - 4$ **45.** $25a^6 - 4b^2$ **47.** $m^2 + 2mt + t^2 - 25$

49. $y^2 - r^2 - 10r - 25$
51. $4y^2 - 4yt + t^2 + 12y - 6t + 9$
53. $9h^2 + 6hk - 6h + k^2 - 2k + 1$
55. $x^2 + 3x - 54$ **57.** $25 - x^2$
59. $6x^2 + 7ax - 20a^2$ **61.** $2t^2 + 2tw - 3t - 3w$
63. $9x^4 + 12x^2y^3 + 4y^6$ **65.** $6y^2 - 4y - 10$
67. $4m^2 - 28m + 49$ **69.** $49x^2 + 42x + 9$
71. $36y^3 + 12y^2 + y$ **73.** $2ah + h^2$
75. $x^3 + 6x^2 + 12x + 8$ **77.** $y^3 + 9y^2 + 27y + 27$
79. $-3x^2 + 34x - 75$ **81.** $16.32x^2 - 10.47x - 17.55$
83. $12.96y^2 + 31.68y + 19.36$ **85.** $x^{3m} + 2x^{2m} + 3x^m + 6$
87. $a^{3n+1} + a^{2n+1} - 3a^{n+1}$ **89.** $a^{2m} + 2a^{m+n} + a^{2n}$
91. $15y^{3m} + 24y^{2m}z^k + 20y^m z^{3-k} + 32z^3$
93. $x^2 + 4x + 3$ **95.** $4x^2 - 36x + 80, 66.24 \text{ km}^2$
97. $4x^3 - 20x^2 + 24x, 5.9 \text{ ft}^3$

Section 5.5 Warm-ups T T T T F F F T F F
1. A prime number is a natural number greater than 1 that has no factors other than itself and 1.
3. The greatest common factor for the terms of a polynomial is a monomial that includes every number or variable that is a factor of all terms of the polynomial.
5. A linear polynomial is a polynomial of the form $ax + b$ with $a \neq 0$.
7. A prime polynomial is a polynomial that cannot be factored.
9. 12 **11.** 3 **13.** $6xy$ **15.** $x(x^2 - 5)$
17. $12w(4x + 3y)$ **19.** $2x(x^2 - 2x + 3)$
21. $12a^3b^2(3b^4 - 2a + 5a^2b)$ **23.** $(x - 6)(a + b)$
25. $(y - 1)^2(y + z)$ **27.** $2(x - y), -2(-x + y)$
29. $3x(2x - 1), -3x(-2x + 1)$
31. $w^2(-w + 3), -w^2(w - 3)$
33. $a(-a^2 + a - 7), -a(a^2 - a + 7)$
35. $(x + y)(a + 3)$ **37.** $(x - 3)(y + 1)$
39. $(a - b)(4 - c)$ **41.** $(x - 1)(y - 6)$
43. $(x - 10)(x + 10)$ **45.** $(2y - 7)(2y + 7)$
47. $(3x - 5a)(3x + 5a)$ **49.** $(12wz - h)(12wz + h)$
51. $(x - 10)^2$ **53.** $(2m - 1)^2$ **55.** $(w - t)^2$
57. $(a - 1)(a^2 + a + 1)$ **59.** $(w + 3)(w^2 - 3w + 9)$
61. $(2x - 1)(4x^2 + 2x + 1)$
63. $(4x + 5)(16x^2 - 20x + 25)$
65. $(2a - 3b)(4a^2 + 6ab + 9b^2)$
67. $2(x + 2)(x - 2)$ **69.** $x(x + 5)^2$ **71.** $(2x + 1)^2$
73. $(x + 3)(x + 7)$ **75.** $3y(2y + 1)$ **77.** $(2x - 5)^2$
79. $2m(m - n)(m^2 + mn + n^2)$ **81.** $(2x - 3)(x - 2)$
83. $a(3a + w)(3a - w)$ **85.** $-5(a - 3)^2$
87. $2(2 - 3x)(4 + 6x + 9x^2)$ **89.** $-3y(y + 3)^2$
91. $-7(ab + 1)(ab - 1)$ **93.** $(x - h)(7 - h)$
95. $(x + 3)(a - 2)(a + 2)$ **97.** 9 **99.** 20 **101.** 16
103. 100 **105. a)** $b - 3$ **b)** 4050 in.^{3} **c)** 30 in.

Section 5.6 Warm-ups T F F F T F F F T T
1. To factor $x^2 + bx + c$, find two integers whose sum is b and whose product is c.
3. Trial and error means simply to write down possible factors and then use FOIL to check until you get the correct factors.

5. $(x + 1)(x + 3)$ **7.** $(a + 10)(a + 5)$
9. $(y - 7)(y + 2)$ **11.** $(x - 2)(x - 4)$
13. $(a - 9)(a - 3)$ **15.** $(a + 10)(a - 3)$
17. $(3w + 1)(2w + 1)$ **19.** $(2x + 1)(x - 3)$
21. $(2x + 5)(2x + 3)$ **23.** $(2x - 1)(3x - 1)$
25. $(3y + 1)(4y - 1)$ **27.** $(6a - 5)(a + 1)$
29. $(2x - 1)(x + 8)$ **31.** $(3b + 5)(b - 7)$
33. $(3w - 4)(2w + 3)$ **35.** $(4x - 1)(x - 1)$
37. $(5m - 2)(m + 3)$ **39.** $(3y + 4)(2y - 5)$
41. $(x^5 - 3)(x^5 + 3)$ **43.** $(z^6 - 3)^2$ **45.** $2x(x^3 + 2)^2$
47. $x(2x^2 + 1)^2$ **49.** $(x^2 - 2)(x^4 + 2x^2 + 4)$
51. $(a^n - 1)(a^n + 1)$ **53.** $(a^r + 3)^2$
55. $(x^m - 2)(x^{2m} + 2x^m + 4)$
57. $(a^m - b)(a^{2m} + a^m b + b^2)$ **59.** $k(k^w - 5)^2$
61. $(x^3 + 5)(x^3 - 7)$ **63.** $(a^{10} - 10)^2$
65. $-2a(3a^2 + 1)(2a^2 + 1)$ **67.** $(x^a + 5)(x^a - 3)$
69. $(x^a - y^b)(x^a + y^b)$ **71.** $(x^4 - 3)(x^4 + 2)$
73. $x^a(x - 1)(x + 1)$ **75.** $(x^a + 3)^2$ **77.** $2(x + 5)^2$
79. $a(a - 6)(a + 6)$ **81.** $5(2a - 1)(a + 6)$
83. $2(x + 8y)(x - 8y)$ **85.** $-3(3x + 1)(x - 4)$
87. $m^3(m + 10)^2$ **89.** $(3x + 4)(2x + 5)$
91. $y(3y - 4)^2$ **93.** $(r - 4s)(r - 2s)$
95. $m(m + 1)(m + 2)$ **97.** $m(2m + n)(3m - 2n)$
99. $(3m - 5n)(3m + 5n)$ **101.** $5(a + 6)(a - 2)$
103. $-2(w - 10)(w + 1)$ **105.** $x^2(w + 10)(w - 10)$
107. $9(3x + 1)(3x - 1)$ **109.** $(4x + 5)(2x - 3)$
111. $3m(m - 2)(m^2 + 2m + 4)$ **113.** a and b
115. a) $(x + 5)^2$ **b)** $(x - 5)^2$ **c)** $(x + 25)(x + 1)$
d) $(x + 5)(x - 5)$ **e)** Not factorable

Section 5.7 Warm-ups F T T F F T F T T F
1. Always factor out the greatest common factor first.
3. In factoring a trinomial, look for the perfect square trinomials.
5. Prime **7.** Not prime **9.** Not prime **11.** Prime
13. Prime **15.** Prime **17.** $(a^2 - 5)^2$
19. $(x^2 - 2)(x - 2)(x + 2)$ **21.** $3(x - 2)(3x - 4)$
23. $2(y - 2)(y^2 + 2y + 4)(y + 2)(y^2 - 2y + 4)$
25. $2(4a^2 + 3)(4a^2 - 3)$ **27.** $(x + 3)(x - 2)(x^2 - x + 6)$
29. $(m + 5)(m + 1)$ **31.** $(3y - 7)(y + 4)$
33. $(y - 3)(y + 3)(y - 1)(y + 1)$
35. $(x - 2)(x + b)$ **37.** $(x - y)(x + a)$
39. $(x + 1 - a)(x + 1 + a)$ **41.** $(x - 2 - w)(x - 2 + w)$
43. $(x + 2 - z)(x + 2 + z)$ **45.** $(3x - 4)^2$
47. $(3x - 1)(4x - 3)$ **49.** $3a(a + 3)(a^2 - 3a + 9)$
51. $2(x^2 + 16)$ **53.** Prime **55.** $(x + y - 1)(x + y + 1)$
57. $ab(a - b)(a + b)$ **59.** $(x + 2)(x - 2)(x^2 + 2x + 4)$
61. $n(m + n)^2$ **63.** $(m + n)(2 + w)$
65. $(2w + 3)(2w - 1)$ **67.** $(t^2 + 7)(t^2 - 3)$
69. $-a(a + 10)(a - 3)$ **71.** $(y + 2)(y + 6)$
73. $-2(w - 5)(w + 5)(w^2 + 25)$ **75.** $4(a^2 + 4)$
77. $8a(a^2 + 1)$ **79.** $(w + 2)(w + 8)$ **81.** $a(2w - 3)^2$
83. $(x - 3y)^2$ **85.** $3x^2(x - 5)(x + 5)$

87. $n(m - 1)(m^2 + m + 1)$ **89.** $2(3x + 5)(2x - 3)$
91. $2(a^3 - 16)$ **93.** $(a^m - 1)(a^{2m} + a^m + 1)$
95. $(a^w - b^{2n})(a^{2w} + a^w b^{2n} + b^{4n})$
97. $(t^n - 2)(t^n + 2)(t^{2n} + 4)$
99. $a(a^n - 5)(a^n + 3)$ **101.** $(a^n - 3)(a^n + b)$

Section 5.8 Warm-ups F T T F T F T T F F
1. The zero factor property says that if $a \cdot b = 0$, then either $a = 0$ or $b = 0$.
3. The hypotenuse of a right triangle is the side opposite the right angle.
5. The Pythagorean theorem says that a triangle is a right triangle if and only if the sum of the squares of the legs is equal to the square of the hypotenuse.

7. $\{-4, 5\}$ **9.** $\left\{\dfrac{5}{2}, -\dfrac{4}{3}\right\}$ **11.** $\{-5, 2\}$ **13.** $\{-5, 0, 5\}$

15. $\{-7, 2\}$ **17.** $\{0, 7\}$ **19.** $\{-4, 5\}$ **21.** $\left\{-5, \dfrac{3}{2}\right\}$

23. $\left\{-4, \dfrac{1}{5}\right\}$ **25.** $\{-3, 4\}$ **27.** $\left\{-4, \dfrac{5}{2}\right\}$ **29.** $\{-2, 0, 2\}$

31. $\left\{-1, 0, \dfrac{1}{4}\right\}$ **33.** $\{-5, -4, 5\}$ **35.** $\{-1, 1, 2\}$

37. $\{-3, -1, 1, 3\}$ **39.** $\{-8, -6, 4, 6\}$ **41.** $\{-4, -2, 0\}$

43. $\{-7, -3, 1\}$ **45.** $\left\{-\dfrac{3}{2}, 2\right\}$ **47.** $\{-6, -3, -2, 1\}$

49. $\{-6, 1\}$ **51.** $\{-5, 2\}$ **53.** $\{-5, -4, 0\}$

55. $\{-3, 0, 3\}$ **57.** $\left\{-3, \dfrac{1}{2}, 3\right\}$ **59.** $\left\{-\dfrac{1}{3}, \dfrac{1}{4}, \dfrac{1}{2}\right\}$

61. $\left\{\dfrac{3}{2}\right\}$ **63.** $\{0, -b\}$ **65.** $\left\{-\dfrac{b}{a}, \dfrac{b}{a}\right\}$ **67.** $\left\{-\dfrac{b}{2}\right\}$

69. $\left\{-\dfrac{3}{a}, 1\right\}$ **71.** Width 4 inches, length 6 inches

73. 4 and 9   **75.** Length 43 inches, width 22 inches
77. a) 4 seconds   **b)** 4 seconds   **c)** 64 feet   **d)** 2 seconds
79. a) 1225 ft   **b)** 20.3125 sec
81. 3 sec   **83.** Width 5 feet, length 12 feet
85. Width 5 feet, length 12 feet   **87.** 12 ft   **89.** -3 or 4
91. 3 and 4, or -4 and -3
93. Length 20 feet, width 12 feet

Chapter 5 Wrap-up

Enriching Your Mathematical Word Power
1. d   **2.** b   **3.** c   **4.** d   **5.** b   **6.** a   **7.** c   **8.** a
9. a   **10.** d   **11.** c   **12.** a   **13.** c   **14.** b   **15.** c
16. a   **17.** c

Review Exercises
1. 2   **3.** 36   **5.** $-\dfrac{1}{27}$ **7.** 1   **9.** $\dfrac{8}{x^3}$ **11.** $\dfrac{1}{y^2}$

13. a^7 **15.** $\dfrac{2}{x^4}$ **17.** 8,360,000   **19.** 0.00057
21. 8.07×10^6 **23.** 7.09×10^{-4} **25.** 1×10^2

27. $\dfrac{1}{a}$ **29.** $\dfrac{n^2}{m^{16}}$ **31.** $\dfrac{81}{16}$ **33.** $\dfrac{25}{36}$ **35.** $-\dfrac{4}{3ab}$

37. $\dfrac{b^{14}}{a^7}$ **39.** 5^{6w-1} **41.** 7^{15a-40} **43.** $8w + 2$

45. $-6x + 3$ **47.** $x^3 - 4x^2 + 8x - 8$ **49.** $-4xy + 22z$
51. $5m^5 - m^3 + 2m^2$ **53.** $x^2 + 4x - 21$ **55.** $z^2 - 25y^2$
57. $m^2 + 16m + 64$ **59.** $w^2 - 10xw + 24x^2$
61. $k^2 - 6k + 9$ **63.** $m^4 - 25$ **65.** $3(x - 2)$
67. $-4(-a + 5)$ **69.** $-w(w - 3)$
71. $(y - 9)(y + 9)$ **73.** $(2x + 7)^2$ **75.** $(t - 9)^2$
77. $(t - 5)(t^2 + 5t + 25)$ **79.** $(x - 10)(x + 3)$
81. $(w - 7)(w + 4)$ **83.** $(2m + 7)(m - 1)$
85. $m(m^3 - 5)(m^3 + 2)$ **87.** $5(x + 2)(x^2 - 2x + 4)$
89. $(3x + 2)(3x + 1)$ **91.** $(x + 1)^2(x - 1)$
93. $-y(x - 4)(x + 4)$ **95.** $-ab^2(a - 1)^2$
97. $(x - 1)(x^2 + 9)$ **99.** $(x - 2)(x + 2)(x^2 + 3)$
101. $a^3(a - 1)(a^2 + a + 1)$ **103.** $-2(2m + 3)^2$
105. $(2x - 7)(2x + 1)$
107. $(x + 2)(x^2 - 2x + 4)(x - 1)(x^2 + x + 1)$
109. $(a^2 - 11)(a^2 - 12)$ **111.** $(x^k - 7)(x^k + 7)$
113. $(m^a - 3)(m^a + 1)$ **115.** $(3z^k - 2)^2$
117. $(y^a - b)(y^a + c)$ **119.** $\{0, 5\}$ **121.** $\{0, 5\}$

123. $\left\{-\dfrac{1}{2}, 5\right\}$ **125.** $\{-5, -1, 1\}$ **127.** $\{-3, -1, 1, 3\}$

129. 6 feet   **131.** 7 m by 9 m   **133.** 7 in. by 24 in.
135. a) 68.7 yr   **b)** 6.5 yr   **137. a)** 15%   **b)** $12,196.46

Chapter 5 Test

1. $\dfrac{1}{9}$ **2.** 36   **3.** 8   **4.** $12x^7$ **5.** $4y^{12}$ **6.** $64a^6b^3$

7. $\dfrac{27}{x^6}$ **8.** $\dfrac{2a^3}{b^3}$ **9.** 3,240,000,000   **10.** 0.0008673

11. 2.4×10^{-5} **12.** 2×10^{-13} **13.** $3x^3 + 3x^2 - 2x + 3$
14. $-2x^2 - 8x - 3$ **15.** $x^3 - 5x^2 + 13x - 14$
16. $x^3 - 6x^2 + 12x - 8$ **17.** $2x^2 - 11x - 21$
18. $x^2 - 12x + 36$ **19.** $4x^2 + 20x + 25$
20. $9y^4 - 25$ **21.** $(a - 6)(a + 4)$ **22.** $(2x + 7)^2$
23. $3(m - 2)(m^2 + 2m + 4)$ **24.** $2y(x - 4)(x + 4)$
25. $(2m + 3)(6m + 5)$ **26.** $(2x^5 - 3)(x^5 + 4)$
27. $(2x + 3)(a - 5)$ **28.** $(x - 1)(x + 1)(x^2 + 4)$

29. $\left\{-5, \dfrac{3}{2}\right\}$ **30.** $\{-2, 0, 2\}$ **31.** $\{-4, -3, 2, 3\}$

32. Width 8 inches, height 6 inches
33. 38.0, 10.8, 7.9
34. a) 96 ft, 96 ft   **b)** 5 sec   **35.** 20 ft by 24 ft

Making Connections Chapters 1–5

1. 16   **2.** -8 **3.** $\dfrac{1}{16}$ **4.** 2   **5.** 1   **6.** $\dfrac{1}{6}$ **7.** $\dfrac{1}{12}$

8. 49   **9.** 64   **10.** 8   **11.** -29 **12.** $\dfrac{11}{30}$ **13.** $\{200\}$

14. $\left\{\dfrac{9}{5}\right\}$ **15.** $\left\{-9, \dfrac{3}{2}\right\}$ **16.** $\left\{-\dfrac{15}{2}, 0\right\}$ **17.** $\left\{2, \dfrac{8}{5}\right\}$

18. $\left\{\dfrac{9}{5}\right\}$ **19.** $\varnothing$ **20.** $\{-3, -2, 1, 2\}$ **21.** $\left\{-5, \dfrac{1}{2}\right\}$

22. $\left[-\dfrac{2}{3}, \dfrac{4}{3}\right]$ **23.** 5×10^{10} **24.** 2.05×10^5

25. a) \$20,000   **b)** \$2,500   **c)** (20,000, 20,000)   **d)** \$0

Chapter 6

Section 6.1 Warm-ups T T F T F F F T T F

1. A rational expression is a ratio of two polynomials with the denominator not equal to zero.

3. The basic principle of rational numbers states that $(ab)/(ac) = b/c$, provided a and c are not zero.

5. We build up the denominator by multiplying the numerator and denominator by the same expression.

7. $(-\infty, 1) \cup (1, \infty)$ **9.** $(-\infty, 0) \cup (0, \infty)$

11. $(-\infty, -2) \cup (-2, 2) \cup (2, \infty)$

13. $(-\infty, -3) \cup (-3, -2) \cup (-2, \infty)$

15. $(-\infty, \infty)$ **17.** $(-\infty, -3) \cup (-3, 0) \cup (0, 2) \cup (2, \infty)$

19. $\dfrac{2}{19}$ **21.** $\dfrac{1}{5}$ **23.** $\dfrac{x+1}{2}$ **25.** $-\dfrac{3}{5}$ **27.** $\dfrac{b}{a^2}$

29. $\dfrac{-w}{3x^2 y}$ **31.** $\dfrac{b^2}{1+a}$ **33.** $-\dfrac{1}{2}$ **35.** $\dfrac{x+2}{x}$

37. $a^2 + ab + b^2$ **39.** $\dfrac{x^2-1}{x^2+1}$ **41.** $\dfrac{6x+2}{2x+5}$

43. $\dfrac{x^2+7x-4}{x^2-16}$ **45.** $\dfrac{a+y}{b-5}$ **47.** $\dfrac{2x-6}{x+5}$

49. $\dfrac{a+b}{2a+3b}$ **51.** $\dfrac{10}{50}$ **53.** $\dfrac{3xy^2}{3x^2y^3}$ **55.** $\dfrac{5x-5}{x^2-2x+1}$

57. $\dfrac{6x+15}{4x^2-25}$ **59.** $\dfrac{-3}{-6x-6}$ **61.** $\dfrac{5a}{a}$ **63.** $\dfrac{x^2+x-2}{x^2+2x-3}$

65. $\dfrac{-7}{1-x}$ **67.** $\dfrac{3x^2-6x+12}{x^3+8}$ **69.** $\dfrac{2x^2+9x+10}{6x^2+13x-5}$

71. $\dfrac{4}{7}$ **73.** $\dfrac{1}{10}$ **75.** Undefined   **77.** $\dfrac{7}{21}$ **79.** $\dfrac{10}{2}$

81. $\dfrac{3a}{a^2}$ **83.** $\dfrac{-2}{b-a}$ **85.** $\dfrac{2x+2}{x^2-1}$ **87.** $\dfrac{-2}{3-w}$

89. $\dfrac{x+2}{3}$ **91.** $\dfrac{a+1}{a}$ **93.** $\dfrac{x^2+x+1}{x^3-1}$ **95.** $x^a - 2$

97. $\dfrac{1+w}{x^a - m}$ **99.** $\dfrac{x^{2b}+x^b+1}{x^b+1}$ **101.** $\dfrac{250}{x}$ mph

103. a) $A(n) = \dfrac{0.50n + 45}{n}$ dollars   **b)** 7.5 cents

   c) Decreases   **d)** Increases

105. a) $p(n) = \dfrac{0.053n^2 - 0.64n + 6.71}{3.43n + 87.24}$

   b) 7.7%, 18.5%, 41.4%

107. The value of $R(x)$ gets closer and closer to $\dfrac{1}{2}$.

Section 6.2 Warm-ups F F T F T T T T T F

1. To multiply rational numbers, multiply the numerators and the denominators.

3. The expressions $a - b$ and $b - a$ are opposites.

5. $\dfrac{5}{11}$ **7.** $\dfrac{ab}{4}$ **9.** $\dfrac{1}{2}$ **11.** $\dfrac{x+1}{x^2+1}$ **13.** $\dfrac{1}{a-b}$

15. $\dfrac{a+2}{2}$ **17.** $-\dfrac{2}{3}$ **19.** $-7a - 14$ **21.** $6x^2 - x - 1$

23. $\dfrac{3}{2}$ **25.** $\dfrac{63}{5}$ **27.** $\dfrac{6b}{5c^8}$ **29.** $\dfrac{w}{w-1}$ **31.** $\dfrac{2}{x-y}$

33. $\dfrac{2}{x}$ **35.** $2x - 2y$ **37.** $2x + 10$ **39.** $\dfrac{a-b}{6}$

41. $3a - 3b$ **43.** $\dfrac{5x}{6}$ **45.** 3   **47.** $\dfrac{1}{12}$ **49.** $\dfrac{2x}{3}$

51. -1 **53.** -2 **55.** $\dfrac{a+b}{a}$ **57.** $\dfrac{x-9}{2}$ **59.** -2

61. $2a + 2b$ **63.** $\dfrac{3x}{5y}$ **65.** $\dfrac{3a}{10b}$ **67.** $\dfrac{7x^2}{3x+2}$

69. $-\dfrac{a^6 b^2}{8c^2}$ **71.** $\dfrac{2m^8 n^2}{3}$ **73.** $\dfrac{2x-3}{8x-4}$ **75.** $\dfrac{h-3}{5h+1}$

77. $\dfrac{-3a-1}{2}$ **79.** $\dfrac{k+m}{m-k}$ **81.** $\dfrac{y^b}{x^a}$ **83.** $\dfrac{x^a - 1}{x^a + 2}$

85. $\dfrac{m^k + 1}{m^k + 2}$ **87.** 7.1%   **89.** $\dfrac{75}{x}$ miles   **91.** e

Section 6.3 Warm-ups F F T F F F T T T F

1. The sum of a/b and c/b is $(a + c)/b$.

3. The least common multiple (LCM) of some numbers is the smallest number that is a multiple of all of the numbers.

5. To add rational expressions with different denominators, you must build up the expressions to equivalent expressions with the same denominator.

7. $4x$ **9.** $\dfrac{-x+1}{x}$ **11.** $\dfrac{5}{2}$ **13.** $\dfrac{2}{x-3}$

15. $\dfrac{3x-5}{x+3}$ **17.** 120   **19.** $30x^3 y$ **21.** $a^3 b^5 c^2$

23. $x(x+2)(x-2)$ **25.** $12a + 24$ **27.** $(x-1)(x+1)^2$

29. $x(x-4)(x+4)(x+2)$

31. $(2x+3)(3x+4)(3x-4)$

33. $\dfrac{17}{140}$ **35.** $\dfrac{1}{144}$ **37.** $\dfrac{3w+5z}{w^2 z^2}$ **39.** $\dfrac{2x-1}{24}$

41. $\dfrac{11x}{10a}$ **43.** $\dfrac{9-4xy}{4y}$ **45.** $\dfrac{-2a-14}{a(a+2)}$

47. $\dfrac{3a-b}{(a-b)(a+b)}$ **49.** $\dfrac{4x+9}{(x+3)(x-3)}$ **51.** 0

53. $\dfrac{11}{2x-4}$ **55.** $\dfrac{-x+3}{(x-1)(x+2)(x+3)}$

57. $\dfrac{3x^2+5x-3}{(x+1)(2x-1)(3x-1)}$ **59.** $\dfrac{8x-2}{x(x-1)(x+2)}$

61. $\dfrac{7}{12}$ **63.** $-\dfrac{19}{40}$ **65.** $\dfrac{5x}{6}$ **67.** $\dfrac{3a-2b}{3b}$ **69.** $\dfrac{3a+2}{3}$

71. $\dfrac{a+3}{a}$ **73.** $\dfrac{3}{x}$ **75.** $\dfrac{8x+3}{12x}$ **77.** -3

79. $\dfrac{-13}{15(x-2)}$ **81.** $\dfrac{-4x}{(x+1)(x-1)(2x+1)}$

83. b **85.** $\dfrac{x^2+10x}{(5x-2)^2}$ **87.** $\dfrac{4x^2+9}{x(2x-3)}$

89. $\dfrac{-w^2 + 2w + 8}{(w + 3)(w^2 - 3w + 9)}$ **91.** $\dfrac{a - 3}{a^2 + 2a + 4}$

93. $\dfrac{-w^3 - 2w^2 - 5w + 6}{(w - 2)(w + 2)(w^2 + 2w + 4)}$

95. $\dfrac{x^3 + x^2 + 2x + 1}{(x - 1)(x + 1)(x^2 + x + 1)}$

97. $\dfrac{16x + 8}{x^2 + x}$ **99.** $\dfrac{3x + 60}{x}$ **101.** $\dfrac{300x + 500}{x^2 + 5x}$ hours

Section 6.4 Warm-ups F T T T F F F F T T

1. A complex fraction is a fraction that contains fractions in the numerator, denominator, or both.

3. $\dfrac{10}{3}$ **5.** -8 **7.** $\dfrac{a^2 + ab}{a - b}$ **9.** $\dfrac{a^2 b + 3a}{a + b^2}$

11. $\dfrac{x - 3y}{x + y}$ **13.** $\dfrac{60m - 3m^2}{8m + 36}$ **15.** $\dfrac{a^2 - ab}{b^2}$

17. $\dfrac{xy + x^2}{y^2 - x^2 y^2}$ **19.** $\dfrac{x + 2}{x - 2}$ **21.** $\dfrac{y^2 - y - 2}{(y - 1)(3y + 4)}$

23. $\dfrac{4x - 10}{x - 4}$ **25.** $\dfrac{6w - 3}{2w^2 + w - 4}$ **27.** $\dfrac{2b - a}{a - 3b}$

29. $\dfrac{-y^2 - 12}{y^2 - 3}$ **31.** $\dfrac{3a - 7}{5a - 2}$ **33.** $\dfrac{3m^2 - 12m + 12}{(m - 3)(2m - 1)}$

35. $\dfrac{2x^2 + 4x + 5}{4x^2 - 2x - 6}$ **37.** $\dfrac{yz + wz}{wy + wz}$ **39.** $\dfrac{x}{x + 1}$

41. $\dfrac{a^2 + b^2}{ab^3}$ **43.** $\dfrac{a - 1}{a}$ **45.** $\dfrac{1}{x^2 - x + 1}$ **47.** $2m - 3$

49. $-\dfrac{1}{ab}$ **51.** $-x^3 y^3$ **53.** $x - 2$ **55.** $\dfrac{xy}{x + y}$

57. $-1.7333, -\dfrac{26}{15}$ **59.** $0.1667, \dfrac{1}{6}$ **61.** 47.4%

63. 49.5 mph   **67.** $\dfrac{2x + 1}{3x + 2}, x = 0, -1, -\dfrac{1}{2}, -\dfrac{2}{3}$

Section 6.5 Warm-ups F F T T T F F T T

1. If $a \div b = c$, then the divisor is b, the dividend is a, and the quotient is c.

3. If the term x^n is missing in the dividend, insert the term $0 \cdot x^n$ for the missing term.

5. Synthetic division is used only for dividing by a binomial of the form $x - c$.

7. $12x^4$ **9.** -2 **11.** $2b - 3$ **13.** $x + 1$

15. $-5x^2 + 4x - 3$ **17.** $\dfrac{7}{2}x^2 - 2x$

19. $2, -3$ **21.** $\dfrac{2}{3}x + \dfrac{1}{3}, 4x - 3$

23. $2x^2 + x, -6x - 7$ **25.** $x + 5, -2$

27. $x - 4, 8$ **29.** $x^2 - 2x + 4, 0$

31. $a^2 + 2a + 8, 11$ **33.** $x^2 - 2x + 3, -6$

35. $x^3 + 3x^2 + 6x + 11, 21$

37. $-3x^2 - 1, x - 4$ **39.** $3x + 5, -1$

41. $2b - 5, -2$ **43.** $x^2 + x - 2, 0$ **45.** $x - 5, 0$

47. $2 + \dfrac{10}{x - 5}$ **49.** $x - 1 + \dfrac{1}{2x + 1}$

51. $x^2 - 2x + 4 + \dfrac{-8}{x + 2}$ **53.** $x + \dfrac{2}{x}$

55. $x - 6 + \dfrac{2}{2x + 1}$ **57.** $3x^2 - x - 1 + \dfrac{6}{x - 1}$

59. $6x^2 + 12x + 20 + \dfrac{45}{x - 2}$ **61.** $x^2 - x + 2 + \dfrac{-2}{x + 1}$

63. $x^2 - 3x, -3$ **65.** $2x - 6, 11$

67. $3x^3 + 9x^2 + 12x + 43, 120$

69. $x^4 + x^3 + x^2 + x + 1, 0$ **71.** $x^2 - 2x - 1, 8$

73. $x^2 + 2x + 10, 55$ **75.** No   **77.** Yes, $(x - 4)(x - 2)$

79. Yes, $(w - 3)(w^2 + 3w + 9)$ **81.** No

83. Yes, $(y - 2)(y^2 - 2y + 2)$ **85.** -15 **87.** 9   **89.** 28

91. a) $AC(x) = 0.03x + 300$ **b)** No   **c)** Because $AC(x)$ is very close to 300 for x less than 15, the graph looks horizontal.

93. $x - 1$ ft   **95.** 6,333.3 m^3

Section 6.6 Warm-ups T F F T F T F F F T

1. The first step is to multiply each side of the equation by the LCD.

3. A proportion is an equation expressing equality of two rational expressions.

5. In $a/b = c/d$ the extremes are a and d.

7. $\{-24\}$ **9.** $\left\{\dfrac{22}{15}\right\}$ **11.** $\{5\}$ **13.** $\{1, 6\}$ **15.** $\{20, 25\}$

17. $\varnothing$ **19.** $\{-2\}$ **21.** $\varnothing$ **23.** $\{-5, 1\}$ **25.** $\left\{\dfrac{8}{3}\right\}$

27. $\left\{-\dfrac{3}{4}\right\}$ **29.** $\left\{-\dfrac{14}{5}\right\}$ **31.** $\{20\}$ **33.** $\{-3, 3\}$

35. $\{-5, 6\}$ **37.** $\varnothing$ **39.** $\left\{\dfrac{11}{2}\right\}$ **41.** $\{0\}$

43. $\{-6, 6\}$ **45.** $\{8\}$ **47.** $\{2, 4\}$

49. $\{-1\}$ **51.** $\{5\}$ **53.** $\{-3, 3\}$ **55.** $\{8\}$ **57.** $\left\{\dfrac{25}{2}\right\}$

59. $\varnothing$ **61.** $\{4\}$ **63.** $\{-5, 2\}$ **65.** $\left\{\dfrac{16}{3}\right\}$

67. $\dfrac{3x + 16}{4x}$ **69.** $\left\{\dfrac{8}{5}\right\}$ **71.** $\dfrac{-5x + 8}{4x}$ **73.** \$166,666.67

75. 138   **77.** Width 132 cm, length 154 cm

79. 20%, 96%   **81. a)** \$17,142.86   **b)** \$57,142.86

83. To solve the equation, multiply each side by the LCD. To find the sum, build up each rational expression so that its denominator is the LCD.

Section 6.7 Warm-ups F T F T T T F T F F

1. $y = 5x - 7$ **3.** $y = -\dfrac{1}{3}x + 1$

5. $y = mx - bm + a$ **7.** $y = -\dfrac{7}{3}x - \dfrac{29}{3}$

9. $f = \dfrac{F}{M}$ **11.** $D^2 = \dfrac{4A}{\pi}$ **13.** $m_1 = \dfrac{Fr^2}{km_2}$

15. $q = \dfrac{pf}{p - f}$ **17.** $a^2 = \dfrac{b^2}{1 - e^2}$ **19.** $T_1 = \dfrac{P_1 V_1 T_2}{P_2 V_2}$

21. $h = \dfrac{3V}{4\pi r^2}$ **23.** $\dfrac{1}{2}$ **25.** 24   **27.** $\dfrac{32}{3}$

29. -6.517 **31.** 19.899   **33.** 1.910   **35.** 4 mph

37. Patrick 24 min, Guy 36 min, 100 mph, no

39. 10 mph   **41.** 6 hours   **43.** 60 minutes

45. 30 minutes   **47.** 10 pounds apples, 12 pounds oranges

49. 6 ohms   **51. a)** 80   **b)** $C(n) = \dfrac{24{,}000}{n}$

53. 25.255 days

Chapter 6 Wrap-Up

Enriching Your Mathematical Word Power

1. b   **2.** d   **3.** b   **4.** d   **5.** b   **6.** a   **7.** a   **8.** d
9. a   **10.** b   **11.** d   **12.** d   **13.** a   **14.** c   **15.** d

Review Exercises

1. $(-\infty, 1) \cup (1, \infty)$ **3.** $(-\infty, -1) \cup (-1, 2) \cup (2, \infty)$

5. $\dfrac{c^2}{a^2 b}$ **7.** $\dfrac{4x^2}{3y}$ **9.** $-a$ **11.** $\dfrac{3}{2}$ **13.** $6x(x - 2)$

15. $12a^5 b^3$ **17.** $\dfrac{3x + 11}{2(x - 3)(x + 3)}$ **19.** $\dfrac{aw - 5b}{a^2 b^2}$

21. $\dfrac{21}{10x - 60}$ **23.** $\dfrac{7 - 3y}{4y - 3}$ **25.** $\dfrac{b^3 - a^2}{ab}$

27. $x^2 + 3x - 5, 0$ **29.** $m^3 - m^2 + m - 1, 0$

31. $a^6 + 2a^3 + 4, 0$ **33.** $m^2 + 2m - 6, 0$

35. $x + 1 + \dfrac{-4}{x - 1}$ **37.** $3 + \dfrac{6}{x - 2}$ **39.** Yes

41. Yes   **43.** No   **45.** Yes   **47.** $\left\{ -\dfrac{16}{3} \right\}$

49. $\varnothing$ **51.** $\{10\}$ **53.** $y = mx + b$ **55.** $m = \dfrac{Fr}{v^2}$

57. $r = \dfrac{3A}{2\pi h}$ **59.** $y = 2x - 17$ **61.** $\dfrac{10 + 7y}{6xy}$

63. $\dfrac{8a + 10}{(a - 5)(a + 5)}$ **65.** $\{-8, 8\}$ **67.** $-\dfrac{3}{2}$ **69.** $\{-9, 9\}$

71. $\dfrac{1}{x - m}$ **73.** $\dfrac{8a + 20}{(a - 5)(a + 5)(a + 1)}$

75. $\dfrac{-15a + 10}{2(a + 2)(a + 3)(a - 3)}$ **77.** $\{2\}$

79. $\left\{ -\dfrac{5}{2} \right\}$ **81.** $-\dfrac{1}{3}$ **83.** $\dfrac{x - 2}{3x + 3}$ **85.** $\dfrac{3a^2 + 7a + 16}{a^3 - 8}$

87. $\dfrac{3 - x}{(x + 1)(x + 3)}$ **89.** $\dfrac{a + w}{a + 4}$ **91.** $\{-6, 8\}$

93. $\dfrac{18}{3x}$ **95.** $\dfrac{-3}{b - a}$ **97.** $\dfrac{4x}{x}$ **99.** $10x$ **101.** $\dfrac{1}{3}$

103. $\dfrac{1}{a + 3}$ **105.** $\dfrac{3}{10}$ **107.** $\dfrac{5a}{6}$ **109.** 28,000

111. 10 hours   **113.** 400 hours

Chapter 6 Test

1. $(-\infty, 4/3) \cup (4/3, \infty)$ **2.** $(-\infty, -3) \cup (-3, 3) \cup (3, \infty)$

3. $(-\infty, \infty)$ **4.** $\dfrac{3a^3}{2b}$ **5.** $\dfrac{-x - y}{2x - 2y}$ **6.** $-\dfrac{1}{36}$

7. $\dfrac{7y^2 + 3}{y}$ **8.** $\dfrac{5}{a - 9}$ **9.** $\dfrac{4a + 3b}{24a^2 b^2}$ **10.** $\dfrac{a^3}{30b^2}$

11. $-\dfrac{3}{a + b}$ **12.** $\dfrac{1}{x^2 - 1}$ **13.** $\dfrac{-4x + 2}{(x + 2)(x - 2)(x - 5)}$

14. $\dfrac{m + 1}{3}$ **15.** $\left\{ \dfrac{12}{7} \right\}$ **16.** $\{4, 10\}$ **17.** $\{-2, 2\}$

18. $t = \dfrac{a^2}{W}$ **19.** $b = \dfrac{2a}{a - 2}$ **20.** $\dfrac{16}{9 - 6x}$ **21.** $w - m$

22. $\dfrac{3a^2}{2}$ **23.** $3x + 2, -8$ **24.** $-1, 0$ **25.** $5 + \dfrac{-15}{x + 3}$

26. $x + 5 + \dfrac{4}{x - 2}$ **27.** 24 minutes   **28.** 30 miles   **29.** 9

Making Connections Chapters 1–6

1. $\left\{ \dfrac{15}{4} \right\}$ **2.** $\{-4, 4\}$ **3.** $\left\{ \dfrac{12}{5} \right\}$ **4.** $\{-6, 3\}$ **5.** $\left\{ \dfrac{1}{4} \right\}$

6. $\{6\}$ **7.** $\left\{ \dfrac{1}{2} \right\}$ **8.** $\left\{ \dfrac{3}{2} \right\}$ **9.** $\{-3, 3\}$ **10.** $\{-8, 3\}$

11. $\left\{ \dfrac{1}{3}, \dfrac{2}{3} \right\}$ **12.** $\{-3, 9\}$ **13.** $\left\{ -\dfrac{9}{2}, \dfrac{1}{2} \right\}$ **14.** $\varnothing$

15. $y = \dfrac{C - Ax}{B}$ **16.** $y = -\dfrac{1}{3}x + \dfrac{4}{3}$ **17.** $y = \dfrac{C}{A - B}$

18. $y = A$ or $y = -A$ **19.** $y = 2A - 2B$

20. $y = \dfrac{2AC}{2B + C}$ **21.** $y = \dfrac{3}{4}x - \dfrac{3}{2}$ **22.** $y = A$ or $y = 2$

23. $y = \dfrac{2A - BC}{B}$ **24.** $y = B$ or $y = -C$ **25.** $12x^{13}$

26. $3x^5 + 15x^8$ **27.** $25x^{12}$ **28.** $27a^9 b^6$ **29.** $-4a^6 b^6$

30. $\dfrac{1}{32x^{10}}$ **31.** $\dfrac{27x^{12} y^{15}}{8}$ **32.** $\dfrac{a^2}{4b^6 c^2}$

33. $\dfrac{ab + a^2 b^4}{b + a^2}$ **34.** $a + b$

35. a) 2188 calories   **b)** increases
 c) $B = 9.56W + 918.7$ **d)** $B = 2328 - 4.68A$

Chapter 7

Section 7.1 Warm-ups T F T F T F F F T T
1. If $b^n = a$, then b is an nth root of a.
3. If $b^n = a$, then b is an even root of a provided n is even or an odd root of a provided n is odd.
5. The product rule for radicals states that $\sqrt[n]{a} \cdot \sqrt[n]{b} = \sqrt[n]{ab}$ provided all of the roots are real.
7. 6   **9.** 10   **11.** -3 **13.** 2   **15.** -2 **17.** 2
19. 10   **21.** Not a real number   **23.** -2 **25.** m
27. x^8 **29.** y^3 **31.** y^5 **33.** m **35.** w^3 **37.** $3\sqrt{y}$
39. $2a$ **41.** $x^2 y$ **43.** $m^6 \sqrt{5}$ **45.** $2\sqrt[3]{y}$
47. $a^2 \sqrt[3]{3}$ **49.** $2\sqrt{5}$ **51.** $5\sqrt{2}$ **53.** $6\sqrt{2}$ **55.** $2\sqrt[3]{5}$
57. $3\sqrt[3]{3}$ **59.** $2\sqrt[4]{3}$ **61.** $2\sqrt[8]{3}$ **63.** $a\sqrt{a}$
65. $3a^3 \sqrt{2}$ **67.** $2x^2 \sqrt{5xy}$ **69.** $2m\sqrt[3]{3m}$
71. $2a\sqrt[4]{2a}$ **73.** $2x\sqrt[5]{2x}$ **75.** $4xy^4 z^3 \sqrt{3xz}$

77. $\dfrac{\sqrt{t}}{2}$ 79. $\dfrac{25}{4}$ 81. $\sqrt{10}$ 83. $\dfrac{\sqrt[3]{t}}{2}$ 85. $\dfrac{-2x^2}{y}$

87. $\dfrac{2a^3}{3}$ 89. $\dfrac{2\sqrt{3}}{5}$ 91. $\dfrac{3\sqrt{3}}{4}$

93. $\dfrac{a\sqrt[3]{a}}{5}$ 95. $\dfrac{3\sqrt[3]{3}}{2b}$ 97. $\dfrac{x\sqrt[4]{x^3}}{y^2}$ 99. $\dfrac{a\sqrt[4]{a}}{2b^3}$

101. 1, $[2, \infty)$ 103. $\sqrt{14}$, $[-4, \infty)$ 105. No $f(3)$, $(-\infty, 1]$

107. $-4°F$, $-10°F$ 109. a) $t = \dfrac{\sqrt{h}}{4}$ b) $\dfrac{\sqrt{10}}{2}$ sec

c) 100 ft   111. 5.8 knots   113. 114.1 ft/sec, 77.8 mph

115. a) Yes b) No c) Yes d) Yes

117. Arithmetic mean

Section 7.2 Warm-ups T F F T T T T T F T T

1. The nth root of a is $a^{1/n}$.

3. The expression $a^{-m/n}$ means $\dfrac{1}{a^{m/n}}$.

5. The operations can be performed in any order, but the easiest is usually root, power, and then reciprocal.

7. $7^{1/4}$ 9. $(5x)^{1/2}$ 11. $\sqrt[5]{9}$ 13. $\sqrt{a}$ 15. 5

17. -5 19. 2   21. Not a real number

23. $w^{7/3}$ 25. $2^{-10/3}$ 27. $\sqrt[4]{\dfrac{1}{w^3}}$ 29. $\sqrt{(ab)^3}$

31. 25   33. 125   35. $\dfrac{1}{81}$ 37. $\dfrac{1}{64}$ 39. $-\dfrac{1}{3}$

41. Not a real number   43. $3^{7/12}$ 45. 1   47. $\dfrac{1}{2}$

49. 2   51. 6   53. 4   55. 81   57. $\dfrac{1}{4}$ 59. $\dfrac{9}{8}$

61. $|x|$ 63. a^4 65. y 67. $|3x^3y|$ 69. $\left|\dfrac{3x^3}{y^5}\right|$

71. $x^{3/4}$ 73. $\dfrac{y^{3/2}}{x^{1/4}}$ 75. $\dfrac{1}{w^{8/3}}$ 77. $12x^8$ 79. $\dfrac{a^2}{b}$

81. $8w^{13/4}$ 83. $\dfrac{h^{1/6}}{3k^{1/2}}$ 85. 9   87. $-\dfrac{1}{8}$ 89. $\dfrac{1}{625}$

91. $2^{1/4}$ 93. 3   95. 3   97. $\dfrac{4}{9}$ 99. Not a real number

101. $\dfrac{4}{3}$ 103. $-\dfrac{216}{125}$ 105. $3x^{9/2}$ 107. $\dfrac{a^2}{27}$ 109. $a^{5/4}b$

111. $k^{9/2}m^4$ 113. 1.2599   115. -1.4142 117. 2

119. 2.5   121. $a^{3m/4}$ 123. $a^{2m/15}$ 125. $a^n b^m$

127. $a^{4m}b^{2n}$ 129. 13 inches   131. 274.96 m²

133. 26.3%   135. 6.1%   137. Second is incorrect.

Section 7.3 Warm-ups F T F F T F T F F T

1. Like radical are radicals with the same index and same radicand.

3. In the product rule the radicals must have the same index, but do not have to have the same radicand.

5. $-\sqrt{3}$ 7. $9\sqrt{7x}$ 9. $5\sqrt[3]{2}$ 11. $4\sqrt{3} - 2\sqrt{5}$

13. $5\sqrt[3]{x}$ 15. $2\sqrt[3]{x} - \sqrt{2x}$ 17. $2\sqrt{2} + 2\sqrt{7}$

19. $5\sqrt{2}$ 21. 0   23. $-\sqrt{2}$ 25. $x\sqrt{5x} + 2x\sqrt{2}$

27. $7\sqrt[3]{3}$ 29. $-4\sqrt[4]{3}$ 31. $ty\sqrt[3]{2t}$

33. $\sqrt{15}$ 35. $30\sqrt{2}$ 37. $6a\sqrt{14}$ 39. $3\sqrt[4]{3}$

41. 12   43. $6\sqrt{2} + 18$ 45. $5\sqrt{2} - 2\sqrt{5}$

47. $3\sqrt[3]{t^2} - t\sqrt[3]{3}$ 49. $-7 - 3\sqrt{3}$ 51. 2

53. $-8 - 6\sqrt{5}$ 55. $-6 + 9\sqrt{2}$ 57. $\sqrt[6]{3^5}$ 59. $\sqrt[12]{5^7}$

61. $\sqrt[6]{500}$ 63. $\sqrt[12]{432}$ 65. -1 67. 3   69. 19

71. 13   73. $25 - 9x$ 75. $11\sqrt{3}$ 77. $10\sqrt{30}$

79. $8 - \sqrt{7}$ 81. $16w$ 83. $3x^2\sqrt{2x}$

85. $28 + \sqrt{10}$ 87. $\dfrac{8\sqrt{2}}{15}$ 89. 17

91. $9 + 6\sqrt{x} + x$ 93. $25x - 30\sqrt{x} + 9$

95. $x + 3 + 2\sqrt{x + 2}$ 97. $-\sqrt{w}$ 99. $a\sqrt{a}$

101. $3x^2\sqrt{x}$ 103. $13x\sqrt[3]{2x}$ 105. $\sqrt[6]{32x^5}$

107. $3\sqrt{2}$ ft²   109. $\dfrac{9\sqrt{2}}{2}$ ft²   111. No

113. a) $(y - \sqrt{3})(y + \sqrt{3})$, $(\sqrt{2}a - \sqrt{7})(\sqrt{2}a + \sqrt{7})$

b) $\{\pm 2\sqrt{2}\}$ c) $\{\pm\sqrt{a}\}$

Section 7.4 Warm-ups T T F T F T F T T T

1. $\dfrac{2\sqrt{5}}{5}$ 3. $\dfrac{\sqrt{21}}{7}$ 5. $\dfrac{\sqrt[3]{2}}{2}$

7. $\dfrac{\sqrt[3]{150}}{5}$ 9. $\dfrac{\sqrt{15}}{6}$ 11. $\dfrac{1}{2}$ 13. $\dfrac{\sqrt{2}}{2}$ 15. $\dfrac{\sqrt[3]{18}}{3}$

17. $\dfrac{\sqrt[3]{14}}{2}$ 19. $\dfrac{\sqrt{xy}}{y}$ 21. $\dfrac{a\sqrt{ab}}{b^4}$ 23. $\dfrac{\sqrt{3ab}}{3b}$

25. $\dfrac{\sqrt[3]{ab^2}}{b}$ 27. $\dfrac{\sqrt[3]{20b}}{2b}$ 29. $\sqrt{3}$ 31. $\dfrac{\sqrt{15}}{5}$

33. $\dfrac{3\sqrt{2}}{10}$ 35. $\dfrac{\sqrt{2}}{3}$ 37. $\dfrac{\sqrt{3a}}{3}$ 39. $\sqrt[3]{10}$ 41. 2

43. $\dfrac{2}{w}$ 45. $2 + \sqrt{5}$ 47. $1 - \sqrt{3}$ 49. $2\sqrt{2} - 2$

51. $\dfrac{\sqrt{11} + \sqrt{5}}{2}$ 53. $\dfrac{1 + \sqrt{6} + \sqrt{2} + \sqrt{3}}{2}$

55. $\dfrac{2\sqrt{3} - \sqrt{6}}{3}$ 57. $\dfrac{6\sqrt{6} + 2\sqrt{15}}{13}$

59. $128\sqrt{2}$ 61. $x^2\sqrt{x}$ 63. $-27x^4\sqrt{x}$ 65. $8x^5$

67. $4\sqrt[3]{25}$ 69. x^4 71. $\dfrac{\sqrt{6} + 2\sqrt{2}}{2}$ 73. $2\sqrt{6}$

75. $\dfrac{\sqrt{2}}{2}$ 77. $\dfrac{2}{3}$ 79. $\dfrac{2 - \sqrt{2}}{5}$ 81. $\dfrac{1 + \sqrt{3}}{2}$

83. $a - 3\sqrt{a}$ 85. $4a\sqrt{a} + 4a$ 87. $12m$ 89. $4xy^2z$

91. $m - m^2$ 93. $5x\sqrt[3]{x}$ 95. $8m\sqrt[4]{8m^2}$ 97. $\sqrt{x} + 3$

99. $\dfrac{3k - 3\sqrt{7k}}{k - 7}$ 101. $2 + 8\sqrt{2}$ 103. $\dfrac{3\sqrt{2} + 2\sqrt{3}}{6}$

105. $7\sqrt{2} - 1$ 107. $\dfrac{4x + 4\sqrt{x}}{x - 4}$ 109. $\dfrac{x + \sqrt{x}}{x - x^2}$

111. a) $x^3 - 2$ b) $(x + \sqrt[3]{5})(x^2 - \sqrt[3]{5}x + \sqrt[3]{25})$ c) 3

d) $(\sqrt[3]{a} + \sqrt[3]{b})(\sqrt[3]{a^2} - \sqrt[3]{ab} + \sqrt[3]{b^2})$, $(\sqrt[3]{a} - \sqrt[3]{b})(\sqrt[3]{a^2} + \sqrt[3]{ab} + \sqrt[3]{b^2})$

Section 7.5 Warm-ups F T F F T F F T T T

1. The odd-root property states that if n is an odd positive integer, then $x^n = k$ is equivalent to $x = \sqrt[n]{k}$ for any real number k.

3. An extraneous solution is a solution that appears when solving an equation but does not satisfy the original equation.

5. $\{-10\}$ 7. $\left\{\dfrac{1}{2}\right\}$ 9. $\{1\}$ 11. $\{-2\}$ 13. $\{-5, 5\}$

15. $\{-2\sqrt{5}, 2\sqrt{5}\}$ 17. No real solution   19. $\{-1, 7\}$

21. $\{-1 - 2\sqrt{2}, -1 + 2\sqrt{2}\}$ 23. $\{-\sqrt{10}, \sqrt{10}\}$

25. $\{3\}$ 27. $\{-2, 2\}$ 29. $\{52\}$ 31. $\left\{\dfrac{9}{4}\right\}$ 33. $\{9\}$

35. $\{3\}$ 37. $\{3\}$ 39. $\{-5, 3\}$ 41. $\{1\}$ 43. $\varnothing$

45. $\{4\}$ 47. $\{2\}$ 49. $\{6\}$ 51. $\{7\}$ 53. $\{-5\}$

55. $\varnothing$ 57. $\{0\}$ 59. $\{-3\sqrt{3}, 3\sqrt{3}\}$

61. $\left\{-\dfrac{1}{27}, \dfrac{1}{27}\right\}$ 63. $\{512\}$ 65. $\left\{\dfrac{1}{81}\right\}$ 67. $\left\{0, \dfrac{2}{3}\right\}$

69. $\left\{\dfrac{4 - \sqrt{2}}{4}, \dfrac{4 + \sqrt{2}}{4}\right\}$ 71. No real solution

73. $\{-\sqrt{2}, \sqrt{2}\}$ 75. $\{-5\}$ 77. No real solution

79. $\{-9\}$ 81. $\left\{\dfrac{5}{4}\right\}$ 83. $\varnothing$ 85. $\left\{-\dfrac{2}{3}, 2\right\}$

87. $\{-2 - 2\sqrt[4]{2}, -2 + 2\sqrt[4]{2}\}$ 89. $\{0\}$ 91. $\left\{\dfrac{1}{2}\right\}$

93. $4\sqrt{2}$ feet   95. $5\sqrt{2}$ feet   97. 50 feet

99. a) 1.89   b) $d = \dfrac{64b^3}{C^3}$ c) $d > 19{,}683$ pounds

101. $\sqrt[6]{32}$ meters   103. $\sqrt{73}$ km

105. $S = P(1 + r)^n$, $P = S(1 + r)^{-n}$ 107. 9.5 AU

109. $\{-1.8, 1.8\}$ 111. $\{4.993\}$ 113. $\{-26.372, 26.372\}$

Section 7.6 Warm-ups T F F T T T T F T F

1. A complex number is a number of the form $a + bi$, where a and b are real numbers.

3. The union of the real numbers and the imaginary numbers is the set of complex numbers.

5. The conjugate of $a + bi$ is $a - bi$.

7. $-2 + 8i$ 9. $-4 + 4i$ 11. -2 13. $-8 - 2i$

15. $6 + 15i$ 17. $-2 - 10i$ 19. $-4 - 12i$

21. $-10 + 24i$ 23. $-1 + 3i$ 25. $-5i$

27. 29   29. 2   31. 20   33. -9 35. -25

37. 16   39. i 41. 34   43. 5   45. 5

47. 7   49. $\dfrac{12}{17} - \dfrac{3}{17}i$ 51. $\dfrac{4}{13} + \dfrac{7}{13}i$ 53. $3 - 4i$

55. $1 + 3i$ 57. $\dfrac{1}{13} - \dfrac{5}{13}i$ 59. $-2i$ 61. $2 + 2i$

63. $5 + 6i$ 65. $7 - i\sqrt{6}$ 67. $5i\sqrt{2}$ 69. $1 + i\sqrt{3}$

71. $-1 - \dfrac{1}{2}i\sqrt{6}$ 73. $-2\sqrt{3}$ 75. -9 77. $-i\sqrt{2}$

79. $\{\pm 6i\}$ 81. $\{\pm 2i\sqrt{3}\}$ 83. $\left\{\dfrac{\pm i\sqrt{10}}{2}\right\}$ 85. $\{\pm i\sqrt{2}\}$

87. $18 - i$ 89. $5 + i$ 91. $-\dfrac{6}{25} - \dfrac{17}{25}i$ 93. $3 + 2i$

95. -9 97. $3i\sqrt{3}$ 99. $-5 - 12i$ 101. $-2 + 2i\sqrt{2}$

Chapter 7 Wrap-Up

Enriching Your Mathematical Word Power

1. d   2. b   3. b   4. b   5. d   6. b   7. c   8. a
9. d   10. c   11. a   12. c   13. d   14. b

Review Exercises

1. 2   3. 10   5. $6\sqrt{2}$ 7. x^6 9. x^2 11. $x^4\sqrt{2x}$

13. $2w^2\sqrt{2w}$ 15. $2x\sqrt[3]{2x}$ 17. $a^2b\sqrt[4]{ab}$ 19. $\dfrac{x\sqrt{x}}{4}$

21. $\dfrac{1}{9}$ 23. 4   25. $\dfrac{1}{1000}$ 27. $27x^{1/2}$ 29. $a^{7/2}b^{7/2}$

31. $x^{3/4}y^{5/4}$ 33. 13   35. $3\sqrt{5} - 2\sqrt{3}$

37. $30 - 21\sqrt{6}$ 39. $6 - 3\sqrt{3} + 2\sqrt{2} - \sqrt{6}$

41. $\dfrac{5\sqrt{2}}{2}$ 43. $\dfrac{\sqrt{10}}{5}$ 45. $\dfrac{\sqrt[3]{18}}{3}$ 47. $\dfrac{2\sqrt{3x}}{3x}$

49. $\dfrac{y\sqrt{15y}}{3}$ 51. $\dfrac{3\sqrt[3]{4a^2}}{2a}$ 53. $\dfrac{5\sqrt[4]{27x^2}}{3x}$ 55. 9

57. $1 - \sqrt{2}$ 59. $\dfrac{-\sqrt{6} - 3\sqrt{2}}{2}$ 61. $\dfrac{3\sqrt{2} + 2}{7}$

63. $256w^{10}$ 65. $\{-4, 4\}$ 67. $\{3, 7\}$

69. $\{-1 - \sqrt{5}, -1 + \sqrt{5}\}$ 71. No real solution

73. $\{10\}$ 75. $\{9\}$ 77. $\{-8, 8\}$ 79. $\{124\}$ 81. $\{7\}$

83. $\{2, 3\}$ 85. $\{9\}$ 87. $\{4\}$ 89. $5 + 25i$ 91. $7 - 3i$

93. $-1 + 2i$ 95. $2 + i$ 97. $2 - i\sqrt{3}$ 99. $\dfrac{5}{17} - \dfrac{14}{17}i$

101. $\{\pm 10i\}$ 103. $\left\{\pm\dfrac{3i\sqrt{2}}{2}\right\}$ 105. False

107. True   109. True   111. False   113. False

115. False   117. False   119. True   121. False

123. True   125. False   127. False   129. True

131. True   133. $5\sqrt{30}$ seconds   135. $10\sqrt{7}$ feet

137. $200\sqrt{2}$ feet   139. $26.4\sqrt[3]{25}$ ft^2

141. a) 4.9%   b) \$1600 billion   143. $V = \dfrac{29\sqrt{LCS}}{CS}$

Chapter 7 Test

1. 4   2. $\dfrac{1}{8}$ 3. $\sqrt{3}$ 4. 30   5. $3\sqrt{5}$ 6. $\dfrac{6\sqrt{5}}{5}$

7. 2   8. $6\sqrt{2}$ 9. $\dfrac{\sqrt{15}}{6}$ 10. $\dfrac{2 + \sqrt{2}}{2}$ 11. $4 - 3\sqrt{3}$

12. $2ay^2\sqrt[4]{2a}$ 13. $\dfrac{\sqrt[3]{4x}}{2x}$ 14. $\dfrac{2a^4\sqrt{2ab}}{b^2}$ 15. $-3x^3$

16. $2m\sqrt{5m}$ 17. $x^{3/4}$ 18. $3y^2x^{1/4}$ 19. $2x^2\sqrt[3]{5x}$

20. $19 + 8\sqrt{3}$ 21. $\dfrac{5 + \sqrt{3}}{11}$ 22. $\dfrac{6\sqrt{2} - \sqrt{3}}{23}$

23. $22 + 7i$ 24. $1 - i$ 25. $\dfrac{1}{5} - \dfrac{7}{5}i$ 26. $-\dfrac{3}{4} + \dfrac{1}{4}i\sqrt{3}$

27. $\{-5, 9\}$ 28. $\left\{-\dfrac{7}{4}\right\}$ 29. $\{-8, 8\}$ 30. $\left\{\pm\dfrac{4}{3}i\right\}$

31. $\{3\}$ 32. $\{5\}$ 33. $\dfrac{3\sqrt{2}}{2}$ feet   34. 25 and 36

35. Length 6 ft, width 4 ft   36. 39.53 AU, 164.97 years

Making Connections Chapters 1–7

1. $\left\{-\dfrac{4}{7}\right\}$ **2.** $\left\{\dfrac{3}{2}\right\}$

3. $(-\infty, -3) \cup (-2, \infty)$

4. $\left\{\dfrac{3}{2}\right\}$ **5.** $(-\infty, 1)$

6. $\varnothing$ **7.** $\{9\}$ **8.** $\varnothing$ **9.** $\{-12, -2\}$ **10.** $\left\{\dfrac{1}{16}\right\}$

11. $(-6, \infty)$

12. $\left\{-\dfrac{1}{64}, \dfrac{1}{64}\right\}$ **13.** $\left\{-\dfrac{\sqrt{3}}{3}, \dfrac{\sqrt{3}}{3}\right\}$ **14.** R

15. $\left(-\dfrac{1}{3}, 3\right)$

16. $\left\{\dfrac{1}{3}\right\}$ **17.** $\{82\}$ **18.** $\left\{\dfrac{6}{5}, \dfrac{12}{5}\right\}$ **19.** $\{100\}$ **20.** R

21. $\{4\sqrt{30}\}$ **22.** $\{400\}$ **23.** $\left\{\dfrac{13 + 9\sqrt{2}}{3}\right\}$

24. $\{-3\sqrt{2}, 3\sqrt{2}\}$ **25.** $\{5\}$ **26.** $\{7 + 3\sqrt{6}\}$

27. $\{-2, 3\}$ **28.** $\{-5, 2\}$ **29.** $\{-2, 3\}$ **30.** $\left\{\dfrac{1}{2}, 3\right\}$

31. 3 **32.** -2 **33.** $\dfrac{1}{2}$ **34.** $\dfrac{1}{3}$

35. a) 48.5 cm^3 **b)** 14% **c)** 56 cm^3

Chapter 8

Section 8.1 Warm-ups F F F F T F F T F F

1. In this section quadratic equations are solved by factoring, the even-root property, and completing the square.

3. The last term is the square of one-half the coefficient of the middle term.

5. $\{-2, 3\}$ **7.** $\{-5, 3\}$ **9.** $\left\{-1, \dfrac{3}{2}\right\}$ **11.** $\{-7\}$

13. $\{-4, 4\}$ **15.** $\{-9, 9\}$ **17.** $\left\{-\dfrac{4}{3}, \dfrac{4}{3}\right\}$ **19.** $\{-1, 7\}$

21. $\{-1 - \sqrt{5}, -1 + \sqrt{5}\}$ **23.** $\left\{\dfrac{3 - \sqrt{7}}{2}, \dfrac{3 + \sqrt{7}}{2}\right\}$

25. $x^2 + 2x + 1$ **27.** $x^2 - 3x + \dfrac{9}{4}$ **29.** $y^2 + \dfrac{1}{4}y + \dfrac{1}{64}$

31. $x^2 + \dfrac{2}{3}x + \dfrac{1}{9}$ **33.** $(x + 4)^2$ **35.** $\left(y - \dfrac{5}{2}\right)^2$

37. $\left(z - \dfrac{2}{7}\right)^2$ **39.** $\left(t + \dfrac{3}{10}\right)^2$ **41.** $\{-3, 5\}$ **43.** $\{-5, 7\}$

45. $\{-4, 5\}$ **47.** $\{-7, 2\}$ **49.** $\left\{-1, \dfrac{3}{2}\right\}$

51. $\{-2 - \sqrt{10}, -2 + \sqrt{10}\}$

53. $\{-4 - 2\sqrt{5}, -4 + 2\sqrt{5}\}$ **55.** $\left\{\dfrac{1 \pm \sqrt{2}}{2}\right\}$

57. $\left\{\dfrac{-3 \pm \sqrt{41}}{4}\right\}$ **59.** $\{4\}$ **61.** $\left\{\dfrac{1 + \sqrt{17}}{8}\right\}$

63. $\{1, 6\}$ **65.** $\{-2 - \sqrt{2}, -2 + \sqrt{2}\}$

67. $\{-1 - 2i, -1 + 2i\}$ **69.** $\{3 + i\sqrt{2}, 3 - i\sqrt{2}\}$

71. $\left\{\pm\dfrac{i\sqrt{2}}{2}\right\}$ **73.** $\{-2i\sqrt{3}, 2i\sqrt{3}\}$ **75.** $\left\{\dfrac{2 \pm i}{5}\right\}$

77. $\{\pm 11i\}$ **79.** $\left\{-\dfrac{5}{2}i, \dfrac{5}{2}i\right\}$ **81.** $\{-2, 1\}$

83. $\left\{\dfrac{-2 - \sqrt{19}}{5}, \dfrac{-2 + \sqrt{19}}{5}\right\}$ **85.** $\{-6, 4\}$

87. $\{2 \pm 3i\}$ **89.** $\{-2, 3\}$ **91.** $\{3 - i, 3 + i\}$ **93.** $\{6\}$

95. $\left\{\dfrac{9 - \sqrt{65}}{2}, \dfrac{9 + \sqrt{65}}{2}\right\}$ **101.** 136.9 ft/sec **103.** 12

105. c **109.** $\{4.56, 2.74\}$ **111.** $\{3.53\}$

Section 8.2 Warm-ups T F T F T T T T F F

1. The quadratic formula can be used to solve any quadratic equation.

3. Factoring is used when the quadratic polynomial is simple enough to factor.

5. The discriminant is $b^2 - 4ac$. **7.** $\{-3, -2\}$

9. $\{-3, 2\}$ **11.** $\left\{-\dfrac{1}{3}, \dfrac{3}{2}\right\}$ **13.** $\left\{\dfrac{1}{2}\right\}$ **15.** $\left\{\dfrac{1}{3}\right\}$ **17.** $\left\{-\dfrac{3}{4}\right\}$

19. $\{-4 \pm \sqrt{10}\}$ **21.** $\left\{\dfrac{-5 \pm \sqrt{29}}{2}\right\}$ **23.** $\left\{\dfrac{3 \pm \sqrt{7}}{2}\right\}$

25. $\left\{\dfrac{3 \pm i}{2}\right\}$ **27.** $\left\{\dfrac{3 \pm i\sqrt{39}}{4}\right\}$ **29.** $\{5 \pm i\}$ **31.** $28, 2$

33. $-23, 0$ **35.** $0, 1$ **37.** $-\dfrac{3}{4}, 0$ **39.** $97, 2$ **41.** $0, 1$

43. $140, 2$ **45.** $1, 2$ **47.** $\{-2 \pm 2\sqrt{2}\}$ **49.** $\left\{-2, \dfrac{1}{2}\right\}$

51. $\left\{\dfrac{-1 \pm \sqrt{13}}{3}\right\}$ **53.** $\{0\}$ **55.** $\left\{\dfrac{13}{9}, \dfrac{17}{9}\right\}$

57. $\{\pm 5\sqrt{3}\}$ **59.** $\{4 \pm 2i\}$ **61.** $\{2 \pm i\sqrt{6}\}$

63. $\left\{-\dfrac{3}{4}, \dfrac{5}{2}\right\}$ **65.** $\{-4.474, 1.274\}$ **67.** $\{3.7\}$

69. $\{-2.979, -0.653\}$ **71.** $\{-4792.983, -0.017\}$

73. $\{-0.079, 0.078\}$

75. $\dfrac{1 + \sqrt{65}}{2}$ and $\dfrac{-1 + \sqrt{65}}{2}$, or 4.5 and 3.5

77. $3 + \sqrt{5}$ and $3 - \sqrt{5}$, or 5.2 and 0.8

79. $W = \dfrac{-1 + \sqrt{5}}{2} \approx 0.6 \text{ ft}, L = \dfrac{1 + \sqrt{5}}{2} \approx 1.6 \text{ ft}$

81. $W = -2 + \sqrt{14} \approx 1.7 \text{ ft}, L = 2 + \sqrt{14} \approx 5.7 \text{ ft}$

83. 3 sec **85.** 7.0 sec **87.** 4 in. **89.** 4

95. 2 **97.** 0 **99.** 0

Section 8.3 Warm-ups T F T T F T T T T F

1. A quadratic function is a function of the form $f(x) = ax^2 + bx + c$ with $a \neq 0$.

3. If $a > 0$ then the parabola opens upward. If $a < 0$ then the parabola opens downward.

5. The vertex is the highest point on a parabola that opens downward or the lowest point on a parabola that opens upward.

7. $(3, -6), (4, 0), (-3, 0)$ **9.** $(4, -128), (0, 0), (2, 0)$

11. Domain $(-\infty, \infty)$, range $[2, \infty)$

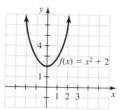

13. Domain $(-\infty, \infty)$, range $[-4, \infty)$

15. Domain $(-\infty, \infty)$, range $(-\infty, 5]$

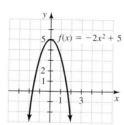

17. Domain $(-\infty, \infty)$, range $(-\infty, 5]$

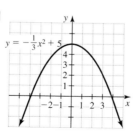

19. Domain $(-\infty, \infty)$, range $[0, \infty)$

21. Vertex $\left(\dfrac{1}{2}, -\dfrac{9}{4}\right)$, intercepts $(0, -2), (-1, 0), (2, 0)$, domain $(-\infty, \infty)$, range $\left[-\dfrac{9}{4}, \infty\right)$

23. Vertex $(-1, -9)$, intercepts $(0, -8), (-4, 0), (2, 0)$, domain $(-\infty, \infty)$, range $[-9, \infty)$

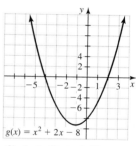

25. Vertex $(-2, 1)$, intercepts $(0, -3), (-1, 0), (-3, 0)$, domain $(-\infty, \infty)$, range $(-\infty, 1]$

27. Vertex $\left(\dfrac{3}{2}, \dfrac{25}{4}\right)$, intercepts $(0, 4), (4, 0), (-1, 0)$, domain $(-\infty, \infty)$, range $\left(-\infty, \dfrac{25}{4}\right]$

29. Vertex $(3, -25)$, intercepts $(0, -16), (8, 0), (-2, 0)$, domain $(-\infty, \infty)$, range $[-25, \infty)$

31. Minimum -8 **33.** Maximum 14

35. Minimum 2   **37.** Maximum 2

39. Maximum 64 feet

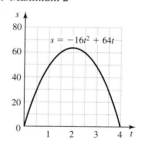

41. 100   **43.** 625 square meters
45. 2 P.M.   **47.** 15 meters, 25 meters
49. The graph of $y = kx^2$ gets narrower as k gets larger.
51. The graph of $y = x^2$ has the same shape as $x = y^2$.
53. a) Vertex $(0.84, -0.68)$, domain $(-\infty, \infty)$,
    range $[-0.68, \infty)$, $(1.30, 0)$, $(0.38, 0)$
  b) Vertex $(5.96, 46.26)$, domain $(-\infty, \infty)$,
    range $(-\infty, 46.26]$, $(12.48, 0)$, $(-0.55, 0)$

Section 8.4 Warm-ups T F F T F F F T F F
1. If the coefficients are integers and the discriminant is a perfect square, then the quadratic polynomial can be factored.
3. If the solutions are a and b, then the quadratic equation $(x - a)(x - b) = 0$ has those solutions.
5. Prime   **7.** Prime   **9.** $(3x - 4)(2x + 9)$ **11.** Prime
13. $(4x - 15)(2x + 3)$ **15.** $x^2 + 4x - 21 = 0$
17. $x^2 - 5x + 4 = 0$ **19.** $x^2 - 5 = 0$ **21.** $x^2 + 16 = 0$
23. $x^2 + 2 = 0$ **25.** $6x^2 - 5x + 1 = 0$ **27.** $\left\{-\dfrac{3}{2}, \dfrac{3}{2}\right\}$

29. $\left\{\dfrac{-3 \pm \sqrt{5}}{2}\right\}$ **31.** $\{\pm\sqrt{5}, \pm 3\}$ **33.** $\{-2, 1\}$

35. $\{-1 \pm \sqrt{5}, -3, 1\}$ **37.** $\{-3, -2, 1, 2\}$ **39.** $\{16, 81\}$

41. $\{9\}$ **43.** $\left\{-\dfrac{1}{3}, \dfrac{1}{2}\right\}$ **45.** $\{64\}$ **47.** $\left\{\dfrac{2}{3}, \dfrac{3}{2}\right\}$

49. $\left\{\pm\dfrac{\sqrt{14}}{2}, \pm\dfrac{\sqrt{38}}{2}\right\}$ **51.** $\{-1 + \sqrt{2}, -1 - \sqrt{2}\}$

53. 2:00 P.M.
55. Before $-5 + \sqrt{265}$ or 11.3 mph, after $-9 + \sqrt{265}$ or 7.3 mph
57. Andrew $\dfrac{13 + \sqrt{265}}{2}$ or 14.6 hr, John $\dfrac{19 + \sqrt{265}}{2}$ or 17.6 hr
59. Length $5 + 5\sqrt{41}$ or 37.02 ft, width $-5 + 5\sqrt{41}$ or 27.02 ft
61. $14 + 2\sqrt{58}$ or 29.2 hr   **63.** $-5 + 5\sqrt{5}$ or 6.2 meters
65. a) $x^2 - 6x + 4 = 0$ **b)** $x^2 - 8x + 20 = 0$
  c) $x^2 - x + 1 = 0$
67. $\{-10, -4, 4, 10\}$ **69.** $\{4.27\}$

Section 8.5 Warm-ups F F F F T T T T T F
1. A quadratic inequality has the form $ax^2 + bx + c > 0$. In place of $>$ we can also use $<$, $\leq$, or $\geq$.
3. A rational inequality is an inequality involving a rational expression.
5. $(-3, 2)$

7. $(-\infty, -2) \cup (2, \infty)$

9. $(-\infty, -4] \cup \left[\dfrac{3}{2}, \infty\right)$

11. $(-\infty, 0] \cup [2, \infty)$

13. $(-\infty, 0) \cup \left(\dfrac{1}{2}, \infty\right)$

15. $(-\infty, \infty)$

17. $(-\infty, 0) \cup (3, \infty)$

19. $[-2, 0)$

21. $(-\infty, -6) \cup (3, \infty)$

23. $(-\infty, -2) \cup (-1, \infty)$

25. $(-13, -4) \cup (5, \infty)$

27. $(-\infty, -5) \cup (1, 3) \cup (5, \infty)$

29. $[-6, 3) \cup [4, 6)$

31. $(-\infty, 1 - \sqrt{5}) \cup (1 + \sqrt{5}, \infty)$

33. $\left(-\infty, \dfrac{3 - \sqrt{3}}{2}\right] \cup \left[\dfrac{3 + \sqrt{3}}{2}, \infty\right)$

35. $\left[\dfrac{3 - 3\sqrt{5}}{2}, \dfrac{3 + 3\sqrt{5}}{2}\right]$

37. $[-3, 3]$ **39.** $(-4, 4)$ **41.** $(-\infty, 0] \cup [4, \infty)$
43. $\left(-\dfrac{3}{2}, \dfrac{5}{3}\right)$ **45.** $(-\infty, -2] \cup [6, \infty)$
47. $(-\infty, -3) \cup (5, \infty)$ **49.** $(-\infty, -4] \cup [2, \infty)$
51. $(-3, 4]$ **53.** $[-1, 2] \cup [5, \infty)$
55. $(-\infty, -3) \cup (-1, 1)$ **57.** $(-27.58, -0.68)$
59. $(-\infty, -2 - \sqrt{6}) \cup (-3, -2 + \sqrt{6}) \cup (2, \infty)$
61. $6, 7, 8, \ldots$ **63.** 4 seconds
65. a) 900 ft   **b)** 3 sec   **c)** 3 sec
67. a) (h, k) **b)** $(-\infty, h) \cup (k, \infty)$
  c) $(-k, -h)$ **d)** $(-\infty, -k] \cup [-h, \infty)$
  e) $(-\infty, h] \cup (k, \infty)$ **f)** $(-k, -h]$
69. c   **71.** b

Chapter 8 Wrap-up

Enriching Your Mathematical Word Power
1. b   **2.** a   **3.** d   **4.** c   **5.** b   **6.** c
7. c   **8.** a   **9.** c   **10.** a   **11.** c

Review Exercises

1. $\{-3, 5\}$ **3.** $\left\{-3, \dfrac{5}{2}\right\}$ **5.** $\{-5, 5\}$ **7.** $\left\{\dfrac{3}{2}\right\}$

9. $\{\pm 2\sqrt{3}\}$ **11.** $\{-2, 4\}$ **13.** $\left\{\dfrac{4 \pm \sqrt{3}}{2}\right\}$ **15.** $\left\{\pm\dfrac{3}{2}\right\}$

17. $\{2, 4\}$ **19.** $\{2, 3\}$ **21.** $\left\{\dfrac{1}{2}, 3\right\}$ **23.** $\{-2 \pm \sqrt{3}\}$

25. $\{-2, 5\}$ **27.** $\left\{-\dfrac{1}{3}, \dfrac{3}{2}\right\}$ **29.** $\{-2 \pm \sqrt{2}\}$

31. $\left\{\dfrac{5 \pm \sqrt{13}}{6}\right\}$ **33.** $0, 1$ **35.** $-19, 0$ **37.** $17, 2$

39. $\left\{\dfrac{2 \pm i\sqrt{2}}{2}\right\}$ **41.** $\left\{\dfrac{3 \pm i\sqrt{15}}{4}\right\}$ **43.** $\left\{\dfrac{-1 \pm i\sqrt{5}}{3}\right\}$

45. $\{-3 \pm i\sqrt{7}\}$

47. Vertex $(3, -9)$, intercepts $(0, 0)$, $(6, 0)$

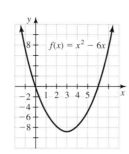

49. Vertex $(2, -16)$, intercepts $(0, -12)$, $(-2, 0)$, $(6, 0)$

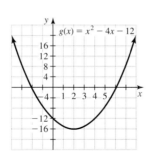

51. Vertex $(2, 8)$, intercepts $(0, 0)$, $(4, 0)$

53. Vertex $(1, 4)$, intercepts $(0, 3)$, $(-1, 0)$, $(3, 0)$

55. Domain $(-\infty, \infty)$, range $[-3, \infty)$
57. Domain $(-\infty, \infty)$, range $(-\infty, 4.125]$

59. $(4x + 1)(2x - 3)$ **61.** Prime   **63.** $(4y - 5)(2y + 5)$
65. $x^2 + 9x + 18 = 0$ **67.** $x^2 - 50 = 0$
69. $\{-2, 1\}$ **71.** $\{\pm 2, \pm 3\}$ **73.** $\{-6, -5, 2, 3\}$
75. $\{-2, 8\}$ **77.** $\left\{-\dfrac{1}{9}, \dfrac{1}{4}\right\}$ **79.** $\{16, 81\}$

81. $(-\infty, -3) \cup (2, \infty)$ **83.** $[-4, 5]$

85. $(0, 1)$ **87.** $(-\infty, -2) \cup [4, \infty)$

89. $(-3, \infty)$ **91.** $(-2, -1) \cup \left(-\dfrac{1}{2}, \infty\right)$

93. $\left\{\dfrac{5}{12}\right\}$ **95.** $\left\{\dfrac{-3 \pm \sqrt{5}}{2}\right\}$ **97.** $\left\{\dfrac{4 \pm 2i}{3}\right\}$ **99.** $\left\{\dfrac{5}{2}\right\}$

101. $\left\{-2, -\dfrac{1}{4}\right\}$ **103.** $\{625, 10{,}000\}$

105. $-2 + 2\sqrt{2}$ and $2 + 2\sqrt{2}$, or 0.83 and 4.83

107. Width $\dfrac{4 + \sqrt{706}}{2}$ or 15.3 inches, height $\dfrac{-4 + \sqrt{706}}{2}$ or 11.3 inches

109. 2 inches   **111.** Width 5 ft, length 9 ft
113. \$20.40, 400   **115.** 0.5 sec and 1.5 sec

Chapter 8 Test

1. $-7, 0$ **2.** $13, 2$ **3.** $0, 1$ **4.** $\left\{-3, \dfrac{1}{2}\right\}$

5. $\{-3 \pm \sqrt{3}\}$ **6.** $\{-5\}$ **7.** $\left\{-2, \dfrac{3}{2}\right\}$ **8.** $\{-4, 3\}$

9. $\{\pm 1, \pm 2\}$ **10.** $\{11, 27\}$ **11.** $\{\pm 6i\}$ **12.** $\{-3 \pm i\}$

13. $\left\{\dfrac{1 \pm i\sqrt{11}}{6}\right\}$

14. Domain $(-\infty, \infty)$, range $(-\infty, 16]$

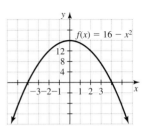

15. Domain $(-\infty, \infty)$, range $\left[-\dfrac{9}{4}, \infty\right)$

16. $x^2 - 2x - 24 = 0$ **17.** $x^2 + 25 = 0$

18. $(-6, 3)$

$-6\ -5\ -4\ -3\ -2\ -1\ \ 0\ \ 1\ \ 2\ \ 3$

19. $(-1, 2) \cup (8, \infty)$

$-1\ 0\ 1\ 2\ 3\ 4\ 5\ 6\ 7\ 8\ 9\ 10$

20. Width $-1 + \sqrt{17}$ feet, length $1 + \sqrt{17}$ feet

21. $\dfrac{5 + \sqrt{37}}{2}$ or 5.5 hr   **22.** $(1, 0), (5, 0)$

23. 36 feet

Making Connections Chapters 1–8

1. $\left\{\dfrac{15}{2}\right\}$ **2.** $\left\{\pm\dfrac{\sqrt{30}}{2}\right\}$ **3.** $\left\{-3, \dfrac{5}{2}\right\}$ **4.** $\left\{\dfrac{-2 \pm \sqrt{34}}{2}\right\}$

5. $\left\{-\dfrac{7}{2}, -2\right\}$ **6.** $\left\{-3, \dfrac{1}{4}, \dfrac{-11 \pm \sqrt{73}}{8}\right\}$ **7.** $\{9\}$

8. $\left\{-\dfrac{3}{2}, \dfrac{13}{2}\right\}$ **9.** $(-4, \infty)$ **10.** $\left[\dfrac{1}{2}, 5\right]$ **11.** $\left[\dfrac{1}{2}, 5\right)$

12. $(2, 8)$ **13.** $[-3, 2)$ **14.** $(-\infty, \infty)$ **15.** $y = \dfrac{2}{3}x - 3$

16. $y = -\dfrac{1}{2}x + 2$ **17.** $y = \dfrac{-c \pm \sqrt{c^2 - 12d}}{6}$

18. $y = \dfrac{n \pm \sqrt{n^2 + 4mw}}{2m}$ **19.** $y = \dfrac{5}{6}x - \dfrac{25}{12}$

20. $y = -\dfrac{2}{3}x + \dfrac{17}{3}$ **21.** $\dfrac{4}{3}$ **22.** $-\dfrac{11}{7}$ **23.** -2

24. $\dfrac{58}{5}$ **25.** 40,000, 38,000, \$32.50

26. \$800,000, \$950,000, \$40 or \$80, \$60

Chapter 9

Section 9.1 Warm-ups T T T T T F T T F T

1. A linear function is a function of the form $f(x) = mx + b$, where m and b are real numbers with $m \neq 0$.

3. The graph of a constant function is a horizontal line.

5. The graph of a quadratic function is a parabola.

7. $(-\infty, \infty), \{-2\}$

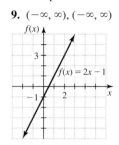

9. $(-\infty, \infty), (-\infty, \infty)$

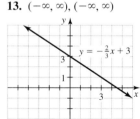

11. $(-\infty, \infty), (-\infty, \infty)$

13. $(-\infty, \infty), (-\infty, \infty)$

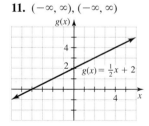

15. $(-\infty, \infty), (-\infty, \infty)$

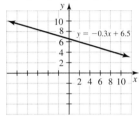

17. $(-\infty, \infty), [1, \infty)$

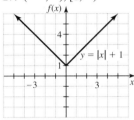

19. $(-\infty, \infty), [0, \infty)$

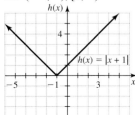

21. $(-\infty, \infty), [0, \infty)$

23. $(-\infty, \infty), [0, \infty)$

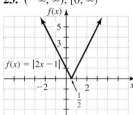

25. $(-\infty, \infty), [1, \infty)$

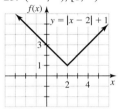

27. $(-\infty, \infty), [2, \infty)$

29. $(-\infty, \infty), [0, \infty)$

31. $(-\infty, \infty), (-\infty, 6]$

33. $[0, \infty), [0, \infty)$

35. $[1, \infty), [0, \infty)$

37. $[0, \infty), (-\infty, 0]$

39. $[0, \infty)$, $[2, \infty)$

41. $[0, \infty)$, $(-\infty, \infty)$

61. $(-\infty, \infty)$, $(-\infty, \infty)$

63. $(-\infty, \infty)$, $(-\infty, 0]$

43. $(-\infty, 0]$, $(-\infty, \infty)$

45. $\{5\}$, $(-\infty, \infty)$

65. The graph of $f(x) = \sqrt{x^2}$ is the same as the graph of $f(x) = |x|$.

67. For large values of k the graph gets narrower and for smaller values of k the graph gets broader.

69. The graph of $y = (x - k)^2$ moves to the right for $k > 0$ and to the left for $k < 0$.

71. The graph of $y = f(x - k)$ lies to the right of the graph of $y = f(x)$ when $k > 0$.

47. $[-9, \infty)$, $(-\infty, \infty)$

49. $[0, \infty)$, $[0, \infty)$

Section 9.2 Warm-ups F T T F T T F T T F

1. The graph of $y = -f(x)$ is a reflection in the x-axis of the graph of $y = f(x)$.

3. The graph of $y = f(x) + k$ for $k < 0$ is a downward translation of $y = f(x)$.

5. The graph of $y = f(x + k)$ for $k > 0$ is a translation to the left of $y = f(x)$.

51. $[0, \infty)$, $(-\infty, \infty)$

53. $(-\infty, \infty)$, $(-\infty, 1]$

7.

9.

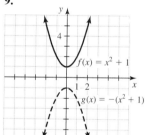

55. $(-\infty, \infty)$, $[-1, \infty)$

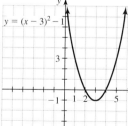

57. $(-\infty, \infty)$, $[1, \infty)$

11.

13.

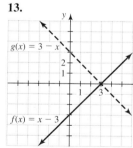

59. $[0, \infty)$, $[-3, \infty)$

15.

17.

19.

21.

43.

45.

23.

25.

47.

49.

27.

29.

51.

31.

33.

53.

35.

37.

55. d   **57.** e   **59.** h   **61.** c   **63.** $y = x^2 + 8$
65. $y = \sqrt{x + 5}$ **67.** $y = |x + 3| + 5$
69. Move f to the right 20 units and upward 30 units.

Section 9.3 Warm-ups T T F F F F T T T T
1. The basic operations of functions are addition, subtraction, multiplication, and division.
3. In the composition function the second function is evaluated on the result of the first function.
5. $x^2 + 2x - 3$ **7.** $4x^3 - 11x^2 + 6x$ **9.** 12   **11.** -30
13. -21 **15.** $\dfrac{13}{8}$ **17.** $y = 6x - 20$ **19.** $y = x + 2$
21. $y = x^2 + 2x$ **23.** $y = x$ **25.** -2 **27.** 5   **29.** 7
31. 5   **33.** 5   **35.** 4   **37.** 22.2992   **39.** $4x^2 - 6x$

39.

41.

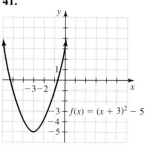

41. $2x^2 + 6x - 3$ **43.** x **45.** $4x - 9$ **47.** $\dfrac{x+9}{4}$

49. $F = f \circ h$ **51.** $G = g \circ h$ **53.** $H = h \circ g$

55. $J = h \circ h$ **57.** $K = g \circ g$ **67. a)** 50 ft^2 **b)** $A = \dfrac{d^2}{2}$

69. $P(x) = -x^2 + 20x - 170$ **71.** $J = 0.025I$

73. a) 397.8 **b)** $D = \dfrac{1.116 \times 10^7}{L^3}$ **c)** Decreases

75. $[0, \infty), [0, \infty), [16, \infty)$ **77.** $[0, \infty), [0, \infty)$

Section 9.4 Warm-ups F F F T T T F T T T F
1. The inverse of a function is a function with the same ordered pairs except that the coordinates are reversed.
3. The range of f^{-1} is the domain of f.
5. A function is one-to-one if no two ordered pairs have the same second coordinate with different first coordinates.
7. The switch-and-solve strategy is used for finding a formula for an inverse function.
9. No   **11.** Yes, $\{(4, 16), (3, 9), (0, 0)\}$ **13.** No
15. Yes, $\{(0, 0), (2, 2), (9, 9)\}$ **17.** No   **19.** Yes
21. Yes   **23.** Yes   **25.** Yes   **27.** No

29. $f^{-1}(x) = \dfrac{x}{5}$ **31.** $g^{-1}(x) = x + 9$ **33.** $k^{-1}(x) = \dfrac{x+9}{5}$

35. $m^{-1}(x) = \dfrac{2}{x}$ **37.** $f^{-1}(x) = x^3 + 4$ **39.** $f^{-1}(x) = \dfrac{3}{x} + 4$

41. $f^{-1}(x) = \dfrac{x^3 - 7}{3}$ **43.** $f^{-1}(x) = \dfrac{2x + 1}{x - 1}$

45. $f^{-1}(x) = \dfrac{1 + 4x}{3x - 1}$ **47.** $p^{-1}(x) = x^4$ for $x \geq 0$
49. $f^{-1}(x) = 2 + \sqrt{x}$ **51.** $f^{-1}(x) = \sqrt{x - 3}$
53. $f^{-1}(x) = x^2 - 2$ for $x \geq 0$

55. $f^{-1}(x) = \dfrac{1}{2}x - \dfrac{3}{2}$ **57.** $f^{-1}(x) = \sqrt{x + 1}$

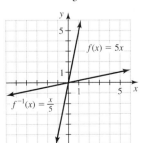

59. $f^{-1}(x) = \dfrac{x}{5}$ **61.** $f^{-1}(x) = \sqrt[3]{x}$

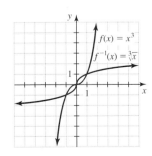

63. $f^{-1}(x) = x^2 + 2$ for $x \geq 0$

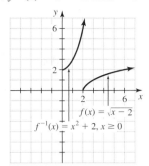

65. $(f^{-1} \circ f)(x) = x$ **67.** $(f^{-1} \circ f)(x) = x$
69. $(f^{-1} \circ f)(x) = x$ **71.** $(f^{-1} \circ f)(x) = x$

73. a) 33.5 mph   **b)** Decreases   **c)** $L = \dfrac{S^2}{30}$

75. $T(x) = 1.09x + 125, \ T^{-1}(x) = \dfrac{x - 125}{1.09}$

77. An odd positive integer   **79.** Not inverses

Section 9.5 Warm-ups T F F T F T F F F T
1. If y varies directly as x, then $y = kx$ for some constant k.
3. If y is inversely proportional to x, then $y = k/x$.
5. If y is jointly proportional to x and z, then $y = kxz$ for some constant k.
7. $a = km$ **9.** $d = k/e$ **11.** $I = krt$ **13.** $m = kp^2$
15. $B = k\sqrt[3]{w}$ **17.** $t = \dfrac{k}{x^2}$ **19.** $v = \dfrac{km}{n}$ **21.** $y = \dfrac{3}{2}x$

23. $A = \dfrac{30}{B}$ **25.** $m = \dfrac{36}{\sqrt{p}}$ **27.** $A = \dfrac{2}{5}tu$

29. $y = \dfrac{1.067x}{z}$ **31.** $-\dfrac{21}{5}$ **33.** $-\dfrac{3}{2}$ **35.** $\dfrac{1}{2}$

37. 3.293 **39.** Inverse   **41.** Direct
43. Combined   **45.** Joint   **47.** $420
49. 9 cm^3 **51.** $360   **53.** $18.90
55. a) $d = 16t^2$ **b)** 4 feet   **c)** 2.5 sec
57. 400 pounds   **59.** 7.2 days

61. a) $G = \dfrac{Nd}{c}$ **b)** 84   **c)** 23, 20, 17, 15, 13
   d) Decreases

63. $(1, 1)$, y_1 increasing, y_2 decreasing, y_1 direct variation, y_2 inverse variation

Chapter 9 Wrap-up

Enriching Your Mathematical Word Power
1. a   **2.** b   **3.** d   **4.** d
5. a   **6.** b   **7.** d
8. c   **9.** d   **10.** b
11. a   **12.** d

Review Exercises

1. $(-\infty, \infty), (-\infty, \infty)$

$f(x) = 3x - 4$

3. $(-\infty, \infty), [-2, \infty)$

$h(x) = |x| - 2$

5. $(-\infty, \infty), [0, \infty)$

$y = x^2 - 2x + 1$

7. $[0, \infty), [2, \infty)$

$k(x) = \sqrt{x} + 2$

9. $(-\infty, \infty), (-\infty, 30]$

$y = 30 - x^2$

11. $\{2\}, (-\infty, \infty)$

$x = 2$

13. $[1, \infty), (-\infty, \infty)$

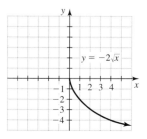

$x = |y| + 1$

15.

$y = \sqrt{x}$

17.

$y = -2\sqrt{x}$

19.

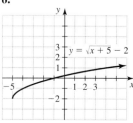

$y = \sqrt{x - 2}$

21.

$y = \tfrac{1}{2}\sqrt{x}$

23.

$y = -\sqrt{x + 1} + 3$

25. -4 **27.** $\sqrt{2}$ **29.** 99 **31.** 17

33. $3x^3 - x^2 - 10x$ **35.** 20 **37.** $F = f \circ g$ **39.** $H = g \circ h$

41. $I = g \circ g$ **43.** No **45.** Yes, $f^{-1}(x) = x/8$

47. Yes, $g^{-1}(x) = \dfrac{x + 6}{13}$ **49.** Yes, $j^{-1}(x) = \dfrac{x + 1}{x - 1}$ **51.** No

53. $f^{-1}(x) = \dfrac{1}{3}x + \dfrac{1}{3}$ **55.** $f^{-1}(x) = \sqrt[3]{2x}$

$f^{-1}(x) = \dfrac{x + 1}{3}$

$f(x) = 3x - 1$

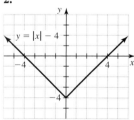

$f^{-1}(x) = \sqrt[3]{2x}$

$f(x) = \tfrac{1}{2}x^3$

57. 24 **59.** -16 **61.** 256 ft **63.** $B = \dfrac{2A}{\pi}$

65. $a = 15w - 16$ **67.** $A = s^2, s = \sqrt{A}$

Chapter 9 Test

1.

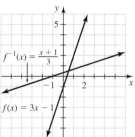

$f(x) = -\tfrac{2}{3}x + 1$

2.

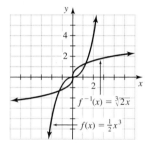

$y = |x| - 4$

3.

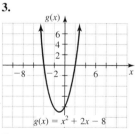

$g(x) = x^2 + 2x - 8$

4.

$x = y^2$

5.

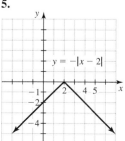

$y = -|x - 2|$

6.

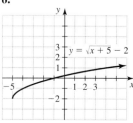

$y = \sqrt{x + 5} - 2$

7. 11　**8.** 125　**9.** -3　**10.** $\dfrac{x-5}{-2}$

11. $x^2 - 2x + 9$　**12.** 15　**13.** 1776　**14.** $\dfrac{1}{8}$

15. $-2x^2 - 3$　**16.** $4x^2 - 20x + 29$　**17.** $H = f \circ g$

18. $W = g \circ f$　**19.** Not invertible　**20.** $f^{-1}(x) = (x-9)^3$

21. $(-\infty, \infty), [0, \infty)$　**22.** $f^{-1}(x) = \dfrac{x+1}{x-2}$　**23.** $\dfrac{32\pi}{3}$ ft^3

24. $\dfrac{36}{7}$　**25.** $5076

Making Connections Chapters 1–9

1. $\dfrac{1}{25}$　**2.** $\dfrac{3}{2}$　**3.** $\sqrt{2}$　**4.** x^8　**5.** 2　**6.** x^9

7. $\{\pm 3\}$　**8.** $\{\pm 2\sqrt{2}\}$　**9.** $\{0, 1\}$　**10.** $\{2 \pm \sqrt{10}\}$

11. $\{81\}$　**12.** $\varnothing$　**13.** $\{\pm 8\}$　**14.** $\left\{-\dfrac{17}{5}, 5\right\}$

15. $\{2\}$　**16.** $\left\{\dfrac{5}{3}\right\}$　**17.** $\{42\}$　**18.** $\{11\}$

19.

20.

21.

22.

23.

24.

25. $(2, 4), (3, 8), (1, 2), (4, 16)$

26. $\left(\dfrac{1}{2}, 2\right), \left(-1, \dfrac{1}{4}\right), (2, 16), (0, 1)$

27. $[0, \infty)$　**28.** $(-\infty, 3]$　**29.** $(-\infty, \infty)$

30. $(-\infty, 1) \cup (1, 9) \cup (9, \infty)$

31. a) $C = 0.12x + 3000$　**b)** $P = 1 \times 10^{-6}x + 0.15$

32. a) \$0.44, \$0.40, \$0.39

b)

c) 60,000 miles　**d)** $[50,000, 60,000]$

Chapter 10

Section 10.1 Warm-ups T T F T T T T T T T

1. A zero of the function f is a number a such that $f(a) = 0$.

3. Two statements are equivalent means that they are either both true or both false.

5. If the remainder is zero when $P(x)$ is divided by $x - c$, then $P(c) = 0$.

7. Yes　**9.** Yes　**11.** No　**13.** Yes　**15.** No　**17.** Yes

19. Yes　**21.** $(x - 3)(x^2 + 3x + 3)$

23. $(x + 5)(x + 3)(x + 1)$　**25.** No

27. $(x + 1)(x - 2)(x^2 + 2x + 4)$

29. $(2x - 1)(x - 3)(x + 2)$

31. $\{-4, 1, 3\}$　**33.** $\left\{-\dfrac{1}{2}, 2, 3\right\}$　**35.** $\left\{-4, -\dfrac{1}{2}, 6\right\}$

37. $\{-3, 1\}$　**39.** $\{-1, 1, 2\}$

41. a) $f(x) = x + 2$　**b)** $f(x) = x^2 - 25$

c) $f(x) = (x - 1)(x + 3)(x - 4)$

d) Yes. The degree is the same as the number of zeros.

43. a) $\{-2, 1, 5\}$　**b)** $\left\{-\dfrac{3}{2}, \dfrac{3}{2}, \dfrac{5}{2}\right\}$

Section 10.2 Warm-ups F F T T F T F T F F

1. A polynomial function is a function for which the value of the dependent variable is determined by a polynomial.

3. A zero of a function $f(x)$ is a number c such that $f(c) = 0$.

5. The rational root theorem states that if a rational number p/q (in lowest terms) is a zero of a polynomial, then its p is a factor of the constant term and q is a factor of the leading coefficient.

7. 0　**9.** 15　**11.** 3　**13.** -15　**15.** 0　**17.** 17

19. Yes　**21.** No　**23.** Yes　**25.** No　**27.** $\dfrac{9}{5}$

29. 2, 3　**31.** $3i, -3i$　**33.** $-2i, 2i, 3$　**35.** $-\dfrac{1}{2}, 0, 3$

37. $-1, \pm\sqrt{7}$　**39.** $\dfrac{-1 \pm i\sqrt{3}}{2}, 1$　**41.** $\pm 1, \pm 2, \pm\dfrac{1}{2}$

43. $\pm 1, \pm 2, \pm 3, \pm 4, \pm 6, \pm 8, \pm 12, \pm 24$

45. $\pm 1, \pm 2, \pm 3, \pm 6$　**47.** $-\dfrac{1}{2}, 1, 2$　**49.** $-4, -3, -2$

51. $-3 - \sqrt{3}, -3 + \sqrt{3}, 1$　**53.** $-2 \pm 2i, 2$　**55.** $\dfrac{1}{2}, \dfrac{1}{3}, \dfrac{1}{4}$

57. \$1000, 0 or 20　**59.** $-0.2, 0.1, 0.3$　**61.** 10, 20, 30

Section 10.3 Warm-ups F T T F F T F F T T

1. Multiplicity of a root c is the number of times that $x - c$ occurs as a factor.
3. The conjugate pairs theorem states that for a polynomial equation with real coefficients if $a + bi$ ($b \neq 0$) is a root, then $a - bi$ is also a root.
5. If there are no roots greater than c, then c is an upper bound for the roots.
7. Degree 5, -2, 2, 0 multiplicity 3
9. Degree 4, 0 multiplicity 2, -1 multiplicity 2
11. Degree 4, $-\sqrt{3}$ multiplicity 2, $\sqrt{3}$ multiplicity 2
13. Degree 4, 1 multiplicity 2, -2 multiplicity 2
15. Degree 4, -1 multiplicity 2, 1 multiplicity 2
17. $x^3 - 7x^2 + 17x - 15 = 0$
19. $x^3 + 2x^2 + x + 2 = 0$ **21.** $x^3 + 2x = 0$
23. $x^4 - 2x^3 + 3x^2 - 2x + 2 = 0$
25. $x^2 - 3x + 2 = 0$ **27.** $x^3 - 4x^2 + x + 6 = 0$
29. 3 negative, or 1 negative and 2 imaginary
31. 1 positive and 2 negative, or 1 positive and 2 imaginary
33. 4 positive, or 2 positive and 2 imaginary, or 4 imaginary
35. no positive, no negative, 4 imaginary
37. 1 positive and 2 imaginary   **39.** 4 imaginary and 0
41. Between -3 and 3   **43.** Between -1 and 3
45. Between -5 and 4   **47.** Between -1 and 7
49. $-2, 1 \pm 2i$ **51.** $\dfrac{1}{2}, 1 \pm \sqrt{5}$ **53.** $-\dfrac{1}{2}, \dfrac{2 \pm \sqrt{2}}{2}$
55. $-1, 1, 2, 3$ **57.** 1, 2, 3   **59.** $0, 1, \pm i\sqrt{5}, \pm\sqrt{3}$
61. 6 feet   **63.** $\dfrac{1}{2}$ in.   **65.** 3.3315, 0.9492, -0.9492, -3.3315
67. $-2.4495, -1.4142, -1, 1, 1.4142, 2.4495$

Section 10.4 Warm-ups F F F F T T F F T F

1. The graph of $y = f(x)$ is symmetric about the y-axis if $f(x) = f(-x)$ for all x in the domain of the function.
3. An x-intercept is a point at which a graph intersects the x-axis.
5. Symmetric about y-axis   **7.** Neither symmetry
9. Neither symmetry   **11.** Neither symmetry
13. Symmetric about y-axis   **15.** Symmetric about origin
17. Does not cross at $(5, 0)$ **19.** Crosses at $(4, 0)$ and $(-1, 0)$
21. Does not cross at $(0, 0)$
23. Crosses at $(-5, 0)$, does not cross at $(3, 0)$
25. Crosses at $(1, 0)$, does not cross at $(0, 0)$
27. Crosses at $\left(\dfrac{1}{2}, 0\right)$, does not cross at $(-1, 0)$
29. d   **31.** a   **33.** c   **35.** e

37.

39.

41.

43.

45.

47.

49.

51.

53.

Section 10.5 Warm-ups F F F F T F T F T T
1. A rational function is of the form $f(x) = P(x)/Q(x)$, where $P(x)$ and $Q(x)$ are polynomials with no common factor and $Q(x) \neq 0$.
3. A vertical asymptote is a vertical line that is approached by the graph of a rational function.
5. An oblique asymptote is a nonhorizontal, nonvertical line that is approached by the graph of a rational function.
7. $(-\infty, 1) \cup (1, \infty)$ 9. $(-\infty, 0) \cup (0, \infty)$
11. $(-\infty, -4) \cup (-4, 4) \cup (4, \infty)$
13. Vertical: $x = -4$; horizontal: x-axis
15. Vertical: $x = 4, x = -4$; horizontal: x-axis
17. Vertical: $x = 7$; horizontal: $y = 5$
19. Vertical: $x = 3$; oblique: $y = 2x + 6$
21. c   23. b   25. g   27. f
29. $x = -4$, x-axis   31. $x = 3, x = -3$, x-axis

33. $x = -3, y = 2$ **35.** y-axis, $y = x - 3$

37. $x = 1, y = 3x + 1$

39. $x = 0, y = 0$

41. $x = -3, x = 2,$
$\quad y = 0, \left(0, \frac{1}{2}\right), \left(\frac{3}{2}, 0\right)$

43. $x = 0, y = 0, (-1, 0)$

45. $x = 0, x = \pm 3,$
$\quad y = 0, \left(\frac{1}{2}, 0\right)$

47. $x = \pm 1, y = 0, (0, 0)$

49. $y = 0$, $(0, 2)$

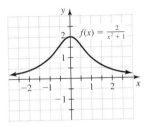

51. $x = -1$, $y = x - 1$, $(0, 0)$

53. $f(20) = \$2.35$,
$f(30) = \$1.46$,
average approaches 0

55. **a)** $y = 25,000$ **b)** $\$39,000$ **c)** $140,000$

57. The graph of $f(x)$ is an asymptote for the graph of $g(x)$.
59. The graph of $f(x)$ is an asymptote for the graph of $g(x)$.
61. The graph of $f(x)$ is an asymptote for the graph of $g(x)$.

Chapter 10 Wrap-up

Enriching Your Mathematical Word Power
1. c   **2.** b   **3.** a   **4.** d   **5.** a   **6.** a   **7.** d
8. d   **9.** a   **10.** b   **11.** a

Review Exercises
1. $\{-3, 2, 5\}$ **3.** $\{-2, 3, 4\}$ **5.** $(x - 3)(x + 2)(x + 5)$

7. No   **9.** $-45, \dfrac{5}{2}$ **11.** $\pm 1, \pm 2, \pm 4, \pm\dfrac{1}{3}, \pm\dfrac{2}{3}, \pm\dfrac{4}{3}$

13. $\pm 1, \pm 3, \pm\dfrac{1}{2}, \pm\dfrac{3}{2}, \pm\dfrac{1}{4}, \pm\dfrac{3}{4}$ **15.** $\dfrac{3}{2}$ **17.** ± 10

19. $4, -2 \pm 2i\sqrt{3}$ **21.** $\pm 2\sqrt{2}, \pm 2i\sqrt{2}$

23. $\dfrac{1}{3}, \pm\dfrac{1}{2}$ **25.** $2x^2 - 5x + 2 = 0$ **27.** $x^2 - 10x + 29 = 0$

29. $x^3 - 5x^2 + 16x - 30 = 0$
31. 4 imaginary and 0 with multiplicity 2
33. 3 positive, or 1 positive and 2 imaginary
35. Between -2 and 4   **37.** Between -2 and 5

39. $\dfrac{1}{2}, 4, 5$ **41.** $-\dfrac{3}{2}, \dfrac{1}{2}, \dfrac{5}{2}$ **43.** $5, \dfrac{1}{2} \pm i$

45. 3 with multiplicity 2, $\dfrac{1 \pm \sqrt{2}}{2}$ **47.** 1 with multiplicity 3

49. Symmetric about y-axis   **51.** Symmetric about origin
53. $(1, 0), (-2, 0), (0, 2)$

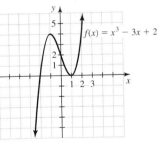

55. $(1, 0), (-1, 0), (0, -1)$

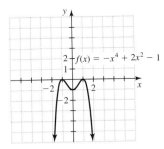

57. $(0, 0), (2, 0), (-2, 0)$

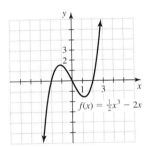

59. $\left(-\infty, -\dfrac{3}{2}\right) \cup \left(-\dfrac{3}{2}, \infty\right)$ **61.** $(-\infty, \infty)$

63. $x = 3$, x-axis   **65.** $x = 2$, $x = -2$, x-axis

          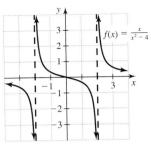

67. $x = 1$, $y = 2$ **69.** $x = 2$, $y = x$

71.

73.

18.

19.

20.

75.

77.

79. 3 in.

Making Connections Chapters 1–10

1. -2 **2.** $\dfrac{3}{2}, 5$ **3.** $\dfrac{3}{2}$ **4.** $\pm\dfrac{\sqrt{6}}{2}$ **5.** -9

6. $\pm\dfrac{\sqrt{6}}{2}, \pm i\sqrt{5}$ **7.** $-5, 2$ **8.** $-\dfrac{1}{3}, -\dfrac{1}{5}, \dfrac{3}{2}$

9.

10.
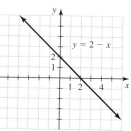

Chapter 10 Test

1. 52 **2.** 7 **3.** $\pm1, \pm2, \pm3, \pm6$ **4.** $\pm1, \pm3, \pm\dfrac{1}{2}, \pm\dfrac{3}{2}$

5. $-4, 1, 3$ **6.** $\dfrac{1}{2}, 2\pm i$ **7.** $x^3 - 2x^2 - x + 2 = 0$

8. $x^3 - 8x^2 + 22x - 20 = 0$ **9.** Yes
10. $(x-3)(x-4)(x-5)$
11. 3 positive, or 1 positive and 2 imaginary
12. 4 imaginary roots and 0 **13.** Between -2 and 3
14. Between -2 and 3 **15.** Symmetry about origin
16. Symmetry about y-axis

17.

11.

12.

13.

14.

15.

16.

17.

18.

19.

20.

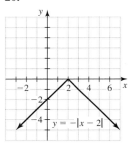

Chapter 11

Section 11.1 Warm-ups F T F T T F T F T F

1. An exponential function has the form $f(x) = a^x$, where $a > 0$ and $a \neq 1$.

3. The two most popular bases are e and 10.

5. The compound interest formula is $A = P(1 + i)^n$.

7. 16   **9.** 2   **11.** 3   **13.** $\dfrac{1}{3}$ **15.** -1 **17.** $-\dfrac{1}{4}$

19. 1   **21.** 100   **23.** 2.718   **25.** 0.135

27.

29.

31.

33.

35.

37.

39.

41.

43.

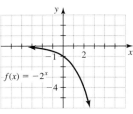

45. $\{6\}$ **47.** $\{-3\}$ **49.** $\{-2\}$ **51.** $\{-1\}$ **53.** $\{-2\}$

55. $\{-2\}$ **57.** $\{-3, 3\}$ **59.** 2   **61.** $\dfrac{4}{3}$ **63.** -2

65. 0   **67.** $\dfrac{3}{2}$ **69.** $\dfrac{1}{2}$ **71.** \$9861.72

73. a) \$53,277.30   **b)** 2010   **75.** \$45, \$12.92

77. \$616.84   **79.** \$6230.73

81. 300 grams, 90.4 grams, 12 years, no

83. 2.66666667, 0.0516, 2.8×10^{-5}

85. The graph of $y = 3^{x-k}$ lies k units to the right of $y = 3^x$ when $k > 0$ and $|k|$ units to the left of $y = 3^x$ when $k < 0$.

Section 11.2 Warm-ups T F T T F F F F T T

1. If $f(x) = 2^x$, then $f^{-1}(x) = \log_2(x)$.

3. The common logarithm uses the base 10 and the natural logarithm uses base e.

5. The one-to-one property for logarithmic functions states that if $\log_a(m) = \log_a(n)$, then $m = n$.

7. $2^3 = 8$ **9.** $\log(100) = 2$ **11.** $5^y = x$ **13.** $\log_2(b) = a$

15. $3^{10} = x$ **17.** $\ln(x) = 3$ **19.** 2   **21.** 4   **23.** 6

25. 3   **27.** -2 **29.** 2   **31.** -2 **33.** 1   **35.** -3

37. $\dfrac{1}{2}$ **39.** 2   **41.** 0.6990   **43.** 1.8307

45.

47.

49.

51.

53. $f^{-1}(x) = \log_6(x)$ **55.** $f^{-1}(x) = e^x$

57. $f^{-1}(x) = \left(\dfrac{1}{2}\right)^x$ **59.** $\{4\}$ **61.** $\left\{\dfrac{1}{2}\right\}$ **63.** $\{0.001\}$

65. $\{6\}$ **67.** $\left\{\dfrac{1}{5}\right\}$ **69.** $\{\pm 3\}$ **71.** $\{0.4771\}$

73. $\{-0.3010\}$ **75.** $\{1.9741\}$ **77.** 5.776 years

79. 1.9269 years   **81. a)** 14.58%   **b)** \$66,576.60

83. 4.1   **85.** 6.8   **87.** 90 db

89. $f^{-1}(x) = 2^{x-5} + 3,\ (-\infty, \infty),\ (3, \infty)$

91. $y = \ln(e^x) = x$ for $-\infty < x < \infty$, $y = e^{\ln(x)} = x$ for $0 < x < \infty$

Section 11.3 Warm-ups T F T T F T F F F T

1. The product rule for logarithms states that $\log_a(MN) = \log_a(M) + \log_a(N)$.

3. The power rule for logarithms states that $\log_a(M^N) = N \cdot \log_a(M)$.

5. Since $\log_a(M)$ is the exponent you would use on a to obtain M, using $\log_a(M)$ as the exponent produces M: $a^{\log_a(M)} = M$.

7. $\log(21)$ **9.** $\log_3(\sqrt{5x})$ **11.** $\log(x^5)$ **13.** $\ln(30)$

15. $\log(x^2 + 3x)$ **17.** $\log_2(x^2 - x - 6)$ **19.** $\log(4)$

21. $\log_2(x^4)$ **23.** $\log(\sqrt{5})$ **25.** $\ln(h - 2)$

27. $\log_2(w - 2)$ **29.** $\ln(x - 2)$ **31.** $3\log(3)$

33. $\dfrac{1}{2}\log(3)$ **35.** $x\log(3)$ **37.** 10   **39.** 19   **41.** 8

43. 4.3   **45.** $\log(3) + \log(5)$ **47.** $\log(5) - \log(3)$

49. $2\log(5)$ **51.** $2 \cdot \log(5) + \log(3)$ **53.** $-\log(3)$

55. $-\log(5)$ **57.** $\log(x) + \log(y) + \log(z)$

59. $3 + \log_2(x)$ **61.** $\ln(x) - \ln(y)$ **63.** $1 + 2 \cdot \log(x)$

65. $2\log_5(x - 3) - \dfrac{1}{2}\log_5(w)$

67. $\ln(y) + \ln(z) + \dfrac{1}{2}\ln(x) - \ln(w)$ **69.** $\log(x^2 - x)$

71. $\ln(3)$ **73.** $\ln\left(\dfrac{xz}{w}\right)$ **75.** $\ln\left(\dfrac{x^2 y^3}{w}\right)$ **77.** $\log\left(\dfrac{(x-3)^{1/2}}{(x+1)^{2/3}}\right)$

79. $\log_2\left(\dfrac{(x-1)^{2/3}}{(x+2)^{1/4}}\right)$ **81.** False   **83.** True   **85.** True

87. False   **89.** True   **91.** True   **93.** True   **95.** False

97. $r = \log(I/I_0),\ r = 2$ **99.** b

101. The graphs are the same because

$$\ln(\sqrt{x}) = \ln(x^{1/2}) = \dfrac{1}{2}\ln(x).$$

103. The graph is a straight line because $\log(e^x) = x\log(e) \approx 0.434x$. The slope is $\log(e)$ or approximately 0.434.

Section 11.4 Warm-ups T T T F T T T F T F

1. The exponential equation $a^y = x$ is equivalent to $\log_a(x) = y$.

3. $\{7\}$ **5.** $\{31\}$ **7.** $\{e\}$ **9.** $\{2\}$ **11.** $\{3\}$ **13.** $\varnothing$

15. $\{6\}$ **17.** $\{3\}$ **19.** $\{2\}$ **21.** $\{4\}$ **23.** $\{\log_3(7)\}$

25. $\left\{\dfrac{\ln(7)}{2}\right\}$ **27.** $\{-6\}$ **29.** $\left\{-\dfrac{1}{2}\right\}$

31. $\dfrac{5\ln(3)}{\ln(2) - \ln(3)}, -13.548$ **33.** $\dfrac{4 + 2\log(5)}{1 - \log(5)}, 17.932$

35. $\dfrac{\ln(9)}{\ln(9) - \ln(8)}, 18.655$ **37.** 1.5850   **39.** -0.6309

41. -2.2016 **43.** 1.5229   **45.** $\dfrac{\ln(7)}{\ln(2)}, 2.807$

47. $\dfrac{1}{3 - \ln(2)}, 0.433$ **49.** $\dfrac{\ln(5)}{\ln(3)}, 1.465$

51. $1 + \dfrac{\ln(9)}{\ln(2)}, 4.170$ **53.** $\log_3(20), 2.727$ **55.** $\dfrac{3}{5}$ **57.** $\dfrac{1}{2}$

59. 41 months   **61.** 594 days

63. 10 g, 9163 years ago   **65.** 7524 ft^3/sec   **67.** 7.1 years

69. 16.8 years   **71.** 2.0×10^{-4} **73.** 0.9183

75. 2.2894   **77.** (2.71, 6.54)   **79.** (1.03, 0.04), (4.73, 2.24)

Chapter 11 Wrap-up

Enriching Your Mathematical Word Power

1. a   **2.** d   **3.** b   **4.** d   **5.** d   **6.** b   **7.** a

8. b   **9.** b   **10.** c

Review Exercises

1. $\dfrac{1}{25}$ **3.** 125   **5.** 1   **7.** $\dfrac{1}{10}$ **9.** 4   **11.** $\dfrac{1}{2}$ **13.** 2

15. 4   **17.** $-\dfrac{5}{2}$ **19.** 2   **21.** 8.6421   **23.** 177.828

25. 0.02005   **27.** 0.1408

29.

31.

33.

35.

37. $\log(n) = m$ **39.** $k^h = t$ **41.** -3 **43.** -1 **45.** 2

47. 0   **49.** 256   **51.** 6.267   **53.** -5.083 **55.** 5.560

57. $f^{-1}(x) = \log(x)$ **59.** $f^{-1}(x) = \ln(x)$

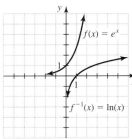

61. $2\log(x) + \log(y)$ **63.** $4\ln(2)$ **65.** $-\log_5(x)$

67. $\log\left(\dfrac{\sqrt{x+2}}{(x-1)^2}\right)$ **69.** $\{256\}$ **71.** $\{3\}$ **73.** $\{2\}$

75. $\{3\}$ **77.** $\left\{\dfrac{\ln(7)}{\ln(3)-1}\right\}$ **79.** $\left\{\dfrac{\ln(5)}{\ln(5)-\ln(3)}\right\}$

81. $\left\{\dfrac{1}{3}\right\}$ **83.** $\{22\}$ **85.** $\left\{\dfrac{200}{99}\right\}$ **87.** $\{1.3869\}$

89. $\{0.4650\}$ **91.** $\$51,182.68$ **93.** 161.5 grams

95. 5 years   **97.** 4347.5 ft³/sec

Chapter 11 Test

1. 25   **2.** $\dfrac{1}{5}$ **3.** 1   **4.** 3   **5.** 0   **6.** -1

7.

8.

9.

10.

11. 10   **12.** 8   **13.** $\dfrac{3}{2}$ **14.** 15   **15.** -4

16. $\{\log_3(12)\}$ **17.** $\{\sqrt{3}\}$ **18.** $\left\{\dfrac{\ln(8)}{\ln(8)-\ln(5)}\right\}$

19. $\{5\}$ **20.** $\{3\}$ **21.** $\{0.5372\}$ **22.** $\{20.5156\}$

23. 10; 147,648   **24.** 1.733 hours

Making Connections Chapters 1–11

1. $\{3 \pm 2\sqrt{2}\}$ **2.** $\{259\}$ **3.** $\{6\}$ **4.** $\left\{\dfrac{11}{2}\right\}$

5. $\{-5, 11\}$ **6.** $\{67\}$ **7.** $\{6\}$ **8.** $\{4\}$ **9.** $\left\{-\dfrac{52}{15}\right\}$

10. $\left\{\dfrac{3 \pm \sqrt{3}}{3}\right\}$ **11.** $f^{-1}(x) = 3x$ **12.** $g^{-1}(x) = 3^x$

13. $f^{-1}(x) = \dfrac{x+4}{2}$ **14.** $h^{-1}(x) = x^2$ for $x \geq 0$

15. $j^{-1}(x) = \dfrac{1}{x}$ **16.** $k^{-1}(x) = \log_5(x)$

17. $m^{-1}(x) = 1 + \ln(x)$ **18.** $n^{-1}(x) = e^x$

19.   **20.**

21.   **22.**

23.   **24.**

25.   **26.**

27. a)

b) Linear 155.7 million, exponential 156.5 million

28. a) $d_1 = 0.135v$ **b)** $d_2 = 0.216v$ **c)** $d_1 = 200.2$ m

Chapter 12

Section 12.1 Warm-ups T F F T F T T T T T

1. If the graph of an equation is not a straight line, then it is called nonlinear.

3. Graphing is not an accurate method for solving a system and the graphs might be difficult to draw.

5. $\{(2, 4), (-3, 9)\}$ **7.** $\{(-2, 2), (6, 6)\}$

9. $\{(8, 4)\}$ **11.** $\left\{\left(-\dfrac{3}{4}, -\dfrac{4}{3}\right), \left(3, \dfrac{1}{3}\right)\right\}$

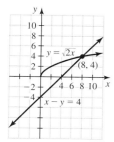

13. $\left\{\left(\dfrac{\sqrt{2}}{2}, \dfrac{1}{2}\right), \left(-\dfrac{\sqrt{2}}{2}, \dfrac{1}{2}\right)\right\}$

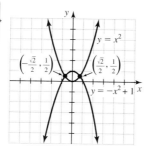

15. $\{(0, -5), (3, 4), (-3, 4)\}$ **17.** $\{(4, 5), (-2, -1)\}$

19. $\left\{\left(-3, -\dfrac{5}{3}\right)\right\}$

21. $\{(\sqrt{5}, \sqrt{3}), (\sqrt{5}, -\sqrt{3}), (-\sqrt{5}, \sqrt{3}), (-\sqrt{5}, -\sqrt{3})\}$

23. $\{(\sqrt{2}, \sqrt{3}), (\sqrt{2}, -\sqrt{3}), (-\sqrt{2}, \sqrt{3}), (-\sqrt{2}, -\sqrt{3})\}$

25. $\left\{\left(\dfrac{3}{2}, -\dfrac{3}{13}\right)\right\}$ **27.** $\{(3, 4)\}$ **29.** $\left\{\left(-\dfrac{5}{3}, \dfrac{36}{5}\right), (2, 5)\right\}$

31. $\{(2, 5), (19, -12)\}$

33. $\{(\sqrt{2}, 2), (-\sqrt{2}, 2), (1, 1), (-1, 1)\}$

35. $\{(3, 1)\}$ **37.** $\varnothing$ **39.** $\{(-6, 4^{-7})\}$

41. $\sqrt{3}$ feet and $2\sqrt{3}$ feet

43. Height $5\sqrt{10}$ inches, base $20\sqrt{10}$ inches

45. Pump A 24 hours, pump B 8 hours

47. 40 minutes   **49.** 8 feet by 9 feet   **51.** $4 - 2i$ and $4 + 2i$

53. Side of square 8 feet, height of triangle 2 feet

55. a) $(1.71, 1.55), (-2.98, -3.95)$ **b)** $(1, 1), (0.40, 0.16)$

 c) $(1.17, 1.62), (-1.17, -1.62)$

Section 12.2 Warm-ups F T T F F T T T T T

1. A parabola is the set of all points in a plane that are equidistant from a given line and a fixed point not on the line.

3. A parabola can be written in the forms $y = ax^2 + bx + c$ or $y = a(x - h)^2 + k$.

5. We use completing the square to convert $y = ax^2 + bx + c$ into $y = a(x - h)^2 + k$.

7. $\sqrt{13}$ **9.** $2\sqrt{17}$ **11.** $\sqrt{65}$

13. Vertex $(0, 0)$, focus $\left(0, \dfrac{1}{8}\right)$, directrix $y = -\dfrac{1}{8}$

15. Vertex $(0, 0)$, focus $(0, -1)$, directrix $y = 1$

17. Vertex $(3, 2)$, focus $(3, 2.5)$, directrix $y = 1.5$

19. Vertex $(-1, 6)$, focus $(-1, 5.75)$, directrix $y = 6.25$

21. $y = \dfrac{1}{8}x^2$ **23.** $y = -\dfrac{1}{2}x^2$ **25.** $y = \dfrac{1}{2}x^2 - 3x + 6$

27. $y = -\dfrac{1}{8}x^2 + \dfrac{1}{4}x - \dfrac{1}{8}$ **29.** $y = x^2 + 6x + 10$

31. $y = (x - 3)^2 - 8$, vertex $(3, -8)$, focus $(3, -7.75)$, directrix $y = -8.25$, axis $x = 3$

33. $y = 2(x + 3)^2 - 13$, vertex $(-3, -13)$, focus $(-3, -12.875)$, directrix $y = -13.125$, axis $x = -3$

35. $y = -2(x - 4)^2 + 33$, vertex $(4, 33)$, focus $\left(4, 32\dfrac{7}{8}\right)$, directrix $y = 33\dfrac{1}{8}$, axis $x = 4$

37. $y = 5(x + 4)^2 - 80$, vertex $(-4, -80)$, focus $\left(-4, -79\dfrac{19}{20}\right)$, directrix $y = -80\dfrac{1}{20}$, axis $x = -4$

39. Vertex $(2, -3)$, focus $\left(2, -2\dfrac{3}{4}\right)$, directrix $y = -3\dfrac{1}{4}$, $x = 2$, upward

41. Vertex $(1, -2)$, focus $\left(1, -2\dfrac{1}{4}\right)$, directrix $y = -1\dfrac{3}{4}$, $x = 1$, downward

43. Vertex $(1, -2)$, focus $\left(1, -1\dfrac{11}{12}\right)$, directrix $y = -2\dfrac{1}{12}$, $x = 1$, upward

45. Vertex $\left(-\dfrac{3}{2}, \dfrac{17}{4}\right)$, focus $\left(-\dfrac{3}{2}, 4\right)$, directrix $y = \dfrac{9}{2}$, $x = -\dfrac{3}{2}$, downward

47. Vertex $(0, 5)$, focus $\left(0, 5\dfrac{1}{12}\right)$, directrix $y = 4\dfrac{11}{12}$, $x = 0$, upward

49. $(3, 2)$, $\left(\dfrac{13}{4}, 2\right)$, $x = \dfrac{11}{4}$

51. $(-2, 1), (-1, 1)$, $x = -3$ **53.** $(4, 2)$, $\left(\dfrac{7}{2}, 2\right)$, $x = \dfrac{9}{2}$

55.

57.

59.

61.

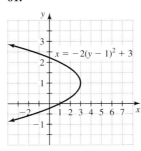

63. $y = \dfrac{1}{60} x^2$

65. $\{(-1, 2), (1, 2)\}$

67. $\{(1, -1)\}$

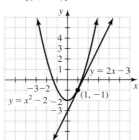

69. $\left\{\left(\dfrac{3}{2}, \dfrac{11}{4}\right), (-4, 0)\right\}$

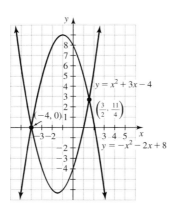

71. $\{(-3, -4), (2, 6)\}$

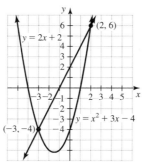

73. $(3, 0), (-1, 0)$ **75.** $(20, 4), (-20, 4)$ **77.** $(0, 0), (1, 1)$
81. The graphs have identical shapes.

Section 12.3 Warm-ups F F T F F F T F T F
1. A circle is the set of all points in a plane that lie at a fixed distance from a fixed point.

3. $x^2 + (y - 3)^2 = 25$ **5.** $(x - 1)^2 + (y + 2)^2 = 81$

7. $x^2 + y^2 = 3$ **9.** $(x + 6)^2 + (y + 3)^2 = \dfrac{1}{4}$

11. $\left(x - \dfrac{1}{2}\right)^2 + \left(y - \dfrac{1}{3}\right)^2 = 0.01$ **13.** $(3, 5), \sqrt{2}$

15. $\left(0, \dfrac{1}{2}\right), \dfrac{\sqrt{2}}{2}$ **17.** $(0, 0), \dfrac{3}{2}$ **19.** $(2, 0), \sqrt{3}$

21.

23.

25.

27.

29.

31. $(x + 2)^2 + (y + 3)^2 = 13, (-2, -3), \sqrt{13}$
33. $(x - 1)^2 + (y - 2)^2 = 8, (1, 2), 2\sqrt{2}$
35. $(x - 5)^2 + (y - 4)^2 = 9, (5, 4), 3$

37. $\left(x - \dfrac{1}{2}\right)^2 + \left(y + \dfrac{1}{2}\right)^2 = \dfrac{1}{2}, \left(\dfrac{1}{2}, -\dfrac{1}{2}\right), \dfrac{\sqrt{2}}{2}$

39. $\left(x - \dfrac{3}{2}\right)^2 + \left(y - \dfrac{1}{2}\right)^2 = \dfrac{7}{2}, \left(\dfrac{3}{2}, \dfrac{1}{2}\right), \dfrac{\sqrt{14}}{2}$

41. $\left(x - \dfrac{1}{3}\right)^2 + \left(y + \dfrac{3}{4}\right)^2 = \dfrac{97}{144}, \left(\dfrac{1}{3}, -\dfrac{3}{4}\right), \dfrac{\sqrt{97}}{12}$

43. $\{(1, 3), (-1, -3)\}$ **45.** $\{(0, -3), (\sqrt{5}, 2), (-\sqrt{5}, 2)\}$

9.

11.

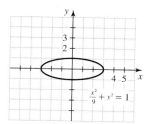

13.

47. $\{(0, -3), (2, -1)\}$ **49.** $(0, 2 + \sqrt{3})$ and $(0, 2 - \sqrt{3})$

15.   **17.**

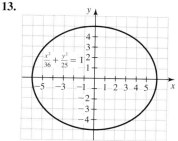

51. $\sqrt{29}$ **53.** $(x - 2)^2 + (y - 3)^2 = 32$

55. $\left(\frac{5}{2}, -\frac{\sqrt{11}}{2}\right)$ and $\left(\frac{5}{2}, \frac{\sqrt{11}}{2}\right)$ **57.** $755{,}903$ mm^3

59. $(0, 0)$ only   **61.**

19.   **21.**

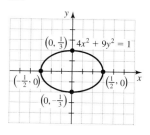

63. B and D can be any real numbers, but A must equal C, and $4AE + B^2 + D^2 > 0$. No ordered pairs satisfy $x^2 + y^2 = -9$.

65. $y = \pm\sqrt{4 - x^2}$ **67.** $y = \pm\sqrt{x}$ **69.** $y = -1 \pm \sqrt{x}$

Section 12.4 Warm-ups F F T T T F F T T T

1. An ellipse is the set of all points in a plane such that the sum of their distances from two fixed points is constant.

3. The center of an ellipse is the point that is midway between the foci.

5. The equation of an ellipse centered at (h, k) is $\frac{(x - h)^2}{a^2} + \frac{(y - k)^2}{b^2} = 1.$

7. The asymptotes of a hyperbola are the extended diagonals of the fundamental rectangle.

23.   **25.**

27.

29. $y = \pm\dfrac{3}{2}x$

43.

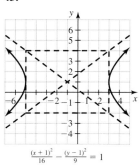

$$\frac{(x+1)^2}{16} - \frac{(y-1)^2}{9} = 1$$

45.

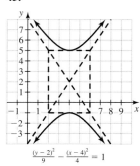

$$\frac{(y-2)^2}{9} - \frac{(x-4)^2}{4} = 1$$

47. $\left(\dfrac{2\sqrt{10}}{5}, \dfrac{3\sqrt{15}}{5}\right), \left(\dfrac{2\sqrt{10}}{5}, -\dfrac{3\sqrt{15}}{5}\right),$

$\left(-\dfrac{2\sqrt{10}}{5}, \dfrac{3\sqrt{15}}{5}\right), \left(-\dfrac{2\sqrt{10}}{5}, -\dfrac{3\sqrt{15}}{5}\right)$

31. $y = \pm\dfrac{2}{5}x$

33. $y = \pm\dfrac{1}{5}x$

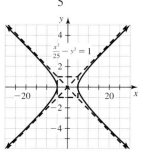

49. No points of intersection

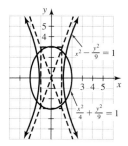

35. $y = \pm 5x$

37. $y = \pm\dfrac{3}{4}x$

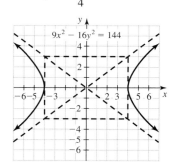

51. $\left(\dfrac{\sqrt{10}}{2}, \dfrac{\sqrt{6}}{2}\right), \left(\dfrac{\sqrt{10}}{2}, -\dfrac{\sqrt{6}}{2}\right),$

$\left(-\dfrac{\sqrt{10}}{2}, \dfrac{\sqrt{6}}{2}\right), \left(-\dfrac{\sqrt{10}}{2}, -\dfrac{\sqrt{6}}{2}\right)$

39. $y = \pm x$

41.

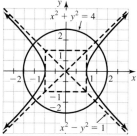

53. $\left(\dfrac{3\sqrt{6}}{4}, \dfrac{\sqrt{10}}{4}\right), \left(\dfrac{3\sqrt{6}}{4}, -\dfrac{\sqrt{10}}{4}\right),$
$\left(-\dfrac{3\sqrt{6}}{4}, \dfrac{\sqrt{10}}{4}\right), \left(-\dfrac{3\sqrt{6}}{4}, -\dfrac{\sqrt{10}}{4}\right)$

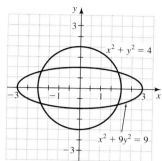

55. $\left(\dfrac{\sqrt{17}}{3}, \dfrac{8}{9}\right), \left(-\dfrac{\sqrt{17}}{3}, \dfrac{8}{9}\right), (0, -1)$

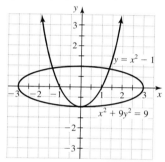

57. $(2, 0), \left(-\dfrac{5}{2}, -\dfrac{9}{4}\right)$

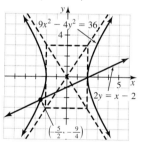

59. a) $(2.5, 1.5)$ **b)** $(\sqrt{7}, \sqrt{2})$

Section 12.5 Warm-ups F T T T F F F T T T
1.

3.

5.

7.

9.

11.

13.

15.

17.

19.

21.

23.

25.

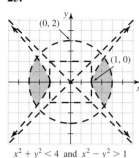

$x^2 + y^2 < 4$ and $x^2 - y^2 > 1$

27.

$y > x^2 + x$ and $y < 5$

41.

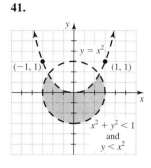

$x^2 + y^2 < 1$
and
$y < x^2$

43.

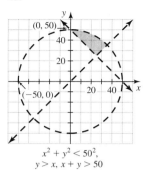

$x^2 + y^2 < 50^2$,
$y > x$, $x + y > 50$

45. No solution

Chapter 12 Wrap-up

Enriching Your Mathematical Word Power

1. c   **2.** a   **3.** d   **4.** a   **5.** c   **6.** d   **7.** b   **8.** d
9. c   **10.** a

Review Exercises

1. $\{(3, 9), (-5, 25)\}$

29.

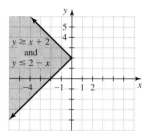

$y \geq x + 2$
and
$y \leq 2 - x$

31.

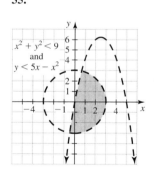

$x^2 + 4y^2 > 4$ and $4x^2 - y^2 < 4$

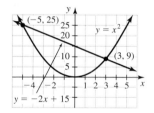

3. $\left\{\left(\dfrac{\sqrt{3}}{3}, \sqrt{3}\right), \left(-\dfrac{\sqrt{3}}{3}, -\sqrt{3}\right)\right\}$

33.

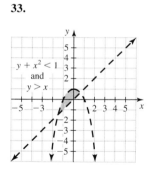

$y + x^2 < 1$
and
$y > x$

35.

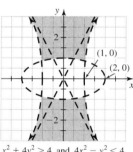

$x^2 + y^2 < 9$
and
$y < 5x - x^2$

5. $\{(\sqrt{3}, 1), (-\sqrt{3}, 1)\}$ **7.** $\{(-5, -3), (3, 5)\}$

9. $\{(5, \log(2))\}$ **11.** $\{(2, 4), (-2, 4)\}$ **13.** $2\sqrt{2}$ **15.** $2\sqrt{58}$

17. Vertex $\left(-\dfrac{3}{2}, -\dfrac{81}{4}\right)$, axis of symmetry $x = -\dfrac{3}{2}$, focus
$\left(-\dfrac{3}{2}, -20\right)$, directrix $y = -\dfrac{41}{2}$

19. Vertex $\left(-\dfrac{3}{2}, -\dfrac{1}{4}\right)$, axis of symmetry $x = -\dfrac{3}{2}$, focus $\left(-\dfrac{3}{2}, 0\right)$,
directrix $y = -\dfrac{1}{2}$

37.

$x \leq 1$ and
$y \geq 3$

39.

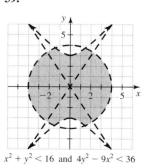

$x^2 + y^2 < 16$ and $4y^2 - 9x^2 < 36$

21. Vertex $(2, 3)$ axis of symmetry $x = 2$, focus $\left(2, \dfrac{5}{2}\right)$,
directrix $y = \dfrac{7}{2}$

23. $y = 2(x - 2)^2 - 7$, $(2, -7)$

25. $y = -\dfrac{1}{2}(x + 1)^2 + 1$, $(-1, 1)$

27. $(0, 0)$, 10

29. $(2, -3)$, 9

45.

47.

31. $(0, 0)$, $\dfrac{2}{3}$

49.

51.

33. $x^2 + (y - 3)^2 = 36$ **35.** $(x - 2)^2 + (y + 7)^2 = 25$
37.   **39.**

53.

55. Hyperbola   **57.** Circle   **59.** Circle   **61.** Circle
63. Hyperbola   **65.** Hyperbola
67.   **69.**

41.

43.

71.

73.

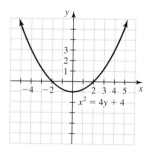

75. $x^2 + y^2 = 25$ **77.** $(x + 1)^2 + (y - 5)^2 = 36$
79. $y = \frac{1}{4}(x - 1)^2 + 3$ **81.** $y = x^2$ **83.** $y = \frac{2}{9}x^2$
85. $\{(4, -3), (-3, 4)\}$ **87.** $\varnothing$ **89.** 6 ft, 2 ft

Chapter 12 Test

1.

2.

3.

4.

5.

6.

7.

8.

9.

10.

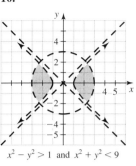

$x^2 - y^2 > 1$ and $x^2 + y^2 < 9$

11.

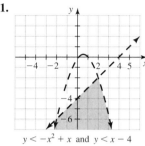

$y < -x^2 + x$ and $y < x - 4$

12. $\{(-5, 27), (3, -5)\}$ **13.** $\{(\sqrt{3}, 3), (-\sqrt{3}, 3)\}$
14. $2\sqrt{2}$ **15.** $(-1, -5)$, 6
16. Vertex $\left(-\frac{1}{2}, \frac{11}{4}\right)$, focus $\left(-\frac{1}{2}, 3\right)$, directrix $y = \frac{5}{2}$, axis of symmetry $x = -\frac{1}{2}$, upward
17. $y = \frac{1}{2}(x - 3)^2 - 5$ **18.** $(x + 1)^2 + (y - 3)^2 = 13$
19. 12 ft, 9 ft

Making Connections Chapters 1–12

1.

2.

3.

4.

5.

6.

7.

8.

9.

10.

11. $x^2 + 4xy + 4y^2$ **12.** $x^3 + 3x^2y + 3xy^2 + y^3$
13. $a^3 + 3a^2b + 3ab^2 + b^3$ **14.** $a^2 - 6ab + 9b^2$
15. $6a^2 - 7a - 5$ **16.** $x^3 - y^3$ **17.** $\{(1, 2)\}$
18. $\{(3, 4), (4, 3)\}$ **19.** $\{(1, -2, 3)\}$ **20.** $\{(-1, 1), (3, 9)\}$

21. $x = -\dfrac{b}{a}$ **22.** $x = \dfrac{-d \pm \sqrt{d^2 - 4wm}}{2w}$

23. $B = \dfrac{2A - bh}{h}$ **24.** $x = \dfrac{2y}{y - 2}$ **25.** $m = \dfrac{L}{1 + xt}$

26. $t = \dfrac{y^2}{9a^2}$ **27.** $y = -\dfrac{2}{3}x - \dfrac{5}{3}$ **28.** $y = -2x$

29. $(x - 2)^2 + (y - 5)^2 = 45$ **30.** $\left(-\dfrac{3}{2}, 3\right), \dfrac{3\sqrt{5}}{2}$

31. $-10 + 6i$ **32.** -1 **33.** $3 - 5i$ **34.** $7 + 6i\sqrt{2}$

35. $-8 - 27i$ **36.** $-3 + 3i$ **37.** 29 **38.** $-\dfrac{3}{2} - i$

39. $-\dfrac{1}{2} + \dfrac{9}{2}i$ **40.** $2 - i\sqrt{2}$

41. a) $q = -500x + 400$ **b)** $R = -500x^2 + 400x$
    c)   **d)** \$0.40 per pound
    e) \$80

Chapter 13

Section 13.1 Warm-ups T T T F F F T F T T
1. A sequence is a list of numbers.
3. A finite sequence is a function whose domain is the set of positive integers less than or equal to some fixed positive integer.
5. 1, 4, 9, 16, 25, 36, 49, 64

7. $-1, \dfrac{1}{2}, -\dfrac{1}{3}, \dfrac{1}{4}, -\dfrac{1}{5}, \dfrac{1}{6}, -\dfrac{1}{7}, \dfrac{1}{8}, -\dfrac{1}{9}, \dfrac{1}{10}$

9. 1, -2, 4, -8, 16   **11.** $\dfrac{1}{2}, \dfrac{1}{4}, \dfrac{1}{8}, \dfrac{1}{16}, \dfrac{1}{32}, \dfrac{1}{64}$

13. $-1, 1, 3, 5, 7, 9, 11$ **15.** $1, \dfrac{\sqrt{2}}{2}, \dfrac{\sqrt{3}}{3}, \dfrac{1}{2}, \dfrac{\sqrt{5}}{5}$

17. $\dfrac{1}{2}, \dfrac{1}{6}, \dfrac{1}{12}, \dfrac{1}{20}$ **19.** $-\dfrac{1}{3}, -1, 1, \dfrac{1}{3}$ **21.** $-1, 0, -1, 4$

23. $1, \dfrac{1}{4}, \dfrac{1}{9}, \dfrac{1}{16}$ **25.** $a_n = 2n - 1$

27. $a_n = (-1)^{n+1}$ **29.** $a_n = 2n - 2$ **31.** $a_n = 3n$
33. $a_n = 3n + 1$ **35.** $a_n = (-1)^n 2^{n-1}$

37. $a_n = (n - 1)^2$ **39.** $4, 2, 1, \dfrac{1}{2}, \dfrac{1}{4}$ yard line

41. \$36,687, \$38,521, \$40,447, \$42,470, \$44,593, \$46,823
43. \$1,000,000, \$800,000, \$640,000, \$512,000
45. 27 in., 13.5 in., 9 in., 6.75 in., 5.4 in.
47. 137,438,953,500, larger
51. a) 0.9048, 0.3677, 0.00004517   **b)** a_n goes to zero

Section 13.2 Warm-ups T F F F F T T T T F
1. Summation notation provides a way to write a sum without writing out all of the terms.
3. A series is the indicated sum of the terms of a sequence.

5. 30   **7.** 24   **9.** $\dfrac{31}{32}$ **11.** 50   **13.** -7 **15.** 0

17. $\displaystyle\sum_{i=1}^{6} i$ **19.** $\displaystyle\sum_{i=1}^{6} (-1)^i(2i - 1)$ **21.** $\displaystyle\sum_{i=1}^{6} i^2$ **23.** $\displaystyle\sum_{i=1}^{4} \dfrac{1}{2 + i}$

25. $\displaystyle\sum_{i=1}^{3} \ln(i + 1)$ **27.** $\displaystyle\sum_{i=1}^{4} a_i$ **29.** $\displaystyle\sum_{i=1}^{48} x_{i+2}$ **31.** $\displaystyle\sum_{i=1}^{n} w_i$

33. $\displaystyle\sum_{j=0}^{4} (j + 1)^2$ **35.** $\displaystyle\sum_{j=1}^{13} (2j - 3)$ **37.** $\displaystyle\sum_{j=1}^{5} \dfrac{1}{j + 3}$

39. $\displaystyle\sum_{j=0}^{3} x^{2j+5}$ **41.** $\displaystyle\sum_{j=0}^{n-1} x^{j+1}$

43. $x + x^2 + x^3 + x^4 + x^5 + x^6$ **45.** $x_0 - x_1 + x_2 - x_3$

47. $x + 2x^2 + 3x^3$ **49.** $\displaystyle\sum_{i=1}^{9} 2^{-i}$ **51.** $\displaystyle\sum_{i=1}^{4} 1{,}000{,}000(0.8)^{i-1}$

53. A sequence is basically a list of numbers. A series is the indicated sum of the terms of a sequence.

Section 13.3 Warm-ups F F F F F F T T T F
1. An arithmetic sequence is one in which each term after the first is obtained by adding a fixed amount to the previous term.
3. An arithmetic series is an indicated sum of an arithmetic sequence.

5. $a_n = 6n - 6$ **7.** $a_n = 5n + 2$
9. $a_n = 2n - 6$ **11.** $a_n = -4n + 9$
13. $a_n = -7n + 5$ **15.** $a_n = 0.5n - 3.5$
17. $a_n = -0.5n - 5.5$ **19.** 9, 13, 17, 21, 25
21. 7, 5, 3, 1, −1   **23.** −4, −1, 2, 5, 8
25. −2, −5, −8, −11, −14
27. −7, −11, −15, −19, −23   **29.** 4.5, 5, 5.5, 6, 6.5
31. 1020, 1040, 1060, 1080, 1100
33. 51   **35.** 4   **37.** 26   **39.** 17   **41.** 1176
43. 330   **45.** −481   **47.** 435   **49.** −540   **51.** 150
53. −308   **55.** $25,000   **57.** 1085   **59.** b

Section 13.4 Warm-ups F F T T T T F F T F
1. A geometric sequence is one in which each term after the first is obtained by multiplying the preceding term by a constant.
3. A geometric series is an indicated sum of a geometric sequence.
5. The approximate value of r^n when n is large and $|r| < 1$ is 0.
7. $a_n = \dfrac{1}{3}(3)^{n-1}$ **9.** $a_n = 64\left(\dfrac{1}{8}\right)^{n-1}$ **11.** $a_n = 8\left(-\dfrac{1}{2}\right)^{n-1}$

13. $a_n = 2(-2)^{n-1}$ **15.** $a_n = -\dfrac{1}{3}\left(\dfrac{3}{4}\right)^{n-1}$ **17.** $2, \dfrac{2}{3}, \dfrac{2}{9}, \dfrac{2}{27}, \dfrac{2}{81}$

19. 1, −2, 4, −8, 16   **21.** $\dfrac{1}{2}, \dfrac{1}{4}, \dfrac{1}{8}, \dfrac{1}{16}, \dfrac{1}{32}$

23. 0.78, 0.6084, 0.4746, 0.3702, 0.2887

25. 5   **27.** $\dfrac{1}{3}$ **29.** $-\dfrac{1}{9}$ **31.** $\dfrac{511}{512}$ **33.** $\dfrac{11}{32}$

35. $\dfrac{63,050}{729}$ **37.** 5115   **39.** 0.111111   **41.** 42.8259

43. $\dfrac{1}{4}$ **45.** 9   **47.** $\dfrac{8}{3}$ **49.** $\dfrac{3}{7}$ **51.** 6   **53.** $\dfrac{1}{3}$

55. $\dfrac{4}{33}$ **57.** $3,042,435.27   **59.** $21,474,836.47

61. $5,000,000   **63.** d   **65.** $\dfrac{8}{33}$

Section 13.5 Warm-ups F F F T T T T T T T
1. The sum obtained for a power of a binomial is called a binomial expansion.
3. The expression $n!$ is the product of the positive integers from 1 through n.
5. 10   **7.** 56
9. $r^5 + 5r^4t + 10r^3t^2 + 10r^2t^3 + 5rt^4 + t^5$
11. $m^3 - 3m^2n + 3mn^2 - n^3$
13. $x^3 + 6ax^2 + 12a^2x + 8a^3$
15. $x^8 - 8x^6 + 24x^4 - 32x^2 + 16$
17. $x^7 - 7x^6 + 21x^5 - 35x^4 + 35x^3 - 21x^2 + 7x - 1$
19. $a^{12} - 36a^{11}b + 594a^{10}b^2 - 5940a^9b^3$
21. $x^{18} + 45x^{16} + 900x^{14} + 10,500x^{12}$
23. $x^{22} - 22x^{21} + 231x^{20} - 1540x^{19}$

25. $\dfrac{x^{10}}{1024} + \dfrac{5x^9y}{768} + \dfrac{5x^8y^2}{256} + \dfrac{5x^7y^3}{144}$

27. $1287a^8w^5$ **29.** $-11,440m^9n^7$ **31.** $448x^5y^3$

33. $635,043,840a^{28}b^6$ **35.** $\displaystyle\sum_{i=0}^{8} \dfrac{8!}{(8-i)!\,i!}a^{8-i}m^i$

37. $\displaystyle\sum_{i=0}^{5} \dfrac{5!(-2)^i}{(5-i)!\,i!}a^{5-i}x^i$

39. $a^3 + b^3 + c^3 + 3a^2b + 3a^2c + 3ab^2 + 3ac^2 + 3b^2c + 3bc^2 + 6abc$

Chapter 13 Wrap-up

Enriching Your Mathematical Word Power
1. a   **2.** d   **3.** c   **4.** b   **5.** a   **6.** c   **7.** d   **8.** b
9. d   **10.** a

Review Exercises
1. 1, 8, 27, 64, 125   **3.** 1, 1, −3, 5, −7, 9   **5.** $-1, -\dfrac{1}{2}, -\dfrac{1}{3}$

7. $\dfrac{1}{3}, \dfrac{1}{5}, \dfrac{1}{7}$ **9.** 4, 5, 6   **11.** 36   **13.** 40   **15.** $\displaystyle\sum_{i=1}^{\infty} \dfrac{1}{2(i+1)}$

17. $\displaystyle\sum_{i=1}^{\infty} (i-1)^2$ **19.** $\displaystyle\sum_{i=1}^{\infty} (-1)^{i+1}x_i$ **21.** 6, 11, 16, 21

23. −20, −22, −24, −26   **25.** 3000, 4000, 5000, 6000

27. $a_n = \dfrac{n}{3}$ **29.** $a_n = 2n$ **31.** 300   **33.** $\dfrac{289}{6}$ **35.** 35

37. $3, \dfrac{3}{2}, \dfrac{3}{4}, \dfrac{3}{8}$ **39.** $1, \dfrac{1}{2}, \dfrac{1}{4}, \dfrac{1}{8}$

41. 0.23, 0.0023, 0.000023, 0.00000023

43. $a_n = \dfrac{1}{2}(6)^{n-1}$ **45.** $a_n = 0.7(0.1)^{n-1}$ **47.** $\dfrac{40}{81}$

49. 0.3333333333   **51.** $\dfrac{3}{8}$ **53.** 54

55. $m^5 + 5m^4n + 10m^3n^2 + 10m^2n^3 + 5mn^4 + n^5$
57. $a^6 - 9a^4b + 27a^2b^2 - 27b^3$

59. $495x^8y^4$ **61.** $372,736a^{12}b^2$ **63.** $\displaystyle\sum_{i=0}^{7} \dfrac{7!}{(7-i)!\,i!}a^{7-i}w^i$

65. Neither   **67.** Arithmetic   **69.** Arithmetic

71. $\dfrac{1}{\sqrt[3]{180}}$ **73.** $-1 + \dfrac{1}{2} - \dfrac{1}{6} + \dfrac{1}{24} - \dfrac{1}{120}$

75. $a^5 + 5a^4b + 10a^3b^2 + 10a^2b^3 + 5ab^4 + b^5$
77. 26   **79.** $118,634.11   **81.** $13,784.92

Chapter 13 Test
1. −10, −4, 2, 8   **2.** 5, 0.5, 0.05, 0.005

3. $-1, \dfrac{1}{2}, -\dfrac{1}{6}, \dfrac{1}{24}$ **4.** $1, \dfrac{3}{4}, \dfrac{5}{9}, \dfrac{7}{16}$ **5.** $a_n = 10 - 3n$

6. $a_n = -25\left(-\dfrac{1}{5}\right)^{n-1}$ **7.** $a_n = (-1)^{n-1}2n$ **8.** $a_n = n^2$

9. 5 + 7 + 9 + 11 + 13
10. 5 + 10 + 20 + 40 + 80 + 160
11. $m^4 + 4m^3q + 6m^2q^2 + 4mq^3 + q^4$

12. 750   **13.** $\dfrac{155}{8}$ **14.** 5   **15.** 10,100

16. $\dfrac{1}{2}$ **17.** $\dfrac{511}{128}$ **18.** ±2   **19.** 11   **20.** $1365r^{11}t^4$

21. $-448a^{10}b^3$ **22.** $86,545.41

Making Connections Chapters 1–13

1. 6   **2.** $n^2 - 3$

3. $x^2 + 2xh + h^2 - 3$ **4.** $x^2 - 2x - 2$ **5.** 11

6. 6   **7.** 4   **8.** 32   **9.** $\dfrac{1}{2}$ **10.** 3   **11.** 1

12. x **13.** $-\dfrac{27}{2}$ **14.** $-\dfrac{8}{3}$ **15.** $-\dfrac{128}{9}$ **16.** 16

17.

18.

19.

20.

21.

22.

23.

24.

25.

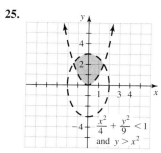

26. $\dfrac{a^2 + b^2}{ab}$ **27.** $\dfrac{y - 3}{y}$ **28.** $\dfrac{10}{(x - 3)(x + 3)(x + 1)}$

29. $\dfrac{2(x^3 - 64)}{x^3 - 16}$ **30.** $\dfrac{a^7}{b^4}$ **31.** 1   **32.** 4   **33.** $\dfrac{1}{32}$

34. -2 **35.** $\dfrac{1}{9}$ **36.** $-\dfrac{1}{8}$ **37.** $\dfrac{1}{4}$ **38.** $\dfrac{1}{5}$ **39.** 25

40. a) 105.8 cm or 41.7 in.   **c)** 1.3 years

Chapter 14

Section 14.1 Warm-ups F F T T T F T T F T

1. A tree diagram shows the number of different ways that a sequence of events can occur.

3. A permutation is an ordering or arrangement of distinct objects in a linear manner.

5. 12   **7.** 1024   **9.** 8   **11.** 120   **13.** 1320
15. 35,904   **17.** 1.0995×10^{12} **19.** 1.01989×10^{46}
21. 180   **23.** 9,000,000   **25.** 5040
27. 26,000,000, 156,000,000   **29.** 8   **31.** 1×10^{10}
33. 24   **35.** 336   **37.** 1   **39.** 210   **41.** 220
43. 364   **45.** 152,096

Section 14.2 Warm-ups T T F F F T T F T T
1. A combination of n things taken r at a time is a subset of size r taken from a set of n elements.
3. In a labeling problem we want the number of ways of labeling n objects with n labels, where some of the labels are identical.
5. 2,598,960   **7.** 10   **9.** 15,504   **11.** 13,983,816
13. 35   **15.** 120   **17.** 56   **19.** 479,001,600
21. 591,600,030   **23.** 3, 6, 10, $C(n, 2)$ **25.** 36   **27.** 8
29. $C(n, r) = \dfrac{n!}{(n - r)!r!}$ and $C(n, n - r) = \dfrac{n!}{r!(n - r)!}$
31. 60   **33.** 21,162,960   **35.** 576   **37.** 960,960
39. 5.36447×10^{28}, larger   **41.** 180, 2,520, 50,400
43. 698,377,680   **45.** 630   **47.** 2520   **49.** 56

Section 14.3 Warm-ups F F T T F F T F F F
1. An experiment is a process for which the outcomes are uncertain.
3. An event is a subset of a sample space.
5. The addition rule says that if A and B are events in a sample space, then $P(A \cup B) = P(A) + P(B) - P(A \cap B)$.
7. $\dfrac{1}{2}, \dfrac{5}{6}, \dfrac{5}{6}, 0, 1$ **9.** $\dfrac{1}{4}, \dfrac{3}{4}, \dfrac{1}{4}, \dfrac{3}{4}$ **11.** $\dfrac{1}{36}, \dfrac{11}{36}, \dfrac{6}{36}, 1, 0$
13. $\dfrac{1}{4}, \dfrac{2}{3}, \dfrac{2}{3}, \dfrac{1}{3}$ **15.** $\dfrac{1}{90}, \dfrac{1}{45}, \dfrac{2}{45}$ **17.** $\dfrac{1}{2,598,960}, \dfrac{1,024}{2,598,960}$
19. 0.79   **21.** $\dfrac{1}{4}$ **23.** $\dfrac{4}{13}$ **25.** 0.995   **27.** $\dfrac{1}{36}, \dfrac{35}{36}, \dfrac{35}{36}$
29. 3 to 2   **31.** 3 to 2, 2 to 3   **33.** 1 to 3, $\dfrac{3}{4}$ **35.** 3 to 5
37. 5 to 31   **39.** 1 to 999,999   **41.** $\dfrac{1}{32}$
43. $\dfrac{1}{7,059,052}, \dfrac{7,059,051}{7,059,052}$, 1 to 7,059,051

Chapter 14 Wrap-up

Enriching Your Mathematical Word Power
1. c   **2.** a   **3.** b   **4.** d   **5.** b   **6.** a   **7.** d   **8.** b
9. d   **10.** a

Review Exercises
1. 14,348,907   **3.** 120   **5.** 144   **7.** 70   **9.** 126, 5, 60
11. 120   **13.** 4620   **15.** 3360, 120   **17.** 64
19. $\dfrac{1}{4096}, \dfrac{1}{4096}$ **21.** $\dfrac{5}{14}, \dfrac{9}{14}, 0, 1$ **23.** 1 to 7   **25.** 3 to 2
27. 0.9   **29.** 40,320   **31.** 20   **33.** 1680   **35.** 28
37. 1680   **39.** 8

Chapter 14 Test
1. 72   **2.** 6840   **3.** 10   **4.** 1848   **5.** 495   **6.** 165
7. 2,522,520   **8.** 120   **9.** $\dfrac{3}{4}$ **10.** 1   **11.** 1 to 3
12. 7 to 1   **13.** 20 to 1, $\dfrac{1}{21}, \dfrac{20}{21}$ **14.** $\dfrac{11}{36}, \dfrac{1}{6}, \dfrac{1}{18}, \dfrac{5}{12}$
15. 4950   **16.** 7,880,400   **17.** 4200

Appendix A

Geometry Review Exercises
1. 12 in.   **2.** 24 ft^2 **3.** 60°   **4.** 6 ft   **5.** 20 cm
6. 144 cm^2 **7.** 24 ft^2 **8.** 13 ft   **9.** 30 cm   **10.** No
11. 84 yd^2 **12.** 30 in.   **13.** 32 ft^2 **14.** 20 km
15. 7 ft, 3 ft^2 **16.** 22 yd   **17.** 50.3 ft^2 **18.** 37.7 ft
19. 150.80 cm^3 **20.** 879.29 ft^2 **21.** 288 in.^{3}, 288 in.^{2}
22. 4 cm   **23.** 100 mi^2, 40 mi   **24.** 20 km
25. 42.25 cm^2 **26.** 33.510 ft^3, 50.265 ft^2
27. 75.4 in.^{3}, 100.5 in.^{2} **28.** 56°   **29.** 5 cm
30. 15 in. and 20 in.   **31.** 149°
32. 12 km   **33.** 10 yd

INDEX

DEFINITIONS, RULES, AND FORMULAS

Subsets of the Real Numbers

Natural Numbers $= \{1, 2, 3, \ldots\}$

Whole Numbers $= \{0, 1, 2, 3, \ldots\}$

Integers $= \{\ldots -3, -2, -1, 0, 1, 2, 3, \ldots\}$

Rational $= \left\{\dfrac{a}{b} \,\middle|\, a \text{ and } b \text{ are integers with } b \neq 0\right\}$

Irrational $= \{x \mid x \text{ is not rational}\}$

Properties of the Real Numbers

For all real numbers a, b, and c

$a + b = b + a; \; a \cdot b = b \cdot a$ Commutative

$(a + b) + c = a + (b + c); \; (ab)c = a(bc)$ Associative

$a(b + c) = ab + ac; \; a(b - c) = ab - ac$ Distributive

$a + 0 = a; \; 1 \cdot a = a$ Identity

$a + (-a) = 0; \; a \cdot \dfrac{1}{a} = 1 \; (a \neq 0)$ Inverse

$a \cdot 0 = 0$ Multiplication property of 0

Absolute Value

$|a| = \begin{cases} a & \text{for } a \geq 0 \\ -a & \text{for } a < 0 \end{cases}$

$\sqrt{x^2} = |x|$ for any real number x.

$|x| = k \leftrightarrow x = k \text{ or } x = -k \quad (k > 0)$

$|x| < k \leftrightarrow -k < x < k \quad (k > 0)$

$|x| > k \leftrightarrow x < -k \text{ or } x > k \quad (k > 0)$

(The symbol $\leftrightarrow$ means "if and only if.")

Interval Notation

$(a, b) = \{x \mid a < x < b\}$ $[a, b] = \{x \mid a \leq x \leq b\}$

$(a, b] = \{x \mid a < x \leq b\}$ $[a, b) = \{x \mid a \leq x < b\}$

$(-\infty, a) = \{x \mid x < a\}$ $(a, \infty) = \{x \mid x > a\}$

$(-\infty, a] = \{x \mid x \leq a\}$ $[a, \infty) = \{x \mid x \geq a\}$

Exponents

$a^0 = 1$

$a^{-1} = \dfrac{1}{a}$

$a^{-r} = \dfrac{1}{a^r} = \left(\dfrac{1}{a}\right)^r$

$\dfrac{1}{a^{-r}} = a^r$

$a^r a^s = a^{r+s}$

$\dfrac{a^r}{a^s} = a^{r-s}$

$(a^r)^s = a^{rs}$

$(ab)^r = a^r b^r$

$\left(\dfrac{a}{b}\right)^r = \dfrac{a^r}{b^r}$

$\left(\dfrac{a}{b}\right)^{-r} = \left(\dfrac{b}{a}\right)^r$

Roots and Radicals

$a^{1/n} = \sqrt[n]{a}$

$a^{m/n} = \left(\sqrt[n]{a}\right)^m = \sqrt[n]{a^m}$

$\sqrt[n]{ab} = \sqrt[n]{a} \cdot \sqrt[n]{b}$

$\sqrt[n]{\dfrac{a}{b}} = \dfrac{\sqrt[n]{a}}{\sqrt[n]{b}}$

Factoring

$a^2 + 2ab + b^2 = (a + b)^2$

$a^2 - 2ab + b^2 = (a - b)^2$

$a^2 - b^2 = (a + b)(a - b)$

$a^3 - b^3 = (a - b)(a^2 + ab + b^2)$

$a^3 + b^3 = (a + b)(a^2 - ab + b^2)$

Rational Expressions

$\dfrac{a}{b} + \dfrac{c}{b} = \dfrac{a + c}{b}$

$\dfrac{a}{b} - \dfrac{c}{b} = \dfrac{a - c}{b}$

$\dfrac{ac}{bc} = \dfrac{a}{b}$

$\dfrac{a}{b} + \dfrac{c}{d} = \dfrac{ad + bc}{bd}$

$\dfrac{a}{b} \cdot \dfrac{c}{d} = \dfrac{ac}{bd}$

$\dfrac{a}{b} \div \dfrac{c}{d} = \dfrac{a}{b} \cdot \dfrac{d}{c}$

If $\dfrac{a}{b} = \dfrac{c}{d}$, then $ad = bc$.

Quadratic Formula

The solutions to $ax^2 + bx + c = 0$ with $a \neq 0$ are

$$x = \frac{-b \pm \sqrt{b^2 - 4ac}}{2a}.$$

Distance Formula

The distance from (x_1, y_1) to (x_2, y_2), is

$$\sqrt{(x_2 - x_1)^2 + (y_2 - y_1)^2}.$$

Midpoint Formula

The midpoint of the line segment with endpoints (x_1, y_1) and (x_2, y_2) is

$$\left(\frac{x_1 + x_2}{2}, \frac{y_1 + y_2}{2}\right).$$

Slope Formula

The slope of the line through (x_1, y_1) and (x_2, y_2) is

$$\frac{y_2 - y_1}{x_2 - x_1} \quad (\text{for } x_1 \neq x_2).$$

Linear Function

$f(x) = mx + b$ with $m \neq 0$

Graph is a line with slope m.

A constant function
$f(x) = 2$

The identity function
$f(x) = x$

Absolute Value Function

$f(x) = |x|$

Quadratic Function

$f(x) = ax^2 + bx + c$ with $a \neq 0$

Graph is a parabola.

$f(x) = x^2$ (the squaring function)

Square-Root Function

$f(x) = \sqrt{x}$

Exponential Function

$f(x) = a^x$ for $a > 0$ and $a \neq 1$

One-to-one property: $a^m = a^n \leftrightarrow m = n$

$f(x) = a^x$ for $a > 1$ $f(x) = a^x$ for $0 < a < 1$

Logarithmic Function

$f(x) = \log_a(x)$ for $a > 0$ and $a \neq 1$

One-to-one property: $\log_a(m) = \log_a(n) \leftrightarrow m = n$

Base-a logarithm: $y = \log_a(x) \leftrightarrow a^y = x$

Natural logarithm: $y = \ln(x) \leftrightarrow e^y = x$

Common logarithm: $y = \log(x) \leftrightarrow 10^y = x$

$f(x) = \log_a(x)$
for $a > 1$

$f(x) = \log_a(x)$
for $0 < a < 1$

Properties of Logarithms

$\log_a(a) = 1$ $\qquad\qquad \log_a(1) = 0$

$\log_a(a^M) = M$ $\qquad\quad a^{\log_a(M)} = M$

$\log_a(MN) = \log_a(M) + \log_a(N)$

$\log_a\left(\dfrac{M}{N}\right) = \log_a(M) - \log_a(N)$

$\log_a(M^N) = N \cdot \log_a(M)$

$\log_a\left(\dfrac{1}{N}\right) = -\log_a(N)$

$\log_a(M) = \dfrac{\log_b(M)}{\log_b(a)} = \dfrac{\ln(M)}{\ln(a)} = \dfrac{\log(M)}{\log(a)}$

Interest Formulas

A = amount and P = principal

Compound interest: $A = P(1 + i)^n$, where n = number of periods and i = interest rate per period

Continuous compounding: $A = Pe^{rt}$, where r = annual interest rate and t = time in years

Variation

Direct: $y = kx$ $\quad (k \neq 0)$

Inverse: $y = \dfrac{k}{x}$ $\quad (k \neq 0)$

Joint: $y = kxz$ $\quad (k \neq 0)$

Straight Line

Slope-intercept form: $y = mx + b$

Slope: m $\qquad$ y-intercept: $(0, b)$

Point-slope form: $y - y_1 = m(x - x_1)$

Slope: m $\qquad$ Point: (x_1, y_1)

Standard form: $Ax + By = C$

Horizontal: $y = k$ $\qquad$ Vertical: $x = k$